PLANT DISEASE HANDBOOK

by

CYNTHIA WESTCOTT

"The Plant Doctor"

D. VAN NOSTRAND COMPANY, INC.

TORONTO NEW YORK LONDON

NEW YORK
D. Van Nostrand Company, Inc., 250 Fourth Avenue, New York 3
TORONTO
D. Van Nostrand Company (Canada), Ltd., 228 Bloor Street, Toronto
LONDON
Macmillan & Company, Ltd., St. Martin's Street, London, W.C. 2

Published simultaneously in Canada by
D. VAN NOSTRAND COMPANY (Canada), LTD.

PRINTED IN THE UNITED STATES OF AMERICA

In Memoriam

HERBERT HICE WHETZEL

Beloved "Prof," who taught me how to learn from plants and sent me forth to doctor them.

where she appeared
in A.H. 1st mag.

PREFACE

The *Plant Disease Handbook* was designed as a companion volume to *The Gardener's Bug Book,* a reference book for professional and amateur gardeners and those who advise them. It turns out to be a formidable tome, and a hybrid to boot, composed of purely technical information crossed with admonitions to the layman. The result is neither a comforting bedside volume for the first-year gardener nor a treatise for the specialist in any one field. It is a compendium (and that word means inclusion within *small* compass of a *large* subject) of available information on diseases of plants grown in gardens or in the home in continental United States. It includes some references to Alaska and the subtropical region of southern Florida, but excludes the purely tropical problems of Hawaii, the Canal Zone, and Puerto Rico. It includes florists' crops grown for home decoration and native plants sometimes grown in wild gardens, but excludes cotton, wheat, and other field crops.

This information is filtered through, and somewhat colored by, my own experience. Once upon a time I was a normal plant pathologist. Since 1933 I have been a practicing plant physician called upon to minister to private garden patients and expected to act as a liaison agent between the university and the gardening public. When requests for free information get so numerous I cannot salvage enough time to take care of the paying patients I write a book—first, to save my time in finding the answers, second, to encourage a few gardeners to look up the answers for themselves.

The Plant Doctor, published in 1937, was quickly written, for it was based entirely on the doctor's casebook and limited to diseases and pests found most commonly in northeastern gardens. The day that galley proofs went back to the printer I set out to discover how many of my observations were true for the rest of the country. This handbook has been in the making ever since. While New Jersey gardens sleep in the winter the Ford and I have wandered thousands of miles. I have visited tiny backyard gardens and large estates, public gardens and parks, commercial nurseries and greenhouses, universities and experiment stations, from New England to Florida, from New York to California. To cite individually the people who have opened their homes and gardens, answered questions, provided bulletins and reprints, and shown experiments in progress, would fill many pages. I can give here only a collective thank-you. Garden visiting is by no means a sunny weather proposition and I am particularly grateful to the indefatigable souls who trudged around with me in the cloudbursts of "sunny" Florida and California, in Texas snowstorms, Louisiana icestorms, Iowa windstorms, and Virginia high tides. We who garden in the heat and humidity of New Jersey summers have no monopoly on bad weather.

Superimposed on such a background is the literature summary presented here, arranged for finger-tip reference. I hope that it will prove useful not only to gardeners but to those who serve them—the landscape architects who design their plantings, the florists and nurserymen who grow their plants and cut-flowers, the dealers who supply their seeds and fungicides, the arborists who care for their trees and shrubs, the county agents who answer their questions, and the plant pathologists who diagnose their diseased specimens.

The charge has been made that plant pathologists can tell you what a disease is but seldom what to do about it except to "Remove diseased plants or parts; rake up and burn fallen leaves." The charge has been made against this handbook, reviewed in manuscript, that too many possible control measures are offered without indication of the best. I plead guilty on both counts. We really know very little about disease control in home gardens and, while sanitary measures do not always lessen the incidence of disease, they work fairly well in some instances. In no instance is it possible for me to recommend a single chemical that will control a given disease in all parts of the country in all seasons without plant injury. I can make no such recommendation for rose diseases, and I have tested fungicides on roses for a quarter of a century. The most I can say is that a certain spray is expedient in the conditions under which I practice. I can cite numerous instances where the same chemical applied in the same dilution on the same dates controlled black spot in one rose garden and not in the one across the street.

The use of chemicals by amateurs is hazardous in any event. Many of the control measures mentioned have been developed for professional growers and in some cases should be left to them. It is far better for the grower to sell a healthy plant than for the gardener to try to cure a sick one. Without implying that any reputable nurseryman would deliberately sell a diseased plant, I think that there is room for a good deal of education. For that reason disease symptoms which remain constant are given more prominence than control measures which are constantly changing. The grower must learn not to sell, and the gardener to reject, dangerously diseased plants. While scouting for azalea petal blight in Georgia some years ago I met a conscientious nurseryman who said he would certainly like to see that disease and learn to recognize it. I asked him what he thought was the matter with the row of azaleas he was standing by. "That? Oh, that's just weather! We had rain a couple of days ago and the blossoms all collapsed." The blossoms had collapsed from the petal blight, encouraged by the weather.

On the other hand, I found it equally difficult to persuade a park superintendent that his azaleas were actually suffering from drought and not petal blight. Because few gardeners realize the importance of distinguishing between a disease caused by a living organism and that caused by an unfavorable environmental influence I have stressed the latter in the section on Physiogenic Diseases and have included spray injuries under the same heading.

The backbone of the handbook is the list of diseases under host plants in Chapter 5. Credit for this section goes almost entirely to Freeman Weiss whose *Check List Revision, Diseases of Economic Plants of the United States* has been published in installments, from 1940 to 1949, in the *Plant Disease Reporter,* issued by The Plant Disease Survey, Division of Mycology and Disease Survey, Bureau of Plant Industry, Soils, and Agricultural Engineering, Agricultural Research Administration, United States Department of Agriculture. A very particular thank-you goes to Dr. Weiss, not only for permission to adapt the check list for my purposes but for painstakingly going over Chapter 5 and making many suggestions as to nomenclature. The record of states where diseases are found is compiled by The Plant Disease Survey from reports by collaborators all over the country. My grateful appreciation goes to these collaborators and to Paul R. Miller, head of the Survey. Dr. Miller has read the entire manuscript and made helpful suggestions.

The bibliography must stand as my acknowledgment of debt to many authors. A great many others, uncited, have also provided information.

The decision to sandwich in classification of the pathogen along with the usual description of the disease (for the benefit of people with a microscope and most especially myself) has added many unexpected months to the preparation of the manuscript. During the years of working in gardens I had forgotten that names could be so baffling and that classifications changed almost as rapidly as control measures. Authorities used in naming bacteria, fungi, and viruses are given in the text.

Finding no consistency in present-day usage of host names—e.g. horsechestnut, horse-chestnut and horse chestnut, mountain ash, mountain-ash and mountainash—I have taken the middle-of-the-road policy and followed *Hortus Second.* The hyphen is used to designate plants which are not what the name implies. That is, mountain-ash (Sorbus) is not a true ash (Fraxinus) nor horse-chestnut (Aesculus) a chestnut (Castanea). This distinction seems useful in dealing with diseases, for they are often confined to a single genus or family.

The photographs are of material collected in doctoring gardens or on cross-country jaunts and are intended to emphasize the more common home garden problems. Many were taken by my former assistant, Lacelle Stites, who deserves special thanks. The drawings are diagrams adapted from various sources.

It is easy enough to start a book on plant disease. It is impossible to finish it. Every garden visited, every meeting attended, every journal read, means additions, deletions, and corrections. So I chop it off, unfinished, while the river of knowledge keeps rolling along.

CYNTHIA WESTCOTT

Glen Ridge, New Jersey
October, 1949

CONTENTS

HOW TO USE THIS BOOK

This is a reference manual. You need not read it through from cover to cover, but I hope you will read the first chapter and then the introduction to garden chemicals, page 7, and the few pages, 22 to 27, on spraying, with particular attention to the conversion table on page 27. Note for future reference that chemicals are listed alphabetically, along with some trade names, and that comments are given on their compatibility and incompatibility with each other and with insecticides.

Chapter 3 on the classification of plant pathogens can be taken or not as desired. It provides a mycological background for students and a brief review for professional workers.

The rest of the book is in two main sections. Chapter 4, starting on page 43, describes specific diseases and gives remedies when known. The diseases are grouped according to their common names into thirty-five types treated in alphabetical order: Anthracnose (p. 44), Bacterial Diseases (p. 58), Black Knot (p. 83), Black Leg (p. 85), Black Mildew (p. 86), Black Spot (p. 88), Blights (p. 95), Blotch Diseases (p. 142), Broomrapes (p. 145), Cankers and Diebacks (p. 145), Club Root (p. 173), Damping-off (p. 174), Dodder (p. 176), Downy Mildews (p. 179), Fruit Spots (p. 185), Leaf Blister and Leaf Curl Diseases (p. 186), Leaf Galls (p. 188), Leaf Scorch (p. 191), Leaf Spots (p. 193), Mistletoe (p. 232), Molds (p. 235), Needle Casts (p. 237), Nematode Diseases (p. 241), Physiogenic Diseases (p. 250), Powdery Mildews (p. 267), Rots (p. 279), Rusts (p. 324), Scab (p. 352), Scurf (p. 361), Smuts (p. 363), Snowmold (p. 367), Sooty Mold (p. 369), Virus Diseases (p. 371), White Rusts (p. 391), Wilts (p. 392). These types are briefly defined on page 407.

Chapter 5, starting on page 405, gives nearly a thousand host plants in alphabetical order, from Abelia to Zinnia, according to common names except in cases where the Latin name means less confusion. Under the hosts the diseases are sorted out into the thirty-five types and the geographical distribution given. From then on it is a process of checking back into the disease section to get the information applicable to your particular problem. Chapter 4 has a running head of disease types, from Anthracnose to Wilts, but exigencies of manufacture have placed this in the inner margin, not readily seen by riffling the pages, so that the Index may provide a quicker means to the same end. In both disease and host sections the Latin name of the pathogen is given in **boldface** type and provides the key word, for the individual diseases in each group are listed in alphabetical order according to the names of their pathogens.

A specific example in the use of this book is given on page 406.

Addresses of state agricultural experiment stations, sources of help for every gardener, are given on pages 669 and 670, followed by a glossary, page 671, and a bibliography where references likely to be of interest to gardeners are separated from those acknowledging source material.

The index includes common and Latin names of host plants, Latin names of pathogens, and common names of the described diseases.

The very best way to use this book is to take it in small doses as needed. Do not let the hundreds of diseases you will never meet worry you too much. And remember that most plants survive, despite their troubles!

PLANT DISEASE HANDBOOK

CHAPTER 1

INTRODUCTION

The chief hazard any garden plant has to endure is its owner, or gardener. I make this statement unequivocally, after nearly twenty years of visiting home gardens across the country, doctoring gardens in the East, and answering countless inquiries.

Undoubtedly many plants will suffer undue hardship from the publication of this Handbook. It is human nature to read symptoms of an ailment and immediately assume it is your own affliction. Jumping to conclusions is as dangerous to plants as to humans. A sore throat does not necessarily mean diphtheria. Only a trained physician can diagnose probable diphtheria, and a laboratory culture is necessary for positive confirmation.

A spotted or yellowed rose leaf does not necessarily mean rose black spot. More than half the specimens sent to me as black spot are examples of spray injury and most of the rest show reaction to weather conditions, yet gardeners blithely go on increasing the spray dosage, confident that more and stronger chemicals will lick the "disease" and seldom noticing they are nearly killing the patient in the process.

A browning azalea flower does not necessarily mean the dreaded petal blight. This past spring an article of mine on possible azalea troubles appeared in print about the time some azalea bloom in this vicinity was turning brown from a combination of unusual weather conditions. Some gardeners immediately suspected the worst, thought that the southern blight had arrived in the North, and started spraying. The poor plants, suffering from drought and a heat wave, found this very hard to take.

All chemicals used as sprays or dusts are injurious to plants under some conditions, the injury varying with the chemical, the dosage, with the species and even the variety of plant, with the temperature, with the soil moisture, and many other factors. Plants suffering from drought are commonly injured by certain sprays.

So please, please don't jump to conclusions. Don't do anything in a hurry because the plants are getting sick fast and there is no time for a proper diagnosis. Don't rush to the seedstore to buy some chemical just as good as the one you vaguely remember reading about. Sit down; relax! You have all the time in the world for a proper diagnosis, because, by the time the disease is bad enough for you to notice it, it is probably too late for protective spraying this season anyway.

Browning of an azalea flower means nothing as a diagnostic symptom. It could just as well come from frost or heat or old age as from disease. If the flowers had been limp and collapsed with a *slimy* feel, those would have been good symptoms, but signs of the fungus are needed, too. Thin, slightly curved black bodies (sclerotia) formed at the base of petals would have been distinctive, but most conclusive would have been spores taken from the inside of the petals and examined under the microscope. If they were one-celled but had a little boxlike appendage, then one might have reasonably concluded that *Ovulinia azaleae,* the cause of petal blight, had jumped from Maryland, its present northern limit, to New York.

This is a book of garden diseases, but it is not expected that anyone, amateur or professional, can read a brief description, look at an unfamiliar disease in the garden, and make a very reliable diagnosis. I certainly cannot, and after compiling this tome I am less likely to try than ever before. I have written "water-soaked" or "reddish brown" too many hundreds of times for different diseases to make such symptoms seem very distinctive.

However, if you are a gardener you can narrow the field down considerably by consulting Chapter 5 where host plants are listed in alphabetical order and under each the type of disease—Blight, Canker, Leaf Spot, etc., and then the organisms causing these diseases by their scientific names and the states where they have been reported. Eliminating the types of disease that are obviously different from yours and eliminating diseases that are reported only on the West Coast when you live in New York, you may find only two or three possibilities to look up in Chapter 4 which lists, under the different disease groups, the pathogens in alphabetical order, followed by a discussion of the disease. Don't let all the scientific names worry you. It is the only way to make this a quick and easy reference, for there are very few common names of plant diseases that can be used without confusion. It works just like the telephone book. While thumbing your way down to Smith, John, you do not worry about spelling Smiecinski, C., you pass on the way.

If you are a quasi-professional, like me, with your formal mycology far in the past but trying to keep abreast of a flood of miscellaneous specimens, there is a brief review of the salient, microscopic characters of each genus, together with its classification. This is in small type and can be readily passed over by those interested solely in macroscopic characters.

What Is Plant Disease?

There are many definitions of plant disease, the simplest being any deviation from the normal. I still like the one learned in student days, concept of the late Professor H. H. Whetzel, to whose inspiration I owe this plant doctoring vocation and whose assistant I was privileged to be for ten years. Disease in plants is an injurious physiological process, caused by the *continued* irritation of a primary causal factor, exhibited through abnormal cellular activity and expressed in characteristic pathological conditions called symptoms. The causal factor is a living organism or an environmental condition. Injury differs from disease in being due to the *transient* irritation of a causal factor, as the wound of an insect, sudden freezing or burning, application of a poison.

Plant diseases may be **necrotic,** with dying or death of cells, tissues or organs, **hypoplastic,** resulting in dwarfing or stunting, or **hyperplastic** with an overgrowth of plant tissue, as in crown gall, or club root.

Plant Diseases Are Not New

All species of plants, wild and cultivated, are subject to disease. Fossil remains suggest that plant diseases were present on earth before man himself. Certainly man has been punished by them ever since the garden of Eden. "I smote you with blasting and with mildew and hail in all the labors of your hands yet ye turned not to me, saith the Lord" (Haggai 2:17).

Man's attempts at controlling plant disease go back at least to 700 B.C. when the Romans instituted the Robigalia to propitiate the rust gods with prayer and sacrifice. About 470 B.C. Pliny reported that amurca of olives should be sprinkled on plants to prevent attacks of blight, this being our earliest known reference to a fungicide.

In 1660, at Rouen, France, a law was passed calling for eradication of the barberry as a means of fighting wheat rust, two centuries before the true nature of rust was known or how the barberry affected the wheat.

In the latter part of the eighteenth century the English Forsyth discoursed on tree surgery and treatment of wounds and cankers. His seemingly fantastic recommendation of a paste of cow dung to promote healing of tree wounds has modern corroboration in research showing that urea speeds up healing of such wounds.

Much of our progress in dealing with plant disease has followed spectacular catastrophes. Modern plant pathology had its start with the blight which swept the potato fields of Europe in 1844 and 1845, resulting in the Irish famine. This lesson in the importance of plant disease to the economic welfare of mankind marked the beginning of public support for investigations on the cause of disease. Two men, both German, laid the firm foundations of our present knowledge. Mycologist Anton de Bary, 1867 to 1888, first proved beyond doubt that fungi found associated with plant diseases were pathogenic, while Julius Kuhn, farmer with a doctor's degree in science, first showed the relation between science and practice in the problems of plant disease control. His textbook on *Diseases of Cultivated Plants,* published in 1858, is still useful.

The accidental discovery of bordeaux mixture in France in 1882 marks the beginning of protective spraying for disease control, although sulfur dust had been recommended as an eradicant for powdery mildew back in 1824.

Plant Pathology in the United States

Organized plant pathology in America started in 1885 with a section of Mycology in the U.S. Department of Agriculture. In 1904 the start of the great epiphytotic of chestnut blight which was to wipe out our native trees stimulated more public interest and support for plant pathology. In 1907 the first University Chair of Plant Pathology was established at Cornell University.

The United States Quarantine Act of 1912 officially recognized the possibility of introducing pests and diseases on imported plants, after low-priced nursery seedlings from Europe had brought in the white pine blister rust, and this was our first attempt at control by exclusion.

In 1917, during World War I, the Plant Disease Survey was organized as an office of the Bureau of Plant Industry "to collect information on plant diseases in the United States, covering such topics as prevalence, geographical distribution, severity, etc. and to make this information immediately available to all persons interested, especially those concerned with disease control." This information comes to the Survey from volunteer collaborators all over the country and is distributed in a mimeographed bulletin, *The Plant Disease Reporter.*

During World War II, the Plant Disease Survey was in charge of the Emergency Plant Disease Prevention Project to "protect the country's food, feed, fiber and oil supplies by ensuring immediate detection of enemy attempts at crop destruction through the use of plant diseases and providing production specialists and extension workers with prompt and accurate information regarding outbreaks of plant diseases whether introduced inadvertently or by design while still in incipient stages." The role of the G-men of plant disease and the methods they used is not yet fully told, but as a by-product of these wartime surveys we accumulated a great deal of evidence on the presence and prevalence of new and established diseases across the country and this included home gardens as well as farms. Much of the material in this Handbook can be regarded as another by-product of these surveys.

In 1946, a century after *Phytophthora infestans* had made history with the potato blight, a strain of the same fungus started an unprecedented epiphytotic of tomato blight, as devastating in home gardens as in canning crops. And this disaster led directly to the latest service of the Plant Disease Survey, A Crop Plant Disease Forecasting Project authorized under the Research and Marketing Act. Clearing through key pathologists in each state, information flows to and from the Survey in time to warn dealers to lay in their stocks of chemicals and growers to be ready to spray when disease is imminent. Late blight of potato and tomato, tobacco blue mold, and cucurbit downy mildew are the three diseases for which forecasts were attempted the first year, but doubtless the service will be expanded as the need develops.

Principles of Control

Control of a plant disease means reduction in the amount of damage caused. Perfect control is rare, but there is profitable control when the increased yield more than covers the cost of chemicals and labor, or when the ornamentals in our gardens stay beautiful instead of becoming unkempt horrors.

The four fundamental principles of control are Exclusion, Eradication, Protection, and Immunization.

1. EXCLUSION means preventing the entrance and establishment of pathogens in uninfested gardens, states, or countries. For home gardeners it means using certified seed or plants, sorting bulbs before planting, discarding any that are doubtful, possibly treating seeds or tubers or corms before they are put in the garden, and, most especially, refusing obviously diseased specimens from nurseryman or dealer. For states and countries, exclusion means quarantines, prohibition by law. Sometimes restricted entry of nursery stock is allowed, the plants to be grown under isolation and inspected for one or two years before distribution is permitted.

2. ERADICATION means the elimination of a pathogen once it has become established on a plant or in a garden. It can be accomplished by *removal* of diseased specimens, or parts, as in roguing to control virus diseases, or cutting off cankered tree limbs; by *cultivating* to keep down weed hosts and deep ploughing or spading to bury diseased plant debris; by *rotation* of susceptible with nonsusceptible crops, trying to starve out the pathogen; and *disinfection,* usually by chemicals, sometimes by heat treatment. Spraying or dusting foliage with sulfur after mildew mycelium is present is eradication, and so is treating the soil with chloropicrin to kill nematodes and fungi.

3. PROTECTION is the interposition of some protective barrier between the susceptible part of the suscept or host and the pathogen. In most instances this is a protective spray or dust applied to the plant in advance of the arrival of the fungus spore; sometimes it means killing insects or other inoculating agents, sometimes the erection of a windbreak or other mechanical barrier.

Chapter 2 gives an alphabetical list of chemicals used in present-day protective spraying and dusting, along with eradicant chemicals, and includes notes on compatibility and possibilities of injury. It is here that home gardeners, sometimes commercial growers, can do their plants irreparable harm instead of the good they intend. Spraying is never to be undertaken lightly, or thoughtlessly. Stop and think! Read all of the fine print on the labels; be sure of your dosage, and the safety of that particular chemical on the plant you want to protect.

4. IMMUNIZATION is control by the development of resistant varieties or by inoculating the plant with something which will inactivate the pathogen.

The latter is a very recent phase of plant disease control. We call it chemotherapy, and promising results have been obtained with Dutch elm disease, bleeding canker of maples, and one or two others. Resistant varieties are as old as time. Nature has always eliminated the unfit, but since about 1890 man has been speeding up the process by deliberate breeding, selecting, and propagating plants resistant to the more important diseases. It was estimated in 1937 that disease-resistant varieties of 17 farm crops added upwards of 70 million dollars a year to farm incomes. Some crops could not be grown at all if it were not for resistant varieties.

Resistant ornamental plants have lagged behind food plants but we do have wilt-resistant asters, rust-resistant snapdragons, and we hope that elms that can withstand Dutch elm disease and wilt-resistant mimosas are on the way. Here is the ideal way for home gardeners to control their plant diseases —in the winter when the seed order and the nursery list is made out—so easy, and so safe!

CHAPTER 2

GARDEN CHEMICALS AND THEIR APPLICATION

FUNGICIDES, BACTERICIDES, NEMATOCIDES

A **fungicide** is a toxicant or poison for fungi, a chemical or physical agent that kills or inhibits the development of fungus spores or mycelium. It may be an **eradicant,** applied to a plant, plant part, or the environment to destroy fungi *established* within a given area or plant, or it may be a **protectant,** applied to protect a plant or plant part from infection by killing or inhibiting the development of fungus spores or mycelium that *may arrive* at the infection court. The term fungicides as generally used includes **bactericides,** toxicants for bacteria.

A **disinfectant** is an agent that frees a plant or plant part from infection by destroying the pathogen established *within* it. A **disinfestant** kills or inactivates organisms present *on the surface* of the plant or plant part or in the immediate environment. Chemicals for seed treatment can be either eradicants or protectants but most of them are disinfestants in that they kill organisms on the surface of the seed rather than those within. In common usage, however, they are called disinfectants.

A **nematocide** is, of course, a chemical that kills nematodes in the soil or in the plant. Most nematocides are **fumigants,** chemical toxicants applied in volatile form.

Not so long ago the chemicals on the garden medicine shelf consisted of copper and sulfur for protectants, lime sulfur as an eradicant, mercuric chloride as a disinfectant, and formalin and carbon bisulfide as fumigants. You sometimes got plant injury; you did not always get the best possible control but at least you did not have to be an organic chemist. Now we have added "fixed" coppers, organic sulfurs or dithiocarbamates, phenyl mercury derivatives, chlorinated quinones and naphthoquinones, metallic quinolinolates, quaternary compounds, glyoxalidines, nitrated phenols or dinitro derivatives, compounds of chromium, cadmium, silver, and zinc as fungicides; and the fumigants chloropicrin, dichloropropylene and dichloropropane, methyl bromide, ethylene dibromide, and ethylene dichloride as nematocides.

Many of these were developed to meet an emergency—the sudden need for fungicides to combat tropical fungi deteriorating fabrics and equipment during World War II, but the search for new fungicides goes on, with hundreds of synthetic organic compounds being screened each year. This screening is often a cooperative venture between manufacturers, state experiment stations, and the U.S. Department of Agriculture. The first question asked of any new material is, "Does it have any fungicidal value?" the second, "What diseases will it control?" the third, "Is it **phytotoxic,** injurious to plants, at the concentration required to control the disease?"

Phytotoxicity is an elusive factor, not to be pinned down in a few tests. It varies not only with the kind of plant but with the particular variety, with the amount of moisture in the soil when the spray is applied, the temperature, whether or not the application is followed by rain or high humidity, with the section of the country, with the compatibility of the chemical with spreaders or wetting agents, other fungicides or insecticides. Coordinated tests with new materials in many different states are extremely valuable. Some compounds give rather uniform results over the country, others vary widely with climatic conditions.

The 1947 Federal Insecticide, Fungicide and Rodenticide Act provides that all fungicides must be registered with the U.S. Department of Agriculture before being marketed. Materials highly toxic to humans must be prominently marked, instructions given for avoiding injury to plants or animals, the toxicant chemical must be named and the percentage of active or inactive ingredients given. All labels submitted for registration must be accompanied by some sort of proof that the claims for performance are valid.

The consumer, therefore, is well protected against fraud and, if he is willing to read fine print, should be able to choose fairly intelligently from among the bewildering array of proprietary compounds on his dealer's shelves. Too many gardeners, however, seem unable to read when confronted with a packaged garden chemical. This ability must be reacquired. Don't leave your glasses at home when you start out to buy garden chemicals. Within the first six months after the 1947 Act went into effect 2,660 brand names were registered and label reading became a first requirement in getting the right fungicide for a specific disease.

You should, of course, follow manufacturer's directions for dosage, unless you have learned otherwise through past experience; but even following exactly directions of a reliable manufacturer is no guarantee against injury, since no tests are comprehensive enough to cover all the combinations of weather, soil, and plant varieties you may encounter. Keep your eyes open. Keep a notebook. Put down the date you sprayed and the dosage used, the approximate temperature and humidity, whether it was in a period of drought, and whether rain followed soon afterward. Go around later and check for burning or leaf spotting or defoliation, or too much unsightly residue. Note which varieties can take the spray and which cannot. Rose varieties, for example, show a wide variation in tolerance to certain chemicals.

The following alphabetical list includes chemicals already commercially available and a few others that may be marketed before this manuscript is in print. The trade names, given in small capital letters, are only a sample of the thousands now registered and listed with no thought that they are better than those excluded. For a comprehensive list of trade names of insecticides and fungicides, together with addresses of manufacturers, see *Entoma,* Eighth (1949) edition. The search for better chemicals is unending. No listing can be really up to date.

Acetic Acid, present in vinegar, one of the oldest preservatives, and suggested as a soil disinfectant about 20 years ago, particularly for damping-off of evergreen seedlings, 3/4 quart per square foot of an 0.8% solution being applied 5 to 6 days before sowing. For a brief period acetic acid was suggested as a flower spray for azalea blight.

Ammoniacal Copper Carbonate, occasionally used in place of bordeaux mixture, since it does not discolor foliage. Directions for preparing this vary. One formula calls for moistening 1 level teaspoon of copper carbonate with 2 tablespoons of household ammonia and adding 1 gallon of water. I have never mixed my own but use it in the three-in-one proprietary spray Triogen, which gives excellent control of powdery mildews and fair control of rose black spot.

Ammonium Sulfate, used around trees and shrubs affected with Phymatotrichum root rot. Make a circular ridge about the tree the diameter of the plant top, apply 1 pound chemical to each 10 square feet in this basin, and follow with 3- to 4-inch irrigation. Repeat in 5 to 10 days, but not again the same season.

ANTI-DAMP (Andrew Wilson), oxyquinoline benzoate, used for damping-off.

ARASAN (Du Pont), tetramethyl thiuram disulfide, sold under this name for seed treatment and as Tersan for turf and bulb treatments. Recommended for peanut, corn, bean, pea, beet, carrot, and some other vegetable and flower seeds, and mixed with fertilizer for onion smut control. Arasan SF is a slurry form for large-scale operations.

ARATHANE (Rohm & Haas), dinitro capryl phenyl crotonate, under test as a miticide, fungicide, and insecticide on fruit, vegetables, and ornamentals, promising for apple scab, rose powdery mildew; may be injurious to young foliage in emulsion form, safer as a wettable powder.

Arsenate of Lead apparently has some slight fungicidal value—at least sprays and dusts containing it are sometimes more potent than the fungicide used alone.

BASI-COP (Sherwin-Williams), basic copper sulfate.

Bentonite, hydrated aluminum silicate, a clay mineral used as a diluent in dusts.

Benzol vapor used to control downy mildew, tobacco particularly, in seed beds. The benzol is evaporated overnight in a flat pan or wick-type evaporator under canvas covering the bed.

Bismuth Subsalicylate, sometimes used as a spray for downy mildew, under test as a corm and bulb treatment.

BIOQUIN 1 (Monsanto), copper 8-quinolinolate, a green, organic copper fungicide promising for apple scab, blotch and Brooks's fruit spot, for some potato and tomato diseases, suggested for delphinium black spot, as a soil treatment for carnation. In California tests it has given moderate control of sycamore anthracnose and good control of avocado fruit rot; used at ½ to 1 pound per 100 gallons.

BIOQUIN 100 (Monsanto), zinc 8-quinolinolate.

Borax, used as a wash for citrus fruit molds, a dip for sweet potato sprouts, in small quantities in boron-deficient soils to control black heart of beets, cracked stem of celery, internal cork of apples, and in large quantities (4 pounds per 100 square feet) as an herbicide, especially good for poison ivy eradication.

Bordeaux Mixture, made from copper sulfate and lime water and forming a membranous coating over plant parts, the first protective spray and perhaps still the most widely used. Although others had previously used the chemicals, to the Frenchman Millardet is given the credit of discovering and publicizing the efficacy of bordeaux mixture, so named because it was used on grapes along the highway to Bordeaux. About 1878 downy mildew, introduced into France from America, was threatening the vineyards. Millardet, one of the workers assigned to the problem, noticed, in 1882, that where grapes near the highway had been treated with a poisonous-looking blue mixture of copper and lime to prevent stealing there was little or no downy mildew. A description of the preparation of bordeaux mixture was published in 1885, and it remains to this day one of our most efficient and widely used fungicides. It does, however, have a most conspicuous residue, and is injurious to many plants.

Bordeaux mixture is made in varying concentrations. The most usual formula is 8–8–100 (often stated as 4–4–50) which means 8 pounds copper sulfate, 8 pounds hydrated lime to 100 gallons of water. Stock solutions are made up for each chemical (1 pound per gallon of water), the lime solution placed first in the sprayer, diluted to nearly the full amount and the copper sulfate solution added. Or, for power sprayers, finely divided copper sulfate (snow) can be washed through the strainer into the spray tank and when this is two-thirds full the weighed amount of hydrated lime can also be washed through the strainer while the agitator is running. Casein or other spreader is added toward the end.

For ornamentals a 4–4–100 bordeaux mixture is usually strong enough and can be made in small amounts by dissolving 2 ounces of copper sulfate in 1 gallon of water, 2 ounces hydrated lime in 2 gallons of water, pouring the copper sulfate solution into the lime water and straining into the spray tank through fine cheesecloth.

For some plants, as stone fruits, the proportion of lime is increased; for others, as azaleas, a low-lime bordeaux is used. Once the two solutions have been mixed together the preparation must be used immediately. Fresh lime is essential, not some left over from a previous season. Somewhat less effective than homemade bordeaux but easier for the home gardener and usually less injurious to plants are the various prepared powders and pastes available under many trade names.

Compatibility. Bordeaux mixture is compatible with lead arsenate, calcium arsenate, Paris green, rotenone, pyrethrum, nicotine sulfate, DDT, summer and dormant oils, wettable sulfurs, glyoxalidines; *incompatible* with cryolite, benzene hexachloride, tetraethyl pyrophosphate, lime sulfur; *questionable* with chlordane, toxaphene, parathion, quinones, organic mercuries, dithiocarbamates (Fermate, Dithane, Zerlate), dinitro compounds.

Phytotoxicity comes from both the lime and the copper. Plants are often stunted with yield reduced; fruit-setting of tomatoes may be delayed. Bordeaux is not safe on peaches during the growing season, may burn and russet apples (both foliage and fruits), may cause red spotting, yellowing and dropping of rose leaves (often confused with black spot by amateur and sometimes professional gardeners), and may cause defoliation of Japanese plums. Injury is most prominent early in the season and in dull, cloudy weather when light rain or high humidity prevents rapid drying of the spray. Bordeaux may also make some plants more susceptible to early fall frosts.

Bordeaux-Oil Emulsion, for citrus fruits. Enough oil emulsion is added to the dilute bordeaux mixture to make 1% actual oil. The copper kills the beneficial fungi keeping down scale insects, so the oil is added to kill the scales.

Bordeaux Paint. Raw linseed oil stirred into dry bordeaux powder until thin enough to apply with a brush on pruning wounds, especially on apple trees after cutting out fire blight.

Bordeaux Paste or **Wash.** Water is added to dry bordeaux powder and half as much lime until the mixture is like thin paint. It is applied to the lower trunk of citrus trees to prevent brown rot gummosis.

BROMOFUME 10, 20 and 40 (Eston Chemicals), ethylene dibromide, soil fumigant.

Burgundy Mixture, a soda bordeaux formerly used when good lime was not obtainable and on resistant plants such as potatoes; sometimes more injurious to plants but with less visible residue than bordeaux. For a 8–10–100 mixture, 8 pounds copper sulfate dissolved in 8 gallons of water are added to a spray tank two-thirds full of water and with the agitator running 10 pounds sodium carbonate (washing soda) added in water to dissolve it.

Calcium Cyanamid (American Cyanamid), an herbicide, and also used to inhibit development of apothecia of the fungus causing lettuce soft rot or drop and sometimes those causing brown rot of stone fruits.

CALO CHLOR (Mallinckrodt), 2:1 mixture of calomel and mercuric chloride, used as a turf fungicide; may cause burning unless used cautiously.

CALO GREEN (Mallinckrodt), mercuric chloride.

Calomel, mercurous chloride, for control of brown patch and some other turf diseases, usually used in a mixture of 2 parts calomel and 1 part mercuric chloride, with 1½ to 3 ounces of the mixture applied with sand or with a power sprayer per 1000 square feet. Also a corm treatment for gladiolus, at 5 ounces to 1 gallon of water, and a seed treatment for celery, 1 ounce suspended in 1 gallon of water.

Carbon Disulfide, soil fumigant used for control of Armillaria root rot and sometimes for nematodes. Holes 18 inches apart are made in staggered rows, with 1⅗ liquid ounces injected per hole. This chemical is highly inflammable, also dangerous to living plants. Use only on fallow soil.

Casein, one of the proteins in dried skim milk, used as a spreader for sprays, to reduce surface tension.

CERESAN (Du Pont), 2% ethyl mercuric chloride, for treating cotton, peas, flower bulbs.

CERESAN M (Du Pont), ethyl mercuric p-toluene sulfanilide, less toxic than Ceresan and replacing it for the same uses. On gladiolus corms it is used at rate of 1 ounce to 3 gallons of water.

CERESAN, NEW IMPROVED (Du Pont), ethyl mercuric phosphate, for seed treatment of cereals, cotton, sugar beets, peas, and bulbs. The recommended strength for gladiolus corms is 1 ounce to 3 gallons water plus 2 tablespoons of Dreft. The corms are soaked for 15 minutes only (30 minutes for cormels) and planted *immediately*. If allowed to dry out overnight they may be injured.

Chloropicrin, tear gas, sold as Larvacide, a fumigant for soil nematodes and some fungi, not to be used around living plants. The soil should be prepared as for planting and be moderately loose. Spot injections, 10 inches apart, are made with a hand applicator resembling a huge hypodermic needle. The chemical should be injected 6 inches deep with 2½ to 3 cc. (½ teaspoon) per injection. It helps to mark the area like a checkerboard with crosswise and lengthwise lines 10 inches apart. On the first row injections are made at the intersection of lines, and on the next staggered halfway between, then at the intersections on the third row, and so on. Tear gas is, of course, disagreeable to handle and must be applied with a special applicator, which can be rented. A gas mask is required for indoor application and preferably for outdoor handling. The gas works much better at high temperatures, with most rapid killing of root-knot nematodes at 98° F. It should not be used in early spring before the ground has warmed up to 60° or above. Soil moisture is also necessary. Apply a water seal immediately after smoothing the soil, wetting the surface for an inch or more. A delay of two hours after injection means great reduction in effectiveness of the treatment.

Other fumigants can be substituted for nematode control, but chloropicrin remains one of the most effective for soil fungi, including the sclerotia of *Sclerotium rolfsii,* cause of southern blight and crown rot.

C O C S (Niagara Sprayer), copper oxychloride sulfate, one of the fixed coppers rather widely used as a substitute for bordeaux mixture on vegetables and sometimes ornamentals. On roses and azaleas it is sometimes injurious at effective concentrations.

Coposil (California Spray Chemical), copper ammonium silicate, a nonstaining, usually noninjurious copper compound, useful for diseases of ornamentals, such as laurel leaf spots.

Copper Compounds. More than a hundred million pounds of copper sulfate are used annually in the preparation of bordeaux mixture and other copper fungicides. Although tried many years ago for seed treatment, the modern use of copper dates from about 1882 with the discovery of bordeaux mixture (see above). Substitutes for bordeaux, the so-called "fixed coppers," are easier to use, sometimes safer for plants, and leave less objectionable residue. They include basic sulfates (Tennessee Tribasic, Basicop, Bordow), basic chlorides (Compound A, Cupro K, C O C S), copper oxides (Cuprocide), copper ammonium silicate (Coposil), copper phosphate, and copper zeolite. Copper sprays control many blights, leaf spots, downy and powdery mildews.

Compatibility. Fixed coppers are compatible with lead arsenate, calcium and zinc arsenates, Paris green, rotenone, pyrethrum, summer and dormant oils, DDT, chlordane, toxaphene, parathion, glyoxalidines, quinones, wettable sulfur, zinc sulfate and lime; *incompatible* with lime sulfur; *questionable* with cryolite, benzene hexachloride, tetraethyl pyrophosphate, organic mercuries, and dithiocarbamates.

Phytotoxicity. Plant injury may occur when application is followed by light rain or high humidity with consequent slow drying, or in cold weather of early spring or in fall. Injury to apples and roses varies from reddish spots on leaves to yellowing and defoliation.

Copper-A Compound (Du Pont), copper oxychloride, adapted for use on potatoes and other vegetables, claimed to be a safer fungicide for copper-sensitive plants.

Copper Carbonate, a greenish powder made from copper sulfate and sodium carbonate, formerly used as a seed treatment for wheat, but now largely replaced by organic mercurials, still used for sorghum seed, sold as Copper Carb, Carbo, etc.

Copper Ammonium Silicate, complex combination of copper sulfate with sodium silicate and ammonium hydroxide. See Coposil.

Copper Hydro (Chipman Chemical), a fixed copper to be used as a dust or spray, claimed to be especially effective against tomato blight and cherry leaf spot.

Copper 8-Quinolinolate, or 8-hydroxy quinoline. See Bioquin 1.

Copper-Lime Dust, usually made up of 20% monohydrated copper sulfate and 80% hydrated lime, sometimes used on potatoes and other vegetables as a substitute for bordeaux mixture. To be effective it should be applied when foliage is wet, but this leaves a residue entirely too objectionable for ornamentals.

Copper Naphthenate, made by reacting hot naphthenic acids, by-product of the petroleum industry, with copper carbonate, and used in the treatment of fabric and wood against mildew and rot. In aerosol form it is also promising for plant disease control, but at present seems better adapted for greenhouse than garden use.

Copper Oxalate, from oxalic acid and a copper salt; has controlled walnut blight in the Northwest.

Copper Oxide, see **Cuprocide.**

Copper Phosphate, a gelatinous precipitate formed from copper sulfate and sodium or ammonium phosphate with bentonite and hydrated lime; limited tests showed promise for apple scab, cherry leaf spot, pear blight.

Copper Sulfate, mostly used in the preparation of bordeaux mixture, but used alone as a spray for disinfesting storage houses and in weak concentration as an eradicant for powdery mildews.

Copper Zeolite, a complex copper alumino-silicate, with the copper held firmly, reducing injury from soluble copper.

Corrosive Sublimate, see **Mercuric Chloride.**

CRAG 341 B and 341 C (Carbide & Carbon), glyoxalidine compounds marketed as fruit fungicides, 341 B for cherry leaf spot and 341 C for apple scab; some tests have given good results, but performance is still somewhat erratic with occasional phytotoxicity. *Compatible* with lead arsenate, nicotine sulfate, tetraethyl pyrophosphate, and parathion; *incompatible* with Neotran and benzene hexachloride.

CRAG POTATO FUNGICIDE (Carbide & Carbon), an inorganic copper-zinc-chromate complex promising for early and late blight of potatoes, perhaps other diseases, at 1½ to 2 pounds per 100 gallons.

CRAG TURF FUNGICIDE 531 (Carbide & Carbon), calcium-zinc-copper-cadmium-chromate, effective against dollar spot or small brown patch at 3 ounces per 1000 square feet, applied with water or sand, at 10- to 14-day intervals.

CUPROCIDE (Rohm & Haas) red or yellow copper oxide, the color being a function of particle size, yellow being the smallest; used as a seed disinfectant, except on cabbage, and as a spray for post-emergence damping-off and certain vegetable diseases.

CUPRO K (Rohm & Haas), copper oxychloride, suggested for cherry leaf spot and other fruit and vegetable diseases.

D–D MIXTURE (Shell Chemical), 1,2-dichloropropane and 1,3-dichloropropylene, soil fumigant for nematodes, well-suited for large-scale operation since fumes need not be confined. Injections of 4 to 5 cc. (¾ to 1 teaspoon) are made 12 inches apart. There is little or no control of soil fungi.

Diluents, relatively inert materials used as carriers and conditioners in dust mixtures—hydrated lime, bentonite, talc, kaolin, pyrophyllite, walnut-shell flour.

Dinitro compounds, derivatives of cresol and phenol used as dormant sprays for some insects, and as herbicides. See Elgetol.

DITHANE D–14 (Rohm & Haas), disodium ethylene bisdithiocarbamate, used to control potato and tomato late blight at the rate of 2 quarts liquid Dithane, 1 pound 36% zinc sulfate, and 1/2 pound hydrated lime per 100 gallons of water. For azalea petal blight 1 to 1 1/3 quarts Dithane are used with 1 pound of 25% zinc sulfate, 1/2 pound lime and Triton B 1956 or Dreft as a spreader. In small quantities this reduces to 2 1/2 teaspoons Dithane plus 1 teaspoon each of zinc sulfate and lime, with 5 to 10 drops of spreader. The mixture must be continuously agitated. Dithane also gives good control of Botrytis on gladiolus flowers and Stemphylium leaf spot. It is one spray which can be used on open bloom without much injury or discoloration.

DITHANE Z 78 (Rohm & Haas), zinc ethylene bisdithiocarbamate, a wettable powder used at 1 1/4 pounds (for azalea petal blight) to 2 pounds (for vegetables) per 100 gallons of water, or around 1 tablespoon per gallon, and also used in a 6 to 8% dust. This is easier to prepare than the liquid Dithane, but leaves a more noticeable residue on ornamentals. It is effective in the control of downy mildew of cucurbits. In my own rose test garden it controls black spot but not powdery mildew.

Dithiocarbamates, organic sulfur fungicides, derivatives of dithiocarbamic acid. See Arasan, Dithane, Fermate, Parzate, Zerlate and Zac. In general these carbamates are *compatible* with lead arsenate, cryolite, rotenone, pyrethrum, nicotine, DDT, chlordane, benzene hexachloride, toxaphene, parathion, dormant and summer oils, wettable sulfur; *incompatible* with Paris green; *questionable* with calcium arsenate, tetraethyl pyrophosphate, lime sulfur, lime (except at manufacturer's directions) fixed coppers, and bordeaux mixture.

DOWFUME G (Dow Chemical), methyl bromide, with carbon tetrachloride and ethylene dichloride as diluents, soil fumigant giving good control of nematodes and some control of fungi and weeds. See also Methyl Bromide.

DOWFUME N (Dow Chemical), same ingredients as D–D Mixture (See above).

DOWFUME W–40 (Dow Chemical), ethylene dibromide, soil fumigant for nematodes and wireworms, adapted for large-scale use.

Dow 9 (Dow Chemical), zinc trichlorophenate, seed treatment for cotton, peas, and other crops, and dip for bulbs.

DREFT, detergent used as a wetting agent in sprays.

ELGETOL (Standard Agricultural Chemical), sodium dinitro-o-cresolate, used as a dormant spray to kill aphid eggs and some scales, and also as an eradicant ground spray for apple scab, grape black rot, and similar diseases where fungi overwinter in leaves on ground. It has also been effectively used on junipers to inhibit formation of telial horns from rust galls but is somewhat phytotoxic.

Ethylene Dibromide, soil fumigant, a relatively cheap nematocide sold as Dowfume, Iscobrome D, Soilfume-caps, for small gardens, Bromofume, used at 5 to 6 cc. per injection (of materials 20% by weight) and injections spaced 12 inches apart. No water seal is required.

Ethyl Mercuric Chloride, 2% Ceresan, seed treatment for cotton, corn and flax, dip for flower bulbs.

Ethyl Mercuric Iodide, DuBay 1155–HH, effective in a California nursery for pre- and post-emergence damping-off.

Ethyl Mercuric Phosphate, seed and bulb disinfectant. See Ceresan, New Improved.

Ethylmercuric-p-toluene Sulfonanilide, Ceresan-M, DuBay 1451, 1452, replacing the older Ceresan as seed and bulb treatment.

Ferbam, common name for ferric dimethyl dithiocarbamate (Fermate).

FERMATE (Du Pont), ferric dimethyl dithiocarbamate, one of the leading new organic fungicides. Used at 1½ to 2 pounds per 100 gallons as a spray and as a 7 to 10% dust, often with sulfur. The iron gives a black color sometimes objectionable on light flowers, although seldom noticeable on foliage. Fermate gives good control of apple scab, apple rust, brown rot of stone fruits, some Botrytis blights, anthracnoses, downy mildews, and excellent control of grape black rot and rose black spot. It does not control powdery mildews. It is compatible with wettable sulfur and is usually used with sulfur in fruit sprays; also compatible with lead arsenate and acts as a safener for it. See Dithiocarbamates for the complete compatibility list.

Formaldehyde, soil fumigant effective in controlling fungi causing damping-off and other diseases but not very efficient against nematodes. It is sold as Formalin, a 35 to 40% solution of a colorless gas in water and methanol. In preparing soil for flats, mix 2½ tablespoons formalin with 1 cup of water and sprinkle over, then mix with 1 bushel of soil. Fill flats, plant seed, after waiting 24 hours, then water. As a drench for fallow soil dilute 1 part formalin to 50 parts water and apply ½ to 1 gallon to each square foot of soil. As a treatment for potato scab 1 pint formalin is used to 30 gallons water and tubers are soaked for 2 hours. As a disinfectant for tools, a 5% solution of formalin is sometimes used.

FULEX Soil Treatment (Fuller System), copper 8-quinolinolate, manufactured for treatment of growing carnations to control wilt and stem and root rots; considered promising by some commercial growers, but results are not conclusive.

GARDEN DOWFUME (Dow Chemical), ethylene dibromide for small-scale use.

Glyoxalidine Derivatives, recently promising as fungicides and available now as Crag Fruit Fungicides—compounds 341 B and C.

GOOD RITE P.E.P.S. (B. F. Goodrich), polyethylene polysulfide, a latex-like material used as a sticker for fruit sprays. It has some fungicidal value but not enough, alone, to control apple scab. It does reduce the number of sprays required during the season.

Hot Water, used in disinfection of seeds, bulbs, and sometimes living plants to kill internal bacteria, fungi, or nematodes, the temperature and time of treatment varying with the plant.

HYAMINE COMPOUNDS (Rohm & Haas), quaternary ammonium compounds of possible use in disinfesting storage rooms and containers, effective against molds and bacteria but not insects.

Iodine, used in impregnating wrappers for fruits in storage.

ISCOBROME 1 (Innis, Speiden), 15% methyl bromide, for soil fumigation in greenhouses and seedbeds for nematodes and some fungi; can be used near living plants.

ISCOBROME D (Innis, Speiden), ethylene dibromide in high-flash naphtha, field fumigant for nematodes and wireworms.

ISOTHAN Q 15 (Onyx Oil & Chemical), lauryl isoquinolinium bromide, a quaternary ammonium compound readily wetting plant surfaces but only fair as a fungicide. Reported as somewhat effective for powdery mildew on live oaks.

KARBAM BLACK (Sherwin-Williams), ferric dimethyl dithiocarbamate, same active ingredient as Fermate.

KARBAM WHITE (Sherwin-Williams), zinc dimethyl dithiocarbamate. See Zerlate.

KOLODUST (Niagara Sprayer), a finely divided and adhesive sulfur dust.

KOLOFOG (Niagara Sprayer), fused bentonite sulfur used as a spray for apple scab, brown rot of stone fruits, etc.

KOPPER KING (Acme White Lead & Color Works), basic copper sulfate.

LARVACIDE (Innis, Speiden), chloropicrin, which see.

Lime, Hydrated, calcium hydroxide, used in preparing bordeaux mixture, as a safener when lead arsenate is added to lime sulfur, and as a filler in insecticidal and fungicidal dusts. Until recently it has been considered relatively inert, but now some of the dwarfing and hardening of bordeaux-sprayed plants are attributed to the lime.

Lime Sulfur, polysulfides formed by boiling together sulfur and milk of lime. The standard liquid has a specific gravity of 32 Baumé and the commercial product is far superior to the homemade. Lime sulfur dates back to 1851 when the head gardener, Grison, at Versailles, France, boiled together sulfur and lime for a vegetable fungicide, called "Eau Grison." In 1886 it was used in California as a dormant spray for San José scale and later for peach leaf curl. A dry form of lime sulfur was marketed about 1915.

Because this was injurious to many plants as a summer spray a self-boiled lime sulfur made without heat was produced in 1908 for sensitive plants; later it was replaced by wettable sulfurs in the fruit-spray program.

Lime sulfur is still used as a dormant spray for fruits, roses, and some other plants at a 1 to 9 dilution, and sometimes in summer sprays at a 1 to 50 dilution, being especially valuable for the Volutella blight of boxwood. It should not be used at temperatures above 85° F.

Compatible with calcium arsenate, nicotine sulfate, glyoxalidines; *incompatible* with soaps, Paris green, cryolite, rotenone, pyrethrum, dormant and summer oils, dinitro compounds, benzene hexachloride, tetraethyl pyrophosphate, organic mercuries, bordeaux mixture, fixed coppers; *questionable* with chlordane, toxaphene, parathion, dinitro compounds, and dithiocarbamates.

LYSOL, sometimes used for treatment of gladiolus corms, at 1 pint to 25 gallons, or 1½ tablespoons per gallon, and soaking for 3 hours, but injurious on occasion; in 5% solution used for dipping cutting knife to prevent potato ring rot.

Magnesium Sulfate, epsom salts, sometimes used as a safener.

MAGNETIC 70 (Stauffer Chemical), a wettable sulfur paste produced by emulsification and atomization of molten sulfur.

MERCAD (Merck & Co.), an organic cadmium, turf fungicide.

Mercuric Chloride, bichloride of mercury, corrosive sublimate, a very effective disinfectant at 1 to 1000 dilution or one 7-grain tablet to a pint of water. This is poison, sometimes difficult to buy except by presenting a doctor's prescription at the drug store, but very useful for disinfecting iris rhizomes (30-minute soak), treating gladiolus corms for scab (soak 2 hours just before planting), and some seeds, soaking for 2 to 20 minutes according to the kind, then rinsing in running water and drying before planting. Make the solution in a glass or enamel container; metals are corroded. Mercuric chloride is also used mixed with calomel as a turf fungicide.

Mercurous Chloride. See calomel.

METHASAN (Monsanto) zinc dimethyl dithiocarbamate. See Zerlate.

MERSOLITE 8 (F. W. Berk & Co.), phenyl mercuric acetate, effective in control of basal rot of narcissus.

Methyl Bromide, soil fumigant available as Dowfume G and Iscobrome 1, less toxic to plants than other fumigants and so useful in greenhouses and sometimes for balled or potted nursery stock in special fumigating chambers. It is toxic to humans and should be used with caution. Some fungi will be killed if 7 to 8 cc. are used per injection, with injections spaced 10 inches apart, but 5 to 6 cc. is considered sufficient dosage for nematodes.

MICROGEL (Tennessee Corp.), neutral, insoluble copper readily miscible with oil emulsion for dormant sprays.

MIKE (Dow Chemical), micronized wettable sulfur.

Monocalcium Arsenite, used as an eradicant fungicide, at 3 pounds per 100 gallons, with or without 4–4–100 bordeaux mixture and ½% petroleum oil, to suppress brown rot and blossom blight conidia in stone fruits.

MYCOTOX (Givauden Delawanna), trichlorophenylacetate with Pyrax, now under test as a fungicide.

Nabam, common name for disodium ethylene bisdithiocarbamate (Dithane D–14).

ORANGE HELIONE (Standard Agricultural Chemicals), diamino azobenzene dihydrochloride, for chemotherapy, treating maple trees for bleeding canker.

Oxyquinoline Benzoate, 8-quinolinol benzoate, used as chemotherapeutant for Dutch elm disease and also in a proprietary compound for damping-off. Soil applications at 1 to 1000 concentration, applied at the rate of 5 gallons per diameter inch of tree trunk at breast height are quite effective in protecting elms from the toxic effects of the Dutch elm disease fungus. The chemical is more successful as a preventive than as a curative, but treatment of already infected trees in many cases prolongs life.

Oxyquinoline Sulfate, promising for post-emergence damping-off, and some wilts.

PARZATE (Du Pont), zinc ethylene bisdithiocarbamate, the same active ingredient as in Dithane but in a formulation somewhat more injurious to cucurbits, also injurious to apple fruit. Effective at 2 pounds per 100 gallons in control of tomato and potato late blight and snapdragon rust, and in some cases as a 15-minute soak for gladiolus at 6 ounces to 3 gallons water.

PHYGON (U.S. Rubber, dichloronaphthoquinone, a most effective fungicide, at 1 pound per 100 gallons, for a wide variety of diseases, including apple scab, peach brown rot, rose black spot, azalea petal spot, but somewhat injurious even with magnesium sulfate added as a safener (Phygon XL). The injury varies from a faint light spotting of azalea flowers, or a faint blackening of rose foliage, to a great reduction in yield of potatoes. Phygon is also an excellent seed treatment, although irritating to the operator in large-scale handling.

Phenyl Mercuric Nitrate, added, in 0.2% solution, to gilsonite varnish used for canker stain of plane trees.

P.M.A.S., phenyl mercuric acetate, promising as a turf fungicide, effective against dollar spot and copper spot, and also marketed as a crabgrass control.

PURATIZED AGRICULTURAL SPRAY (Gallowhur Chemical), phenyl mercuric triethanol ammonium lactate, an organic mercury used at great dilution—1 to 5000 to 1 to 10,000. It is more effective as an eradicant than as a protectant for apple scab and is usually used with sulfur or Fermate in the spray schedule and during the early part of the season for fear of mercury residue from late applications. At 1 to 5000 it has given good control of sycamore anthracnose and walnut leaf spot. Tested for azalea petal blight it took the color out of the flowers at effective concentrations. It is incompatible with lime sulfur but compatible with wettable sulfur and most insecticides.

PURATIZED 111–5 (Gallowhur Chemical), mercury-copper quaternary ammonium complex, effective for potato blight in mist blower applications.

Potassium Permanganate, occasionally used as a disinfectant and has given some promise as a chemotherapeutant for the Dutch elm disease; can be used as a disinfectant for grafting knives and other tools at 1 ounce in 2 gallons of water.

Puraturf 177 (Gallowhur Chemical), phenyl amino cadmium lactate, turf fungicide effective in the control of dollar spot.

Rosin Lime Sulfur, a homemade rosin soap added to lime sulfur to increase adhesiveness and performance, apparently safer on the West Coast than in the more humid East. The soap is made with 25 parts rosin, 5 parts potash lye, 1 part alcohol, and 69 parts water, by weight, melted together with heat. The soap is added to the water before the lime sulfur, but in equal volume—that is, one part rosin soap, 48 parts water, and 1 part lime sulfur for a summer spray for rust and some other diseases.

Semesan (Du Pont), mercuric chlorophenol sulfate, an organic mercury first marketed in Germany as Uspulun, used for treatment of vegetable and flower seeds and sometimes for brown patch of turf.

Semesan Bel (Du Pont), 2% chlorophenol mercury and 12% nitrophenol mercury, used for treating white or sweet potatoes, or for woody cuttings and grafts.

Sodium Selenate, applied to soil and taken up by plants; makes chrysanthemums resistant to leaf nematodes and some boxwood to root nematodes. It is poisonous, has a long residual effect in the soil, and must not be used on land intended later for vegetables. The form P–40 (Plant Products Co.) is 2% sodium selenate impregnated on superphosphate and can be applied in dry form.

Spergon (U.S. Rubber), tetrachlorobenzoquinone, seed treatment for vegetables, especially legumes and corn, some flowers, bulb treatment for lilies, root and sprout treatment for sweet potatoes, and a spray or dust for cabbage downy mildew.

Sulforon (Du Pont), wettable sulfur.

Sulfur, the oldest known fungicide, antedating written history. Around 150 million pounds are used annually in the United States in fungicides and insecticides. As a dust the particles should be fine enough to go through a 325-mesh screen. Flowers of sulfur, small crystals produced by sublimation, are not fine enough for dusts.

Wettable sulfurs have wetting agents added for ready mixing with water for use in sprays. Flotation sulfurs are by-products of the manufacture of fuel gas from coal, so finely divided they are almost colloidal. They are available in paste or powder form. Micronized sulfurs also have particles approaching colloidal size and are prepared in special impact and air separator mills.

Sulfur sprays and dusts are more useful for ornamentals and fruits than for vegetables, and are used for control of powdery mildews, rusts, apple scab, brown rot of stone fruits, rose black spot, etc.

Compatibility. Wettable sulfurs are compatible with lead arsenate, calcium arsenate, cryolite, pyrethrum, rotenone, nicotine, DDT, chlordane, benzene hexachloride, toxaphene, tetraethyl pyrophosphate, lime sulfur, fixed coppers, bordeaux mixture, dithiocarbamates, quinones, and organic mercuries; *incom-*

patible with oil sprays, Paris green; *questionable* with dinitro compounds and parathion.

Phytotoxicity. Sulfur is unsafe on many varieties of cucurbits, causing stunting and decrease in yield in squash and melons particularly, except for sulfur-resistant varieties. Wettable sulfurs and sulfur dusts are safer than lime sulfur at high temperatures but may injure fruit at 85° and foliage at 100° F. On roses there may be some foliage burn above 90°.

TAG FUNGICIDE 331 (California Spray-Chemical), organic mercury, promising as an eradicant for apple scab and rust.

TENNESSEE COPPER 34 (Tennessee Corp.), 34% metallic copper, often used with sulfur for rose black spot, especially in the South, in proportion to give about 3½% copper in the dust.

TERSAN (Du Pont), tetramethyl thiuram disulfide, turf fungicide, rather effective for large brown patch.

Thiourea, under test for bulb treatment.

Thiram, common name for tetramethyl thiuram disulfide (Arasan, Tersan).

Tree Paints or Wound Dressings. Many commercial tree paints are not particularly fungicidal, as evidenced by the spread of the plane-tree canker-stain fungus in wound dressings. Orange shellac is effective on a fresh cut, for the alcohol acts as a sterilizing agent after which spar varnish, house paint, or an asphaltum tree paint may be applied. Creosote paints destroy wood-decay fungi but are toxic to live tissues and should be confined to dead heartwood. See also Bordeaux paint.

TRITON B 1956 (Rohm & Haas), spreader used with Dithane and some other fungicides. Triton X 100 is used with DDT in control of elm disease vectors.

URAMON (Du Pont), urea, somewhat effective as a soil treatment for root-knot nematodes.

VASCO 4 (Virginia Smelting), zinc oxide, sometimes used in seed treatment, especially for crucifers sensitive to copper oxide.

ZAC (Goodrich), zinc dimethyl dithiocarbamate-cyclohexamine.

ZERLATE (Du Pont), zinc dimethyl dithiocarbamate, one of the best materials for controlling tomato anthracnose but ineffective against late blight, also good for cucurbit anthracnose and downy mildew. On tomatoes it can be alternated with copper in the spray schedule.

Zinc Sulfate, used with liquid Dithane and also to control little-leaf or mottle-leaf, zinc deficiency disease.

Zineb, common name for zinc ethylene bisdithiocarbamate (Dithane Z–78, Parzate).

Ziram, common name for zinc dimethyl dithiocarbamate (Zerlate, Karbam White).

Applying the Chemicals

Spraying is the application of a chemical to a plant in *liquid* form, **dusting** the application of a dust fine *dry* powder. This difference between spraying and dusting was very clear cut until aerosol bombs, mist blowers, and fog machines were developed to apply liquids in such concentrated form that the particles are practically dry when they reach the plant and spray-dusters were made to deliver wetted dusts.

Sprayers vary from a flit gun or small pint atomizer, which takes an hour to discharge a gallon, to power apparatus that discharges 60 gallons a minute at 800 pounds pressure from a 600-gallon tank. Dusters vary from the small cardboard carton in which the dust is purchased to helicopters. Applicators for aerosols vary from the one-pound "bomb" for household insects to the truck-mounted fog generators or air blast machines.

MIST SPRAYERS

Basic research on improving the methods of applying insecticides was started by the U.S. Department of Agriculture in 1928, the first published reports were in 1936, and in 1948 S. F. Potts and R. R. Whitten who conducted the work were publicly cited as having accomplished means of producing aerosols by mechanical methods, for treatment of over 600,000 acres of forest for pest control by aircraft and mist blowers, and for increasing the value of the 1948 corn crop by 100 million dollars, through the application of 2,4–D in atomized concentrates. The total cost of all this was said to be $25,000 for salaries, a fine example of how a little money spent on research pays dividends. The present mist blowers can disperse finely atomized sprays 100 feet vertically and several hundred feet horizontally—sprays which are 100 times more concentrated than the conventional hydraulic sprays. There is no refilling of spray tanks, no bothering with a great excess of water, no drenching of plants to leave an unsightly residue. There are, of course, drawbacks. Only as many trees can be treated as will be reached from the truck on the road; in most cases trees can be treated from only one side, and great care must be taken so that the oils used in formulation are not toxic to plants. Also, it is impossible to differentiate between plants; everything within reach of the "wafted air" gets a dose.

Starting with DDT for mosquito control and going on to various shade tree pests the mist sprayers have been chiefly used for insecticides, but now formulations for fungicides are being prepared. Lime sulfur can be used undiluted with glycerine (I shudder to think what that will do to painted houses along the route); basic copper sulfate and Coposil can be used with refined oils, and Puratized with water. Mist spraying is also under test for vegetable row crops, with a couple of copper products satisfactory in control of potato late blight.

Aerosol application of insecticides in greenhouses is far ahead of that of fungicides, but preliminary work indicates the latter is possible. Copper naphthenate has given good results in control of snapdragon rust and rose mildew.

HYDRAULIC SPRAYERS

Mist sprayers will probably never eliminate hydraulic sprayers which have the advantage of a long hose to reach every side of a tree or part of a property, can use any compatible combination of insecticide and fungicide, and can work under more unfavorable weather conditions.

For trees high gallonage per minute and great pressure to drive sprays high in the air have advantages, but for garden plants the emphasis should be on cutting down gallonage and pressure. Estate sprayers come in different sizes, from a 15-gallon tank and 1 horsepower engine up to orchard size. For the orchard, a spray gun is satisfactory; but for flowering shrubs—azaleas, roses, etc.—a spray rod, curved at the end, or with an angle nozzle, is easier on the plants and more effective. The size of the hole in the nozzle disc and the pressure determine the amount of spray used. A No. 2 disc delivers .17 gallon per minute at 50 pounds pressure and .42 gallon at 300 pounds pressure. A No. 3 disc delivers .32 gallon at 50 pounds and .78 at 300 pounds. Spray guns deliver much more spray and are very wasteful for garden operations. If a proprietary spray costs, as many do, from 15 to 30 cents a diluted gallon, keeping the pressure down and the nozzle hole small becomes very important.

My own conviction is that a hand-operated sprayer of the 12-gallon Paragon type is far more economical of material and probably of time than a power sprayer for roses and other garden plants. Probably I am biased by habit, but with a good assistant (one born with a sense of timing and rhythm for pumping) I can spray more roses faster with less material than I have ever seen done by two men operating a power sprayer in a public rose garden. We sometimes spray 3000 or more roses a day, to say nothing of various other plants, and these may be divided up in as many as 14 gardens, anywhere from 1 to 20 miles apart. Yet with a Paragon in the back of the Ford business coupe (much quicker packing than a station wagon), we can unpack and pack up 14 times and make up 14 fresh batches of spray material in about the same hours it may take to do the same number of roses in one large garden by power sprayer. The latter applies more gallons per minute but does not cover more roses per minute, and the hand pump is so much easier to maneuver around beds!

The same hand-pumped sprayer can do large shrubs and small trees with the addition of an extension rod, and with 25 feet of heavy duty spray hose replacing the 10 feet purchased with the sprayer it is possible to get into odd corners behind shrubbery.

Knapsack sprayers are next best if you have no one to help spray. Worn on

Fig. 1. Twelve-gallon Paragon sprayer in action, using one extension rod with angled spray rod. A second extension can be added for spraying of small trees.

Fig. 2. Knapsack sprayer, for one-man operation. The angle nozzle allows coverage of under surface of foliage.

Fig. 3. Knapsack sprayer in action. The shoulder straps should have been shortened to bring the sprayer higher on the back.

the back with the weight distributed evenly they are not too heavy, and they are pumped without effort by moving a lever up and down with the right hand while spraying with the left. The spray residue may be somewhat more spotty than that applied with greater pressure, and knapsacks cost as much as larger sprayers.

Compressed air sprayers are less expensive, but are pumped up with great effort. After pumping you sling the tank over one shoulder, spray while the pressure lasts, then stop and pump again. If you are affluent, you can purchase a tank on wheels, and pressure cylinders to replace the pumping.

Atomizer or **plunger-type sprayers** are hard on the operator if used for more than one or two plants, and it is difficult to place the spray on the underside of the foliage. They work better for insects on house plants than for garden diseases.

In addition to the regular sprayers there are all kinds of gadgets to be inserted in pails or attached to hoses, all of which have some value but often call forth more effort than they are supposed to save, and sometimes limit the choice of fungicide.

DUSTERS

A cheesecloth bag beaten with a stick is not recommended as a duster, but it is far better than a can with holes in the top to be used like a salt shaker. Many of the expensive combination dusts come in small cardboard cylinders to be used as dusters, and they work fairly well for awhile if the cardboard is well paraffined to slide easily and the dust does not get damp and clog. There

FIG. 4. A collection of dusters: small cardboard carton at right; 2-quart, 1-quart, 1-pint dust guns with extension rods; bellows duster.

FIG. 5. Bellows duster provides easy coverage from underneath the bushes up through the foliage.

comes a time, however, when the effort gets too great and you transfer the contents to a **dust gun,** which can be glass but preferably metal, of 1 pint to 2 quart capacity, and with an extension tube with some sort of flaring arrangement at the end to send dust up through a plant. There are a number of satisfactory small dust guns.

If you have much dusting to do you will rejoice with me that the Platz type **bellows duster** that we used to get from Germany is now made in the United States in an improved but similar model. You can walk down a row of beans or around a rosebed and dust almost as fast as you can walk, with no stooping and no need to stop too frequently for refilling.

There are also **rotary dusters** that you carry over one shoulder and operate with a crank, and **knapsack dusters** that are worn on the back like the sprayers but are more suited to large gardens or small farms. For a large farm with orchard crops there are power dusters. And in most states there is a surprisingly long list of companies who take on custom dusting by airplane or helicopter.

SPRAYING VS. DUSTING

There is really no answer to the question of whether it is better to dust or to spray. In most gardens you will do both, depending on the weather, the plant, the fungicide you want to use, and how much time and help you have. I dust vegetables to save time, and sometimes roses early in the season; but when they are coming into full bloom I prefer to use a spray that will not dull the glowing color with a dusty film.

Some orchardists prefer dusting because they can get around the trees quickly in a rain, whereas to apply a spray they must wait until the foliage is dry. But for ornamentals exactly the opposite is true! You cannot dust a shrub even slightly wet with rain or dew without having a hideous splotchy effect that persists for a long time. If absolutely necessary you can spray while plants are still somewhat wet with dew. It is easier to spray than to dust on a windy day and you don't have to cry the dust particles out of your eyes before you can go to sleep at night. Dusting does have points, however, the two chief ones being speed of application and not having to clean out the duster after use.

Sprayers have to be cleaned, and the *Gardener's Bug Book* goes into some detail on this chore. I'll not repeat it here except to say that sprayers should be rinsed between each kind of solution and with at least two changes of water at the end of the day. Occasionally they must be taken apart, the tank soaked in trisodium phosphate or washing soda, the strainers and nozzles in kerosene, wire run through the spray rods, then all put together and rinsed again with water.

MIXING THE CHEMICALS

A few hours after I wrote the opening paragraph about garden owners being their plants' worst enemies the telephone rang and an anxious voice asked if too much —— would hurt her roses. "Of course, how much did you use?"

"Well, I don't know, I just poured a little in some water in the sprayer." It seems incredible to me that so many gardeners still treat their plants that way.

Buy a set of measuring spoons and a glass measuring cup, marked in ounces, also a large pail and mark it off in gallons. Then measure, exactly!

Dosage directions are usually given per 100 gallons of water, with or without translation into small amounts. Not much arithmetic is required to figure a smaller dosage, if you remember a few measurements:

Conversion Table

3 teaspoons = 1 tablespoon
2 tablespoons = 1 fluid ounce
16 tablespoons or 8 fluid ounces = 1 cup
16 ounces, 2 cups = 1 pint
2 pints, 4 cups = 1 quart
16 cups, 8 pints, 4 quarts = 1 gallon
1 acre = 43,560 square feet

Suppose you want to make 3 gallons of a 2 to 100 dilution of lime sulfur. That is the same as a 1 to 50 dilution. Three gallons constitute 48 cups, so if you add 1 cup of lime sulfur to your 3 gallons you will have a 1 to 49 dilution which is close enough.

Or suppose you want to make 4 gallons of Dithane Z 78 at the rate of 1½ pounds per 100 gallons. That is 24 ounces per 100 gallons or .24 ounce per gallon, or .96 ounce for 4 gallons, which is approximately 1 ounce to weigh on your small scales. It also works out at about 1 level tablespoon of the Dithane powder per gallon and it is easier to measure than to weigh. There is, however, a good deal of variation in measuring, depending on how fluffed up or packed down the material is at the time, so weighing is preferable.

Sometimes materials for soil treatment are given in pounds per acre. Knowing that one acre contains 43,560 square feet you can make a proportion to find out how many pounds are required per 1000 square feet.

ALL-PURPOSE SPRAYS AND DUSTS

The practicability of combination insecticide-fungicide mixtures is sometimes argued. The proprietary compounds are more expensive, but they are more properly prepared than could be done at home and certainly save a lot of time. Nobody in these days could put on all the materials needed in separate applications. The trouble is that the mixtures follow fads, as in human medicine, and I am not sure that I always want to be on the band wagon. Just as penicillin was given for most human ills, so DDT was put in all plant mixtures. I am not for a minute decrying the great good each has done, but my roses don't need DDT unless they get midge, which they are free of to date, and they don't like DDT as much as they do old-fashioned lead arsenate. Fermate is fine for black spot but not much help when powdery mildew is on a rampage in a dry summer. And so, although I try out everything possible in my own garden and find many good points in the new combinations, for my clients I continue to use, for roses, the all-purpose spray known as Triogen which still has lead arsenate and still has the copper so effective for mildew and so relatively safe when the spray must go on in the hot noonday sun of our most fiendish days. The Fermate which has been added does not particularly improve black spot control but seems to lessen phytotoxicity from the lead arsenate and copper. Triogen is not always safe in very cool weather, nor on some varieties; it does not give perfect control of black spot nor is it too effective against red spiders. In my particular situation, where I must spray regardless of high temperature and into blooms which may be cut for a flower show, it happens to be the safest and least disfiguring mixture I have tried. For gardeners at home, who can dust with sulfur in the evening when it is cool or who can cut their open blooms before dust is applied, it may not be the best. My point is that you should stick with whatever spray or dust mixture—e.g. Pomogreen (sulfur and lead arsenate), Protexall or Ortho Rose Dust (DDT and Fermate), Floral Dust (with methoxyclor instead of DDT) Endopest Dust (with Zerlate), Pestmaster (copper and DDT)—that has, over a period of time, given *you* good results and should adopt new methods only after tests promise better results for *your* garden.

CHAPTER 3

CLASSIFICATION OF PLANT PATHOGENS

The plant diseases described in this Handbook are caused by bacteria, fungi, nematodes, a few seed plants, as dodder and mistletoe, viruses, and physiological disturbances grouped under the heading of Physiogenic Diseases. The classification of bacteria, fungi, and viruses is somewhat involved and is given here as a background for the specific descriptions in Chapter 4. Perhaps I should say that there are many classifications of bacteria, fungi, and viruses and that I have, with far too little knowledge of all the specialized fields, tried to choose that which is widely accepted and most readily adapted to the alphabetical requirements of a reference that works like a dictionary.

Classification of the bacteria is based on that given in the sixth (1948) edition of *Bergey's Manual of Determinative Bacteriology,* the sections on bacterial plant pathogens having been prepared by Walter H. Burkholder. Classification of the viruses is that given by Francis O. Holmes, also in the sixth edition of *Bergey's Manual.* So far as possible the genera, orders, and families of the fungi agree with those given in *A Dictionary of the Fungi,* by G. C. Ainsworth and G. R. Bisby but with some changes to American usage. Ainsworth and Bisby give G. W. Martin's *Key to the Families of Fungi,* but do not always follow it. In some cases where they have hesitated to assign a genus to a family I have chosen one of several possibilities, often helped by *The Fungi,* by Frederick A. and Frederick R. Wolf. *The Lower Fungi: Phycomycetes,* by H. M. Fitzpatrick, has also been a guide. The generic descriptions in Chapter 4 are largely based on *Genera of the Fungi,* by F. E. Clements and C. L. Shear.

Classification in accordance with convention or law is called taxonomy. Common names vary from locality to locality and country to country. Scientific names are international and are based on the binomial system. Each kind of bacterium, or fungus, or higher plant is a species and it has two Latin words for its name. The first indicates the genus to which the species belongs and the second the species itself. The latter name is usually descriptive. *Diplocarpon rosae* means that Diplocarpon, the black spot fungus, is found on rose. Sometimes the species name honors a person, as *Coniothyrium wernsdorffiae* for the fungus causing brand canker of rose. Although under the recommendations of the Rules of Nomenclature adopted at the International Botanical Congress species names derived from proper names should be capitalized, most American plant pathologists find it simpler to decapitalize all species names. Correctly, the author of the name should be written after the species. Then, if someone else comes along and places the species in a new genus, the name of the first author is put in parentheses and after that the name of the second author. When a number of taxonomists have worked on a species, the list of authors gets quite unwieldy. For simplicity all authors have been omitted from the scientific names in this text. The correct name for a fungus with more than one stage in the life-cycle is that given to the perfect stage.

Species are grouped into genera, related genera into families, designated with the suffix *aceae,* as Erysiphaceae, and families into orders with the suffix *ales,* Erysiphales. Groups of related orders form classes.

BACTERIA CAUSING PLANT DISEASE

Class Schizomycetes. Typically unicellular plants, cells usually small, some times ultramicroscopic; cells lack the definitely organized nucleus found in cells of higher plants and animals.

Order I. EUBACTERIALES. Simple and undifferentiated rigid cells which are spherical or rod-shaped, the latter being short or long, straight or curved, some nonmotile, others with flagella. Elongated cells divide by transverse fission and may remain attached in chains. Spherical cells (cocci) may divide in two or three planes producing tetrads and cubes, but these do not include plant pathogens.

Family 2. **Pseudomonadaceae.** Cells without endospores, elongate rods, straight or more or less spirally curved, mostly Gram-negative, aerobic.

Tribe 1. *Pseudomonadeae.* Straight rods; soil and water bacteria with many plant pathogens in genera Pseudomonas and Xanthomonas.

Family 4. **Rhizobiaceae.** Cells without endospores, rod-shaped, usually motile but sparsely flagellated; usually Gram-negative, aerobic.

Rhizobium. Cells capable of fixing free nitrogen when growing symbiotically on roots of Leguminosae. These are the desirable root-nodule bacteria. Different species are required for the inoculation of pea, sweet pea, and broad bean; bean; soybean; clover; sweet clover and alfalfa; lupine.

Agrobacterium. Producing hypertrophies or galls on roots and stems, but not capable of fixing free nitrogen; cause of crown gall and hairy root.

Family 8. **Corynebacteriaceae.** Nonmotile rods frequently banded or beaded with metachromatic granules; usually aerobic and Gram-positive.

Corynebacterium. Slender, straight to slightly curved rods, with irregularly stained segments or granules, often with pointed or club-shaped swellings at ends; causing potato ring rot, canker of tomato.

Family 10. **Enterobacteriaceae.** Gram-negative straight rods, motile with peritrichous flagella or nonmotile; some plant parasites causing blights and soft rots, some saprophytes causing decomposition of plant material.

Tribe 2. *Erwiniae.* Motile rods normally requiring nitrogen compounds for growth; invading tissues of living plants and producing dry necrosis, galls, wilts, and soft rots. There is a single genus, Erwinia.

Family 12. **Bacteriaceae.** Rod-shaped cells without endospores, motile or nonmotile, Gram-positive and Gram-negative, aerobic to facultative anaerobic, all in a single form genus, Bacterium, which contains the corn wilt organism and a few other plant pathogens.

FUNGI

Fungi are organisms having no chlorophyll, reproducing by sexual or asexual spores and not by fission as the bacteria and typically possessing a mycelium or mass of interwoven threads (hyphae) containing well-marked nuclei. Fungi are divided into three classes, the Phycomycetes with mycelium generally non-septate, the Ascomycetes with septate mycelium and sexual spores in asci, and the Basidiomycetes, with septate mycelium, frequently clamp connections, and sexual spores on basidia. A fourth group, the Fungi Imperfecti, includes those forms where only the imperfect state or asexual spore stage is known.

Ainsworth and Bisby claim 3,585 valid genera in the fungi, as many more which are synonymous, and 37,200 species living as parasites or saprophytes on other organisms or their residues.

PHYCOMYCETES

The word Phycomycetes means algal fungi, and the lower forms in this class resemble algae. The mycelium has many nuclei not marked off by cross-walls except where reproductive structures arise, a condition known as coenocytic. Asexual reproduction is by means of spores borne in sacs called sporangia. In the lower orders these sporangia germinate by breaking up into zoospores or swarmspores, which swim about by means of one or two little whips called flagella or cilia. In higher forms the asexual spores are nonmotile and known as conidia or sporangiospores. Sexual spores are zygospores, formed by the union of two similar sex cells or gametes, or oospores formed from unlike gametes. Phycomycetes are divided into the subclasses Oomycetes, with oospores, and Zygomycetes, with zygospores.

OOMYCETES

Order I. Chytridiales. Simple aquatic fungi with almost no mycelium, the thallus at maturity acting as a single sporangium, or dividing to become a sorus of sporangia; zoospores posteriorly uniflagellate. The families are sometimes separated into two series: inoperculate with the sporangia opening by the rupturing of one or more papillae and operculate, opening by a lid.

Inoperculate Chytridiales

Family 1. **Olpidiaceae.** Inside living organisms, holocarpic or the whole thallus functioning as a sporangium.

2. **Achlyogetonaceae.** Thallus converted into a linear series of sporangia.

3. **Synchytriaceae.** Thallus converted into a prosorus or sorus surrounded by a common membrane.

4. **Phlyctidiaceae.** Thallus divided into reproductive and vegetative portions, inside plant tissue or with reproductive bodies on surface of host.

5. **Rhizidiaceae.** Thallus between host cells; sporangium, prosporangium or resting spore formed from enlarged body of encysted zoospore.

6. **Cladochytriaceae.** Mycelium widespreading with terminal and intercalary enlargements transformed wholly or in part into sporangia or resting spores.

7. **Physodermataceae.** Sporangia and resting spores formed on separate thalli; the former on the surface, the latter abundant in host; parasites on terrestrial angiosperms.

Operculate Chytridiales

8. **Chytridiaceae.** Occurring in algae.

9. **Megachytriaceae.** Thallus with many centers, in living tissue or saprophytic.

II. Blastocladiales. Saprophytes in water or soil; thallus anchored in substratum by tapering rhizoids.

III. Monoblepharidales. Saprophytes in water; thallus of much-branched delicate hyphae.

IV. Plasmodiophorales. The placement of this group has always been uncertain. Some put it in the Myxomycetes or slime molds, others place it between the Myxomycetes and true fungi, and it has also been considered a family under the Chytridiales. Parasitic, assimilative phase a multinucleate thallus within host cells, chiefly of vascular plants and often causing hypertrophy, and germinating in place by amoeboid zoospores (occasionally uniciliate). There is a single family, **Plasmodiophoraceae.** Two genera are important plant pathogens: Plasmodiophora causing club root and Spongospora, cause of potato scab.

V. Saprolegniales. Marine forms, parasites of diatoms and algae, or in fresh water and soil, the water molds, with abundant mycelium; hyphae without constrictions; oogonium with several oospores.

VI. Leptomitales. Also water forms; hyphae constricted with cellulin plugs; oogonium with a single oospore.

VII. Lagenidiales. Primarily aquatic, mostly parasitic on algae and water molds; thallus simple; zoospores formed by cleavage within sporangium or partly or wholly in an evanescent external vesicle.

VIII. Peronosporales, the downy mildews and white rusts. Primarily terrestrial, living in soil or parasitic on vascular plants, in the latter case, zoosporangia functioning as conidia.

1. **Albuginaceae,** the white rusts. Conidia (sporangia) in chains on club-shaped conidiophores borne in dense sori beneath epidermis of host, the sori forming white blisters; intercellular mycelium with globose haustoria.

2. **Pythiaceae.** Conidiophores differing little from assimilative hyphae; mycelium saprophytic or parasitic but if latter within cells and without haustoria. Two genera, Phytophthora, which includes the potato blight organism and many other pathogens, and Pythium, responsible for much damping-off, are especially important.

3. **Peronosporaceae.** Downy mildews. Conidia are borne singly or in clusters at tips of usually branched, rarely clavate, conidiophores emerging through stomata; haustoria various.

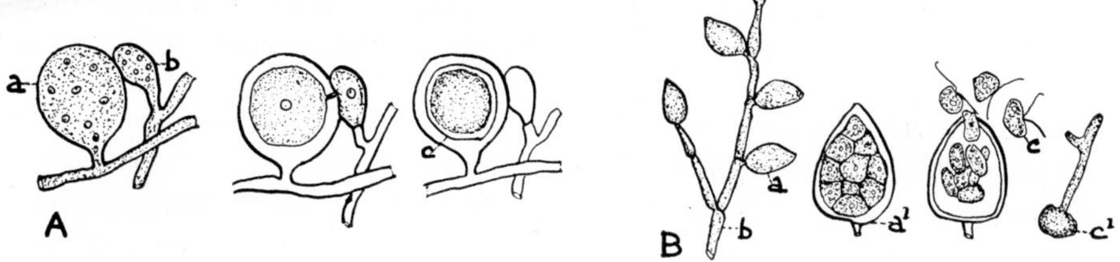

FIG. 6. Reproduction of an Oomycete (*Phytophthora,* order Peronosporales): A, multinucleate oogonium (a) and male antheridium (b) in contact; fertilization tube formed between gametes after all nuclei except one have disintegrated; thick-walled oospore (c) formed inside oogonium. B, asexual reproduction by sporangium (a) formed on sporangiophore (b); a¹ sporangium germinating by formation of ciliate zoospores; c¹ zoospore germinating with germ tube.

ZYGOMYCETES

IX. MUCORALES. Profuse mycelium, much branched; asexual reproduction by sporangia, mero-sporangia or conidia; sexual reproduction by zygospores from union of two branches of same mycelium or from different mycelia (heterothallic, with + and − sexes). Some species damage fruits and vege-

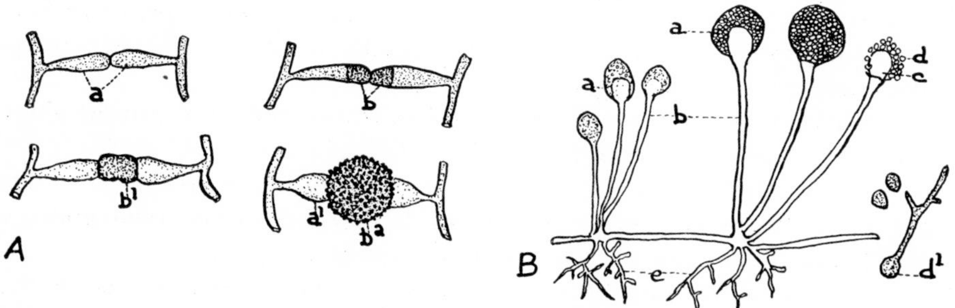

FIG. 7. Reproduction of a Zygomycete (*Rhizopus,* order Mucorales). A, suspensors (a) from different hyphae cut off gametes (b) of equal size which fuse (b¹) to form a spiny zygospore (b²). B, asexual sporangiospores (d) formed inside a sporangium (a) formed on a sporangiophore (b) around a columella (c). Hyphae are attached to substratum by rhizoids (e). Sporangiospore germinates by a germ tube (d¹).

tables in storage. Of the six families only two are of much interest to pathologists.

2. **Mucoraceae.** Sporangiospores liberated by breaking up of thin sporangial wall; zygospores rough. Mucor and Rhizopus cause storage molds.

6. **Choanephoraceae.** Both sporangia and conidia present, the latter borne on swollen tips; zygospores naked. Choanephora is a weak parasite causing blossom blight or blossom-end rot of young fruits.

X. ENTOMOPHTHORALES. Profuse mycelium, species frequently parasitic on insects or other animals, rarely on plants; imperfect spores modified sporangia functioning as conidia; zoospores free within a gametangial vesicle.

ASCOMYCETES

The diagnostic characteristics of this Class are a septate mycelium (hyphae with cross-walls) and the ascus, a sac, typically club-shaped or cylindrical, bearing the sexual spores, ascospores, frequently 8 in number. Asci may be formed on or in hyphae or cells but are usually grouped in structures, ascocarps, either in locules in a stroma or lining an open cup-shaped fruiting body called an apothecium or the walls of an enclosed round or flask-shaped

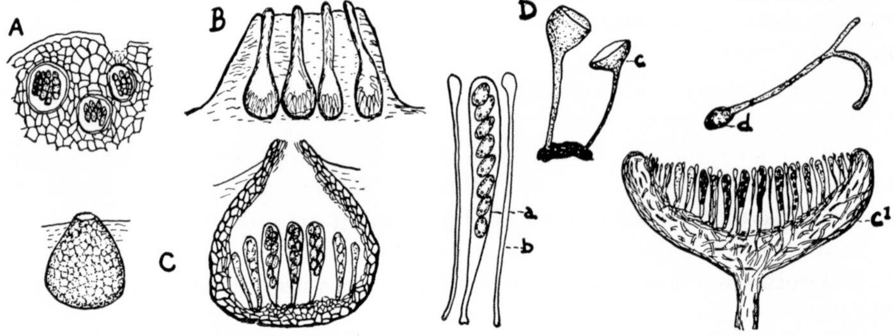

FIG. 8. Sexual reproduction in the Ascomycetes. A, asci borne singly in locules in stroma (Myriangiales). B, perithecia with long necks or beaks immersed in stroma (Sphaeriales). C, Papillate perithecium in host tissue, opening with a mouth or ostiole (Sphaeriales). D, Discomycetes (Helotiales), ascus (a) and paraphyses (b) formed in a hymenial layer in a cuplike apothecium (c) and (c^1); ascospore (d) germinates by germ tube.

perithecium. The young ascus has two nuclei which fuse and then undergo generally three divisions to give the 8 spores. In many genera paraphyses, thin, sterile clubs, are formed between the asci.

Many ascomycetes have both a parasitic and a saprophytic stage. In their parasitic stage they usually produce conidia or imperfect spores, sometimes on groups of conidiophores growing out of the mycelium, sometimes in a special pycnidium. Similar structures sometimes found are spermagonia containing spermatia, small sex cells.

Order I. ENDOMYCETALES. Single cells transformed directly into asci.

Family 1. **Ascoideaceae.** Asci many-spored.

2. **Endomycetaceae.** Asci on well-developed mycelium; ascospores 8 or fewer.

3. **Saccharomycetaceae,** the yeasts or budding fungi. Mycelium lacking; reproduction by budding; asci formed by transformation of a single cell or fusion of two cells.

II. TAPHRINALES. Hyphal cells becoming chlamydospores, each of which germinates to become a single ascus; parasitic on vascular plants.

1. **Protomycetaceae.** Chlamydospores thick-walled, germinating after a rest period, the exospore splitting and the endospore emerging to form a large, many-spored ascus.

2. **Taphrinaceae.** Chlamydospores thin-walled, endospores on germination protruding from host and cut off by a septum to form an 8-spored ascus, which may become many-spored by budding. The genera Exoascus and Taphrina cause leaf curl and leaf blisters.

III. EUROTIALES. Asci borne in tufts or singly at various levels in interior of ascocarp or stroma, but extensive stroma lacking.

1. **Gymnoascaceae.** Peridium around asci of loosely interwoven hyphae.

2. **Eurotiaceae.** Ascocarp sessile, small, peridium weak, tardily and irregularly dehiscent.

3. **Onygenaceae.** Ascocarp stalked and capitate, small to medium; peridium tough, opening above.

4. **Elaphomycetaceae.** Ascocarp sessile, underground, not opening; medium to large.

IV. MYRIANGIALES. Stroma well-developed, often gelatinous; asci borne singly in locules.

1. **Atichiaceae.** Tropical fungi, on insect secretions; thallus superficial, of yeast-like cells.

2. **Myriangiaceae.** Stroma massive, homogeneous, naked, asci arising at various levels.

Ainsworth and Bisby give only these two families. Martin adds **Elsinoaceae,** with effused stroma, gelatinous interior and crustose rind, **Saccardiaceae** with naked stroma, asci in a single layer, and **Dothioraceae,** stroma with rind, tissue between locules compressed to form pseudoparaphyses.

V. DOTHIDEALES. Mycelium immersed in substratum; stroma with hard, dark rind, soft and pale within; locules more or less spherical resembling perithecial cavities.

1. **Capnodiaceae,** sooty molds. Often on living plants associated with insect secretions. Stroma massive, carbonaceous, often excessively branched; fruiting bodies borne singly at tips of branches, resembling perithecia.

2. **Coryneliaceae.** Stroma pluriloculate to lobed, each lobe with a single locule which is finally wide open.

3. **Dothideaceae.** Stroma not markedly lobed, locules immersed in groups; at maturity stroma is erumpent and superficial.

4. **Phyllachoraceae.** Locules immersed in groups; stroma covered by host tissue at maturity.

VI. Microthyriales (Hemisphaeriales of Ainsworth and Bisby). The wall of the fruit-body, frequently in the form of a shieldlike half perithecium, is a stroma.

1. **Stigmateaceae.** Stroma subcuticular, mycelium scanty or lacking.

2. **Polystomellaceae.** Mycelium largely internal, forming a hypostroma but fruiting stroma superficial.

3. **Micropeltaceae.** (Hemisphaeriaceae). Internal mycelium scanty, stromatic cover not of radially arranged hyphae; chiefly tropical species.

4. **Microthyriaceae.** Stromatic cover radial; superficial mycelium reticulate or lacking.

5. **Trichopeltaceae.** Superficial mycelium radial or parallel, forming a flat thallus one cell thick.

6. **Trichothyriaceae.** Superficial mycelium irregular or lacking; ascomata with basal tissue; parasitic on other fungi.

VII. Erysiphales (Perisporiales). Parasites of higher plants; mycelium generally on surface of host; perithecia with no true ostioles.

1. **Erysiphaceae,** the powdery mildews. White mycelium; perithecia rupturing with an apical tear or slit.

2. **Meliolaceae,** dark or black mildews. Mycelium dark, ascocarp not becoming gelatinous above at maturity.

3. **Englerulaceae.** Mycelium dark; asci exposed by gelatinization of upper portion of ascocarp.

Martin puts the last two families in a separate order, the Meliolales.

VIII. Hypocreales. Ostiole (mouth) present; perithecia and stromata bright-colored, soft and fleshy.

1. **Nectriaceae.** Perithecia superficial, stroma present or absent.

2. **Hypocreaceae.** Perithecia partially or entirely immersed in a stroma or stromatic base.

IX. Laboulbeniales. Minute parasites on insects or spiders; mycelium represented by a small number of basal cells functioning as haustorium and stalk.

X. Sphaeriales, Pyrenomycetes. Mycelium well-developed; perithecia dark, more or less hard, carbonaceous, with an ostiole typically circular in section; with or without stromata; asci inoperculate (without a lid) but spores discharged with force. Paraphyses and periphyses present.

1. **Chaetomiaceae.** Perithecia superficial, hairy, walls membranous, asci deliquescent.

2. **Sordariaceae.** Perithecia superficial, walls membranous, naked or sparsely setose; asci discharging spores forcibly.

3. **Sphaeriaceae.** Perithecia superficial, walls carbonous, mouths papillate.

4. **Ceratostomataceae.** Perithecia superficial, carbonous, with long, hair-like beaks.

5. **Cucurbitariaceae.** Stroma present but perithecia completely emergent at maturity, in groups (caespitose) .

6. **Amphisphaeriaceae.** Bases of perithecia persistently immersed in stroma; mouths circular; walls membranous.

7. **Lophiostomataceae.** Bases of perithecia persistently immersed in stroma; mouths compressed, elongate.

8. **Mycosphaerellaceae** (Sphaerellaceae) . Perithecia immersed in substratum; stroma lacking or poorly developed; asci not thickened at tips; mouths of perithecia papillate.

9. **Gnomoniaceae.** Perithecia immersed in substratum; usually beaked; asci thickened at tips.

10. **Clypeosphaeriaceae.** Stroma a shield-like crust (clypeus) over perithecia, through which necks protrude.

11. **Valsaceae.** Stroma composed of mixed host and fungal elements; perithecia immersed with long necks; conidia borne in cavities in stroma.

12. **Melanconidiaceae.** Like Valsaceae but conidia borne superficially on the stroma.

13. **Diatrypaceae.** Stroma composed wholly of fungus elements; in some genera present only in conidial stage; perithecia develop under bark; ascospores small, allantoid, hyaline to yellow-brown.

14. **Melogrammataceae.** Conidia typically borne in hollow chambers in stroma composed of fungal elements; ascospores 1 to many-celled, hyaline or brown.

15. **Xylariaceae.** Conidia borne in superficial layer on surface of stroma; ascospores 1 to 2-celled, blackish brown.

XI. HYSTERIALES. Ostiole an elongated slit on a usually flattened, elongate perithecium, bearing asci in a flat, basal layer.

1. **Ostropaceae.** Ascocarps first immersed in substratum, then erumpent.

2. **Hysteriaceae.** Ascocarps superficial from the first, black, carbonous, round or elongate.

3. **Acrospermaceae.** Ascocarps brown, tough-membranous, clavate, erect.

XII. PHACIDIALES. Discomycetes in which the hymenium is covered by a membrane finally broken stellately or irregularly.

1. **Stictidiaceae.** Ascocarps soft, fleshy, bright, waxlike, never black.

2. **Phacidiaceae.** Ascocarps leathery or carbonous, black, remaining imbedded in host tissue or in stroma; hypothecium thin.

XIII. HELOTIALES. Discomycetes without a membrane; asci inoperculate, opening by a definite pore.

1. **Tryblidiaceae** (Martin places this under Phacidiales) . Ascocarps leathery, immersed, hypothecium thick.

2. **Geoglossaceae.** Ascocarps clavate or cap-like, hymenium covering convex upper portion; ascospores elongate to threadlike.

3. **Dermateaceae.** Apothecia arise innately and rupture overlying tissues at maturity, corneous to leathery, excipulum thick, of dark, thick-walled cells.

4. **Patellariaceae.** Apothecia leathery, horny, cartilaginous or gelatinous, tips of paraphyses united to form an epithecium; asci thick-walled.

5. **Mollisiaceae.** Apothecia waxy or fleshy, peridium of rounded or angular, mostly thin-walled and dark cells forming a pseudoparenchyma.

6. **Helotiaceae.** Apothecia soft, fleshy, stalked, peridium of elongate, thin-walled, bright-colored hyphae, arranged in parallel strands.

7. **Sclerotiniaceae.** Apothecia arising from a definite sclerotium or stromatized portion of the substratum; stalked, cup-shaped, funnel-form or saucer-shaped; usually brown; asci inoperculate, usually 8-spored, spores ellipsoidal, often flattened on one side, usually hyaline; spermatia globose to slightly ovate; conidial forms lacking in many genera.

XIV. Pezizales. Asci operculate, opening by a lid; hymenium exposed before maturity of spores; apothecia often brightly colored; most forms saprophytic.

1. **Cyttariaceae.** A pear-shaped stroma with numerous apothecial pits; parasitic.

2. **Pezizaceae.** Apothecia cup-shaped or discoid; sessile or stalked; saprophytic.

3. **Helvellaceae.** Fruit bodies upright, columnar or with a stalk and cap, sometimes edible; saprophytic.

XV. Tuberales. Fruiting body mostly subterranean, remaining closed; including edible truffles.

BASIDIOMYCETES

The chief diagnostic character of the Basidiomycetes is the basidium, the structure on which the sex spores, basidiospores, are formed. Typically these

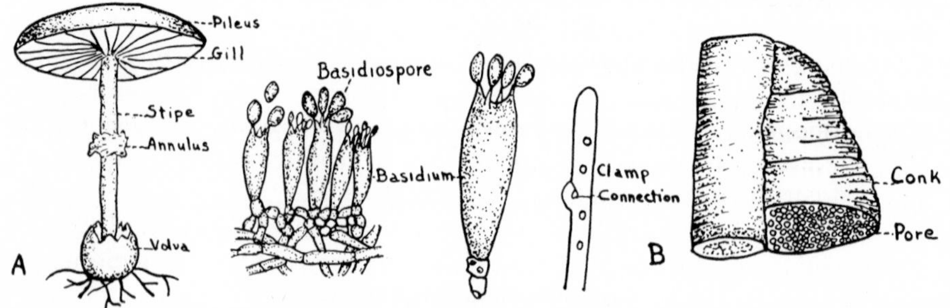

Fig. 9. Reproduction in Basidiomycetes. A, Mushroom (Agaricaceae) with cap or pileus lined with gills bearing basidia germinating by basidiospores. B, sporophore, or conk, in Polyporaceae where basidia line pores instead of gills. Mycelium in basidiomycetes sometimes has a structure around a septum called a clamp connection.

are four, formed on four little horns or sterigmata which are extensions of the basidial wall. The mycelium frequently has clamp-connections, hyphal outgrowths formed at the time of cell division and forming a connection between two cells. The basidiomycetes are divided into two sub-classes: the Heterobasidiomycetes, including the rusts and smuts, and the true, or Homobasidiomycetes, which include the mushrooms, bracket fungi formed on trees, etc.

HETEROBASIDIOMYCETES

Order I. Ustilaginales, the Smuts. Spore masses usually black; spores are heavy walled, chlamydospores, germinating by a promycelium (basidium) and 4 or more sporidia (basidiospores).

Family 1. **Ustilaginaceae.** Basidiospores are produced on sides of a 4-celled promycelium.

2. **Tilletiaceae.** Elongated basidiospores produced in a cluster at tip of a nonseptate promycelium or basidium.

3. **Graphiolaceae.** False smuts. Black, erumpent sori and spores in chains; on palms in warmer regions.

II. Uredinales, the Rusts. Always parasitic in vascular plants; teliospores or probasidia germinate with a promycelium divided transversely into 4 cells, each producing a single basidiospore on a sterigma; spore masses are yellowish or orange, and there are several spore forms (see Rusts in Chapter 4).

1. **Melampsoraceae.** Teliospores sessile, in crusts, cushions or cylindrical masses, or solitary, or in clusters in mesophyll or epidermis of host.

2. **Pucciniaceae.** Teliospores usually stalked, separate, or held together in gelatinous masses; sometimes several on common stalks; less frequently sessile, catenulate, breaking apart.

III. Tremellales (Trembling fungi). Basidiocarp usually well-developed, often gelatinous, varying to waxy or leathery horn-like when dry; mostly saprophytic, sometimes parasitic on mosses, vascular plants, insects or other fungi.

1. **Auriculariaceae.** Basidia with transverse septa, typically gelatinous. The genus Helicobasidium causes violet root rot.

2. **Septobasidiaceae** (Felt fungi). Arid, lichenoid, parasitic on scale insects; probasidia often with thickened walls.

There are six other families, of no particular interest from the standpoint of plant disease.

HOMOBASIDIOMYCETES

I. Agaricales. Hymenium, fruiting layer, present, often exposed from beginning and always before spores are matured.

1. **Exobasidiaceae.** Hymenium on galls or hypertrophied tissues of hosts, which are vascular plants.

2. **Thelephoraceae.** Hymenium more or less smooth, roughened or corrugated; basidiocarp web-like or membranous, leathery or woody; hymenium on lower side.

3. **Clavariaceae.** Hymenium smooth, pileus more or less clavate or club-shaped, erect, simple or branched, fleshy or rarely gelatinous, cartilaginous or tough; hymenium on all surfaces.

4. **Hydnaceae.** Hymenium covering downward directed spines, warts or teeth.

5. **Polyporaceae.** Hymenium borne on surface of pores; hymenophore woody, tough or membranous, rarely subfleshy, poroid or pitted, rarely more or less laminate.

6. **Boletaceae.** Fruiting surface poroid, pores easily separable; soft, fleshy, putrescent.

7. **Agaricaceae,** the Mushrooms. Fruiting bodies usually fleshy, sometimes tough or membranous, often with a stipe and cap, hymenophore lamellate, with gills.

II. Hymenogastrales. Hymenium present in early stages, lining chambers of the gleba, closed fruiting body, which is fleshy or waxy, sometimes slimy and fetid at maturity.

III. Phallales. Gleba slimy and fetid; exposed at maturity on an elongated or enlarged receptacle.

IV. Lycoperdales, the Puffballs. Gleba powdery and dry at maturity; spores commonly small, pale.

V. Sclerodermatales. Gleba powdery at maturity; chambers not separating from peridium or each other; spores commonly large, dark.

VI. Nidulariales, Bird's Nest Fungi. Gleba waxy; chamber with distinct walls forming peridioles (the eggs in the nest) which serve as organs of dissemination.

FUNGI IMPERFECTI

Imperfect fungi are those for which a perfect stage is not yet known or does not exist. Most of them are in the Ascomycetes. The groupings are based on the conidia, whether they are hyaline or colored, have one or two or several cells, and whether they are formed in pycnidia, on acervuli (little cushions of hyphae) or free on the surface of the host.

I. Sphaeropsidales (Phyllostictales). Conidia borne in pycnidia.

1. **Sphaerioidaceae** (Phyllostictaceae). Pycnidia more or less globose, ostiolate (with a mouth) or closed; walls dark, tough, leathery or carbonaceous.

2. **Nectrioidaceae.** As above but walls or stroma bright-colored, fleshy or waxy.

3. **Leptostromataceae.** Pycnidia dimidiate (having the outer wall covering only the top half), usually radiate or long and cleft.

4. **Excipulaceae.** Pycnidia discoid or cupulate.

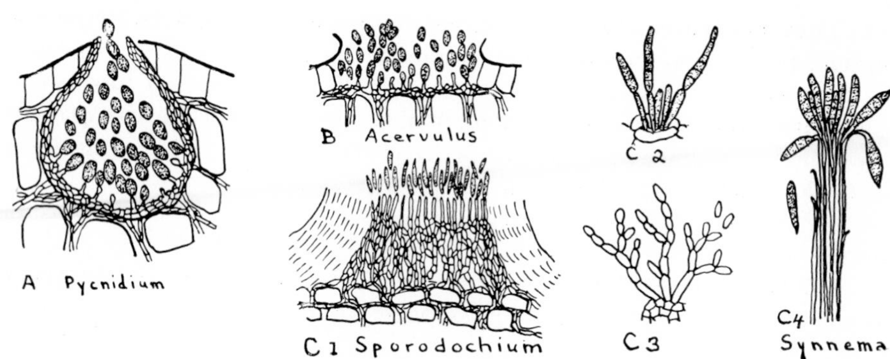

FIG. 10. Spore formation in the Fungi Imperfecti. A, Sphaeropsidales, conidia in pycnidium; B, Melanconiales, conidia in acervulus; C, Moniliales—C[1], sporodochium of Tuberculariaceae; C[2], dark conidiophores and conidia of Dematiaceae; C[3], hyaline conidia in chains, Moniliaceae; C[4], conidiophores grouped into a synnema, Stilbaceae.

II. MELANCONIALES. Conidia borne in definitely circumscribed acervuli, erumpent (breaking through the substratum) ; a single family, **Melanconiaceae.**

III. MONILIALES. Conidiophores (specialized hyphae bearing conidia) if present, entirely free or bound in tufts or pulvinate (cushionlike) masses.

1. **Pseudosaccharomycetaceae,** false yeasts. Hyphae scanty or nearly lacking; reproduction by budding.

2. **Sporobolomycetaceae.** Reproduction by budding and germinating by repetition; probably imperfect species of the Tremellales, in the Basidiomycetes.

3. **Moniliaceae.** Hyphae and spores hyaline or brightly colored; conidiophores not grouped.

4. **Dematiaceae.** Same as Moniliaceae but hyphae or conidia or both brownish to black.

5. **Stilbaceae** (Stilbellaceae). Conidiophores united into a coremium or synnema, an upright group of hyphae.

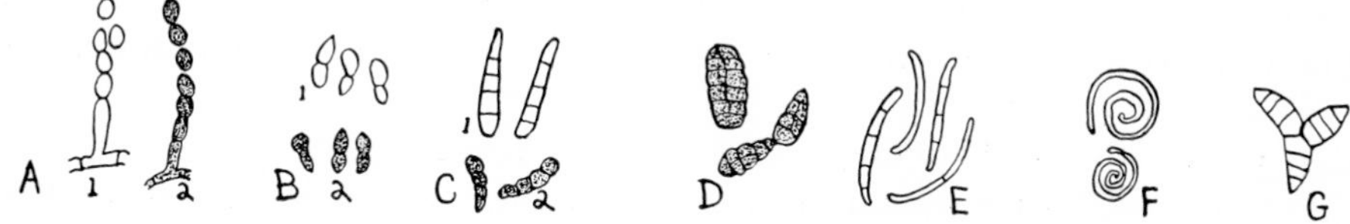

FIG. 11. Spore forms in the Fungi Imperfecti, commonly designated by letters and figures. A, Amerosporae, 1-celled, A1, Hyalosporae, spores hyaline, A2, Phaeosporae, spores dark; B, Didymosporae, 2-celled-B1, Hyalodidymae, hyaline, B2, Phaeodidymae, dark; C, Phragmosporae, spores with 2 or more cross septa-C1, Hyalophragmiae, hyaline or light, C2, Phaeophragmiae, dark; D, Dictyosporae, muriform spores; E, Scolecosporae, filiform spores; F, Helicosporae, spirally coiled spores; G, Staurosporae, star-like spores.

6. **Tuberculariaceae.** Hyphae and conidiophores combined in a sporodochium, or tight, spore-bearing mass.

IV. Mycelia Sterilia. No spores known; mycelium or masses of fungus cells forming sclerotia or resting bodies; in a few cases connected with Basidiomycetes.

FILTERABLE VIRUSES

Any classification of the viruses is artificial, but putting them into the same binomial system as known living organisms is an aid to quick reference.

VIRALES

Etiological agents of disease, typically of small size and capable of passing filters that retain bacteria, increasing only in the presence of living cells.

Suborder I. Phagineae. Infecting bacteria, the bacteriophages.

III. Zoophagineae. Infecting animals—insects and mammals.

II. Phytophagineae. Infecting plants; vectors typically homopterous or hemipterous insects (leafhoppers, aphids, whiteflies, true bugs) or thrips.

Family 1. **Chlorogenaceae.** Inducing yellows-type diseases; vectors typically cicadellid or fulgorid leafhoppers.

2. **Marmoraceae.** Inducing mosaic diseases; vectors typically aphids.
3. **Annulaceae.** Inducing ringspot diseases; vectors unknown.
4. **Rugaceae.** Inducing leaf-curl diseases; vectors typically whiteflies.
5. **Savoiaceae.** Inducing leaf-savoying diseases; vectors, true bugs.
6. **Lethaceae.** Inducing spotted wilt; vectors, thrips.

CHAPTER 4

PLANT DISEASES AND THEIR PATHOGENS

Since this is a reference book and not one to be read for pleasure or continuity, most of you will come to the material you need in this section by way of the index or the lists of diseases given under the different hosts in Chapter 5. On page 407, you will find a list of headings under which diseases are grouped and described from Anthracnose to Wilts. In the Host Section the key word, rot or blight, is given in capitals, followed by the name of the pathogen (agent causing disease) in bold face. In this Disease Section the pathogens are listed in bold face in alphabetical order under each heading of rot or blight, followed by the common name of the disease in small capitals. This system was adopted for quick and easy reference, because trying to alphabetize hundreds of similar common names would lead to endless confusion. Also, it allows a very brief summary of the classification and diagnostic characters of each genus before going on to consider the diseases caused by the various species. This part is in small type, so that it can be readily skipped by readers uninterested in the technical details. Perhaps I am the only one who feels the need for this quick review, to be used in conjunction with the classification given in Chapter 3; perhaps others who have to answer questions over a broad field instead of their own specialty can make use of these capsules sandwiched in between nontechnical descriptions.

An alphabetical arrangement has the great disadvantage of being thrown out of alignment every time the name of a fungus is changed, as it so frequently is. It is disconcerting to learn at the last minute that certain wood rots treated under Hydnum should now be considered under Steccherinum. In some such cases the old name is retained to avoid change in order, but the present accepted name is also given. Sometimes names have been changed under several hosts and the old name inadvertently retained under others. And sometimes the old name is purposely retained because it is so familiar to everyone. This is true particularly of a few fungi far better known by their imperfect stages than by the correct name of the perfect stage.

A fungus not only can have several names; it can cause more than one type of disease. For instance, **Pellicularia filamentosa** is the present name of the fungus formerly known as *Corticium vagum* when causing Rhizoctonia rot of potatoes, and *Corticium microsclerotia* when causing web blight of beans. As *Rhizoctonia solani,* the name given to the sclerotial stage, the same fungus causes damping-off and root rot of many plants, and also brown patch of lawn grasses. There are lots of plant diseases and there are lots of fungi causing them, but there are not nearly as many separate pathogenic organisms as all the names would indicate.

I can't think of anything more deadly than ploughing straight through this section from Anthracnose to Wilts. By doctor's orders, take it in small doses, as needed. But do read the few introductory words as you use each section, and please, please before starting any control measures read the opening remarks in Chapter 2 on Garden Chemicals, and look up, in the list of chemicals, any material you propose to use, noting all precautions to be taken along the lines of compatibility, weather relations, and phytotoxicity.

I regret to confess that, with all the new materials listed in that chemical chapter, most of the control directions end with the old refrain, "Spray with bordeaux mixture and cut out and burn infected plant parts." The latter part is usually a safe policy, but the bordeaux may or may not be safe. Probably somebody suggested trying bordeaux for a disease about fifty years ago and ever since then each writer on that disease has copied the recommendation from the one before him. Frankly I don't like bordeaux mixture very much on ornamentals, but I am likewise scared of most new materials until they have had several years' testing on many plants under many climatic conditions. And so, where I have little personal experience with a disease and new materials, and where literature on the new materials is nonexistent or conflicting, I, too, am copying the writer before me with the same old conservative refrain. Where my own tests or recent literature indicate the value of new materials, these have been included in suggested control measures.

Although the disease descriptions, fungus life-cycles, and general principles of control given here will remain fairly valid, it must be stressed that chemicals suggested for control are constantly changing. Today's discovery may be obsolete tomorrow. This *Plant Disease Handbook* should, therefore, be used in conjunction with the latest advice from your own county agent or experiment station. Addresses of the state agricultural experiment stations are given on page 669.

ANTHRACNOSE

The term anthracnose has been used for two distinct types of disease, one characterized by a typical necrotic spot, or lesion of dead tissue, and the other by some hyperplastic symptom, such as a raised border around a slightly depressed center. The word was coined in France for the latter type, to differentiate a grape disease from a smut of cereals, both of which were called *charbon*. The new word was taken from the Greek *Anthrax* (coal, carbuncle) and *noses* (disease) and was first used for the grape disease, caused by *Sphaceloma ampelophagum,* the chief symptom of which was a bird's-eye spot with a raised border.

Soon a bramble disease was named anthracnose of raspberry and blackberry because it looked like the grape anthracnose. The fungus, however, instead of being correctly placed in the genus Sphaceloma was mistakenly named *Gloeosporium venetum*. The next disease entering the picture was a bean trouble and, because the fungus was identified as Gloeosporium, though later transferred to the genus Colletotrichum, this common bean disease, with typical necrotic symptoms, was also called anthracnose and came to typify diseases so designated. Recently the term spot anthracnose has been given to those diseases similar to the original hyperplastic grape disease.

Anthracnose, in the modern sense, is a disease characterized by distinctive limited lesions on stem, leaf or fruit, often accompanied by dieback and usually caused by a Gloeosporium or a Colletotrichum, imperfect fungi producing slime spores oozing out of fruiting bodies (acervuli) in wet, pinkish pustules. These spores (conidia), on germinating, form an appressorium or organ of attachment before entering the host plant. The perfect stage of the fungus, when known, is Gnomonia or Glomerella.

In many instances spraying with one of the dithiocarbamates, Fermate, Dithane or Zerlate, is replacing bordeaux mixture in anthracnose control, but experimental work has been limited to a few diseases of economic importance.

A spot anthracnose is a disease caused by a Sphaceloma, or its perfect stage Elsinoë, characterized by some overgrowth of tissue. When this hyperplasia is pronounced, the disease is known as scab and is treated in the section on Scab. Spot anthracnoses with slight hyperplastic symptoms, still commonly called anthracnose, are included in this section.

COLLETOTRICHUM

Fungi Imperfecti, Melanconiales, Melanconiaceae

Spores are formed in acervuli, erumpent, cushion-like masses of hyphae bearing conidiophores and one-celled, hyaline, oblong to fusoid conidia. Acervuli have marginal setae or bristles, sometimes hard to see. Conidia are held together by a gelatinous coating and appear pinkish in mass. They are not wind-borne but can be disseminated by wind-splashed rain. On landing on a suitable host the conidium sends out a short germ tube, which, on contact with the epidermis, enlarges at the tip into a brown, thick-walled appressorium, from which a peg-like infection hypha ruptures the cuticle.

Colletotrichum antirrhini. SNAPDRAGON ANTHRACNOSE, on snapdragon, chiefly in greenhouses, sometimes outdoors in late summer.

Stems have oval, sunken spots, grayish white with narrow brown or reddish borders, fruiting bodies showing as minute black dots in center. Spots on leaves are circular, yellow green turning dirty white, with narrow brown borders. Stem cankers may coalesce to girdle plant at base, causing collapse of upper portions, with leaves hanging limp along the stem.

Control. Spray with bordeaux mixture; take cuttings from healthy plants; provide air circulation; keep foliage dry.

Colletotrichum atramentarium. POTATO ANTHRACNOSE; Black Dot Disease, on potato stems and stolons following wilt and other stem diseases, of general distribution, but of minor importance.

Starting below soil surface brown, dead areas extend up and down the stem. The partial girdling causes vines to lose fresh color and lower leaves to fall. Infection may extend to stolons and roots. The black dots embedded in epidermal cells, inside hollow stems and on tubers are sclerotia to carry the fungus over winter and to produce conidia the following spring.

The fungus is a wound parasite, ordinarily not serious enough to call for control measures other than cleaning up old refuse.

Colletotrichum bletiae and other species. ORCHID ANTHRACNOSE; Leaf Spot, on orchids coming in from tropics.

Lemon-colored acervuli are formed in soft, blackish spots in ragged leaves. Burn diseased plants, or parts. Spray with a copper fungicide.

Colletotrichum erumpens. RHUBARB ANTHRACNOSE; Stalk Rot. Oval, soft watery areas on petioles increase until whole stalk is included; leaves wilt and die. Small, dark fruiting bodies with setae survive winter in stems, producing conidia in spring. Clean up all old rhubarb remains in fall.

Colletotrichum fragariae. STRAWBERRY ANTHRACNOSE, apparently confined to Florida.

Runners are girdled and killed before young runner plants are rooted, sometimes rhizomes of rooted plants are infected, or leaf petioles. The disease is more severe after August first, during warm, moist weather. Spots are light brown, oval, sunken, small at first, but gradually increasing to length of runner, which turns brown to black and is covered with bristle-like tufts of setae (seen with a hand lens). Spores are produced in great abundance.

Control. Spray with 8–8–100 bordeaux mixture at 10-day intervals during late July, August, and September.

Colletotrichum fuscum. FOXGLOVE ANTHRACNOSE. Spots are circular to angular, light or purplish brown, up to 1/8 inch in diameter, with indefinite purple borders, and minute, black acervuli, with bristles, in center of spots. Infected seedlings damp off.

Colletotrichum gloeosporioides. ANTHRACNOSE or WITHERTIP of citrus fruits, orange, lemon and grapefruit, also of avocado, aucuba, cherimoya, fig, loquat, roselle, rose-mallow, royal palm, rubber-plant and other ornamentals and fruits. The fungus is mostly secondary, growing in tissues weakened from other causes, and is connected with *Glomerella cingulata,* the perfect stage.

On ripening fruits in storage the fungus produces decayed spots. On citrus there is a dying back or withertip of twigs, also spots on nearly mature leaves, first light green but soon turning brown, with the pinkish spore pustules prominent in moist weather. Lack of water, nutrient deficiency, or other environmental influences predispose the trees to infection by this weak parasite.

Control. Rather drastic pruning may be needed to remove infected twigs and branches, taking care to make smooth cuts at base of limbs and painting surfaces with a wound dressing.

Colletotrichum graminicolum. Cereal Anthracnose, widely distributed on cereals—barley, oats, rye, wheat—and also on cultivated lawn grasses, causing a root decay and stem rot. Black acervuli develop on dead leaf blades. Improved soil fertility reduces damage from this disease.

Colletotrichum higginsianum. Anthracnose of Crucifers, on Chinese cabbage and turnips. Very small, circular gray spots on leaves and elongated spots on stems show pink pustules in center of dead tissue. The disease is not very destructive or important.

Colletotrichum lagenarium. Melon Anthracnose, chiefly important on watermelons and muskmelons but seriously infecting cucumbers, and also found on squash, pumpkin, chayote, balsam-apple and balsam-pear. The disease is general except for the Pacific Coast and is very destructive in melon areas east of the Rocky Mountains. In 1943 one-fourth of the Iowa crop was destroyed and the next year Oklahoma lost a quarter of its crop, estimated at $80,000.

Leaf symptoms are small, yellow or water-soaked areas which enlarge and turn black in watermelon, brown on other cucurbits; the dead tissue shatters and leaves shrivel up and die. Elongated lesions on stems may kill vines. Young fruit darkens, shrivels, and dies if the pedicels are infected, older fruit shows circular, black, sunken cankers or depressions, from ¼ to 2 inches on watermelon and up to ⅓ inch deep. In moist weather the black center of these spots is covered with a gelatinous mass of salmon-colored spores. Infected fruit either has a bitter taste or the flesh is tough and insipid. Soft rots often follow the anthracnose. Epidemics or epiphytotics occur only in periods of high rainfall and a temperature optimum of around 75° F.

Control. Use a 3-year crop rotation with non-cucurbits; destroy plant refuse; treat seed with mercuric chloride, 1 tablet to a pint of water, for 5 minutes, rinsing in water, and drying thoroughly; spray or dust with Fermate, or perhaps Dithane or Zerlate, or an insoluble copper (bordeaux mixture is injurious to young vines), making three or four applications at 10- to 14-day intervals after vines start to run.

Resistant varieties include watermelon Black Kleckly, Kleckly Hybrid, Dixie Hybrid, Georgia Home Garden Melon No. 2.

Colletotrichum liliacearum found on dead stems of daylilies and many other plants and perhaps weakly parasitic.

Colletotrichum lindemuthianum. Bean Anthracnose, a major bean disease, sometimes mistakenly called "rust," generally present in eastern and central states, and rare from the Rocky Mountains to the Pacific Coast. Anthracnose is occasionally found on lima beans in the East and South and sometimes on scarlet runner beans. It is world-wide in distribution, being known in the United States since 1880.

The most conspicuous symptoms are on the pods—small, brown specks enlarging to black, circular sunken spots, in moist weather showing the typical pinkish ooze of the slime spores. Older spots often have narrow reddish borders and, after spores are washed away, the acervuli appear dark and pimple-like.

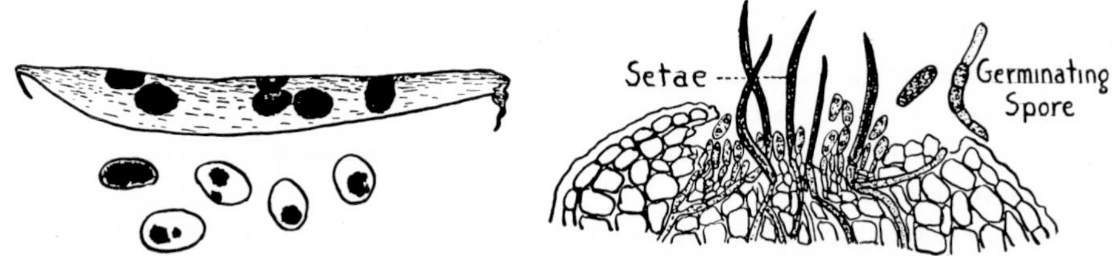

FIG. 12. Bean Anthracnose. Pod and seeds with dark, sunken areas; section through bean seed showing spores formed in an acervulus marked with prominent black setae.

If pods are infected when young, the disease extends through to the seed, which turns yellow, then rusty brown or black under the pod lesion. The infection may extend deep enough to reach the cotyledons.

Leaf lesions are dark areas along veins on underside of the blade and on petioles. Seedlings may show stem spotting below diseased cotyledons. The fungus is spread by splashing rain, tools, and gardeners working with beans when they are wet. Optimum temperature is between 63° and 75°, and maximum around 85°.

The fungus has several different races, at least 34 strains in 3 different groups being known, so that breeding for resistance has been difficult but not impossible.

Control. Use western-grown seed. Saving home-grown seed usually turns out to be very expensive unless you can be sure of selecting from perfectly healthy plants and pods. Clean up or spade under old bean tops; rotate crops; and never pick or cultivate beans while vines are wet.

Varieties showing some resistance are: snapbeans, Livingston's Pencil Pod Wax, Keeney's Rustless Golden Wax, Longfellow, Black Valentine; dry beans, Michigan Robust Pea, Perry Marrow, Yellow Eye, Wells Red Kidney.

Colletotrichum malvarum. HOLLYHOCK ANTHRACNOSE; Seedling Blight, on hollyhock, mallow and abutilon, particularly destructive to greenhouse seedlings. Black blotches are formed on veins, leaf blades, petioles, and stems. Remove and burn all old plant parts in fall; spray with 6–6–100 bordeaux mixture in severe infections.

Colletotrichum omnivorum. ANTHRACNOSE, on aspidistra and hosta. Large, whitish spots with brown margins are formed on leaves and stalks. Remove and burn infected plant parts.

Colletotrichum phomoides. TOMATO ANTHRACNOSE, common rot of ripe tomatoes, most frequent in Northeast and North Central districts. Symptoms appear late in season, causing particular loss to canning crops. Small, circular sunken spots, increasing to an inch in diameter, penetrate deeply into the flesh. At first water-soaked, the spots turn dark, with pinkish, cream or brown spore masses in the depressed centers often arranged in concentric rings. The disease is worse in warm, moist weather. The fungus winters in tomato refuse.

Control. Clean up tomato trash and rotting fruit; spray with Fermate or Zerlate or a copper fungicide, the latter being third choice.

Colletotrichum pisi. PEA ANTHRACNOSE; Leaf and Pod Spot, commonly associated with Ascochyta blight and often a secondary parasite. Spots on pods, stems, and leaves are sunken, gray, circular, with dark borders. Avoid infected seed; rotate crops.

Colletotrichum schizanthi. ANTHRACNOSE, on butterfly-flower. Symptoms are small, brown spots on leaves and water-soaked areas on young stems and leaf stalks. Canker on stems and main branches of old plants may cause leaves to turn yellow and branches to die back from the tip, followed by death of all parts above canker. Spraying with bordeaux mixture may help.

Colletotrichum spinaciae. SPINACH ANTHRACNOSE. Known on spinach since 1880 but unimportant in most years. Leaves have few to many circular spots, water-soaked, turning gray or brown, with setae or bristles evident in spore pustules.

Colletotrichum trichellum, general on English ivy, but recently attributed to *Amerosporium*. See under Leaf Spots.

Colletotrichum truncatum. STEM ANTHRACNOSE, of lima and kidney beans. Pods are russeted, and reddish brown circular areas appear on upper leaf surfaces. Young pods may be killed or stunted. Fruiting bodies are black, with prominent setae. Phygon and Fermate seem promising for control.

Colletotrichum violae-tricoloris. ANTHRACNOSE OF VIOLET AND PANSY. Dead spots with black margins appear on leaves; flowers may have petals spotted or not fully developed and produce no seed; entire plants are sometimes killed. Remove and burn infected plant parts or whole plants; clean up all old leaves in fall. Violets and pansies are sensitive to copper. Use sprays with caution.

ELSINOË

Ascomycetes, Myriangiales, Myriangiaceae

Asci are borne singly, at different levels, in an effused stroma, having gelatinous interior and a crustose rind. The imperfect stage is Sphaceloma, causing diseases known as spot anthracnoses.

Elsinoë ampelina. GRAPE ANTHRACNOSE; Bird's Eye Rot, widespread on grape. Small, sunken dark spots with light centers on fruit, and also young shoots, tendrils, petioles, leaf veins. Leaves may be distorted, and ragged from diseased portions dropping out. The disease is occasionally serious but confined to a few varieties, including Catawba.

Control. Apply a dormant spray of lime sulfur, at 1 to 9 dilution, and four or five applications of bordeaux mixture. Anthracnose is not known on variety Concord; Delaware and Niagara are highly resistant.

Elsinoë cinnamomi. Spot Anthracnose, on camphor tree, found in Mississippi in 1945.

Elsinoë corni. Spot Anthracnose of Dogwood, on flowering dogwood, first collected in Georgia in 1939. Leaf spots are small, 1 to 2 mm., slightly raised at margin, reddish gray paling to yellow gray at centers which may be broken in a shot-hole effect; few to numerous, up to 100 on a single leaf. Spots on flower bracts have light tan centers with purple to brown borders.

Elsinoë ledi. Ledum Anthracnose, on Labrador tea and Salal. Leaf spots are grayish white with red brown borders and purple margins. The disease is not serious.

Elsinoë parthenocissi. Anthracnose of Virginia Creeper. Leaf spots are few to numerous, circular, scattered or along midribs and veins, with buff centers and narrow brown margins. Fruit spots are grayish white, while lesions on petioles and stems are more or less raised.

Elsinoë piri. Anthracnose of Pome Fruits, on pear, apple, quince in moist sections of western Washington and Oregon. The disease was first noticed in 1943 and is more prevalent in neglected home gardens than in commercial orchards. Late yellow varieties such as Grimes Golden seem to be most susceptible. Fruit spots are small, up to 2 mm. across, numerous, up to 100 per apple, red or reddish purple with pale centers. Leaf spots are also small, ½ to 3 mm., and equally numerous.

Elsinoë randii. Pecan Anthracnose; Nursery Blight, on pecan in the Southeast, most important as a nursery disease and a limiting factor in the production of budded pecans in wet seasons. Small reddish lesions develop on both leaf surfaces, those on upper surface later turning to ash-gray. Single spots unite to form continuous lesions along veins and midribs. Diseased tissues become brittle and fall out, leaving ragged margins and perforations.

Control. Spray nursery trees with 4–1–100 bordeaux mixture about April 5 to 15 (dates for Florida) and follow with 3 sprays of 6–2–100 bordeaux at monthly intervals. Destroy fallen leaves, which carry the fungus over winter.

Elsinoë veneta. Bramble Anthracnose, general on blackberry, dewberry, and raspberry and one of the most serious canefruit diseases. It is present on all raspberry varieties, but most common on black caps.

Symptoms are circular, reddish brown, sunken spots with purple margins and light gray centers. On young shoots these are up to ⅜ inch in diameter, but on older canes grow together to form large cankers. Similar spots, but not always with purple margins, are formed on fruit, leaf, and flower stalks. On leaves spots are first yellowish, then develop a light center and red margin, and sometimes drop out, leaving shot holes. Leaves may fall prematurely and fruit may dry up, due to loss of water from infected canes. The fungus winters in old canes, primary spring infection coming from ascospores with secondary spread by conidia during wet weather in early spring.

Control. Cut old canes or "handles" from black raspberries after setting; remove and burn old fruiting canes after harvest; apply a delayed dormant spray of a 1 to 12 dilution of lime-sulfur, or 1% Elgetol, followed by 4–8–100 bordeaux mixture or Fermate, 2 pounds to 100 gallons, a week before blooming and again after blossoming is over. In some tests the single delayed dormant spray has controlled anthracnose without the later sprays, and in others three foliage sprays with Fermate have been effective without the delayed dormant application.

GLOEOSPORIUM

Fungi Imperfecti, Melanconiales, Melanconiaceae

Genus characters are about the same as for Colletotrichum except that there are no setae, bristles, in or around acervuli. Conidia are hyaline, 1-celled, appearing in masses or pustules on leaves or fruit. Leaf spots are usually light brown, with foliage appearing scorched.

Gloeosporium allantosporum. ANTHRACNOSE; Dieback, of raspberry in Oregon, Washington. See *Elsinoë veneta* for common raspberry anthracnose.

Gloeosporium apocryptum. MAPLE ANTHRACNOSE; Leaf Blight, an important leaf disease of silver maple, common also on sugar and other maples and on boxelder. The spots are indefinite light brown, enlarging and merging until the whole leaf is killed. Leaves with limited dead areas appear scorched. In rainy seasons there may be almost complete defoliation. On Norway maples the leaf lesions are purple to brown narrow lines along the veins.

Control. Standard treatment is two or three applications of bordeaux mixture in spring, starting when buds are breaking and repeating at two-week intervals. Parzate, Fermate or other of the new organic sprays offer some promise but have not yet had enough testing. Do not confuse this pathogenic disease with physiogenic leaf scorch.

Gloeosporium aridum. ASH ANTHRACNOSE; Leaf Scorch, in Eastern and Central States. Brown spots occur over large leaf areas and at margins, sometimes with premature defoliation in wet seasons. If the tree value justifies expense two or three sprays early in the season with bordeaux mixture, 8–8–100, or one of the carbamate sprays, should control the disease. In most years gathering and burning fallen leaves is said to be sufficient, although such measures may not reduce the incidence of disease to any great extent.

Gloeosporium limetticolum. LIME ANTHRACNOSE; Withertip, only on lime, in southern Florida. Shoots, leaves, and fruits infected when young; mature tissues are immune. Twigs wither and shrivel for one to several inches back from tip; young leaves have dead areas or are distorted; buds fail to open and may drop; fruits drop, or are misshapen, or have shallow spots or depressed cankers.

Control. Spray with bordeaux-oil emulsion as fruit is setting, with two or three applications of 1 to 40 lime-sulfur at one- to two-week intervals.

Gloeosporium melongenae. EGGPLANT ANTHRACNOSE; Ripe Rot, an occasional trouble. Yellow to brown spots on leaves and small to medium depressed spots on fruit show pink spore masses following rain or heavy dew. Spores are splashed by rain or spread by tools, insects, and workmen. Rotation of crops and sanitary measures may be sufficient control.

Gloeosporium piperatum. PEPPER ANTHRACNOSE; Fruit Spot. Sometimes a leaf and stem spot but more often a disease of ripe fruit appearing as water-soaked, dark depressed areas turning lighter with age and producing great numbers of pinkish spores.

Control. Rotate crops; remove and burn or bury diseased plants; treat seed with mercuric chloride, 1 tablet to 3 pints of water, for 5 minutes, then rinse in running water 15 minutes and dry.

Gloeosporium thuemenii f. tulipi. TULIP ANTHRACNOSE, a relatively new disease found in 1939 in California. Lesions on peduncles and leaf blades of Darwin tulips are small to large, elliptical in shape, first water-soaked then dry with black margins, and numerous black acervuli in center of spots.

Gloeosporium sp. PEONY ANTHRACNOSE, on stems, leaves, flowers, petals, sometimes causing death of plant.

GLOMERELLA

Ascomycetes, Sphaeriales, Gnomoniaceae

Perithecia are dark, hard, carbonaceous, usually beaked and immersed in substratum so only the neck protrudes. Ascospores are hyaline, 1-celled; asci are thickened at tips, inoperculate but spores sometimes discharged with force; paraphyses present.

Glomerella cingulata. ANTHRACNOSE, Canker, Dieback, Withertip, Fruit Rot of a great many plants: apple (see under Rots), avocado, camphor tree, camellia (see Dieback), century plant, citrus fruits, dieffenbachia, guava, nandina, pepper, privet, snowberry, sweet pea, and many other plants. This fungus is generally distributed, except on the Pacific Coast, but most common in the South.

Anthracnose appears on outdoor sweet peas about flowering time and is one of the more destructive diseases, often more serious near apple orchards where the fungus winters on cankered apple limbs and in bitter rot apple mummies. The fungus also winters in sweet-pea refuse and on seed from inflected pods. White areas appear on leaves which wither and fall; flower stalks often dry up before blossoms develop; infected seed pods lose green color and shrivel. There may be general wilting of plants, or dying back of shoots.

Control. Use only plump, sound seed from healthy pods; treat seed with Arasan before planting; rake up and burn all plant parts at end of season.

On privet, anthracnose and twig blight are widespread. Leaves dry and cling to stem, cankers are formed at base of main stems and dotted with pink spore pustules. Bark turns brown and splits, with death following complete girdling of stem. Amur, Ibota, Regal's border and California privets are fairly resistant.

Snowberry fruits show cinnamon-colored spots, then turn black and mummify, dropping prematurely. The more common snowberry anthracnose is caused by Sphaceloma.

Glomerella glycines. SOYBEAN ANTHRACNOSE, first reported from North Carolina in 1920. Numerous black acervuli are scattered over surface of affected stem and pods. Setae or spines are numerous and can be readily seen with a hand lens. Diseased plants die prematurely; pods do not fill properly. The fungus winters as mycelium inside seed as well as spores on the outside, and also on diseased stems left in the field. Use healthy seed and clean up plant refuse.

Glomerella nephrolepis. FERN ANTHRACNOSE; Tip Blight, on Boston and sword ferns. The soft growing tips of fronds turn brown and shrivel. Keep foliage dry, remove and burn diseased leaves.

GNOMONIA

Ascomycetes, Sphaeriales, Gnomoniaceae

Perithecia innate, beaked, separate; paraphyses absent; ascospores 2-celled, hyaline, imperfect stage Gloeosporium or Marssonina. Diseases caused by Gnomonia are classified as anthracnose, scorch, or leaf spot.

Gnomonia leptostyla (imperfect state *Marssonina juglandis*). WALNUT ANTHRACNOSE; LEAF SPOT, general on butternut, hickory, and walnut. Spring infection comes from ascospores shot from dead leaves wintered on ground; secondary infection from conidia. Irregular dark brown spots appear on leaflets in early summer; if numerous the leaves fall. General unthrifty condition of black walnuts and butternuts is often due to this disease, which can be controlled with two or three sprays of bordeaux mixture. Zerlate or Parzate may be satisfactory.

Gnomonia tiliae (conidial stage *Gloeosporium tiliae*). LINDEN ANTHRACNOSE, LEAF SPOT, leaf blotch, scorch on American and European linden. Small, circular to irregular brown spots with dark margins form blotches along main veins in leaves, leaf stalks, and young twigs. In wet seasons defoliation in early summer can be followed by wilting and death of branches. Rose-colored spore pustules are formed on stems.

Control. Spray early with bordeaux mixture; cut out and burn infected branches.

Gnomonia veneta (conidial stage *Gloeosporium nervisequum*). ANTHRACNOSE OF SYCAMORE AND OAK, general on American and Oriental planes, California and Arizona sycamores, most damaging to white oaks, but attacking other species. London plane is rather resistant.

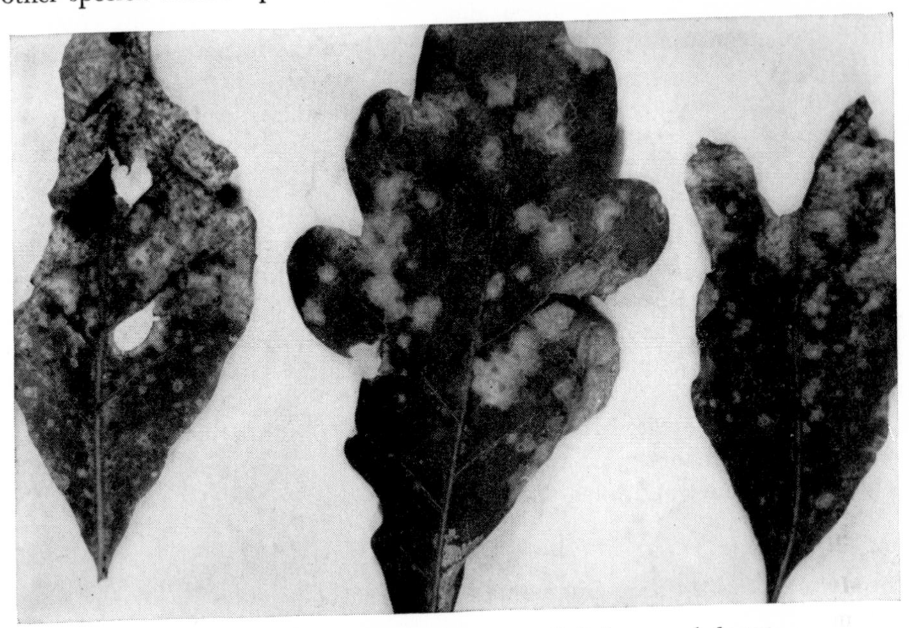

FIG. 13. Anthracnose of Sycamore and Oak, on oak leaves.

The disease, first found in the United States in 1888, is now present wherever the hosts are found.

The fungus winters as mycelium in fallen leaves, producing perithecia toward spring and discharging ascospores when young foliage is breaking out. Young sycamore leaves turn brown and die, looking as if hit by late frost, but later infection appears as brown areas along the veins, extending in brown, dead triangles between them. Conidia ooze out from acervuli on underside of veins in cream or flesh-colored masses in rainy weather, and are splashed to other leaves producing secondary infection. Native sycamore may be nearly completely defoliated and smaller twigs are killed. Sunken cankers form on twigs and branches, with more acervuli. In the South the fungus can winter in spore form on dormant buds, or in twig cankers. After defoliation trees usually put out a second crop of leaves, but the process is weakening and two or three successive years of early leaf fall is most injurious.

On oak the foliage usually looks scorched, but some leaves show small scattered brown spots and on white oaks there may be premature defoliation.

Control. Standard treatment is bordeaux mixture in three applications starting when buds burst and repeating at ten-day to two-week intervals. Puratized Agricultural Spray has given good results in experimental spraying in Illinois. Prune out and burn dead or cankered twigs. A dormant lime-sulfur spray would be helpful but probably impossible in residential areas because of its effect on paint.

MARSSONINA

Fungi Imperfecti, Melanconiales, Melanconiaceae

Two-celled, hyaline spores are formed in acervuli without setae. Spores are rounded at ends and are formed in pale to black masses on leaves. (The imperfect stage of the rose black spot fungus is in this genus.)

Marssonina panattoniana. LETTUCE ANTHRACNOSE. Small dead, brown spots appear on blades and midribs, centers often falling out leaving black-margined shot holes. Spots progress from older to inner young leaves; outer leaves are broken off and blown around by wind. The disease is important only during prolonged periods of wet weather, when it may cause heavy losses. Sanitary measures suffice for control.

MYCOSPHAERELLA

Ascomycetes, Sphaeriales, Mycosphaerellaceae

Perithecia not beaked, not setose, paraphyses lacking; spores hyaline, 2-celled.

Mycosphaerella opuntiae. CACTUS ANTHRACNOSE on Cereus, Echinocactus, Mamillaria, and Opuntia. The curved spores of the imperfect stage (*Gloeosporium cactorum*) form light pink pustules on surface of moist, light brown, rotted areas. Cut out and destroy diseased segments.

NEOFABRAEA

Ascomycetes, Helotiales, Mollisiaceae

This is one of the cup fungi or discomycetes. The apothecia are bright colored, formed in spots on living leaves, having a peridium of dark cells forming a pseudoparenchyma. The spores are hyaline, oblong to fusoid with several cross walls.

Neofabraea malicorticis. NORTHWESTERN ANTHRACNOSE, on apple, crabapple, pear, quince, chiefly in the Pacific Northwest where it is a native disease, serious in regions with heavy rainfall.

Cankers are formed on younger branches—elliptical, dark, sunken, up to 3 or 4 inches wide and 10 to 12 inches long, delimited when mature by a crack in the bark. Conidia of imperfect stage (*Gloeosporium malicorticis*) are formed in cream-colored cushions, turning black with age, in slits in bark. Young cankers, reddish brown circular spots, show in late fall.

Control. Prune properly, cutting out larger cankers and removing all dead bark; spray with bordeaux mixture before fruit is picked and fall rains start, repeating after harvest and two to three weeks later.

PSEUDOPEZIZA

Ascomycetes, Helotiales, Mollisiaceae

Apothecia bright colored, in spots on living leaves, not setose, spores 1-celled hyaline.

Pseudopeziza ribis. CURRANT ANTHRACNOSE; Leaf, Stem and Fruit Spot, generally distributed on currant, flowering currant, and gooseberry. This anthracnose was first reported on black currants in Connecticut in 1873. The first symptoms are very small, brown, circular spots on lower, older leaves, the leaves turning yellow if spots are numerous. Conidia of the imperfect stage (*Gloeosporium ribis*) are formed in moist flesh-colored masses in center of spots. In severe infections there is progressive defoliation from below upward.

Other occasional symptoms are black, sunken spots on leaf stalks, light brown to pale yellow lesions on canes, and black flyspeck spots on green berries, with considerable reduction in yield. Apothecia are formed on fallen leaves; ascospores are forcibly discharged in spring and carried by wind to young leaves.

Control. Clean up and burn, or plow under, fallen leaves. Spray when leaves are unfolding, again in 10 to 20 days, and repeat if needed. Tests in New York showed two sprays of 3–3–100 bordeaux mixture adequate (and preferred to new organics), the first spray applied about three weeks after blossoming and the second immediately after picking. A good spreader is required, and both leaf surfaces should be thoroughly covered.

SPHACELOMA

Fungi Imperfecti, Melanconiales, Melanconiaceae

Spores are 1-celled, hyaline, borne on a conidial stroma; perfect stage when known is Elsinoë, cause of spot anthracnose disease, sometimes called scab if there is appreciable amount of raised tissue. See also Scab Diseases.

Sphaceloma cercocarpi. ANTHRACNOSE of birch-leaf mahogany, in California. Leaf spots are nearly circular, up to 3 mm. across, with pale centers and slightly elevated purple margins.

Sphaceloma lippiae. ANTHRACNOSE OF LIPPIA, on fog-fruit in Indiana, closely resembling mint anthracnose and found in same fields. Numerous spots on leaves and stems are scattered or grouped to be almost confluent; centers are depressed, buff-colored, with purple margins.

Sphaceloma mattirolianum. SPOT ANTHRACNOSE, on *Arbutus menziesii,* in California.

Sphaceloma menthae. MINT ANTHRACNOSE, Leopard Spot Disease, on peppermint and other mints. Circular to irregular or oval spots on leaves, stems, and rootstocks are black with light centers, to 5 mm. in diameter. This disease formerly caused considerable damage, but is now controlled in commercial mint fields by fall plowing, covering old plants deeply.

FIG. 14. Spot Anthracnose of Rose.

Sphaceloma rosarum. ROSE ANTHRACNOSE, widespread on rose, collected on wild roses as early as 1898.

Symptoms appear on all above-ground plant parts. On leaves, spots are scattered or grouped, sometimes running together, usually circular, size variable up to 1/4 inch in diameter. At first spots are brown to dark purplish black with a dull brown border, but on aging the center turns ashen white, with a dark red margin. Leaves often turn yellow or reddish in area of spots and may have slits or perforations when the centers of the spots fall out.

On canes, spots are circular to elongated, raised, brown or purple, with depressed light centers; similar lesions, with ashen centers, occur on hips. Acervuli appear as barely visible dark masses on the light centers. Spore germination is prompt, and secondary cycles may be completed within two weeks.

The severity of the disease seems to vary with location. It was common in the rose test gardens during the years I worked at Cornell University, yet I have seen it very infrequently in suburban gardens near New York City. In parts of California it is reported more often than black spot. Climbing roses, particularly Dr. Van Fleet, are quite susceptible.

Control. The spraying or dusting program used for black spot will probably keep anthracnose in check but little test spraying has been done.

Sphaceloma symphoricarpi. SNOWBERRY ANTHRACNOSE, widespread on snowberry, impairing beauty of ornamental plants, first described from New York in 1910. Leaf spots, showing in early spring, are minute, dark purple to black, acquiring the distinctive dirty gray center with age, enlarging and coalescing into large areas subject to cracking. Misshapen leaves come from early marginal infections. Flower spotting is inconspicuous, but pronounced on the berries, with purple areas becoming sunken and pinkish. Secondary infection by an Alternaria causes fruit to shrivel into dry, brown mummies.

Control. A dormant lime-sulfur spray in spring, followed by treatments with copper-lime dust, has been suggested.

BACTERIAL DISEASES

The fact that bacteria can cause plant disease was discovered almost simultaneously in four different countries, with America claiming first honors. In 1878 Professor T. J. Burrill of the University of Illinois advanced the theory that fire blight was due to the bacteria which he found constantly associated with blighted tissues. In 1879 the French scientist Prillieux published a paper on bacteria as the cause of rose-red disease of wheat; in 1880 the Italian Comes recognized bacteria as pathogenic to plants; in 1882 Burrill named his fire-blight organism *Micrococcus amylovorus;* and in 1883 Wakker in Holland reported the bacterial nature of yellows disease of hyacinth. It remained, however, for Erwin F. Smith, of the U.S. Department of Agriculture, to do most of the pioneer work in this field and to convince the world that bacteria were to blame for so many diseases. He spent a lifetime in the process, starting with peach yellows, and going on to a study of crown gall and its relation to human cancer. In 1905 the first volume of his monumental work *Bacteria in Relation to Plant Diseases* was published.

Bacterial diseases fall into three categories: 1, a wilting, as in cucumber wilt, due to invasion of the vascular system, or water-conducting vessels; 2, necrotic blights, rots and leaf spots where the parenchyma tissue is killed, as in fire blight, delphinium black spot, soft rot of iris and other plants with rhizomes or fleshy roots; 3, an overgrowth or hyperplasia, as in crown gall or hairy root.

Pathogenic bacteria apparently cannot enter plants directly through unbroken cuticle but get in through insect or other wounds, through stomata, through water-pores, possibly through lenticels and often through flower nectaries. They can survive for some months in an inactive state in plant tissue, as in holdover cankers of fire blight, and perhaps years in the soil, although claims for extreme longevity of the crown-gall organism in soil are discounted.

Most of these plant-disease bacteria have had their genus names changed several times since they were first described, although the specific names have survived unchanged. The genera used in this text agree with those given in the sixth edition (1948) of *Bergey's Manual of Determinative Bacteriology.* Walter H. Burkholder, of Cornell University, who revised the portions of the Manual dealing with plant pathogens has followed in the footsteps of Erwin F. Smith by spending his life with bacterial diseases of plants, and so has Charlotte Elliott, of the U.S. Department of Agriculture, from whose *Manual of Bacterial Plant Pathogens* I have taken much information on disease symptoms.

In many cases the general nature of the symptoms and the name of the host plant will leave little doubt as to the identity of a bacterial disease. In the case of the soft rot due to *Erwinia carotovora* the nose alone is a reliable guide. In other cases identification is a job which has to be left to the technically trained bacteriologist. It involves special staining technique, for examination of form and motility under the microscope, and to see if it is Gram-negative or Gram-positive, and special culture technique to determine shape, color and texture of colonies on agar and gelatin, production of gases, fermentation of sugar, coagulation of milk, etc. If you are in doubt about a plant disease, and the absence of fungus fruiting bodies leads you to believe bacteria may be at work, send a specimen to your State Experiment Station for expert diagnosis.

AGROBACTERIUM

Eubacteriales, Rhizobiaceae

Small, motile, short rods, with 1 to 4 peritrichous flagella, ordinarily Gram-negative, not producing visible gas or detectable acid in ordinary culture media; gelatin liquefied slowly or not at all; not fixing free nitrogen but utilizing inorganic forms of nitrogen; optimum temperature 25° to 30° C. Found in soil, or plant roots in soil, or in hypertrophies or galls on stems of plants.

Agrobacterium gypsophilae, on gypsophila and related plants. Galls are formed at crown and root of grafted plants, from 1/4 to 1 inch in diameter, but with a flat nodular growth rather than the usual globose crown gall.

Agrobacterium rhizogenes. HAIRY ROOT OF APPLE, also recorded on cotoneaster, hollyhock, honey locust, honeysuckle, mulberry, peavine, peach, quince, Russian olive, rose, and spirea. "Woolly root" and "woolly knot" are other names given to this disease which was long considered merely a form of crown gall. Both diseases may occur on the same plant and in early stages be confused. In hairy root a great number of small roots protrude either directly from stems or roots or from localized hard swellings that frequently occur at the unions, the disease being common on grafted nursery apple trees 1, 2, or 3 years old, and the root development as profuse as a witches' broom. Control measures are the same as for crown gall.

Agrobacterium rubi. CANE GALL OF BRAMBLES, on blackberry, black and purple raspberries, and very rarely on red raspberry. Symptoms appear on fruiting canes in late May or June as small, spherical protuberances or elongate ridges of white gall tissue, which turns brown after several weeks. Canes often split open and dry out, producing small seedy berries. The disease is not as important as crown gall, but may be controlled by the same measures.

Agrobacterium tumefaciens. CROWN GALL, on a great variety of plants in more than 40 families, general on blackberry, raspberry and other brambles, on grapes and on rose; on fruit trees—apple, apricot, cherry, fig, peach and nectarine, pear, rarely, plum; on nuts—almond very susceptible, walnut, fairly susceptible, and pecan occasionally so; on shade trees, willow particularly and other hard woods but rare on conifers, although reported on incense cedar and juniper; on many shrubs and vines, particularly honeysuckle and euonymus; on perennials such as asters, daisies, and chrysanthemums; and on beets, turnips, and a few other vegetables, with tomato widely used in experiments.

FIG. 15. Crown Gall on Euonymus.

Crown gall was first noticed on grape in Europe in 1853 and the organism was first isolated in America, from galls on Paris daisy, about 1904. It is of first importance as a disease of nursery stock, but may cause losses of large productive trees in neglected orchards, especially almonds and peaches in California and other warm climates.

Symptoms. The galls are usually rounded, with an irregular rough surface, ranging up to several inches in diameter, usually occurring near the soil line, commonly at the graft union, but sometimes on roots or aerial parts. On euonymus, galls are formed anywhere along the vine. This is primarily a disease of the parenchyma, starting with a rapid proliferation of cells in the meristematic tissue and the formation of more or less convoluted soft or hard overgrowths or tumors. The close analogy of the unorganized cell growth of plant galls to wild cell proliferation in human cancer has intrigued scientists for many years. In some fashion bacteria provide stimulus for this overdevelopment, but similar galls have been produced on plants experimentally by injecting growth-promoting substances. Again experimentally, the injection of penicillin and other antibiotics has inhibited the development of bacterial crown galls.

Entrance of bacteria into plants for natural infection is exclusively through wounds. In nurseries and orchards the plow, the disc, or the hoe may be responsible; on the propagating bench grafting tools are indicted. Many claims have been made for the longevity of the bacteria in soil, but it now seems to be established that they do not live in the absence of host plants more than a couple of years and that sudden outbreaks of crown gall in land not previously growing susceptible crops is due to irrigation water bringing in viable bacteria from other infected orchards. The addition of lime to the soil may encourage crown gall, since bacteria do not live in an acid medium. The period of greatest activity is during warm months of the year.

Control. For home gardens rigid exclusion of all suspected planting stock is the very best control. Do not accept from your nurseryman blackberries or raspberries or roses or fruit trees showing suspicious bumps. If you have had previous trouble choose a different location for new, healthy plants. Be careful not to wound stems in cultivating.

For nurserymen, sanitary propagating practices are a must. Stock should be healthy, and perhaps certified by state nursery inspectors. Incidence of crown gall is greatly reduced by dipping rose cuttings in mercuric chloride, 1 to 1000, for 20 minutes, or in Semesan 1 to 400 for 10 minutes. Grafting knives should be sterilized by frequent dipping in potassium permanganate, 1 ounce in 2 gallons of water, or in denatured alcohol. If nursery soil is infested two years' growth of cowpeas, oats, or crotalaria between rose crops will minimize crown gall.

Fruit and nut growers can perhaps plant less susceptible varieties, although fruit that is resistant in one locality may be diseased in another. American grape varieties are considered more resistant than European; Jonathan apples and nut trees on black walnut understock may be less susceptible.

Painting galls with a solution of Elgetol-methanol has given control of crown gall on almonds and peaches in California. One part Elgetol (sodium dinitrocresol) is shaken with four parts synthetic wood alcohol and applied with a brush, covering the surface of the gall and extending ½ to 1 inch beyond the margin into healthy bark.

Some years ago it was found that colchicine inhibited some plant tumors, and since 1945 there have been intriguing reports on the effects of penicillin and streptomycin, applied by hypodermic injection, by immersing galled roots, or by applying a cotton pad soaked with the antibiotic to a gall. The practical development of this idea is still in the future.

BACTERIUM

Eubacteriales, Bacteriaceae

This is a form genus to take care of a heterogeneous collection of species whose relationships are not clear. Bacteria are rod-shaped, without endospores. The plant pathogens are Gram-negative.

Bacterium pseudotsugae. GALL DISEASE on Douglas fir and big-cone spruce in California. Galls are formed on twigs and upper branches, but trees older than 15 years are not subject to new infection. Occasionally galls are on main stems, which may be girdled with death of the tops or formation of a secondary, staghead leader. Galls are globular, rough, spongy, fissured, varying from pin-head size to several inches across. Bacteria are spread by Cooley spruce gall aphid.

Bacterium stewartii. BACTERIAL WILT OF CORN; Stewart's Disease, on sweet corn, sometimes on field corn, in the middle regions of the United States, from New York to California. This is a vascular disease with yellow slime formed in the water-conducting system, resulting in browning of nodes, and dwarfing of plants or long pale green streaks on leaf blades, followed by wilting and death of whole plant. Tassels may be formed early and die before rest of plant.

The bacteria are chiefly disseminated by corn flea beetles and winter either in the beetles or in seed. Primary infections come from beetles feeding in spring, from infected seed, or occasionally from soil, but secondary spread is mostly by insects.

Corn grown in rich soil is more susceptible to the disease, which is most prevalent on variety Golden Bantam. Winter temperatures influence the amount of wilt the following summer. If the winter index, which is the sum of mean temperatures for December, January, and February, is above 100, bacterial wilt will be present in destructive amounts on susceptible varieties. If the winter index is below 90 the disease will be almost absent in northeastern states. With an index between 90 and 100 there may be a moderate amount of wilt. Disease surveys over a period of years testify to the reliability of such forecasts, but with the increasing use of hybrid sweet corn resistant to wilt the importance of winter temperatures is lessened.

Control. When winter index is above 100 do not grow Golden Bantam but substitute resistant Golden Cross Bantam, Carmelcross, Ohio Gold, Ioana, Marcross, Spancross, or Whipcross. Substitute commercial fertilizer for manure.

Bacterium tardicrescens. Bacterial Blight of Iris, apparently widespread. Early symptoms are translucent spots of irregular shape on leaves, appearing dark green in reflected light. The lesions may coalesce to cover the entire leaf, but infection occurs only in continued moist weather and rhizomes are not involved as with soft rot.

CORYNEBACTERIUM

Eubacteriales, Corynebacteriaceae

Slender, straight to slightly curved rods, with irregularly stained segments or granules, often with pointed or club-shaped swellings at ends; nonmotile or questionably motile; Gram-variable.

Corynebacterium agropyri. Yellow Gum Disease, on western wheat grass. Enormous masses of surface bacteria form yellow slime between stem and upper sheath and glumes of flower head; plants dwarfed or bent; normal seeds rare.

Corynebacterium fascians. Fasciation, widespread on sweet pea, also on carnation, chrysanthemum, gypsophila, geranium, petunia, and pyrethrum. Sweet pea symptoms are masses of short, thick, and aborted stems with misshapen leaves developing near soil line at first or second nodes of stem. On old plants the fasciated growth may have a diameter of 3 inches but does not extend more than an inch or two above ground. The portion exposed to light develops normal green color. Plants are not killed, but the stem is dwarfed and blossom production reduced.

Control. Sterilize infested soil or use fresh; disinfect seed by dipping 1 minute in alcohol, then 20 minutes in 1 to 1000 solution of mercuric chloride, rinsing and drying before planting.

Corynebacterium flaccumfaciens. Bacterial Wilt of Bean, widespread on kidney and lima beans, causing considerable loss. Plants wilt at any stage from seedling to pod-production, with leaves turning dry and brown, ragged after rains. Plants are often stunted. Bacteria winter on or in seed, which appear yellow, or wrinkled and varnished. When infected seed is planted bacteria pass from cotyledons into stems and xylem vessels. Other plants are infected by mechanical injury and perhaps by insects, but there is not much danger from splashed rain. Plants girdled at nodes may break over.

Control. Use seed grown in Idaho or California.

Corynebacterium michiganense. Bacterial Canker of Tomato, widespread, formerly causing serious losses of tomato canning crops. This is a vascular wilt disease, seedlings remaining stunted, symptoms on older plants starting with wilting of margins of leaflets of lower leaves, often on only one side of leaf, with leaflets curling upward, then browning and withering but remaining attached to stem. The one-sided infection may continue up through the plant. Open cankers may extend from pith to outer surface of stem. Fruit infection starts with small, raised, snow-white spots, with the center later browned and roughened but with the white color persisting as a halo to give a bird's-eye spot. Fruits may also be distorted and stunted with a yellowish interior discoloration. Seed from such fruits carry bacteria both internally and on seed coat. In the field bacteria are spread by splashed rain. They can persist in soil for two years.

Control. Use certified seed; a two-year rotation; clean up all tomato refuse at end of season, and diseased plants throughout season. Fermenting tomato pulp for four days at a temperature near 70° F. will kill bacteria on surface of seeds, but hot-water treatment, 25 minutes at 122° F., is required for internal bacteria. Seedlings should be started in soil that has not previously grown tomatoes, and framework of coldframes disinfected with formaldehyde.

Corynebacterium poinsettiae. Stem Canker and Leaf Spot of Poinsettia, a relatively new disease of poinsettia first noted in greenhouses in 1941. Longitudinal water-soaked streaks appear on one side of green stems, sometimes continuing through leaf petioles to cause spotting or blotching of leaves and complete defoliation. The cortex of the stems turns yellow and the vascular system brown. Stems may crack open and bend down, with glistening, golden-brown masses of bacteria oozing from stem ruptures and leaf lesions.

Control. Discard diseased stock plants; isolate rooted cuttings and young plants obtained from questionable sources; avoid overhead watering and syringing.

Corynebacterium sepedonicum. Bacterial Ring Rot of Potato, widespread since 1931, when it probably was introduced from Europe. All commercial varieties are susceptible and losses amount to millions of dollars in decay of tubers in field and storage. Symptoms appear when plants are nearly full grown, with one or more stems in a hill wilted and stunted while the rest seem healthy. Lower leaves have pale yellow areas between veins, then deeper yellow color with upward rolling of leaf margins. A creamy exudate is expelled when stem is cut across.

Tuber infection takes place at the stem end. Most prominent symptoms appear some time after storage with the vascular ring turning creamy yellow to light brown, with a crumbly or cheesy odorless decay, followed by decay from secondary organisms. Bacteria are not spread from plant to plant in the field but on cutting knife and fingers at planting. A knife used to cut one infected tuber may contaminate the next 20 seed pieces.

Control. Use certified seed potatoes; disinfect knife between cuts in a 1 to 10 solution of formalin or 1 to 500 mercuric chloride. Use several knives and rotate them in disinfectant after each few cuts. Commercial growers use a rotating knife passing through a chemical or hot-water bath between cuts. Disinfect tools, grader, digger and bags with formalin; sweep storage house clean and spray with copper sulfate, 1 pound to 5 gallons of water.

ERWINIA

Eubacteriales, Enterobacteriaceae

Motile rods, which normally require organic nitrogen compounds for growth; producing acid with or without visible gas from a variety of sugars; invading tissues of living plants, producing dry necrosis, galls, wilts, or soft rots. The genus is named for Erwin F. Smith, pioneer in plant diseases caused by bacteria.

Erwinia amylovora. Fire Blight, general on many species in several tribes of the Rosaceae, particularly serious on pear, apple, and quince, also on almond, amelanchier (serviceberry) apricot, blackberry, cherry, chokecherry, cotoneaster, crabapples, hawthorn, Japanese quince, loquat, mountain-ash, plum, pyracantha, raspberry, rose, spirea, and strawberry. Apparently a native disease, first noticed near the Hudson River in 1780, fire blight spread south and west with increased cultivation of pears and apples. By 1880 it had practically wrecked pear orchards in Illinois, Iowa, and other states in the Northern Mississippi Valley. Then it devastated pears on the Texas Gulf. Reaching California by 1910 it played havoc up the coast to Washington, although it has not developed in western Washington.

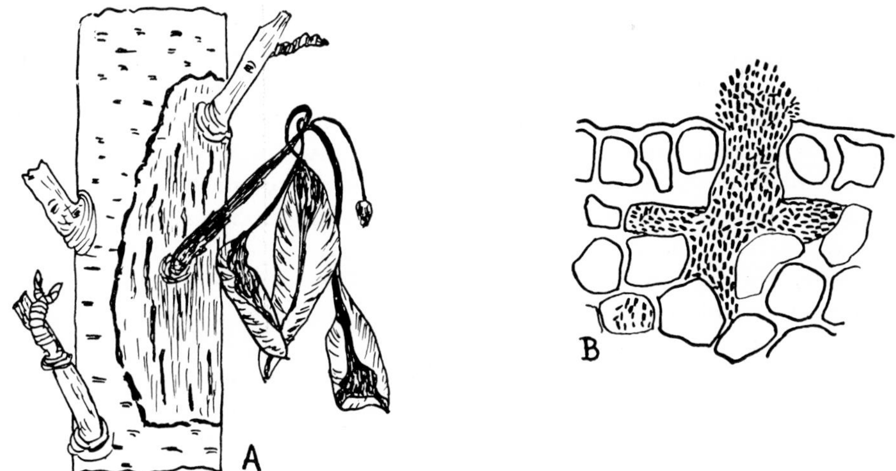

Fig. 16. Fire Blight. A, hold-over canker developed on apple limb at base of blighted twig; B, bacteria swarming through tissue.

Symptoms. Blossoms and leaves of infected twigs suddenly wilt, turn dark brown to black, shrivel and die, but remain attached to twigs. The bark is shrunken, dark brown to purplish, and sometimes blistered with gum oozing out. Brown or black blighted branches with dead persistent leaves look as if scorched by fire.

The bacteria survive the winter in living tissue at the edge of "holdover cankers" on limbs. These are dead, slightly sunken areas with a definite margin or slight crack where dead tissue has shrunk away from living. In moist weather bacteria appear on the surface of cankers in pearly viscid drops of ooze which is carried by wind-blown rain or insects to blossoms. Infection spreads from the blighted bloom to the young fruit, then down the pedicel to adjacent leaves which turn brown, remaining hanging around the blighted blossom cluster. Leaf and fruit blight is also possible by direct invasion, a secondary infection via bacteria carried from primary blossom blight by ants, aphids, flies, wasps, fruit-tree bark beetles and honeybees, sometimes tarnished plant bugs.

The tissue first appears water-soaked, then reddish, then brown to black as the bacteria swarm between the dying parenchyma cells. Division may take place every half hour so they multiply rapidly and are usually well in advance of discolored external tissue. A collar rot may develop when cankers are formed near the base of a tree. Water sprouts are common sources of infection.

As spring changes to summer, the bacteria gradually become less active and remain dormant at the edge of a woody canker until the next spring at sap flow. Ordinarily they do not winter on branches smaller than ½ inch in diameter.

Control. Surgery is the surest method, cutting out cankered limbs during the dormant season, taking the branch off at least 4 inches back from the margin of the visible canker. Large cankers on main trunks can be excised with a knife, scraping away all bark inside the area and for an inch outside the margin and disinfecting the wound before covering with a wound dressing. In place of the extremely poisonous mixture of cyanide of mercury and mercuric chloride used as a disinfectant, two other mixtures have been suggested.

I		II	
1	qt. denatured alcohol	100	gms. cobalt nitrate
¼	pt. distilled water	50	cc. glycerine
¾	oz. muriatic acid	100	cc. oil of wintergreen
1½	lbs. zinc chloride	50	cc. acetic acid
		800	cc. denatured alcohol

A druggist could probably prepare either formula which should be kept in a glass container. The solution is painted over the canker, without cutting out the bark, and over apparently healthy tissue 5 or 6 inches from the edge of the canker.

When blighted branches have to be cut out during the growing season, either from fruit trees or ornamental shrubs and trees, it pays to cut 6 inches to a foot below the visibly blighted portion, disinfecting the pruning saw or shears between cuts with formaldehyde or denatured alcohol. Large cut surfaces can be covered with bordeaux paint, prepared by stirring dry bordeaux powder into raw linseed oil until a workable paste is formed.

Spraying fruit trees coming into full bloom with a weak bordeaux mixture (2–6–100) aids in control of blossom blight. Sometimes copper-lime dust can be substituted. No insecticide should be added to a full blossom spray for fear of poisoning bees and preventing pollination.

Resistant varieties are possibilities. Asiatic species of pears are more resistant than our common *Pyrus communis.* Varieties Old Home and Orient are blight resistant, and the common Kieffer pear we use for preserving, but Bartlett, Flemish Beauty, Howell, and Clapps Favorite are especially susceptible. More or less resistant apple varieties are Baldwin, Ben Davis, Delicious, Duchess, Golden Delicious, McIntosh, Northern Spy, Stayman and Winter Banana.

At the University of California some work has been done on susceptibility of ornamentals to fire blight. *Pyracantha angustifolia* is quite susceptible but *P. coccinea, P. crenulata,* and *P. gibbsii* are rather resistant. *Cotoneaster salicifolia* is susceptible, *C. dammeri, C. pannosa,* and *C. horizontalis* are more resistant, and *C. adpressa* and *C. microphylla* show marked resistance.

Cultural methods also influence the degree of fire blight, which is worse on fast-growing, succulent tissue. Avoid excessive nitrogen in fertilizers, or compensate with potassium and phosphorus. Feed trees susceptible to fire blight in autumn rather than spring.

Erwinia aroideae. Soft Rot of Calla, originally described from common calla, found on golden calla, and also on beet, cactus, cabbage, cauliflower, celery, cucumber, carrot, eggplant, geranium (Pelargonium), hyacinth, iris, onion, parsnip, pepper, potato, salsify, sansevieria, tomato, and turnip.

On calla lily the soft rot starts in upper portion of the corm and progresses upward into leaf and flower stalks or down into roots, with the corm becoming soft, brown, and watery. Sometimes infection starts at edge of petiole which turns slimy, with brown margins and spots on leaves which die entirely, or rot off at base before losing green color. Flowers turn brown; stalks fall over; roots become soft and slimy inside the epidermis. Corms may rot so fast the plant falls over without other symptoms, or diseased portion may dry down to sunken dark spots, in which the bacteria stay dormant to the next season.

On tomatoes, infection takes place through growth cracks, insect wounds or sunscald areas. The tissue is at first water-soaked then opaque, and in 3 to 10 days the whole fruit is soft, watery, colorless, with an offensive odor.

Control. Scrub calla corms, cut out rotted spots, and let cork over for a day or two. Before planting soak for 1 hour in a 1 to 50 dilution of formalin, or in New Improved Ceresan, 1 ounce mixed with a heaping teaspoon of Dreft to 3 gallons water, or in a 1 to 1000 solution of mercuric chloride. Plant in fresh or sterilized soil in sterilized containers and keep pots on clean gravel or wood racks, never on beds where diseased callas have grown previously. Grow at cool temperatures and avoid overwatering.

Erwinia atroseptica. POTATO BLACKLEG, basal stem rot, tuber rot, general on potato in the North, less frequent in South. This is a systemic disease perpetuated by naturally infected tubers. Lower leaves turn yellow; upper leaves curl upward; stems and leaves tend to grow up rather than spread out; stem is black spotted, more or less softened at base and up to 3 or 4 inches from ground, and may be covered with bacterial slime; shoots may wilt and fall over. Tubers are infected through the stem end. The disease is most rapid in warm, moist weather but may continue in storage. The bacteria are spread on the cutting knife as with ring rot.

Control. Use certified seed; rogue infected plants during season; practice long rotation; disinfest cutting knife. Late varieties seem to be more resistant than early.

Erwinia carnegiana. BACTERIAL NECROSIS OF GIANT CACTUS, in the entire habitat of *Carnegia gigantea.* Long present in southern Arizona this disease was not described until 1942, after it had encroached on cactus parks and private estates and had infected an area of about 200 by 250 miles near Tucson. In the Saguaro National Monument about one-fifth of the cacti have been attacked, with heaviest mortality in trees 150 to 200 years old.

Symptoms start with a small, circular, light spot, usually with a water-soaked margin. The tissues underneath then turn nearly black, the spot enlarges and has a purplish hue with the center cracking and bleeding a brown liquid. The rotten tissues dry, break up into granular or lumpy pieces and fall to the ground. Rotting on one side means leaning to that side, but when the trunk is girdled near the base the giant may fall in a wind storm. If it does not break it stands as a bare, woody skeleton, with all parenchyma tissue disintegrated. An insect vector is now known to transmit the disease.

Control. Incipient spots should be cut out, disinfected and painted with asphalt paint. Fallen trees should be destroyed, a difficult job since they will not burn. They are cut into short lengths (and even a 5-foot length may weigh 1500 pounds), dragged to a burial pit, covered with a disinfectant and then with a tarpaulin for a few days; afterward the pit is filled with soil.

Erwinia carotovora. SOFT ROT, general on many vegetables, in field, storage and transit, and many ornamentals, but most particularly on iris. The bacteria were first isolated from rotted carrots, whence the name, but they are equally at home in asparagus, cabbage, turnips and other crucifers, celery, cucumbers, eggplant, endive, garlic, horseradish, melon, parsnip, pepper, spinach, sweet potato, tomato. Besides wide distribution on iris, soft rot has been reported on chrysanthemum, dahlia, Easter lily, geranium, sansevieria, and yellow calla among ornamentals.

The bacteria enter through wounds, causing a rapid, wet rot with a most offensive odor. The middle lamella is dissolved and roots become soft and pulpy. In iris infection often follows borer infestation. Tips of the leaves are withered, but the basal portions are wet and practically shredded. The entire interior of a rhizome may disintegrate into a vile yellow mess but the epidermis remains firm. The rot is more serious in shaded locations, when iris is too crowded, planted too deeply.

Control. Most iris needs to be divided every three or four years. At that time cut away all rotted portions, cut leaves back to short fans and disinfect in 1 to 1000 mercuric chloride (2 tablets to a quart of water) for 30 minutes, allow to dry in the sun a day or two, then replant in well-drained soil, in full sun, with upper portion of rhizome slightly exposed to sun. (Many good iris growers do not agree with this "sitting duck" method, preferring to cover with an inch of soil.) Clean off all old leaves in late fall after frost.

Prevent rot on stored vegetables by saving only sound, dry tubers, in straw or sand, in a well-ventilated room with temperature not too much above freezing.

In the garden use a rather long rotation, with leafy vegetables changing places with those having fleshy roots.

Erwinia cytolytica. BACTERIOSIS OF DAHLIA, on dahlia stem and tubers. Stems near crown are blackened, softened, with a moist decay of pith and tubers, accompanied by foul odor.

Erwinia dissolvens. CORN ROT. Corn leaves show light or dark brown rotting at base; husks and leaf blades have dark brown spots; lower portion of stalk is rotted, soft, brown, with strong odor of decay; plants may break over and die. As the tissue dies all that is left is a mass of shredded remnants of fibrovascular bundles. Bacteria enter through hydathodes (water pores), stomata, and wounds.

Erwinia lathyri. BACTERIAL STREAK OF SWEET PEA, also on bean, broad bean, pea, soy bean. Symptoms appearing on sweet pea at blossom time are light reddish brown to dark brown spots and streaks along stems near the ground, the lesions turning purple with age. The cambium and parenchyma are destroyed and plants are finally killed. Petioles and leaves may show water-soaked spots. The bacteria are seed-borne.

Control. Unless seed is known to be clean, treat before planting. Soak 5 minutes in a 1 to 20 solution of formalin or for 20 minutes in 1 to 1000 mercuric chloride, rinsing thoroughly and drying.

Erwinia nimipressuralis. WETWOOD OF ELM, slime flux, due to bacteria pathogenic in elm trunk wood. A water-soaked dark discoloration of the heartwood is correlated with chronic bleeding at crotches and wounds and abnormally high sap pressure in trunk, with wilting a secondary symptom. The pressure in diseased trees increases from April to August or September, reaching 5 to 30 pounds per square inch, and as much as 60 in one record. The bacteria inhabit chiefly ray cells and do not cause a general clogging of water-conducting tissues. That slime flux occurs with increased pressure has been known for many years for many kinds of trees. The bacterial connection was not demonstrated until 1945, and then only on elm.

Control. Install drains of ½-inch copper pipe in tree trunk to provide outlet for abnormal sap and gases. Pipe should extend far enough so sap does not fall on bark.

Erwinia rhapontici. Rhubarb Crown Rot, similar to soft rot.

Erwinia tracheiphila. Bacterial Wilt of Cucurbits, on cucumber, pumpkin, squash and muskmelon, but not watermelon. The disease is general east of the Rocky Mountains and is also present in parts of the West, most serious north of Tennessee. Total loss of vines is rare, but a 10 to 20% loss is common.

This is a vascular wound disease transmitted by insects—the striped and 12-spotted cucumber beetles. Dull, green flabby patches on leaves are followed by sudden wilting and shriveling of foliage, drying of stems. Bacteria form a viscous mass which oozes from cut stems. Partially resistant plants may be dwarfed with excessive blooming and branching, wilting during day but with partial recovery at night.

The bacteria winter solely in the digestive tract of the beetles and are deposited on leaves in spring with excrement, entering through feeding wounds or stomata.

Control is directed chiefly at the insects. Start vines under Hotkaps and spray or dust with rotenone, calcium arsenate, or cryolite when the mechanical protection is removed. Controlling the wilt directly with copper sprays is possible but not advisable on very young vines for fear of phytotoxicity. Rogue infected young plants as soon as noticed.

Erwinia phytophthora, not clearly distinguished from E. carotovora but listed for Delphinium Foot Rot; Blackleg. Bacteria enter through stem cracks; flower stalks are killed, tan exudate is present; fostered by wet soil. Avoid overhead watering. Bioquin 1 has been suggested as a spray.

PSEUDOMONAS

Eubacteriales, Pseudomonadaceae

Cells are straight rods and most are Gram-negative. Many species produce a fluorescent, greenish, water-soluble pigment. These are soil and water bacteria with many plant pathogens causing leaf spots, leaf stripes, or similar diseases.

Pseudomonas aceris. Maple Leaf Spot, found in California on big leaf maple. Small, water-soaked spots, surrounded by yellow zones, turn brown or black; cankers develop on petioles and bracts in serious cases; leaves may drop; disease present in cool, damp weather of early spring.

Pseudomonas alboprecipitans. Bacterial Spot of cereals, grasses, and corn. Light or dark brown spots or streaks on grass blades. Bacteria enter through stomata or water pores.

Pseudomonas aleuritidis. Leaf Spot on tung-oil, bean and castor bean. Dark angular lesions, most destructive to young trees.

Pseudomonas alliicola. Onion Bulb Rot, a storage disease, inner scales of bulb water-soaked and soft, sometimes entire bulb rotting.

Pseudomonas andropogoni. Bacterial Stripe, of sorghum and corn through sorghum growing sections of central and northern states. Red streaks and blotches appear on leaves and sheaths, with abundant exudate drying down to red crusts or scales, readily washed off in rains. Bacteria enter through stomata.

Pseudomonas angulata. Angular Leaf Spot of Tobacco, in all tobacco areas, also on flowering tobacco. Irregular angular spots on leaves, bounded by veins; centers are tan or reddish brown, with thin dark borders, but may dry, turn whitish and drop out. Remove diseased leaves.

Pseudomonas apii. Bacterial Blight of Celery. Small, irregularly circular rusty leaf spots, with a yellow halo, are occasionally numerous enough to cause death of foliage, but commonly only disfiguring.

Control. Spray plants in seedbed with 8–4–100 bordeaux mixture or dust weekly with 20–80 copper-lime dust; clean up all old refuse.

Pseudomonas aptatum. Bacterial Spot, on beets and nasturtium. Spots on nasturtium leaves are water-soaked, brownish, 1/8 to 1/4 inch across. On beets they are dark brown or black, irregular, and in addition there are narrow streaks on petioles, midribs, and larger veins. Petiole tissue may be softened as with soft rot. Infection occurs only through wounds.

Pseudomonas berberidis. Bacterial Leaf Spot of Barberry. Small, irregular, dark green water-soaked areas on leaves turn purple brown with age; occasional spotting occurs on leaf stalks and young shoots. Buds do not develop the next season if twigs are infected, and if they are girdled the entire twig is blighted. Cut out infected twigs and spray with bordeaux mixture.

Pseudomonas caryophylli. Bacterial Wilt of Carnation, usually under glass. Plants wilt, turn dry, colorless, with roots disintegrating. Grayish-green foliage is the first symptom, but leaves rapidly turn yellow and die. Yellow streaks of frayed tissue in vascular areas extend a foot or two up the stem. It takes a month for disease to show up after inoculation but it can be transmitted on cuttings taken from plants previous to appearance of symptoms. The sticky character of diseased tissue distinguishes this from Fusarium wilt.

Most susceptible varieties are Miller's Gold, Yellow Gold, Charm, Coronet, Dorothy Napier, King Cardinal, Pelargonium, Pollyanna, Maine Sunshine, Spitfire, Virginia Dare, Virginia Supreme, and Woburn. Resistant varieties include Dairy Maid, Dimity Derigo, Peter Fisher, Dark Pink Fisher, Marchioness of Headfort, Seth Parker.

Control. Take cuttings early from healthy plants in benches and not from those close to diseased plants; treat cuttings 15 to 30 minutes in potassium permanganate, 1 ounce to 5 gallons of water; sterilize sand with steam or chloropicrin. Soil treatments are under test.

Pseudomonas cichorii. Rot, of chicory and French endive. A yellowish olive center rot, affecting young inner leaves.

Pseudomonas columnae. Bacterial Leaf Spot of Turkish hazelnut. Circular to angular, brown, necrotic spots on leaves start as small, water-soaked areas, turning dark, oily, much shrunken.

Pseudomonas delphinii. Delphinium Black Spot, on delphinium and aconite (monkshood). Irregular tarry black spots on leaves, flower buds, petioles, and stems may coalesce in late stages to form large black areas. The bacteria enter through stomata or water pores. Occasionally this bacterial leaf spot results

Fig. 17. Bacterial Black Spot of Delphinium, right, compared with "blacks," deformed condition caused by cyclamen mite, left.

in some distortion but most abnormal growth and blackening of buds is due to the cyclamen mite, which is usually much more serious than black spot.

Control. Remove diseased leaves as noticed; cut and burn all old stalks at end of season. In a wet spring and summer, spray with bordeaux mixture. Drenching crowns with mercuric chloride has been suggested but is seldom necessary.

Pseudomonas erodii. Bacterial Leaf Spot on heronbill (*Erodium*) and geranium (*Pelargonium*). On heronbill the diseased areas are circular to angular, or elongated, bounded by veins, reddish brown becoming black and watery; leaves wither and fall. On geranium minute pellucid dots turn reddish brown with colorless borders; the dead tissue becomes dry and seared, making a "frogeye" spot.

Control. Remove infected leaves; avoid overhead watering.

Pseudomonas gardeniae. BACTERIAL LEAF SPOT OF GARDENIA. Ovoid to circular spots, varying from pin-points to 1/4 inch in diameter, have brown to reddish brown centers and usually narrow, water-soaked margins. Severe spotting is followed by yellowing and defoliation. The bacteria are weakly parasitic, operating under high humidity in cloudy weather.

Control. Destroy infected leaves of plants; disinfect pots and benches; sterilize soil; take cuttings from healthy plants; avoid syringing.

Pseudomonas glycinea. BACTERIAL BLIGHT OF SOYBEAN, perhaps the most common and conspicuous disease of soybean, appearing in fields when plants are half-grown and remaining active until maturity, with defoliation during periods of high humidity or heavy dews. Small, angular, translucent leaf spots, yellow to light brown, turn dark reddish brown to nearly black with age. There is often a white exudate drying to a glistening film on under leaf surface. Black lesions appear on stems and petioles, and on pods water-soaked spots enlarge to cover a wide area, darken, and produce an exudate drying to brownish scales; seeds are often infected. Seedlings from infected seed may have brown spots on cotyledons and sometimes die.

Control. Use seed only from disease-free pods. Resistant varieties are a possibility.

Pseudomonas helianthi. BACTERIAL LEAF SPOT OF SUNFLOWER. Leaves show brown, necrotic spots, first water-soaked, then dark and oily.

Pseudomonas intybi. BACTERIAL ROT of endive and lettuce, a center rot affecting young, inner leaves.

Pseudomonas lachrymans. ANGULAR LEAF SPOT OF CUCURBITS, general on cucumber, muskmelon, summer squash, gourds, bryanopsis. Leaves or stems may have irregular, angular, water-soaked spots, with bacteria oozing out in tear-like droplets which dry down to a white residue. Eventually the spots turn gray, die and shrink, leaving holes in foliage. Fruit spots are small, nearly round, with the tissue turning white, sometimes cracking. The bacteria overwinter in diseased plant refuse and on seed and are spread from the soil to stems and later to fruit in rainy weather, also transferred from plant to plant on hands and clothing of gardeners. Infection is through stomata, usually in early morning in warm, rainy weather.

Control. Plow under or remove vines immediately after harvest; treat seed in 1 to 1000 mercuric chloride (1 tablet to a pint of water, for 5 minutes, then rinse in running water; spray with 6–6–100 bordeaux mixture (4–4–100 for melons) or use copper-calcium arsenate-lime dust, 15–15–70.

Pseudomonas maculicola. BACTERIAL LEAF SPOT OF CRUCIFERS, pepper spot of cabbage, cauliflower, chinese cabbage and turnip, mostly in northeastern and Middle Atlantic states. Numerous brown or purple spots range from pin points to 1/8 inch in diameter. If they are very numerous leaves turn yellow and drop off. Cauliflower is more commonly affected than cabbage. Bacteria, disseminated on seed or in diseased plant parts, enter through stomata, and visible symptoms appear in three to six days. Disease is most severe in seedbeds.

Control. Change location of hotbed starting seedlings; use two-year rotation in field; have seed hot-water treated.

Pseudomonas marginalis. KANSAS LETTUCE DISEASE. Leaf margins are dark brown to almost black, first soft, then like parchment. Yellowish red spots, turning dark, are scattered over leaves. The bacteria live in the soil, which should not be splashed on the plants by uncareful watering.

Pseudomonas marginata. GLADIOLUS SCAB, stem rot, neck rot, widespread on gladiolus, also on iris and trigridia. Lesions on corms are pale yellow, water-soaked, circular spots deepening to brown or nearly black, eventually sunken with raised, horny or brittle margins that are scablike and exude a gummy substance. Bacteria overwinter on corms. First symptoms after planting are tiny, reddish, raised specks on leaves, mostly near the base, enlarging to dark sunken spots which grow together into large areas with a firm or soft rot. Sometimes plants fall over, but generally the disease is not very damaging with chief loss to grower in disfigured, unsalable corms. Brown streaks in husks sometimes disintegrate, leaving holes.

Control. Use well-drained soil, preferably sandy loam and combine corm treatments with crop rotation. Soak unhusked corms for 2 hours in 1 to 1000 mercuric chloride just before planting, or dip for 1 minute in calomel, 1 pound to 5 gallons water prepared with a little Dreft or other spreader as a wetting agent. Occasionally mercury compounds are injurious, especially if treatment is continued too long, and in some soils seem to be ineffective. Fresh manure in soil seems to reduce effectiveness of treatment.

Pseudomonas martyniae. LEAF SPOT on unicorn plant. Very small, angular, sunken, translucent spots, with raised margins coalesce to form irregular patches of dry, light-brown tissue. Petioles and stems may also be affected and plants die; fruits may be brown, shriveled.

Control. Destroy diseased foliage or plants; use seed from healthy pods.

Pseudomonas mellea. WISCONSIN TOBACCO DISEASE, "rust" on tomato, *Nicotiana* spp. in Kentucky and Wisconsin. Small rusty specks or spots with chlorotic halos often coalesce to large, irregular areas. Do not use plants from infected seedbeds.

Pseudomonas melophthora. APPLE ROT, probably widespread. This is a decay of ripe apples following after apple maggots and eventually rotting whole fruit.

Pseudomonas mori. BACTERIAL BLIGHT OF MULBERRY, general on black and white mulberry. Numerous water-soaked leaf spots join to form brown or black areas with surrounding yellow tissue. Young leaves may be distorted with dark, sunken spots on midribs and veins. Dark stripes with translucent borders, on young shoots, exude white or yellow ooze from lenticels. Dead twigs and brown leaves resemble fire blight; trees are stunted but seldom killed.

Control. Remove and burn blighted branches; do not plant young mulberry trees near infected specimens.

Pseudomonas papulans. Blister Spot Canker, on apple. Small, dark brown blisters on fruit and rough bark cankers on limbs start at lenticels. Bark may have rough, scaly patches from a few inches to a yard long, bordered with a pimpled edge, and with outer bark sloughing off in spring.

Pseudomonas phaseolicola. Bean Halo Blight, halo spot, on common, lima and scarlet runner beans. The symptoms are those of other bean blights except that there are wide green or yellowish green halos around water-soaked leaf spots, such spots later turning brown and dry. Leaves wilt and turn brown; young pods wither and produce no seed, or sometimes plants are dwarfed with top leaves crinkled and mottled. In hot weather spots may be angular, reddish brown, and without halo. Stem streaks are reddish, with gray ooze; pod spots are red to brown with silver crusts; seed are small, wrinkled with cream-colored spots.

Control. Use seed from blight-free areas. Blight is extremely rare in California, and very occasional in Idaho, in very wet weather. Somewhat resistant varieties include some strains of Red Kidney and Refugee, Scotia, New Stringless Green Pod, Black and Extra Early Valentine, Refugee 1000 to 1, Excelsior Wax, Logan and Tendergreen.

Pseudomonas pisi. Bacterial Blight of Pea, general on field and garden peas, especially in East and South, and causing leaf spot of sweet peas. Dark green, water-soaked dots on leaves enlarge and dry to russet brown; stems have dark green to brown streaks. Flowers may be killed or young pods shriveled, with seed covered with bacterial slime. Bacteria enter through stomata or wounds and if they reach vascular system either leaflets or whole plants wilt. Vines infected when young usually die.

Control. Avoid wounding vines during cultivation, also Alaska and Telephone varieties which are particularly susceptible. Sow peas in early spring, in well-drained soil.

Pseudomonas primulae. Bacterial Leaf Spot of Primrose, in ornamental and commercial plantings in California. Infection confined to older leaves, showing as irregularly circular brown lesions surrounded by conspicuous yellow halos. Spots may coalesce to kill part or all of leaf. Spraying with 4–4–100 bordeaux mixture seems to prevent infection.

Pseudomonas rhizoctonia. Bacterial Rosette of Lettuce, apparently a greenhouse problem. Plant growth is retarded or shows a tendency to rosette, with yellowed, flaccid, outer leaves; young plants do not mature for marketing. Infection starts in fibrous roots and spreads to larger roots. Treat soil with formaldehyde before planting.

Pseudomonas savastanoi. Olive Knot, bacterial knot, of olive, and var. **fraxini** on ash. Irregular, spongy, more or less hard, knotty galls on roots, trunk, branches, leaf or fruit pedicels start as small swellings and increase to several inches with irregular fissures. Terminal shoots are dwarfed or killed, or whole tree dies. Bacteria enter through wounds, often leaf scars or frost cracks. Variety Manzanilla is most susceptible of the olives commonly grown in California. Symptoms of the disease on ash are similar.

Control. Cut out galls carefully, disinfecting tools and cuts with 1 to 1000 mercuric chloride; paint larger cuts with bordeaux paste and spray trees thoroughly with 8–8–100 bordeaux mixture in early November, repeating in December and March if infection has been abundant. Do not plant infected nursery trees, or bring equipment from an infected orchard into a healthy one.

Pseudomonas solanacearum. SOUTHERN WILT; also called brown rot, bacterial wilt, bacterial ring disease, slime disease, Granville wilt (of tobacco), present in many states but particularly prevalent in the South, from Maryland around the coast to Texas. Southern wilt is common on potatoes in Florida but also appears on many other vegetables—bean, lima bean, castor bean, soybean, velvet bean, beet, carrot, cowpea, peanut, sweet potato, tomato, eggplant, pepper, and rhubarb. Ornamentals sometimes infected include ageratum, dwarf banana, garden balsam, canna, cosmos, croton, chrysanthemum, dahlia, hollyhock, lead tree, marigold, nasturtium, Spanish needle, sunflower, and zinnia.

The symptoms are those of a vascular disease, with dwarfing or sudden wilting, shriveling of foliage, with a brown stain in vascular bundles, and dark patches or streaks in stems. Often the first symptom is a slight wilting of leaves at end of branches in the heat of the day, followed by recovery at night, but each day the wilting is more pronounced and recovery less until plant dies. Young plants are more susceptible than older. In potatoes and tomatoes there may be a brown mushy decay of stem with bacterial ooze present. Potato tubers often have a browning of vascular ring, followed by general decay.

Bacteria are said to live in the soil six years and may persist indefinitely in the presence of susceptible plants. They are spread by irrigation water or crop debris or in fragments of soil carried on farm implements or wheels of carts or tractors, or on hooves of farm animals. Optimum temperatures are high, ranging from 77° to 97° F. with inhibition of disease below 55°.

Control. Use northern-grown seed potatoes and resistant varieties Green Mountain and Katahdin in place of susceptible Triumph and Cobbler. A long rotation is needed for tomatoes since there are no resistant varieties. Soil can be acidified with sulfur to kill bacteria, followed by liming in the fall before planting for commercial acreages, using 800 pounds sulfur and 3000 pounds limestone per acre.

Pseudomonas stizolobii. BACTERIAL LEAF SPOT OF VELVET BEAN. Translucent, angular brown leaf spots have lighter centers and chlorotic surrounding tissue; there is no exudate. Bacteria enter through stomata and fill intercellular spaces of parenchyma.

Pseudomonas syringae. BACTERIAL SHOOT BLIGHT, CITRUS BLAST, lilac blight or black pit, on citrus fruits, lilacs, and many unrelated plants such as beans, cowpeas and cherries, apple, peach, pear, almond, and avocado.

On *lilac,* brown, water-soaked spots on leaves and internodes of young shoots, in early spring, in rainy weather, blacken and enlarge rapidly. Young leaves are entirely killed, older leaves have large portions of the blade affected. When twigs are girdled the stem bends over, the upper part withers and dies. On mature stems spots may spread to petioles; leaves may be killed but not the twigs. The bacteria are primarily in the parenchyma, spreading through intercellular spaces, blackening and killing cells, forming cavities. But sometimes the vascular system is also affected, followed by wilting of upper leaves.

On *citrus,* and particularly lemons, dark sunken spots, called black pit, are formed on fruit rind but there is no decay. The blast form of the disease is most often on oranges and grapefruit—water-soaked areas in leaves which may drop or hang on; twigs are blackened and shriveled. The disease is most serious in seasons with cold, driving rainstorms.

Control. Prune out infected twigs. Grow bushy, compact citrus trees less liable to wind injury; use windbreaks for orchards. Spray nursery trees in northern California with bordeaux mixture about November first.

Pseudomonas tabaci. TOBACCO WILDFIRE, on tobacco, tomato, eggplant, soybean, cowpea, pokeberry and ground cherry, in all tobacco districts sporadically. Leaf spots have tan to brown dead centers with chlorotic halos. The disease appears first on lower leaves and spreads rapidly in wet weather. The bacteria persist in crop refuse and enter through stomatal cavities.

Control. Spray seedbed with bordeaux mixture; clean up crop residues.

Pseudomonas tomato. BACTERIAL SPECK OF TOMATO. Numerous, dark brown raised spots on fruit are very small, less than 1/16 inch across. They do not extend into flesh and are more disfiguring than harmful.

Control. Treat seed with mercuric chloride or New Improved Ceresan; rotate crops; destroy old vines.

Pseudomonas tonelliana. BACTERIAL GALL on oleander. Galls or tumors are formed on branches, herbaceous shoots, leaves, and flowers but not on underground parts. Small swellings develop on leaf veins, surrounded by yellow tissue, with bacterial ooze coming from veins in large quantity. Young shoots have longitudinal swellings with small, secondary tubercles, young leaves and seed pods may be distorted and curled. On older branches tumors are soft, or spongy and rough with projecting tubercles, and slowly turn dark.

Control. Prune out infected portions, sterilizing shears between cuts; propagate only from healthy plants.

Pseudomonas viburni. BACTERIAL LEAF SPOT OF VIBURNUM, widespread. Circular water-soaked spots appear on leaves, and irregular sunken brown cankers on young stems, the bacteria wintering here or in buds.

Control. Remove and burn infected leaves. Spray with bordeaux mixture two or three times at weekly intervals.

Pseudomonas viridilivida. LOUISIANA LETTUCE DISEASE, on lettuce and tomato. Numerous, water-soaked leaf spots fuse to infect large areas, first with a soft rot, then a dry shriveling. Sometimes outer leaves are rotted and the heart sound.

Pseudomonas woodsii. BACTERIAL SPOT OF CARNATION. Leaf lesions are small, elongated, brown with water-soaked borders, withering to brown sunken areas, with masses of bacteria oozing out of stomata. Bacteria are spread by syringing in greenhouses or by rain outdoors.

Control. Keep foliage dry; avoid syringing; remove and burn diseased leaves. Sulfur dust or lime-sulfur spray may help.

XANTHOMONAS

Members of this genus are aerobic, Gram-negative small rods, motile with a single polar flagellum, and form abundant, slimy yellow growth on sugar media. Most of them are plant pathogens causing necrosis.

Xanthomonas barbareae. BLACK ROT OF WINTER-CRESS (*Barbarea vulgaris*), similar to black rot of cabbage; small greenish spots turn black.

Xanthomonas begoniae. BEGONIA BACTERIOSIS, leaf spot of both fibrous and tuberous begonias, probably general in the United States. Blister-like, roundish dead spots are scattered over surface of leaves. Spots are brown with yellow translucent margins. Leaves fall prematurely and in severe cases the main stem is invaded with gradual softening of all tissues and death of plants. Bacteria are present on surface of dried leaves in yellow ooze which remains viable at least three months. Leaves are infected through upper surfaces during watering, with rapid spread of disease when plants are crowded together under conditions of high humidity.

Control. Keep top of leaves dry, avoiding syringing or overhead watering; keep pots widely spaced; spray with bordeaux mixture and dip cuttings in it.

Xanthomonas beticola. BEET GALL, on sugar and garden beets, sometimes called bacterial pocket disease. Deeply indented nodular growths which soon disintegrate are formed on crown of roots. Avoid excessive nitrogen in the soil.

Xanthomonas campestris. BLACK ROT OF CRUCIFERS, bacterial blight, stump rot of cabbage, cauliflower, broccoli, brussels sprouts, kale, mustard, radish, rutabaga, stock, and turnip. Black rot was first observed in Kentucky and Wisconsin about 1890 since when it has been generally distributed in this country and capable of causing losses of 40 to 50% of the total crop. It is one of the most serious crucifer diseases, present each season, but epidemic in warm, wet seasons.

The bacteria invade leaves through water pores or wounds and progress to the vascular system. The veins are blackened and leaf tissue may brown in a

V-shape. With early infections plants either die or are dwarfed with a one-sided growth. Late infection results in defoliation, leaving long bare stalks with a tuft of leaves at top. When stems are cut across they show a black ring, result of the vascular invasion, and sometimes the yellow bacterial ooze. Black rot itself is a hard odorless rot, but may be followed by secondary decays. Primary infection comes from bacteria carried on seed, or in refuse in soil, but drainage water, rain, farm implements and animals all spread bacteria for secondary infection.

Control. Use seed grown in disease-free areas in the West or treat with 1 to 1000 mercuric chloride for 30 minutes. Tie in a loose cheesecloth bag before dipping and then rinse in running water after treatment. Plan a three-year rotation with plants other than crucifers. Clean up all crop refuse.

Xanthomonas campestris var. **armoraciae.** HORSE-RADISH LEAF SPOT. Leaves are spotted but there is no vascular infection.

Xanthomonas cannae. CANNA BUD ROT. Bacteria enter through stomata of young leaves rolled in bud, then spread through parenchyma of young leaf blades, petioles and stalks. Leaf spots are in turn water-soaked, yellow, brown, and ragged with irregular thin gray to brown areas extending several inches along the leaf blade. Leaves are sometimes distorted. Stalks may have gummy sap exuding from blackened areas but roots are not affected. Flowers are ruined by stem decay or bud infection.

Control. Select rootstalks from healthy stock. Soak dormant corms for 2 hours in mercuric chloride, 1 to 1000, before planting. Keep plants well spaced; water carefully to keep new growth dry.

Xanthomonas carotae. BACTERIAL BLIGHT OF CARROT. The chief damage is to flower heads grown for seed, which may be entirely killed. Symptoms include irregular dead spots on leaves, dark brown lines on petioles and stems, blighting of floral parts, which may be one-sided. Use clean seed, or treat with hot water; rotate crops.

Xanthomonas citri. CITRUS CANKER, on all citrus fruits, an introduced disease now apparently eradicated from the United States. It came from the Orient and appeared in Texas around 1910, becoming of major importance in Florida and the Gulf States by 1914, ranking with chestnut blight and white pine blister rust as a national calamity. But here is one of the few cases on record where man has won the fight, where a disease has been eradicated by spending enough money and having enough cooperation early in the game. Several million dollars, together with concerted intelligent effort by growers, quarantine measures, destruction of every infected tree, sanitary precautions so rigid they included walking the mules through disinfectant, sterilization of clothes worn by workers, all saved us from later untold losses.

Symptoms of citrus canker are rough, brown corky eruptions on both sides of leaves and fruit. On foliage the lesions are surrounded by oily or yellow halos and may be grouped to form good-sized cankers.

Xanthomonas corylina. FILBERT BLIGHT OR BACTERIOSIS, the most serious disease of filberts in the Pacific Northwest, known since 1913 from the Cascade Mountains west in Oregon and Washington. The disease is similar to walnut blight (see *Xanthomonas juglandis*) with infection on buds, leaves, and stems of current growth, on branches, and on trunks from one to four years old. The bacteria are weakly pathogenic to nuts.

Control. Copper-lime dusts seem to be effective with 4 to 6 weekly applications, starting at the early pre-bloom stage.

Xanthomonas cucurbitae. BACTERIAL SPOT, on winter squash and pumpkin. Leaf spots are first small and round, then angular between veins, with bright yellow halos, sometimes translucent and thin, but not dropping out, often coalescing to involve whole leaf. Bacterial exudate is present.

Xanthomonas dieffenbachiae. DIEFFENBACHIA LEAF SPOT. Spots are formed on all parts of leaf blade except midrib, but not on petioles and stems. They range from minute, translucent specks to lesions 3/8 inch in diameter, circular to elongated, yellow to orange yellow with a dull green center. Spots may grow together to cover large areas, which turn yellow, wilt, and dry. Dead leaves are dull tan to light brown, thin and tough, but not brittle. The exudate on lower surface of spots dries to a waxy, silver white layer.

Control. Separate infected from healthy plants; keep temperature low; avoid syringing.

Xanthomonas geranii. GERANIUM LEAF SPOT, on *Geranium* spp., but not on Pelargonium or common house geranium. Leaf spots are small, brown, necrotic, sometimes with reddish tinge on upper surface and a slightly water-soaked condition on underside. Young leaves may die and drop. Petioles are occasionally spotted. Bacteria winter in old leaves or under mulch.

Xanthomonas gummisudans. BACTERIAL BLIGHT OF GLADIOLUS. Narrow, horizontal water-soaked, dark green spots turn into brown squares or rectangles between veins, covering entire leaf, particularly a young leaf, or middle section of blade. Bacteria ooze out in slender, twisted white columns or in a gummy film in which soil and insects get stuck. Disease is spread by planting infected corms or by bacteria splashed in rain from infected to healthy leaves. The small, dark brown corm lesions are almost unnoticeable.

Control. Treat corms as for scab; soak unhusked for 2 hours in mercuric chloride before planting.

Xanthomonas hederae. BACTERIAL LEAF SPOT OF ENGLISH IVY. Small water-soaked areas on leaves develop dark brown to black centers as they increase in size, sometimes cracking on drying, with reddish purple margins. Spots are sometimes formed on petioles and stems, with plants dwarfed and foliage yellow green.

Control. Spray with bordeaux mixture; avoid overhead watering and high humidity.

Xanthomonas hyacinthi. YELLOW DISEASE or yellow rot of Dutch hyacinth, occasionally entering the country in imported bulbs. The disease was first noted in Holland in 1881 and named for the yellow slime or bacterial ooze seen when a bulb is cut. The bulbs rot either before or after planting, producing no plants above ground or badly infected specimens which do not flower and have yellow to brown stripes on leaves or flower stalks. Bacteria are transmitted by wind, rain, tools, and clothes with rapid infection in wet or humid weather, particularly among luxuriantly growing plants.

Control. In Holland frequent inspection of bulb fields prevents spread from infection centers. An inverted imperforate flower pot is placed over every "miss" or empty space where a plant should have appeared and over every suspected hyacinth, and nearby plants are sprayed with formaldehyde or carbolineum. At the end of season, after harvesting healthy bulbs, dig and destroy those under pots; avoid excessive manure.

Xanthomonas incanae. BACTERIAL BLIGHT OF GARDEN STOCKS, causing, since 1933, serious losses on flower-seed ranches in California; also present in home gardens. This is a vascular disease of main stem and lateral branches, often extending into leaf petioles and seed peduncles. Seedlings may suddenly wilt when they are 2 to 4 inches high, with stem tissues yellowish, soft and mushy, and sometimes a yellow exudate along stem. On older plants dark, water-soaked areas appear around leaf scars near ground, stem is girdled, and lower leaves turn yellow and drop; or entire plants wilt or are broken by the wind at ground level. Bacteria persist in soil and on or in seed; they are also spread in irrigation water.

Control. Use a two- to three-year rotation or disinfect soil with formaldehyde. Commercial growers can treat seed with hot water, at 127.5° to 131° F. for 10 minutes, followed by rapid cooling.

Xanthomonas juglandis. WALNUT BLIGHT, or bacteriosis, on English or Persian walnut, also black walnut, butternut, Siebold walnut. Black, dead spots appear on young nuts, green shoots, and leaves. Many nuts fall prematurely, but others reach full size with husk, shell, and kernel more or less blackened and destroyed. Bacteria winter in old mummified nuts or in buds and may be carried by the walnut erinose mite.

Control. Standard control in California has been to spray trees with bordeaux mixture, 12–6–100, at pre-bloom and immediately after bloom, but this has sometimes caused injury and has also increased the number of walnut aphids. Ammoniacal copper carbonate (Solcopper) and copper oxide (Yellow Cuprocide) are less injurious and seem to produce a higher yield even though somewhat less effective in blight control. Another possibility is a low-lime, weak bordeaux mixture (4–2–100) plus a summer oil emulsion (1 pint to 100 gallons) and applying up to three pre-blossom sprays.

Xanthomonas papavericola. BACTERIAL BLIGHT OF POPPY, on corn poppy, Oriental, opium, and California poppies. Minute, water-soaked areas darken to intense black spots bounded by a colorless ring. Spots are scattered, circular, small, often zonate, with tissue between yellow and then brown. There is a noticeable, slimy exudate. Infection is through stomata and often into veins. Stem lesions are long, very black, sometimes girdling and causing young plants to fall over. Flower sepals are blackened, petals stop developing; pods show conspicuous black spots.

Control. Remove and destroy infected plants; do not replant poppies in the same location.

Xanthomonas pelargonii. Bacterial Leaf Spot of Geranium or Pelargonium. Irregular to circular brown leaf spots start as water-soaked dots on under surface, becoming sunken as they enlarge and with tissue collapsing. With numerous spots the entire leaf turns yellow, brown, and shriveled, and then drops.

Control. Pick off and burn infected leaves; keep pots well spaced; provide proper ventilation; use care in watering; spray with 4–4–100 bordeaux mixture.

Xanthomonas phaseoli. Bacterial Bean Blight, general on beans, and serious, but rare in some western states. Leaf spots are first very small, water-soaked, or light green wilted areas, which enlarge, turn brown, are dry and brittle, and have a yellow border around edge of lesions and often a narrow, pale green zone outside of that. Leaves become ragged in wind and rainstorms. Reddish brown horizontal streaks appear in stem which may be girdled and break over at cotyledons or first leaf node.

Pod lesions are first dark green, water-soaked, then dry, sunken and brick red, sometimes with a yellowish encrustation of bacterial ooze. White seeds turn yellow, are wrinkled, with a varnished look.

Control. Use disease-free seed (California-grown beans are free from blight) and varieties showing some resistance, such as Robust Pea, Yellow Eye, and White Marrow for field beans; and for garden beans Refugee 1000–1, Late Stringless Refugee, Refugee Wax, or White Imperial. Spraying or dusting is not practical, but cleaning up old vines is helpful. Do not cultivate or pick beans when vines are wet.

Xanthomonas phaseoli var. **sojense.** Bacterial Pustule of Soybean, similar to regular bean blight, but chiefly a foliage disease, with angular reddish brown leaf spots, and portions dropping out to give a ragged appearance.

Xanthomonas pruni. Bacterial Spot of Stone Fruits, also called canker or shot hole or black spot, general on plum, Japanese plum, prune, peach, and nectarine east of the Rocky Mountains. This is one of the most destructive stone-fruit diseases, causing heavy losses in some states.

Symptoms on leaves are numerous, round or angular, small reddish spots with centers turning brown and dead, dropping out to leave shot holes. Spots may run together to give a burned, blighted or ragged appearance, followed by defoliation, with losses running high in devitalized trees. On twigs dark blisters dry out to sunken cankers. Fruit spots turn into brown to black, saucer-shaped depressions, with small masses of gummy, yellow exudate, and often crack through the spots.

Control. Plant new orchards from nurseries free from the disease. Prune, cultivate, and feed properly. Trees with sufficient nitrogen do not defoliate so readily. Zinc sulfate-lime sprays may aid in control but spraying is not very effective. Some reports indicate that Elgetol or other Dinitro compound is useful as a dormant spray.

Xanthomonas vesicatoria. BACTERIAL SPOT on tomato and pepper, common in wet seasons. Small, black, scabby fruit spots, sometimes with a translucent border, provide entrance points for secondary decay organisms. Leaves may die, after small circular spots have become black and sunken. Elongated black spots may appear on stems and petioles. Bacteria are carried on seed.

Control. Treat seed with mercuric chloride or New Improved Ceresan; rotate crops; destroy diseased vines. Spraying or dusting with copper fungicides may reduce leaf infection.

Xanthomonas vesicatoria var. **raphani.** LEAF SPOT of radish, turnip and other crucifers, similar to bacterial spot on tomato.

Xanthomonas vignicola. COWPEA CANKER, on cowpeas and beans, a new and destructive disease, first described in 1944. Beans are blighted, cowpea stems have swollen, cankerlike lesions, with the cortex cracked open and a white bacterial exudate. The plants tend to break over. Leaves, stems, pods, and seeds may also be affected. Chinese Red cowpeas seem particularly susceptible, but the disease appears on other varieties.

Xanthomonas vitians. SOUTH CAROLINA LETTUCE DISEASE, a wilting and rotting of lettuce leaves and stems. In early stages plants are lighter green than normal. Wilting may follow stem infection or leaves may have definite brown spots which coalesce to large areas.

Control. Use windbreaks to prevent injuries.

BLACK KNOT

The term black knot is ordinarily used to designate one specific disease, characterized by black, elongated overgrowths.

DIBOTRYON

Ascomycetes, Dothidiales, Dothidiaceae

Asci are in locules, without well-marked perithecial walls, immersed in groups in a massive, carbonaceous stroma, erumpent, and superficial at maturity. Spores are hyaline, unequally 2-celled.

Dibotryon morbosum. BLACK KNOT OF PLUMS AND CHERRIES, plum wart, widespread on garden plum, sweet and sour cherries, chokecherry, and apricot, in eastern states and often causing serious losses on plums. This is apparently a native disease, destructive in Massachusetts as early as 1811.

The chief symptoms are black, rough, cylindrical or spindle-shaped enlargements of the twigs into two to four times their thickness and knots several inches long.

Infection takes place in spring but swelling is not usually evident until growth starts the following spring, at which time the bark ruptures and a light yellowish growth fills the crevices, turning greenish in late spring and

FIG. 18. Black Knot on Cherry.

covered with an olive green velvety layer made up of brownish conidiophores and one-celled hyaline conidia of the imperfect Hormodendron stage. Conidia are spread by wind.

In late summer black stromata cover the affected tissues and the galls become hard. Asci are formed during the winter in cavities in the stroma and ascospores are discharged and germinate in early spring, completing the two-year cycle. The knots are produced from primary infection by the ascospores or from secondary infection by mycelium formed in old knots and growing beyond to invade new tissue.

Control. Cut out infected twigs and branches 3 or 4 inches beyond the knot so as to get any perennial mycelium which may be advancing; prune in winter or very early spring. Eradicate or thoroughly clean up wild plums and cherries near orchards. Spray at the green-tip or delayed dormant stage with 6–12–100 bordeaux mixture plus 3% lubricating oil or with lime sulfur at 1 to 8 dilution.

GIBBERIDEA

Ascomycetes, Sphaeriales, Sphaeriaceae

Perithecia in clusters on wood; spores dark, with several cells.

Gibberidea heliopsidis. Black Knot, Black Patch, on goldenrod and sunflower.

BLACK LEG

The term black leg is used to describe darkening at the base of a stem or plant. Black leg of potatoes is described under Bacterial Diseases.

PHOMA

Fungi Imperfecti, Sphaeropsidales, Sphaerioidaceae

Spores 1-celled, hyaline, in dark carbonous pycnidia with an ostiole, usually formed on stems (Fig. 42).

Phoma lingam. Black Leg of Crucifers, foot rot, Phoma wilt of plants of mustard family, including cabbage, cauliflower, Chinese cabbage, brussels sprouts, charlock, garden cress, pepper grass, kale, kohlrabi, mustard, rape, radish, rutabaga, turnip, stock and sweet alyssum, generally distributed east of the Rocky Mountains. The disease was first known in France in 1849 and was reported in Ohio in 1911. It formerly caused from 50 to 90% loss but is less important with improved seed and seed treatment.

The first symptom is a sunken area on the stem near the ground which extends until the stem is girdled, and the area turns black. Leaves, seed stalks, and seed pods may have circular, light brown spots. The small black pycnidia appearing on all lesions distinguish black leg from other cabbage maladies. The leaves sometimes turn purple and wilt, but there is no defoliation as in black rot.

The fungus reaches the soil via infected plant debris, remaining alive two or more years. Spores are spread during the season by splashing rain, on manure, and on tools, and perhaps by insects, with new lesions resulting in 10 to 14 days. But the chief spread of the disease is through infected seed, where the mycelium winters.

When infected seed is planted fruiting bodies are formed on cotyledons as they are pushed above ground and serve as source of inoculum for near-by plants. A few diseased seeds can start an epidemic in wet weather.

Control. Use seed grown in the Puget Sound area of Washington or other disease-free locations. In the last year or two, even western-grown seed has been occasionally diseased and responsible for epidemics in most of the cabbage-producing areas. Hence it is safest to have all seed treated with hot water—25 minutes at 122° F.—and it is usually possible to purchase treated seed.

Sterilize soil for the seedbed unless it is free from the fungus; plan a three-year rotation; do not splash seedlings when watering, do not transplant any seedlings if disease appears in seedbed; do not feed cabbage refuse to cattle; do not transfer cultivators and other tools from a diseased to a healthy field without cleaning with a disinfectant.

BLACK MILDEW

The terms black mildew, sooty mold, and black spot have been used somewhat interchangeably. In this text the use of sooty mold is restricted to those fungi living on insect exudate and hence not true parasites. Included here under black mildew are parasitic fungi which have a superficial dark mycelium, either members of the Erysiphales, and similar to powdery mildews, except for the dark color, or members of the order Hemisphaeriales, characterized by a dark stroma simulating the upper portions of a perithecium.

APIOSPORINA

Ascomycetes, Erysiphales, Meliolaceae

Perithecia and mycelium superficial; mycelium with setae and perithecia usually hairy; paraphysoids present; spores 2-celled, dark.

Apiosporina collinsii. WITCHES' BROOM of serviceberry (*Amelanchier*) widespread. Perennial mycelium stimulates the development of numerous stout branches into a broom. A sooty growth develops on underside of leaves, first olive brown, then black. Numerous globose, beadlike black perithecia appear in late summer. The damage to the host is not serious.

ASTERINA

Ascomycetes, Hemisphaeriales, Microthyriaceae

Asterina species are parasites on the surface of leaves and usually occur in warm climates. In some cases the disease is called black mildew; in others, black spot. The perithecia are dimidiate, having the top half covered with a shield-shaped stroma composed of radially arranged dark hyphae. Underneath this stromatic cover, scutellum, there is a single layer of fruiting cells; paraphyses are lacking. Spores are dark, 2-celled. The mycelium, which is free over the surface, has lobed appendages, called hyphopodia.

Asterina anomala. BLACK MILDEW on California-laurel, California.
Asterina gaultheriae. BLACK MILDEW on bearberry, Wisconsin.
Asterina lepidigena. BLACK MILDEW on lyonia, Florida.

DIMERIUM

Ascomycetes, Erysiphales, Meliolaceae

Perithecia are smooth, spores 2-celled, dark, paraphyses lacking.

Dimerium juniperi. BLACK MILDEW on Rocky Mountain juniper, California.

DIMEROSPORIUM

According to some authorities this is the same as Asterina, but Dimerosporium is in common use.

Dimerosporium abietis. Black Mildew on Pacific silver and lowland white firs. Black patches are formed on older needles, usually on under surface. There is no apparent injury to trees.

Dimerosporium hispidulum. Black Mildew on boxelder.

Dimerosporium pulchrum. Black Mildew on ash.

Dimerosporium robiniae. Black Mildew on ailanthus.

Dimerosporium tropicale. Black Mildew on bignonia, Mississippi.

IRENE

Ascomycetes, Erysiphales, Meliolaceae

Mycelium with capitate hyphopodia; perithecia with larviform appendages; spores dark, with several cells.

Irene araliae. Black Mildew on magnolia, Mississippi.

Irene calastroma. Black Mildew on waxmyrtle, Gulf States.

Irene perseae. Black Mildew on avocado, Florida.

IRENINA

Like Irene except perithecia have no appendages.

Irenina manca. Black Mildew on waxmyrtle, Mississippi.

IRENOPSIS

Like Irene except that perithecia have setae (stiff hairs) and not larviform appendages.

Irenopsis martiniana. Black Mildew on redbay, swampbay.

LEMBOSIA

Ascomycetes, Hemisphaeriales, Microthyriaceae

Free mycelium present with hyphopodia; ascoma linear with a single fruiting layer under scutellum; paraphyses present; spores dark, 2-celled.

Lembosia cactorum. Black Mildew on cactus, Opuntia, Florida.

Lembosia coccolobae. Black Mildew on sea-grape, Florida; also **L. portoricensis** and **L. tenella.**

Lembosia illiciicola. Black Mildew on anise-tree, Alabama, Mississippi.

Lembosia rugispora. Black Mildew on redbay, swampbay, Mississippi, North Carolina.

MELIOLA

Ascomycetes, Erysiphales, Meliolaceae

Superficial dark mycelium with hyphopodia and setae; perithecia coal-black, without ostiole or appendages but often with setae (stiff hairs); spores several-celled, dark; paraphyses lacking. Conidia are lacking in most species, of Helminthosporium type in others. Species occur most abundantly in tropics.

Meliola amphitricha. Black Mildew on boxelder, magnolia, redbay, swampbay.

Meliola bidentata. Black Mildew on bignonia.

Meliola camelliae. Black Mildew. Abundant black growth may cover camellia leaves and twigs. Spraying with a light, summer oil is sometimes effective.

Meliola cookeana. Black Mildew on callicarpa, lantana.

Meliola cryptocarpa. Black Mildew on gordonia.

Meliola lippiae. Black Mildew on lippia.

Meliola magnoliae. Black Mildew on *Magnolia virginiana.*

Meliola nidulans. Black Mildew on blueberry, wintergreen.

Meliola palmicola. Black Mildew on palmetto.

Meliola tenuis. Black Mildew on bamboo.

Meliola wrightii. Black Mildew on chinaberry.

MORENOELLA

Considered by some authorities same as Lembosia. Genus description under Blotch.

Morenoella angustiformis; M. ilicis; M. orinoides. Black Mildew on holly, *Ilex* spp., Mississippi.

BLACK SPOT

Diseases under this heading are primarily leaf spots but commonly designated black spot from their sooty appearance. Some, as black spot of rose, and elm black spot, are more injurious than the general run of leaf spots. Delphinium black spot is included in Bacterial Diseases.

ASTERINA

See under Black Mildew for genus description.

Asterina delitescens. Black Spot on redbay.

Asterina diplodioides. Black Spot on leucothoë.

Asterina orbicularis. Black Spot on American holly and *Ilex* spp.

ASTERINELLA

Ascomycetes, Hemisphaeriales, Microthyriaceae

Like Asterina but lacking hyphopodia and with paraphyses. Spores dark, 2-celled.

Asterinella puiggarii. Black Spot on eugenia.

ASTEROMA

Fungi Imperfecti, Sphaeropsidales, Sphaerioidaceae

Pycnidia globose with a radiate subicle, a compact, crust-like growth of mycelium underneath, without an ostiole or mouth; spores hyaline, 1-celled.

Asteroma garretianum. Black Spot on primrose.
Asteroma solidaginis. Black Spot, black scurf, on goldenrod.
Asteroma tenerrimum. Black Spot on erythronium.

DIPLOCARPON

Ascomycetes, Helotiales, Dermateaceae

Apothecia arise innately and at maturity rupture overlying tissues. They are horny to leathery with a thick margin or outer wall (excipulum) of dark, thick-walled cells; spores 2-celled, hyaline; paraphyses present. Imperfect stage Marssonina with 2-celled hyaline spores formed in an acervulus.

Diplocarpon rosae. Black Spot of Rose, general on rose, but less serious in the semi-arid Southwest; reported from all states except Arizona, Nevada, and Wyoming.

For nearly a hundred years the fungus was known only by its imperfect stage which has had about twenty-five different names. The first definite record is by Fries in Sweden in 1815, under the name *Erysiphe radiosum,* but the first valid description was by Libert in 1827 as *Asteroma rosae.* Later Fries called it *Actinonema rosae* and that has been the most general term until recently when Actinonema species were transferred to Marssonina. The black-spot fungus was first reported in America, in Philadelphia, in 1831, but it was not until 1912 that the connection was made with the perfect stage and the correct name became *Diplocarpon rosae.*

Black spot is probably the most widely distributed and best known rose disease. It is confined to roses, garden and greenhouse, and may affect practically all varieties, although not all are equally susceptible. Probably no rose yet grown is truly immune to black spot, but some of the newer sub-zero roses, like Pink Princess, are quite resistant. Roses with the Pernetiana parentage which has given us the lovely yellows and coppers and blends are especially prone to black spot, but there is promise of resistant varieties even in this group. Some roses, like Radiance, are tolerant of black spot, even though they cannot be considered resistant.

Symptoms are primarily more or less circular black spots, up to ½ inch in diameter which have radiating fimbriate or fringed margins. This fimbriate margin is a special diagnostic character, differentiating black spot from other leaf spots and from discolorations due to cold or chemicals. The spots vary

FIG. 19. Rose Black Spot. Note fimbriate margin to spot.

FIG. 20. Rose black spot, on lower leaflet, compared with cold injury, upper.

from one or two to a dozen or more on a leaf, usually on the upper surface, and show small, black dots or pimples (the acervuli bearing conidia) in the center.

In susceptible varieties the appearance of black spots is soon followed by yellowing of a portion or all of leaflets and then defoliation. Some roses lose almost all their leaves, put out another set and lose those and often are trying to leaf out for a third time by late summer. The process is so devitalizing that bushes frequently die during the winter. On tolerant varieties the spots are not so numerous, and there is much less yellowing and defoliation. Cane lesions are small, indistinct, black areas, slightly blistered, without fimbriate margins.

Infection occurs through either leaf surface, the fungus sending its germ tube directly through the cuticle by mechanical pressure. The hyphae form a network under the cuticle, joining together into several parallel filaments radiating from the point of infection. The hyphae are actually colorless, the black color of the spot coming from death and disorganization of host cells. The mycelial growth is between the cells, with haustoria, or suckers, obtaining nourishment from the epidermal and palisade cells.

Summer fruiting bodies or acervuli are formed just under the cuticle and bear 2-celled hyaline conidia on short cells of a thin, basal stroma. Splashed by rain, or overhead watering or perhaps spread by gardeners on tools and clothing, the conidia germinate with at least 6 hours of continuous moisture, which can be rain, or from the sprinkler used late in the day so foliage does not dry before night, or heavy dew or fog. New spots show up within a week

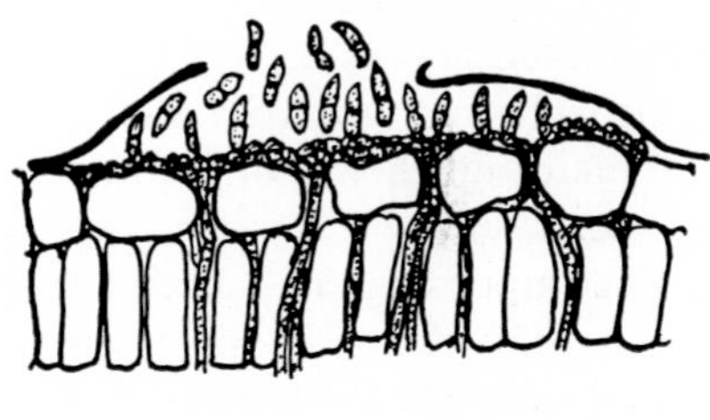

Fig. 21. Rose Black Spot. Two-celled conidia formed in acervulus under cuticle.

and more spores are developed in 10 days or less. The secondary cycles are repeated all summer—from late May to late October around New York City.

In my experience the spread of disease is most rapid in gardens where large numbers of susceptible varieties are massed together. If all the yellows, for instance, are kept together the disease gets such a head start and builds up so much inoculum to spread to the more tolerant red and pink varieties near by that these also are more heavily infected than usual. When the roses are mixed in beds so that one or two particularly susceptible bushes are surrounded by more resistant types, the infective material cannot increase so rapidly and the net result is less disease in the garden as a whole. Protected corners in the garden where the air circulation is poor also increase the disease potentiality.

When old leaves drop to the ground the mycelium continues a saprophytic existence, growing through dead tissue with hyphae which are now dark in color. In spring three types of fruiting bodies may be formed: micro-acervuli or spermagonia containing very small cells which perhaps act as male cells; apothecia, the sexual bodies formed from a stroma between the epidermis and palisade cells and covered with a circular shield of radiating strands; and winter acervuli, formed internally and producing new conidia in spring. The perfect or Diplocarpon stage is apparently not essential and is known only in northeastern United States and south-central Canada. The shield over the apothecium ruptures and the 2-celled ascospores are forcibly discharged into the air to infect lowest leaves.

Where the sexual stage is not formed, primary spring infection comes either from conidia splashed by rain to foliage from overwintered leaves on ground or from acervuli in cane lesions. New roses sometimes bring black spot to a garden previously free of disease via these cane lesions.

Control. Sanitation has some value, although its importance may have been overstressed and it cannot replace routine spraying or dusting. It is certainly a good idea to pick off for burning the first spotted leaves, if this is done when plants are dry and the act of removal does not further spread the fungus. Raking up old leaves from the ground at the end of the season is likewise helpful, and so is a mulch applied in spring after uncovering and first feeding. The mulch acts as a mechanical barrier to prevent spores in old leaves from being splashed up from the ground and, equally important to my mind, eliminates much weeding and cultivation by which the gardener may spread disease.

The importance of a dormant spray is debatable. I like to use liquid lime sulfur, diluted 1 to 8, after pruning, provided the buds have not broken far enough to show the leaflets. I think it helps to kill spores spread in pruning, perhaps burns out some of the cane lesions, prevents some brown canker, and controls scale.

Summer spraying or dusting, from May through October in New Jersey, is essential for most garden roses, if you want to keep enough leaves on the bush for continuous production of fine flowers (it takes food manufactured in several leaves to develop one flower) and for winter survival. Some strong varieties will, however, live and bloom for years without chemical treatment. Since roses can be defoliated as readily from spray injury as from black spot, fungicides must not only be effective against the fungus but safe under the conditions of application.

Some copper sprays or dusts cause red spotting and defoliation in cool cloudy weather. Bordeaux mixture is both unsightly and harmful, unless used in very weak concentration. Used at ordinary strength leaves turn yellow and drop. Dusts containing more than 3 to 4% metallic copper are injurious under some weather conditions.

Dusting sulfur, fine enough to pass through a 325-mesh screen, has been successfully used for years in black spot control, but it does burn margins of leaves somewhat in very hot weather. Fermate has been widely hailed as an advance over sulfur and copper and is certainly effective against the black-spot fungus. It does not, however, control powdery mildew, and in many of the proprietary mixtures there is too little sulfur to take care of mildew. In certain formulations Fermate is rather disfiguring to open blooms.

In experiments in my own garden Dithane, Parzate, and Zerlate have given good control of black spot (but not mildew) without plant injury. Phygon is effective, but spots the petals somewhat when used as a spray and slightly blackens leaves of some varieties. As a dust it seems less injurious, possibly less effective.

There are hundreds of combination sprays and dusts on the market under trade names, and it seems to me easier, and even cheaper considering the time saved, for home gardeners to make use of these to control black spot and other rose diseases, as well as insects, in one operation. The particular best combination depends somewhat on where you live. In Texas and other parts of the South, copper is added to sulfur dust with good results. Fermate and sulfur are widely used in combination with DDT and rotenone, but I am increasingly inclined to use DDT on roses only when it is vitally necessary. For much of my own work I am still using the combination spray (Triogen) of ammoniacal copper, now with Fermate added, lead arsenate, pyrethrum, and rotenone. It is expensive, not entirely efficient against black spot in a wet season, but it is relatively safe and does not disfigure blossoms.

Whatever mixture is chosen, coverage should be complete on upper and lower leaf surfaces, and applications should be repeated at approximately weekly intervals. This may mean every 5 or 6 days in rainy weather when plants are growing rapidly and up to a 9-day interval in dry weather when growth is slow. Once every two weeks seldom gives adequate control. Although most directions call for applications ahead of rains, some growers feel that the next day after a rain is correct timing. Treatment at regular weekly intervals provides enough residue on the foliage to give protection whenever the rains come, and saves a lot of worrying.

GNOMONIA

See under Anthracnose for genus description.

Gnomonia ulmea. Black Spot of Elm, general on American, English and Chinese elms. Imperfect stage of the fungus is *Gloeosporium ulmeum*. Spots on leaves are small but conspicuous, a shining coal black. Leaves may turn yellow and drop, with severe premature defoliation in wet seasons, and especially serious on Siberian elms. When defoliation occurs in spring, damage to elms may be heavy, sometimes with death of twig terminals, but more often defoliation is prevalent toward fall when the loss is not important.

Conidia are produced in the leaf spots in summer, with a creamy exudate of spores, and ascospores develop in spring in perithecia formed in fallen dead leaves. Overwintering is also possible in dormant buds.

Control. Rake and burn fallen leaves. Chemical control is required only in a wet season, which is difficult to determine in advance. A dormant lime-sulfur spray might be useful but is seldom possible for elms near houses. Standard recommendation is for bordeaux mixture, 8–8–100, applied when leaves are unfolding, when they reach full size, and a third application about two weeks later. One or two of these treatments can be incorporated into insecticide sprays for elm leaf beetles and cankerworms, thereby reducing costs.

MICROTHYRIELLA

Ascomycetes, Hemisphaeriales, Micropeltaceae

Stroma superficial, with scanty internal mycelium; a single hymenium, fruiting layer, beneath scutellum or stromatic cover, which is brown, made up of parenchyma-like cells; paraphyses absent; spores 2-celled, hyaline.

Microthyriella cuticulosa. Black Spot of Holly. Dark spot on leaves of American holly.

MYCOSPHAERELLA (or Sphaerella)

Perithecia, with papillate ostioles, immersed in substratum; stroma lacking; paraphyses and paraphysoids lacking; spores 2-celled, hyaline.

Mycosphaerella nigromaculans. Cranberry Black Spot. Apparently not very important.

PHYLLACHORA

Ascomycetes, Dothidiales, Phyllachoraceae

Asci in locules immersed in groups in a dark stroma which is covered by host tissue at maturity; spores 1-celled, hyaline; paraphyses present; asci cylindrical with short pedicels.

Phyllachora graminis. Black Spot of red top and other grasses; also called tar spot. Conspicuous, black, sunken, glossy spots on leaves have mouths or ostioles of the fruiting bodies opening on both leaf surfaces. Although the disease is widespread it does not become general and serious in any one location.

STEVENSEA

Ascomycetes, Myriangiales, Myriangiaceae

Asci borne singly in locules at various levels in a massive stroma; spores dark, several-celled.

Stevensea wrightii. Black Spot or charcoal spot of Opuntia cacti in Florida and Texas, uncommon in North. Dark spots, 1/4 inch or more in diameter, are surrounded by a ring of fruiting bodies.

STIGMATEA

Ascomycetes, Hemisphaeriales, Polystomellaceae

Fruiting structure subcuticular, hymenium a single, disk-like layer covered with a scutellum; spores dark, 2-celled; mycelium scanty.

Stigmatea rubicola. BLACK SPOT OF RASPBERRY. Leaf spot formed in late summer and fall with a membranaceous layer under the cuticle; fruiting bodies produced in spring. The disease is not very important.

Stigmatea geranii. BLACK LEAF SPECK of geranium (cranesbill).

BLIGHTS

According to Webster, blight is "any disease or injury of plants resulting in withering, cessation of growth and death of parts, as in leaves, without rotting." The term is somewhat loosely used by pathologists and gardeners to cover a wide variety of diseases, some of which may have rotting as a secondary symptom; but, in general, the chief characteristic of a blight is sudden and conspicuous leaf and shoot damage in contradistinction to leaf spotting where the dead areas are definitely delimited and to wilt due to a toxin or other disturbance of the vascular system. Fire blight, discussed under Bacterial Diseases, is a typical blight, with twigs and branches dying back but holding withered, dead foliage.

ALTERNARIA

Fungi Imperfecti, Moniliales, Dematiaceae

Dark, muriform conidia are not produced in fruiting bodies but formed in chains from a mycelium made up of long, dark hyphae. The chain-like formation of conidia is hard to demonstrate, and so there has been confusion with Macrosporium which is similar except that spores are not in chains. Many species formerly classified as Macrosporium are now placed under Alternaria (Fig. 22).

There are many saprophytic species in this genus, the spores of which are windborne for many miles and are a common cause of hayfever. There are also parasitic forms causing blights and leaf spots. Sometimes the disease starts as a leaf spot but the spots, which are typically formed in concentric circles, run together to produce a blight, dark and velvety in appearance, from the dark conidia.

Alternaria cucumerina. ALTERNARIA BLIGHT OF CUCURBITS, also known as Macrosporium blight of cucurbits, cucumber blight, black mold; general on cucumbers, cantaloupe or muskmelon, winter and summer squash; known since 1894.

Symptoms appear in the middle of the season, first on leaves nearest the center of the hill. Circular, brown spots with concentric rings are visible only on upper surface of leaves but a black, moldy growth, made up of conidiophores and large brown spores, can be seen on both leaf surfaces. Leaves curl and dry up, cantaloupe foliage being more sensitive than that of other cucurbits. The disease spreads rapidly in warm, humid weather, and with the vines dried up the fruit is exposed to sunburn.

Control. Treat seed 5 minutes in 1 to 1000 mercuric chloride, rinse, and dry. Spray with Dithane Z–78, or with Zerlate, alternating with a fixed copper.

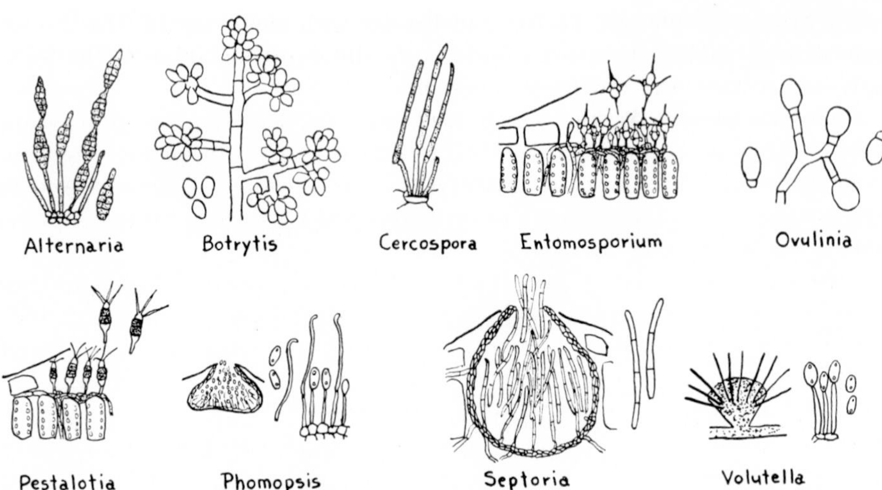

FIG. 22. Conidial production among some fungi causing blights. *Alternaria,* dark muriform spores in chains; *Botrytis,* hyaline spores in clusters; *Cercospora,* pale to dark septate spores on dark conidia protruding from stomata; *Entomosporium,* peculiarly appendaged spores in acervulus; *Ovulinia,* hyaline spore with basal disjunctor cell, borne free on mycelium; *Pestalotia,* in acervulus, median cells colored, end cells hyaline, apical cell with appendages; *Phomopsis,* oval and filiform hyaline spores in pycnidium; *Septoria,* septate hyaline spores in pycnidium; *Volutella,* hyaline spores formed on a hairy sporodochium.

Bordeaux mixture may cause stunting and perhaps a yellow margin to leaves, but it can be used in a weak concentration.

Alternaria dauci. LEAF BLIGHT OF CARROTS, general on carrot and parsley. Affected leaves and petioles are spotted, then turn yellow and brown; entire tops are killed in severe infections. In California the disease is known as late blight, with the peak coming in November. The fungus apparently winters in discarded tops.

Control. Clean up refuse. Spray with bordeaux mixture, starting when plants are 3 inches tall and repeating at 10-day intervals for three to five applications; or use a fixed copper dust or spray.

Alternaria dianthi. CARNATION COLLAR BLIGHT, leaf spot, stem and branch rot, general on carnation, widespread on garden pinks and sweet william. The chief symptom is a blight or rot at leaf bases and around nodes, which are girdled. Spots on leaves are ashy white, but centers of old spots are covered with dark brown to black fungus growth. Older leaves are most seriously affected; branches may die back to girdled area. Conidia are spread in watering, or rains outdoors, and enter through wounds or stomata.

Control. Commercial growers can often avoid Alternaria blight by keeping plants growing continuously in the greenhouse. Plants in the field should be sprayed with 8–8–100 bordeaux, with Fermate as second choice. Recent reports credit Bioquin 1, Phygon, Zerlate and Parzate with good control. Use disease-free cuttings, taking them from midway up the stems, breaking at the joint; start in sterilized soil and keep foliage dry.

Alternaria panax. ALTERNARIA BLIGHT, root rot, leaf spot on ginseng and golden-seal, general. In Ohio the blight appears each year in semi-epidemic form. Spraying with bordeaux mixture, or a fixed copper spray plus wetting agent, starts when plants emerge in early May and is repeated every two weeks until three weeks after bloom.

Alternaria solani. EARLY BLIGHT OF POTATO AND TOMATO, general on these hosts, occasional on eggplant and pepper, first described in Missouri in 1885.

Leaf symptoms are dark brown, circular to oval spots, marked with concentric rings in a target effect, appearing first on lower, shaded foliage, with spots growing together to blight large portions or all of leaves, exposing fruits to sunburn. On tomato there may be a collar rot of young seedlings, sunken spots or cankers on older stems, blossom drop with loss of young fruits, or dark, leathery fruit spots near the stem end.

Foliage symptoms are similar on potatoes and small, round spots on tubers afford entrance to secondary rot organisms. Each leaf spot may produce three or four crops of dark spores, which remain viable more than a year. They are blown by wind, splashed by rain, perhaps carried by flea beetles. The fungus is a weak parasite, often entering through fruit wounds, and thriving in warm, moist weather, with 85° F. as optimum temperature. It can survive in soil so long as host refuse is not completely rotted, and also winters on seed and weed hosts.

Control. Plan, if possible, a three year rotation with crops not in potato family; dig under diseased refuse immediately after harvest; use seed from healthy fruit, or, if plants are purchased, those guaranteed grown from hot-water treated seed or free from collar rot. Spray tests in different states give somewhat conflicting data on disease control and yield, but Dithane, Parzate, and Zerlate are high on most lists. Bordeaux gives excellent control but stunts young plants and may reduce yield or delay ripening.

Alternaria violae. ALTERNARIA BLIGHT, leaf spot, on violet, pansy. Spots vary from greenish yellow to light buff with umber margins. Brown patches run together to form large, blighted areas. Clean up and burn old leaves in fall. If necessary, spray with bordeaux mixture, but blooms may be injured.

Alternaria zinniae. ZINNIA BLIGHT or Alternariosis, on zinnia. Small, reddish brown spots with grayish white centers increase to irregular, large, brown dry areas. Similar spots on stem internodes or at nodes may girdle the stem with dying back of portions above. Dark brown to black basal cankers with sunken centers are common. Roots often turn dark gray, rot, and slough off. Small brown flower spots may enlarge to include whole petals and cause conspicuous blighting. The fungus apparently winters on seed and in soil.

Control. Treat seed with mercuric chloride, Semesan or Cuprocide; practice garden sanitation; use a long rotation if growing plants commercially; spray seedlings and young plants with bordeaux mixture or perhaps Fermate or Dithane.

ASCOCHYTA

Fungi Imperfecti, Sphaeropsidales, Sphaerioidaceae

Pycnidia formed in spots, usually on leaves, separate, innate, finally erumpent, globose with dark walls; spores 2-celled, hyaline, pointed at ends.

Ascochyta asparagina. STEM BLIGHT OF ASPARAGUS FERN or canker, on *Asparagus plumosus*. Small branchlets dry and drop prematurely; small branches are killed if attacked at crown. Blight is more serious in the South. A weak, 2–2–100, bordeaux mixture is said to give control.

Ascochyta chrysanthemi. CHRYSANTHEMUM RAY BLIGHT, a conspicuous and rapid disease of ray flowers. If young buds are infected the head does not open, if the attack is later there may be one-sided development of flowers. A straw or brown discoloration proceeds from base toward tip of each individual flower, followed by withering. Upper portion of stem and receptacle may turn black.

Control. Keep plants well spaced; avoid overhead watering and excessive humidity.

Ascochyta piniperda. SPRUCE TWIG BLIGHT, found on young shoots of red and Norway spruce seedlings in a North Carolina nursery and on blue spruce in Maine, but apparently a minor disease.

Ascochyta pisi, A. pinodes, A. pinodella. ASCOCHYTA BLIGHT OF PEAS. All three fungi may be connected with the disease complex known as Ascochyta blight, but *A. pinodes* has *Mycosphaerella pinodes* as an ascospore stage, while *A. pinodella* causes more of a foot rot than a blight. *A. pisi* causes brown, somewhat circular spots on foliage and is discussed more fully under leaf spots.

BOTRYOSPHAERIA

Ascomycetes, Sphaeriales (also placed in Myriangiales), Dothioraceae

Asci in locules in a stroma; spores 1-celled, hyaline, eight in an ascus. There seems to be a good deal of variation in this genus. The locules may be scattered throughout the stromatic tissue, or seated on the surface, or, as in *Botryosphaeria ribis,* the locules are perithecium-like. In *B. ribis* there are two pycnidial forms, a Dothiorella stage containing very small spores which may function as male cells and a Macrophoma stage, containing larger spores functioning as other conidia.

Botryosphaeria ribis var. chromogena. CURRANT CANE BLIGHT, also canker and dieback of currant, flowering currant, gooseberry, apple, rose, and many other plants (see also under Cankers). There are two forms of this species, one being a saprophyte developing on already dying tissue. The parasitic form, variety chromogena, is so named for its developing a purplish pink color when grown on starch paste. There are also a number of pathogenic strains in this form varying from high to low in virulence. Some currant varieties are quite resistant, but the widely grown Wilder and Red Lake are rather susceptible.

Dieback and death of fruit-bearing branches occur as the berries are coloring, with leaves wilting and fruit shriveling. Cankers can be found at the base of affected areas and small, dark pycnidia are numerous in the dead bark. Rose canes show a similar dying back and wilting above a canker.

Control. Cut out and burn all affected branches below the canker.

BOTRYOTINIA

Ascomycetes, Helotiales, Sclerotiniaceae

Stroma a typical black sclerotium, loaf-shaped or hemispherical, just on or beneath cuticle or epidermis of plant and firmly attached to it; apothecia cupulate, stalked, brown; ascospores hyaline, 1-celled; conidiophores and conidia of the *Botrytis cinerea* type.

Botryotinia convoluta. Gray mold rot of iris. See under Rots.

Botryotinia fuckeliana, presumably apothecial stage of *Botrytis cinerea* but connection somewhat inconclusive.

Botryotinia ricini. Gray Mold Blight of Castor Bean. A pale to olive gray mold develops on inflorescence, and when portions of this drop on to stem and leaves they are infected in turn.

BOTRYTIS

Fungi Imperfecti, Moniliales, Moniliaceae

Egglike conidia, hyaline, 1-celled, are formed on branched conidiophores over the surface, not in special fruiting bodies. The arrangement of the conidia gives the genus its name, which comes from the Greek *botrys* and means a cluster of grapes (Fig. 22). Flattened, loaf-shaped, or hemispherical black sclerotia are formed on or just underneath cuticle or epidermis of the host and are firmly attached to it. These sclerotia have a dark rind and light interior and serve as resting bodies to carry the fungus over winter. There are also very minute spores, formerly called microconidia but now known as spermatia or male cells, which apparently function in the formation of apothecia in the few cases where a definite connection has been made between the Botrytis stage and the ascospore form, Botryotinia.

Botrytis species are the common gray molds, only too familiar to every gardener. Some are saprophytic or weakly parasitic on senescent plant parts, and on a wide variety of hosts; others are true parasites and cause such important diseases as peony blight, lily blight, tulip fire.

Botrytis cinerea. Gray Mold Blight, bud and flower blight, blossom blight, gray mold rot, Botrytis blight, of general distribution on a great many flowers, fruits, and vegetables. There are undoubtedly many strains of this fungus and perhaps more than one species involved, but they have not been definitely separated.

This gray-mold disease is common on soft ripe fruits after picking, as any housewife knows after having to throw out half a box of strawberries or raspberries, but in continued humid weather the blight appears on growing fruits. Gray mold and shoot blight of blackberries are particularly prevalent in the Northwest. On citrus the fungus may produce a twig blight, a gummosis or a fruit rot, the latter mostly a storage decay of lemons. Peaches, plums, and quinces are subject to gray mold.

Vegetables are commonly afflicted as seedlings grown in greenhouses and in storage after harvest. If lettuce plants are set in the garden too close together they may blight at the base in moist weather, as will endive and escarole. Gray mold is common on lima beans, is sometimes found on snap and kidney beans. In rainy or foggy periods globe artichoke may be covered with a brownish-gray, dusty mold, with bud scales rotted. Asparagus shoots are sometimes blighted and tomato stems occasionally rotted.

Among ornamentals *Botrytis cinerea* causes a seedling blight of pine, a flower, twig or seedling blight of rhododendron, a twig blight of arborvitae, shoot blight of lilac and viburnum.

Gray mold is present on flowers and foliage of many plants under greenhouse conditions; but, when these same plants are brought into the home, the dry air of the average living room prevents further trouble.

The following annotated list includes most of the ornamentals on which *Botrytis cinerea* is reported causing trouble.

African-violet—leaf and stem rot, probably cosmopolitan in greenhouses.

Amaryllis—gray mold, mostly in South on outdoor plants after chilling.

Anemone—occasional severe rotting of crowns.

Aster—brown patches in flower head of perennial aster; seed damaged.

Begonia—dead areas on leaves and flowers rapidly enlarging and turning black in a moist atmosphere, and covered with brownish gray mold.

Calendula—gray mold blight.

Camellia—flower and bud blight, common after frost.

Century plant—gray mold after overwatering and chilling.

Chrysanthemum—cosmopolitan on flowers, buds, leaf tips, cuttings. Ray blight on flowers starts as small, water-soaked spots which rapidly enlarge with the characteristic grayish mold.

Dahlia—bud and flower blight.

Dogwood—flower and leaf blight. This is rather unusual, but in the Northeast, during our very wet spring of 1948, Botrytis attacked anthers and petals of aging flowers and when these rotted down onto young leaves the latter were also blighted. The effect was so striking that experiment stations and other agencies were flooded with inquiries about a strange new blight. By summer the dogwoods had recovered without any control measures.

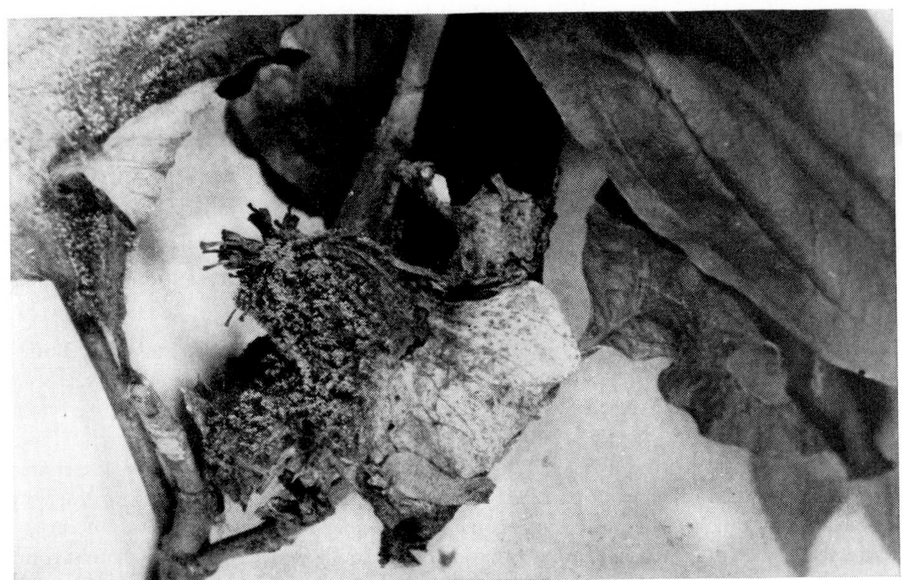

FIG. 23. Dogwood Blight. *Botrytis cinerea* in gray mold form on fading flower and foliage.

Eupatorium—stem blight, common in crowded plantings, at least in New Jersey. A tan area girdles the stem from one to several inches above the ground, with tops wilting or drying to that point.

Geranium (*Pelargonium*)—blossom blight and leaf spot, most common in cool, moist greenhouses where plants are syringed frequently. Petals are discolored, flowers drop, gray mold forms on leaves.

Gladiolus—leaf and flower blight causing much concern in recent years among commercial growers in Florida and the Northwest, and a corm rot causing damage on Long Island and some other sections.

In 1939 Botrytis blight was reported destructive to gladiolus in Oregon, and in 1940 an epiphytotic of blight appeared in Florida. The same year corms grown on Long Island showed large, deep, shriveled and sunken lesions. A similar corm rot in Holland, known for many years on stored corms but assuming alarming form in 1937, has been attributed to *Botrytis gladiolorum*. A gladiolus disease in England has been credited to *B. gladioli* and *B. cinerea*. To date in this country the blight and corm rot are considered due to one or more strains of *B. cinerea*.

The leaf and flower blight is fostered by cool rainy or foggy weather such as occurs in Florida in early winter, and on the Pacific Coast from September to November. In Michigan and other inland states cool rainy weather sometimes brings on leaf blight.

Leaf spots are round or oval, light brown surrounded by a darker brown ring, varying in size with an average of ¼ by ½ inch. In continued wet weather gray mold is produced in these spots and on dead plant material left on the ground. On flower spikes spots are on petals or at base of floral bracts, and sometimes on stems. Since in commercial culture the spikes are cut before buds show color they may appear healthy when packed only to go down in a watery soft rot in transit, or open to tattered, "moth-eaten" blooms. Some shipments are a total loss.

Control. Spraying gladiolus in the field with Dithane D–14 plus zinc sulfate, or Dithane Z–78 or Parzate has been helpful in preventing spike infection, but applications as frequent as every five days are often necessary in rainy periods. Cleaning up all old plant parts is essential.

Because corm rot develops in cool, moist weather after digging, it can be somewhat prevented by curing rapidly at high temperatures. After the infected areas are walled off by cork formation, corms can be stored at normal low temperatures without further loss.

Lily—*Botrytis cinerea* is common on lilies, but see *B. elliptica* for the special lily Botrytis.

Marigold—gray mold prevalent on fading flowers.

Narcissus—occasional.

Peony—late blight, distinguished from early blight (see *B. paeoniae*) by the sparse mold, usually standing far out from affected tissue, instead of thick, short velvety mold and by much larger, flatter sclerotia formed near base of stalk. Late flowers are infected and, when these drop down onto wet foliage, irregular brown areas are formed in leaves.

Poinsettia—tip blight and stem canker.

Primrose—crown rot and decay of basal leaves, with prominent gray mold, very common in greenhouses where plants are heavily watered.

Rose—bud or flower blight, cane canker. When half-open buds ball up, the cause is either an infestation of thrips (which can be seen by looking closely at base of interior petals) or Botrytis blight, which is identified as soon as the gray fuzz forms. Canes kept too wet by a manure mulch or wet leaves, and canes injured in some way, show a gray mold over the affected area.

Sunflower—bud rot and mold.

Sweet pea—blossom blight.

Viola spp.—gray mold and basal rot of violet and pansy, particularly the latter.

Zinnia—petal blight, head blight, moldy seed.

Botrytis cinerea also may infect arabis, cineraria, eucharis, euphorbia, fuchsia, gerbera, gypsophila, heliotrope, hydrangea, iris, lupine, May-apple, pyrethrum, periwinkle or vinca, rose-of-Sharon, stockesia, and wallflower.

Control. Sanitation is more important than anything else. Carry around a paper bag as you inspect the garden; put into it all fading flowers, and blighted foliage; if rot is near the base take up entire plant for burning. Keep greenhouse plants widely spaced, with good ventilation; avoid syringing and overhead watering.

Botrytis douglasii. SEEDLING BLIGHT on giant sequoia and redwood, perhaps a form of *B. cinerea*.

Botrytis elliptica. BOTRYTIS BLIGHT OF LILY, general on lilies. Madonna lily is particularly susceptible, along with *L. chalcedonicum*, *L. pardalinum* (Leopard lily), and *L. testaceum* (Nankeen lily). Easter lilies (*L. longiflo-*

rum) sometimes planted in gardens are moderately susceptible, whereas Hanson, Martagon, and regal lilies are somewhat resistant.

If blight strikes early, the entire apical growth may be killed, with no further development, but more often the disease starts as a leaf spot when stems are a good height. Spots are orange to reddish brown, oval, or sometimes circular. In some species there is a definite red to purple margin around a light center; in others the definite dark margin is replaced by an indefinite water-soaked zone. If spots are numerous they grow together to blight the whole leaf. Infection starts with lowest leaves and works up the stem until, in favorable cool, moist weather, all leaves are blackened and hanging limp.

Fig. 24. Botrytis Blight of Lily.

Buds rot or open to distorted flowers with irregular brown flecks. There are sometimes stem lesions, but the rot rarely progresses into the bulb. Spores formed in the usual gray-mold masses in blighted portions are spread by splashed rain, air currents, and gardeners. Optimum spore germination is at 60° F. but 70° F. promotes most rapid blighting once infection has started. The fungus winters in small, black sclerotia in fallen flowers, or blighted dead stems and leaves, or in leaf spots in rosette of basal leaves of Madonna lilies.

Control. Avoid too dense planting, and shady or low spots with little air circulation and subject to heavy dews. Clean up infected plant parts before sclerotia can be formed. Spray with 8–4–100 bordeaux mixture (4 ounces copper sulfate, 2 ounces lime to 3 gallons water) starting when lilies are 5 to 6 inches high and continuing at 10- to 14-day intervals up to flowering. Some of the new organic chemicals seem to be less effective than bordeaux against this particular Botrytis.

Botrytis galanthina. BOTRYTIS BLIGHT OF SNOWDROP, sometimes found in sclerotial stage in imported bulbs. If the small black dots of sclerotia are found only on outer scales these can be removed before planting; otherwise do not plant infected bulbs.

Botrytis narcissicola is *Sclerotinia narcissicola,* cause of smoulder or neck rot. See under Rots.

Botrytis polyblastis. NARCISSUS FIRE. This is really *Sclerotinia polyblastis,* the connection with the perfect stage having been made some years ago. The disease is serious as a flower blight in parts of England, and occasional in Scotland and Ireland, but is known in this country only on the Pacific Coast, first reported in Washington in 1934 and recently in California. The chief characteristic of this Botrytis species is the very large size of the conidia and their germination by several germ tubes.

In England overwintering sclerotia produce apothecia when *Narcissus tazetta* comes into flower, the ascospores infecting the perianth and causing flower spotting. Withered flowers produce numerous conidia which infect foliage, on which sclerotia are formed late in the season.

Control. Remove immediately all infected flowers and leaves. Early season spraying with bordeaux mixture or Fermate may help.

Botrytis paeoniae. BOTRYTIS BLIGHT OF PEONY, early blight, bud rot, bud blast, gray mold, probably present wherever peonies are grown, also recorded on lily-of-the-valley, but here perhaps only a form of *Botrytis cinerea.* This blight was first noted in epidemic or epiphytotic form in this country in 1897 and has been important in wet springs ever since.

Young shoots may rot off at the base as they come through the ground or when a few inches high, with a dense, velvety gray mold on the rotting portions. In my own experience this early shoot blight is far more common when the young stems are kept moist by having to emerge through a manure mulch. Flowers are attacked at any stage; they may stay as tiny brown to black buds which never develop further, or they may be blasted as half open buds or even as full-blown flowers, with the infection proceeding a few inches down the stem and giving it a brown and tan zoned appearance. Leaf spots develop when infected petals fall on foliage, but in some cases blasting of mature flowers and continued leaf blighting through the summer is due to late blight, caused by *Botrytis cinerea,* differentiated by the sparser mold and conidiophores projecting further from the petal or leaf surface.

Conidia are blown by wind, splashed by rain, carried on gardeners' tools, and sometimes transported by ants. Secondary infection is abundant in cool,

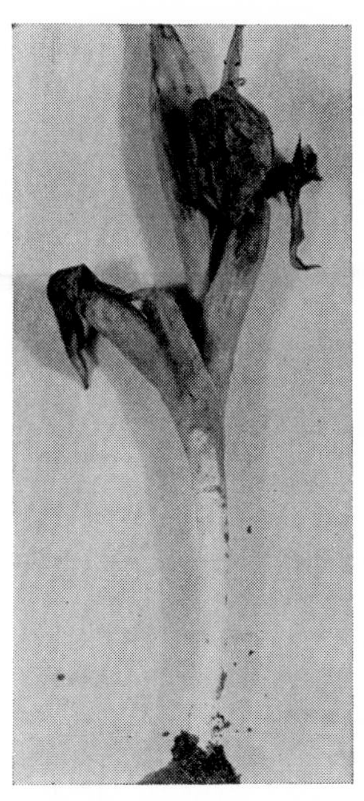

Fig. 29. Botrytis Blight of Tulip: primary infection from diseased bulb.

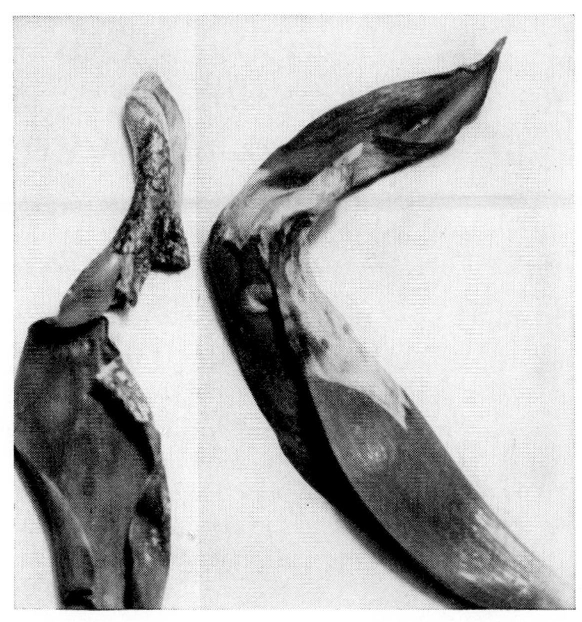

Fig. 30. Tulip Blight, early spring infection; leaves mold at tip or show light patches resembling frost injury.

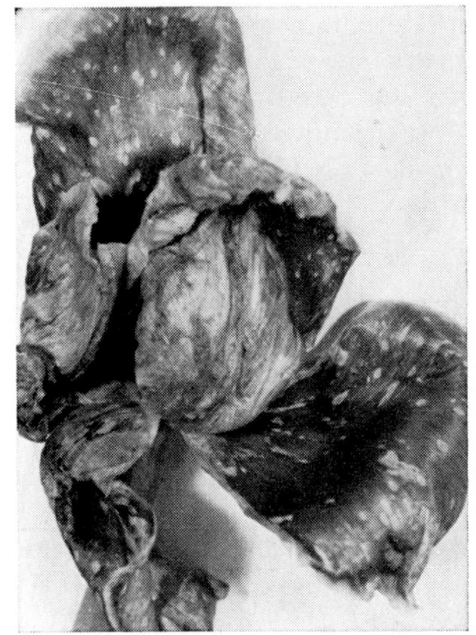

Fig. 31. Tulip Blight, secondary infection; each spot comes from germination of a spore splashed by rain onto petal.

Fig. 32. Tulip Blight, final stage of flower shown in Figure 31, with spores ready to infect other tulips.

trol but leaves a splotchy effect on foliage when applied with a knapsack sprayer. Zerlate and Tersan offer possibilities. Bordeaux mixture is effective but often injurious in the cool weather of early spring. No spraying schedule can be considered a substitute for strict sanitary precautions.

BRIOSIA

Fungi Imperfecti, Moniliales, Stilbaceae

Conidia on synnemata or coremia, erect fascicles of hyphae ending in a small head; spores globose, dark, 1-celled and catenate, formed in chains.

Briosia azaleae (formerly *Sporocybe azaleae*). BUD AND TWIG BLIGHT of azaleas and rhododendrons. The disease was originally noted from New York as early as 1874, reported as a rhododendron bud rot from California in 1920, and in 1931 and 1939 reported as the cause of a very serious azalea disease in western Massachusetts, threatening to exterminate some species, although in that state common rhododendron species seem resistant.

First symptoms in flower and leaf buds appear in July and August. Some flower buds are dwarfed to half size, turn light brown and shrivel, with tips of basal bud scales projecting outward in a rosetted appearance. Other flower buds are shriveled in May with scales turning to silvery gray. Infection of lateral leaf buds is followed by death of twigs. Successive crops of coremia are produced on old dead buds for as long as three years, the first crop appearing the spring after summer infection. The heads of the coremia are dark and buds look as if stuck with minute, round-headed pins.

Control. Prune out and burn infected buds and twigs in late autumn and early spring. Spraying with bordeaux mixture or dusting with copper-lime dust before blossoming and at monthly intervals after blossoming is helpful, but not as essential as pruning.

CENANGIUM

Ascomycetes, Helotiales, Dermateaceae or Helotiaceae

Apothecia small, brown to black, sessile or substipitate on bark; spores hyaline, elliptical, 1-celled; paraphyses filiform.

Cenangium abietis. TWIG BLIGHT OF PINE, Cenangium dieback or "pruning disease," also found on fir. The fungus is ordinarily saprophytic on native pines but may become parasitic when their vigor is reduced by drought. The disease is considered beneficial to ponderosa pine in the Southwest because it prunes off the lower branches, but on exotic pines it can be damaging.

Infection starts near terminal buds in late summer and progresses down the twig to a node, sometimes beyond into two-year wood, or branches. The needles redden and die, being conspicuous in spring but falling in late summer, after which brown to black apothecia with a greenish disc appear on twigs.

Control. Cut off and destroy affected twigs.

CERCOSPORA

Fungi Imperfect, Moniliales, Dematiaceae

Conidia pale to dark, long, filiform, with several cross-walls, not formed in a fruiting body but successively on slender conidiophores which emerge in fascicles or groups from stomata, and usually show joints or scars where conidia have fallen off in turn. Hyphae are olive brown to black (Fig. 22).

This is the largest group genus of the Dematiaceae, there being about 400 species causing blights and leaf spots on nearly every crop species. Some have been connected with Mycosphaerella as a perfect stage.

Cercospora apii. EARLY BLIGHT OF CELERY, general on celery and also found on celeriac, first noted in Missouri in 1884 and since found in varying abundance wherever celery is grown, being most severe from New Jersey southward. The name is misleading, for it rarely appears before the Septoria disease known as late blight.

Foliage spots first show when plants are about six weeks old. Minute yellow areas change to large, irregular, ash gray lesions, covered in moist weather with velvety groups of conidiophores and spores on both sides of leaves. Spores are splashed by rain, carried with manure or cultivators or blown by wind to other plants. Here germ tubes penetrate uninjured tissue and the disease spreads rapidly in warm, moist weather. Sclerotial bodies formed inside host tissue can survive a year if host cells are not disintegrated.

Control. Two-year-old seed will probably be free from viable spores; other seed should be treated with formaldehyde, hot water or calomel, even though this may cause some injury (see *Septoria apii* for directions). Earlier recommendations called for spraying in seedbed and in field with bordeaux mixture or copper-lime dust, but in many states the somewhat less injurious organics are replacing copper. Dithane D–14 plus zinc sulfate, Parzate, and Fermate have good ratings for yield and control in some tests.

Cercospora carotae. EARLY BLIGHT OF CARROT. Leaves and petioles turn yellow, then brown. Whole top may be killed. Fungus winters in old refuse and with seed.

Control. Spray or dust with a copper fungicide.

Cercospora microsora (perfect stage *Mycosphaerella microsora*). LEAF BLIGHT, general on American and European linden. Small, circular brown spots with darker borders coalesce to form large blighted areas, often followed by defoliation, most serious on young trees.

Control. Clean up and burn fallen leaves. If necessary spray with bordeaux mixture or other copper when leaves begin to grow, when half-grown, and when fully expanded.

Cercospora sordida. Leaf Blight on trumpetvine, chiefly east of the Mississippi River and in the South. Small, angular, sordid brown patches run together; upper leaf surface turns yellow to reddish brown. Probably the blight is too unimportant for control measures.

Cercospora thujina. Arborvitae Blight or Fire, on oriental arborvitae and Italian cypress in the South, destructive in ornamental plantings for some years but first reported in Louisiana in 1943 and the fungus named as a new species in 1945. Affected leaves and branchlets are killed, turn brown, and fall off gradually, leaving shrub thin and ragged. The lower two-thirds is infected most severely, with a tuft of healthy growth at the top. When close to a house the side away from the wall may be most affected. Plants crowded in nurseries are killed in one to three years, but in home gardens they may persist indefinitely in a ragged, unsightly condition. Conidiophores in fascicles produce conidia after cankers on young stems have girdled the bark and killed the twigs, often with a swelling above the girdle which looks like an insect gall.

Control. Copper sprays effectively check the disease—8–8–100 bordeaux mixture, Cuprocide at 3 pounds per 100 gallons, or Tribasic at 6 pounds per 100 gallons. Dithane is a possibility. Apply 3 sprays at monthly intervals, starting June 1.

CHOANEPHORA

Phycomycetes, Mucorales, Choanephoraceae

Mycelium profuse; sporangia and conidia present; sporangiola lacking. Sporangium pendent on recurved end of an erect, unbranched sporangiophore with a columella, containing spores provided at both ends and sometimes at side with a cluster of fine, radiating appendages. Conidia formed in heads on a few short branches of an erect conidiophore enlarged at the tip; conidia longitudinally striate, without appendages.

Choanephora cucurbitarum. Blossom Blight, and blossom-end rot, common on summer squash and pumpkin, occasional on amaranth, cowpea, cucumber, okra, and pepper, on fading hibiscus and other flowers.

This blight is often found in home gardens in seasons of high humidity and rainfall. Flowers and young fruits are covered with a luxuriant fungus growth, first white then brown to purple with a definite metallic luster and the fruiting bodies looking like little pins to the naked eye. Both staminate and pistillate flowers may be infected, but from the latter the fungus advances into young fruits producing a soft wet rot at the blossom end. In severe cases all flowers are blighted or all fruits rotted.

There seems to be no control beyond removing affected flowers and fruits as soon as noticed.

Choanephora infundibulifera. Blossom Blight on hibiscus and jasmine.

CIBORIA

Ascomycetes, Helotiales, Sclerotiniaceae

Stroma a dark brown to black sclerotium in catkins or seed, simulating in shape the stromatized organ and not resembling a sclerotium externally. Apothecia cupulate to shallow-saucer-shaped, brown.

Ciboria acerina. INFLORESCENCE BLIGHT of red and silver maple. Apothecia developed in quantities from stromatized inflorescences on ground beneath trees start discharging spores when maple flowers appear overhead. Mycelium spreads through stamens, calyx, and bud scales until flower cluster drops.

Ciboria carunculoides. POPCORN DISEASE OF MULBERRY, a southern disease and not very important. Sclerotia are formed in carpels of fruit which swell to resemble popcorn in shape, but remain green.

CIBORINIA

Ascomycetes, Helotiales, Sclerotiniaceae

Stroma a thin, flat, black sclerotium of discoid type formed in leaves. One to several stalked apothecia arise from sclerotia; they are small, brown, cupulate to flat when expanded.

Ciborinia erythronii and **C. gracilis.** LEAF BLIGHT of erythronium. Flat black sclerotia are prominent in leaves.

CORTICIUM

Basidiomycetes, Agaricales, Thelephoraceae

Hymenium or fruiting surface of basidia consisting of a single resupinate or horizontal layer. This genus has contained a rather heterogeneous collection of species and some of the more important have been transferred to the genus Pellicularia.

Corticium koleroga. THREAD BLIGHT. See *Pellicularia koleroga.*

Corticium microsclerotia. WEB BLIGHT. See *Pellicularia filamentosa.*

Corticium salmonicolor. LIMB BLIGHT of fig, pear, apple in Gulf States. The spore surface is pinkish.

Corticium stevensii. THREAD BLIGHT. See *Pellicularia koleroga.*

Corticium vagum, now *Pellicularia filamentosa,* perfect stage of *Rhizoctonia solani,* causing black scurf of potatoes and damping off and root rot of many, many plants. See both Pellicularia and Rhizoctonia under Rots.

CORYNEUM

Fungi Imperfecti, Melanconiales, Melanconiaceae

Dark spores, with several cross-walls, borne in acervuli (Fig. 42).

Coryneum berckmanii. CORYNEUM BLIGHT OF ORIENTAL ARBORVITAE, on *Thuja orientalis* and Italian cypress, causing serious losses in nurseries and home gardens in Pacific Northwest. Small branches are blighted, turn reddish brown; many small branchlets drop, leaving a tangle of dead gray stems; larger limbs may be girdled. Foliage turns light gray with formation of black pustules bearing 5-septate spores. As new growth develops in blighted areas the fungus is spread by these spores to young, contiguous foliage. Reinfection continues until the plant is so devitalized it dies. The fungus fruits only on scale leaves or young stems.

Control. One application of red copper oxide or basic copper sulfate is satisfactory if made before infection starts in early fall rains.

Coryneum carpophilum (formerly *C. beijerinckii*). Peach Blight, twig blight, Shot-Hole Disease of Stone Fruits, leaf spot, general on peach in West, also on almond, apricot, nectarine, and cherry. *Ascospora* is perfect stage of fungus.

Twig lesions are formed on one-year shoots, reddish spots developing into sunken cankers with fruit buds invaded and copious gum formation. Small spots are formed on foliage and as leaves grow the spots drop out to give typical shot holes, followed by considerable defoliation. There may be spotting, deformation, or dropping of young fruit.

Apricot buds are blackened and killed during winter, and fruits may be roughened with scabby spots. In peaches much fruiting wood is killed before growth starts, and in late rains leaves and fruit are peppered with small, round dead spots. The fungus winters in twig lesions and sometimes in old blighted blossoms on the ground.

Control. Standard spray is a 10–10–100 bordeaux mixture applied in November before heavy rains come, but Fermate now seems promising.

Coryneum microstictum. Twig Blight of American bladdernut. Young twigs are killed, fungus winters in acervuli formed on this dead tissue and spores are disseminated in spring. Prune out and burn diseased twigs during winter.

CRYPTOSPORA

Ascomycetes, Sphaeriales, Sphaeriaceae

Perithecia immersed in a stroma, with long necks converging into a disc; ascospores long, filiform, hyaline; conidia on a stroma.

Cryptospora longispora. Branch Blight of Araucaria. Lower branches are attacked first with disease spreading upward; tip ends are bent and then broken off. Plants several years old may be killed. Prune off and burn infected branches.

CRYPTOSTICTIS

Fungi Imperfecti, Melanconiales, Melanconiaceae

Spores dark, with several cross walls, formed in acervuli.

Cryptostictis sp. Twig Blight of dogwood.

CYLINDROSPORIUM

Fungi Imperfecti, Melanconiales, Melanconiaceae

Conidia hyaline, long filiform, often curved, formed in white to dark masses in acervuli on leaves or branches. Many pathogenic species have Higginsia as a perfect state.

Representative species causing leaf blights are *Cylindrosporium defoliatum* on hackberry, *C. griseum* on western soapberry and *C. juglandis* on walnut. Usually not important, but causing defoliation in some circumstances.

CYTOSPORA

Fungi Imperfecti, Sphaeropsidales, Sphaerioidaceae

Pycnidia globose, with dark walls, formed in a circle in a stroma; conidia 1-celled, hyaline, sausage-shaped, expelled in cirrhi or curls (Fig. 42). Species are imperfect stages of Valsa, which has perithecia grouped in a circle in a stroma and hyaline, 1-celled ascospores.

Cytospora (*Valsa*) **kunzei.** SPRUCE TWIG BLIGHT AND CANKER, common on ornamental Norway and blue spruces in the Northeast. Browning and death of branches starts with those near the ground and progresses slowly upward, with a large flow of resin on affected branches. Needles drop immediately or persist for a while but eventually twigs are left bare and brittle. Cankers are formed near resin spots with small black fruiting bodies extruding yellow tendrils of spores splashed by wind and rain to other branches. Infection is usually through wounds.

Control. Cut off branches a few inches back from infected portions or at main stem; work only in dry weather. Avoid wounding trees with lawn mowers and other tools. Sterilize pruning tools between cuts. Fertilize to renew vigor. Spraying lower branches with bordeaux mixture in spring may be helpful.

Cytospora persicae. TWIG BLIGHT on peach twigs and branches.

DENDROPHOMA

Fungi Imperfecti, Sphaeropsidales, Sphaerioidaceae

Conidiophores branched, with hyaline, 1-celled conidia formed at tips of branches; pycnidia separate, innate but finally erumpent, with ostioles.

Dendrophoma obscurans. STRAWBERRY LEAF BLIGHT, angular leaf spot, on strawberries. Spots are large, circular to angular, reddish-purple, zonated with age, when there is a dark brown center, then a light brown zone with a purple border. Spots may extend in a V-shaped area from a large vein to edge of leaf, with black fruiting bodies showing in central portion.

Control. Use bordeaux mixture as for leaf spots.

DIAPORTHE

Ascomycetes, Sphaeriales, Valsaceae

Perithecia in a hard, black stroma, first immersed, then erumpent; paraphyses lacking; spores 2-celled, hyaline. Imperfect stage a Phomopsis, with small, hyaline, 1-celled spores.

Diaporthe arctii. DIAPORTHE BLIGHT OF LARKSPUR, stem canker, on delphinium, particularly annual larkspur. Lower leaves turn brown and dry but remain attached; brown lesions at base of stems extend several inches upward, and down into roots. Scattered dark pycnidia are present in stems, petioles, leaf blades, and seed capsules, the latter probably spreading the blight. Crowns are sometimes enveloped in a cottony weft of mycelium and perithecia develop on decaying stems.

Control. Remove and destroy diseased plants; use seed from healthy plants.

Diaporthe phaseolorum. LIMA BEAN POD BLIGHT, leaf spot, apparently native in New Jersey where it was noticed first in 1891, more abundant on pole than bush limas. Leaf spots are large, irregular, brown, often with discolored borders and large black pycnidia formed in concentric circles in dead tissue. Necrotic portions may drop out, making leaves ragged. Pod lesions spread in all directions, turning pods black and wilted. They also have prominent black pycnidia. Seed is shriveled or lacking. Spores, produced in great abundance, are disseminated by wind and pickers, enter through stomata or wounds. The disease is most severe along the coast with an optimum temperature around 80° F.

Control. Use clean seed from healthy plants.

Diaporthe sojae. (or *D. phaseolorum* var. *sojae*) SOYBEAN POD AND STEM BLIGHT, also reported on snap bean, cowpea, lima bean, peanut, lupine, pepper, tomato, okra, onions and garlic. There seems to be a difference of opinion as to the pathogenicity of the fungus. Some feel it is merely a vigorous saprophyte, fruiting abundantly on tissue killed by other organisms or adverse growing conditions, or perhaps a weak wound parasite entering tomatoes and peppers through blossom-end rots or sun-scald spots. The blight was first observed in North Carolina in 1920 and has become established in the Corn Belt, where it is considered a distinct menace to soybean production. Blight starts at junction of branch with stem, which is girdled and above portions killed back, then covered with black pycnidia. Seeds are infected from the pods and the fungus winters in dead stems and seed.

Control. Use clean seed from healthy pods; clean up crop refuse.

Diaporthe vaccinii. BLUEBERRY TWIG BLIGHT. The same fungus which causes cranberry rot blights new shoots of cultivated blueberries, entering at tips, progressing toward base and ultimately girdling old branches. Pycnidia develop on leaves and dead twigs. The disease is seldom serious enough for control measures.

DIDYMASCELLA (formerly *Keithia*)

Ascomycetes, Phacidiales, Stictidiaceae (or Phacidiaceae)

Apothecia erumpent on leaves of conifers; spores dark, 2-celled, ovoid, paraphyses filiform; asci 2- to 4-spored.

Didymascella thujina. LEAF BLIGHT, seedling blight of arborvitae in eastern states and of giant arborvitae, sometimes called western red cedar. The fungus is a native of North America and occurs abundantly in the West damaging seedlings and saplings, often killing trees up to four years old, when they are in dense stands in humid regions. Older trees do not die but foliage appears scorched, particularly on lower branches, and young leaf twigs may drop.

Cushion-like, brown to black apothecia are embedded in leaf tissue, usually upper, and are exposed by rupture of epidermis. After discharge of round, brown, unequally 2-celled spores during the summer, the apothecia drop out of the needles, leaving deep pits.

Control. Spray small trees and nursery stock several times during summer and fall with bordeaux mixture.

Didymascella tsugae. HEMLOCK NEEDLE BLIGHT. Needles of Canada hemlock turn brown and drop in late summer. Spores are matured in apothecia on fallen needles with new infection in spring. The damage is not heavy; raking up and burning fallen needles should be sufficient control.

DIDYMELLA

Ascomycetes, Sphaeriales, Sphaeriaceae (or Myriangiales, Pseudosphaeriaceae)

Perithecia (or perithecium-like stromata) are membranous, not carbonous, innate, not beaked, paraphyses present; spores 2-celled, hyaline.

Didymella applanata. RASPBERRY SPUR BLIGHT, purple cane spot, gray bark, general on raspberries, also on dewberry, blackberry. The disease is so named because it partially or completely destroys spurs or laterals of canes. It has been known in America since 1891 and may cause losses up to 75 percent of the crop in individual plantings of red raspberries.

Dark reddish or purple spots on canes at point of attachment of leaves enlarge to surround leaf and bud and may darken lower portion of cane. Affected areas turn brown, then gray. If buds are not killed outright during winter, they are so weakened that the next season's spurs are weak, chlorotic, seldom blossoming. Pycnidia of the imperfect Phoma stage of the fungus and perithecia are numerous on the gray bark; ascospores are discharged during spring and early summer.

In New York State varieties Indian Summer and Taylor seem most susceptible, and Ontario, Viking, Cuthbert, Marcy, and Chief least susceptible.

Control. A delayed dormant or green-tip spray of 1% Elgetol followed by two applications of Fermate, 2 pounds to 100 gallons, or 6–10–100 bordeaux mixture, applied when new shoots are 10 to 12 inches high and again two weeks later gives control. Avoid planting sites with poor air circulation and soil drainage; cut out and destroy fruiting canes as soon as possible after harvest.

DIDYMOSPHAERIA

Ascomycetes, Sphaeriales, Sphaeriaceae

Perithecia innate or finally erumpent, not beaked, smooth, paraphyses present; spores dark, 2-celled.

Didymosphaeria populina (imperfect stage *Napicladium tremulae*). SHOOT BLIGHT OF POPLAR, in Northeast. The blight is similar to willow scab, with young shoots blackened and wilted. In moist weather dark, olive-green masses of spores are formed on leaves.

DIPLODIA

Fungi Imperfecti, Sphaeropsidales, Sphaerioidaceae

Pycnidia separate, innate or finally erumpent, smooth; ostiole present; spores 2-celled, dark, ovoid.

Some species cause not too important twig blights: **Diplodia coluteae** on bladder senna, **D. longispora** on white oak, **D. pinea** on pine, **D. sarmentorum** on pyracantha. **Diplodia natalensis** causes twig blight of peach and citrus. It is the imperfect stage of *Physalospora rhodina*. See further under Rots.

ENDOTHIA

Ascomycetes, Sphaeriales, Melogrammataceae (Sphaeriaceae of Clements, Diaporthaceae of Wolf and Wolf)

Perithecia deeply embedded in a reddish to yellow stroma, with long necks opening to the surface but not beaked; paraphyses lacking; spores 2-celled, hyaline. Conidia borne in hollow chambers or pycnidia in a stroma or pycnidium, and expelled in cirrhi.

Endothia parasitica. CHESTNUT BLIGHT, Endothia Canker, general on chestnut. To most gardeners this disease is now of historical interest for our native chestnuts have long since gone; the disease, however, persists in sprouts starting from old stumps and in the chinkapin. One of the most destructive tree diseases ever known, chestnut blight at least served to awaken people to the importance of plant disease and to the need for research in this field.

First noticed in the New York Zoological Park in 1904, the blight rapidly wiped out the chestnut stands in New England and along the Allegheny and Blue Ridge Mountains, leaving not a single undamaged tree. In 1925 the disease eliminated chestnuts in Illinois and by 1929 had reached the Pacific Northwest.

Conspicuous reddish bark cankers are formed on trunk and limbs, often swollen and splitting longitudinally. As the limbs are girdled the foliage blights, so that brown shriveled leaves are seen at a distance. The fungus fruits abundantly in crevices of broken bark first producing conidia extruded in yellow tendrils from reddish pycnidia, and later ascospores from perithecia embedded in orange stromata. Fans of buff-colored mycelium are found under affected bark.

Ascospores can be spread by the wind many miles, landing in open wounds, but the sticky conidia are carried by birds and insects. The fungus can live indefinitely as a saprophyte, and new sprouts developing from old stumps may grow for several years before they are killed.

Control. All eradication and protective measures proved futile. Hope for the future lies in crossbreeding resistant Asiatic species with the American chestnut (and there has been some success to date) or in substituting Chinese and Japanese chestnuts for our own.

FABRAEA

Ascomycetes, Helotiales, Dermateaceae

Apothecia bright colored, in spots in living leaves; ascospores 2-celled, hyaline. Conidial stage an Entomosporium, in Melanconiales, with distinctive cruciate, 4-celled conidia, each cell ciliate, with an appendage, formed in acervuli (Fig. 22.)

Fabraea maculata (*Entomosporium maculatum*). LEAF BLIGHT, leaf spot generally distributed on pear, quince, on hawthorn (sometimes considered a separate species, *Entomosporium thuemenii*), widespread on amelanchier and sometimes found on cotoneaster, Siberian crab, loquat, medlar, Japanese quince, photinia and mountain-ash.

Pears may be affected as seedlings in nurseries or in bearing orchards. Very small, dark spots are scattered over leaves, with the raised black dot of a fruiting body in center of each spot. Fruit spots are red at first, then dark; the skin is roughened, sometimes cracked. Quince has similar symptoms.

Home gardeners are more familiar with this as a blight of English hawthorn. Small dark or reddish brown spots are numerous over leaves which drop prematurely in August. In wet seasons there may be nearly complete defoliation. The fungus winters in dead leaves on ground and in bark cankers.

Control. Spraying with bordeaux mixture three times, starting when leaves are unfolded gives excellent control of hawthorn leaf blight but may cause some injury, particularly reddish leaf spots that somewhat resemble initial stages of the blight. I have had quite good luck spraying with Triogen, when I have it made up for roses, for the copper in this combination spray is less injurious and less conspicuous. Bioquin 1 and Parzate have controlled pear blight in test spraying at the Morris Arboretum.

GIBBERELLA

Ascomycetes, Hypocreales

Perithecia superficial, blue, violet or greenish; spores hyaline with several cells. Conidial stage in genus Fusarium with fusoid-curved spores, several-septate.

Gibberella baccata (*Fusarium lateritium*). TWIG BLIGHT of ailanthus, citrus, cotoneaster, fig, hibiscus, hornbeam, peach and other plants in warm climates, sometimes associated with other diseases.

Glomerella cingulata (see under Anthracnose). LEAF AND BUD BLIGHT of Cyclamen. Remove blighted leaves, reduce humidity, possibly spray young plants with Fermate or bordeaux mixture.

GLOMERULARIA

Fungi Imperfecti, Moniliales, Moniliaceae

Conidia 1-celled, light, formed in heads; hyphae obsolescent or lacking.

Glomerularia lonicerae. LEAF BLIGHT of honeysuckle.

GNOMONIA—see under Anthracnose

Gnomonia rubi. CANE BLIGHT of blackberry, dewberry, raspberry.

HADROTRICHUM

Fungi Imperfecti, Moniliales, Tuberculariaceae

Conidia 1-celled, dark, formed on sporodochia.

Hadrotrichum globiferum. LEAF BLIGHT of lupine.

HELMINTHOSPORIUM

Fungi Imperfecti, Moniliales, Dematiaceae

Spores and mycelium dark. Conidia large, with several cross-walls, wormlike, borne successively on conidiophores which often protrude from stomata of host.

Helminthosporium turticum. CORN LEAF BLIGHT, on field and sweet corn and grasses, widely distributed but with epidemics more frequent in the East. Long, elliptical greenish-brown lesions on leaves become covered with conidia; corn ears have a smutty decay. Disease is favored by low wet locations and rainy seasons. Some of the new hybrid corn varieties are rather resistant.

HERPOTRICHIA

Ascomycetes, Sphaeriales, Sphaeriaceae

Mycelium dark, perithecia superficial, spores with several cross-walls, olivaceous when mature.

Herpotrichia nigra. BROWN FELT BLIGHT of conifers at high elevations—on fir, juniper, incense cedar, spruce, pine, yew when under snow. When snow melts lower branches are seen covered with dense felty growth of brown to nearly black mycelium, which kills foliage by excluding light and air as well as by invading hyphae. Small, black perithecia are scattered over the felt.

HETEROSPORIUM

Fungi Imperfecti, Moniliales, Dematiaceae

Conidia dark, spiny, with several cells; hyphae long and distinctly different from conidia.

Heterosporium syringae. LILAC LEAF BLIGHT. A velvety, olive-green bloom of spores is formed in blighted, gray-brown leaf areas, which may crack and fall away. The fungus is usually associated with Cladosporium and infection is on mature leaves. If necessary, spray after mid-June with bordeaux mixture.

HIGGINSIA (Coccomyces)

Ascomycetes, Helotiales, Dermateaceae

Dark, leathery to fleshy apothecia are formed on fallen leaves; spores filiform, hyaline; paraphyses present. Conidial stage Cylindrosporium with hyaline, thread-like conidia in acervuli, and also spermatia, formed in conidial acervuli, which apparently function in fertilization.

Higginsia hiemalis. CHERRY LEAF BLIGHT, SHOT HOLE, general on sweet and sour cherries, the most common and destructive leaf disease of cherries.

FIG. 33. Cherry Leaf Blight, or shot-hole, or leaf spot.

Leaf spots are circular, first purplish, then brown, falling out to give the shot-hole effect. If lesions are numerous leaves turn yellow and fall by mid-summer, this premature defoliation reducing next season's harvest. The fungus winters in fallen leaves, producing disk-shaped apothecia for the source of primary infection. Secondary infection comes from conidia, formed in whitish masses on the spots in moist weather, and more numerous on under than upper leaf surface.

Control. Cleaning up or turning under fallen leaves is helpful but usually about four spray applications are also needed—at petal fall, shuck, 10 days after husks split on young fruit, and after harvest. The early sprays are often of lime-sulfur at a 1 to 50 dilution, and later treatments are with weak bordeaux mixture. Fermate, Dithane, Zerlate, Phygon, Isothan Q 15 have all given promising results in some cases. Consult your own Experiment Station for suitable materials and schedule for your location.

Higginsia (*Coccomyces*) ***kerriae*** (imperfect stage *Cylindrosporium kerriae*). KERRIA LEAF AND TWIG BLIGHT, widespread on kerria from Eastern States to Texas. Leaves have small, round to angular, light to reddish brown spots with darker borders; when spots are numerous leaves turn yellow and die. Similar spots on young stems often run together into extended cankers, the bark splitting over cankers to show black pycnidia oozing out a mass of long, white, curved spores. Twigs are slowly killed back. The fungus winters in old dead leaves.

Control. Cut out diseased sprouts; rake up dead leaves. Spraying with bordeaux mixture or dusting with sulfur may help.

HYPODERMA

Ascomycetes, Phacidiales, Phacidiaceae (or Hypodermataceae)

Ascopores formed in hysterothecia, which are elongated perithecia (or apothecia) extending along evergreen needles; ascospores 1-celled hyaline, fusiform, surrounded by a gelatinous sheath (Fig. 58).

Hypoderma lethale. GRAY BLIGHT of hard pines, from New England to Gulf States. Hysterothecia are short, narrow, black, often found on pitch pine.

HYPODERMELLA

Ascomycetes, Phacidiales, Phacidiaceae (or Hypodermataceae)

Like Hypoderma but one-celled spores are club-shaped at upper end, tapering toward base (Fig. 58).

Hypodermella laricis. LARCH NEEDLE AND SHOOT BLIGHT. Yellow spots are formed on needles which turn reddish brown but stay attached, giving a scorched appearance to trees. Hysterothecia are very small, oblong to elliptical, dull black, on upper surface of needles.

HYPOMYCES

Ascomycetes, Hypocreales

Perithecia bright colored, with a subicle (a crustlike mycelial growth underneath); spores 2-celled, light, with a short projection at one end.

Hypomyces ipomoeae. TWIG BLIGHT of bladdernut.

HYPONECTRIA

Ascomycetes, Hypocreales

Perithecia bright colored, soft; innate or finally erumpent, paraphyses lacking; spores 1-celled, light, oblong.

Hyponectria buxi. Leaf Blight, leaf cast of boxwood.

KELLERMANNIA

Fungi Imperfecti, Sphaeropsidales, Sphaerioidaceae

Pycnidia globose, dark; spores hyaline, 2-celled.

Kellermannia anomala. Leaf Blight, general on nonarborescent forms of yucca and in Florida and California on arborescent forms.

Kellermannia sisyrinchi. Leaf Blight of blue-eyed grass.

LABRELLA

Fungi Imperfecti, Sphaeropsidales, Leptostromataceae

Pycnidia with a radiate shield, rounded, innate or erumpent; spores hyaline, 1-celled.

Labrella aspidistrae. Leaf Blight of aspidistra.

LEPTOSPHAERIA

Ascomycetes, Sphaeriales, Sphaeriaceae (or Myriangiales, Pseudosphaeriaceae)

Perithecia membranous, not beaked, opening with an ostiole, innate or finally erumpent, paraphyses present; spores dark, with several cells.

Leptosphaeria coniothyrium (imperfect stage *Coniothyrium fuckelii*). Raspberry Cane Blight, general on raspberry, dewberry, blackberry. The same fungus also causes common or stem canker of rose and apple canker.

On raspberry, brown, dead areas extend into wood, whole canes or single branches wilting and dying, often between blossoming and fruiting. Berries dry up; canes turn brittle. The fungus enters the bark through an insect wound or mechanical injury. Smutty patches on the bark are due to small olive conidia of the Coniothyrium stage, or to the larger dark ascospores.

Control. Cut out diseased canes as soon as noticed; remove fruiting canes right after harvest. The spray schedule for spur blight should suffice for cane blight. (See *Didymella applanata*.)

Leptosphaeria thomasiana. Cane Blight of dewberry, raspberry, in Pacific Northwest.

LOPHODERMIUM

Ascomycetes, Phacidiales, Phacidiaceae (or Hypodermataceae)

Fruiting body a hysterothecium, midway between an elongated perithecium and a compressed apothecium, hard, black, formed along needles, opening with a long narrow slit; paraphyses present, hooked at tip; spores filiform, septate or continuous. Most species are listed under Needle Cast.

Lophodermium piceae. NEEDLE BLIGHT, tar spot of fir, most severe on young specimens. Needles turn yellow, reddish, or brown and drop.

Macrophomina phaseoli. ASHY STEM BLIGHT, charcoal rot. See under Rots.

MICROPELTIS

Ascomycetes, Hemisphaeriales, Micropeltaceae

A single hymenium, or fruiting layer, covered with an open, reticulate, blue-green scutellum, radiate at margin; paraphyses present; spores with several cells, hyaline.

Micropeltis viburni. LEAF BLIGHT of viburnum.

MONILINIA (formerly *Sclerotinia*)

Ascomycetes, Helotiales, Sclerotiniaceae

Stroma a sclerotium formed in fruit by fungus digesting fleshy tissues and replacing them with a layer of broad, thick-walled, interwoven hyphae forming a hollow sphere enclosing core or seed of fruit, which has become a dark, wrinkled, hard mummy. Apothecia funnel-form or cupulate, rarely flat-expanded, some shade of brown; asci 8-spored; ascospores 1-celled, ellipsoidal, often slightly flattened on one side, hyaline. Conidia hyaline, 1-celled, formed in chains in grayish masses, sporodochia.

Monilinia azaleae. SHOOT BLIGHT of native or pinxter azalea (*Rhododendron roseum*), Apothecia are formed on overwintered mummied fruits in leaf mold under shrubs in moist places, ascospores infect leaves and succulent shoots when azalea is in full bloom. The conidial stage is common on young and developing fruits in late June and July, in New York State.

Monilinia johnsonii. LEAF BLIGHT, fruit rot, of hawthorn.

Monilinia (*Sclerotinia*) ***laxa.*** BLOSSOM BLIGHT, brown rot of apricot, sweet and sour cherry, peach, pear, plum in Pacific Coast States. Blossoms and twigs are blighted with much gum formation. Recently this fungus has been found in Wisconsin, causing blossom blight of sour cherries and there controlled with a copper-lime-monocalcium-arsenite dormant spray followed by a bloom spray of 6–8–100 bordeaux mixture.

In the West, *Monilinia laxa* is sometimes coincident with and confused with *M. fructicola* which causes brown rot of stone fruits generally. Both are discussed more fully under Rots.

Monilinia seaveri. TWIG BLIGHT, seedling blight, of sweet cherry.

MYCOSPHAERELLA

Ascomycetes, Sphaeriales, Mycosphaerellaceae

This genus contains more than 1000 species, many of which are destructive to plants and with conidial stages belonging to many form genera. Perithecia immersed in substratum, not beaked, usually with a papillate ostiole; paraphyses absent; spores 2-celled, hyaline. In many species spermatia are present in pycnidium-like spermogonia (Fig. 52.)

Mycosphaerella citrullina (Conidial stage *Phyllosticta citrullina*). GUMMY STEM BLIGHT, stem end rot, leaf spot on watermelon, muskmelon, summer squash, pumpkin.

Gray to brown dead areas in leaves are marked with black pycnidia; leaves may turn yellow and shrivel. Stem infection starts with a water-soaked, oily green area at nodes. The stem is girdled, covered with a dark exuded gum and vine wilts back to that point. Fruit rot is first gray, darkening to nearly jet-black. It may start in the garden, but more often infection is through the wound made at cutting.

Control. Start spraying with bordeaux mixture or dusting with copper-lime dust when vines are 2 to 3 feet long.

Mycosphaerella (*Ascochyta*) **pinodes.** PEA BLIGHT, foot rot, general on pea, sometimes on sweet pea, usually associated with *Ascochyta pisi* and *A. pinodella.* Stem is spotted with purple-black blotches and underground portion is blackened and shriveled. Young plants have blighted leaves, as well as stem and root rot. The disease is seedborne, most serious in cool wet springs.

Control. Use seed from clean fields; avoid land where blight has been present in previous three years; clean up refuse. Dusting seed with Spergon, Phygon or Zerlate will kill spores on surface, but not internal mycelium in cases where there has been direct seed invasion from the pod.

Mycosphaerella sequoiae. NEEDLE BLIGHT of redwood.

MYSTROSPORIUM

Fungi Imperfecti, Moniliales, Dematiaceae

Conidia dark, muriform; hyphae long, different from conidia.

Mystrosporium adustum. LEAF BLIGHT, INK DISEASE of bulbous iris. Black crusty patches make bulb scales look as if splashed with ink. Black streaks enlarge and penetrate inward, the bulb becoming shrunken, hard, black. If diseased bulbs are planted the foliage turns yellow, withers at an early age. The disease is serious in England and Holland and may appear here in imported bulbs.

Control. Examine bulbs carefully before planting; burn all showing signs of this ink disease.

MYXOSPORIUM

Fungi Imperfecti, Melanconiales, Melanconiaceae

Conidia hyaline, 1-celled, in discoid to pulvinate acervuli on branches.

Myxosporium diedicki. TWIG BLIGHT OF MULBERRY.

Myxosporium everhartii. Twig Blight of dogwood, and **M. nitidum** causing twig blight and dieback of native dogwood. Twigs should be pruned back to sound wood, trees fed and watered.

NEOPECKIA

Ascomycetes, Sphaeriales, Sphaeriaceae

Parithecia hairy, not beaked, formed on a mycelial mass; paraphyses present; spores 2-celled, dark.

Neopeckia coulteri. Brown Felt Blight, on pines only, otherwise similar to brown felt blight caused by Herpotrichia, a disease of high altitudes on foliage under snow.

OVULINIA

Ascomycetes, Helotiales, Sclerotiniaceae

Stroma a sclerotium, thin, circular to oval, shallowly cupulate formed in petal tissue but falling away; minute globose spermatia; apothecia of sclerotinia type, small, paraphyses septate with swollen tips; conidia large, obovoid, 1-celled except for basal appendage or disjunctor cell, borne singly at tips of short branches of mycelium forming a mat over surface of petal tissue (Fig. 22).

Ovulinia azaleae. Petal Blight, Flower Spot, very destructive to southern azaleas in humid coastal regions. Occasional on mountain laurel and rhododendron. Starting as a sudden outbreak near Charleston, S. C., in 1931, the disease spread rapidly north to Wilmington, N. C., down the coast to Florida and around the Gulf to Texas, which it reached by 1938. It was reported in California in 1941, Maryland in 1945, and Virginia in 1947. This is the most spectacular disease I have ever witnessed, with most of the bloom on all of the azaleas in a town blighting simultaneously and seemingly overnight under special weather conditions. The blight, however, does not injure the shrubs themselves, so that the loss is esthetic, and economic from the standpoint of tourist trade.

Primary infection comes from very small apothecia produced from sclerotia on the ground under shrubs, usually in January or February, occasionally as early as December. Spores shot into the air are carried by wind drift to low flowers of early varieties, initial spots being somewhat water-soaked. With continued high humidity, as in heavy fogs or dew as well as rain, conidia are produced over inner surface of petals and are widely disseminated by wind, insects, and splashed rain to other azaleas. Within a few hours small white spots appear all over petals of colored varieties, brown spots on white flowers, by the next day flowers have collapsed into a *slimy* mush, the bushes looking as if they had boiling water poured over them, and in a day or two more, if the weather remains humid, the small black sclerotia are being formed in the petals. Infected blooms do not drop normally but remain hanging in unsightly condition for weeks and months, a few even to the next season. Many of the sclerotia, however, drop out and remain in the litter on the ground ready to send up apothecia the next winter.

Both Indian and Kurume varieties are attacked, peak of infection coming with mid-season varieties such as Pride of Mobile or Formosa. In some seasons dry weather during early spring allows a good showing of azaleas before they

FIG. 34. Azalea Petal Blight, spots appearing in moist weather 6 to 12 hours after spores land on petals, each spot representing a separate infection court.

FIG. 35. Azalea Petal Blight, 24 hours after initial infection; at this stage petals are distinctly slimy to the touch.

blight in a rainy spell; in other years blight starts early and there is very little color unless azaleas are sprayed.

Control. Mulching and soil treatments to inhibit apothecial production seem to have no practical value. Spraying gives effective control if started on time, when early varieties are in bloom, and as mid-season azaleas show color, and repeated three times a week (twice a week gives some control) for three or four weeks. Dithane D–14 (at the rate of 1⅓ quarts per 100 gallons, plus 1 pound of 25% zinc sulfate, ½ pound hydrated lime, and 1 ounce spreader Triton B 1956, or 4 ounces Dreft) has given excellent control of azalea petal blight for several years, lengthening the season of the big azalea gardens by several weeks, the additional admission fees paying for the spraying program many times over. For small gardens special kits have been available with the different chemicals and specific directions for mixing and application. Easier to use, and apparently nearly as effective, are Dithane Z–78 at 1¼ pounds per 100 gallons (⅗ ounce to 3 gallons water) or Parzate at 1 pound per 100 gallons (½ ounce to 3 gallons). These two can also be used as 6% dusts. Opening petal surfaces must be protected at all times. The spray should be a very fine mist but applied from several directions to get adequate coverage. In some towns homeowners have banded together to hire custom spraying of their azaleas during the crucial period.

Fig. 36. Control of Azalea Petal Blight: left, Pride of Mobile sprayed with Dithane 3 times a week for about 3 weeks; right, same variety, unsprayed, 48 hours after a rainy spell. The bushes were adjoining, photographed on same date.

PELLICULARIA

Basidiomycetes, Agaricales, Thelephoraceae

Includes some species formerly assigned to Corticium, Hypochnus, and Peniophora. Hyphae stout, very short-celled; mycelium branching at right angles; basidia very stout, formed on a resupinate, cottony or membranous layer of mycelium. Some species have a sclerotial stage known as Rhizoctonia with the resting bodies made up of brown, thin-walled, rather angular cells.

Pellicularia filamentosa (*Corticium vagum*) perfect stage of *Rhizoctonia solani,* cause of Rhizoctonia rot of potatoes and damping-off and root rot of many plants. See under Rots.

A form of this Pellicularia, previously known as *Corticium microsclerotia,* causes Web and Leaf Blight of lima and kidney beans, also reported on fig, elder, hibiscus, hollyhock, tung oil, phoenix tree—from Florida to Texas. On beans many small, brown sclerotia and much weblike mycelium are found on stems, pods, and foliage. Infection starts with very small, circular spots that look water-soaked or scalded. These, enlarging to more than an inch across, become tan with a darker border, and are sometimes zonate. The whitish mycelium grows rapidly over the leaf blade, killing it, and spreading a web from leaf to leaf, over petioles, flowers, and fruit, in wet weather and at temperatures 70° to 90° F.; in dry weather growth is inconspicuous except on fallen leaves. The fungus is spread by wind, rain, irrigation water, cultivating tools and bean pickers; it survives in sclerotial form from season to season.

Control. Destroy infected plants, clean up refuse. Do not plant beans between June and September (in Florida) if blight has been present. Dust with copper-lime dust or spray with weak (2–4–100) bordeaux mixture.

Pellicularia (*Corticium*) **koleroga,** and probably including *Corticium stevensii.* THREAD BLIGHT of apple, azalea, casuarina, chinaberry, citrus, currant, dogwood, euonymus, elder, erythrina, fig, goldenrod, gooseberry, guava, hibiscus, Japanese honeysuckle, Japanese persimmon, ligustrum, lilac, magnolia, pear, pecan, pomegranate, pittosporum, quince, rose, sweet potato, soapberry, Virginia creeper, viburnum in the South—North Carolina to Texas.

The fungus winters as sclerotia on twigs and leaf petioles and in May and June produces thread-like mycelium which grows over lower surface of leaves, killing them and causing premature defoliation, although often dead leaves hang on the trees in groups, matted together by spider-weblike threads. Fruiting patches on leaves are first whitish, then buff-colored webs.

Control. On pecans remove lower limbs and trees that are too crowded, retaining high humidity. Two applications of 6–2–100 bordeaux mixture, as used in the schedule for pecan scab, will prevent thread blight. One application of a bordeaux-oil spray on citrus, ahead of the rainy season, seems satisfactory, and on figs a mixture of 1.5% copper sulfate, 1% lime and zinc arsenite, and 0.25% monocalcium arsenite with 1% fish-oil has given fairly satisfactory results.

Pellicularia rolfsii, name given to perfect stage of *Sclerotium rolfsii,* which see, cause of southern blight, found on climbing fig.

PESTALOTIA

Fungi Imperfecti, Melanconiales, Melanconiaceae

Conidia in acervuli; fusiform, with 3 to 5 cross-walls, median cells colored, end cells hyaline, with short stalk at basal cell and a crest of two or more simple or branched setae or appendages from apical cell (Fig. 22). Species are weak parasites or saprophytes; some are treated under leaf spots.

Pestalotia funerea. NEEDLE BLIGHT of giant sequoia; TIP BLIGHT of chamaecyparis and retinospora; LEAF BLIGHT of juniper; twig blight of cypress, baldcypress, yew, and arborvitae. The fungus is saprogenic on dead and dying tissue and also is a weak parasite infecting living tissue through wounds under moist conditions. It appears in sooty pustules on leaves, bark, and cones. Spores are 5-celled with a crest of 3 to 5 setae.

PHACIDIUM

Ascomycetes, Phacidiales, Phacidiaceae (or Hypodermataceae)

Apothecia innate, concrete above with the epidermis and splitting with it into lobes; spores 1-celled, hyaline.

Phacidium abietinellum. Needle Blight of balsam fir.

Phacidium balsameae. Needle Blight of balsam fir, New England States, white and alpine fir in Northwest.

Phacidium infestans. Snow Blight on fir and young pines in Northeast, also on arborvitae and spruce; variety *abietis* on white and alpine fir in Northwest. A native fungus, it is most damaging in nurseries, attacking foliage under the snow. The needles turn brown, with a covering of white mycelium which shows just as snow melts. In late summer and fall brown to nearly black disc-like apothecia appear on underside of browned needles, and ascospores are spread by wind, primary infection taking place in fall. Additional infection occurs in late winter when mycelium grows out under the snow from diseased to dormant, healthy needles.

Control. Spray nursery beds with dormant-strength lime sulfur in late fall; remove infected trees; dip new stock in lime sulfur before planting.

PHLEOSPORA

Fungi Imperfecti, Sphaeropsidales, Sphaerioidaceae

One of the conidial forms linked with Mycosphaerella as perfect stage. Spores filiform, needle-shaped, in incomplete pycnidia on leaves.

Phleospora adusta. Leaf Blight of clematis.

PHOMA

Fungi Imperfecti, Sphaeropsidales, Sphaerioidaceae

Pycnidia leathery to carbonaceous, with ostiole; spores hyaline, 1-celled; parasitic on seed plants, chiefly on stems and fruits, but rarely on leaves (Fig. 42).

Phoma conidiogena. Boxwood Tip Blight. Ashy-gray necrotic areas at leaf tips, with pycnidia on both leaf surfaces.

Phoma fumosa. Twig Blight, occasional on maple.

Phoma mariae. Twig Blight, Japanese honeysuckle.

Phoma piceina. Twig and Needle Blight, Norway spruce, may cause defoliation and sometimes death of forest trees.

Phoma strobiligena, on cone scales of Norway spruce.

PHOMOPSIS

Fungi Imperfecti, Sphaeropsidales, Sphaerioidaceae

Pycnidia without ostiole, membranous to subcarbonous, smooth, innate, finally erumpent; spores hyaline, 1-celled, of two types—one ellipsoidal, the other long, filamentous and hooked at the upper end, or sickle-shaped (Fig. 22).

Phomopsis ambigua, conidial stage of *Diaporthe eres.* Twig Blight of pear, widespread.

Phomopsis diospyri. Twig Blight of native persimmon.

Phomopsis japonica. Twig Blight of kerria.

Phomopsis juniperovera. Nursery Blight, cedar blight, canker, on red-cedar and other junipers, cypress, chamaecyparis, Japanese yew (*Cephalotaxus*) arborvitae, giant sequoia, and redwood. This disease occurs in virulent form in coniferous nurseries and in ornamental plantings from Connecticut to Florida and Minnesota to Alabama.

Tips of branches turn brown with progressive dying back until a whole branch or even a young tree is killed. Trees over five years are not so seriously injured. Spores produced in quantity in pycnidia on diseased twigs and branches ooze out in little tendrils in moist weather to be spread by wind, rain, and workers. Entrance is through unbroken tissue as well as wounds, with overhead irrigation in a nursery a predisposing factor. A large amount of nursery stock can be blighted in a very short time, with epidemics particularly serious in the Middle West.

Control. Have seedbeds well-drained; water by ditch irrigation rather than overhead; remove and burn diseased seedlings early in season; keep seedbeds away from older cedar trees; do not use cedar branches or needles for mulching. Weekly spraying of older trees with Special Semesan, bordeaux, or Fermate is said to be rather effective, but arduous and expensive.

Phomopsis kalmiae. Leaf Blight of Mountain-Laurel. Circular, brown, often zonate areas on leaves frequently start near edge or tip, gradually enlarging and coalescing until nearly the whole blade is involved and sometimes working down the petiole to cause a twig blight.

Control. Remove blighted leaves, clean up fallen leaves; spray with bordeaux mixture, or less conspicuous fixed copper sprays, three or four times from June to September.

Phomopsis vexans. Phomopsis Blight of Eggplant, or fruit rot, general in field and market, especially in the South. Destruction is often complete, with every above-ground part affected. Seedlings rot at ground level. First foliage spots appear on leaves near ground. They are definite, circular, gray to brown areas with light centers and numerous black pycnidia; leaves later turn yellow and die. Stem cankers are constrictions or light gray lesions. Fruit lesions are pale brown, sunken, marked by many black pycnidia arranged more or less concentrically. Eventually the whole fruit is involved in a soft rotting or shriveling. Spores winter on seed and in contaminated soil.

Control. Use disease-free seed, preferably northern grown, in clean seedbeds. Or treat seed in hot water at 122° F. for 30 minutes, then dry and dust with Semesan or Arasan. Spray with 6–6–100 bordeaux mixture starting when plants are established in field and continuing weekly for five to seven applications; or use a copper-rotenone dust, or a fixed copper spray at 3 pounds per 100 gallons. Black Beauty is very susceptible, but resistant varieties are in the making.

PHYLLOSTICTA

Fungi Imperfecti, Sphaeropsidales, Sphaerioidaceae

Pycnidia with ostiole, in spots in leaves; spores 1-celled, hyaline. This genus is practically the same as Phoma except for location, the latter being chiefly found on twigs. More species listed under Leaf Spots.

Phyllosticta batatas. LEAF BLIGHT OF SWEET POTATO, occasional New Jersey to Florida, more prevalent in South, but not often important enough for control measures. Numerous white spots on leaves are bordered with a narrow, reddish zone; pycnidia are numerous and spores appear in tendrils.

Phyllosticta lagerstroemeria. TIP BLIGHT of crape myrtle.

Phyllosticta pteridis. TIP BLIGHT of fern. Leaves lose green color; spots are ash gray with purple brown margins, and numerous black pycnidia in center. A very weak bordeaux mixture has been suggested for control, but if overhead watering is avoided spraying may not be necessary.

PHYSALOSPORA

Ascomycetes, Sphaeriales, Mycosphaerellaceae

Perithecia papillate, immersed in substratum but without well-defined stromata; paraphyses present; spores 1-celled, hyaline. Most species cause rots. See under Rots.

Physalospora dracaenae. TIP BLIGHT, leaf spot of dracaena. Diseased areas are shrunken and straw colored. Disease starts on lower leaves, with center leaves dead only at tips. Remove infected foliage.

Physalospora gregaria (conidial stage *Phyllostictina hysterella*). TWIG BLIGHT of Taxus or yew.

Physalospora obtusa. CANE BLIGHT OF ROSE, also black rot of apple and dieback and canker of many plants. See under Cankers and also under Rots.

PHYTOPHTHORA

Phycomycetes, Peronosporales, Pythiaceae

This is a most important genus containing many species causing destructive blights, cankers, and rots. The name, which means "plant destroyer," was given in 1876 for the potato late blight fungus.

Sporangia, formed successively on sporangiophores which are slender, sparsely branched hyphae emerging from stomata, germinate either by a germ tube or by zoospores; sexual spore an oospore.

Phytophthora cactorum. PHYTOPHTHORA BLIGHT OF LILAC. Blossoms and succulent growing tips are blighted and turn brown; suckers are killed back 4 or 5 feet. Blight is most severe in wet springs when shrubs are crowded, shaded, and improperly pruned. The same fungus causes a canker, foot rot, and dieback of rhododendron and other plants, and is considered again under Cankers.

Control. Avoid planting lilacs and rhododendrons close together. Prune each year for air circulation and to remove dead twigs. If disease has been serious in previous springs, spray with bordeaux mixture.

Phytophthora capsici. PHYTOPHTHORA BLIGHT OF PEPPER, fruit rot of pepper, tomato, cucumber; first found in New Mexico, in 1918, injuring Chilli peppers.

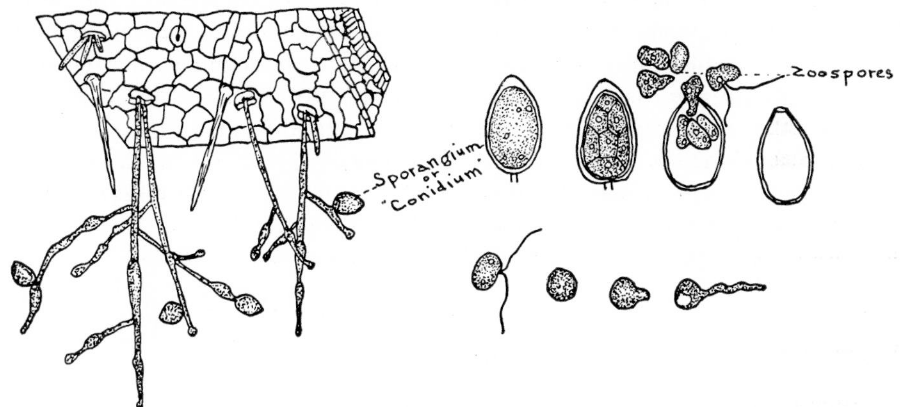

FIG. 37. Late Blight of Potatoes. Sporangiophores of *Phytophthora infestans* emerging from leaf, bearing sporangia, sometimes called conidia, which germinate by zoospores.

Girdling stem cankers at ground level cause death of whole plant, and at base of branch cause wilting and dieback of that portion. Fruit infection starts with a small, water-soaked spot, bleaching to straw color, turning dark from secondary fungi. The fungus grows into the seed from the fruit. Fruit infection sometimes reaches epiphytotic proportions. In 1947 nearly 60 per cent of green fruits were infected in New Mexico fields with pods drying and mummifying in a few days. Wet soil and high temperatures encourage the blight.

Control. Avoid overirrigation; have land well-leveled.

Phytophthora erythroseptica. LEAF BLIGHT OF PINK AND GOLDEN CALLA. Leaf is wilted and distorted. Petiole black and soft.

Phytophthora infestans. LATE BLIGHT OF POTATO AND TOMATO, general on potato in the Northeast, in Middle Atlantic and North Central States, sometimes in Gulf and Western States; on tomato in humid regions and seasons.

Here is a pathogen which has not lost its destructive virulence with passage of time. In 1946, a whole century after potato blight caused the famous Irish famine, tomato blight devastated tomatoes along the eastern seaboard, both in home gardens and canning fields.

The potato went to Europe from South America shortly before 1600, seemingly leaving its pathogens at home. For 200 years potatoes throve in Europe as the main source of carbohydrate food, but in August, 1845, the *Gardener's Chronicle* reported, "A fatal malady has broken out amongst the potato crop. On all sides we hear of destruction. In Belgium the fields are said to have been completely desolated. There is hardly a sound sample in Covent Garden Market." The editor went on to describe the decay and to say, "As to cure for this distemper there is none. One of our correspondents is today angry with us for not telling the public how to stop it; but he ought to consider that Man has no power to arrest the dispensations of Providence. We are visited by a great calamity which we must bear" (and in 1946 American gardeners were blaming the editor for lack of information on tomato blight).

In 1845 the weather was one of continued gloom and fog, with below-average temperatures. The *Gardener's Chronicle* editor was sure blight was due to potatoes being overladen with water. The Rev. M. J. Berkeley disagreed. He insisted blight was due to a fungus, with the weather contributing to the spread of a moisture-loving parasite. The argument raged, for this was long before Pasteur and his germ theory, and the first time anyone believed a fungus could be the cause and not the consequence of plant disease. A French scientist, Montagne, named the fungus *Botrytis infestans,* but the first really good description of it was published by Berkeley, and it remained for the German deBary, in 1876, to actually prove the pathogenic nature of the fungus and to erect the new genus Phytophthora to include it.

Meanwhile the disease was making history. The loss of the potato crop in 1845 and 1846 killed off a million people and caused another million and a half to emigrate, the first Government Relief program was instigated, and the English Corn Laws were repealed with a change to a policy of free trade and unbounded expansion of commerce.

LATE BLIGHT ON POTATO

Symptoms. After blossoming, large, dark green, water-soaked spots appear on leaves in wet weather, first on lower leaves. As the spot enlarges the center is shriveled, dry, dark brown to black and a downy, whitish growth appears on the underside of leaves. Similar lesions are formed on stems and petioles, and there is a characteristic strong odor as tops are blighted. On tubers first symptoms are small brown to purple discolorations of skin on upper side, changing to depressed pits when tubers are removed from soil and put in storage. On cutting through the potato a reddish brown dry rot is seen.

Life History. The primary cycle starts with infected tubers which have harbored mycelium in the dry rot over winter. Infection comes either from piles of old cull potatoes or seed pieces. As the shoots grow they are invaded systematically, but the fungus finally fruits by sending sporangiophores out through the stomata on lower leaf surfaces. These swell at the tips into ovoid bodies, sporangia, after which they branch and produce successively more sporangia. The latter can function as conidia, putting out a germ tube, but more often are differentiated into a number of swarmspores or zoospores with cilia enabling them to swim about after they are splashed by rain to another leaf. Eventually they stop swimming and send a germ tube in through the leaf cuticle or a stoma. Blighting follows rapidly, with first symptom in five days or less from infection and the fungus fruiting again in a whitish layer on underside of leaves.

Tubers with a thin covering of soil can be infected by swarmspores washing down onto them, but they can also be infected if dug early in moist weather while tops are still green. Swarmspores can remain viable in soil for some weeks while awaiting favorable conditions. Oospores, the sexual spores, are apparently not required in the life cycle, for they are not found with potatoes grown in the field, although they have been produced in culture and found on sterile soil and straw.

Weather Relations. This is a disease entirely dependent on weather conditions. Normally temperature and moisture are right for an epiphytotic about two years out of five. Zoospores are produced only in cool weather, 60° F. and lower, although they invade leaves most rapidly at higher temperatures. Since they are swimming spores, rain is needed. A cool, wet July is usually followed by blight in August and September.

Control. 1. Use certified or selected tubers for seed.

2. Resistant varieties, long worked for, are now available. Empire, Placid, Virgil, Ashworth, Potomac, Menonimee, Sebago, Sequoia can be used in different sections. They are not actually immune and sometimes a more virulent strain of the pathogen is built up from lesions on almost blight-free plants.

3. Destruction of dump piles to prevent an occasional diseased sprout is an important sanitation measure. Another is the killing of tops with weedkillers such as Sinox or Ammate to prevent infection at early digging. Home gardeners can well content themselves with early varieties that mature before blight makes much headway.

4. Spraying or dusting is still the chief control measure with 8–8–100 bordeaux mixture the standard for many years. It is now recognized, however, that in a blight-free year bordeaux-sprayed potatoes may have less yield than those unsprayed, and much testing is in progress with fixed coppers and organic materials. Dithane D–14 has given good results for several years from control and yield standpoint; Parzate is about the same; Phygon gives excellent control but greatly reduces yield and delays maturity. A copper-zinc-chromate complex is being tried with fair results.

LATE BLIGHT ON TOMATO

Although there are apparently two strains of *Phytophthora infestans,* a potato and a tomato strain, each is capable of infecting the other host. Ordinarily blight starts with potatoes in midsummer; when the fungus moves over to tomatoes it has to go through several cycles to build up a strain virulent enough to produce general blighting, and by that time the tomato season is nearly over. Hence before 1946 it seemed rather profitless to spray tomatoes. Now we know that it is possible for the tomato strain to winter in potato tubers and be ready to inflict damage to tomatoes with the first crop of zoo-

Fig. 38. Late Blight on Tomatoes; 1946 devastation in a home garden.

spores produced on potato sprouts. Conversely, tomato seedlings brought up from the South and planted near potato fields can start an epidemic of potato late blight.

The 1946 tomato blight saga—the one that awakened eastern gardeners to the fact that plant disease could be as important to home gardeners as to farmers—started in Florida late in November, 1945. By January the disease was extremely destructive in tomato seedbeds and it continued so intermittently whenever temperatures ranged from 60° to 70° F. and relative humidity was nearly 100 per cent for more than 15 hours. Evidence indicated spores could be windborne for as many as 30 miles. The wave of late blight went west to Alabama, taking 75% of the early crop and rolled up the Atlantic Coast, reaching the Carolinas in May, Virginia and Maryland in June, again taking about 75% of the early crop. It rolled into Delaware and New Jersey in July, but did not reach peak epidemic form until after an extended rainy period in August, and ended in Massachusetts in August and September.

In 1947 a blight forecasting service was started, based on weekly graphs prepared by plotting daily the cumulative rainfall and mean temperatures and aided by reports from key pathologists in various states. If conditions are unfavorable for blight we can all save time and money by eliminating useless spraying.

Symptoms. On seedlings small, dark spots on stems or leaves are followed by death within two or three days. On mature plants blight starts with dark, water-soaked leaf spots and large, dark brown spots on fruit, with most of the leaves soon hanging lifeless, and fruit rotting on ground.

Control. Bordeaux mixture applied to young tomato plants will either prevent fruit setting or cause stunting. It can be used after blossoming, or a fixed copper can be substituted. Some spray schedules alternate Zerlate for early blight with copper sprays for late blight. Dithane D–14 plus zinc sulfate, Dithane Z–78, and Parzate give good control of late blight without reducing yield. Proprietary dust mixtures containing 7% copper are available for small gardens.

Phytophthora syringae. CITRUS BLIGHT, also on lilac, but chiefly a European disease on this host, the more common blight on lilac being due to *P. cactorum.* On citrus trees leaves have semi-transparent spots similar to frost damage. Other Phytophthora species may be present with *P. syringae* to cause brown rot of fruits. See under Rots for control.

On lilacs large irregular leaf patches have a lighter zone at margin. There may be some defoliation.

PIRICULARIA

Fungi Imperfecti, Moniliales, Moniliaceae

Spores hyaline with several cross-walls, obclavate (reverse club-shaped) to pear-shaped.

Piricularia grisea. LEAF BLIGHT on creeping bentgrass.

PYRENOCHAETA

Fungi Imperfecti, Sphaeropsidales, Sphaerioidaceae

Pycnidia innate, finally erumpent, hairy or setose; conidiophores branched, conidia hyaline, 1-celled.

Pyrenochaeta phlogis. STEM BLIGHT OF PHLOX.

REHMIELLOPSIS

Ascomycetes, Sphaeriales, Sphaeriaceae

Perithecia single, globose, rupturing irregularly, asci in fascicles, no paraphyses; spores hyaline, 2-celled.

Rehmiellopsis balsameae. TIP BLIGHT, NEEDLE BLIGHT OF BALSAM FIR, on native balsam fir in northern New England, and on ornamental firs in southern New England and New York. Infection is in spring with needles of current season shriveled, curled, and killed, often with a dieback of terminal or lateral shoots and sometimes cankers at base of infected needles.

Control. Satisfactory control on ornamental firs has been obtained by three sprays, at 12-day intervals, of a 8–8–100 bordeaux mixture with casein spreader, the first application being made as new growth starts.

ROSELLINIA

Ascomycetes, Sphaeriales, Sphaeriaceae

Perithecia separate, superficial from the first, carbonous, not beaked, ostioles papillate, spores dark, 1-celled, with a small groove.

Rosellinia herpotrichioides. Needle Blight of hemlock. Needle-bearing portions of twigs become intensely covered on underside with a grayish brown mycelial mat, with black perithecia produced in this mat in abundance. Ovoid, hyaline conidia are formed on Botrytis-like conidiophores.

SCLEROPYCNIUM

Fungi Imperfecti, Sphaeropsidales, Excipulaceae

Pycnidium somewhat like a hysterothecium, rather long and cracked or cleft; spores hyaline, 1-celled.

Scleropycnium aureum. Leaf Blight of mesquite.

SCLEROTINIA

Ascomycetes, Helotiales, Sclerotiniaceae

Apothecia arising from a tuberoid sclerotium which, though formed free on aerial mycelium, is sometimes enclosed in natural cavities of suscept or host, as in hollow stems of perennials; interior (medulla) white with gelatinous matrix lacking, dark rind completely enveloping sclerotium. Conidia are wanting but very small spermatia (formerly called microconidia) are formed on spermodochia borne free or enclosed in special cavities. Apothecia some shade of brown, cupulate to funnel-form, or maturity shallow saucer-shaped to flat expanded; ascospores hyaline, 1-celled, ovoid.

Sclerotinia camelliae. Camellia Flower Blight, long known in Japan, first noted in California in 1938, confirmed in Georgia in 1948, although probably there several years previously, and in Oregon in 1949.

Floral parts only are affected, infection taking place soon after tips of petals are visible in opening buds or later. Few to many small brownish specks on expanding petals soon involve the whole flower which turns brown and drops. In early stages darkened veins are prominent diagnostic symptoms. When flowers are resting on moist earth spermatia are produced on petals in shiny black masses. Hard, dark brown to black sclerotia formed at base of petals frequently unite into a compound structure simulating petal arrangement. This compound sclerotium may be an inch or more in diameter.

Sclerotia lie dormant on ground or in mulching materials until the next winter when, from January on, after wet periods with rising temperature, they produce one to several apothecia on long or short stipes (stems) with brown saucerlike discs ¼ to ¾ inch across. Spores, discharged forcibly, are carried by wind currents to flowers, thus completing the cycle. No conidia

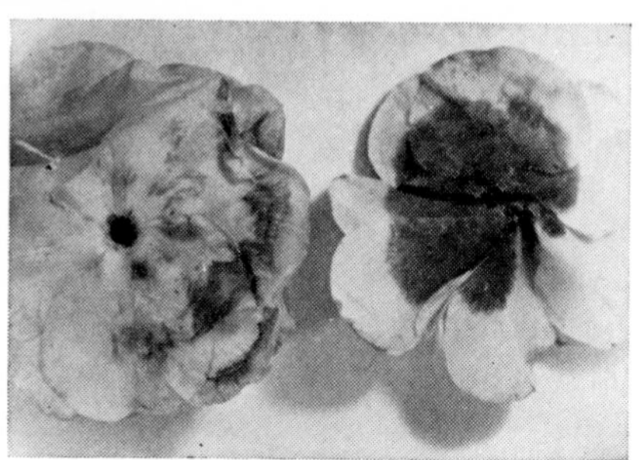

Fig. 39. Camellia Flower Blight; darkening of veins is an early diagnostic symptom.

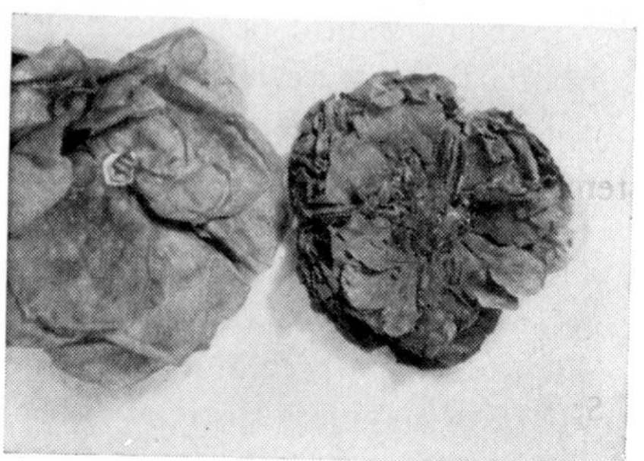

Fig. 40. Camellia Flower Blight; at left, late stage of infection, with bumps showing start of sclerotial formation; at right, dark, compound sclerotium being formed in center of blighted flower.

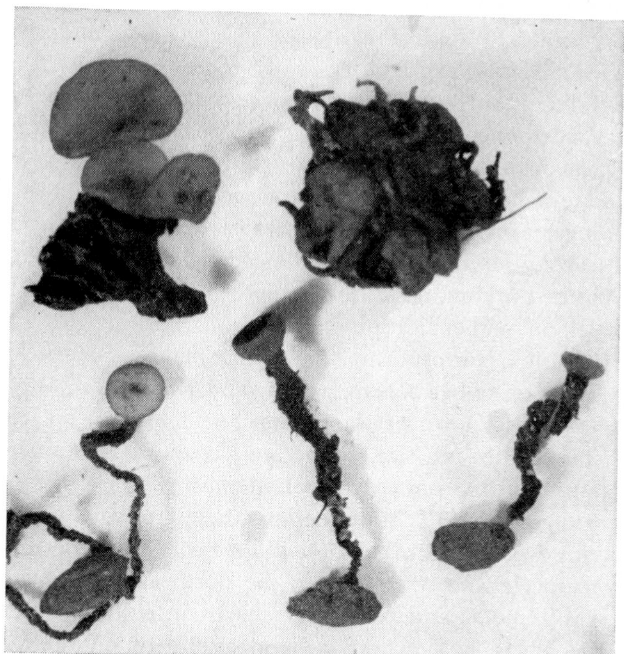

Fig. 41. Sclerotia of *Sclerotinia camelliae,* simple and compound, producing apothecia (about natural size).

are known and hence no secondary infection, but ascospores seem to reach flowers at top of tall shrubs as readily as those near the ground.

Control. With no secondary stage, picking off and destroying *every* infected flower should give complete control, and a fair job of sanitation does reduce the blight. Treating the ground with Fermate has inhibited apothecial production. Spring application of manure, peat, etc., which stimulate apothecial development should be avoided. Flower spraying has not been tried. Where it occurs the disease is sufficiently devastating to cause concern to gardeners in blight-free areas. In ordering camellias from a state where blight is known it should be stipulated that the shrubs be taken up bare-rooted and repacked in fresh peat moss to prevent sclerotia from hitchhiking along. Some southern states are now enforcing such precautions with quarantine measures.

Sclerotinia sclerotiorum. Shoot and Twig Blight of lilac, grape, and malvaviscus. This is an ubiquitous fungus that is more commonly considered a stem rot of its many suscepts. See under Rots.

SCLEROTIUM

Fungi Imperfecti, Mycelia Sterilia

Spores are wanting and there is merely a resting body made up of a rounded mass of hyphae. This is a form genus, and species are removed as soon as they are connected up with some reproductive stage.

Sclerotium rhizodes. White Tip Blight of grass. See under Snowmold.

Sclerotium rolfsii. Southern Blight, crown rot, of hundreds of plants. Fruits and vegetables include Jerusalem artichoke, avocado seedlings, bean, beet, carrot, cabbage, cucumber, eggplant, endive, lettuce, melon, okra, onion, garlic and shallot, pea, peanut, pepper, potato, rhubarb, strawberry, sweet potato, turnip, and watermelon. Ornamentals are too numerous to list in entirety but include ajuga, ageratum, amaryllis, azalea, caladium, calendula, campanula, canna, carnation, cosmos, China aster, chrysanthemum, dahlia, delphinium, daphne, duranta, gladiolus, some grasses, hollyhock, hydrangea, iris, jasmine, lemon verbena, lupine, marigold, morning-glory, myrtle, narcissus, orchids, phlox, pittosporum, rose, rose-mallow, rudbeckia, scabiosa, sedum, sweet pea, star-of-bethlehem, violet, and zinnia.

Sclerotium rolfsii is known as the mustard-seed fungus, its sclerotia being small, round, tan bodies the size, shape, and color of mustard seed. A very similar fungus responsible for crown rot of most of the same plants in the North is *Sclerotium delphinii.* Many believe these are two strains of the same organism. Having worked with both for many years I am loath to relinquish the idea of two species, for *S. delphinii,* the northern form, has much lower temperature requirements and produces, at least in culture, much larger and redder sclerotia. There is, however, a good argument on the other side. In 1945 the perfect stage of *S. rolfsii,* which heretofore had been produced only rarely and in culture, was found in nature on a climbing fig leaf. Single spore cultures were made from this perfect stage (named *Pellicularia rolfsii*) and some were typically *Sclerotium rolfsii,* some *S. delphinii,* and some intermediate.

Whatever its classification the southern blight strain is particular about its temperature, optimum growth being at 85° to 90° F. with little growth below 65°, although the sclerotia survive much cooler temperatures unharmed. Hence, it is much less of a problem on winter crops in the South. It also is somewhat fussy about its soil, shunning organic mixtures high in nitrogen and growing best in rather poor, sandy soil.

The first sign of southern blight is the formation of white wefts of mycelium at the base of the stem, spreading up in somewhat fan-shaped fashion and sometimes spreading out on the ground in wet weather. The sclerotia formed in the wefts are first white, later turning reddish tan or light brown. They can be numerous enough to form almost a crust over the soil for several inches around the stem, or they may be somewhat sparse and scattered. See Fig. 87.

In the white stage droplets of liquid are sometimes formed on the sclerotia. Oxalic acid in this liquid is assumed to kill plant cells in advance of the fungus hyphae. This means that the fungus never has to penetrate living tissue and explains why so many different plants succumb so readily to southern blight. Fruits touching the ground, as well as vegetables with fleshy roots like carrots and beets, and plants with bulbs or rhizomes, like onions, narcissus and iris, seem particularly subject to blight.

Control. The few really resistant plants are field crops like wheat, oats, corn, and sorghum. Sterilizing soil with chloropicrin, which is tear gas and sold as Larvacide, will kill most sclerotia; Formalin, using 1 part of the commercial dilution to 100 parts of water and applying at 3 gallons per square foot is effective but arduous; methyl bromide and ethylene dibromide offer promise, but all these soil disinfectants can be used only on fallow soil, not near living plants.

Home gardeners can best rely on watching for the disease and removing blighted plants with surrounding soil as soon as noticed, going down several inches to get all the sclerotia. Pouring a 1 to 1000 solution of bichloride of mercury over the hole and crowns of surrounding plants will prevent spread of mycelium but will not kill all sclerotia that may be left in soil. Dusting plants with sulfur will slow up mycelial growth. Increasing the organic content of the soil may help. Nitrogenous fertilizers reduce sclerotium rot on sugar beets and ammonium nitrate has been helpful with annual larkspur grown commercially.

SEPTORIA

Fungi Imperfecti, Sphaeropsidales, Sphaerioidaceae

Pycnidia black, globose, innate, then erumpent; conidia hyaline, long threadlike or filiform, with many cells (Fig. 22).

Septoria apii and **S. apii-graveolentis.** Late Blight of Celery, general on celery, also on celeriac. Both species singly or together produce the disease known as late blight, first reported in Delaware in 1891 and since causing much crop destruction, one California county reporting half a million dollars loss from celery blight in 1908, and Michigan a million in 1915. It was not until 1932 that it was known there were two distinct species involved.

Early symptoms are similar. Large leaf spot, due to *S. apii,* starts as a light yellow area which soon turns brown and dies. Spots are up to ¼ inch in diameter. Small black pycnidia appear two or three days from the start of collapse.

In small leaf spot, due to *S. apii-graveolentis* and considered the most destructive, pycnidia appear at first sign of chlorotic spotting or even before, and are often outside the indefinite margin of the spot which is very small, not over 2 mm. If infection is severe spots fuse, leaf turns brownish black and rots. Leaf stalks may also be infected. Pycnidia winter on seed and in plant refuse in garden and compost.

A single pycnidium of the small spot fungus has been shown to have an average of 3675 spores and a single leaf spot as many as 56 pycnidia. Thus there are enormous amounts of inoculum to be spread by rain, wind, insects, men, and tools. Some years ago on Long Island, where celery was intercropped with spinach, it was found that workers spread blight spores on their sleeves as they cut the spinach in early morning dew. And there is a case on record where a man walked through his own blighted celery before taking a diagonal path across his neighbor's healthy field. In a few days blight showed up along that diagonal path.

Control. Seed should be treated unless it is more than two years old. Place in cheesecloth bags and (1) dip in calomel suspension, 1 ounce to 1 gallon of water, for 2 to 3 minutes while it is kept agitated; or (2) immerse in formaldehyde, 1 tablespoon commercial strength to 2 quarts of water, for 25 minutes, then rinse 10 minutes and dry; or (3) suspend in hot water held accurately at 118° F. for 30 minutes. Use crop rotation; do not grow near where celery was grown the year before. Start spraying or dusting program in the seedbed when plants are only half an inch tall. Sulfur added to coppers or Dithane seems to increase effectiveness, decrease injury. For a 8–4–100 bordeaux or 4 pounds of a fixed copper, add sulfur at rate of 8 pounds per 100 gallons, or replace about half the lime with sulfur in a copper-lime dust. Phygon and Parzate have given good control in some tests; when mixed with sulfur there may be an unsightly residue.

Septoria leucanthemi. Leaf Blight, blotch on chrysanthemum, shasta daisy, ox-eye daisy. The generally destructive Septoria on chrysanthemums is *S. chrysanthemi.* See under Leaf Spots.

Septoria petroselini. Leaf Blight of Parsley, similar to late blight of celery.

SEPTOTINIA

Ascomycetes, Helotiales, Sclerotiniaceae

Stroma a definite, small, thin, elongate to angular black sclerotium maturing in host tissue after it has fallen to ground. Apothecia shallow cup-shaped, stipitate; spores hyaline, ovoid, 1-celled. Conidial stage a Septogloeum, spores hyaline, elongate, one or more cross-walls, formed on sporodochia.

Septotinia podophyllina. Leaf Blight of May-apple, found in leaves and stalks of this plant only.

SPHAERULINA

Ascomycetes, Sphaeriales, Sphaeriaceae

Perithecia innate or finally erumpent, not beaked, paraphyses and paraphysoids lacking; spores hyaline, several-celled.

Sphaerulina polyspora. Twig Blight of sourwood, oxydendron.
Sphaerulina taxi. Needle Blight of yew.

SPORODESMIUM

Fungi Imperfecti, Moniliales, Dematiaceae

Hyphae very short, conidia ovoid-oblong, dark, muriform with many cells.

Sporodesmium maclurae. Leaf Blight of osage-orange.

Sporodesmium scorzonerae. Salsify Leaf Blight. Leaves have many circular spots, varying from pinpoint to ¼ inch in diameter, brown with red borders. Leaves die or whole top; roots are small and unsalable. Fungus winters as mycelium and in spore form.

SYSTREMMA

Ascomycetes, Dothideales, Dothideaceae

Asic in locules in an elongate stroma which is erumpent and superficial at maturity; spores light brown, 2-celled. Conidial stage *Lecanosticta* with brown conidia, having 1 to 3 cross-walls, formed on a conidial stroma resembling an acervulus.

Systremma acicola. Brown Spot Needle Blight of Pine, on southern pines, most serious on longleaf pine. The name of the fungus and its classification has been much in dispute. Known in conidial stage since 1876 it was long considered a Septoria, but at the time that a connection was made with an ascospore stage, the imperfect state was more correctly placed in Lecanosticta. *Scirrhia acicola,* the name for the perfect stage given in 1939, has been inacceptable to some workers because that genus has hyaline ascospores, so now the fungus is finally (?) placed in Systremma which allows the colored spores.

Most injurious on seedlings, needle blight can also injure large trees. Small, gray-green spots on needles turn brown and form a narrow brown band, the needle tips dying. Three successive seasons of brown spot kill longleaf seedlings. The fungus is more severe on trees in unburned areas because of accumulation of inoculum.

Control. Spray seedlings in plantations with 8–8–100 bordeaux mixture every two weeks from May to October or November.

THELEPHORA

Basidiomycetes, Agaricales, Thelephoraceae

Fruiting body leathery, somewhat funnel-form, hymenium smooth to roughened but not ribbed; spores 1-celled.

Thelephora terrestris. SEEDLING BLIGHT, SMOTHER. The fungus mycelium ramifies in the soil and the leathery fruiting body grows up around stem of a seedling conifer or deciduous tree, smothering or strangling it without being parasitic on living tissue. The disease most often occurs in crowded stands in nurseries, but the damage is seldom important.

TRYBLIDIELLA

Ascomycetes, Helotiales

Apothecia opening by a wide cleft; spores dark, cylindric, with several cells.

Tryblidiella rufula. TWIG BLIGHT on citrus.

VOLUTELLA

Fungi Imperfecti, Moniliales, Tuberculariaceae

Hyphae compacted into hairy sporodochia, ciliate at margin; conidia 1-celled, light, on simple conidiophores (Fig. 22).

Volutella buxi. BOXWOOD LEAF BLIGHT. Pinkish spore pustules on leaves and twigs. Leaves often turn straw colored. See further under Cankers.

Volutella pachysandrae (perfect stage *Pseudonectria pachysandricola*) PACHYSANDRA LEAF AND STEM BLIGHT. Large areas of leaves turn brown to black, and also portions of stem, in wet weather showing numerous pinkish spore pustules. The blight is most serious when pachysandra has been injured or kept too moist by leaves falling into bed, or too crowded.

Control. Spraying once or twice with bordeaux mixture gives excellent control if severely blighted plants have been removed before treatment. Keep pachysandra thinned and sheared back periodically.

BLOTCH DISEASES

Diseases known as blotch are usually characterized by irregular, superficial, small or large necrotic areas on leaves or fruit. The technical description of many of the genera listed here is given under Blights.

Alternaria porri. PURPLE BLOTCH OF ONION, garlic, shallot. Small, white, circular to irregular spots increase to large purplish blotches, sometimes surrounded by orange to salmon bands, on leaves and flower stalks. Leaves may turn yellow and die beyond the spots and the girdled flower stalks die before seeds mature. Brown muriform spores form a dusky layer on spots.

Control. Rotate crops; spray with copper or Dithane.

Cercospora concors. POTATO LEAF BLOTCH. An unimportant disease consisting of small blackened dead areas and yellowing of leaflets.

Cercospora purpurea. AVOCADO BLOTCH, Cercospora spot, considered the most important avocado disease in Florida with no commercial variety completely resistant. Leaf spots are angular, brown to chocolate brown, scattered and distinct, less than 1/16 inch, or coalescing to irregular patches. Grayish spore patches can be seen with hand lens on either side of spots, and successive crops of spores are borne in moist periods throughout the year.

Fruit spots are 1/4 inch or less in diameter, brown to dark brown, irregular, sunken, with cracked surface, grayish spore tufts. Lesions are confined to rind so fruit is not affected but the cracks furnish entrance to anthracnose and other decay organisms. The fungus winters in leaves and seems to be progressively more abundant.

Control. Three applications of 6–6–100 bordeaux mixture or basic copper sulfate at 6 pounds per 100 gallons, or cuprous oxide at 1½ pounds per 100: (1) between May 1 and 15; (2) 4 to 5 weeks later, in June; (3) 4 to 5 weeks later than (2).

CLADOSPORIUM

Fungi Imperfecti, Moniliales, Dematiaceae

Conidiophores somewhat decumbent, branched; conidia dark, 1 to 4 cells, solitary or in chains of two or three.

Cladosporium herbarum. LEAF BLOTCH OF LILAC, cosmopolitan but probably secondary following blights.

Cladosporium paeoniae. LEAF BLOTCH OF PEONY, red stem spot, or measles. Leaf and stem spots are purplish or brownish red, raised on stems, up to 4 mm. long, small specks on leaves. Small, reddish spots are also present on floral bracts and petals. The disease is widely distributed in commercial plantations and may destroy value of flowers for cutting on occasion.

Control. Cut down all tops in fall, as for Botrytis blight. Spraying the ground in spring with Elgetol before growth starts gives good control in commercial fields.

GLOEODES

Fungi Imperfecti, Sphaeropsidales, Leptostromataceae

Pycnidia dimidiate, having a radiate cover over only the top half, on a dark subicle, or mycelial crust; pseudoparaphyses present; conidia hyaline, 1-celled.

Gloeodes pomigena. Sooty Blotch of Fruit, apple, crabapple, blackberry, pear and citrus, in east and central states down to the Gulf, rare in West. Fruit may be infected by heavy spore dissemination from pycnidia on twigs of various wild trees—persimmon, prickly-ash, white ash, bladdernut, hawthorn, red elm, sassafras, maple, sycamore, willow. On apples clusters of short, dark hyphae make a superficial thallus on the cuticle, which appears as a sooty brown or black blotch 1/4 inch in diameter. Numerous spots may coalesce to cover the apple, a condition known as cloudy fruit. The lesion is superficial, not much affecting the fruit flesh, but reducing grade and market value. On citrus the fungus does not penetrate the rind and spots can be removed by a gentle rubbing.

Control. Use a fungicide in summer codling moth sprays on apple, especially the early June spray.

GUIGNARDIA

Ascomycetes, Sphaeriales, Mycosphaerellaceae

Perithecia immersed in substratum, stroma lacking, mouths papillate; spores hyaline, unequally 2-celled, with lower cell cut off just before maturity. See under Rots for the fungus causing black rot of grapes.

Guignardia aesculi. Horse-Chestnut Leaf Blotch, general on horse-chestnut and Ohio buckeye, sometimes on red and yellow buckeye. Large reddish brown blotches in foliage are usually surrounded by a yellowish area. Numerous pinpoint black dots, pycnidia, distinguish blotch from scorch due to drouth. Petioles often have oval, reddish spots. In a rainy season there is a great deal of secondary infection from spores spread by wind and rain. Blotches appear on nearly every leaflet with much defoliation. Primary infection in spring comes from ascospores developed in perithecia in fallen, overwintered leaves.

Control. Rake up and burn fallen leaves. Spraying with bordeaux mixture, or with lime sulfur 1 to 50 has been recommended, starting soon after buds open in spring and repeating twice at two-week intervals. Recent test spraying indicates that Zerlate or Parzate gives fair control. Nursery trees can be dusted with sulfur.

Mycosphaerella dendroides (conidial stage *Cercospora halstedii*). Pecan Leaf Blotch, on pecan in South, on hickory East and South. This is a foliage disease of nursery and orchard trees. Olive green velvety tufts of conidiophores and spores appear on under surface of mature leaves in June or July (in Florida) and yellow spots over these areas show on upper surface of leaves. Black, pimple-like perithecia appear in the tufts about midsummer and unite to form shiny, black blotches. In nursery trees defoliation may be serious, starting with basal leaves and progressing upward, but the disease is of little consequence to orchard trees unless they have been weakened by overcrowding, borer attack, or other cause. The fungus winters in old, fallen leaves.

Control. Rake up fallen leaves, or plow under; spray with low-lime bordeaux mixture, 6–2–100, in June or rely on the spray schedule for scab.

Mycosphaerella diospyri. Leaf Blotch on Japanese persimmon.

Mycosphaerella (*Cercospora*) **lythraceae.** Leaf Blotch, Fruit Spot of pomegranate.

Phyllosticta congesta. Leaf Blotch of garden plum.

Phyllosticta solitaria. Apple Blotch on apples and crabapples most serious in the South, especially in Ozark section of Missouri, Arkansas, Oklahoma, and Texas. Leaf spots are very small, round, white with a single black pycnidium in center of each. Larger, elongate lesions form on veins and midribs. Leaves do not turn yellow but drop prematurely if spots are numerous. Fruit blotches are brown, irregular, feathery at margin, studded with numerous pycnidia, and afford entrance to secondary decay organisms; sometimes fruit lesions develop into deep cracks. Bark cankers are lens-shaped to oval, smooth, light-colored with many black pycnidia. The fungus winters in pycnosclerotia on bark cankers or mycelium in bark, sometimes in fallen leaves or fruit. Spores are discharged from pycnidia only after heavy rains and at warm temperatures, and well-fertilized trees seem most susceptible. Infected nursery stock is responsible for much spread of apple blotch.

Control. Secure healthy nursery stock. Spray with Fermate (replacing bordeaux mixture in some states) ; use more resistant varieties—Grimes Golden, Jonathan, Stayman Winesap, and Winesap.

Septoria macropoda. Purple Leaf Blotch, general on lawn grasses. Irregular blotches on blades contain flattened to round, light brown pycnidia.

BROOMRAPES

Broomrapes are leafless herbs of the family Orobanchaceae and are parasitic on roots of other plants. There are 130 or more species, mostly from north temperate regions, but few have any garden importance. Lacking chlorophyll, or green coloring matter, broomrapes cannot manufacture their own food. The seeds germinate in the soil, produce a filiform plant body which grows into the ground, penetrating crown or root of host plant and forming a more or less tuberous enlargement, from which aerial flowering shoots arise. Such flowering shoots may be almost naked, clothed with a few scattered rudimentary leaves or covered with conspicuous, overlapping, scale-like leaves.

Orobanche sp. is reported on strawberry in Washington, **C. ludoviciana** on tomato in Wyoming; and **O. ramosa** on tomato in California.

CANKERS AND DIEBACKS

A canker is a localized lesion or diseased area often resulting in an open wound and usually on a woody structure. Starting as a definite necrotic spot it may girdle cane, stem or tree trunk, killing the water-conducting tissue so that the most prominent symptom becomes a dieback. When twigs and branches die back from the tip it may be a blight with the pathogen directly invading that area, or it may be the secondary effect of a canker some distance below.

ALEURODISCUS

Basidiomycetes, Agaricales, Thelephoraceae

Hymenium resupinate, of one layer, with projecting spinose or short-branching cystidia (swollen sterile cells); spores hyaline. Facultative parasite on trees.

Aleurodiscus acerina. BARK PATCH, widespread on maple.

Aleurodiscus amorphus. CANKER OF BALSAM FIR. Cankers are formed on main stems of saplings, which are sometimes killed, but the fungus is also widespread as a saprophyte on dead bark of firs and other conifers. Cankers center around a dead branch, are narrowly elliptical with a raised border and the dead bark is covered with a light-colored fruiting layer of the fungus.

Aleurodiscus oakesii. SMOOTH PATCH OF WHITE OAK. Irregularly circular, smooth, light gray sunken areas in bark vary from several inches to a foot across. The fungus is confined to dead bark and trees are not injured.

APIOPORTHE

Ascomycetes, Sphaeriales

Perithecia in a black, carbonous stroma; spores 2-celled, hyaline.

Apioporthe anomala. CANKER, Twig Blight of hazelnut.

Apioporthe apiospora. TWIG CANKER, Dieback of elm.

ASCOSPORA (or *Plectosphaerina*)

Ascomycetes, Sphaeriales, Sphaeriaceae

Perithecia with a subicle, paraphyses lacking; spores 2-celled, hyaline.

Ascospora ruborum (imperfect stage *Hendersonia rubi*) CANE SPOT, DIEBACK, on dewberry, raspberry.

ATROPELLIS

Ascomycetes, Helotiales, Tryblidiaceae

Apothecia black, sessile or with short stalk; asci clavate, with longer, hairlike paraphyses; spores needlelike to slightly club-shaped, hyaline, 1-celled.

Atropellis pinicola. PINE BRANCH AND TRUNK CANKER on western white sugar and lodgepole pines in Pacific Northwest. Branches are girdled and killed but not the trees. Perennial cankers are smooth, elongated, flattened depressions covered with bark, in which small black apothecia, 2 to 4 mm. in diameter, appear.

Control. Remove dead and weak branches; fertilize to promote vigor.

Atropellis piniphila (*Cenangium piniphilum*), CANKER on lodgepole and ponderosa pines on Pacific Coast and in Southwest, rarely on western white pine and on eastern pines. Trees five to twenty-five years old are damaged by deformation of main stem and branches. Infection is at branch whorls. Cankers are elongated, flattened depressions covered with bark and copious resin. Apothecia have short stalks, are black with brownish discs, 2 to 5 mm. across.

Atropellis tingens. BRANCH AND TRUNK CANKERS of native and exotic hard pines from New England and Lake States to Gulf States. Slash pine saplings are most susceptible. Smaller branches are girdled and perennial target cankers are formed on larger branches and main stems. Cankers persist many years, but extension stops after about ten years.

BOTRYOSPHAERIA (See under Blights)

Botryosphaeria ribis, saprophytic on dying tissue, and parasitic var. **chromogena.** CANKER, DIEBACK of at least 50 woody plants, including apple, avocado, fig, Japanese persimmon, hickory, pecan, pyracantha, quince, redbud, rhododendron, willow. Also a CANE BLIGHT of currant and rose (see under Blights).

On redbud, sunken, oval cankers nearly girdle branches, the fungus entering through wounds and dead and dying twigs. On rhododendron there is a leaf spot and dieback similar to that caused by Phytophthora except that the surface is roughened by protruding fruiting bodies.

Cankers on twigs, larger branches, and trunks of willow may kill trees in a few years. Trunk lesions are very small, 1/4 to 1/2 inch, and numerous, or large, with fissured bark, from the union of several small cankers.

Control. Prune and burn dead twigs and heavily infected branches, painting wounds with a disinfectant followed by tree paint; avoid injuries.

CALICIOPSIS

Ascomycetes, Dothideales, Coryneliaceae

Stroma lobed, each lobe containing a single locule which is finally wide open; perithecia stalked; asci on long slender stalks, spores dark, 1-celled.

Caliciopsis pinea. PINE CANKER, on eastern white pine and other species, also on Douglas fir. Cankers are sharply depressed areas in bark, reddish brown and smoother than rest of bark, up to several inches in diameter. Small, globose, clustered black pycnidia, and stalked perithecia, looking like slender black bristles, arise from stroma in cankered bark. Disease is chiefly serious on suppressed saplings.

CHONDROPODIUM

Fungi Imperfecti, Sphaeropsidales, Sphaerioidaceae

Chondropodium pseudotsugae. BARK CANKER of Douglas-fir. This is a superficial canker with outer layers of bark killed over small circular to elliptical areas, in which pycnidia project as short, blunt black spines. Trees are not noticeably injured.

CONIOTHYRIUM

Fungi Imperfecti, Sphaeropsidales, Sphaerioidaceae

Pycnidia separate, innate, conidiophores obsolete or none; spores small, colored, 1-celled (Fig. 42).

Coniothyrium fuckelii (imperfect stage of *Leptosphaeria coniothyrium*). STEM CANKER OF ROSE, COMMON CANKER, Graft Canker, widespread on rose. Also cause of raspberry cane blight (see Leptosphaeria under Blights), sometimes associated with apple rots, with peach cankers attributed to arsenical injury, and stem canker of Virginia creeper.

Of the three species of Coniothyrium which cause rose cankers, *C. fuckelii* is by far the most common. Any plant part may be affected and pycnidia

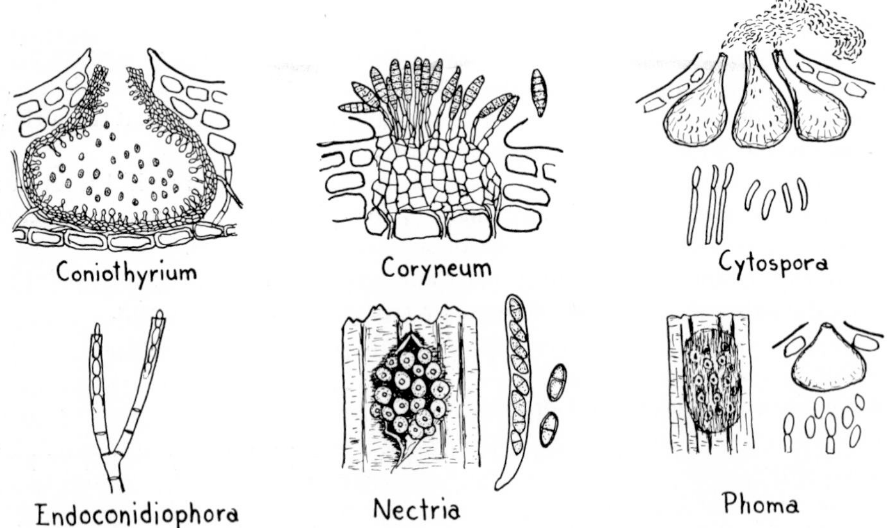

FIG. 42. Spore Formation of some Canker Fungi. *Coniothyrium,* small dark spores on short conidiophores in pycnidium; *Coryneum,* dark, septate spores in acervulus; *Cytospora,* sausage-shaped spores in valsoid pycnidia expelled in cirrhi; *Endoconidiophora,* spores formed inside of conidiophores; *Nectria,* 2-celled bright ascospores in reddish perithecia clustered on bark; *Phoma,* hyaline spores in pycnidia formed in spots on bark.

have even been found within black spot lesions on leaves, but this is primarily a cane disease, starting as a red or yellow spot on bark, drying out and turning brown as it increases in size, with the epidermis somewhat wrinkled and perhaps rupturing irregularly over sooty masses of very small, olive-brown spores. The stem may be girdled, with dieback to that point.

Stem cankers are found around insect punctures, thorn pricks and leaf or thorn scars, abrasions caused by tying, but in garden roses most infection is near cut ends of stems where a stub has been left above a leaf axil or bud. Roses cut properly, *close* to a bud, seldom develop this canker. A rose stub usually dies back to the first node and the fungus is a weak parasite starting most readily in dead wood. When a cut is made at a node it is quickly callused over, a good defense against wound fungi.

Graft canker is a disease of roses under glass, starting at the union of stock and scion in the warm, moist propagating frame and continuing in a large amount of dead wood when plants are removed to the greenhouse bench.

Control. Care in cutting is most important. Make all cuts at a node, not only in spring pruning but in cutting flowers during the season. Cut just barely above a bud or leaf axil and slant the cut in the direction of the bud. Prune out cankered and dying stems whenever noticed.

Coniothyrium rosarum. GRAFT CANKER OF ROSE. There is some doubt as to whether this is a separate species or a form of *C. fuckelii.* Having measured spores of the type specimen, deposited in the Kew Herbarium, I feel that there probably are two different species but that many cases of graft canker are caused by the common canker fungus.

Coniothyrium wernsdorffiae. BRAND CANKER OF ROSE. A rather rare but very serious disease. The pathogen was named in Germany in 1905 but not reported in this country until 1925, although subsequently shown to have been present in Canada in 1912, and in Pennsylvania and Minnesota in 1914 and 1916. In 1926 a severe epiphytotic appeared at Ithaca, N. Y., in the Cornell rose garden, infecting about 90% of the climbers so seriously that canes had to be cut to the ground. Since then it has been reported from a few other states, but in some instances may have been confused with common canker.

Small dark reddish spots on canes enlarge and acquire a more or less definite reddish brown or purple margin, contrasting sharply with the green of the cane. The center of the spot turns light brown as the cells die and little longitudinal slits appear over the developing pycnidia. Spores are olive brown like those of *C. fuckelii,* but they are nearly twice the size and released through those definite slits in the epidermis, instead of being spread in a smutty mass under the epidermis. Cankers formed under the winter protection of soil are black when roses are first uncovered in spring, which explains the name *Brandfleckenkrankheit,* meaning fire-spot disease.

C. wernsdorffiae is a cold temperature fungus infecting rose canes during late winter and early spring under the winter covering and entering through

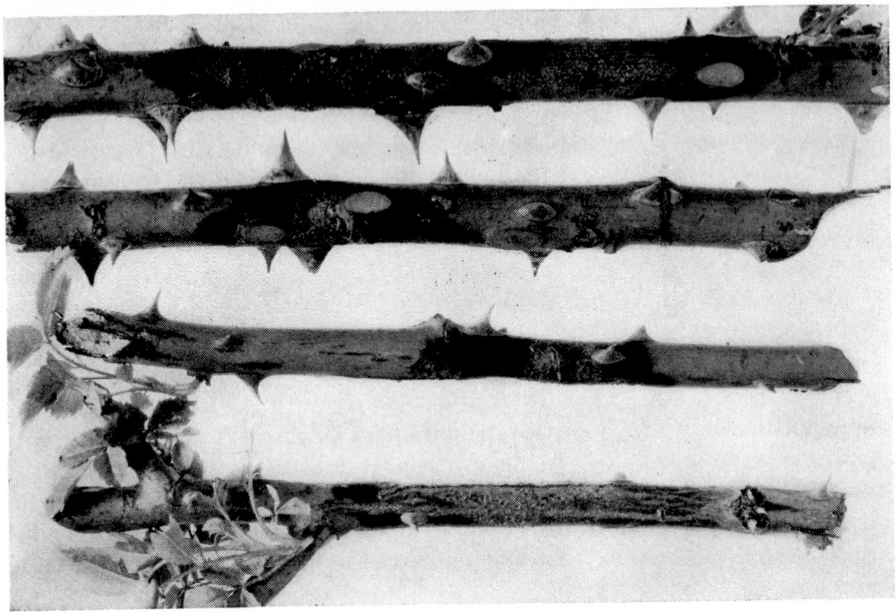

FIG. 43. Brand Canker of Rose; pycnidia breaking through slits in bark.

insect wounds, thorn scars, scratches, and occasionally through dormant buds. During a four-year investigation at Ithaca I found no infection on canes not hilled with earth or other moist cover over winter and no natural infection during the summer.

Control. Omit the usual winter protection of soil or other materials which keep canes moist. If brand canker is a problem, just fasten canes of climbers down near the ground, uncovered, and hope for the best. Loss from winter injury will be less than from the disease. Cut out diseased canes carefully.

CORYNEUM (See under Blights)

Coryneum cardinale. CORYNEUM CANKER OF CYPRESS, Bark Canker of cypress and also incense cedar, common juniper and oriental arborvitae. This disease, since its discovery in 1927, has been gradually exterminating Monterey cypress in most parts of California and is also serious on Italian cypress. Twigs, branches, whole trees turn sickly, lose their leaves, and finally die.

The fungus attacks living bark and cambium, girdling twig and branch. Cankers appear first at base of lateral twigs; they are slightly sunken, dark, resinous, rough with black spore pustules. Conidia have dark median cells, five cross-walls. They are spread by tools in nursery stock, by wind and rain, perhaps birds and insects. Infection appears first in upper parts of trees, usually in spring in moist weather when yellowing and browning of foliage together with gummy ooze at the cankers form conspicuous symptoms.

Control. Drastic surgery, removing wood well below infected parts and spraying foliage heavily with bordeaux mixture helps some, but with heavy infection the price of saving healthy trees is the removal and destruction of all diseased specimens. California citizens, threatened with the loss of the famous native stands of Monterey cypress at Point Lobos and Cypress Point, have voluntarily destroyed their own plantings by the thousands.

Coryneum foliicolum. TWIG CANKER, Fruit Rot, widespread on apple, affecting twigs, foliage and fruit.

CRYPTODIAPORTHE

Ascomycetes, Sphaeriales, Sphaeriaceae

Like Diaporthe but without blackened zones in substratum; spores hyaline, 2-celled.

Cryptodiaporthe aculeans (*Sporocybe rhois*). DIEBACK, CANKER of sumac.

Cryptodiaporthe castanea. DIEBACK, CANKER of Asiatic chestnut, widespread, chiefly on seedlings or larger trees in poor sites. Canker starts as a brown discoloration of bark of trunk, limb, or twig, often girdling twig and then invading larger branch. Leaves on girdled branches wilt without yellowing, turn brown, and die. Bark splitting over callus formation at edge of diseased area forms a pronounced canker. Conidia, 2-celled, fusoid, are formed in pustules in bark and beaked perithecia are formed in groups by midsummer.

Control. Maintain vigor; plant on well-drained, fertile soil. Prune out diseased portions several inches below affected area.

Cryptodiaporthe salicina. TWIG AND BRANCH CANKER of willow.

CRYPTOMYCES

Ascomycetes, Phacidiales, Phacidiaceae

Apothecia effuse, splitting irregularly; paraphyses present; spores hyaline, 1-celled.

Cryptomyces maximum. BLISTER CANKER, on common and purple osier.

CRYPTOSPORELLA

Ascomycetes, Sphaeriales, Melanconidiaceae

Perithecia in a circle in a stroma, with long necks converging in a common canal; spores 1-celled, hyaline; conidia borne on surface of stroma.

Cryptosporella umbrina. BROWN CANKER OF ROSE, a widespread and serious rose disease, first noted in Virginia in 1917 but known from herbarium specimens to have been present since 1903. The fungus was first placed in Diaporthe because of occasional 2-celled spores.

Symptoms are most noticeable on canes, starting with very small purplish spots, but with the center very soon turning white inside a reddish purple margin. Many small spots may be grouped on a single cane. During the winter, and especially on portions of canes covered with earth, cankers or girdling lesions are formed, often several inches long with tan centers and purplish borders, the coloring most striking when moist earth is first removed in spring. In moist weather the surface of these large cankers is often covered with

FIG. 44. Brown Canker of Rose; whitish spots with dark reddish borders.

yellow spore tendrils from pycnidia just under the bark, or there may be extrusion of asci from perithecia, also in tendrils.

Leaf spots are small purple specks or larger dead areas, cinnamon buff to white bordered with purple, with black pycnidia in center. Spots at margins of leaflets are subcircular. On blossoms outer exposed petals may have cinnamon-buff spots without purple border; buds are sometimes blighted.

Infection is either through wounds or uninjured tissue.

Control. The best time to take care of brown canker is at spring pruning. Take out every diseased cane possible. A dormant lime-sulfur spray, 1 to 10 dilution, immediately after pruning kills spores which may have been spread in the process and possibly burns out the fungus in initial lesions. The regular summer spraying or dusting program using either copper or sulfur largely prevents new summer infections. In my own garden, Fermate seems to have been less successful, but it is too early for a definite conclusion.

Cryptosporella viticola. DEAD-ARM DISEASE OF GRAPE, Branch Necrosis, widespread, especially in Northeast, serious in Illinois. Small, angular spots with yellowish margins and dark centers are formed on leaves, leaf stems, canes, and flower-cluster stems, sometimes growing together into large brown areas with numerous darker spots, sometimes splitting to form diamond-shaped cankers. Shoots are occasionally stunted and killed. Lesions on cluster stems advance into fruit late in the season, causing rotting, those on the canes kill buds, and sometimes the fungus kills the arm, whence the name, dead-arm disease.

Control. Cut out and burn all infected wood. A promising dormant spray, applied not earlier than 3 weeks after pruning, is sodium arsenite solution, containing an equivalent of 3 pounds of arsenic trioxide per 100 gallons of water. This may be injurious under certain conditions.

CRYPTOSPORIUM

Fungi Imperfecti, Melanconiales, Melanconiaceae

Conidia formed in acervuli, filiform, curved, dark.

Cryptosporium minimum. Canker on rose.

CYLINDROCLADIUM

Fungi Imperfecti, Moniliales, Moniliaceae

Conidiophores dichotomously branched; spores hyaline, 2-celled.

Cylindrocladium scoparium. Crown Canker of Rose, apparently confined to greenhouse roses. The cane above and at the union of stock and scion is most commonly attacked, the bark darkening into a black water-soaked punky region, cankers often girdling the cane but not causing death. The plants produce fewer and inferior blooms. The fungus lives in the soil and usually enters through pruning or other wounds in presence of abundant moisture.

Control. Change soil or sterilize before replanting with fresh stock. Wash benches with formaldehyde or boiling water before refilling.

CYTOSPORA

Fungi Imperfecti, Sphaeropsidales, Sphaerioidaceae

Cosmopolitan species, imperfect stages of Valsa. Conidia hyaline, 1-celled, allantoid (slightly curved with rounded ends, or sausage-like), expelled in cirrhi or tendrils from pycnidia in a valsoid stroma (Fig. 42).

Cytospora annularis. Canker, Dieback of ash, on twigs and branches.

Cytospora chrysosperma. (*Valsa sordida*) Cytospora Canker on poplar, aspen and cottonwood, and willow, occasionally found on mountain-ash, maple, cherry, and elder. Cankers form on trunks and large branches, most often on trees of low vigor. Bark is discolored in more or less circular areas, sapwood is reddish brown. In old cankers exposed wood is surrounded by layers of callus tissue. In spring, in moist weather, yellow or reddish spore tendrils are extruded from small, pimplelike pycnidia in dead bark. Perithecia are found infrequently on aspen, arranged circularly around a black or grayish disc, flask-shaped with necks pushing through the bark. Twigs and small branches may die back without a definite canker being formed. The fungus can be present on healthy trees, becoming pathogenic only when trees are weakened by neglect, drought, being pollarded, or other causes. Entrance is through wounds.

Control. Use care in pruning, avoid pollarding; maintain high vigor by planting in good land and watering in drought periods. Rio Grande cottonwood is resistant; Valley cottonwood, preferred in semi-arid West, is somewhat resistant.

Cytospora kunzei. CYTOSPORA CANKER OF SPRUCE and TWIG BLIGHT. See under blights.

Cytospora nivea. CANKER, DIEBACK of poplar and willow, similar to that caused by *C. chrysosperma* but only occasional.

Cytospora pinastri. BARK AND TWIG CANKER of balsam fir.

Cytospora sambucicola. BRANCH CANKER on elder.

DASYSCYPHA

Ascomycetes, Helotiales, Helotiaceae

Apothecia stalked, white and hairy on the outside with a bright disc; paraphyses filiform; asci inoperculate (without a lid); spores elliptical to fusoid.

Dasyscypha agassizi, common on blister-rust lesions of white pine; saprophytic on dead branches.

Dasyscypha calycina, on larch, fir, ordinarily a saprophyte, can be a weak parasite, occasional on blister rust cankers.

Dasyscypha ellisiana. CANKER OF DOUGLAS-FIR and pine, in eastern United States. This is a native fungus on twigs and branches of native pines, also on introduced pines and on basal trunk and branches of older Douglas-fir. Bark on trunk may be infected for 10 to 15 feet, with copious resin flow and numerous swellings, but it is not killed. Apothecia are short-stalked, covered with white hairs on outside and with disc orange to chrome yellow; ½ to 2 mm. in diameter.

Dasyscypha pini. DASYSCYPHA CANKER OF PINES, on western white, whitebark, and eastern white pines at high altitudes, or on poor sites. Branches up to 4 inches in diameter can be girdled and killed, but cankers on trunk and large limbs persist for years without retarding growth. Infection is through needles or fascicles when trees are young. Apothecia are cinnamon brown and hairy on the outside, with an orange to yellow disc, 2 to 4 mm. in diameter. Remove trees with trunk cankers early in forest stands.

Dasyscypha pseudotsugae. CANKER, on Douglas-fir. Open cankers, 2 to 3 inches long, swollen, on suppressed saplings.

Dasyscypha resinaria. CANKER of Balsam fir, found only in one locality in Minnesota. Cankers are swollen at base of branches; younger stems are girdled and killed.

Dasyscypha willkommii. EUROPEAN LARCH CANKER. A European disease discovered in eastern Massachusetts in 1927 on diseased nursery stock from Great Britain. Infected trees were removed and the fungus not found again until 1935, near original locations. Perennial branch or trunk cankers are flattened depressions but swollen on the flanks and opposite side of the stem. Neighboring bark is usually somewhat cracked, dark with heavy exudation of resin. Cup-shaped apothecia are 3 to 6 mm. across, white hairy with orange to buff disc, and a very short stalk. Young trees may be killed, but older trees usually survive. Frost wounds are a contributing, but apparently not essential, factor. So far infection in this country has been confined to European larch with slight damage to Japanese larch, although the latter is relatively resistant. Eastern larch is susceptible but not yet attacked.

Control. Remove all trees showing cankers promptly; continue periodic inspection.

DERMATEA

Ascomycetes, Helotiales, Dermateaceae

Apothecia small, brownish to black with a circular opening innate at first, on a stromoid base, rupturing host tissue at maturity; spores 1-celled, hyaline, globose to oblong.

Dermatea acerina. BARK CANKER of maple, occasional.

Dermatea balsamea. TWIG CANKER of hemlock.

Dermatea livida. BARK CANKER of redwood.

DIAPORTHE (See under Blights)

Diaporthe eres. CANKER, DIEBACK of English holly in Northwest. The fungus name is a species complex which may include a Diaporthe on rose petals and a peach constriction disease.

Diaporthe oncostoma. CANKER, DIEBACK of black locust.

Diaporthe pruni. TWIG CANKER on black cherry and **D. prunicola** on American plum.

DIDYMELLA (See under Blights)

Didymella sepincoliformis. DIEBACK of rose.

DIPLODIA (See under Blights)

Diplodia sp. ROSE DIEBACK, sometimes after drouth and other contributing factors. In Texas the disease is most evident in fall, progressing on roses in storage or overwintering in ground. Canes die from tip downward, often starting in the flower stem. Diseased wood and bark turns brown or black, is somewhat shriveled. Pycnidia are found in dead canes.

Control. Improve general vigor; use fungicides as for black spot.

Diplodia camphorae. Canker, Dieback of camphor-tree.

Diplodia infuscans. Ash Canker and dieback, northeastern states.

Diplodia juglandis. Dieback, widespread on branches of walnut.

Diplodia natalensis. Stem Canker of prickly-ash; Dieback of citrus twigs. The fungus is the imperfect stage of *Physalospora rhodina,* cause of citrus stem-end rot.

Diplodia sophorae. Dieback of pagoda tree.

Diplodia sycina. Canker, Dieback of fig.

DISCELLA

Fungi Imperfecti, Sphaeropsidales, Excipulaceae

Pycnidia cupulate or discoid; spores 2-celled, hyaline.

Discella carbonacea. Twig Canker of willow.

DOTHICHIZA

Fungi Imperfecti, Sphaeropsidales, Sphaerioidaceae

Pycnidia innate, finally erumpent; conidiophores lacking, conidia hyaline, 1-celled.

Dothichiza populea. Poplar Canker, European poplar canker, or Dothichiza canker of poplar, widespread as a branch and trunk canker, found sporadically in eastern United States and Canada since 1915 but probably introduced from Europe on black poplar before that. Lombardy poplars are most susceptible but hosts include black and eastern cottonwoods, balsam, black and Norway poplars. Japanese poplar seems rather resistant. Young trees in nurseries are most injured, the cankers frequently starting around wounds.

Cankers are first slightly sunken areas, often at base of twigs and limbs, with diseased bark a shade darker than healthy; they become elongated, paralleling the long axis of the stem; bark is killed to the cambium with a brown discoloration of sapwood. After June, development ceases until the following spring. If a stem has been completely girdled, it dies; if not, callus formation goes on through the summer often growing over the canker and causing bark swelling. The next year the canker starts growth again until finally unhealed cracks appear in bark and the tree dies. If water sprouts grow out below dead limbs, they too die.

Pycnidia appear in bark as hemispherical pustules, pinhead size, with spores extruded in cream or amber tendrils, drying to brown. They are washed by rain, probably carried by birds and insects to wounds in wood and to leaves.

Control. Destroy infected stock in nurseries and plantations; do not move stock, even though apparently healthy, from a nursery where disease is known, to a disease-free location. If pruning is necessary to cut out limbs with small cankers, sterilize tools between cuts and treat wounds. Avoid other pruning and wounding so far as possible. Spray nursery trees with bordeaux mixture when trees are expanding and repeat after heavy rains. A dormant lime-sulfur spray may be helpful.

DOTHIORELLA

Fungi Imperfecti, Sphaeropsidales, Sphaerioidaceae

Pycnidia in a stroma; innate; spores small, hyaline, 1-celled, fusoid.

Dothiorella sp. CANKER OF LONDON PLANE, first noted in New York City in 1947. Infected trees have sparse, undersized foliage and narrow, longitudinal cankers on trunk and branches, varying from 1 to 4 inches wide and often extending from ground level to branch top; bark rough, deeply fissured, inner bark brown, dry, sapwood only superficially discolored. Minute pycnidia in dead bark are not numerous except under ideal weather conditions. Entire branches may wilt and die back.

Control. Since the disease is still limited in distribution, all confirmed cases should be promptly eradicated.

Dothiorella fraxinicola. BRANCH CANKER of ash.

Dothiorella (now *Deuterophoma*) **ulmi.** DIEBACK, WILT of elm. See under Wilts.

ENDOCONIDIOPHORA

Ascomycetes, Sphaeriales, Ceratostomataceae

Perithecia beaked; spores hyaline; 1-celled; rod-like endoconidia formed inside tube-like conidiophores and extruded endwise; ovoid brown conidia. This genus is closely related to Ceratostomella and sometimes still so called (Fig. 42).

Endoconidiophora sp. CANKER STAIN OF PLANE, London Plane Blight, on London plane, also American plane or sycamore. The fungus is closely related to, perhaps a strain of *Endoconidiophora fimbriata* causing black rot of sweet potato.

This serious disease started as a killing epidemic in the Philadelphia area about 1935, destroying city shade trees by the thousands there and in Baltimore, and up to Newark, N. J., in the next few years and also extending south to Wilmington, N. C., and southwest to Vicksburg, Miss.

Trees show sparse foliage, smaller leaves, and elongated sunken regions on trunks and larger branches. Cross sections through cankers reveal blue black or reddish brown discoloration of wood, usually in wedgeshaped sectors. First year cankers may not be more than 2 inches wide and a yard or so long but they widen annually, girdling and killing the trees in three to five years. Several cankers coalescing around the trunk kill more quickly. Once infection starts a tree is doomed.

Ascospores and the two types of conidia are produced in moist springs. They may be spread by rain a short distance, but most dissemination is by man in pruning operations, the spores even being spread in sawdust falling into tree paint (and capable of surviving in ordinary tree wound dressing). Infection is solely through wounds, large or minute.

Control. Do not try to save trees where trunk has been invaded, but diseased branches may sometimes be removed, cutting at least 3 feet from infected area. Do not prune unless absolutely necessary and then only in winter, December 1 to February 15, when trees are practically immune. Do not paint pruning cuts or wounds unless a gilsonite varnish is used, containing 0.2% phenylmercury nitrate (¼ ounce per gallon of varnish). Sterilize pruning tools between cuts.

FUSICOCCUM

Fungi Imperfecti, Sphaeropsidales, Sphaerioidaceae

Pycnidia in a valsoid stroma; conidia 1-celled, hyaline, oblong to rod-shaped, on filiform conidiophores.

Fusicoccum persicae. CANKER, DIEBACK of peach.

GIBBERELLA (See under Blights)

Gibberella baccata (*Fusarium lateritium*). TWIG CANKER of acacia, ailanthus, apple, boxwood, mimosa, mulberry, and on other plants where twig blight is the most prominent symptom. See under Blights.

GLOEOSPORIUM (See under Anthracnose)

Gloeosporium perennans. PERENNIAL CANKER of apple in Pacific Northwest, much like northwestern anthracnose caused by *Neofabraea malicorticis* (see under Anthracnose). Perennial canker may follow in after winter injury, or around pruning cuts where woolly aphids congregate or following an application of wound dressing containing copper arsenite.

GLOMERELLA (See under Anthracnose)

Glomerella cingulata. DIEBACK, CANKER of camellias, widespread, sometimes of azalea, blackberry, bittersweet, rose, raspberry, soapberry, mountain-ash, English ivy. The fungus is perhaps best known as the cause of bitter rot of apples; it also produces anthracnose of many plants, but southern gardeners denounce it most bitterly as producing camellia dieback. Tips die back, leaves wilt, turn dull green and finally brown, stem dries out, turns brown, and there is a girdle of dead bark. Elliptical cankers are also found on older wood. The cause of dieback is still controversial. Both *Gloeosporium* (the imperfect stage of *Glomerella cingulata*) and a Phomopsis have been frequently isolated from stems showing dieback. Infection may be through bud scars in spring, young buds in summer or pruning wounds. Proper control measures are not yet known, but there is a general feeling that a copper fungicide combined with pruning out dead and cankered twigs and limbs is useful.

GLUTINIUM

Fungi Imperfecti, Sphaeropsidales, Sphaerioidaceae

Pycnidia innate, without a stroma; spores borne at tip and sides of conidiophores, hyaline, 1-celled.

Glutinium macrosporium. CANKER, fruit rot, of apple.

GRIPHOSPHAERIA

Ascomycetes, Sphaeriales, Sphaeriaceae

Perithecial walls carbonous, mouths papillate; spores with several cells.

Griphosphaeria corticola (imperfect stage *Coryneum microstictum*). ROSE CANKER, DIEBACK. Cankers are formed near base of canes, often show dark glistening pustules of conidial stage—dark spores with several cross-walls. Occasionally when the canker has girdled the cane a large gall forms above the lesions, resembling crown gall, and apparently due to the prevention of downward transfer of food. Infected canes should be cut out.

FIG. 45. Coryneum Canker of Rose, showing small dark spore masses.

HYMENOCHAETE

Basidiomycetes, Agaricales, Thelephoraceae

Pileus or fruiting structure resupinate, of several layers, cystidia present, hyaline or dark.

Hymenochaete agglutinans. HYMENOCHAETE CANKER on apple, birch, hazelnut, sweetgum, various young hardwoods. When an infected dead stem comes in contact with a live one the mycelium forms a thin leathery fruiting body around the living stem, holding it to the dead one. This resupinate body is deep brown in central portion with creamy-yellow margin. The stem is constricted at point of encirclement and the sapling often dies in two or three years. If the dead stem is removed before girdling, a sunken canker appears on one side, which may be overgrown with callus and disappear.

Control. In nursery stands do not leave severed stems in contact with living seedlings or saplings.

HYPOXYLON

Ascomycetes, Sphaeriales, Xylariaceae

Perithecia in a pulvinate to hemispheric, often confluent and crustose stroma, ascospores 1-, rarely 2-celled, blackish brown; conidia in superficial layer on surface of young stroma.

Hypoxylon pruinatum. TRUNK CANKER on poplar. Aspen and largetooth aspen are most commonly attacked, balsam poplar less frequently. This is more of a forest than an ornamental disease with trees less than thirty years old, on poor sites, most susceptible. The disease starts as small, yellow to reddish brown slightly sunken areas with irregularly lobed advancing margins, centered around a wound. These enlarge and grow together to form a canker marked off by vertical cracks. The bark is mottled, gray with black patches where blackened cortex is exposed. Conidia appear in blister-like stromata on first and second year cankers while perithecia are formed on three-year cankers in hard, black stromata covered with a white pruinose coat.

Infection occurs through wounds. Infected trees should be eliminated in thinning.

MACROPHOMA

Fungi Imperfecti, Sphaeropsidales, Sphaerioidaceae

Like Phoma, with discrete pycnidia arising innately, but with much larger spores, hyaline, 1-celled.

Macrophoma candollei. Associated with DIEBACK of boxwood, but apparently saprophytic only. The large black pycnidia are, however, quite striking on straw-colored leaves.

Macrophoma cupressi. DIEBACK of Italian cypress.

Macrophoma phoradendron. Defoliates mistletoe, but it grows back.

Macrophoma tumefaciens. BRANCH GALL CANKER of poplar. Nearly spherical round galls not over 1½ inches in diameter form at base of twigs, which usually die. The disease is not serious.

MASSARIA

Ascomycetes, Sphaeriales, Sphaeriaceae

Spores dark, with several cells, oblong-fusiform, with mucous sheath.

Massaria platani. CANKER, widespread on branches of American, London, and California planes.

MELANCONIS

Ascomycetes, Sphaeriales, Melanconidiaceae

Perithecia in an immersed black stroma; paraphyses present; spores 2-celled, light; conidia superficial on a stroma.

Melanconis juglandis. MELANCONIS DIEBACK OF BUTTERNUT, widespread on butternut, also on black walnut, Japanese, and English walnut. The disease was first described in Connecticut in 1923, but evidently had been responsible for slow dying of butternuts long before that. It extends over the natural range of butternut and is likewise important on Japanese walnut. If trees are previously weakened the fungus proceeds rapidly; otherwise there is the slow advance of a weak parasite.

Dead limbs are sprinkled with small, black, conidial acervuli, rounded or wartlike, looking like drops of ink in wet weather, occasionally developing spore horns in wet weather. Conidia are olive-gray, oval to kidney-shaped. The perfect stage is rare; perithecia are embedded in the bark singly or in groups, with long necks. Mycelium invades bark and wood, producing a dark discoloration, and grows slowly down a branch to the trunk. When that is reached the tree is doomed. In final stages trees have a stagheaded effect from loss of leaves.

Control. Remove diseased branches promptly, cutting some distance below infection; remove trees developing trunk cankers; keep the rest growing well with proper food and water.

Melanconis stilbostoma. DIEBACK of branches of European birch, on trees weakened by drought.

MONOCHAETIA

Fungi Imperfecti, Melanconiales, Melanconiaceae

Spores in acervuli, dark with several cells, and with one cilium or appendage at upper end; usually cause leaf spots.

Monochaetia mali. CANKER, LEAF SPOT of Apple. Fungus enters through deep wounds, grows deeply into wood, and then attacks resulting wound callus, producing numerous fruiting bodies on exposed wood and callus layer. Killing of successive callus layers results in a canker similar to European apple canker, but the disease is not common enough to be serious.

NECTRIA

Ascomycetes, Hypocreales, Hypocreaceae

Perithecia bright, more or less soft, and fleshy, in groups, basal portion seated on a stroma; spores 2-celled, hyaline, or subhyaline (Fig. 42).

Nectria cinnabarina. DIEBACK, TWIG CANKER, CORAL SPOT, cosmopolitan on hardwoods, most common on maples but also found on ailanthus, amelanchier, apple and crabapple, apricot, ash, blackberry, chokecherry, beech, birch, elm, hickory, horsechestnut, mimosa, linden, paper mulberry, pear, peach, sophora. It also may appear in stem cankers on vines and shrubs—ampelopsis, barberry, boxwood, callicarpa, cotoneaster, currant, gooseberry, fig, honeysuckle, kerria, California laurel, rose, syringa.

The fungus is widespread as a saprophyte. On ornamental trees and shrubs it is weakly parasitic, producing cankers around wounds and at base of dead branches, or a dieback of twigs and branches.

On maple it is more pathogenic, killing twigs, small branches, and young trees, girdling larger branches. Most common on Norway maple and boxelder it may invade red, sycamore, Japanese, and other maples. First symptoms are small, depressed, dead areas in bark near wounds or branch stubs. Conspicuous flesh-colored or coral pink sporodochia, rather hemispherical in shape, are formed in dead bark and bear the conidia. Later the pustules turn chocolate brown and form pockets in which perithecia are produced.

The canker is most common in severely wounded or recently pruned trees. Sapwood has a dark greenish discoloration and open cankers are eventually formed with successive rolls of callus.

Control. Remove diseased wood and bark, cutting beyond the greenish discoloration.

Nectria coccinea var. **faginata.** CANKER, BEECH BARK DISEASE on beech in the Northeast. This disease occurs solely in connection with the woolly beech scale insect (*Cryptococcus fagi*), but it has caused high mortality in Canada, killing 50 per cent of beech stands since 1920 and is now epidemic in Maine on American beech.

The aphids, covered with a woolly white down, cluster thickly around cracks and wounds in bark, often making trunk and branches look as if coated with snow. The small yellow larvae establish themselves on the bark in autumn, each inserting its sucking organ, stylet, into the living bark, which shrinks and cracks. Nectria enters through these cracks and kills surrounding tissue in bark and cambium. With the cells dead the aphids can no longer obtain food and disappear.

White pustules of sporodochia are pushed out through dead bark, bearing elongate, slightly curved macroconidia, 3 to 9-celled. The perithecia are red, slightly lemon-shaped, and appear in clusters—often so abundant that the bark appears red. After the 2-celled ascospores are discharged the upper half of the perithecium collapses and sinks into the lower.

The eventual canker becomes a deeply depressed cavity surrounded by callus. After the cambium dies foliage wilts, and twigs, branches, and finally roots die.

Control. Ornamental trees should be sprayed or scrubbed to kill the aphids. Beeches are sensitive to oil sprays, although Sunoco oil or kerosene soap emulsion is recommended. A dormant lime-sulfur spray is probably safer. In forest stands mortality is greater on steep slopes than on broad ridge tops and among larger trees. Selective cutting should reduce the proportion of beech by removing larger trees and those on slopes first.

Nectria desmazierii (conidial stage *Fusarium buxicola*). CANKER and dieback of boxwood.

Nectria ditissima, sometimes reported but not confirmed in the United States. Reports probably refer to *N. galligena.*

Nectria galligena. NECTRIA CANKER, TRUNK CANKER, widespread on apple, pear, quince, aspen, beech, birch, maple, especially mountain, red and sugar maples, hickory, Pacific dogwood and various other hardwoods. The disease has been called European canker of apple and pear, but there is no evidence that it was introduced from there and may be native here. It was first reported on apple in 1900, is prevalent on pomaceous fruits in the Pacific Northwest, and is the most serious canker disease of hardwood stands in the East.

Young cankers are small, depressed or flattened areas of bark near small wounds or at base of dead side twigs or branches, darker than rest of bark and appearing water-soaked. As the bark cracks at the outer edge, callus tissue is formed. Older cankers are conspicuous and somewhat like a target, with bark sloughed off to expose concentric ridges of callus. Cankers on elm, sugar maple, and yellow and sweet birches are usually circular, those on oaks irregular, on basswood elongated, pointed at ends. If the canker is nearly covered with a callus roll it indicates infection is being overcome.

Small red perithecia are formed singly or in clusters on bark or on wood at margin of cankers. Ascospores discharged during moist weather or disseminated by wind and rain. Creamy-white sporodochia protruding through bark produce cylindrical macroconidia and ellipsoidal microconidia but are usually confined to recently killed bark of young cankers. Invasion is through bark cracks or other wounds in living or dying but not dead wood. Infection is slow, with annual callus formation, so that only the smallest branches are apt to be girdled.

Control. Avoid wounds on ornamental trees; treat all cuts immediately; remove dead branches; increase vigor by feeding, and watering during drought. In hardwood stands trees with trunk infections should be removed first.

Nectria magnoliae. NECTRIA CANKER, similar to the preceding but found on magnolia and tuliptree.

NEOFABRAEA (See under Anthracnose)

Neofabraea malicorticis. CANKER, black spot of pear.

Neofabraea perennans. PERENNIAL CANKER of apple, also bull's-eye rot of fruit. See *Gloeosporium perennans* (the imperfect stage) in this section.

NUMMULARIA

Ascomycetes, Sphaeriales, Xylariaceae

Stroma superficial, composed entirely of fungus elements, covered with a conidial layer when young. Perithecia flask-shaped, embedded in stroma; spores 1-celled, dark.

Nummularia discreta. BLISTER CANKER of apple, crabapple, pear, mountain-ash, a major disease east of Rocky Mountains, especially in Upper Mississippi and Lower Missouri River valleys where millions of apple trees have been killed.

Large and small limbs are affected. Cankers are dead areas, up to 3 feet long, mottled with living wood, and dotted with numerous round cushions of stromata looking like nailheads. Perithecia with dark ascospores are buried in the stromata but hyphae bearing small, light-colored conidia grow over the surface. The fungus enters through branch stubs, bark injuries, and other wounds.

Control. Prune out and burn cankered wood in early stages.

PENICILLIUM

Fungi Imperfecti, Moniliales, Moniliaceae

Conidia in heads, conidiophores unequally verticillate at tip, in whorls, and globose conidia formed in chains.

Penicillium vermoeseni. PENICILLIUM DISEASE OF ORNAMENTAL PALMS, serious in southern California, with symptoms varying according to type of palm. On queen palm (Arecastrum or *Cocos plumosa*) the disease is a trunk canker, which may remain inconspicuous for several years but leads to weakening and breaking of trunk and so should be removed at an early stage. On Canary date palm the disease is a leaf-base rot and on Washingtonia, a bud rot. See under Rots.

PEZICULA

Ascomycetes, Helotiales, Dermateaceae

Apothecia similar to Dermatea but lighter.

Pezicula carpinea. BARK CANKER of hornbeam.

Pezicula corticola (conidial stage is Myxosporium). SUPERFICIAL BARK CANKER and fruit rot, rather common on apple and pears. Hyaline, 1-celled conidia are formed in acervuli.

Pezicula pruinosa. CANKER on branches of amelanchier.

PHOMA (See under Blights)

Phoma abietina. TWIG CANKER of firs.

Phoma persicae. STEM CANKER of peach.

PHOMOPSIS (See under Blights)

Phomopsis boycei. PHOMOPSIS CANKER of lowland white fir. Branches or main stem of saplings may be girdled and killed; there is often a swelling at base of canker where dead tissues join living. Reddish-brown needles of dead branches are prominent against living foliage.

Phomopsis callistephi. STEM CANKER of China aster. Plants sometimes die from canker on basal portion.

Phomopsis gardeniae. GARDENIA CANKER, STEM GALL, widespread in greenhouses. Although not reported until about 1933 this seems to be the most common gardenia disease. Symptoms start with brown dead areas on stem, usually near the soil line, first sunken, then, as the stem enlarges, swollen with a rough, cracked outer cork. The stem is bright yellow for a short distance above the canker, contrast to the normal greenish white. When cankers completely girdle the stem foliage wilts and dies, but plants often live on a few weeks in a stunted condition. Flower buds are apt to fall before opening.

When humidity is high, black pycnidia on cankers exude yellowish spore masses. The fungus enters through wounds and spores are probably spread on the propagator's knife as lower leaves of cuttings are removed. A large percentage of infection starts at leaf joints at base of cuttings after they are set in the rooting medium. Cankers may be only slightly visible on rooted cuttings and wide distribution of the disease across the country probably came from sale of such cuttings.

Control. Use sterilized rooting media. Steam is preferable for a sand and peat mixture but formaldehyde (3 tablespoons commercial formalin per bushel) can be substituted for sand alone. Dipping cuttings in Semesan may be helpful. Infected plants should be destroyed, but it is sometimes safe to wait until the blooming season is over so as to market all possible flowers.

Phomopsis lokoyae. PHOMOPSIS CANKER of Douglas-fir, chiefly a sapling disease in poor sites in California and Oregon. Long and narrow cankers, somewhat pointed at ends, develop during the dormant season from infection through young shoots. If the tree is not girdled during the first season the canker heals over.

Phomopsis livella (*Diaporthe vincae*). CANKER, DIEBACK of vinca, periwinkle.

Phomopsis mali. BARK CANKER of pear.

Phomopsis padina (*Diaporthe decorticans*). CANKER, twig blight of sour cherry.

PHRAGMODOTHELLA

Ascomycetes, Dothideales, Dothideaceae

Asci in locules in a stroma which is cushionlike, spores hyaline, many-celled.

Phragmodothella ribesia. DIEBACK, BLACK PUSTULE, on currant, flowering currant, gooseberry.

PHYSALOSPORA

Ascomycetes, Sphaeriales, Mycosphaerellaceae

Perithecia immersed in stroma, not beaked, mouths papillate, paraphyses present; spores 1-celled, hyaline. Conidial stage a Sphaeropsis or Diplodia with dark spores.

Physalospora corticis. BLUEBERRY CANE CANKER, in Southeast on cultivated blueberries. Fungus enters through unbroken bark, probably through lenticels with cankers starting as reddish, broadly conical swellings, enlarging the next year to rough, black, deeply fissured cankers that girdle the shoots; the portions above cankers are unfruitful and finally die. Cabot and Pioneer are very susceptible. A number of varieties are quite resistant.

Physalospora glandicola (conidial stage *Sphaeropsis quercina*). SPHAEROPSIS CANKER AND DIEBACK of red, chestnut and other oaks. Shade and ornamental trees of all ages may be killed. Infection often starts on small twigs and branches, passing to larger branches and trunk, but it may begin anywhere through wounds. Twigs and branches die, leaves wither, turn brown, infected bark is sunken and wrinkled with small, black pycnidia breaking through it. On larger stems the bark has a ridgelike callus growth around the canker, the sapwood in this area turning dark with black streaks extending longitudinally for several inches. Numerous watersprouts grow below the dead crown. The fungus winters on dead twigs producing a new crop of conidia in spring. These infect most readily trees weakened by unfavorable environmental conditions.

Control. Prune out diseased portions at least 6 inches below cankers. Fertilize well, and water during drought periods to improve vigor. Remove seriously infected trees.

Physalospora miyabeana. BLACK CANKER OF WILLOW, accompanying scab to form the disease complex known as willow blight in New England and

New York. Starting in leaf blades the fungus proceeds through petioles into twigs and also causes cankers on larger stems, followed by defoliation. Pinkish spore masses of the imperfect Gloeosporium stage are formed on dead twigs and cankers, followed by short-necked perithecia which overwinter.

Control. Remove and destroy dead twigs and branches during dormant stage in winter. Spray three times with bordeaux mixture, starting just after leaves emerge in spring.

Physalospora obtusa (conidial stage *Sphaeropsis malorum*). DIEBACK, CANKER of hardwoods, New York apple-tree canker, and black rot of apple. The fungus attacks leaves, twigs and fruits, is more important east of the Rocky Mountains, and is found on many plants, including alder, ampelopsis, birch, bignonia, bittersweet, callicarpa, catalpa, ceanothus, chestnut, currant, cotoneaster, hawthorn, Japanese quince, maple, peach, pear, persimmon. On hardwoods the canker is similar to that caused by *P. glandicola* on oaks, with limbs girdled, large areas of rough bark with numerous black pycnidia protruding through the bark. As a disease of apple and other fruits see discussion under Rots.

Physalospora rhodina. BLACK ROT CANKER of tung, Mississippi, Louisiana. Black sunken cankers on trunks, limbs, twigs, shoots; may girdle and kill trees. Rogue and burn diseased specimens.

PHYTOPHTHORA (See under Blights)

Phytophthora cactorum. BLEEDING CANKER of maple, beech, oak, elm; CROWN CANKER of dogwood; DIEBACK of rhododendron; TRUNK CANKER of apple, almond, apricot, cherry, plum, peach.

Bleeding Canker. This special manifestation of *Phytophthora cactorum* is relatively recent, first noticed in Rhode Island on maple about 1939, found in New Jersey the next year, and now known on Norway, red, sycamore and sugar maples, American beech, elm, and oak in New England and New York.

The most characteristic symptom is the oozing of a watery light brown or a thick reddish brown liquid from fissures in bark at root collar and at intervals on trunk and branches. When dry this sap resembles dried blood, whence the name bleeding canker. Sunken, furrowed cankers are more definite on young than older trees with rough bark. Symptoms are most prominent in late spring and early fall, with trees in moist situations most often affected. The fungus lives in the soil and advances upward from a primary root infection. Wilting of leaves and blighting of branches seems to be due to a toxin. Mature trees have fewer, smaller, yellow green leaves and there is an acute dieback of branches. Reddish brown areas with intense olive-green margins are found in wood extending vertically from roots to dying branches and marked at irregular intervals with cavities containing the water fluid.

Control. Although there is no real "cure," injecting trees with a basic yellow die, Helione Orange, was found to inhibit growth of the fungus and to inactivate the toxin formed. In some cases trees recover without treatment.

Crown Canker or collar rot is the most serious disease of dogwood and probably present in states other than New York, New Jersey, and Massachusetts where it has been reported. First symptom is a general unthrifty appearance, with leaves smaller and lighter green than normal, turning prematurely red in late summer. Leaves may shrivel and curl during dry spells (normal dogwood leaves also curl in dry spells). Twigs and large branches die, often on one side of the tree first. The canker develops slowly on lower trunk near soil level. Inner bark, cambium and sapwood are discolored; the cankered area is sunken, the bark dries and falls away leaving wood exposed. The trees die when the canker extends completely around the trunk base or root collar. The fungus lives in the soil in partially decayed organic matter, and the spores are washed to near-by uninfected trees. Entrance is through wounds, and the disease is one of transplanted dogwoods, not of natives growing in woods.

Control. Transplant carefully, avoiding all unnecessary wounds; avoid hitting base with lawnmower, perhaps by using a guard to protect tree base. It has been difficult to save infected trees, but cutting out small cankers, disinfecting and painting the wood, is worth trying. If trees have died from crown canker do not plant new dogwoods in the same location for several years.

Rhododendron Dieback. Terminal buds and leaves turn brown, roll up and droop as in winter cold. Stem shrivels, a canker encircles the twigs with above portions wilting and dying. In shady moist locations leaves have water-soaked areas, changing to brown, zonate spots. Do not plant rhododendrons near lilacs, which may be blighted by the same fungus. Prune diseased tips well below shriveled part and spray after blooming with 4–4–100 bordeaux mixture, two applications 14 days apart.

Trunk Canker of Apple, an irregular canker often involving entire trunk and base of scaffold branches, the first outward symptom a wet area on bark. Grimes variety is particularly susceptible, with a large percentage of trees partially or completely girdled.

Phytophthora cinnamomi (same as *P. cambivora*). BASAL CANKER of maple, especially Norway maple, also rhododendron wilt (see under Wilts) and chestnut root rot. Maples have a thin crown, fewer and smaller leaves with trees dying a year or two after cankers are formed at base of trunk. Sapwood is reddish brown; root system may decay.

Remove diseased trees, plant new Norway maples in good soil, well drained, rich in organic matter; treat injuries at base of trunk promptly.

PLENODOMUS

Fungi Imperfecti, Sphaeropsidales, Sphaerioidaceae

Pycnidia leathery or carbonous, more or less sclerotoid; spores hyaline, 1-celled, conidiophores lacking.

Plenodomus fuscomaculans. CANKER on apple.

PSEUDONECTRIA

Ascomycetes, Hypocreales

Perithecia superficial, bright colored, smooth; spores 1-celled, hyaline.

Pseudonectria rouselliana. "NECTRIA" CANKER OF BOXWOOD, leaf cast, twig blight. The fungus is considered the perfect stage of *Volutella buxi,* which see, but the connection has not been proved. This stage is usually found on dead leaves.

PSEUDOVALSA

Ascomycetes, Sphaeriales

Perithecia in a stroma; spores dark, with several cells.

Pseudovalsa longipes. TWIG CANKER on Coast live oak and white oak.

RHABDOSPORA

Fungi Imperfecti, Sphaeropsidales, Sphaerioidaceae

Pycnidia globose or depressed, membranous, spores filiform to needle-shaped, hyaline.

Rhabdospora rubi. CANE SPOT, canker of raspberry.

SCLERODERRIS

Ascomycetes, Helotiales (or Phacidiales), Tryblidiaceae

Apothecia black, opening with lobes, crowded together or with a stroma, short stalked; spores hyaline, with several cells, elongate.

Scleroderris abieticola. CANKER of balsam firs on Pacific Coast. An annual canker, starting in autumn and ceasing when cambium is active in spring, is formed on twigs, branches and trunks of saplings. Twigs and small branches only are girdled; and if this does not happen before spring, the wound heals over. Small black apothecia with short stalks appear on dead bark, with infection via ascospores through uninjured bark or leaf scars.

SCOLECONECTRIA (Ophionectria)

Ascomycetes, Hypocreales, Hypocreaceae

Perithecia red to white, globoid, with a round ostiole, superficial, paraphyses lacking; spores needle-shaped to filiform, light.

Scoleconectria balsamea. BARK CANKER of balsam fir, and **S. scolecospora** of balsam and alpine firs.

SEPTOBASIDIUM

Basidiomycetes, Tremellales, Septobasidiaceae

All species are on living plants in association with scale insects, the combination causing damage to trees. Fungus body usually resupinate but variable, dry, crustaceous or spongy, in most species composed of subiculum growing over bark, middle region of upright slender or thick pillars or mounds of hyphae which support top layer in which hymenium is formed. Basidium transversely septate into 2, 3, or 4 cells, rarely 1-celled; basidiospores elliptic, colorless, divided into 2 to many cells soon after formation, budding with numerous sporidia if kept moist; some species with conidia.

The fungus lives by parasitizing scale insects, obtaining food by means of haustoria, but the scales injure the trees, occasionally killing young trees by piercing the bark to the cambium. The fungus may kill a few scales but it protects vast numbers in its enveloping felty or leathery covering so that this really is a symbiotic relationship. Spores seem to be spread by young crawling scales or by birds. Most Septobasidium species are found in the South, often abundant on neglected fruit, nut, or ornamental trees but rare on those well-kept. Pruning out twigs and branches covered with felt is the most effective means of control. Patches on larger limbs can be scrubbed off with a rag soaked in kerosene emulsion.

Septobasidium burtii. FELT FUNGUS CANKER, on southern hackberry, beech, pear, apple, and peach. This is a perennial growth, with a new ring added to the patch each summer. Probasidia are formed during winter and 4-celled basidia in spring.

Septobasidium curtisii. FELT FUNGUS, widespread on many tree species in the Southeast, commonly on sour gum (Tupelo) and American ash, also on hickory, hawthorn, Japanese quince, and others. The felt is purple black throughout and mounded over the insects.

Septobasidium castaneum. FELT FUNGUS, abundant on willow and water oaks, holly, may injure azaleas. The surface is smooth, shiny chocolate-brown to nearly black.

Septobasidium pseudopedicellatum. FELT FUNGUS, on citrus twigs, sometimes on main stem or branches of hornbeam. Surface is smooth, buff-colored over dark brown pillars.

SOLENIA

Basidiomycetes, Agaricales, Thelephoraceae

Fruiting layers erect, cylindric, formed in groups, membranous.

Solenia anomala. BARK PATCH or canker, widespread on alder.

Solenia ochracea. BARK PATCH of birch, hornbeam, hickory.

SPHAEROPSIS

Fungi Imperfecti, Sphaeropsidales, Sphaerioidaceae

Pycnidia innate, finally erumpent, with ostiole; spores 1-celled, dark, large, on filiform conidiophores. Some species are connected with Physalospora as perfect stage. Various species cause cankers, collar rots, seedling blights, or diebacks of hardwoods.

Sphaeropsis ellisii. See **Diplodia pinea,** under Blights.

Sphaeropsis malorum. See **Physalospora obtusa.**

Sphaeropsis quercina. See **Physalospora glandicola.**

Sphaeropsis ulmicola. SPHAEROPSIS CANKER of American elm. The disease spreads downward from small twigs to larger branches with a brown discoloration of wood just under bark. Secondary shoots sometimes develop below the cankers. Trees weakened by drought or poor growing conditions are particularly susceptible.

Control. Prune out infected wood, cutting well below cankers; fertilize to improve vigor.

STRUMELLA

Fungi Imperfecti, Moniliales, Tuberculariaceae

Sporodochia wartlike, gray to black, of interwoven hyphae, conidia lacking or imperfect on living trees, but after death fruiting sporodochia, bearing brown spiny conidia are formed in dead bark.

Strumella coryneoidea. STRUMELLA CANKER OF OAK, especially the red oak group, American beech and chestnut, occasional on pignut and shagbark hickories, red maple, tupelo. Primarily a forest disease, this canker may become important on red and scarlet ornamental oaks.

Starting as a yellowish discoloration of bark around a dead branch or other point of infection the canker develops into a diffuse type of lesion or into the target type with concentric ridges of callus. Whitish mycelium is present near outer corky bark, and that portion of the trunk may be flattened or distorted. Target cankers often are large, up to 2 feet wide by 5 feet long. The diffuse type canker is found on smaller trees where the trunk is rapidly girdled before callus is formed.

The small, black nodules in cankers on living trees bear no spores, but after death rounded, dark brown spore pustules are formed, which blacken with age while new pustules continue to be formed yearly.

Control. Prune out dead branches; remove dead trees immediately before spores can spread infection.

THYRONECTRIA

Ascomycetes, Hypocreales, Hypocreaceae

Stroma valsoid with several perithecia, spores muriform, hyaline to subhyaline.

Thyronectria austro-americana. CANKER, wilt of honey locust. Slightly depressed bark cankers ranging from pinhead size to ½ inch grow together and enlarge to girdle a branch. There is often a gummy exudate, and the underlying wood is streaked reddish brown for several inches from the canker. Some trees die, but many survive.

Thyronectria berolinensis. CANEKNOT CANKER of fruiting and flowering currants.

VALSA

Ascomycetes, Sphaeriales, Valsaceae (or Diaporthaceae)

Many perithecia in a circle in a stroma in bark, flask-shaped with long necks opening to surface; spores hyaline, 1-celled, curved, slender.

Valsa cincta. DIEBACK, CANKER of peach, nectarine. This fungus is apparently infective only during the dormant season, entering through wounds, dead buds, leaf scars, fruit spurs, etc. It forms a canker complex with *V. leucostoma* and the brown-rot fungus.

Valsa leucostoma. APPLE CANKER, DIEBACK, twig blight on apple, apricot, peach, pear, quince, plum, cherry, willow, and mountain-ash.

Valsa salicis (imperfect stage *Cytospora salicis*) . TWIG CANKER of willow.

Valsa sordida. CANKER, DIEBACK of poplar and willow. See under *Cytospora chrysosperma.*

VERMICULARIA

Fungi Imperfecti, Melanconiales, Melanconiaceae

Like Colletotrichum but setae, or bristles, scattered throughout acervuli and not just marginal; spores hyaline, globose to fusoid.

Vermicularia ipomearum. STEM CANKER of morning glory.

VOLUTELLA (See under Blights)

Volutella buxi. BOXWOOD "NECTRIA" CANKER, Volutella blight. The perfect stage of the fungus is assumed (not proved) to be *Pseudonectria rousselliana,*

FIG. 46. Volutella blight or "Nectria" Canker of boxwood.

which see. As a canker the disease often follows after winter injury with salmon-pink spore pustules on dying twigs, branches and main stems. As a blight, the disease spreads rapidly in moist weather in summer, attacking healthy twigs when humidity is high and often discernible at a distance by a straw yellow "flag." On such branches backs of leaves and twigs are both covered with the pinkish spore pustules.

Control. Cut out branches where the bark has been loosened with winter ice and snow. Have a yearly "housecleaning," brushing out accumulated leaves and other debris from interior of bushes (I use a whiskbroom), cutting out all twigs showing the pink pustules. If there has been much sign of canker, follow cleaning with a thorough spraying, from ground up into interior of bushes, with lime sulfur, 1 to 50 dilution. Copper sprays are also recommended with up to three treatments, but one application of lime sulfur is sufficient, in my own work, if applied after cleaning and before August rains start secondary infection.

CLUB ROOT

PLASMODIOPHORA

Phycomycetes, Plasmodiophorales, Plasmodiophoraceae

This genus, founded on the club-root organism, has a somewhat doubtful taxonomic position. Formerly considered a slime-mold, one of the Myxomycetes, it is now included by many workers in the true fungi, placed in the Phycomycetes and until very recently in the Chytridiales, the lowest order, characterized by mycelium wanting or slightly developed. Now the small order Plasmodiophorales has been separated off.

Thallus amoeboid, multinucleate in host cell; frequently causing hypertrophy; spores lying free in host cell at maturity.

Plasmodiophora brassicae. Club Root of Cabbage and other crucifers, finger-and-toe disease, on alyssum, brussels sprouts, cabbage, Chinese cabbage, candytuft, cauliflower, hesperis, honesty, pepper grass, garden cress, mustard, radish, rutabaga, stock, turnip, and western wallflower.

Club root was first noted in England in 1736, but the true cause was not known until the classic paper of the Russian Woronin in 1878. The disease was important in America by the middle of the nineteenth century and is now present in at least 36 states. Losses are both from death of plants and seedlings and infestation of soil, for susceptible crucifers cannot be grown again on the same land for several years.

The first symptom is wilting of tops on hot days, followed by partial recovery at night; affected plants may be stunted and not head; outer leaves turn yellow and drop. The root system becomes a distorted mass of large and small swellings, sometimes several roots swollen like sweet potatoes, sometimes in one massive gall. Lateral and tap roots are affected and they are often scabby or fissured with rot starting from secondary fungi.

When diseased roots are decomposed small spherical spores are liberated in the soil, capable of surviving there many years between crops. In spring, with suitable temperature and moisture, the resting spores germinate, each becoming a motile swarm spore with a flagellum, but this whiplike appendage is soon lost and the organism becomes amoebalike, moving by protoplasmic streaming until it reaches a root hair or other root tissue. The amoeba or plasmodium continues to grow and to divide until it reaches the cambial cells and in these it develops up and down the root, swelling being produced both by division of the plasmodia and of infected cells. Eventually the multinucleate plasmodium breaks up into a great many small resting spores each rounded up around a single nucleus, and set free in the soil when the root rots. Millions of spores can come from a single diseased root, to be spread in moving soil, drainage water, manure and plant refuse. Infected seedlings probably account for long distance spread of club root. Infection takes place only in a neutral to acid soil, pH 5.0 to 7.0, at temperatures below 80° F. and when soil moisture is above 50% of its water-holding capacity.

Control. Inspect seedlings carefully before planting. Dispose of infected crops with caution (resting spores pass through animals uninjured). Combine liming the soil with a long rotation of other crops. Lime must be applied in large doses, at rate of 1500 pounds per acre, and about 6 weeks before crop is set, to bring pH at least to 7.2. Mercuric chloride, 1 tablet to a quart of water, can be used as setting water for seedlings, using ⅓ pint per plant. Seedbeds can be treated with mercuric chloride or chloropicrin before planting.

Turnip varieties that are somewhat resistant include Early White Milan, Early Snowball, Yellow Stone, Yellow Egg, Sweet German, White Swede, Purple Aberdeen, Yellow Rutabaga. Resistant cabbage and kale varieties are coming.

Damping-Off

Damping-off is the destruction of young seedlings by soil organisms. There are two types. *Pre-emergence damping-off* rots the sprouting seed before it breaks through the soil and is recognized by bare spaces in what should be uniform rows. A poor stand may be the result of low viability of seed, but more often it is due to disease. Pre-emergence damping-off is most serious in cold, wet soils when germination is slow.

Post-emergence damping-off is the rotting or wilting of seedlings soon after they emerge from the soil. Succulent stems have a water-soaked, then necrotic and sunken zone at ground level, and the little plants fall over on the ground, or, in woody seedlings, wilt and remain upright. Root decay follows. This type of damping-off is most common in greenhouses or outdoors in warm humid weather and where seedlings are too crowded. Tree seedlings in nursery rows are subject to this type of damping-off and so are perennial flowers started in late summer for the next year.

Many fungi living saprophytically in the upper layers of soil can cause damping-off. *Pythium debaryanum* and *Rhizoctonia solani* are probably most common, but other species of these two genera and Aphanomyces, Botrytis, Cylindrocladium, Diplodia, Fusarium, Macrophomina and Phytophthora may be important on occasion. See under Rots for details.

Damping-off can't be cured, but it can be prevented by starting seed in a sterile medium such as vermiculite or sphagnum moss, or in soil which has been treated with steam, or electricity or formaldehyde or chloropicrin. It can also be largely prevented by treating seed with a protectant dust. Because most of the damping-off organisms are in the soil and not on the seed the chemicals are not used for disinfesting the seed but to coat the seed with a poison which will kill or inhibit the fungi in the soil immediately surrounding the seed after planting and so provide a temporary protection during germination.

Seed treatment should be regarded as crop insurance. It is quite possible to get good stands without it, but it scarcely pays to take the chance. Some materials widely available and often recommended at this writing are *Arasan,* a thiocarbamate; *Ceresan,* ethyl mercury phosphate; *Cuprocide,* red or yellow copper oxide; *Semesan,* an organic mercury; *Spergon,* a naphthoquinone; and *Vasco* 4, zinc oxide. Treating seeds takes practically no extra time. For large lots dosages are given in teaspoons but for a packet of seeds take about as much as you can get on the end of a knife blade, add it to the seeds in a bottle, shake until seeds are coated, then pour out seeds on a strainer to get rid of any excess dust. The following list gives some suggested treatments of vegetable seeds for damping-off, which should follow hot-water or other treatment for bacteria or fungi harbored in the seed.

BEANS, especially lima beans—Spergon or Arasan, ½ level teaspoon per pound of seed.

BEET—Arasan, 1 level teaspoon per pound, or Semesan, 1¼ teaspoons, or Cuprocide (red is safer than yellow), 1½ teaspoons.

CABBAGE and other crucifers—Semesan, ½ level teaspoon per pound of seed. Do not use copper dusts on crucifers.

CARROT—Spergon or Arasan, 1 level teaspoon per pound, but treat only if previous stands are poor.

CELERY—Old seed may not require treatment. Damping-off is not so important as the blights which require hot-water or calomel treatment for new seed.

CORN—Arasan, ¼ level teaspoon per pound, or Semesan Jr., ¼ level teaspoon per pound, or Spergon, 1½ ounces per bushel of seed.

CUCUMBER and other cucurbits, melon, squash, etc.—Spergon, ½ teaspoon per pound, or Semesan, ½ teaspoon per pound of seed.

EGGPLANT—Arasan or Semesan, ½ level teaspoon per pound of seed.

LETTUCE—no treatment unless previous poor stands, then dust *lightly* with Spergon, Semesan or zinc oxide.

PEA—Spergon, or Arasan, ½ level teaspoon per pound.

PEPPER—Semesan, ½ level teaspoon per pound.
RADISH—seldom requires treatment in home gardens, can use Semesan or zinc oxide, 1 level teaspoon per pound.
SPINACH—Arasan, 1 level teaspoon per pound of seed, or Cuprocide, red, 1½ teaspoons per pound, or zinc oxide, 3 level teaspoons.
TOMATO—Arasan, 1 level teaspoon per pound of seed.

Phygon, chemically related to Spergon, can be used in place of it in some seed treatments.

Not too much work has been done on flower seed treatment, but Semesan has been used rather generally and red copper oxide and zinc oxide somewhat. Spergon is useful for sweet peas, and Arasan doubtless has value in many cases. Treating soil is often recommended for flower seedlings. Formaldehyde dust has been used to some extent for soil in flats, but the formaldehyde sprinkle method is about as easy and quite effective. Use 2½ tablespoons of commercial 40% formaldehyde per bushel of soil, or 1 tablespoon per flat, dilute with 5 or 6 times as much water, and sprinkle over soil, mixing thoroughly. Fill flats, allow to stand 24 hours, sow seed and then water soil thoroughly.

Even easier, and apparently giving good results, is the use of oxyquinoline benzoate, sold as Anti-Damp, diluted 1 part to 100 parts of water and used to water flat or seed bed immediately after sowing. The water is repeated a week after sprouting to control post-emergence damping-off. Oxyquinoline sulfate is also promising.

Watering seedbeds with 4–2–100 bordeaux mixture or with red copper oxide or zinc oxide also helps to control post-emergence damping-off, but do not use coppers on crucifers. More important is keeping seedlings less crowded, in a location with good air circulation.

Nurseries growing conifers often suffer heavy losses from damping-off. Here an acid soil is advisable. Many chemicals have been tried—sulfuric acid applied immediately after sowing seed, or commercial phosphoric acid; or acetic acid or formaldehyde applied several days before sowing; or aluminum or ferrous sulfate; or Semesan for longleaf pine seedlings.

DODDER

Dodders are seed plants parasitic on stems and sometimes other parts of cultivated or wild plants. They are leafless, orange to yellow twining vines, without chlorophyll and so incapable of manufacturing food. They are called variously love vine, strangle weed, gold thread, hairweed, devil's hair, devil's ringlet, pull down, clover silk, and hell-bind, the latter being most appropriate. There are about 40 species in the United States, causing serious agricultural losses in clovers, alfalfa, and flax, and becoming more and more important in gardens on ornamentals and sometimes vegetables. Dodders

Fig. 47. Dodder on Chrysanthemum: Upper, in full flower, with tendrils twining around host stem; lower left, tangle of threads; lower right, seed formed and ready to drop. Control depends on removal before this stage.

belong to the single genus Cuscuta, family Cuscutaceae which is close to the morning-glory family.

Dodder seed is grayish to reddish brown, resembling small legume seed but roughened with three flattened sides. It germinates as ordinary seed but is so synchronized that it starts a little later, when the host seedling is well developed. The parasite is a slender, yellowish, unbranched thread with the growing tip circling around in search of support. When it touches something it twines like a morning glory, and if the support is a susceptible host it puts out little suckers or haustoria which penetrate the host stem. The yellow vine below the first stem coil then dries up and there is no further contact with the soil.

Although seedlings can live for a few weeks without a susceptible host they finally die if a connection is not established. Successful parasites continue to twine and to spread orange tendrils from one plant to the next, often making a tangle of matted orange hairs many feet across with a black region in the center where host plants have died. Such tangles are conspicuous in weeds along roadsides.

In ornamental plantings host plants are not often killed but show stunting and pallor, symptoms of starvation. Minute scales or rudimentary leaves form on the dodder tendrils and then dense clusters of beautiful small white blossoms (sometimes pale pink or yellow) which ripen seed in late summer, as many as 3000 seed being produced on a single plant.

Cuscuta spp. Much of the dodder infesting ornamentals is not readily identified as to species but it is widespread on a great many shrubs, perennials, and annuals. I find it very commonly on chrysanthemum, and strangling any other plant near by; I have spent hours cleaning up English ivy and trumpet-vine. Dodder is frequently reported on petunias and asters, on camellias in the South, and on many other plants.

Cuscuta americana, on citrus. **C. californica** on beet.

Cuscuta coryli, hazel dodder. **C. epithymum,** clover dodder on legumes.

Cuscuta exultata on redbud, ilex, sumac.

Cuscuta gronovii. Common Dodder on buttonbush, cucumber, raspberry, solanum spp., willows, and many garden ornamentals and hedge plants.

Cuscuta indecora. Bigseed Alfalfa Dodder on alfalfa from Colorado westward, but also on sweet pea, tomato.

Cuscuta planifera. Littleseed Alfalfa Dodder on some legumes in the West.

Cuscuta paradoxa on rose, Texas and Florida.

Cuscuta pentagona (*C. arvensis*). Field Dodder, widely distributed, most common and serious east of Mississippi on many cultivated and wild herbaceous plants.

Control. Avoid dodder-infested seed. Commercial seed containing one or more dodder seed per 5-gram sample is prohibited entry into the United

States. Many states have laws regulating sale of infested seed, but it may still be included inadvertently in a seed packet. If any contamination with rough, flat-sided seed is found, do not use any of the lot. Commercial dealers sometimes clean infested seed by screening or treating with an iron powder which sticks to the rough dodder to be drawn out by magnets.

Before breaking new ground for a garden on native sod, examine carefully. If dodder is found, burn over the area, then hoe lightly but repeatedly for several weeks to allow buried seed to germinate and die.

When dodder is present on cultivated plants the only thing to do is to remove and burn infested parts before seed is formed. Even a small fraction of a tendril left will start growing again.

DOWNY MILDEWS

Downy mildews, sometimes called false mildews, are Phycomycetes, in the order Peronosporales and all, except Phytophthora, in the family Peronosporaceae. They form mycelium in higher plants and produce sporangiophores which protrude through stomata in great numbers bearing sporangia in white, gray or violet downy patches on leaves. The downy effect distinguishes these mildews from the true or powdery mildews which form white felty or powdery patches.

The sporangia are often branched and bear a single sporangium at the tip of each branch simultaneously (successively in Phytophthora). Sporangia germinate by swarmspores or with a germ tube. An oospore, resting spore, with external ridges or knobs is formed in the oogonium, a large, globular, multinucleate female cell, after fertilization by the antheridium, the smaller male cell. The oospore is set free by weathering and decay of host parts.

BASIDIOPHORA

Sporangiophore a single trunk with a swollen apex from which short branches grow out, each bearing a nearly globose sporangium; germinating by swarmspores; the oospore wall is not confluent with that of the oogonium. Mycelium is intercellular, haustoria small, knoblike (Fig. 48).

Basidiophora entospora. DOWNY MILDEW of aster, China aster, goldenrod, erigeron. Aster losses are reported by commercial growers in the South, but apparently this is not an important garden problem.

BREMIA

Dichotomous branching of sporangiophores; tips enlarged into discs bordered with sterigmata bearing sporangia. Swarmspores are rare; germination is usually by a germ tube protruded through an apical papilla (Fig. 48).

Bremia lactucae. DOWNY MILDEW OF LETTUCE and other composites, endive, cornflower, centaurea, celtuce, escarole, romaine, and various wild plants or

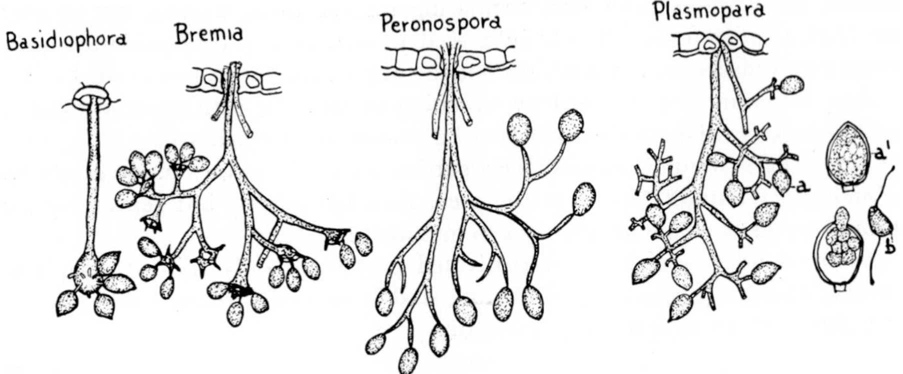

FIG. 48. Downy Mildews fruiting from stomata on underside of leaves. *Basidiophora,* sporangiophore with swollen apex; *Bremia,* sporangiophore tip enlarged to a disc; dichotomous branching; *Peronospora,* sporangia on sharply pointed terminal branches; *Plasmopara,* on obtuse tips; a and a^1, sporangium; b^1, zoospore.

weeds. This disease was first noticed around Boston in 1875. It is serious in greenhouses and in states where outdoor winter crops are grown. Light green or yellowish areas on upper surface of leaves are matched by downy patches on under surface. Affected portions turn brown and leaves die. Older leaves are attacked first. The disease is worse in periods of damp, foggy weather and at low temperatures, 43° to 53° F.

Control. Resistant varieties offer most hope. Imperial 152, 847, 615, and 850 are all resistant to some extent, but there are different strains of mildew in different localities. Bordeaux mixture or copper-lime dust can be used in seedbeds and greenhouses, but is not generally practical in the field.

PERONOSPORA

Mycelium intercellular; haustoria in a few species short and knoblike but in most are filamentous and more or less branched. Sporangiophore with erect trunk 2 to 10 times dichotomously branched, with branches somewhat reflexed and terminal branches sharp-pointed; sporangia colored, lacking an apical papilla, and germinating from an indeterminate point on the side. Oospores more or less smooth or variously marked, germinating by germ tubes (Fig. 48).

Peronospora arborescens. DOWNY MILDEW of prickly-poppy, on leaves, buds, capsules. Yellow or light brown blotches on upper leaf surface turn dark; light gray mold on underside. Fungus winters in old plant parts in soil. Remove and burn infected plants. Use clean seed.

Peronospora arthuri. DOWNY MILDEW of godetia, clarkia, gaura, and evening primrose.

Peronospora destructor. DOWNY MILDEW OF ONION, blight, general on onion, shallot, garlic, one of the most serious diseases of onion, reported in America in 1884. All varieties are susceptible, but red onions are somewhat more resistant. Reduction in yield may be up to 75 per cent.

The first sign of onion mildew is the production of conidiophores with a purplish tinge a short distance back from tips of older leaves. Leaves turn yellow, wither, and break over. Seed stalks may be infected. Onion mildew is sporadic, abundant in years of heavy rainfall. Spores, produced in great numbers in rain or when plants are wet with dew, lose vitality quickly when exposed to sun. Low temperature, optimum 50° F., also favors infection. The fungus winters in or on seed, or in soil.

Control. Rake and burn dead tops; put badly infested soil into other crops for a few years. A rosin soap-lime-sulfur spray has been used in California. At present dusts seem preferable to sprays, with Fermate and Dithane Z–78 giving fair results in some cases.

Peronospora effusa. Downy Mildew of Spinach, and swiss chard, found wherever spinach is grown, absent some seasons and nearly destroying the crop in others. Large pale yellow spots grow together to cover all or part of leaf; lower leaves are infected first, then infection is scattered through the plant. Gray to violet mold forms on underside of leaves and sometimes the whole plant decays and dries. Humidity above 85 per cent and a mean temperature between 45° and 65° F. for a week are required for infection.

Control. Plant spinach on fertile, well-drained soil; do not crowd; cultivate to keep down weeds; if overhead irrigation is used, water early on sunny days; practice a two- to three-year crop rotation. Spraying or dusting has not been very satisfactory because of the residue problem.

Peronospora fragariae. Downy Mildew of strawberry.

Peronospora grisea, on veronica, grayish mildew on underside of leaves.

Peronospora lepidii, on garden cress; **P. leptosperma,** on artemisia; **P. linariae** on linaria; **P. lophanthi,** on agastache.

Peronospora myosotidis. Downy Mildew on forget-me-not, lappula, pale spots on upper surface of leaves with downy growth underneath. Spraying early with bordeaux mixture is said to give control.

Personospora oxybaphi, on sand verbena and four-o'clock.

Peronospora parasitica. Downy Mildew of Crucifers, general on sweet alyssum, arabis, stock, hesperis, cabbage, Chinese cabbage, horse-radish, turnip, cress, peppergrass. Although this mildew occurs wherever crucifers are grown and on nearly all above-ground plant parts it is not ordinarily serious except in a seedbed or with plants grown for seed. Leaf lesions are light green, then yellow with the downy mold on both sides of the leaf in the widening yellow zone but not in the dead, shrunken, gray or tan central portion. Secondary fungi often cover dead parts with a black sooty mold. Fleshy roots of turnips and radishes may have an internal region of discoloration. Warm days and cool nights encourage the disease.

There are several strains of **P. parasitica.** One, often reported as *P. matthiolae,* blights stock in greenhouse and nursery. Leaves have pale green spots on the upper surface and downy mold on the under. Leaves wilt, tender stems and flower parts are stunted and dwarfed.

Control. Avoid crowding plants, remove and burn infected parts; keep foliage dry. Copper sprays or dusts may be helpful on ornamentals. On cabbage Spergon dust seems to give best control.

Peronospora pisi. Downy Mildew of Pea. Water-soaked tissue and white growth on any aerial plant part. Mycelium winters in vetch stems, fruiting there in spring, and spores are disseminated back to peas. The disease is not important enough for control measures.

Peronospora potentillae. Downy Mildew, of agrimony and mock strawberry.

Peronospora rubi. Downy Mildew of blackberry, dewberry, black raspberry.

Peronospora rumicis. Downy Mildew of Rhubarb. Lives over winter in root stalks, grows up with new leaves.

Peronospora schactii. Downy Mildew of Beet, sugar beet, and swiss chard. Inner leaves and seedstalks are curled, dwarfed, covered with violet down; heavily attacked plants are stunted and killed. The disease shows up during the fall rainy season on the Pacific Coast. Oospores can survive in the soil several years.

Control. There is little direct control except to eliminate infected seedlings. Some varieties are less susceptible than others.

Peronospora sojae. Downy Mildew of Soybeans. Indefinite chlorotic areas change to grayish-brown irregular lesions with well-defined dark brown borders and a dense grayish coating of sporangiophores on lower surface.

Peronospora sparsa. Downy Mildew of Rose, chiefly on cuttings under glass. Young foliage is spotted followed by dropping of leaflets. Plants are not killed but blooming is delayed. Abundant spores are produced on underside of leaves. Proper ventilation to regulate temperature and humidity and spraying with bordeaux mixture are considered helpful.

Peronospora tabacina. Blue Mold, Downy Mildew of Tobacco, also on eggplant, pepper, and tomato. This is a seedling disease often controlled in tobacco seedbeds by benzol vapor, evaporated overnight from a flat pan, or by paradichlorobenzene sprinkled on a cloth over seedlings. Fermate or Dithane can be used as a spray.

Peronospora trifoliorum. Downy Mildew of lupine, alfalfa.

PHYTOPHTHORA (See under Blights)

Phytophthora phaseoli. Downy Mildew of Lima Bean, most important in eastern and central states, but decreasing in destructiveness from the Atlantic shore inland. In a rainy season it may take from 50 to 90 per cent of the crop and be of little consequence in a normal season.

White downy mold is conspicuous on the pod, either in patches or covering it. The fungus grows through the pod wall into the bean, then the pod dries, turns black. On leaves the white mycelial weft appears sparingly, but veins are often twisted, purplish, or otherwise distorted. Young shoots and flowers are also attacked, bees and other insects carrying spores from diseased to healthy blossoms. The fungus fruits abundantly on pods, stems, and leaves and is spread by wind and rain as well as insects. In rainy weather, when night temperatures are low and day temperatures high, there can be disastrous results, for the incubation period is very short.

Control. Select healthy seed; plan a long rotation; destroy diseased vines in autumn. Copper sprays and dusts give fair control and Dithane D–14 plus zinc sulfate is promising. In New York State the middle of July is early enough to start treatments.

PLASMOPARA

Sporangiophores with monopodial branches, with obtuse tips, arising more or less at right angles; haustoria unbranched and knoblike; sporangia small, hyaline, papillate, germinating sometimes by germ tubes but usually by swarmspores; oospores yellowish brown, outer wall wrinkled, sometimes reticulate, oogonial wall persistent but not fused with oospore wall (Fig. 48).

Plasmopara acalyphae. Downy Mildew of acalypha.

Plasmopara halstedii. Downy Mildew of bur-marigold, centaurea, erigeron, eupatorium, gnaphalium, goldenrod, hymenopappus, Jerusalem artichoke, ratibida, rudbeckia, senecio, silphium, verbesina, vernonia.

Swarmspores or zoospores germinate in soil moisture and invade seedlings and root hairs; mycelium moves upward into stem and leaves causing early wilt and death. Older plants may not die but have mosaic patterns of light yellow mottling. Sporangiophores project through stomata on underside of leaves. The fungus winters on seed and as oospores in soil.

Control. Rotate plantings. Spray with bordeaux mixture during summer to prevent extensive spread.

Plasmopara geranii, on geranium. **P. gonolobi,** on gonolobus.

Plasmopara nivea. Downy Mildew of Carrot, parsley, parsnip, chervil. Yellow spots on upper surface of foliage and white mycelial wefts on under surface turn dark brown with age. Many tops can be killed but the disease is chiefly important where plants are so crowded they cannot dry off quickly after rain or heavy dew.

Control. Space rows properly.

Plasmopara pygmaea, on anemone, hepatica. Fine white mildew covers under surface of leaves; plants are distorted, stems aborted.

Plasmopara viburni, on viburnum.

Plasmopara viticola. Downy Mildew of Grape, general on grape, also on ampelopsis—Virginia creeper and Boston ivy. This is a native disease, endemic in eastern United States, first observed in 1834 on wild grapes. It had spread to France by 1878, probably imported with American stock resistant to the phylloxera aphid, and in four years it had invaded nearly every vine-growing district in France, some in Germany and Italy, and had become about as ruinous to the wine industry as the potato blight had been to the people of Ireland. The efficacy of bordeaux mixture was first discovered in connection with this mildew.

In this country grape downy mildew is most destructive on European grape varieties east of the Rocky Mountains. Pale yellow spots, varying in form but often nearly circular, and somewhat transparent, appear on the upper leaf surface, while the same region on the lower surface has the conspicuous white downy coating. The spots turn brown with age, and in dry weather the downy growth is scanty. Young canes, leaf stalks and tendrils may be infected in the same way; flowers may blight or rot; fruits infected when young stop growing, turn dark and dry with a copious grayish growth. Older fruits have a brown rot but lack the mildew effect. Fruits from infected vines have less juice, and the bunches are very poorly filled.

Initial infection comes from a swarmspore stopping on the lower side of a leaf, putting out a germ tube, and entering through a stoma. In 5 to 20 days the mycelium has spread through the leaf between cells, obtaining food via thin-walled, globular haustoria. Then the hyphae mass in compact cushions just beneath stomata, and under humid conditions a few hyphae grow out through the openings and develop into branched conidiophores. Occasionally conidiophores also break through crushed and killed epidermal cells. Each one has three to six main branches which branch again. The terminal branches end in two to four short, slender sterigmata, each of which produces a single multinucleate spore. In moisture each nucleus with adjacent protoplasm is organized into a swarmspore, motile with two cilia. These swim around for awhile, then settle down, absorb their cilia, and put out a germ tube. If they happen to be on the upper surface of a leaf nothing happens; but, if they are on the lower surface, the germ tube may reach a stoma and infection follows.

Toward the end of the growing season thick-walled resting spores, oospores, are produced in intercellular spaces of infected parts. These are set free in spring by disintegration of host tissue, are windborne to other vines, and germinate by production of a short, unbranched hypha bearing a single large sporangium which produces swarmspores to start the cycle anew.

Control. Although Fermate is recommended for black rot of grapes, bordeaux mixture seems to be better for downy mildew, applied when shoots are 6 to 8 inches long, just after blossoming, and before fruit changes color. Fallen leaves should be destroyed by burning.

PSEUDOPERONOSPORA (Peronoplasmopara)

Like Plasmopara but with branches of sporangiophores forming more or less acute angles, and tips more acute.

Pseudoperonospora celtidis. DOWNY MILDEW of hackberry.

Pseudoperonospora cubensis. DOWNY MILDEW OF CUCURBITS, general on cucumber, melon, squash, pumpkin, gourds, Chinese wax gourd, bryonopsis. This mildew is most severe on muskmelon, rare on watermelon, and along the Atlantic shore, north of Virginia, south of Maine. It was first noted in 1889 in New Jersey, in 1896 destroyed most of the cucumbers on Long Island, and the next year caused great losses in Ohio.

Irregular yellow spots show on upper surface of foliage, often that nearest the center of the hill. The lesion is brown on the opposite side but covered with a purple growth in dew or rain. The whole leaf may wither and die, with the fruit dwarfed to "nubbins" and of poor flavor. The fungus does not live in the soil and is not prevalent in the North until July or August. It winters in greenhouses or comes up from the South by degrees. The disease is favored by cool temperatures, high humidity.

Control. Copper sprays and dusts control the mildew but from standpoint of yield the zinc dithiocarbamates, like Dithane Z–78, seem better in some states. There are some resistant varieties: Chinese cucumber crosses with Black Diamond, Porto Rican selections, and Texas resistant cantaloupe No. 1.

SCLEROSPORA

Oospore wall confluent with that of oogonium; sporangiophore typically stout with heavy branches clustered at apex; mycelium intercellular, with small, knoblike, unbranched haustoria; germination by germ tube or swarmspores. The genus is common and serious in moist tropic regions on corn, millet, sorghum, and sugar cane.

Sclerospora farlowii. DOWNY MILDEW of Bermuda grass in Southwest. Short, black dead areas prune off tips of leaves without serious damage to grass. Tissues are filled with thick-walled, hard oospores.

FRUIT SPOTS

Many fruit blemishes are symptoms of rot diseases and are treated under Rots; others are due to physiological disturbances and are discussed under Physiogenic Diseases; a few others, limited to fruits and known primarily as fruit spots or specks, are included in this section.

CRIBROPELTIS

Fungi Imperfecti, Sphaeropsidales, Leptostromataceae

Brown mycelium, branched profusely; black, irregularly circular pycnidia; simple, hyaline clavate conidiophores and pale, hyaline, oblong, straight to slightly curved conidia.

Cribropeltis citrullina. FLY SPECK of watermelon fruits.

LEPTOTHYRIUM

Fungi Imperfecti, Sphaeropsidales, Leptostromataceae

Pycnidium flattened with a more or less radiate shield, opening with an ostiole; spores 1-celled, hyaline on simple conidiophores.

Leptothyrium pomi. FLY SPECK, general on apple, also on pear, quince, citrus fruits, Japanese persimmon, plum, blackberry, raspberry, and grape.

Black specks that look like fly specks and formed of closely woven hyphae of the fungus may be numerous over surface of fruit. The disease is disfiguring but not very injurious. Flyspeck and sooty blotch often go together on apples but are controlled by the usual spray schedule for codling moth and apple scab.

MYCOSPHAERELLA (See under Anthracnose, Leaf Spots)

Mycosphaerella pomi. BROOKS FRUIT SPOT of apple. Small spots, less than 1/4 inch in diameter, are red or black on red apple skin but green on yellow fruit surface. Spots are irregular, slightly sunken, more abundant near the calyx end of the apple, usually with centers flecked with black. They are often inconspicuous at picking but become larger, more sunken with a corky layer under the skin if not placed at once in cold storage.

Control. Regular summer spray schedule with a sulfur fungicide.

LEAF BLISTER, LEAF CURL DISEASES

A single genus, Taphrina, is responsible for most of the hyperplastic (overgrowth) deformities known sometimes as leaf blisters, sometimes as leaf curl, and occasionally as pockets.

TAPHRINA

Ascomycetes, Taphrinales, Taphrinaceae (Exoascaceae)

Parasitic on vascular plants, causing hypertrophy. Asci in a single palisade layer, not formed in a fruiting body; hyphal cells become thin-walled chlamydospores and on germination the inner spore protrudes from the host and is cut off by a septum to form an 8-spored ascus, which may become many-spored by budding of the ascospores.

Taphrina spp. MAPLE LEAF BLISTER. Leaves after expanding in spring show dark spots, shrivel, and fall; more common in shaded locations; may be locally epidemic.

Taphrina aesculi. LEAF BLISTER of California buckeye; yellow, turning to dull red; witches' brooms formed.

Taphrina aurea. YELLOW LEAF BLISTER OF POPLAR. Conspicuous blisters, small to an inch or more in diameter, are brilliant yellow on concave side when asci are fully developed; later the color changes to brown.

Taphrina caerulescens. LEAF BLISTER OF OAK, common on oaks in the East, with red oaks particularly susceptible and most damage in the South where trees are sometimes killed by repeated defoliation. Blisters start on young, partly grown leaves as gray areas on undersurface, yellow above, soon bulging with the convex side on the upper surface. Individual blisters are ¼ to ½ inch across but often become confluent, causing the leaf to curl. Ascospores are borne on the surface of blistered or curled area.

Control. Early spring spraying with bordeaux mixture is said to control the disease on valuable individual specimens.

Taphrina cerasi. LEAF BLISTER, WITCHES' BROOM on cherry.

Taphrina communis, T. longipes, T. mirabilis, T. pruni. PLUM POCKETS. Hypertrophy of leaves, shoots, and fruits, which become puffy and enlarged into reddish or white swollen bladders. Native American plum is more affected than garden plums. Perennial mycelium persists in trees.

Control. Prune back branches severely; spray two or three times in early spring with lime sulfur.

Taphrina deformans. PEACH LEAF CURL, general on peach, also on nectarine and apricot. This is an old disease, present in the United States for more than a century and in all major peach districts, but not quite so important in the last half century, after a successful control method was worked out.

FIG. 49. Peach Leaf Curl: deformed leaf; palisade layer of asci formed on curled portion; germinating spore.

Young leaves are arched and reddened, or paler than normal, as they emerge from the bud, then become much curled, puckered, and distorted, greatly increased in thickness. Any portion or the entire leaf may be curled, and one or all leaves from a bud. The leaves often look as if a gathering string had been run along the midvein and pulled tight. Leaves may drop, lowering vitality of tree with partial or total failure to set fruit and increasing chance of winter injury. Young fruits may be distorted or cracked. Defoliation for several seasons kills trees outright.

The fungus has no conidial or summer spore stage and the asci are formed not in a fruiting body but in a layer over infected surfaces giving them a silvery sheen. Before leaves fall, ascospores are discharged from this layer and land on bark of twigs and bud scales, there to germinate by budding into yeastlike spores which remain viable over winter. In spring they are washed by spring rains to opening leaf buds.

Control. The simple life history of *T. deformans* makes it comparatively easy to control peach leaf curl with one thorough dormant spray applied at any time before buds start to swell but with many growers preferring fall. Use lime sulfur at a 1 to 15 dilution (1 to 9 if San Jose scale is a problem) or 10–10–100 bordeaux mixture, or even 6–6–100, wetting every bud and following out all terminals to the tips. Fermate and Elgetol are possibilities. If the spray is not applied in fall and spring work is delayed until buds swell, lime sulfur can still be used at a 1 to 50 dilution, which will reduce amount of curl, although not eliminating all infection.

Taphrina faulliana. Leaf Blister of Christmas fern; **T. filicina,** of sensitive fern; **T. struthiopteridis,** of ostrich fern.

Taphrina flava. Yellow Leaf Blister of gray and paper birches in northeastern states.

Taphrina macrophylla. Leaf Curl on red alder. Young leaves are enlarged to several times normal size and curled, but dry up after ascospore discharge. Then a new crop of healthy leaves is formed.

Taphrina rugosa, T. robinsoniana, T. occidentalis, T. amentorum. Catkin Hypertrophy of alder. Scales of catkins enlarge and project as curled reddish tongues covered with a white glistening layer. Infection can be reduced with a 1 to 40 lime-sulfur spray.

Taphrina ulmi. Leaf Blister of Elm. Very small blisters form on elm leaves. The disease is controlled in one nursery by dusting trees with sulfur before buds open.

LEAF GALLS

Leaf galls are hyperplastic abnormalities similar to leaf blisters but with somewhat more definite form. Those considered in this section are caused by the Basidiomycete Exobasidium and the Phycomycete Synchytrium. Other leaf galls are caused by Rusts.

EXOBASIDIUM

Basidiomycetes, Agaricales, Exobasidiaceae

Mycelium intercellular with branched haustoria entering host cells; basidia extend above the layer of epidermal cells much like the layer of asci in Taphrina; each basidium bears 2 to 8 basidiospores; causing marked hypertrophy on species of Ericaceae.

Exobasidium azaleae. Leaf Gall, widespread on flame azalea.

Exobasidium burtii. Leaf Gall, yellow leaf spot, on azalea and rhododendron.

Exobasidium camelliae. Camellia Leaf Gall, on camellia in the Southeast. Symptoms are a striking enlargement and thickening of leaves and thickening of stems of new shoots. Diseased leaves are four or more times as wide and long as normal leaves and very thick and succulent. Color of the upper surface is nearly normal, but the underside is white with a thin membrane which cracks and peels back in strips or patches exposing the spore-bearing layer. There is seldom more than one diseased shoot on a stem and not many on the whole plant so the disease does not cause serious damage.

Control. Hand-picking of affected parts, searching carefully for affected leaves at base of new growth and removing before spores are formed, keeps sporadic infection at a minimum. Spraying with low-lime bordeaux mixture might be effective but is considered unnecessary.

Exobasidium oxycocci. CRANBERRY ROSE BLOOM, shoot hypertrophy, on cranberry, manzanita. The disease appears in cranberry bogs soon after water is removed in spring. Bud infection results in abnormal lateral shoots with enlarged, swollen pink or light rose distorted leaves, which somewhat resemble flowers. Excessive water supply seems to promote this gall.

Control. Remove water early in spring. Early spraying with bordeaux mixture may be helpful.

Exobasidium rhododendri. LEAF GALL on rhododendron. Large, vesicular galls, especially on *Rhododendron catawbiense* and *R. maximum.*

Exobasidium symploci. BUD GALL on sweetleaf.

Exobasidium uvae-ursi. SHOOT HYPERTROPHY on bearberry.

Exobasidium vaccinii. AZALEA LEAF GALL, red leaf spot, shoot hypertrophy of andromeda, arbutus (*A. menziesii*), bearberry, blueberry, box sandmyrtle, chamaedaphne, cranberry, farkleberry, huckleberry, ledum, leucothoë, manzanita, rhododendron. On azaleas and other ornamentals the galls are bladder-shaped enlargements of all or part of leaf, white or pink and succulent when young, turning brown and hard with age. Normally not a serious disease, but in wet seasons, in shaded gardens, and particularly in the South, the number of galls may become rather alarming.

On cranberries and huckleberries the gall is a small, round red blister in the leaf, with spores formed in a dense layer on the underside.

Control. In the small garden picking off azalea galls is usually sufficient control. A low-lime (6–2–100) bordeaux mixture is effective but must be carefully prepared since there is a low margin of safety. Control measures are seldom necessary for red leaf spot of fruits.

Exobasidium vaccinii-uliginosi. SHOOT AND LEAF GALL, WITCHES' BROOM, of rhododendron, manzanita, mountain-heath. An excessive number of twigs are formed on infected branches. Leaves are yellowish white covered with a dense mealy fungus growth. The mycelium penetrates the whole plant, so that it is wisest to remove the shrub rather than to attempt remedial measures.

FIG. 50. Azalea Leaf Gall.

SYNCHYTRIUM

Phycomycetes, Chytridiales, Synchytriaceae

Mycelium lacking, thallus converted into a sorus with a membrane, at maturity either functioning in entirety as a resting sporangium or divided to form many sporangia enclosed in a common membrane; zoospores or swarmspores with one cilium at posterior end. Species cause excrescences of leaves and fruits, and also potato wart.

Synchytrium anemones. LEAF GALL, flower spot of anemone and thalictrum. Flowers are spotted, distorted, dwarfed, and may fall. Red spots are formed on leaves and stems.

Synchytrium aureum. RED LEAF GALL, false rust, on many plants, 130 species in widely separated genera and including acalypha, artemisia, clintonia, delphinium, geum, golden-glow, marsh-marigold, viola.

Control. Pick off and burn affected parts.

Synchytrium endobioticum. POTATO WART, black wart of potatoes. This is not a leaf gall but a warty hypertrophy of the tubers. A European disease, wart was found in 1918, and later, in backyard gardens in mining towns of Pennsylvania, Maryland and West Virginia. Diseased tubers were apparently brought in by immigrants. A strict quarantine was placed on infested districts and there has been no spread to commercial potato fields.

The disease shows as prominent outgrowths or warts originating in the eyes and varying from the size of a pea to that of the tuber itself. Numerous yellow sporangia are released into the soil by decay of the malformed tissue. Either contaminated soil or affected tubers can spread the disease.

Synchytrium vaccinii. RED LEAF GALL on azalea, cranberry, chamaedaphne, gaultheria, ledum, from New Jersey northward. On cranberry the disease appears just before blossoms open. Buds, young leaves and shoots are covered with small, red, somewhat irregular, globular galls about the size of bird shot, affected shoots producing no fruit. The disease is erratic in appearance, but is most frequent in bogs which have excessive or uneven water supply.

LEAF SCORCH

According to the dictionary scorching means to heat so as to change color and texture without consuming. Sometimes leaves are literally scorched in midsummer heat (see Physiogenic Diseases) and sometimes symptoms caused by fungi resemble those of a heat scorch. This section includes some of the latter.

CERATOSTOMELLA

Perithecia superficial with long, often hairlike beaks; spores hyaline, 1-celled. The most famous species, *C. ulmi,* cause of Dutch elm disease, has Graphium as an imperfect stage (see under Wilts). The imperfect stage of *C. paradoxa* is Thielaviopsis (Moniliales, Dematiaceae) characterized by two kinds of conidia, both formed in chains: small, cylindric, hyaline endogenous spores, that is, spores formed inside the conidiophores, and larger ovate dark conidia formed in the usual way.

Ceratostomella (*Thielaviopsis*) **paradoxa.** BLACK SCORCH, bud scorch, heart rot of date palm, coconut palm, also affecting Canary palm, fan palm (Washingtonia) and Guadaloupe palm. A black, irregular, rough, necrotic condition of the leaf stalk is the most striking symptom. The tissues look as if they had been burned, giving the name black scorch. Young leaves are dwarfed, growing point is twisted, fruit stalks and fruit strands are scorched. Furled pinnae of leaf fronds show pale yellow spots with a brown margin that later converge and turn black; infection spreads rapidly and in severe cases the heart leaves dry up. The heart rot discolors trunk tissues and rots the pithy material between cells.

Infection is through wounds during periods of relatively high humidity or through roots, or sometimes through uninjured fruit strands, petioles, or pinnae. Palms with vitality lowered, as when the normal crown of leaves has been reduced but water supply to roots not reduced, are most susceptible.

Control. Destruction of infected parts of palms seems to be the chief control measure. It is easier to bury than to burn trunks.

DIPLOCARPON (See under Black Spot)

Diplocarpon earliana. STRAWBERRY LEAF SCORCH. Dark purplish spots about 1/4 inch in diameter are scattered profusely over upper surface of leaves in all stages of development. The spots lack the white centers which distinguish Mycosphaerella leaf spot. Scorch lesions are found on petioles, stolons, and fruitstalks as well as leaves. If fruitstalks are girdled, death of flowers and young fruits follows. Rarely the disease shows on green berries as a superficial red or brown discoloration and flecking. Spores, produced in quantity in acervuli in lesions, are distributed by birds, insects, and pickers on tools and clothing.

Control. Spray with 8–8–100 bordeaux mixture at 10-day intervals, starting in January in Louisiana, late February in North Carolina. For home gardens this means 2 level tablespoons of copper sulfate and 6 of hydrated lime to each gallon of water. Southland, Fairfax, Howard 17, Dorsett, and some other varieties are rather resistant.

HENDERSONIA

Fungi Imperfecti, Sphaeropsidales, Sphaerioidaceae

Pycnidia dark, separate, innate or finally erumpent, spores dark with several cells.

Hendersonia opuntiae. SCORCH, SUNSCALD, common and serious on prickly pear cactus (Opuntia). Segments turn reddish brown and die; center of the area is grayish brown and cracked.

SEPTORIA (See under Blights)

Septoria azaleae. AZALEA LEAF SCORCH or leaf spot. Small, yellowish round spots enlarge irregularly, turn reddish brown with dark brown centers. Leaves fall prematurely; black fruiting bodies form in fallen leaves. Disease is most serious in greenhouses and under high humidity.

Control. Bordeaux mixture is recommended but Dithane or other carbamate spray might be satisfactory.

STAGONOSPORA

Fungi Imperfecti, Sphaeropsidales, Sphaerioidaceae

Pycnidia dark, globose, separate, innate or finally erumpent; spores hyaline, with several cells, not pointed at ends.

Stagonospora curtisii. NARCISSUS LEAF SCORCH, RED BLOTCH OF AMARYLLIS, red leaf spot, red fire disease, also on crinum, eucharis, hymenocallis, leucojum, nerine, sternbergia, valliota, and zephyranthes.

Leaf tips of narcissus are blighted as in frost injury for 2 or 3 inches, and separated off from healthy basal portions of leaves by a definite margin or yellow area. Spores formed in pycnidia in the dead area furnish inoculum for secondary infection, which consists of lesions in lower portions of leaves —minute water-soaked or yellowish spots becoming raised, scabby, dark reddish brown areas. Flower stalks may be spotted, and brown spots appear on petals. Bulbs suffer loss in weight due to killing of foliage a month or two before normal dying down. Most susceptible varieties are in Leedsii and Polyanthus groups, but all types may be infected.

Although the fungus was described on narcissus in 1878 it was not considered a threat to narcissus nor known to be connected with the amaryllis red blotch before 1929.

On amaryllis or hippeastrum red spots are formed on leaves, flower stems and petals. On foliage the spots are bright red to purplish, small to start but often increasing to 2 inches. Leaves or flower stalks are bent or deformed at the point of attack. This disease should not be confused with "red disease" due to mites.

The spores of this species are variable in size and number of cells, which can be from 1 to 6. They are embedded in a gelatinous matrix, and spread in rain. The fungus apparently winters in or on the bulbs, infecting new leaves as they grow out of the bulb in spring.

Control. Treat suspected narcissus bulbs before planting. Presoak 1 hour, then dip 30 minutes in mercuric chloride, 1 to 750 dilution, or formaldehyde at 1 to 120 parts of water. Control secondary infection in field with bordeaux mixture or 20–80 copper-lime dust. Discard badly infected amaryllis bulbs; remove infected leaves and bulb scales; avoid syringing and heavy watering.

LEAF SPOTS

Leaf spots are the most prevalent of plant diseases, so common we seldom notice them, and rightly so, for if we should attempt to control all the miscellaneous leaf spots that appear in a small suburban garden in a single season we'd quickly go mad. A typical leaf spot is a rather definitely delimited necrotic lesion, often with a brown, sometimes white, center and a darker margin. When the spots are so numerous that they grow together to form large dead areas the disease becomes a blight, or perhaps a blotch, or scorch. Certain types of lesions are called anthracnose, others black spot. All of these have been segregated out in their different sections. What is left is a very large collection of names.

The genus Cercospora, for instance, has about 400 species, chiefly identified by the hosts on which they appear. *Cercospora beticola* is so named because it causes a leaf spot of beet, *C. apii* is named for its celery host, etc. *Cercospora rosicola* becomes *Mycosphaerella rosicola* when the ascospore stage is found in connection with the rose leaf spot so now we have two names in place of one. A large proportion of the 400 Cercospora species are listed under their respective hosts. They are not repeated here unless the leaf spot is of some importance or there is some useful information that can be added to the name, and the same holds true of other genera with large numbers of species separated only by the name of the host on which the spot is found.

Most leaf spot diseases flourish in wet seasons. Some may be serious enough to call for control measures other than general sanitation. But protection of trees and shrubs against leaf spots means starting as leaves are coming out, in most cases, and repeating sprays two or three times. For trees, calling in an expert with high pressure apparatus may be an expensive proposition, and the amount of damage expected must be weighed against the cost. If the budget

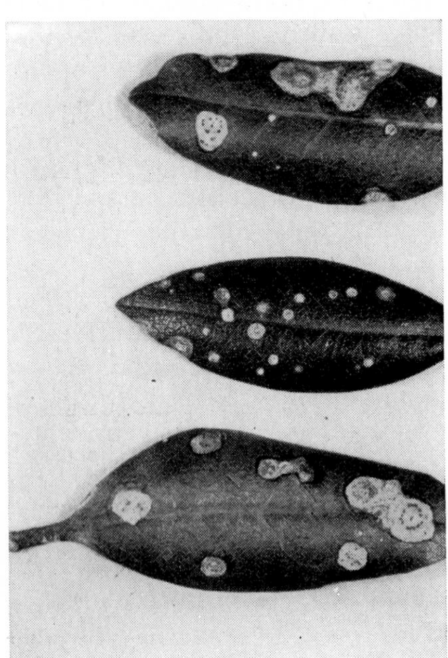

Fig. 51. Leaf Spots; left, typical limited spot with prominent dark pycnidia; right, indefinite type of spot often called blotch, scorch, or leaf blight.

is limited it is more important to have an elm sprayed for elm leaf beetle which causes much defoliation every season than for elm leaf spot (black spot) which might cause some defoliation about one season in three. When it comes to rose black spot (not related to elm black spot), spraying is essential for most garden varieties with fungicides more important than insecticides, although they can usually be combined.

ACTINOTHYRIUM

Fungi Imperfecti, Sphaeropsidales, Leptostromataceae

Pycnidia superficial, globose, with a more or less fimbriate shield; spores filiform, hyaline.

Actinothyrium gloeosporioides. Leaf Spot on sassafras.

ALTERNARIA (See under Blights)

Alternaria brassicae (Berk.) Sacc. BLACK LEAF SPOT OF CRUCIFERS—cabbage, Chinese cabbage, collards, turnip, garden cress, radish, horse-radish; HEAD BROWNING, leaf and pod spot of cauliflower; DAMPING-OFF, wire-stem of seedlings.

There are three Alternaria species causing leaf spots of cabbage and other crucifers and their names have been very much mixed up. (See also *A. herculea* and *A. oleracea.*) *Alternaria brassicae,* as here used, has small dark spores, formed in long chains (on culture media) which germinate over a wide range of temperature.

Seedlings are subject to pre- or post-emergence damping off, with dark brown to black sunken spots on cotyledons, narrow dark spots on stems followed by "wire-stem," a blackening toward the base.

Leaf spots are small, circular, yellowish, enlarging in concentric circles with a sooty black color from the spores. In storage, the spots unite to form a moldy growth over the entire leaf. On seed pods spots are purplish in the beginning, later brown. In moist weather the whole pod may be infected.

Cauliflower infection is a browning of the head, starting at the margin of an individual flower or cluster.

The spores are blown, splashed by rain, carried on tools, feet of men and animals. Spores are also seedborne and the fungus is sometimes present as latent mycelium in seed. Wounds are not necessary for infection.

Control. Hot-water seed treatment seems not to kill all latent mycelium but treatment with Semesan or Arasan reduces amount of damping-off from spores on seed surface. Use long rotations for cauliflower, avoiding all other crucifers in intermediate years.

Alternaria catalpae. CATALPA LEAF SPOT, widespread on catalpa in rainy seasons. Small, water-soaked spots appear over leaf, reach a diameter of ¼ inch and turn brown, sometimes dropping out, leaving shot holes. There is also more or less defoliation. The fungus is possibly secondary following bacterial infection or midge infestation.

Control. Rake up and burn fallen leaves. In occasional cases three applications of bordeaux mixture, starting as leaves unfurl, may be worth-while.

Alternaria citri. Cherry leaf spot, occasionally, more often rot of citrus fruits. See under Rots.

Alternaria fasciculata. LEAF SPOT on rose–acacia and asclepiodora.

Alternaria herculea (*A. brassicae* (Berk.) Bolle). GRAY LEAF SPOT OF CRUCIFERS, general on cabbage and other crucifers, causing browning of cauliflower and broccoli heads like *Alternaria brassicae* (see above). *A. herculea* spores are large, light brown, and sensitive to temperature variations, with optimum germination between 63° and 70° F.

Alternaria longipes. BROWN SPOT OF TOBACCO, including ornamental nicotiana. Small spots on lower leaves rapidly enlarge and turn brown. Fungus winters on old stalks. Remove and burn plants at end of season.

Alternaria mali. Apple leaf spot and storage rot. See under Rots.

Alternaria oleracea. Black Leaf Spot, brown rot of crucifers. This name was first given to a species causing a disease in California similar to that caused by *A. brassicae* elsewhere, but since then the name has been widely used for the pathogen of crucifer leaf spots and head browning.

Alternaria passiflorae. Brown Spot of Passion Flower. Minute brown leaf spots, enlarging to an inch across, are concentrically ridged and zoned with various shades of brown. Dark green water-soaked spots on fruits change to brown spots; fruit shrivels but the spots stay firm.

Control. Prune carefully once a year. Spray with bordeaux mixture or ammoniacal copper carbonate or dust with sulfur.

Alternaria polypodii. Fern Leaf Spot. Brown, circular to oblong, concentrically zonate spots are found along margins of fronds. Chains of spores are spread by syringing or air currents. Keep foliage dry; remove and burn diseased leaves.

Alternaria tenuis. Leaf Spot of magnolia, hibiscus, clarkia, and many ornamental and other hosts. The fungus is a general saprophyte and an occasional weak parasite. It discolors beet, chard, spinach seed.

Alternaria tomato. Nailhead Spot of Tomato, a leaf, stem, and fruit spot. On leaves and stems the disease is much like early blight (see *A. solani* under *Blights*) but on fruits infection is quite different. Very small tan spots, 1/16 to 1/8 inch in diameter, become slightly sunken with grayish brown centers and darker margins. They are shallow unless secondary organisms cause a deeper rot. Spores are produced abundantly on fruit and foliage and are spread by winds and splashing rain.

Control. Treat seed and spray as for early blight. Marglobe, Pritchard, Glovel, and Break o' Day are quite resistant to the fruit spot.

AMEROSPORIUM

Fungi Imperfecti, Sphaeropsidales, Excipulaceae

Pycnidia superficial, discoid to cupulate, hairy; spores 1-celled, hyaline.

Amerosporium trichellum. Leaf and Stem Spot of English ivy. In some cases stems are girdled, causing collapse and death.

ARISTASTOMA

Fungi Imperfecti, Sphaeropsidales, Sphaerioidaceae

Pycnidia dark, globose; spores with several cells, hyaline.

Aristastoma oeconomicum. Leaf Spot on kidney bean.

ASCOCHYTA (See under Blights)

Ascochyta abelmoschi. LEAF SPOT of rose mallow; POD SPOT, stem spot of okra, not widespread but occasionally severely infecting young pods. Dark, small, water-soaked spots slowly enlarge, turn brown with many black pycnidia in concentric rings in dead tissue. Pycnidia are large and spores have either

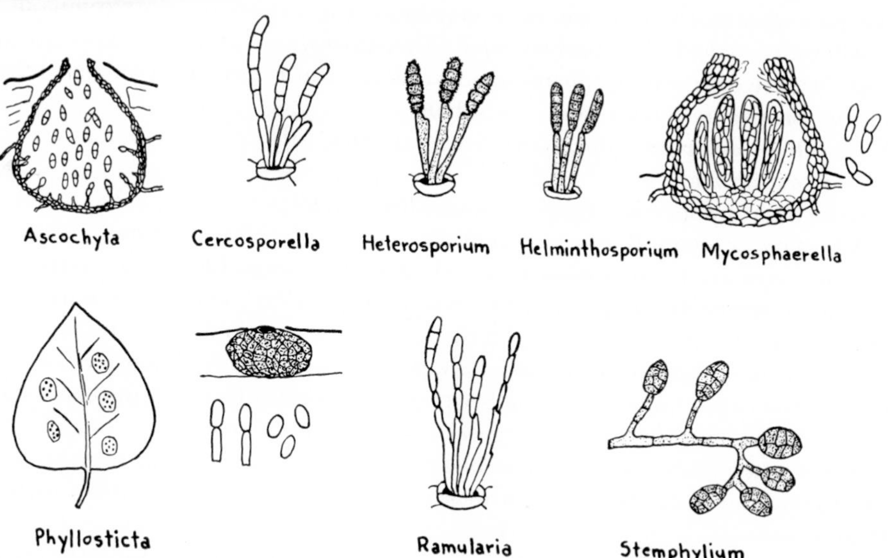

FIG. 52. Some Leaf-spot Fungi. *Ascochyta,* hyaline, 2-celled conidia in Pycnidium; *Cercosporella,* hyaline, septate spores on conidiophores emerging from a stoma; *Heterosporium,* spiny, dark, septate spores; *Helminthosporium,* smooth, dark, septate spores; *Mycosphaerella,* 2-celled hyaline ascospores in a perithecium; *Phyllosticta,* hyaline, 1-celled conidia in pycnidia formed in spots on leaves; *Ramularia,* hyaline spores, becoming septate, formed successively on conidiophores; *Stemphylium,* colored muriform spores borne free on mycelium.

one or two cells. Mycelium in pod grows through wall into seed and is disseminated in it.

Ascochyta aspidistrae. LEAF SPOT on aspidistra. Large, irregular, pale spots on leaves.

Ascochyta asteris. LEAF SPOT of China aster. Treat seed with mercuric chloride; spray foliage with bordeaux mixture.

Ascochyta boltshauseri. LEAF SPOT, POD SPOT OF BEANS, on snap, kidney, lima, and scarlet runner beans, first reported in America in 1933 in Oregon. Spots on leaves and pods are dark to drab, zonate; pycnidia are numerous, light to dark brown, spores predominantly 1-septate.

Ascochyta cheiranthi. LEAF AND STEM SPOT OF WALLFLOWER. Grayish spots, up to ½ inch long, may girdle stems. Leaf spots are circular to elongated, brown with darker brown margins; dark pycnidia contain hyaline 2-celled spores. Leaves wilt and fall; potted plants may be infected.

Control. Spray with bordeaux mixture, keep greenhouse dry.

Ascochyta clematidina. LEAF AND STEM SPOT OF CLEMATIS, widespread. On outdoor plants stems are infected near the ground and are often girdled with upper portions dying back. Spores for initial infection probably come from pycnidia on stumps of old stems. In greenhouses leaf spots are more common—small, water-soaked, then buff with reddish margins.

Control. Remove and destroy infected leaves and stems; spray or dust with sulfur; propagate from disease-free plants.

Ascochyta compositarum. LEAF SPOT on aster, eupatorium, goldenrod, silphium, sunflower.

Ascochyta lycopersici (perfect stage *Didymella lycopersici*). LEAF SPOT, ASCOCHYTA BLIGHT of tomato, eggplant, and potato. Brown spots with concentric rings are formed on leaves and stems and sometimes cankers at base of young stems. Black pustules in center of spots are pycnidia discharging spore tendrils in wet weather. The fungus winters in old plant refuse, is a weak parasite, and ordinarily too unimportant for control measures.

Ascochyta pisi. LEAF SPOT, POD SPOT OF PEA, general but rare in the Northwest. This is one of the three species of Ascochyta that cause the disease complex often known as Ascochyta blight (see under Blights). All three species are seed-borne, carry from season to season in pea refuse, and flourish in wet weather.

Spots on foliage are circular to irregular, pinhead size to ½ inch. Stem lesions are brown to purplish black, are formed at nodes or base of stem. Clusters of brown pycnidia exude spore tendrils in wet weather, the spores being distributed by splashed rain. When pods are spotted the fungus can grow through the pod wall into the seed but most seed contamination is on the surface when peas are harvested.

Control. Seed grown in arid regions is generally free from blight, but in unusual years blight appears even in the western seed fields. The more arid the region the less chance of infested seed. Inspection of seed fields is important. Rotate crops and clean up all pea refuse.

CEPHALEUROS

One of the green algae, possessing chlorophyll, but not differentiated into root, stem and leaves; forming motile spores in sporangia.

Cephaleuros virescens. ALGAL SPOT, RED LEAF SPOT, GREEN SCURF, in the far South or in greenhouses on acacia, albizzia, ardisia, avocado, bixa, bischofia, camellia, camphor-tree, cinnamon-tree, citrus, grevillea, guava, jasmine, jujube, loquat, magnolia, mango, pecan, Japanese persimmon, privet, rhododendron, viburnum.

On some hosts this is a disease of twigs and branches which may be girdled and stunted, and covered with reddish-brown hairlike fruiting bodies. On magnolia leaves velvety, reddish-brown to orange cushionlike patches are formed, but in the absence of sporangia, tiny globular heads on fine, dense reddish hairs, the leaf spots are greenish to brown. Occasionally citrus fruits, as well as leaves and twigs, are attacked.

The sporangia formed on the fine hairs germinate in moisture, producing zoospores which enter through stomata and form myceliumlike chains of algal cells in host tissue. On twigs the alga invades outer cortical tissue which may swell abnormally and afford entrance to injurious fungi. Weakened trees are most susceptible; spread of the disease is most rapid in periods of frequent and abundant rains.

Control. Improve drainage and other growing conditions. Spray with bordeaux mixture or commercial lime sulfur. Since the bordeaux will also kill any beneficial scale fungi present, 1½% oil emulsion should be added to take care of the scales.

CEPHALOSPORIUM

Fungi Imperfecti, Moniliales, Moniliaceae

Spores formed in heads, kept together by slime to make a rounded mass, bright colored; sterile hyphae long, decumbent.

Cephalosporium cinnamomeum. Leaf Spot of syngonium. Small, irregular water-soaked areas develop into reddish brown spots with pale yellow borders and grayish, papery centers. In severe infections leaves turn yellow and die.

Control. Keep greenhouse temperature low, avoid syringing. Try a copper spray that does not leave too objectionable residue.

Cephalosporium dieffenbachiae. Leaf Spot of dieffenbachia. Small, reddish lesions on young leaves with dark borders sometimes run together to cause yellowing and death of whole leaf. Infection is often through mealybug wounds.

Control. Avoid promiscuous syringing; keep temperature and humidity low; control mealybugs, and the ants which carry them around.

CERCOSEPTORIA—Cercospora, according to some workers.

CERCOSPORA (See under Blights)

Cercospora alabamensis. Leaf Spot of morning-glory and jacquemontia. One application of a copper spray is said to control this.

Cercospora althaeae. Leaf Spot on hollyhock and abutilon. More or less angular, grayish spots are scattered irregularly over the leaf, the dead tissue often falling out, leaving shot holes. The fungus winters in old plant parts.

Control. Remove diseased plant parts; spray with bordeaux mixture.

Cercospora angulata. LEAF SPOT on philadelphus, currant, flowering currant and gooseberry.

Cercospora arachidicola. LEAF SPOT OF PEANUT. One of two Cercospora leaf spots of peanuts and probably the least destructive. Irregularly circular, often confluent spots, surrounded with a bright yellow halo vary from 1 mm. to 1 cm. in size. Older spots are dark brown to almost black on the upper surface, lighter brown on underside. Conidiophores formed on both sides of the leaf emerge from stomata or break out of epidermal cells. Conidia are colorless to pale yellow or olive and have 4 to 12, averaging 5 to 7, cross-walls. For control see *C. personata*.

Cercospora beticola. CERCOSPORA LEAF SPOT OF BEET, general on garden and sugar beets, also on swiss chard, spinach. The disease is common in home gardens but is of more economic importance on sugar beets. Brown flecks with reddish-purple borders become conspicuous spots with ash gray centers and a purplish border. The brittle central tissue often drops out leaving ragged holes. Spots usually stay small but may be so numerous foliage is killed. When successive crops of leaves are lost the crown of the beet root is elongated and roughened. The leaf spotting is of little direct importance, except in swiss chard where foliage is used for greens, but the root yield is reduced.

The grayish color of the spots is due to long thin septate conidia produced on conidiophores protruded through stomata in fascicles or groups, coming from a knotted mass of mycelium resembling a sclerotium. Conidia are spread by rain, wind, tools, and insects. Infection is through stomata so that disease spread is most rapid under conditions of high humidity which keep stomata open. Hot weather also favors the disease. Spores winter in old plant refuse or on seed.

Control. In a small garden picking off the first spotted leaves is practical. A copper dust will control spotting but is not too desirable if foliage is to be used for greens. Seed treatment helps to decrease early infection. Use crop rotation, space rows well apart, clean up crop refuse in fall.

Cercospora brunkii. LEAF SPOT of geranium (Pelargonium) mostly in the South. Spots are circular, light reddish-brown with dark brown borders, sometimes coalescing to kill entire leaf.

Cercospora calendulae. CALENDULA LEAF SPOT, perhaps the most serious disease of calendula. Spots run together to blight and kill leaves; entire plants are often destroyed early in season. Spores enter through stomata of plants more than a month old.

Control. Dust with sulfur.

Cercospora capsici. LEAF SPOT, STEM-END ROT OF PEPPER wherever crop is grown, serious in rainy seasons. Spots 1/8 to 1 inch in diameter are first water-soaked, then white with dark brown margins. Leaves turn yellow and drop. Fungus grow through pedicel into fruit, causing stem-end rot.

Control. Spray or dust with copper fungicides.

Cercospora carotae. LEAF SPOT; EARLY BLIGHT OF CARROT, general but seldom very important. Gray to brown spots appear on leaves and petioles. See *Alternaria dauci* under Blights for the more serious late blight of carrots.

Cercospora circumscissa. LEAF SPOT, shot hole of apricot, plum, sweet and sour cherries, cherry laurel, oriental cherry, chokecherry. Dead spots are somewhat larger than those caused by other shot-hole fungi, but the damage is not serious.

Cercospora citrullina. LEAF SPOT of watermelon, muskmelon, and other cucurbits. Spots are small, circular, black with grayish centers, occurring first on leaves in center of watermelon hills. On cucumber, muskmelon, and squash, spots are larger and gray-ochre. Defoliation of vines may cause some reduction in fruit size, but the disease is not considered important.

Control. Clean up diseased vines; use a two- to three-year rotation, spray or dust as for bacterial wilt.

Cercospora cornicola. LEAF SPOT of flowering dogwood. Spraying with bordeaux mixture will prevent occasional defoliation.

Cercospora fusca. PECAN LEAF SPOT, prevalent through the pecan belt but a minor disease, serious in localities with high rainfall and in neglected orchards where trees lack vigor. Spots are circular to irregular, reddish brown and often with grayish concentric zones. Fungus winters in old spots on leaves. In Florida the disease appears first in June or July on mature leaves and may cause premature defoliation in October. Stuart variety is particularly susceptible, the others are more or less resistant.

Control. One application of bordeaux mixture (6–2–100) between May 15 and June 15.

Cercospora melongenae. LEAF SPOT of eggplant. Lesions first yellow, then large brown areas with concentric rings.

Cercospora nandinae. LEAF SPOT of nandina, one of the few diseases of this usually healthy shrub. Reddish spots are formed on leaves.

Cercospora personata. PEANUT LEAF SPOT. Spots are circular, 1 to 7 mm. across, sometimes pale yellow-green and with a bright yellow halo on upper leaf surface. Conidiophores are produced on both sides of leaf but are more numerous on the lower, arranged concentrically in tufts and rupturing epidermis. Spores are pale brown to olivaceous, 1- to 7-septate. Spots are formed on stems. In wet years this disease may nearly defoliate vines.

Control. Sulfur dust gives good control and markedly increases yield. Bordeaux mixture is also helpful.

Cercospora resedae. LEAF SPOT, BLIGHT of mignonette, a rapid disease killing much of the foliage. Numerous small, circular spots, pale yellow with reddish brown borders run together discoloring entire leaf. Lower leaves are most affected; spores are spread by wind and rain.

Control. Spray with bordeaux mixture or less conspicuous copper spray.

Cercospora rhododendri. LEAF SPOT on rhododendron. Angular dark brown spots with grayish down in center, due to spores. Control measures are usually unnecessary.

Cercospora richardiaecola. LEAF SPOT on calla lily, sometimes injurious. Avoid syringing, keep plants well spaced, ventilate greenhouse.

Cercospora smilacis. LEAF SPOT on smilax. Spots are more or less circular, up to 1/4 inch in diameter, dark purplish red, centers fading with age but margins remaining definite and dark colored. Cinnamon brown conidiophores with colorless spores emerge in clusters from stomata.

Control. Dust with sulfur or spray with bordeaux mixture.

Cercospora sojina. FROG-EYE DISEASE OF SOYBEAN. Typical frog-eye spots are formed on leaves; elongated reddish lesions appear on stems, changing to brown then gray or nearly black with age; pods of late varieties are also infected. Fungus overwinters on diseased leaves and stems. Early varieties escape much injury.

Cercospora symphoricarpi. LEAF SPOT on snowberry, coralberry, and wolfberry.

CERCOSPORELLA

Fungi Imperfecti, Moniliales, Moniliaceae

Spores more or less broadly filiform, typically more than 10 times longer than wide, septate, hyaline, on leaves (Fig. 52).

Cercosporella albomaculans. WHITE SPOT of turnip, cabbage, Chinese cabbage. Sclerotial-like bodies give rise to hyaline conidiophores beneath dead epidermal cells. The leaf spots are circular with paper white centers crossed by dark brown veinlets. The disease is most severe in autumn and sometimes Chinese cabbage foliage is killed. Ordinarily white spot is too unimportant for control measures other than sanitation. All diseased refuse should be cleaned up at end of the season.

Cercosporella pastinacae. LEAF SPOT on parsnip occasionally. Spots are small, circular, first brown, then with a white center and brown border. No control is needed.

CLADOSPORIUM (See under Blights)

COLLETOTRICHUM (See under Anthracnose)

Colletotrichum gloeosporioides. LEAF SPOT of jasmine, passion flower, leaf and stem spot of calendula; on many other hosts as anthracnose.

CONIOTHYRIUM (See under Cankers)

Coniothyrium concentricum. LEAF SPOT of century plant and yucca. Spots are zoned, light grayish brown, an inch or more in diameter, with concentric rings of tiny black pycnidia. Large portions of leaves may be destroyed.

Control. Remove and burn diseased leaves.

Coniothyrium hellebori. Black Spot of Christmas Rose. Large, irregular black spots on both sides of leaves, often running together and with concentric zonation; many leaves turn yellow prematurely and die; plants are weakened, fail to mature normal number of leaves. Stems may have canker-like spots, shrivel and fall over, with wilting of unopened flower buds. Open petals sometimes have black spots.

Control. Cut off and destroy diseased parts; spray or dust with a copper fungicide.

Coniothyrium pyrina. Leaf and Fruit Spot of apple, pear.

CRYPTOMYCINA

Ascomycetes, Phacidiales, Phacidiaceae

Apothecium splitting irregularly into lobes, hyphal layer thin; spores hyaline, 1-celled.

Cryptomycina pteridis. Tar Spot of fern. Spots are usually on lower surface and between veins; sometimes there is a leaf roll.

CRYPTOSTICTIS

Fungi Imperfecti, Melanconiales, Melanconiaceae

Conidia formed in acervuli; dark, with several cells, with one cilium or appendage at base.

Cryptostictis arbuti. Leaf Spot on *Arbutus menziesii*, manzanita, ledum.

CURVULARIA

Fungi Imperfecti, Moniliales, Dematiaceae

Dark spores with 3 or 4 cross-walls, generally curved, with 1 or 2 or middle cells larger than the others.

Curvularia lunata. Leaf and Flower Spot of Gladiolus. This fungus has been known as a pest of crop plants, chiefly tropical, for many years but in August, 1947, it suddenly showed up in Florida as a most serious threat of the gladiolus cut-flower industry, ruining hundreds of acres there and in Alabama in the next few months. The disease is now recorded as far north as New York and Wisconsin, but weather conditions make epidemics less likely in the North.

Curvularia spots on leaf or stem are oval, tan to dark brown, showing on both sides of the leaf, bordered with a brown ring, slightly depressed, and with a narrow yellowish region between the spot and the normal green of the leaf. Tan centers of spots are covered with black spores resembling powder. Petal lesions are brownish, varying from pin-point size to an inch or more, but if there is much stem damage the florets fail to open. There are many gladiolus varieties more or less resistant, but Picardy and some others are very susceptible.

This is a high temperature fungus with optimum for growth 75° to 85° F. and no infection under 55° F. A 13-hour dew period is sufficient moisture, with leaf spots showing up in 4 to 5 days, spots on florets and stems in only 2 or 3 days and the complete cycle to spore production as short as a week in warm weather.

Control. So far, the dithiocarbamates offer best protection. Spray regularly, weekly or as often as every 3 to 5 days for spikes, with Dithane D–14 plus zinc sulfate and lime or Dithane Z–78 or Parzate.

CYCLOCONIUM

Fungi Imperfecti, Moniliales, Dematiaceae

Mycelium coiled, spores small, dark, 2-celled; scarcely different from short hyphae.

Cycloconium oleaginum. OLIVE LEAF SPOT, PEACOCK SPOT, ring spot. Blackish more or less concentric rings on leaves, especially those weakened or old, are not serious enough for control measures.

CYLINDROCLADIUM

Fungi Imperfecti, Moniliales, Moniliaceae

Spores 2-celled, hyaline; conidiophores dichotomously branched.

Cyclindrocladium macrosporium. LEAF SPOT, leaf blight of Washington palm. Numerous small, dark brown spots with light margins are somewhat disfiguring.

Cylindrocladium pteridis. FERN LEAF SPOT, leaf blotch. Reddish brown lesions run together to cover large areas. Pick off and burn infected fronds.

CYLINDROSPORIUM

Fungi Imperfecti, Melanconiales, Melanconiaceae

Conidia in acervuli, spores filiform, typically continuous, often curved, hyaline; spore masses white or dark, not setose; on leaves or branches.

Cylindrosporium betulae. BROWN LEAF SPOT OF BIRCH, sometimes serious enough to defoliate but not often found on ornamental trees.

Cylindrosporium chrysanthemi. LEAF SPOT on chrysanthemum. Spots are dark brown with yellowish margins, increasing to involve whole leaf, which hangs down along the stem, as it does with the more common Septoria leaf spot.

Cylindrosporium clematidinis. LEAF SPOT of clematis. Reddish brown spots on lower leaves which may drop; dusting with sulfur is suggested.

Cylindrosporium salicinum. Leaf Spot of willow, sometimes causes defoliation; can be controlled with bordeaux mixture if necessary.

DIDYMARIA

Fungi Imperfecti, Moniliales, Moniliaceae

Conidiophores simple; spores 2-celled, hyaline.

Didymaria didyma. Leaf Spot on anemone. Angular brown spots.

DIDYMELLINA

Ascomycetes, Sphaeriales, Mycosphaerellaceae

Perithecia separate, innate or finally erumpent, not beaked; spores 2-celled, hyaline.

Didymellina macrospora (conidial stage *Heterosporium iridis,* formerly considered *H. gracilis*). Iris Leaf Spot or leaf blotch, on both bulbous and rhizomatous iris. The leaf spotting is conspicuous toward the end of the season

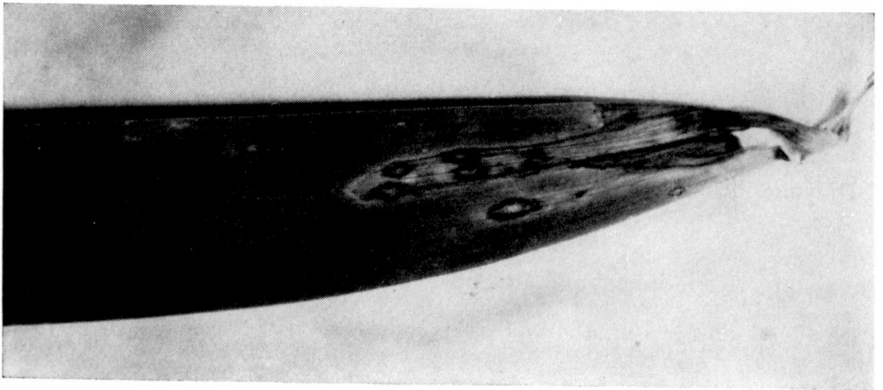

Fig. 53. Iris Leaf Spot.

and on upper half of foliage, but in a normally dry season the disease is not too serious. When plants are crowded and shaded and the summer is wet, the spotting appears earlier and is more damaging.

Spots are first dark brown, surrounded by a water-soaked then yellowing region, but spots later enlarge into yellow brown more or less oval lesions, ¼ to ½ inch long with a deep red-brown border. In bulbous iris this border is lacking. Tufts of conidia turn the centers gray, the spores being produced in abundance and splashed by rain to neighboring leaves. Infection is either through stomata or directly through epidermis. The fungus ordinarily winters as mycelium in old leaves and in spring produces either a fresh crop of conidia or perithecia of the Didymellina stage. The disease is considered more serious when soils are deficient in lime. Repeated spotting reduces bloom and after a number of years may cause death of plants.

The taxonomy of the fungus has been confused, the conidial stage once named *Heterosporium gracile* but with *H. iridis* now accepted in this country. The connection with the perithecial stage has been made fairly recently. Conidia are septate, olivaceous, cylindric but rounded at ends, spiny, usually with 3 cells, sometimes 5 or 6 (Fig. 52). Perithecia are smooth, globose, dark brown to black, with thick, somewhat beaked ostioles (mouths), and ascospores hyaline, elliptical to spindle-shaped, unequally 2-celled.

Control. Usually it is sufficient to remove and burn all old leaves at the end of the season; sometimes shearing back spotted leaves in midsummer is advisable. In some seasons and locations, spraying with bordeaux mixture to which a good sticker is added may be profitable.

Didymellina ornithogali (conidial stage *Heterosporium ornithogali*). Leaf Spot on star-of-bethlehem. Occasional sooty spots on leaves, with foliage blackened and killed in severe infections.

Didymellina poecilospora, a weak parasite sometimes causing black discoloration of iris leaves.

DIDYMOSPORIUM

Fungi Imperfecti, Melanconiales, Melanconiaceae

Conidia are slime spores in acervuli, dark, 2-celled.

Didymosporium arbuticola. Leaf Spot on *Arbutus menziesii.*

DILOPHOSPORA

Fungi Imperfecti, Sphaeropsidales, Sphaerioidaceae

Pycnidia distinct in a stroma; conidia very long, filiform, with brushlike hairs at each end.

Dilophospora geranii. Leaf Spot on native geranium.

DIPLODINA

Fungi Imperfecti, Sphaeropsidales, Sphaerioidaceae

Pycnidia smooth, innate or finally erumpent; conidia 2-celled, hyaline, ovoid, on simple conidiophores.

Diplodina eurhododendri. Leaf Spot on rhododendron.

DOTHICHIZA (See under Cankers)

Dothichiza caroliniana. Leaf Spot, double spot of blueberry, found only on *Vaccinium australis* in North Carolina, but there causing extensive leaf spotting and defoliation. Leaf spots are small, circular, with brown centers and a dark brown ring, but in late summer infection spreads to a secondary necrotic area around the original spot, giving the common name of double spot. Black pycnidia are formed sparsely in the spots. All varieties of high bush blueberries are somewhat susceptible, but Cabot, Dixie, Pioneer, and Rancocas are most damaged.

ECTOSTROMA

Mycelia Sterilia—black stromata formed in leaves and stems.

Ectostroma liriodendri. TAR SPOT, widespread on tulip-trees but perhaps secondary after insect injury.

EPICOCCUM

Fungi Imperfecti, Moniliales, Tuberculariaceae

Sporodochia globose to convex, fleshy; conidiophores short; conidia globose, dark, roughened, 1-celled but sometimes muriform with age.

Epicoccum asterinum. LEAF SPOT of yucca; **E. neglectum** of royal palm; **E. nigrum** on *Magnolia grandiflora;* and **E. purpurascens** on amaryllis but perhaps secondary.

EXOBASIDIUM (See under Leaf Galls)

Exobasidium burtii. YELLOW LEAF SPOT of azalea and rhododendron. See Leaf Galls.

EXOSPORIUM

Fungi Imperfecti, Moniliales, Tuberculariaceae

Conidia on subglobose to convex sporodochia; spores dark, 2 to several cells, sort of club-shaped.

Exosporium concentricum. LEAF SPOT, on *Euonymus japonicus* and ligustrum (privet) in the South.

Exosporium liquidambaris. LEAF SPOT on sweet gum.

Exosporium palmivorum. LEAF SPOT OF PALMS in greenhouses and in the South. Small, round, yellowish, transparent spots run together to form large, irregular, gray-brown blotches. Leaves may die, the disease being most serious in greenhouses with insufficient light. The spores are long, club-shaped, brown, with many cells.

Control. Remove and burn infected leaves; spray with bordeaux mixture.

FUSICLADIUM

Fungi Imperfecti, Moniliales, Dematiaceae

Spores dark, 2-celled, borne at tip of conidiophores which are simple or sparsely branched. In some cases Fusicladium is the imperfect stage of Venturia and the cause of scab diseases.

Fusicladium pisicola. Black Leaf of peas, first reported in Utah, in 1921, causing trouble in canning peas. Spots start as small, irregular whitish areas on undersurface of leaflets and stipules, but they darken to gray or black from the closely packed layer of dark conidia. The disease is not very serious.

Fusicladium robiniae. Leaf Spot and seedling leaf blight of black locust. Spots are small, with light centers and dark margins. There is frequently defoliation of seedlings, sometimes stunting and death.

GLOEOSPORIUM (See under Anthracnose)

Gloeosporium betularum. Leaf Spot, anthracnose of river birch. Spots are more or less circular, 1/8 inch across, brownish with pale centers and yellow margins. They are sometimes numerous enough to cause some damage.

Gloeosporium inconspicuum. Elm Leaf Spot, on American and English elms. Subcircular brown spots with darker margins and centers are visible on both upper and lower leaf surfaces.

Gloeosporium mezerei. Leaf Spot on daphne. Small brown spots on both sides of leaves.

Gloeosporium rhododendri. Leaf Spot on tulip-tree and rhododendron.

Gloeosporium ulmicolum. Elm Leaf Spot. Elongated spots are formed along midribs, veins and margins, visible on both leaf surfaces.

GLOEOCERCOSPORA

Fungi Imperfecti, Moniliales, Tuberculariaceae

Sporodochia formed on surface of host above stomatal opening from hyphae emerging through stomata; conidiophores hyaline, simple or branched; conidia hyaline, elongate to filiform, 1 to many-septate, straight or curved, in a slimy matrix.

Gloeocercospora inconspicua. Leaf Spot of highbush and rabbiteye blueberry. Circular to angular, brownish spots on leaves, with sporodochia more frequent on upper surface. These are flat discs when dry, but glistening globules when wet, containing curved, septate conidia.

GLOMERELLA (See under Anthracnose)

Glomerella cincta. Leaf Spot widespread on queen palm, dracaena, maranta, orchids. In the latter the disease is sometimes called Sobralia blight. Dark discoloration starts at tip of leaves and advances toward base.

Glomerella cingulata. Leaf Spot on aucuba, wampi, croton. See under Anthracnose for this fungus on many other hosts.

GNOMONIA (See under Anthracnose)

Gnomonia caryae. Hickory Leaf Spot, anthracnose, widespread. The disease is common in the eastern states and causes defoliation in wet seasons. Large more or less circular spots are reddish brown on upper leaf surfaces and dull brown underneath. The fruiting bodies are minute brown specks, the fungus overwintering in dead leaves on ground.

Gnomonia caryae (*Leptothyrium*) var. **pecanae.** LEAF SPOT, LIVER SPOT OF PECAN.

Gnomonia nerviseda (*Leptothyrium nervisedum*). VEIN SPOT OF PECAN.

Gnomonia tiliae. LINDEN LEAF SPOT, leaf blotch, scorch, on American and European linden. See under Anthracnose.

GNOMONIELLA

Ascomycetes, Sphaeriales

Perithecia in substratum, beaked, membranous separate; spores hyaline, 1-celled.

Gnomoniella coryli. LEAF SPOT on hazel, frequent in northern states, controlled with bordeaux mixture aided by cleaning up fallen leaves.

Gnomoniella fimbriata. LEAF SPOT of hornbeam.

GONATOBOTRYUM

Fungi Imperfecti, Moniliales, Dematiaceae

Hyphae dark, with spiny inflations at intervals around which are borne ovoid conidia.

Gonatobotryum maculicola. LEAF SPOT on witchhazel.

GRAPHIUM

Fungi Imperfecti, Moniliales, Stilbaceae

Spores formed on upright hyphae joined together to form a synnema or coremium; conidia 1-celled, dark, in mucus.

Graphium sorbi. LEAF SPOT of mountain-ash.

GUIGNARDIA (See under Blotch Diseases)

Guignardia bidwellii f. **parthenocissi.** LEAF SPOT widespread on Boston ivy, pepper-vine, Virginia creeper. Leaf spots are numerous, angular, reddish to grayish brown, usually dark brown at the margin, with minute pycnidia of the imperfect Phyllostictina stage of the fungus, which is a form of that causing black rot of grapes. Leaves are most unsightly and there is some defoliation.

Control. Two or three properly-timed sprays of bordeaux mixture will give some control, but the "cure" looks about as bad as the disease. Fermate is less conspicuous and seems to be somewhat effective. Spraying should start as leaves are coming into full size.

HELMINTHOSPORIUM (See under Blights)

Helminthosporium erythrospilum. LEAF SPOT of redtop and bent grasses, widespread in eastern and middle-western states. Under wet conditions lesions have small, pale centers with russet border, but in dry weather leaves wither

FIG. 54. Common Leaf Spot of Boston Ivy.

as in drought with less evident spotting. Conidia are typically cylindrical, rounded at both ends, yellowish, and germinate from any or all cells.

Helminthosporium giganteum. ZONATE LEAF SPOT. Eye spot, on bent grasses, Canada and Kentucky bluegrass, Bermuda grass. The disease is present in turf and in nursery rows. Spots are small, 1/16 to 1/8 inch, bleached to straw color in center. In the presence of moisture the fungus grows periodically into new areas giving the zoned appearance. In continued wet weather entire leaves are killed and grass turns brown.

Control. Choose resistant Washington or Metropolitan bent rather than susceptible Virginia strain. Organic mercuries sprayed on turf are promising —phenyl mercury acetate and ethyl mercury arsenate. Chlorophenol mercury, mercuric chloride, and calomel are not satisfactory, whereas lime sulfur is effective but injurious.

Helminthosporium triseptatum. LEAF SPOT on redtop, velvet grass, timothy. Leaf lesions are small with a pale center surrounded by a salmon zone in wet weather.

Helminthosporium vagans and sp. LEAF SPOT, foot rot of bluegrass. Spots are bluish black with gray or straw-colored centers. This disease was very serious in hot, humid summer of 1949. A new bluegrass, B27, is resistant.

Helminthosporium vignae. ZONATE LEAF SPOT of soybean.

HENDERSONIA

Fungi Imperfecti, Sphaeropsidales, Sphaerioidaceae

Pycnidia smooth, innate or finally erumpent; conidia dark, many-celled.

Hendersonia concentrica. LEAF SPOT on rhododendron.

Hendersonia crataegicola. LEAF SPOT on hawthorn. Spots irregular, dark brown.

HETEROSPORIUM

Fungi Imperfecti, Moniliales, Dematiaceae

Conidia solitary or few in a group, dark, spiny, with several cells, small oval cells sometimes formed by budding from hyphae or conidiophores (Fig. 52).

Heterosporium allii. LEAF SPOT on onion and leek.

Heterosporium echinulatum. FAIRY RING SPOT, leaf mold on carnation, occasional through range of greenhouse culture. Bleached spots develop on leaves with black spore groups in ring formation.

Control. Syringe as little as possible, and on bright days; control ventilation.

Heterosporium gracile. LEAF SPOT on chlorogalum, daylily, confused with *H. iridis* on iris.

Heterosporium iridis (conidial stage of *Didymellina macrospora,* which see). LEAF SPOT on iris, blackberry lily (belamcanda), freesia, gladiolus.

Heterosporium variabile. LEAF SPOT, pinhead "rust," of spinach, cabbage mold, sometimes severe in cold, wet weather. Small brown spots enlarge and multiply until they cover most of the leaf surface; the rest turns yellow, later dies. Spots are conspicuous from the greenish-black mold on both leaf surfaces. The fungus is a weak parasite entering the host only after it is weakened by too much rain, cold weather, malnutrition, or insect pests. The conidia are large, olive, 1- to 3-septate but small oval spores are formed singly or in chains by budding.

Control. Keep plants growing vigorously on well-drained soil.

HIGGINSIA (See under Blights)

Higginsia (*Cylindrosporium*) **lutescens.** LEAF SPOT, SHOT HOLE on cherry-laurel, black cherry, choke-cherry, similar to leaf blight and shot hole caused by *H. hiemalis* (see under Blights).

Higginsia (*Cylindrosporium*) **prunophorae.** LEAF SPOT, SHOT HOLE on garden plum, apricot. Reddish to brown spots (dark blue at very beginning) produce pinkish spore masses on underside of leaves in wet weather. The shot-hole effect from dropping out of dead tissue may be very prominent and may be accompanied by a heavy fruit drop.

Control. Spray when shucks are off young fruit, two to three weeks later, and before fruit ripens, with lime-sulfur at a 1 to 50 dilution or with wettable sulfur, or dust with sulfur.

ILLOSPORIUM

Fungi Imperfecti, Moniliales, Tuberculariaceae

Conidia superficial on bright-colored sporodochia; conidiophores lacking or imperfect; spores hyaline, 1-celled.

Illosporium malifoliorum. Leaf Spot of apple and crabapple.

ISARIOPSIS

Fungi Imperfecti, Moniliales, Stilbaceae

Fertile hyphae aggregated into cylindric fascicles, or synnemata, which are pale or dark; conidia with several cells, in a loose head.

Isariopsis griseola. Angular Leaf Spot, pod spot, of beans, also sweet pea. Small, angular brown spots are so numerous that they give a checkerboard appearance to leaves. The fungus forms a gray moldy covering over dead areas on underside of leaf, and when dry the fruiting bodies look like small black stromata. The pod spots are very conspicuous—black with red or brown centers, the two zones sharply divided from each other and adjoining healthy tissue, and varying in size from a speck to whole width of the pod. Small dark fungal growths are scattered over the surface bearing large, 2- to 4-celled conidia at top of stalks. They are probably wind-disseminated. Control measures, other than sanitation, are seldom practical.

Isariopsis laxa. Leaf Spot on kidney bean.

KABATIA

Fungi Imperfecti, Sphaeropsidales, Leptostromataceae

Pycnidia with a radiate shield or scutellum with an ostiole; spores 2-celled, hyaline, like a tooth at the apex.

Kabatia lonicerae. Leaf Spot on honeysuckle.

LAESTADIA (Guignardia?)

Laestadia asarifolia. Leaf Spot on wild ginger.

Laestadia prenanthis. Leaf Spot on prenanthes.

LASIOBOTRYS

Ascomycetes, Erysiphales, Meliolaceae

Perithecia in a ring around a sclerotial stroma; spores dark, 2-celled.

Lasiobotrys affinis. Leaf Spot on honeysuckle. Spot is well-marked with small dark wartlike stromas.

LEPTOSTROMELLA

Fungi Imperfecti, Sphaeropsidales, Leptostromataceae

Pycnidia elongate, with a cleft, separate; spores filiform, with rounded ends, hyaline, continuous to septate, on simple conidiophores.

Leptostromella elastica. LEAF SPOT of rubber-plant. The disease appears in spots and streaks but spreads until the entire leaf is involved. Black lines outline spots, in which small black pycnidia produce long, colorless spores.

Control. Remove and burn infected leaves. Spray with ammoniacal copper carbonate or other copper spray which will not leave a conspicuous residue.

LEPTOTHYRELLA

Fungi Imperfecti, Sphaeropsidales, Leptostromataceae

Pycnidia with a radiate shield, separate; spores 2-celled, hyaline.

Leptothyrella liquidambaris. LEAF SPOT, red, on sweet gum.

LEPTOTHYRIUM (See under Fruit Spots)

Leptothyrium californicum. LEAF SPOT on coast live oak.
Leptothyrium dryinum. LEAF SPOT on white oak.
Leptothyrium periclymeni. LEAF SPOT on honeysuckle, widespread.

LINOSPORA

Ascomycetes, Sphaeriales

Perithecia innate, beaked, beak often lateral, with a shield, paraphyses lacking; spores spindle-shaped to filiform, hyaline.

Linospora gleditsiae. LEAF SPOT, tar spot on honey locust in the South. Numerous flat black fruiting bodies are formed on undersurface of leaves.

LOPHODERMIUM (See under Blights)

Lophodermium rhododendri. LEAF SPOT on rhododendron. Large silvery white spots with red raised margins have very prominent oval black fruiting bodies on upper surface. Lower side of spots is a light chocolate brown. Infected portions may fall out, leaving irregular holes. The disease is more common on native than hvbrid varieties.

MACROPHOMA

Fungi Imperfecti, Sphaeropsidales, Sphaerioidaceae

Spores 1-celled, hyaline, larger than 15μ; same as Phoma except for larger spores.

Macrophoma candollei. LEAF SPOT of Boxwood. Conspicuous black pycnidia on dead leaves which are straw colored, sometimes tan or brown. The fungus is a weak parasite coming in secondarily after winter injury or other predisposing factors.

MARSSONINA (Sometimes found as *Marssonia*)

Fungi Imperfecti, Melanconiales, Melanconiaceae

Spores hyaline, 2-celled, formed in pale to black masses in acervuli on leaves (Fig. 21).

Marssonina daphnes. LEAF SPOT on daphne. Small, thick brown spots on both sides of leaf, which turns yellow, dies.

Marssonina delastrei. LEAF SPOT on corncockle and campion.

Marssonina fraxini. LEAF SPOT OF ASH, sometimes serious in nursery stock, controlled by spraying with bordeaux mixture.

Marssonina juglandis. LEAF SPOT OF HICKORY. Large yellow blotches on leaves, glistening white on lower surface; if blotches are numerous leaflets fall prematurely.

Control. Gather and burn all fallen leaves. Spray with 4–4–100 bordeaux mixture.

Marssonina populi. POPLAR LEAF SPOT. Brown spots with darker brown margins cause premature defoliation and may kill twigs.

Marssonina ochraleuca. LEAF SPOT on oak, American chestnut. Spots are circular, yellow to brown with concentric markings, small on chestnut, up to an inch in diameter on oak.

Marssonina rosae, imperfect stage of *Diplocarpon rosae,* cause of rose black spot (see under Black Spot).

MASTIGOSPORIUM

Fungi Imperfecti, Moniliales, Moniliaceae

Hyphae very short, little different from conidia; spores several-celled, hyaline, some species with appendages, conidiophores often obsolete.

Mastigosporium rubricosum. RED EYE-SPOT or leaf fleck, on redtop and bent grasses. Spores with rounded ends, without appendages.

MELANCONIUM

Fungi Imperfecti, Melanconiales, Melanconiaceae

Spores dark, 1-celled, globose to oblong, formed in acervuli, masses setose (with hairs).

Melanconium pandani. LEAF SPOT on pandanus.

MELASMIA

Fungi Imperfecti, Sphaeropsidales, Leptostromataceae

Pycnidia with a stroma, innate; conidia sausage-shaped, hyaline, 1-celled; a stage of *Rhytisma.*

Melasmia menziesiae. LEAF SPOT, tar spot of azalea.
Melasmia falcata. Tar spot of persimmon.

MICROPELTIS (See under Blights)

Micropeltis alabamensis. BLACK LEAF SPOT on magnolia.

MICROSTROMA

Fungi Imperfecti, Melanconiales, Melanconiaceae

Spores hyaline, 1-celled; conidiophores are club-shaped and look like basidia with sterigmata to bear conidia.

Microstroma juglandis. LEAF SPOT, white mold, witches' broom of pecan, walnut and hickory. Yellow blotching of upper side of leaves and a glistening white coating on under surface of leaves, due to pustules containing enormous numbers of spores, may be accompanied by premature defoliation. On shagbark hickory the fungus also invades the stems causing witches' brooms, often numerous and up to 3 feet across. Leaves formed on witches' brooms in spring are yellow green with the white powdery fungus on the underside. Leaflets are small, curled, and soon drop.

Control. Prune out witches' brooms; spray with bordeaux mixture.

MONOCHAETIA

Fungi Imperfecti, Melanconiales, Melanconiaceae

Spores in acervuli, with several cells, center cells dark, with one appendage, at apex.

Monochaetia desmazierii. LEAF SPOT on chestnut, white oak, red oak, coast live oak, winged elm, hickories, especially destructive in the Southeast. Spots are large, 1 to 2 inches in diameter, with pale green or yellow centers surrounded with a red and brown border or concentric zones of gray, yellow, and brown. Symptoms appear most often in late summer when loss of green tissue is not so important.

Control. Bordeaux sprays would be effective but perhaps unnecessary.

MORENOELLA

Ascomycetes, Hemisphaeriales, Microthyriaceae

Apothecia linear, with a shield, hyphopodia present, paraphyses lacking; spores dark, 2-celled.

Morenoella quercina. LEAF SPOT of red and black oaks, twig blight of white oak, common in Southeast. Spots are purplish black, roughly circular, up to $\frac{1}{3}$ inch across, on upper surface and irregular brown areas on under leaf surface. Mycelium is superficial in early summer, but by late summer there are subcuticular hyphae and a black shield formed over a flat cushion of fertile cells. Asci are mature and shield is fissured by spring.

MYCOSPHAERELLA

Ascomycetes, Sphaeriales, Mycosphaerellaceae

Perithecia sparse to gregarious, innate to erumpent, not beaked, typically membranous; spores 2-celled, hyaline, paraphyses and paraphysoids lacking (Fig. 52). Imperfect stages are often in the Moniliales—Cercospora, Ramularia, Phyllosticta, Septoria, etc.

These are more than 1000 species in this unwieldy genus, the conidial stage present during the pathogenic portion of the life cycle and the perithecial stage initiated in late summer and fall, maturing in spring. Spermagonia containing spermatia, presumably male cells, have been often taken for pycnidia and conidia of Phyllosticta.

Mycosphaerella arachidicola. Leaf Spot of peanut, general in southern states. Pycnidia-like spermogonia are formed during autumn on spots produced by Cercospora stages.

Mycosphaerella berkleyi, perfect stage of *Cercospora personata.* Leaf Spot, general on peanut.

Mycosphaerella (*Cercospora*) **bolleana.** Leaf Spot on fig, rubber-tree.

Mycosphaerella (*Phyllosticta*) **brassicicola.** Ring Spot of Crucifers on cabbage, broccoli, brussels sprouts, cauliflower, turnip. Dead spots in leaves, small to ½ inch in diameter, are surrounded by a green zone which keeps its color even if rest of leaf turns yellow. Small black pycnidia deeply embedded in tissue are scattered over the dead surface and are most numerous at margin of leaf. In moist weather conidia ooze from pycnidia in pink tendrils. The fungus winters in old plant refuse. Ascospores are forcibly ejected from perithecia in spring.

Control. Spraying with bordeaux mixture has been advised but results are inconclusive.

Mycosphaerella caroliniana. Leaf Spot, purple blotch of oxydendron or sourwood. Reddish or purple spots on foliage in midsummer have dry and brown centers. Pycnidia embedded in tissue break through lower surface. Spores are formed in large numbers.

Mycosphaerella caryigena. Downy Spot of Pecan, first reported as a new leaf spot in 1927. Conidial stage has been given as a Cercosporella and as *Cylindrosporium carigenum.* Leaf spots are pale yellow when young, turning yellow brown, brown, or black. Conidia produced in minute acervuli on under side of leaves form a white downy or frosty coating; spores are spread in rain, fog, and dew. Tissue in spots may die and leaves drop early. The fungus overwinters in leaves, liberating ascospores in spring to infect new foliage. Orchard trees are more subject to damage than nursery stock, with varieties Moneymaker and Stuart most susceptible.

Control. Turn under old leaves before spring (plowing under winter cover crops takes care of this). The first two sprays for scab will control downy spot: (1) 4–1–100 bordeaux mixture when first leaves are half-grown; (2) 6–2–100 bordeaux mixture plus 4 pounds zinc sulfate when tips of small nuts have turned brown.

Mycosphaerella cerasella. LEAF SPOT of sweet and sour cherries, choke-cherry. Spermagonia are formed late in season in bases of conidial stromata of Cercospora stage.

Mycosphaerella (*Cercospora*) **cercidicola.** REDBUD LEAF SPOT, general on redbud (Cercis). Spots are circular to angular or irregular with raised, dark brown borders. With age, lesions become grayish above and rusty brown on the under surface. The leaf tissue is yellow-green outside the border. Spores are formed on fascicles of conidiophores projecting through stomata. The fungus winters on fallen leaves, producing perithecia in spring. Twigs may be attacked as well as foliage.

Control. Spray with bordeaux mixture in spring.

Mycosphaerella colorata (*Phyllosticta kalmicola*) LEAF SPOT on mountain-laurel. Spots are irregular to circular, with gray centers, dark purple-brown borders, black fruiting bodies. See under Phyllosticta.

Mycosphaerella confusa (*Cercospora rubi*) LEAF SPOT on raspberry, blackberry, dewberry.

Mycosphaerella (*Cercospora*) **cruenta.** LEAF SPOT, leaf blotch of soybean, kidney bean.

Mycosphaerella fragariae. STRAWBERRY LEAF SPOT, black-seed disease, general on strawberries. Reddish spots with brown or grayish centers, 1/8 to 1/4 inch in diameter, are formed on leaves and occasionally black spots on fruits, the blackened achenes prominent against the white of unripe berries.

Control. Set healthy plants in well-drained soil; remove diseased leaves before planting; spray with bordeaux mixture before planting, and follow with two or three more applications. The conidia are very sensitive to copper, which prevents sporulation and kills nongerminated spores.

Mycosphaerella fraxinicola (spermagonial stage *Phyllosticta viridis*). LEAF SPOT on ash, east of the Rocky Mountains.

Mycosphaerella liriodendri (*Phyllosticta liriodendrica*). LEAF SPOT on tulip-tree.

Mycosphaerella louisianae. PURPLE LEAF SPOT OF STRAWBERRY, in the South. Large, irregular, reddish purple areas.

Mycosphaerella mori. MULBERRY LEAF SPOT, widespread, with the conidial stage reported variously as Cercosporella, Cylindrosporium, Phleospora, Septogloeum, and Septoria. Yellow areas on upper leaf surface are matched by whitish patches on under surface with the fungus forming a white downy or powdery coating. The disease is most serious in shady places.

Mycosphaerella nyssaecola (*Phyllosticta nyssae*). LEAF SPOT on sour-gum or tupelo and water tupelo. Purplish, irregular blotches, an inch or more across, are scattered on upper leaf surface, with the lower surface dark brown. There may be heavy defoliation. Perithecia mature in spring on fallen leaves.

Mycosphaerella personata (conidial stage *Isariopsis clavispora*) widespread on muscadine and other grapes after midseason. Spots are dark brown, 1/4 to 1/2 inch in diameter, surrounded by a yellow circle with a narrow band of normal leaf color between spot and circle.

Mycosphaerella pinodes. LEAF SPOT, STEM BLIGHT of peas, including sweet pea. See under Blights.

Mycosphaerella (*Septoria*) **populicola,** and **M. populorum.** LEAF SPOT of poplar. Conidial stage of the latter is *Septoria musiva,* cause of a canker on branches and twigs of some hybrid poplars. The leaf spot occurs only on native poplars.

Mycosphaerella (*Septoria*) **ribis** (formerly *M. grossulariae*). LEAF SPOT of gooseberry, currant, and flowering currant. Numerous small brown spots with grayish centers are formed on both sides of leaves and cause premature defoliation. The fungus winters in leaves, producing ascospores in late spring.

Control. Two sprays of bordeaux mixture, 3–5–100, plus 1 pint of self-emulsifying cottonseed oil (S.E.C.) per 100 gallons has given good control of leaf spot on gooseberries in New York State. The first application is about June 1 and the second in July immediately after fruit is picked.

Mycosphaerella (*Cercospora*) **rosicola.** LEAF SPOT ON ROSE, general except far South. Spots start as small, yellow-green dots, then change into small, light brown areas with purplish borders, with the tissue sometimes falling out in a shot-hole effect. Perithecia are formed in fallen leaves.

Control. Rake up and burn old leaves. The spraying or dusting schedule for black spot should control this leaf spot.

Mycosphaerella (*Septoria*) **rubi.** LEAF AND CANE SPOT OF RASPBERRY, general, also on blackberry, dewberry, loganberry, youngberry, boysenberry in West. Spots are small, first reddish then ashen gray, circular, with black pycnidia visible in center. Spotting occurs late in season but there is defoliation in severe attacks which makes the canes more subject to winter killing.

Control. The spray schedule for other diseases should give control. In the West, spraying with bordeaux mixture before the fall rains and after first leaves are developed is suggested.

Mycosphaerella sentina (*Septoria pyricola*). LEAF SPOT, ASHY FRUIT SPOT on apple and pear, chiefly in the East.

MYROTHECIUM

Fungi Imperfecti, Moniliales, Tuberculariaceae

Sporodochia dark, shield or disc-shaped, with white setae (hairs) at margin; spores 1-celled, dark.

Myrothecium roridum. LEAF SPOT on stock, eremurus, hollyhock. Tissues are dry, brittle, with black sporodochia.

NEOTTIOSPORA

Fungi Imperfecti, Sphaeropsidales, Sphaerioidaceae

Pycnidia dark, smooth, innate; spores hyaline, 1-celled with two to several appendages at the apex.

Neottiospora yuccifolia. Leaf Spot on yucca.

OPHIODOTHELLA

Ascomycetes, Dothideales, Phyllachoraceae

Asci in locules immersed in groups in a stroma, covered by host tissue at maturity; paraphyses lacking; spores filiform.

Ophiodothella vaccinii. Leaf Spot on huckleberry, farkleberry.

OVULARIA

Fungi Imperfecti, Moniliales, Moniliaceae

Spores 1-celled, hyaline, in living leaves, solitary or somewhat in chains, formed on simple or branched hyphae.

Ovularia aristolochiae. Leaf Spot on Dutchman's-pipe.

Ovularia pulchella. Tan Leaf Spot on creeping bent grass.

PESTALOTIA (See under Blights)

Pestalotia aucubae. Leaf Spot on aucuba. Fungus comes in on sunscalded areas or after other fungi as a weak wound parasite.

Pestalotia aquatica. Leaf Spot on arrow-arum. Irregular, chestnut brown spots, up to an inch in diameter have purplish or dark borders and are wrinkled concentrically. Acervuli are sparse, black, erumpent on upper side of leaf. Spores are 5-celled with 3 widely divergent setae.

Pestalotia cliftoniae. Leaf Spot on buckwheat-tree. Ashy or pale brown spots; spores usually curved, constricted at septa; 3 setae at crest.

Pestalotia funerea. Leaf Spot, bark and cone spot on conifers. Pathogenicity of the fungus is questionable. Median spore cells are dark brown; apical hyaline cell has 4 to 5 erect setae.

Pestalotia guepini. Camellia Leaf Spot, widespread on camellia and tea. Numerous, punctiform black fruiting bodies are scattered over gray papery spots. The spores are 5-celled, bright olivaceous, with 1 to 4 divergent, sometimes branched setae, with an inconspicuous knob at the apex, and a short, straight pedicel. This species apparently can be a true parasite.

Pestalotia leucothoës. Leaf Spot of Leucothoë, apparently following winter injury or other disease.

Pestalotia macrotricha. Rhododendron Leaf Spot, gray blight, twig blight, widespread on azalea and rhododendron after winter injury. Black raised pustules are scattered over the stems and on leaves in dark or pale spots or areas at tips and along margins. Spots are often silvery gray on the upper surface, brown below, with the acervuli densely gregarious and sooty from the dark spores.

Pestalotia palmarum. Leaf Spot, gray leaf of palms. Black pustules are sparsely produced on both surfaces of pale, dead areas with definite, reddish brown borders. The fungus is a wound parasite. Spores are 5-celled, with 2 or 3, often knobbed, setae.

Pestalotia rhododendri. Leaf Spot of rhododendron. Black pustules are scattered without order on dried brown areas of living leaves. Spores are broader than those of *P. macrotricha* and have shorter setae.

PESTALOZIELLA

Fungi Imperfecti, Melanconiales, Melanconiaceae

Conidia hyaline, 1-celled, with a branched appendage or awn at apex.

Pestaloziella subsessilis. Leaf Spot on geranium.

PEZIZELLA

Ascomycetes, Helotiales, Helotiaceae

Apothecia sessile, bright-colored, smooth; paraphyses filiform, blunt; spores elliptic to fusoid, hyaline, 1-celled.

Pezizella oenotherae. Leaf Spot, fruit rot of blackberry, raspberry, strawberry, also leaf spot of evening primrose, eugenia, galax, loosestrife, ludwigia, mock-strawberry, May-apple, peony, sumac. Spots are irregular, gray in center with a dark brown border, with light amber, disclike fruiting bodies and spores that are amber in mass.

PHACIDIUM (See under Blights)

Phacidium curtisii. Tar Spot, leaf spot of American holly, also English holly. Small, yellow spots appear in early summer, turning reddish brown with narrow yellow borders. At end of the season flat, black, cushion-shaped masses, stromata, develop underneath the epidermis. Leaves do not often drop prematurely, but the infected areas may fall out, leaving holes.

Control. Clean up and burn diseased leaves; possibly spray with bordeaux mixture, but this may be injurious.

PHLEOSPORA

Fungi Imperfecti, Sphaeropsidales, Sphaerioidaceae

Pycnidia incomplete, on leaves; spores hyaline, needle-shaped.

Phleospora aceris. Leaf Spot of maples, including vine and dwarf maples. The spot is small, rather angular; common but not important.

PHLYCTAENA

Fungi Imperfecti, Sphaeropsidales, Excipulaceae.

Pycnidia innate to erumpent, globose to oblong, more or less cleft; spores needle-shaped to filiform, hyaline.

Phlyctaena ficuum. LEAF SPOT on strangler fig (*Ficus aurea*).

PHOMA (See under Cankers)

Phoma lupini. LEAF SPOT on various native lupines.

PHYLLACHORA (See under Black Spot)

Phyllachora graminis. TAR SPOT of grasses, widespread but seldom a general nuisance. Black glossy spots are conspicuous; perithecia immersed in the black stroma have openings on both sides of the leaf. There is no conidial stage.

PHYLLOSTICTA

Fungi Imperfecti, Sphaeropsidales, Sphaerioidaceae

Pycnidia innate, or finally erumpent, smooth, globose, black, with an ostiole, in spots in leaves; spores 1-celled, hyaline, ovoid (Fig. 52).

The word Phyllosticta literally means leaf spot and this genus is separated from Phoma chiefly on the basis of the organ attacked, Phoma usually, although not always, being found on stems or fruits. There are about 500 species, distinguished almost entirely on the basis of the host. Most can be controlled with bordeaux mixture or other sprays but in many cases picking off infected leaves is sufficient.

Phyllosticta althaeina. LEAF SPOT, stem canker on abutilon and hollyhock. Ashy spots have black dots of pycnidia. The tissue sometimes becomes brittle and falls away, leaving jagged holes.

Phyllosticta aucubae. LEAF SPOT on aucuba. Brown or black zonate spots are mostly along margins of leaves, sometimes with much defoliation. Spores are exuded from leaves in yellow tendrils then spread by rain or syringing in the greenhouse.

Control. Spray with copper ammonium silicate or other colorless copper fungicide.

Phyllosticta camelliae and **P. camelliaecola.** LEAF SPOT ON CAMELLIA. Lesions are more or less irregular brown spots.

Phyllosticta catalpae. LEAF SPOT ON CATALPA. Dark brown or black spots, 1/8 to 1/4 inch in diameter may run together to give a blotched appearance. Minute black fruiting bodies are visible in spots which are often associated with the spotting caused by the catalpa midge. Heavy infection may mean defoliation.

Control. Gather and burn fallen leaves. Spray with bordeaux mixture.

Phyllosticta circumscissa. Leaf Spot on apricot, peach, sour cherry, garden plum, choke-cherry, widespread.

Phyllosticta concentrica. Leaf Spot of English Ivy, also twig blight, widespread. Plants look ragged; fruiting bodies are arranged in concentric circles in spots.

Phyllosticta cookei. Leaf Spot of Magnolia. Spots are grayish without definite margins.

Phyllosticta decidua. Leaf Spot of agrimony, aralia, basil weed, betony, cynoglossum, eupatorium, germander, hierachia, hoarhound, motherwort, lycopus, mint, monarda.

Phyllosticta hamamelidis. Leaf Spot of Witch Hazel. Small spots enlarge to reddish brown blotches, causing some defoliation.

Phyllosticta hydrangeae. Leaf Spot of Hydrangea, widespread. Brown spots are usually near leaf margins. In severe cases both leaves and blossoms are killed.

Control. Spraying with bordeaux mixture or dusting with sulfur has been recommended.

Phyllosticta kalmicola (imperfect stage of *Mycosphaerella colorata*). Leaf Spot of Mountain-laurel. Circular, grayish white to silvery spots with red

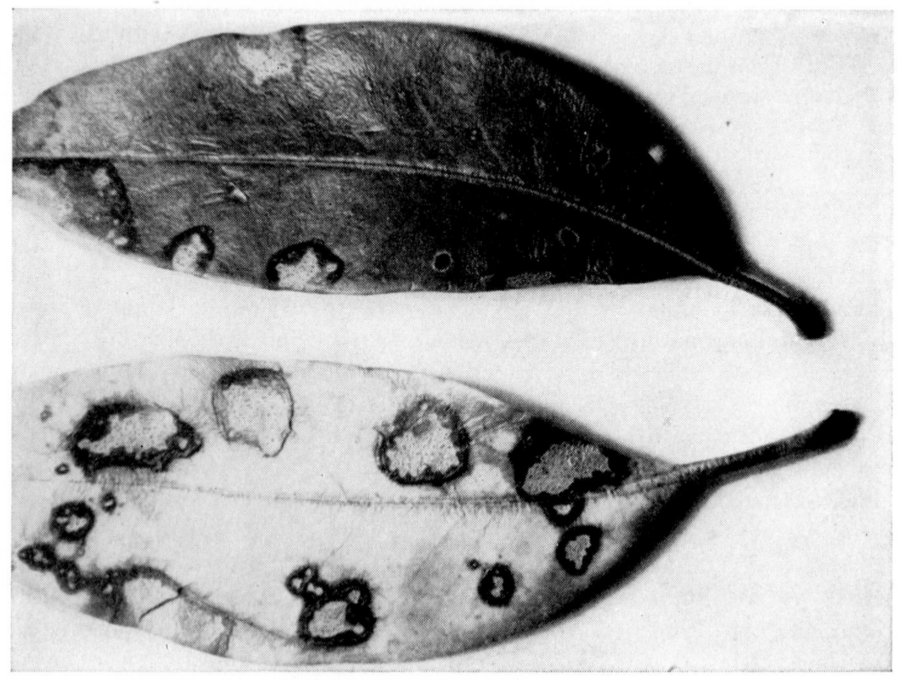

Fig. 55. Phyllosticta Leaf Spot of Mountain-laurel. Black pycnidia are visible in centers of spots; lower leaf has turned yellow and is ready to drop.

or purplish borders, up to ¼ inch across, are sparsely or thickly covered with black pycnidia. Heavy infection means disfigured foliage and some defoliation. The disease is worse in shady locations and where shrubs are under drip of trees.

Control. Spray with 4–4–100 bordeaux mixture, or a less conspicuous copper compound such as Coposil, three or four times from June to September. In some seasons and locations sprays should start in May soon after new growth comes out.

Phyllosticta maculicola. Leaf Spot of Dracaena. Irregular small brown spots have yellowish margins and long coils of spores from black pycnidia.

Phyllosticta maxima. Leaf Spot of Rhododendron, widespread. Spots are marginal or terminal—large, dark brown, zonate.

Phyllosticta minima. Leaf Spot, Gray Spot of Maple, including boxelder, widespread. Spots are more or less irregular, ¼ inch or more across, with brownish centers, containing black pycnidia, and purple-brown margins. The disease is seldom serious enough for control measures.

Phyllosticta richardiae. Leaf Spot of Calla Lily. Small, round ash-gray spots run together, producing irregular decayed areas.

Phyllosticta sanguinariae. Leaf Spot of Bloodroot. Spots reddish brown with a darker border, then a zone of Indian red.

Phyllosticta vaccinii. Leaf Spot on farkleberry and highbush blueberry.

Phyllosticta wistariae. Wistaria Leaf Spot, more important in the South.

PHYLLOSTICTINA

Fungi Imperfecti, Sphaeropsidales, Sphaerioidaceae

Pycnidia membranous, with an ostiole, conidiophores obsolete or none, spores hyaline, 1-celled, ovoid.

Phyllostictina vaccinii. Leaf Spot of Blueberry, also fruit rot. Small circular gray spots, with 1 to 6 pycnidia in center, have a brown margin. Leaf spot is unimportant; fruits may have a hard, dry rot.

PHYSALOSPORA (See under Cankers)

Physalospora ilicis (conidial stage *Phyllosticta ilicis*). Leaf Spot on American holly, English holly, and winterberry.

PHYSODERMA

Phycomycetes, Chytridiales, Cladochytriaceae

Definite mycelium with terminal and intercalary enlargements which are transformed wholly or in part into sporangia and resting spores; sporangia rare, resting spores abundant, globose or ellipsoidal. Affected plant parts are discolored or slightly thickened.

Physoderma zeae-maydis. Brown Spot of Corn, corn measles, corn pox, dropsy, most prevalent in the South. Very small bleached or yellowish spots darken to brown or reddish brown with a light margin. Adjacent spots may coalesce to give the whole blade a rusty appearance. Spots on midrib and leaf sheath are larger, up to 1/4 inch, irregular to square, darker than leaf lesions. The entire sheath may turn brown on death of host cells and accumulation of brown spores. The epidermis finally ruptures, exposing brown spore dust. In severe infections lower nodes of culm are girdled so that stalks break over.

The resting spores remain in soil or plant refuse over winter, germinating by swarmspores the next spring. A fairly high temperature for germination and low wet lands are most favorable to the disease.

Control. Remove plant refuse early; rotate crops.

PIGGOTIA

Fungi Imperfecti, Sphaeropsidales, Leptostromataceae

Pycnidia innate, stellately arranged; conidia in chains, globose-ellipsoid, 1-celled, light or dark.

Piggotia fraxini (perfect stage *Mycosphaerella effigurata*) . Leaf Spot of Ash, general east of the Plains. Spots are small, purple to brown with yellow borders.

PIROSTOMA

Fungi Imperfecti, Sphaeropsidales, Leptostromataceae

Pycnidia superficial, with a shield; spores 1-celled, dark.

Pirostoma nyssae. Leaf Spot on Tupelo.

PLACOSPHAERIA

Fungi Imperfecti, Sphaeropsidales, Sphaerioidaceae

Pycnidia in a discoid stroma; spores hyaline, 1-celled; perfect stage in the Dothideales.

Placosphaeria graminis. Tar Spot on redtop grass.

Placosphaeria haydeni. Black Spot, Tar Spot on goldenrod, stems and leaves.

PLEOSPHAERULINA (Pringsheimia)

Ascomycetes, Sphaeriales

Perithecia innate, not beaked, paraphyses and paraphysoids lacking; spores muriform, hyaline.

Pleosphaerulina sojaecola. Leaf Spot of Soybean.

PLEOSPORA

Ascomycetes, Sphaeriales, Sphaeriaceae (or Myriangiales, Pseudosphaeriaceae)

Perithecia membranous, paraphyses present; spores muriform, dark. Species have wide saprophytic and pathogenic relationships. Some have Alternaria as imperfect stage, some Stemphylium.

Pleospora herbarum (conidial stage *Stemphylium botryosum,* and also *S. sarcinaeforme*). LEAF SPOT OF CLOVERS, also leaf blight of lilac. Seed mold of China aster and other plants.

Spots on legumes are small, irregular, dark brown, sunken, changing to concentric zonated light and dark brown areas. In final stages leaves are wrinkled, dark brown, sooty. Conidia as well as ascospores are muriform, olivaceous.

RAMULARIA

Fungi Imperfecti, Moniliales, Moniliaceae

Hyphae distinct from conidia, which are cylindric to clublike, often in chains, hyaline, with 1 to 2 cells; found on living leaves causing leaf spots or white mold (Fig. 52).

Ramularia armoraciae. PALE LEAF SPOT OF HORSE-RADISH. Few to numerous light green to yellowish spots appear on leaves in early summer, the invaded areas quickly turning thin and papery with dead areas dropping out late in season leaving ragged holes. Innumerable small sclerotium-like bodies in the dead tissue carry the fungus over winter and produce short, knobby conidiophores in spring which either push out through stomata or break through either epidermis.

There is no special control.

Ramularia lactea. WHITE SPOT OF PANSY. Pale circular spots become white on drying and the fungus produces a whitish bloom on undersurface of leaves.

Ramularia pastinacae. LEAF SPOT OF PARSNIP. Lesions are circular, very small, at first all brown, then with a white center and brown border. Long, slender, septate, hyaline conidia are produced on exposed conidiophores. No control is necessary.

Ramularia primula. LEAF SPOT OF PRIMROSE. Yellow blotches have ash-colored centers.

Ramularia vallisumbrosae. WHITE MOLD OF NARCISSUS, sometimes destructive on Pacific Coast. Small, sunken, grayish or yellow spots appear on leaves especially near tips, increasing to dark green to yellow brown patches on which, in moist weather, spores of the fungus appear in white powdery masses. Disease may become epidemic and foliage killed several weeks before normal ripening. Flower stalks of late varieties may also be attacked. Black "sclerotia" winter in leaf fragments on ground, producing spores in spring to infect young shoots.

Control. Three applications of bordeaux mixture, starting when shoots are 4 to 6 inches high, have given control. If disease has been present, rake over beds and burn infected foliage as soon as leaves have died down. A short rotation will help.

Ramularia variabilis. Leaf Spot of Foxglove. Irregular spots, up to 1/4 inch in diameter, brown with a reddish border, are formed most often on lower leaves. Spores in tufts give a white moldy appearance.

Control. Spraying with bordeaux mixture has been recommended, but perhaps some less conspicuous spray can be substituted.

RAMULISPORA (Titaeospora)

Fungi Imperfecti, Tuberculariales, Tuberculariaceae

Conidia on sporodochia, two- to many-septate, hyaline to subhyaline, oblong to fusoid irregularly united or branched at base.

Ramulispora sorghi. Copper Spot of turf grasses, sooty stripe of sorghum, Sudan grass, Johnson grass. Black superficial sclerotia on both leaf surfaces; with conidia in pinkish gelatinous masses. Spots on leaves are straw-colored with purple borders. Dead areas in turf are small, copper red in color. Cadmium fungicides are effective in control.

RHYTISMA

Ascomycetes, Phacidiales, Phacidiaceae

Apothecia concrete with epidermis and in black, stroma-like spots—tar spots—on leaves; spores filiform, typically hyaline.

Rhytisma acerinum. Tar Spot of Maple, especially cut-leaf varieties. Black, thickened, raised tarlike spots, up to 1/2 inch in diameter, are formed on upper leaf surface. They may be numerous enough to cause some defoliation but ordinarily are more disfiguring than destructive. Red and silver maples are

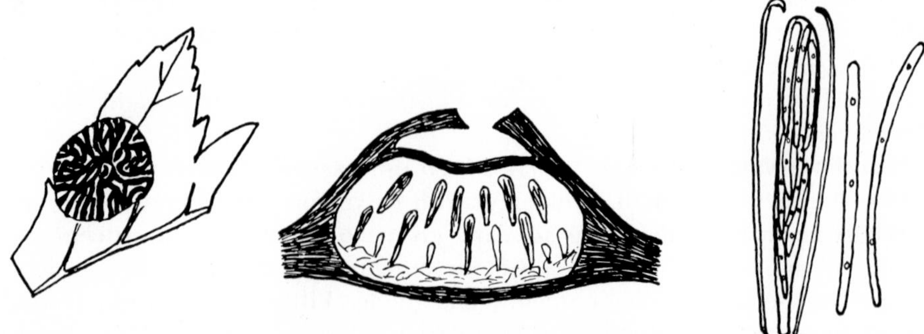

Fig. 56. Tar Spot of Maple; black tarry spot on leaf; section through spot; ascus, paraphyses, and filiform ascospores.

more commonly affected in the East. The lesions are light yellow-green at first, forming the black stromata in summer along with the conidial stage (*Melasmia acerina*). Ascospores are developed in spring in tar spots on fallen overwintered leaves and are forcibly ejected, to be carried by air currents to young leaves overhead.

Control. Collect and burn fallen leaves. Spray nursery trees with bordeaux mixture.

Rhytisma andromedae. TAR SPOT on bog-rosemary and lyonia.

Rhytisma bistorti. TAR SPOT on polygonum. Black, tar-like spots similar to those on maple.

Rhytisma punctatum. SPECKLED TAR SPOT OF MAPLE, a black speckled leaf spot on all species, but especially silver, striped, and bigleaf maple in Pacific Coast States, rare in the East. Black raised specks, pinhead size, are formed in groups on upper leaf surface, in yellowish green areas about a half inch in diameter. These areas retain their color even after leaves have faded in the fall.

Rhytisma salicinum. TAR SPOT OF WILLOW, on pussy willow, and other varieties. Spots are very thick, jet black, definitely bounded, 1/4 inch in diameter. The fungus winters in old leaves, which should be raked up and burned.

SCLEROTINIA (See under Blights)

Sclerotinia bifrons and **S. whetzelii.** BLACK LEAF SPOT, INK SPOT OF POPLAR. These are the names as often given to denote diseases of poplar leaves characterized by saucerlike, thin, black sclerotia which fall out of the leaves and produce apothecia in spring from sclerotia on the ground. There is often considerable defoliation and small trees may be killed.

There has been confusion in names. Whetzel, who long worked on the Sclerotinia group, made, just before his death, a new genus, Ciborinia, to take care of the species with sclerotia formed in leaves. He called the form in eastern poplars *Ciborinia bifrons* and the western form *C. confundens,* because of its confused status, Seaver having called the western form *Sclerotinia bifrons* and the eastern species *C. whetzelii.* See also Ciborinia under Blights.

SCHIZOTHYRIUM

Ascomycetes, Hemisphaeriales, Micropeltaceae

Brown scutellum or shield, radiate at margin, with a single hymenium underneath; apothecia round to linear, opening with a cleft or lobes; spores hyaline, 2-celled.

Schizothyrium gaultheriae. LEAF SPOT on wintergreen.

SCOLECOTRICHUM

Fungi Imperfecti, Moniliales, Dematiaceae

Conidiophores short, mostly erect, in fascicles; spores dark, 2-celled, borne at tips and sides.

Scolecotrichum graminis. Leaf Spot, Brown Stripe, streak on Lawn Grasses—bluegrass and redtop. Grayish brown to dark brown linear streaks on leaf blade may extend into leaf sheath and cause defoliation. Dark gray masses of conidiophores are arranged in rows as they emerge through stomata of upper leaf surface. Conidia are elongate, brown to olive brown, without cross-walls.

SELENOPHOMA

Fungi Imperfecti, Sphaeropsidales, Sphaerioidaceae

Pycnidia black, innate, with ostiole; spores hyaline, crescent-shaped, 1-celled but septate during germination.

Selenophoma donacis. Speckle, leaf blotch on bluegrass, and other grasses. Small brown flecks appear on blades in early spring, enlarging to blotches in which pycnidia develop. The pycnidia may drop out, leaving holes.

SEPTOCYLINDRIUM

Fungi Imperfecti, Moniliales, Moniliaceae

Hyphae very short or obsolete; spores with several cells, hyaline or light, cylindric, formed in chains.

Septocylindrium hydrophyllis. Leaf Spot of Hydrophylum.

SEPTOGLOEUM

Fungi Imperfecti, Melanconiales, Melanconiaceae

Spores in acervuli, hyaline, with 2 or more cross-walls.

Septogloeum acerinum. Leaf Spot of Maple. A small leaf spot, occasionally defoliating Norway and Schwedler maples in the Middle West.

Septogloeum parasiticum. Leaf Spot, twig blight of elm.

SEPTORIA (See under Blights)

This cosmopolitan genus with about 1000 species produces blights, blotches, and leaf spots. The latter are definite lesions with dark margins and grayish centers speckled with black fruiting bodies.

Septoria bataticola. Leaf Spot of Sweet Potato, occasional, and most common in northern tier of sweet potato states. Minute white spots on leaves are bordered with a narrow, reddish zone. Older lesions have one or more pycnidia just visible to the naked eye, the spores oozing out in tendrils when water is present on the leaf, to be spread by rain and insects.

Control. None required, except cleaning up old refuse.

Septoria callistephi. Leaf Spot, damping-off, stem rot of China aster. Treat seed with mercuric chloride to kill spores.

Septoria chrysanthemi. CHRYSANTHEMUM LEAF SPOT, also on ox-eye daisy, general throughout east and central states to Florida, also reported in the West. This disease is sometimes confused with nematode injury, but the leaf nematode browns the leaves in rather wedge-shaped areas between veins, whereas the fungus causes definite spots, first small and yellowish then dark brown to nearly black. Sometimes the spots coalesce to give a blotched appearance. Minute black fruiting bodies are faintly visible in affected areas. Part of the leaf may turn yellow and drop prematurely or leaves may dry and hang down along the stem as do those afflicted with nematodes. Spores are splashed from plant to plant by watering or rain, also in cultivation.

Control. Avoid syringing greenhouse plants; do not cultivate when wet. Spray with Fermate (at the rate of 1½ pounds per 100 gallons) or perhaps Parzate. Bordeaux mixture is effective but causes a slight dwarfing; Phygon is likewise effective but slightly injurious; lime sulfur seems quite injurious.

Septoria citri. SEPTORIA SPOT OF CITRUS, on leaves and fruits, but more serious on the fruits. Spots start as small, shallow, light brown depressions on green immature fruit, with a green marginal ring remaining as the fruit colors. This is usually a minor trouble, but is perhaps increasing in importance in California.

Septoria citrulli. WATERMELON LEAF SPOT. Like *S. cucurbitacearum* (see below) except that spores are shorter.

Septoria cornicola. DOGWOOD LEAF SPOT. Lesions are grayish with dark purple margins.

Septoria cucurbitacearum. SEPTORIA LEAF SPOT OF CUCURBITS, on cucumber, winter squash, muskmelon, watermelon. Foliage spots are small, gray, circular, rather conspicuous, often bordered with a zone of yellow tissue. The fungus fruits abundantly on upper side of leaves, with long, thin, septate spores in black pycnidia, and winters in old plant parts.

Control. Clean up all plant refuse at end of season.

Septoria dianthi. SEPTORIA LEAF SPOT OF DIANTHUS, on carnation and sweet william. Spots are more or less circular, light brown with purplish-brown borders, scattered over leaves and stems but particularly on lower leaves. The spots may enlarge and the leaves die.

Control. Take cuttings from disease-free plants. Avoid syringing or do it early in the day. Spray with Fermate or bordeaux mixture.

Septoria divaricata. SEPTORIA LEAF SPOT OF PHLOX. Dark brown circular spots, up to ¼ inch in diameter, have light gray to white centers and often run together into blotches.

Septoria gladioli. LEAF SPOT of gladiolus but more important as a hard rot of corms. See under Rots.

Septoria glycines. BROWN SPOT OF SOYBEAN. This is primarily a foliage disease but may appear on stems and pods, starting as irregular brown patches on cotyledons, then reddish brown spots on both sides of leaves, often with pale green or chlorotic zones surrounding the lesions. Spots may cover the whole leaf, with subsequent defoliation, starting with lowest leaves. On stems brown discolorations, with indistinct margins, may extend an inch or more. The fungus winters in diseased leaves and probably survives in seed. Some varieties are quite resistant.

Septoria lactucae. SEPTORIA LEAF SPOT OF LETTUCE, occasionally destructive to lettuce, more so on some varieties than others. Lesions are irregular reddish marks, dotted sparsely with black pycnidia. The fungus is probably disseminated with seed, but no control measures are suggested.

Septoria lycopersici. SEPTORIA LEAF SPOT, LEAF BLIGHT, OF TOMATO, quite destructive in Atlantic and central states, less important in the South and West. In seasons with moderate temperature and abundant rainfall so much foliage may be destroyed fruits do not mature properly and are subject to sunscald.

The disease appears at any age, but most often after fruit is set. First infection is on older leaves near the ground with small, thickly scattered water-soaked spots, which soon become roughly circular with gray centers and prominent dark margins. Spots are smaller, 1/16 to 1/8 inch, and more numerous than those of early blight. Leaflets may die and drop, and there may be progressive loss of foliage from the bottom up.

The fungus winters on tomato refuse, solanaceous weed hosts, and other decaying vegetation. Spores are washed from pycnidia by rain or spread by brushing moist leaves. Optimum temperature is 60° to 80° F.

Control. Bury plant remains deeply in soil or, in small gardens, clean up and burn plant refuse; control weeds; use long rotations; spray with a fixed copper or bordeaux mixture or use a copper dust.

Septoria paeoniae. SEPTORIA LEAF SPOT OF PEONY, stem canker. Round gray spots with reddish borders are found on stems and leaves. Control with sanitation, possibly by spraying with bordeaux mixture.

SPHAERULINA

Ascomycetes, Sphaeriales

Perithecia separate, innate to erumpent, not beaked, lacking paraphyses and paraphysoids; spores hyaline, with several cells; clavate-cylindrical.

Sphaerulina rubi. RASPBERRY LEAF SPOT, on red and black raspberry only, common east of the Rocky Mountains. This disease and a similar one on blackberry and dewberry were considered due to *Septoria rubi* for many years and then attributed to Mycosphaerella as the perfect stage. More recently it has been shown that two species are involved, with the ascomycete a Sphaerulina and not infecting blackberry. The name of the blackberry fungus has reverted back to *Septoria rubi.*

The spots are small, circular to angular, first greenish-black, then grayish. Pycnidia produce elongate, 3- to 9-septate spores (*Cylindrosporium rubi*).

Perithecia are formed in fallen leaves. They are black, subepidermal but later erumpent. Ascospores are cylindrical, curved, pointed at both ends, usually 4-septate.

SPORONEMA

Fungi Imperfecti, Sphaeropsidales, Excipulaceae (or Discellaceae)

Pycnidia dark, membranous to carbonous, innate, opening with torn lobes; spores hyaline, 1-celled.

Sporonema camelliae. LEAF SPOT of camellia.

STAGONOSPORA (See under Leaf Scorch)

STEMPHYLIUM

Fungi Imperfecti, Moniliales, Dematiaceae

Spores muriform, dark; conidiophores decumbent (Fig. 52).

Stemphylium sp. GLADIOLUS LEAF SPOT, causing annual loss to Florida cut-flower growers. Spots are small, round, translucent, pale yellow with reddish brown centers. The leaves may be killed before flowering, or after spikes are cut, resulting in smaller corms. Infection can take place in ten hours' wetting with dew or fog—rain is unnecessary. Optimum temperature is 75° F. Leaves can be killed as early as two weeks after first infection.

Picardy variety is moderately susceptible but has more disease if grown near very susceptible Stoplight and Casablanca. The disease, starting on very susceptible varieties, spreads radially to less susceptible plants, decreasing in severity with distance from focal point. The leaf spot disappears in summer and autumn, reappearing in winter 3 weeks after a cold period.

Control. Dithane D–14 plus zinc sulfate and lime, Dithane Z–78 and Parzate give good results if sprayed frequently. Phygon is effective but injurious. Very susceptible varieties should be separated from partly susceptible varieties by resistant varieties.

Stemphylium botryosum. LEAF SPOT, black seed rot, seed mold, on kidney bean, pea, onion, garlic, shallot, salsify, asparagus, pepper, and tomato.

Stemphylium cucurbitacearum. LEAF SPOT OF CUCURBITS, on cucumber, muskmelon, winter and summer squash. Small brown spots with lighter centers have mycelium growing over the spot producing globose, multiseptate spores. Mycelium winters in old plant tissue.

Control. Rotate crops; clean up diseased vines.

Stemphylium solani. GRAY LEAF SPOT, Stemphylium leaf spot, in pepper, tomato, groundcherry, eggplant, and other Solanum species, mostly in the South, but a tomato problem in New Jersey in 1949. In warm, humid weather, plants may be defoliated in seedbed or in field.

First infection is on older leaves, which show numerous, small, dark brown spots extending through to the undersurface. Centers are often a glazed gray-brown with cracking and tearing. Leaves turn yellow and wither; sometimes all leaves are killed except those at the tip; seedbeds are often destroyed.

Control. Use clean soil for the seedbed; treat seed with mercuric chloride or ethyl mercury phosphate; spray seedlings at weekly intervals with one of the fixed copper compounds and continue in the field.

STICTOCHLORELLA (Asteromella)

Fungi Imperfecti, Sphaeropsidales, Sphaerioidaceae

Pycnidia smooth, with ostiole, densely gregarious in asteroma-like spots; spores hyaline, 1-celled.

Stictochlorella lupini. LEAF SPOT on lupine.

STIGMELLA

Fungi Imperfecti, Moniliales, Dematiaceae

Hyphae very short, scarcely different from conidia which are densely aggregated on them; spores dark, muriform, globose-ovoid.

Stigmella platani-racemosae. LEAF SPOT of California sycamore, sometimes causing premature defoliation.

VENTURIA (See under Scab Diseases)

VERMICULARIA (See under Cankers)

VOLUTELLA (See under Blights)

MISTLETOE

Mistletoes are seed plants belonging to the family Loranthaceae. In America true mistletoes are in the genus Phoradendron and dwarf mistletoes in Arceuthobium. They are semiparasites or partial parasites, the plant furnishing water and mineral salts but the mistletoe manufacturing food.

The mistletoe seed is a naked embryo and endosperm invested with a fibrous coat and borne in white, straw-colored, pink or red fruits—"berries"—embedded in a sticky, gelatinous pulp enabling them to cling to bark of trees or stick to feet and beaks of birds which disseminate them.

The seeds can germinate almost anywhere but penetrate only young thin bark, by means of a haustorium sent out from a flattened disc. Branches of the haustorium extend up and down and about the tree and occasionally produce secondary haustoria. The number of annual rings on a tree between the tip of the primary haustorium and the bark tells the age of the mistletoe. Many are 60 to 70 years old, and one has been reported as living 419 years.

The aerial portions of mistletoes are leafy, evergreen tufts of shoots on the stems of host plants, most conspicuous on hardwoods after leaf fall. The stems and leaves contain chlorophyll and are green, but often with a yellowish, brown or olive cast depending on the season. All species have opposite leaves, round, jointed stems, and are dioecious with inconspicuous petal-less flowers.

FIG. 57. Mistletoe, common in southern trees.

Growth is slow at first, but in 6 to 8 years the tufts may be 3 feet across. The aerial part does not survive many years longer than that but the haustoria live as long as the tree, producing new bunches from adventitious buds.

Because they manufacture their own food mistletoes require a lot of sun, which may be one reason why they flourish so in the Southwest. Leafy mistletoes are relatively harmless in some situations; in others, they handicap shade and forest trees and sometimes kill hackberries and oaks. The dwarf mistletoes seriously retard growth of forest trees and predispose them to attack by bark beetles.

Control. Some people desire mistletoe, others want to get rid of it. For the latter group a few fungous diseases help the good work along. For complete eradication the infected branch must be cut off several inches to a foot closer to the trunk. Breaking off the bunches sometimes leads to development of more shoots in a widening area, but it is said to be fairly satisfactory to keep on removing the aerial portions with a curved mistletoe hook.

The dwarf mistletoe is important to forest trees, ranking next to heart rots in western coniferous forests. Infected branches should be pruned out, but if trunks are infected the trees should be felled and removed.

PHORADENDRON (American Mistletoe)

Phoradendron means tree thief. The genus is restricted to the Americas, ranging from southern New Jersey and Oregon southward. Of the 28 species most are on hardwoods.

Phoradendron californicum. CALIFORNIA MISTLETOE, ranging from southern California to Arizona, chiefly on Leguminosae—mesquite, carob, squaw-bush, creosote bush, parkinsonia. This is a leafless species generally pendent, with long stems and reddish pink berries.

Phoradendron flavescens. EASTERN MISTLETOE, from southern New Jersey west to Ohio and Missouri and south to the Gulf, on many hardwoods—oaks, elm, maple, sycamore, gums, hickory, pecan, hackberry, hawthorn, persimmon, black locust, western soapberry, sassafras, trumpet-vine. This species has white berries and is the common Christmas mistletoe.

Phoradendron engelmanni. TEXAS MISTLETOE, abundant in Texas on elms, oaks, mesquite, Osage orange, sugarberry; has white berries.

Phoradendron juniperinum. JUNIPER MISTLETOE, a leafless species with straw or wine-colored berries, ranging from Colorado and Utah through New Mexico and Arizona.

Phoradendron libocedri. INCENSE CEDAR MISTLETOE, confined to incense cedar and occurring throughout its range in Oregon, California, and Nevada. The pendent plants are leafless with straw-colored berries. It may injure plants severely, causing spindle-shaped swellings in limbs at point of attack and living in the trunk as a parasite for hundreds of years after external portions have disappeared.

Phoradendron villosum. HAIRY MISTLETOE, ranging from Oregon through California, usually on oaks, also on Oregon myrtle, California buckeye, and manzanitas. It has pinkish white berries and may cause large hypertrophies on oaks.

ARCEUTHOBIUM (Dwarf Mistletoe)

The genus is restricted to conifers, and most species are found in the Northwest. Trees of any age may be deformed or killed, but the greatest mortality is among seedlings and saplings, with lodgepole and ponderosa pines most susceptible.

The most striking symptom is the formation of witches' brooms with sometimes the whole crown transformed into a huge broom. In other cases fusiform swellings in trunks turn into cankers. Foliage of affected trees is reduced.

The mistletoes themselves are small, rarely attaining a maximum of 8 inches, sometimes less than an inch. They are perennial shoots, simple or branched, jointed, with the leaves reduced to opposite pairs of scales at the top of each segment. Stems range in color from yellow to brown to olive green. Berries are olive green to dark blue; each contains a single seed, rarely two. The seed is ejected with force and is spread horizontally for some feet. Animals and birds account for infection at a distance.

Arceuthobium americanum. LODGEPOLE PINE DWARF MISTLETOE, common on the Rocky Mountain form but not the Pacific lodgepole pine, rare on other pines. The flowers bloom in spring, accessory branches forming a whorl.

Arceuthobium campylopodum. WESTERN DWARF MISTLETOE, widespread in West on pines, firs, larches, spruces. It forms witches' brooms and flowers late in summer.

Arceuthobium douglasii. DOUGLAS FIR DWARF MISTLETOE, confined to this host. Plants are small, only 1½ inches high.

Arceuthobium pusillum. EASTERN DWARF MISTLETOE, the only species in the East, from Minnesota to New Jersey and north to Canada, common on black spruce, less common on other spruces, tamarack, pines. The fruit matures in autumn; shoots are very short, less than an inch.

Arceuthobium vaginatum. SOUTHWESTERN DWARF MISTLETOE on pines.

MOLDS

The word mold, or mould, has many meanings. The first one given in Webster is "a growth, often woolly, produced on various forms of organic matter, especially when damp and decaying, by saprophytic fungi." Leaf mold is organic matter reduced to friable earth by these saprophytic fungi. When rhododendrons are fed with a fertilizer having a cottonseed meal base you can often see a moldy growth showing that beneficial organisms are at work breaking down the material for plant use.

Some of these saprophytic fungi have a harmful, parasitic phase. The common black bread mold, *Rhizopus nigricans,* causes soft rot of sweet potatoes, "leak" of strawberries and grapes. *Penicillium* spp., the common blue molds on jellies, cause a decay of citrus and other fruits. Such diseases are discussed under Rots.

Using the word mold loosely to cover any profuse fungus growth on the surface of plant tissue we have Botrytis gray mold, considered under Blights, brown mold of Alternaria, white mold caused by Ramularia. Sooty molds, the black growths on insect exudate, are discussed under that heading, and the diseases known as snowmold are likewise treated separately. Left for this section is a heterogeneous collection of leaf, seed, and graft molds.

BOTRYOSPORIUM

Fungi Imperfecti, Moniliales, Moniliaceae

Conidiophores long with many short laterals with 3 to many spines bearing conidia in heads; spores globose, hyaline, 1-celled.

Botryosporium pulchrum. LEAF MOLD on tomato, also geranium (pelargonium) occasionally in greenhouse.

CHALAROPSIS

Fungi Imperfecti, Moniliales, Dematiaceae

Mycelium at first hyaline, then greenish; two types of conidia—macroconidia hyaline at first, olive green when mature, sessile or borne on short conidiophores in compact groups; endoconidia, hyaline to dark formed inside the end cell of a dark endoconidiophore, and extruded in chains.

Chalaropsis thielavioides. Black Mold of Rose Grafts, Manetti mold, usually on grafted roses, sometimes on budded roses in nursery fields. The fungus grows over and blackens cut surfaces of stock and scion preventing union and resulting in death of the scions. When outdoor roses are budded on Manetti understock, the bud often turns black and dies. Infection is only through wounds. *Rosa odorata* and *R. chinensis* var. *Manetti* are both very susceptible understocks; *R. multiflora* is moderately so and Ragged Robin is immune.

Control. Use healthy understock or disinfect for 2 hours with formaldehyde at a dilution of 1 part to 320; soak cuttings for 1 hour in Ceresan (at rate of 1 pound per 100 gallons water) before setting in field. Spray greenhouse benches, tools, etc., with copper sulfate; prevent spread of spores by workmen on hands, clothing, and budding knife.

CLADOSPORIUM

Fungi Imperfecti, Moniliales, Dematiaceae

Conidiophores more or less branched, somewhat decumbent, dark; spores dark, with 1 or more cells, formed in chains.

Cladosporium fulvum. Leaf Mold of Tomatoes, general on greenhouse crops, occasionally serious in gardens in wet seasons in the Southeast, and sometimes present in other states. Diffuse, whitish spots on upper surface of older leaves enlarge, turn yellow, while the undersurface of the patches has a velvety olive-brown coating of spores, which are spread by air currents and watering. The spores remain viable about the greenhouse for several months after plants are removed and are sometimes carried on seed. Infection occurs only when humidity is high.

Control. Zerlate has helped with outdoor tomatoes. In greenhouses some night heat in spring and fall months and maximum ventilation reduces humidity. Varieties Globelle, Bay State, and Vetomold are somewhat resistant.

Cladosporium herbarum. Leaf Mold, Pod and Seed Spot. The fungus is a weak parasite reported as causing black mold of peanut, pod spot and seed mold of lima and kidney beans, glume spot of blue grass, leaf mold of pepper and tomato and sometimes of fruit.

EROSTROTHECA

Ascomycetes, Hypocreales

Perithecia bright, more or less soft, without beak, paraphyses lacking; spores ellipsoid, yellow to olivaceous. Conidial stage has many spore forms.

Erostrotheca multiformis (*Cladosporium album*). WHITE MOLD OF SWEET PEA, white blight, also on perennial pea, observed on greenhouse crops. Leaflets are covered with tan or buff, circular to irregular, small to large spots with cinnamon brown pustules giving a granular appearance. White tufts of mold represent the Cladosporium stage. Pseudosclerotia are also formed in the leaves, which may die and drop. The fungus enters through stomata, under conditions of high humidity.

Control. Dusting with sulfur has been suggested.

Heterosporium variabile. LEAF MOLD of cabbage but chiefly a leaf spot of spinach. See under Leaf Spots.

Pleospora herbarum, weak parasite causing seed mold, leaf spot, and blights. See under Leaf Spots.

Ramularia vallisumbro. WHITE MOLD OF NARCISSUS. See under Leaf Spots.

TORULA

Fungi Imperfecti, Moniliales, Dematiaceae

Hyphae dark; conidia in chains but breaking up readily, globose to oblong.

Torula maculans. LEAF MOLD on yucca.

NEEDLE CASTS

Certain diseases of conifers which result in conspicuous shedding of needles are termed needle casts. Most of the fungi causing such symptoms are members of the Phacidiales. The terms "needle cast" and "needle blight" are used somewhat interchangeably, and more diseases of this type are included under Blights.

ADELOPUS (Phaeocryptopus)

Ascomycetes, Erysiphales, Meliolaceae

One of the black mildews, with superficial, dark mycelium; perithecia innate, with a central foot, without ostiole; spores 2-celled, hyaline.

Adelopus gäumanni. ADELOPUS NEEDLE CAST OF DOUGLAS-FIR, Swiss needle cast. Although first noted in Switzerland in 1925 this seems to be a native American disease occurring in relatively harmless fashion on the Pacific Coast, somewhat injurious to native Douglas-fir in the Southwest, and recently quite injurious to trees in New England and New York. Needles fall prematurely, leaving only the current season's growth. If this happens for several consecutive years trees have thin foliage, appear yellow or brown, and finally die. Needles are yellow-green to brown, often mottled and on undersurface tiny black perithecia, issuing from stomata, appear as sooty streaks, one on each side of the middle nerve. No method of control is yet known.

BIFUSELLA

Ascomycetes, Phacidiales, Phacidiaceae

Apothecia elongate, slitting with a cleft; paraphyses lacking; spores hyaline, 1-celled, club-shaped at both ends with halves joined by a narrow neck (Fig. 58).

Bifusella faullii. Needle Cast of Balsam Fir, the most common and destructive of the needle casts of this host. Ascospores are discharged in July but infected young needles do not change color until spring, then turning light brown to buff. Effused pycnidia in the same color appear in the groove on upper surface of the needle followed by dusky brown hysterothecia (apothecia with a covering) maturing ascospores the second summer.

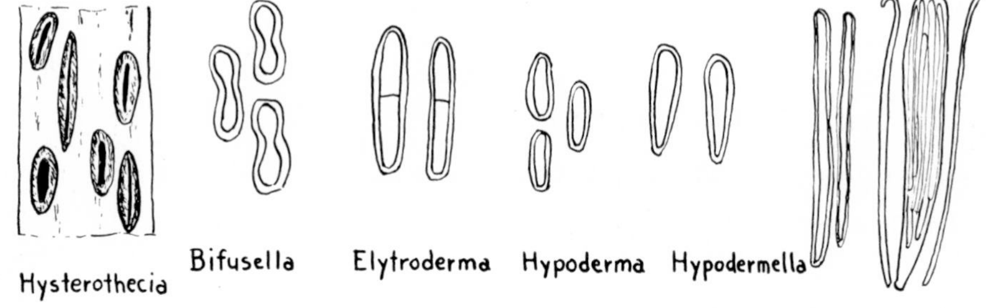

Fig. 58. Needle-cast Fungi, which form ascospores in hysterothecia, elongate apothecia opening with a cleft. *Bifusella,* spores constricted in middle; *Elytroderma,* fusiform spores; *Hypoderma,* short fusiform spores; *Hypodermella,* spores tapering at base; Lophodermium, ascus with filiform spores, and paraphyses.

Bifusella abietis. Needle Cast of Fir, on Alpine and corkbark fir from New Mexico to Idaho. Dark brown to black hysterothecia extend the entire length of the middle nerve on under surface of needle. Pycnidia are in two rows on upper surface.

Bifusella linearis. Needle Cast of Pine, tar spot, on various pine species. Hysterothecia are variable in length, shining black, on 2-year needles.

ELYTRODERMA

Ascomycetes, Phacidiales, Phacidiaceae

Ascospores 2-celled, broadly fusiform (Fig. 58).

Elytroderma deformans. NEEDLE CAST, witches' broom, on ponderosa, lodgepole, Jeffrey, piñon, and Jack pines. Elongated dull, dark hysterothecia are on both needle surfaces. The tissues of ponderosa and Jeffrey pines may be penetrated and loose witches' brooms formed. Saplings may have entire crown converted and die or make little growth.

HYPODERMA

Ascomycetes, Phacidiales, Phacidiaceae

Apothecia or hysterothecia elliptic to oblong, opening by a cleft; asci long-stalked; spores hyaline, fusiform or rod-shaped (Fig. 58).

Hypoderma desmazierii. NEEDLE CAST, tar spot of pines, most frequent on eastern white pine. Infected needles are at first yellow, then reddish brown, and finally deep brown with a grayish cast. The tips are infected first, the fungus being a weak parasite, completing its cycle in a year. Hysterothecia are shining black, elliptical.

Hypoderma hedgecockii. NEEDLE CAST of hard pines, in southeastern states. Elliptical shining black hysterothecia are in discolored areas on green needles. Each ascus contains four normal and four aborted spores.

Hypoderma lethali. GRAY BLIGHT, NEEDLE CAST of hard pines, from New England to Florida and Louisiana, common on pitch pine. Hysterothecia are short, narrow, black.

Hypoderma robustum. NEEDLE CAST OF FIRS, in West, usually white fir. Concolorous pycnidia, which form two rows, one on each needle wing, often turn black after spore discharge.

HYPODERMELLA

Ascomycetes, Phacidiales, Phacidiaceae

Like Bifusella but with paraphyses present; apothecia elongates, with a cleft; spores hyaline, 1-celled, club-shaped at upper end, tapering toward base (Fig. 58).

Hypodermella abietis-concoloris, on firs and southern balsam.

Hypodermella ampla. NEEDLE CAST OF JACK PINE. All needles may drop except those of current season. Short, elliptical, dull black hysterothecia are scattered over light buff-colored areas.

Hypodermella concolor. NEEDLE CAST OF JACK AND LODGEPOLE PINES. Virulent fungus infects young needles, in summer, which turn brown the next season. Short hysterothecia are concolorous with the leaf and appear as shallow depressions.

Hypodermella laricis. LARCH NEEDLE AND SHOOT BLIGHT, on eastern and western larches. Needles and secondary shoots that bear them are both killed. Killed needles are not cast but remain to give a brown, scorched appearance to trees normally deciduous. Very small, oblong to elliptical dull-black hysterothecia are formed on upper surface of needles.

Hypodermella nervata. NEEDLE CAST OF BALSAM FIR. Pycnidia are in a groove along upper surface of needle in continuous or occasionally interrupted row, turning nearly black after spores are discharged.

LOPHODERMIUM

Ascomycetes, Phacidiales, Phacidiaceae.

Apothecia or hysterothecia opening by a cleft, elongate; paraphyses simple, hooked at tip; spores filiform.

Lophodermium filiforme. SPRUCE NEEDLE CAST, sometimes causing serious defoliation of red and black spruce. Hysterothecia are long or short, shining black.

Lophodermium juniperinum, widespread and abundant on common juniper and red cedar but apparently not parasitic. Hysterothecia are elliptical, shining black, on both leaf surfaces.

Lophodermium nitens, frequent but apparently saprophytic on 5-needle pines. Hysterothecia short, black, shining.

Lophodermium piceae. NEEDLE CAST, tar spot of fir and spruce. The fungus is a weak parasite. Short, shining black hysterothecia are formed on all needle surfaces.

Lophodermium pinastri. PINE NEEDLE CAST, widespread. Pycnidia appear in spring or early summer as tiny black spots on browned needles followed by dull, occasionally shining, black, short elliptical hysterothecia. The fungus is a weak parasite but can be epidemic in nurseries where it can be controlled by spraying with bordeaux mixture.

NAEMACYCLUS

Ascomycetes, Phacidiales, Stictidiaceae

Apothecia bright colored, soft, opening with a cleft; paraphyses much branched; spores worm-shaped.

Naemacyclus niveus. NEEDLE CAST, occasional on various pines. Fruiting bodies tiny, elliptical, first waxy, dark brown, later concolorous with leaf surface.

RHABDOCLINE

Ascomycetes, Phacidiales, Phacidiaceae or Stictidiaceae

Apothecia innate, brown, exposed by irregular rupture of epidermis; paraphyses present; spores, 1-celled, becoming septate after discharge from ascus, rounded at ends and constricted in the middle.

Rhabdocline pseudotsugae. Needle Cast of Douglas-Fir, needle blight, common on Pacific Coast and in Rocky Mountain States on native Douglas-fir, and in northeastern states on ornamental forms. The disease has reached Europe on trees from western North America and is causing much concern there.

Needles are infected in spring or early summer, with first symptoms showing as slightly yellow spots, usually at ends of needles, in autumn or winter. By the next spring the color is reddish brown and leaves have a mottled appearance. In severe infections needles turn a more uniform brown and the entire tree appears scorched.

Apothecia are usually on undersurface of needle, sometimes on upper. They are at first round cushions, then the epidermis ruptures to expose a brown, elongated disc. Infected needles drop after ascospore discharge, so that they live only a year instead of the normal life of about eight years.

Control. Spraying with bordeaux mixture when new needles develop, repeating twice at 10- to 14-day intervals, has been suggested; as well as spraying with lime sulfur at time of ascospore discharge in early summer, but not much experimental work has been done. In forests, control will probably depend on early elimination of susceptible trees.

RHIZOSPHAERA

Fungi Imperfecti, Sphaeropsidales, Sphaerioidaceae

Pycnidia brown, on a stalk; spores ovoid, 1-celled, hyaline.

Rhizosphaera kalkhoffi. Needle Cast of blue spruce. Lowest needles are affected first, becoming mottled yellow; and the disease progresses up the tree. It has been controlled in ornamentals with three sprays of bordeaux mixture.

NEMATODES

Nematodes (nemas, eelworms or roundworms) belong to the animal phylum Nemathelminthes, which means threadworms. They live in moist soil, water, decaying organic matter and tissues of other living organisms. Some cause diseases of man or animals, others cause plant diseases. The animal parasites may attain some size, but those on plants are seldom large enough to be seen with the naked eye. They move through the soil with a kind of threshing motion but don't get very far, rarely more than 30 inches a year, by their own efforts. They are spread much greater distances with surface or irrigation water, or soil on machinery, shoes of workers, hoofs of farm animals, or infested plants.

Nematodes have a hollow, spearlike organ, called the buccal spear, with which they suck plant juices from living cells. In this process the root-knot nematode and some others inject a chemical that stimulates gall formation. The meadow or root nematode pierces the roots, affording entrance to rot fungi, but does not cause galls. The stem and bulb nematode produces deformities in many plants, and the leaf nematode produces a definite necrosis.

In some nematodes both males and females are wormlike; in others the female is pear-shaped and the male is long and narrow, with blunt head and pointed tail. This difference is a diagnostic feature, as well as the lobes at the base of the spear or stylet, and the type and position of sexual organs. Nematodes are unsegmented but have a stiff cuticle and muscular wall which makes possible the movements by which they can practically tie themselves into knots.

Nematodes have some enemies—other nemas—and nematode-trapping fungi. One of these, Dactylella, has a series of loops in the mycelium which contract and hold the nematode in place while the hyphae invade its body.

APHELENCHOIDES

Adults of both sexes are elongate, wormlike. Species cause death or deformation and stunting of leaves, stems, and flowers; and there has been much confusion over names.

Aphelenchoides besseyi. STRAWBERRY SUMMER DWARF, or CRIMP, French bud, chiefly in southeastern and Gulf states, where the winter is mild and zero temperatures absent, a major disease in Florida. The nematodes live in the soil and are washed into the buds by rains or irrigation water affecting the young leaves as they develop. Leaflets are crimped or crinkled, cupped, narrow, with a reddish cast to veins and petioles. Older leaves are darker green, more brittle than normal. The disease is common from July to October. Cold weather checks its progress and often masks the symptoms, but plants do not recover. Runner plants from infested mother plants are diseased. In spring the nematode population may be low, allowing nearly normal formation of early leaves, but in summer a single bud may harbor 50 to 1300 nemas, causing center leaves to be deformed and dwarfed.

Control. Buy certified plants wherever possible. Do not accept even apparently healthy plants from a nursery where summer dwarf is known to be present. Rogue out and burn diseased plants whenever they appear.

Aphelencoides fragariae. STRAWBERRY SPRING DWARF, "cauliflower," a cold-weather disease, established along the eastern seaboard from Cape Cod to Norfolk, Va., occasional in other states. Although spring dwarf was first observed in Massachusetts in 1932 it seems to be the same as the English "red plant" from which the nematode was named in 1891, by Ritzema Bos. Dr. J. R. Christie, senior nematologist with the U.S. Department of Agriculture, assures me that this species, *A. fragariae,* is still restricted to strawberries, although it has been reported from many other plants by workers who considered *A. olesistus* and *A. ritzemi-bosi* synonyms instead of valid species.

The nematodes persist through winters with subzero temperatures, and several thousand may be present in a single bud in spring as the first leaves are unfolded. The leaves are small, narrow, twisted, glossy; most blossom buds are killed before they show. Some plants are killed; others recover and produce runners in hot summer, but these runner plants are usually infested.

Control. Nursery plants should be inspected and certified in spring; infested plants in a garden should be rogued and burned.

Aphelenchoides olesistus. Begonia Leaf-Blight Nematode, Fern Leaf Nematode, Bud and Leaf Nematode of Lilies, recorded also on anemone, bouvardia, calceolaria, chrysanthemum, clematis, coleus, crassula, dianthus, doronicum, geranium, hydrangea, peony, primrose, saintpaulia, scabiosa, zinnia, and other ornamentals; but in many cases identification is not certain.

Fern leaves have a patchy or blotched appearance with dark brown to black areas on the fronds. In some species these are rather narrow dark bands from midribs to border, limited by parallel side veins; in bird's-nest fern there is a diffuse brown discoloration from the base halfway up the leaf.

On begonias, the disease is most serious on semi-tuberous varieties such as Lady Mac, Melior and others grown largely in greenhouses for the Christmas trade. Small brown spots with a water-soaked margin on undersides of leaves enlarge and coalesce, turn dark brown, become visible from upper surface. Often the whole leaf is a dark blotch, and plants are stunted. On fibrous-rooted begonias, spots stay small, leaves become shiny with a tendency to curl, then lose color and drop. The nematodes are spattered from plant to plant by syringing or careless watering. There is no spread when leaves are kept dry.

The disease of Easter lilies in the Pacific Northwest is rather recent, and quite serious, in both greenhouse and field plantings. It is called dieback or bunchy top. Leaves are bronzy and strongly undercurled; they turn brown and die back. If bulbs from such plants are planted there may be hundreds of nematodes between bulb scales, to blast growing tip and bud.

Control. Sanitation, removal of infested leaves, and care in watering—avoiding syringing and overhead watering—are important for greenhouse plants. Submersion in hot water is the generally accepted treatment against leaf nematodes. Potted begonias can be treated at 121°–120° F. for 1 minute, 119°–117° for 2 minutes, or 118°–115° for 3 minutes. Plants should be in small pots and treatment should be at least 3 months before the marketing season. The suggested temperature for ferns is 110° F. for 10 to 15 minutes.

For the lily bunchy top and dieback, rigid roguing in the field is coupled with treating the bulbs before planting with hot water, held for 1 hour at 111° F. Formalin at the rate of 1 pint to 25–30 gallons is added to the hot water to prevent increase in basal rot. After immersion, bulbs are dipped in wettable Spergon (1 pound to 25 gallons) or Tersan (1 pound to 8 gallons) as a precaution against bulb and root rots. Planting should be immediately after treatment, on land which has not grown lilies for 2 years.

Such hot-water measures are, of course, for commercial growers. The individual should expect, and get, healthy plants from his florist.

Aphelenchoides parietinus, a common species in soil and in decaying plant tissues, recorded as causing a necrosis of root plate and scales of bulbous iris.

Aphelenchoides ribes, a bud parasite of black currants and gooseberries in England but reported only once, on gooseberry in one locality in California, in this country.

Aphelenchoides ritzema-bosi. LEAF NEMATODE OF CHRYSANTHEMUMS, widespread and very important in the home garden on this host, also recorded on many other ornamentals but not as causing serious trouble.

The first symptoms are dark spots or areas on underside of leaves, but by the fifth day after infestation discolored veins stand out sharply on upper leaf surface and the diseased leaves turn brown or black often in distinct wedges between the veins. Later the leaves dry, wither, and hang down along the stems. The nematodes swim up from the soil in a film of water along the

FIG. 59. Leaf Nematode of Chrysanthemum. Wormlike male and female nemas cause wedge-shaped browning between veins, followed by general blighting of leaf.

stem so the disease goes from lowest leaves progressively upward. Almost any variety may be attacked, but the Koreans are particularly susceptible.

Control. Anything that discourages upward movement of the nemas from the soil is helpful—a good mulch, keeping tops dry by avoiding sprinkling, even a ring of vaseline around each stem. Spraying with nicotine sulfate or other contact insecticide helps a little but is not too effective. The ground can be treated with sodium selenate which is taken up by the plant and kills the nematodes as they feed. This is a poison which must be used with great care and never on land that may be turned into vegetables in the future because there is a residual effect of the poison. The form known as P–40 is considered relatively safe for gardeners to use; directions must be carefully followed.

Soil infested with nematodes can be treated with chloropicrin, after all plants are removed, but this does little good unless the garden is replanted with healthy cuttings. If there is any doubt, rooted cuttings can have their roots wrapped in damp cotton and tops immersed in hot water at 122° F. for 5 minutes, although this is drastic treatment.

Aphelenchoides subtenuis, a parasite of narcissus, invading all plant parts except roots, widespread but reported mostly from Virginia and the Carolinas. Only occasional plants are infected, but these are killed or severely injured.

Aphelenchoides sp. This designation has been given in the host lists for those nematodes reported as *A. fragariae* but not from strawberry.

DITYLENCHUS

Male and female adults both wormlike.

Ditylenchus dipsaci. STEM AND BULB NEMATODE, causing EELWORM DISEASE OF NARCISSUS, RING DISEASE OF HYACINTH, ONION BLOAT, also found on grape-hyacinth, scilla, tulip, galtonia, garlic, shallot, and other bulbs, on some vegetables, and on strawberry, and as a stem nematode, on phlox and many other flowers. This species apparently has many strains, the two on hyacinths and narcissus not being reciprocally infective, although the narcissus strain does infect onions.

Hyacinths have yellow flecks or blotches on the leaves, which are often twisted, short, and split. In narcissus there are pustules or blisters on the leaves, "spikkels" in Dutch, which can be felt when a leaf is drawn through the fingers. The nematodes are in these pustules and probably entered the young leaves as they were pushing up through the soil. Bulbs badly diseased at planting either produce no foliage or a few leaves that are premature, twisted and bent. Often in a planting, the central bulbs show such symptoms at the same time that plants on the periphery of the group, infected subsequent to planting, show only the yellowish spikkels on the foliage.

When the leaves are dry the nematodes are inactive, but when the foliage is moist and decayed the nemas revive and pass down into the soil or into the neck of the bulb and the bulb scales, then to the basal plate and into the bases of other scales. The infected scales are brown, but since there is little lateral movement of the nemas the cut surface of a bulb shows one or more brown rings contrasting with healthy tissue. Eggs, larvae, and adults are all present in this brown tissue. Male and female adults are both wormlike and up to 1.8 mm. long. Infective larvae issue in large numbers in white or creamy tufts in a break between basal plate and scales and work through the soil to invade adjacent plants. They are also spread in irrigation water, on tools, and by animals. Some winter in weed hosts, some in seed of composites. In moist soil they die after a year or so but they have been recovered from plants after 5 or 6 years.

The strain on phlox attacks campanula, sweet william, evening primrose, goldenrod, schizanthus. The leaves are very narrow, crinkled and waved, often brittle, with a tendency to lengthened petioles. Stems may be swollen near the tops, or bent sidewise; plants are stunted, often fail to bloom, may die prematurely.

Control. Immersion in hot water held at 110° F. for periods up to 3 hours is used to treat bulbs for this nematode. Formalin is added to the water as a precaution against basal rot. Infected foliage should be cleaned up and burned at the end of the season. Phlox and similar plants should be removed as soon as noticed.

Ditylenchus iridis, on bulbous iris, similar to *D. dipsaci,* but now considered a separate species.

HETERODERA

Male wormlike, female pear-shaped.

Heterodera marioni. Root Knot, the common nematode disease with the root galls familiar to nearly every gardener. This nematode attacks more than 1400 species of plants, in fact most field, garden, ornamental, and fruit crops except grains and grasses, and special resistant strains of legumes and other vegetables and some fruits. It flourishes in greenhouses in the North, and outdoors to some extent, but as a garden problem it is far more serious in the South.

Infected plants are stunted; they often wilt, turn yellow, and die. The chief diagnostic symptom is the presence of small or large swellings or galls on the

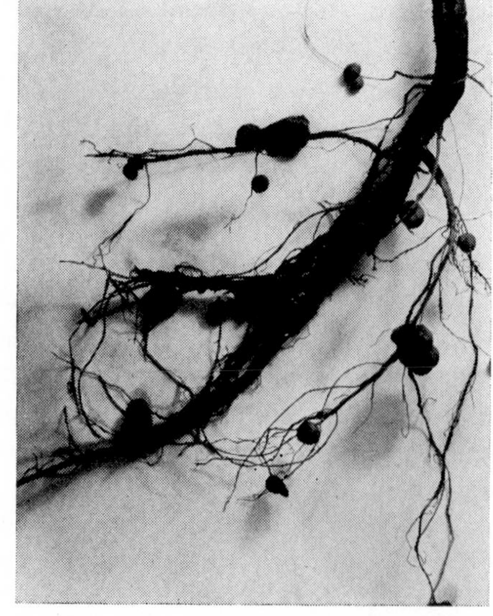

Fig. 60. Root-knot Nematode Galls on Clematis, left. Compare with soybean nodules of beneficial legume bacteria, right.

roots. These may be nearly round or long and irregular, but they can always be differentiated from the nodules produced on legumes by nitrogen-fixing bacteria by the fact that they are an actual part of the root and cannot be broken off. The desirable bacterial nodules are formed at one side of the root and can be readily broken off.

Larvae develop to maturity within the root gall and mate there. The female is pear-shaped, white, glistening, and can just be seen as a white dot with

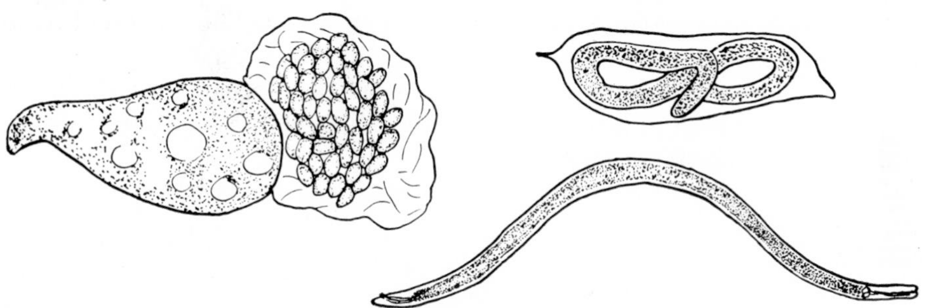

FIG. 61. Root-knot Nematode: pear-shaped female with egg sac; encysted young larva; and wormlike adult male.

the unaided eye. It extrudes a sac full of brownish eggs, about the size of dust particles, and just before hatching, the larva can be seen under the microscope, coiled up inside the egg. Each female lays from 500 to 2000 or more eggs in the course of 2 or 3 months. The larvae move from the decaying knot and attack the same root at a new point or a new root, secreting a chemical that stimulates the gall or knot formation around the larva. At high temperatures, about 80° F., a generation takes only about 25 days; at 67°, it takes an average of 87 days; and below 55°, activity stops.

The adult female cannot live long outside the gall, but the free-living larvae can survive in the soil for some months without food and the eggs, up to 2 years. Larvae and eggs are distributed in infested nursery stock, in root crops, in soil transported on tools and equipment. They are most numerous in light sandy soils which aid free movement, although they seldom travel more than a foot a month. They are usually only 3 to 10 inches deep in the soil but have been found at 6 feet in connection with deep-rooted plants. High organic matter in the soil favors parasitic nemas, mites, and fungi which destroy the root-knot forms.

Control. Chemically treating the soil may pay off in increased yield. Dichloropropylene-dichloropropane (D–D Mixture or Dowfume–N) and ethylene dibromide (Garden Dowfume Soilfume-Caps) are both used at the present time with about comparable results. Chloropicrin (Larvacide) is a little too expensive for large-scale operations but is used for small plots and greenhouses. It does not penetrate fresh galls as readily but has a long residual effect and controls fungi better than the other materials. Special applicators can be rented for injecting liquids which should be placed at exact intervals, usually every 10 inches in the row and the rows 10 inches apart. With chloropicrin, soil temperature should be above 60° F. and a water seal used to hold in the gases; with D–D, temperature is not so important, and the water seal is less necessary. Two weeks or more should elapse before planting. Soil for a young orchard or for ornamental trees and shrubs can be spot treated with chemicals at the place where each tree will be put. The same spot treatment can be used for hill crops like watermelons.

In some cases treating the soil with cyanamid before planting reduces the nematode population as well as having a fertilizer effect. Mulching with organic materials increases nematode enemies.

Crop rotation is possible on a limited scale. There are only a few resistant plants, but these can be grown as green manure crops and plowed under—Crotalaria; bur clover; cowpeas in varieties Brabham, Conch, Iron, Monetta, and Victor; soybeans in varieties Biloxi, Laredo, O-too-tan, Acme, and Haberlandt; and velvet beans. Many other crops will give a fair yield even though somewhat susceptible, whereas some of the more susceptible crops can be grown in the winter, in the South, rather than summer.

Somewhat resistant ornamentals include African marigold, amaryllis, azalea, bittersweet, camellia, day-lily, dogwood, euonymus, evening primrose, ferns, gaillardia, holly, lantana, lupine, narcissus, rhododendron, tulip, and zinnia. Roses are susceptible but can be budded on resistant understock.

Most important is keeping the root-knot nematode out in the first place. Do not plant any seedling or nursery stock that shows the slightest trace of galls. Wherever possible buy certified tomato, cabbage, and other seedlings.

Heterodera rostochiensis. Golden Nematode Disease of Potatoes, first discovered in the United States near Hicksville, Long Island, in 1941, and still confined to about 6000 acres in that area, by a rigorous quarantine. The golden nematode overwinters in soil as eggs enclosed in protective cysts. The larvae hatch in spring, feed internally on roots for 3 or 4 weeks, then the females are fertilized and appear as glistening white swellings on roots. These swellings turn yellow, then golden brown and when the females die their bodies are transformed into cysts to protect the enclosed eggs, which can remain viable in soil for as many as 8 years. Potato yields are reduced by 30 to 70 per cent.

Control methods have not been worked out. Fumigating with D–D Mixture kills the majority of cysts but enough are left to increase so that only one or two potato crops can be grown without injury.

Heterodera schachtii, Sugar-Beet Nematode. The larvae penetrate roots of sugar beets but instead of causing galls stimulate the rootlets to extra activity so that many fine fibrous roots are produced around the stunted main root. The disease is sometimes called celery root. As with the golden nematode the female can turn into a brown cyst to protect eggs for several years, so that crop rotations must be long.

Hoplolaimus sp., Root Nematode in Lycoris.

Hoplolaimus coronatus, Root Nematode of sugar cane, corn, and now found rather constantly associated with a new disease of pin oaks and red oaks in Delaware, the symptoms of which resemble illuminating gas injury.

PRATYLENCHUS

Males and females wormlike, 0.5 mm. long; larvae attack root cortex.

Pratylenchus pratensis and other species, MEADOW OR ROOT NEMATODES, widely distributed, known for many years, but only recently indicted as a primary factor in various root rot disease complexes. These nemas do not produce galls but mutilate the roots by their feeding. Yellow to brown or black lesions are formed on the fine feeder roots, followed by extensive sloughing of the cortex. Most of the root system is destroyed, but there is often a brush of feeder roots near the surface.

More work has been done on brown root rot of tobacco than on other plants, and here the evidence points quite conclusively to the nemas as primary agents. During 1948 in Connecticut the disease caused losses of hundreds of thousands of dollars but in experiments using nematocidal fumigants—Iscobrome, Dowfume 40 and D–D Mixture—treated plots produced normal healthy growth while adjacent untreated plots were not worth harvesting.

A slow decline of peach trees in Connecticut, and of apple, almond, fig, walnut, and cherry trees in other sections, is now attributed to *Pratylenchus* spp. Even more important, from the homeowner's viewpoint, is the connection between meadow nematodes and a serious boxwood disease.

The boxwood decline has become serious in eastern United States in recent years. Above-ground symptoms include defoliation, sudden death of branches, sometimes resulting in a "stag-head," sickly stunted growth, and various types of foliage discoloration. This is often some sort of chlorosis, appearing in thin lateral streaks or in leaf tips or other localized areas. The foliage of lightly infected plants is dark greenish bronze which ranges to light orange-yellow for heavier infection. Symptoms are more pronounced during periods of drought or freezing temperatures.

When the root system is examined, brownish black lesions or entirely black rootlets are found and a proliferous lateral root formation in upper soil layers. The migratory nematodes move away from nearly dead roots so they are not always found in connection with serious cases of the disease.

Control. Although soil for annual crops can be treated with D–D or ethylene dibromide in advance of planting we do not yet have selective chemicals, except perhaps sodium selenate, or the very poisonous parathion, which can be used in the soil around living shrubs. Proper watering in times of drought will help compensate for loss of root system, and organic mulches are probably helpful. Propagation from clean plants, in clean sand, is essential.

TYLENCHULUS

Males wormlike, females flask-shaped.

Tylenchulus semi-penetrans, CITRUS NEMATODE, a root nematode, not forming galls, attacking smaller roots of citrus trees, retarding growth of tops and producing yellow leaves. Soil particles cling to the rootlets due to the gelatinous material in which eggs are embedded, the cortex readily separates from the woody cylinder, and there is a scarcity of healthy growing root tips. When roots are spread out in water and examined with a low-power microscope the long cylindrical males and broad, flask-shaped females can be seen sticking out from the roots, with their heads embedded in the tissue.

Control. All measures for the general health of trees, including use of bulky organic fertilizers, are helpful.

PHYSIOGENIC DISEASES

Plants in poor health from one or more environmental conditions far outnumber those afflicted with bacterial or fungous diseases. When foliage turns yellow from lack of nitrogen, or from unavailability of iron in an alkaline soil, or from lack of oxygen in a waterlogged soil, we call it a physiogenic disease. The adverse condition may be continuing, as it is with a nutrient deficiency, or it may be transitory, an ice-storm, perhaps, lasting but a day but with resultant dieback continuing for the next two years. Spray injury is also included in this section, albeit not a disease in the strict sense of the word.

Trees and crops can be insured against hail, hurricanes, lightning, and other acts of God but not from the misguided zeal of gardeners. Years of working in gardens in my own state and visiting gardens in other states from coast to coast have convinced me that plants often suffer more from their owners than from pests and diseases. Azaleas die from an overdose of aluminum sulfate applied to correct acidity when the original cause of ill health was a too-wet soil. Rhododendrons die when a deep, soggy mass of maple or other "soft" leaves is kept around the trunks. Roses die when the beds are edged with a spade and soil mounded up in the center, burying some plants too deeply and exposing roots of others. Seedlings die from an overdose of fertilizer in hot weather. Trees die from grading operations.

Spray injury is exceedingly common, with the gardener thinking the red or brown spots are fungous leaf spots and increasing the chemical dosage until all foliage is lost. Weed killers take their unexpected toll of near-by ornamentals.

Either deficiency or excess of plant nutrients can cause a physiogenic disease. Greenhouse operators and commercial growers in the field must watch nutrition very carefully. The backyard farmer gets along pretty well by using a "complete" fertilizer containing nitrogen, phosphorus, and potassium in large amounts and minor elements in trace amounts. The deficiency symptoms listed below are not meant to encourage amateur diagnosticians. Send a soil sample to your State Experiment Station for a correct interpretation of nutrients and soil acidity. Take a slice down through the soil to spade or trowel depth from several places in the garden, mix together, and send a small sample of the mixture.

Acidity, Excess. Soil acidity or alkalinity is measured on a pH scale which runs from 0 to 14. When the number of acid or hydrogen ions balance the number of alkaline or hydroxyl ions, we have pH 7.0 or neutral. Above pH

FIG. 62. Simple Kit for Testing Soil pH. A pinch of soil is placed in larger well of porcelain plate, saturated with indicator solution, allowed to stand 30 seconds, liquid then tilted into smaller well and color compared with chart.

7.0 the soil is alkaline and may contain free lime, below it, the soil is acid. Few crop plants will grow below pH 3.5 or above pH 9. Some, like the broad-leaved evergreens, thrive at a pH of 4 to 6, but for most crop plants the most favorable pH range is about 6.2 to 7.2. If the soil becomes very acid roots are poorly developed and may decay, growth is slow, foliage is mottled or chlorotic. This result is due either to actual excess of hydrogen ions or to physical structure of the soil and solubility of nutrients. Lime is added in amounts varying with the type of soil, the original pH, and the crop.

To bring a sandy soil from pH 4 to above 6 takes only ½ pound of hydrated lime per square yard, whereas it takes about 2 pounds lime to change a clay soil the same amount. The small Kits for home testing of soils include lists of plants with their soil preferences and amounts of lime required.

Alkali Injury. Some semiarid soils are nearly barren from excess of chemicals with a basic reaction. Composition varies, but three common salts are sodium chloride, sulfate of soda, and carbonate of soda which may become concentrated at the soil surface with a whitish incrustation. Other soils are black alkali, where the organic matter has been dissolved. Applications of gypsum or sulfur, cultivation, and mulching are correctives.

FIG. 63. Alkali Injury, from salts in irrigation water.

Alkalinity. Either aluminum sulfate or sulfur or both mixed together can be used to reduce the pH for plants doing best in a somewhat acid soil. The dosage of aluminum sulfate should not exceed 5 pounds per 100 square feet at one application; the usual sulfur dosage is about 2 to 3 pounds per 100 square feet.

Aluminum Toxicity, occasional, if used in excess.

Arsenical Injury. Leaves of peaches, apricots, and other stone fruits are readily spotted or burned with lead arsenate unless lime or zinc sulfate is added as a corrective, and there may be similar leaf spotting and defoliation when these tender fruits are grown in old apple land which has accumulated a residue of lead arsenate over a period of years. Even apple trees can be severely injured by arsenical sprays under some weather conditions.

Baldhead. In beans this is loss of the growing point.

Bitter Pit. On apples, this is often called stippen and is characterized by small circular, slightly sunken spots on fruit, increasing in storage, especially at warm temperatures, most frequent on varieties Jonathan, Baldwin, Spy, Rhode Island Greening. It seems to be related to a fluctuating moisture supply in soil and increased by abundant rainfall shortly before harvest. On pear, bitter pit is sometimes associated with moisture deficiency, and with overnutrition in olives.

Black End. In pear, the whole blossom end of the fruit may turn black and dry; the disease appears when oriental pear rootstocks are used in poor soil. In walnut, black end of nuts is probably drought injury.

Black Heart. In beets, this is generally boron deficiency (see below); occasionally it is potassium or phosphorus deficiency. In apple wood it comes from freezing injury; in potatoes, it may be lack of oxygen; in celery, fluctuating soil moisture.

Black Root. Defective soil drainage and accumulation of toxins are associated with black roots, but so too are soil fungi and root nematodes.

Blasting of inflorescence and failure to produce seed seem associated with extremes of soil moisture, too wet or too dry, at blossom time.

Blindness of tulips and other bulbs. Failure to flower may be due to Botrytis blight or other disease but sometimes comes from root failure in dry soil, or heating of bulbs in storage or transit. Too early forcing may result in blindness.

Blossom-end Rot, very common on tomatoes, also on pepper, squash, watermelon. The tissues at blossom end of fruit shrink, causing a dark, flattened or sunken, leathery spot which may include nearly half the fruit. The disease is most common on plants which have had an excess of rainfall in early part of the season, followed by a period of drought; but there are many contributing factors, such as shallow root system, root killing in waterlogged soil, excessive nitrogen, perhaps deficiency of calcium or phosphorus. Deep soil preparation, use of a complete balanced fertilizer, and mulching to conserve moisture all reduce blossom-end rot.

Bordeaux Injury. Both the copper and the lime in bordeaux mixture can be injurious to some crops. Cucurbits are stunted, and blossoming and fruit-setting are delayed in tomatoes. Red-spotting of foliage of roses and apples is followed by yellowing and defoliation. See Copper Injury; Lime Injury.

Boron Deficiency. A small quantity of boron is required for normal growth of most plants. For some plants there is not much leeway between necessary and toxic amounts; others require or tolerate large amounts. Deficiency symptoms vary with the crop.

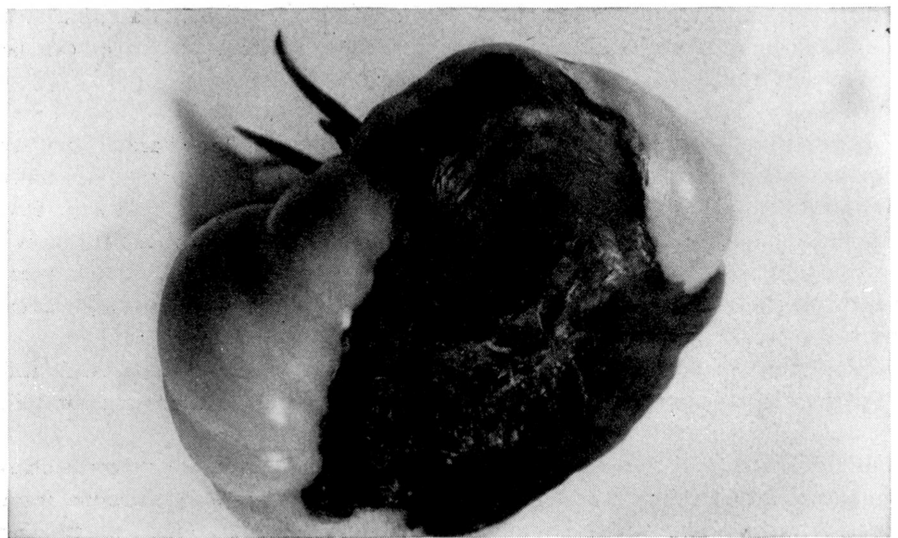

FIG. 64. Blossom-end Rot of Tomato.

Apples. Internal and external cork, dieback, rosette. Leaves on terminal shoots turn yellow, are convex with red veins; twigs die back from tip; dwarfed, thickened, brittle leaves are in tufts at nodes; internodes are abnormally shortened. Chief symptoms are in fruit—dry corky lesions throughout flesh, or diffuse brown lesions, with bitter taste. On varieties McIntosh, Baldwin, Rome, Northwestern Greening, and Jonathan we also get external cork, with severe russeting of surface. Control by broadcasting borax by hand in a ring under tips of branches—2 ounces for 4- to 6-year trees with 3½-inch trunk diameter, up to 12 ounces for a 24-year old tree with 14-inch trunk diameter. Very young trees may be injured by treatment. One application may last 2 or 3 years.

Beets, turnips, other root crops. Black Heart, Brown Heart. Roots have dark spots, plants are gradually stunted and dwarfed, leaves are small, sometimes variegated, twisted. The interior of the beet or turnip has a dark-brown to nearly black, water-soaked area, sometimes with a hollow center that shows when the root is cut open. The amount of borax that can be added without injury depends on type of soil and moisture content. In alkaline soil about 50 pounds borax per acre broadcast with the fertilizer is safe for beets and can be increased with low soil mixture, but with high soil moisture and an acid soil there is more chance of injury. Boron deficiency seems somewhat more prevalent in alkaline soils.

Celery. Cracked Stem. Leaves have a brownish mottling, stems are brittle, cracked with brown stripes. Apply borax as for beets; avoid excessive liming.

Lettuce shows boron deficiency by malformation of young leaves, death of growing point; cauliflower may have browning of the head. In some flowering plants the terminal bud dies and the top leaves are thick and brittle.

Boron Toxicity. Beans are extremely sensitive to boron with injury from as little as 4 pounds borax broadcast per acre. If borax has been added for root crops, boron-tolerant cabbage should follow before beans in the rotation. Retardation or prevention of germination, death or stunting of plants, bleaching or yellowing of tops, disappearance of color along midrib and veins in apple leaves are all indications of excess boron.

Brown Bark Spot of fruit trees. Perhaps arsenical injury from residue in soil.

Brown Heart, of turnip, cabbage, cauliflower. See Boron Deficiency.

Bud Drop. In sweet pea very young flower buds turn yellow and drop off when there is a deficiency of phosphorus and potassium during periods of low light intensity. Water sparingly at such periods, avoid excess of nitrogen. Gardenias often drop their buds when taken from greenhouses to dry homes, but there is also bud drop in greenhouses with high soil moisture, temperature, and lack of sunlight in winter.

Calcium Deficiency. All plants require calcium, which is built into the walls of cells, neutralizes harmful by-products, and maintains a balance with magnesium and potassium. Calcium is leached out of the soil as calcium carbonate and should be replaced by adding ground limestone, or dolomite, which is calcium magnesium carbonate, or gypsum, calcium sulfate, which does not increase the pH of the soil.

In fruits, calcium deficiency shows first in the roots which are short and stubby with a profuse growth of new roots behind the tips which have died back. Basal immature peach leaves sometimes have reddish discolorations and twigs may die back. Corn and legumes require large amounts of calcium, which seems to become unavailable under conditions of high soil acidity.

Calcium Chloride Injury. Trees may be damaged when this dust-laying chemical is washed off country roads or driveways down to roots.

Catface. Fruit Deformity. Due to insects or growth disturbances.

Chlorine Injury. A tank of chlorine gas for the swimming pool carelessly opened too close to trees and shrubs causes foliage browning and sometimes death. Leaf margins are sometimes killed by chlorine gas from manufacturing processes.

Chlorosis. Yellowing or loss of normal green color may be due to deficiency of nitrogen, magnesium, or manganese, occasionally boron, insufficient oxygen to the roots in a waterlogged soil, or alkali injury; but in the majority of cases, and particularly with broad-leaved evergreens, it is because iron is unavailable in an alkaline soil. See Iron Deficiency.

Copper Deficiency. Exanthema or dieback of fruits—apple, apricot, citrus, olive, pear, prune; failure of vegetables on muck soils. Copper deficiency in fruits is widespread in Florida and occurs frequently in California. Leaves are unusually large and dark green, or very small and quickly shed, on twigs that die back, with a reddish-brown gummy discharge. Citrus fruits will be bumpy and drop or have insipid flavor and dry pulp. Application of copper sulfate to the soil corrects the deficiency, but often spraying trees once or twice in the spring with bordeaux mixture provides sufficient copper indirectly. (Avoid fumigation with cyanide several weeks before or after treatment.)

Unproductive muck or peat soils in New York now grow normal crops of onions and lettuce with the addition of 100 to 300 pounds of copper sulfate per acre. On copper-deficient Florida soils many truck plants fail to grow or are stunted, bleached, and chlorotic.

Copper Spray Injury. Some fixed copper sprays are less injurious than bordeaux mixture, but all coppers may be injurious to some plants under some conditions. Foliage spots are small, numerous, reddish, sometimes brown. In peaches the center may fall out, leaving a shot hole. Rosaceous plants follow

FIG. 65. Copper Injury. Reddish spots on leaf at left followed a copper spray. Compare with cold injury, center, and true black spot on small leaflet at right.

spotting with yellowing and dropping of leaves. Treated leaves are often harsher than normal and more subject to frost injury. Dwarfing and stunting are important symptoms on many crops, especially cucurbits. Tomato flowering is injured or delayed; apple and tomato fruits are russeted. Copper injury is most severe when cool, wet, or cloudy weather follows treatment. Tree roots are injured by overflow from pools treated with copper for algae.

Fig. 66. Copper Injury. Roses to the left were treated in cool weather with dust containing 7% copper; to the right, same varieties, untreated, in adjoining bed, photographed same day.

Cork. Boron deficiency, in apple.

Cracked Stem. Boron deficiency, in rhubarb, celery.

DDT Injury. Foliage of some plants—cucurbits particularly, roses occasionally—turns yellow or orange, often with stunting. Certain camellia varieties have been injured when shrubs are under trees sprayed with DDT. Continued spraying with DDT builds up a residue in the soil which may eventually have a toxic effect on the root system, the effect varying with the type of soil and plant.

Fig. 67. DDT Injury? Dark lesions appeared on stems of camellias in a California lathhouse soon after a DDT spray.

Fig. 68. Frost Injury on Rose.

Dieback. Deficiency or excess of moisture, nutrients; winter injury; also due to cankers, nematodes, borers.

Drought Spot. Boron deficiency, of apple.

End spot of avocado. Unequal maturity in two ends of fruits seems to be a factor in withering, spotting, and cracking at lower end. Pick promptly, instead of leaving on trees.

Exanthema. Copper deficiency, in fruits.

Frost Injury, from low temperatures after plants have started growth in spring or before they are dormant in fall (see also Winter Injury for freezing during dormant period). Yellow color of some leaves in early spring is due to temperatures unfavorable for chlorophyll formation. Some leaves, including those of rose, are reddened or crinkled with frost. Blossom buds of fruit trees are critically injured by frost late in spring. In the South, where plants come out of dormancy early, orchard heaters, smudge fires, power fans, and airplanes flying low to stir up the air are all used to help save the crop.

Many ornamentals are injured when a long, warm autumn ends in a sudden very cold snap, or warm weather in February or March is followed by heavy frosts. Cracks in tree trunks come from such temperature fluctuations.

Gas Toxicity. Illuminating gas escaping from aging gas mains causes slow decline or sudden death, depending on the plant. Tomatoes are extremely sensitive and indicate the slightest trace of gas by leaves and stems bending sharply downward. Plane trees develop "rosy canker"—long, narrow cankers near the trunk base with inner bark watermelon pink and swollen. With large amounts of gas escaping foliage wilts and browns suddenly, followed by death of twigs and branches; with slow leaks the symptoms appear gradually over a year or two. After the leak is repaired it is sometimes possible to save trees by digging a trench to aerate the roots, applying large quantities of water, burning out severely injured roots, then replacing soil and feeding to stimulate new growth.

Girdling Roots. Unfavorable conditions sometimes deflect roots from their normal course, and one or two may grow so closely appressed to a tree as to almost strangle it. If one side of a tree shows lighter green leaves with tendency to early defoliation, dig down on that side to see if a root is choking the trunk under the soil surface. The root should be severed and removed, then all cut surfaces painted.

Grading Injuries. Many shrubs die when they are planted much deeper than the level at which they were grown in the nursery. Similarly, many trees die when they are covered over with fill from house excavations. Roots require oxygen for survival, and a sudden excess of soil cuts off most of the supply. The tree expert should be on hand giving advice before any digging starts. Afterward is too late. And if grading means filling in soil around trees, a little well around the trunk is not enough. There must also be radial and circular trenches laid with tile, and then crushed stone and gravel before the top soil goes in place. Consult *Maintenance of Shade and Ornamental Trees* by P. P. Pirone for clear descriptions and diagrams for protecting trees from contractors.

Graft Incompatibility. Lilacs are sometimes blighted from incompatibility of the lilac scion on privet stock. Walnut girdle is caused by incompatibility of scions on black walnut roots.

Gummosis. Formation of gum on bark of fruit trees is commonly formed in cases of bacterial canker, brown rot, crown rot, and root rots from soil fungi and in connection with the peach tree borer, but other cases of gummosis seem connected with adverse sites and soil moisture conditions irrespective of parasitic organisms.

Heart Rot. Boron deficiency, in root crops.

Heat Injury. There are many ways in which excessive high temperatures can injure plants ranging from death to retarded growth or failure to mature flowers and fruit. Sunstroke, outright killing of plants, is a limiting factor in flower and vegetable production in summer in the South. Seedlings, especially tree seedlings, may have heat cankers, with stem tissues killed at the soil line. See also sunburn, sun scald, leaf scorch, tipburn.

Hollow Heart. Sometimes due to excessive soil moisture.

Hopperburn. Marginal chlorosis, burning, or curling of leaves of potatoes and dahlias is caused by leafhoppers.

Internal Browning or Cork of apple. Boron deficiency.

Iron Deficiency. Iron is seldom or never actually deficient in the soil but it is often in such an insoluble form in neutral or alkaline soils that plants cannot

FIG. 69. Iron Deficiency in Laurel; healthy leaf at right.

absorb it, or it may be precipitated as insoluble iron phosphate where excessive amounts of phosphates are added to the soil. Chlorosis is an indication of lack of iron, necessary for the formation of chlorophyll, the green pigment. In acid soils iron is usually available. In alkaline soils leaves turn uniformly yellowish green, or remain green along the veins and turn yellow in interveinal areas. Terminal growth of twigs is small and the shrub or tree is generally stunted.

To obtain a quick response it is possible to spray leaves with a solution of ferrous sulfate. For chlorotic pin oaks a solution of 5 pounds ferrous sulfate and 2 pounds soybean flour per 100 gallons water has been recommended and for chlorotic azaleas, 1 ounce of the iron sulfate to 2 gallons of water. More lasting is a soil treatment of a 50–50 mixture of ferrous sulfate and sulfur using, for oaks, 1 pound for each inch of trunk diameter, or for shrubs, 1 to 1½ pounds per 100 square feet.

Leaf Scorch of maple, horse-chestnut, sometimes walnut and other trees. Scattered areas in the leaf, between the veins or along the margin, turn light or dark brown, with all leaves on a branch affected more or less uniformly; canopy of the tree looks dry and scorched; leaves may dry and fall, with new leaves formed in late summer. Lack of fruiting bodies and position of scorched leaves on side of the tree exposed to sun or wind distinguishes this from a fungous leaf spot. Scorch appears during periods of high temperature and drying winds and often after a rainy period has produced succulent growth. Sugar maples along paved streets are especially subject to scorch.

Fertilizing or other means of improving the root system, top pruning to improve water supply to remaining leaves, and watering during periods of drought are all helpful.

Leaf Scorch, marginal leaf blight. Calcium or potassium deficiency.

Lightning Injury. Trees may be completely shattered or a narrow strip of bark and a shallow layer of wood torn down the trunk. Tall trees or those growing alone in the open are most likely to be struck. Valuable trees can be protected with lightning conductors, installed by a competent tree expert.

Lime-Induced Chlorosis. Plants sickly with yellow foliage in calcareous soils or near cement foundations. See iron deficiency.

FIG. 70. Lime-induced Chlorosis in Rhododendron, growing near cement foundation.

Little Leaf, on almond, apricot, avocado and other fruits. See zinc deficiency.

Magnesium Deficiency. Large areas in the Atlantic and Gulf Coast truck crop areas are low in magnesium because of natural lack of magnesium rock, extensive leaching from heavy rainfall, removal of large quantities in crops, and use of fertilizers lacking this element. In tomatoes, veins remain dark green while rest of leaf is yellow or chlorotic. Cabbages have lower leaves puckered, chlorotic, mottled, turning white at the margin and in center. In strawberries, leaves are thin, bright green, then with necrotic blotches. On fruit trees, fawn-colored patches are formed on mature, large leaves, with affected leaves dropping progressively toward the tip. In flowering plants there is greatly reduced rate of growth, yellowing between veins of lower leaves, sometimes dead areas between veins, sometimes puckering.

Control by using Dolomite limestone or fertilizers containing magnesium. Azaleas can be treated with magnesium sulfate (Epsom salts).

Manganese Deficiency. Top leaves become yellow between veins but even smallest veins retain green color, giving a netted appearance. Manganese sulfate can be added to the soil and the pH should be lowered below 7.

Marginal Browning. Potassium deficiency.

Mottle Leaf. Zinc deficiency.

Nitrogen Deficiency. Symptoms are paleness or yellowing of leaves and stems, firing or burning of lower leaves, stunted growth, reduced yield with small fruit or seeds, sometimes red pigments along veins. Immediate results can be gotten by side-dressing with a quickly available nitrogenous fertilizer, but long-range planning includes use of legumes in the rotation, green manure crops, and balanced fertilizers.

Nitrogen Excess. Too much nitrogen leads to overdevelopment of vegetative growth at the expense of flowers and fruit, bud drop of roses, sweet peas, tomatoes, and, in very high concentrations, to stunting, chlorosis and death. Excessive nitrogen decreases resistance to such diseases as fire blight, powdery mildews, apple scab.

Oedema. Small, wartlike, sometimes corky, excrescences are formed on underside of leaves of many plants—cabbage, tomatoes, geraniums, begonia, camellias, etc. When the roots take up more water than is given off by leaves the pressure built up may cause enlarged mesophyll cells to push outward through the epidermis. This condition is rare outdoors but is found in greenhouses and in house plants occasionally, when they have been overwatered. Copper sprays sometimes produce similar intumescences. Camellias frequently have corky swellings on back of leaves. These have been thought due to water relations but in some cases Sphaceloma, a scab fungus, has been isolated.

Oxygen Deficiency, Asphyxiation. Overwatered house plants and crops in low, poorly drained places in the garden often show the same symptoms as those caused by lack of water, for the roots cannot respire properly and so cannot take up water. Improve drainage; lighten soil with compost and sand; avoid too much artificial watering.

Phosphorus Deficiency. Young leaves are dark green, mature leaves are bronzed, old leaves are mottled light and dark green, and in some plants there is yellowing around the margins. Stems and leaf stalks develop reddish or purplish pigment; plants are stunted, with short internodes; growth is slow, with delayed maturity. Most "complete" commercial fertilizers have adequate phosphorus but it can be used separately in the form of superphosphate. In making rose beds it is a good idea to apply a liberal amount at the second spade depth as well as in the upper soil.

Potassium Deficiency. Marginal bronzing or scorching appears first on lower leaves and advances up the plant which is stunted. Leaves are often crinkled, develop necrotic areas, whole plant may look rusty. The lack of potash can be made up with a complete fertilizer containing 4 or 5 per cent potash. Wood ashes also help to supply potassium.

Ring Spot. Yellow rings on African-violet foliage are believed due to watering with water considerably colder than leaf temperature.

Rosette. Zinc deficiency in pecan and walnut, boron deficiency in apple.

"Rust." This term is used for any rusty discoloration—for a leaf blight of phlox of unknown cause, for a spot necrosis of gladiolus, discoloration of asparagus fern, and other troubles that have nothing to do with the true fungus rust.

Salt Spray Injury. Trees and shrubs along the seacoast are injured by the ocean spray, and after hurricanes and high winds traces of injury can be found 35 to 40 miles inland. Conifers are usually affected the most, looking as if damaged by fire, with needles bright yellow or orange red. Eastern white pine is very susceptible, but blue spruce, Austrian and Japanese black pines, and live oak are highly resistant. Roses survive submersion in salt water during hurricanes.

Scald, of apple. Asphyxiation injury to fruit in storage from accumulation of harmful gases, most important when immature fruit is stored without adequate ventilation at too high temperature and humidity. Wrapping fruit in oiled paper or coating skin with wax or oil, and storage of mature fruit at 32° F., with a high concentration of carbon dioxide at the start, controls scald.

Scorch. See Leaf Scorch.

Shot Berry, of grape. Defective pollination.

Smoke Injury. The most important agent in smoke injury is sulfur dioxide, a colorless gas with a suffocating odor released from smelters and many industrial processes. Acute smoke injury shows in rapid discoloration of the foliage, defoliation, sometimes death. Conifer needles turn wine red, in whole or part, then brown. Leaves of deciduous trees have yellow to dark brown dead areas between veins, with tissue next to larger veins remaining green. Chronic injury results in unhealthy, stunted trees, but less apparent discoloration and defoliation.

Plants vary widely in susceptibility. Roses, grapes, legumes, and some conifers are seriously injured; whereas beets, potatoes, cabbages and other crucifers, ailanthus, gingko, Carolina poplar, London plane, pin oak, and Norway maple are quite resistant. Control of injurious smoke can only be at the source—with filters, tall smoke stacks, neutralizing the acid gases, or using them in the manufacturing of sulfur and sulfuric acid.

Soot Injury. City trees and shrubs acquire an accumulation of soot, the solid residue of smoke, which screens out the sunlight. Evergreens can be sprayed with a soapy solution of Calgon (sodium hexametaphosphate) followed by syringing with clear water.

Stigmonose. Dimpling of fruit by insect punctures.

Sulfur Injury. Sulfur sprays and dusts are likely to burn foliage in hot weather, when temperature is 90° F. and over. There is often a browning of tip or margin of leaves. Lime sulfur is injurious to some plants in any weather, russeting peach foliage, causing apple drop, etc. When roses or other plants are continuously dusted with sulfur over a period of years the soil may become too acid and need lime as a corrective.

Sunscald. Trees with smooth bark are subject to sunscald when trunks or branches are suddenly exposed to the sun, as when a tree standing near-by

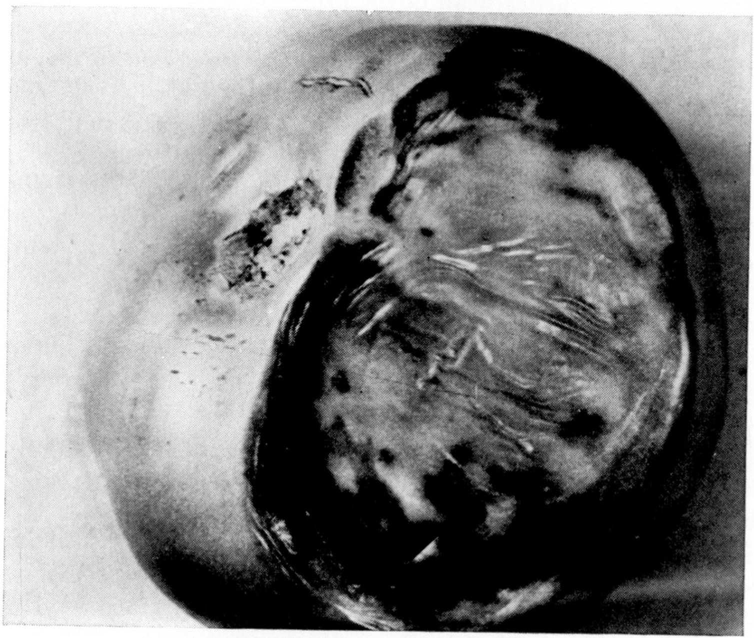

FIG. 71. Tomato Sunscald.

is removed. Young trees are also subject to sunscald the first year or two after planting and should have trunks wrapped in burlap or sprayed with a protective wax to prevent the cambium from drying out under the thin bark.

Boxwood is subject to sunscald in spring after winter covering is removed, particularly if this is done on a sunny day with drying winds.

Sunscald is common on green tomatoes when fruits are exposed to sun in hot, dry weather. This happens when foliage is lost through disease, or excessive irrigation, or when too much is removed in training tomatoes to a single stem. A yellow or white patch appears on side of tomato nearest sun, often developing into a blister, then into a large, flattened spot with a papery white surface darkened by the growth of secondary fungi and internal decay.

Sunstroke. Outright killing in excessive heat.

Tipburn. Potassium deficiency may produce a tipburn, but more often this is a reaction to heat, common in potatoes and particularly in lettuce, which shows marginal browning of the leaves and small brown or black spots in tissues near larger veins. A regular supply of moisture and avoidance of excessive fertilization in warm weather reduce tipburn, but most dependence should be placed on growing more resistant varieties in summer, such as Imperial 456, New York 515, and others listed in seed catalogues.

Variegation. Chlorophyll deficiency, genetic factors, and virus diseases may all produce variegated plants.

Water Deficiency. Practically all of the injury laid to excessive heat or cold is basically due to lack of water. Winter winds and summer sun evaporate it from cells faster than it can be replaced from the roots, and so they collapse and die.

Winter Injury. Most winter browning of evergreens is due not so much to actual cold as to evaporation of water in sudden warm or windy spells faster than it can be supplied from the cold roots. Copious watering late in the fall, a mulch, and windbreaks are needed for broad-leaved evergreens. A little care in matching plants to locations will eliminate most of the need for unsightly burlap or windbreaks other than those supplied by living trees and shrubs. Boxwood in many states requires winter protection. Where it does, I feel it is better relegated to the back garden than having to live with burlap desecrating the front planting four to five months of the year. Have pity on the passers-by.

Sudden icestorms not only cause obvious breaking in trees and shrubs, but in boxwood and similar shrubs they result in bark sloughing off and gradual dieback for months, even years, afterward.

Weed-Killer Injury. There has always been some unintentional injury to neighboring plants when weed killers of the kill-all variety were used on driveways, but now that we have 2,4–D as a selective weed killer for lawns the damage to innocent by-standers has been enormous, not only from spray drift and volatile material in the atmosphere (I saw roses last summer seriously malformed when a factory several hundred feet away worked with this hormone) but from using equipment which has applied 2,4–D for regular spraying purposes. Symptoms of injury are curling, twisting and other distortions, and sometimes a fern-leaf effect instead of normal-size foliage. Don't apply weed killers near valuable plants without preparing some sort of barrier; don't use sprayers for any other purpose.

FIG. 72. Weed-killer Injury. Left, rhododendron near lawn sprayed with 2,4–D; right, rose growing near a factory where 2,4–D was formulated.

Yellows. This term is used for some deficiency diseases but also for various virus diseases and Fusarium wilts.

Zinc Deficiency. Little Leaf of almond, apricot, apple, grape, peach, plum; Mottle Leaf of citrus; Rosette of pecan and walnut. On fruits, foliage is small, narrow, more or less crinkled, chlorotic at tips of new growth, with short internodes producing rosettes of leaves. Defoliation progresses from base to top of twigs. The method of supplying of zinc depends on the fruit.

Little Leaf

Apple. Spray trees in dormant season with zinc sulfate, 50 pounds per 100 gallons the first year, 25 pounds to 100 gallons the second year.

Apricot. Spray as for apple.

Grapes. Swab wounds and other parts of vine with zinc sulfate, 2 pounds to a gallon of water, immediately after pruning, if this is done in December or January before vines bleed.

Peaches, Plums. Spray as for apple, or drive galvanized nails into trunk.

Mottle Leaf. On citrus, leaves are reduced in size, pointed, with a sharply contrasting pattern of green along midrib and main laterals and light green or yellow between veins. The disease can be cured or reduced by spraying with a mixture of 5 pounds zinc sulfate and 2½ pounds hydrated lime in 50 gallons of water, or dusting with a mixture of sulfur and a pulverized zinc compound.

Rosette. This was formerly a problem of the majority of pecans in southeastern states, but now most growers have corrected the deficiency by treating soil with zinc sulfate, usually 5 pounds broadcast on soil under each tree in winter. Affected trees have narrow, crinkled leaflets with dead or perforated areas, short internodes to give the rosette appearance; they often bear no nuts. Variety Money-maker is resistant.

POWDERY MILDEWS

Mildew is a disease in which the pathogen is seen as a growth on the surface of plants. Powdery mildews are Ascomycetes, members of the order Erysiphales, family Erysiphaceae. They have white mycelium, in a delicate weft or a thicker felt, made up of a criss-cross tangle of hyphae. Colorless spores borne in chains on upright conidiophores give the white powdery effect. Black or dark mildews are parasites in the family Meliolaceae with a dark mycelium to give a sooty effect. These are common in the South or on tropical plants in greenhouses (see Black Mildew). False or downy mildews are Phycomycetes and the conspicuous growth is not vegetative mycelium but fruiting structures and conidia protruding through stomata or epidermis and giving a white frosty appearance in moist weather.

True powdery mildews, and we usually just call them mildew, are widely distributed, but are sometimes more important in semi-arid areas than in regions with abundant rainfall where other diseases flourish. Unlike those

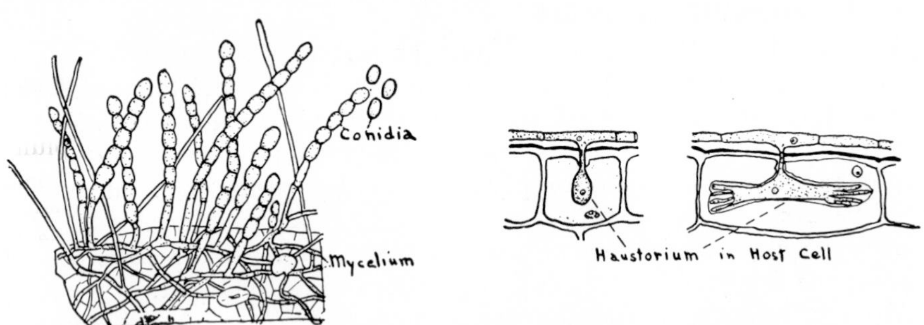

Fig. 73. Powdery Mildew: mycelium and conidia formed on surface of a leaf and two types of the haustoria in host cells.

of most other fungi, powdery mildew spores do not require free water for germination. High humidity at the leaf surface is quite sufficient. This occurs when cold nights change to warm days, when plants are crowded in low areas in gardens, or grown in shade without sufficient air circulation.

When the mildew spore lands on the leaf and puts out its germ tube, it does not make its nearest way inside the leaf but produces a tangle of septate threads, hyphae, on the surface. Special sucking organs, haustoria, penetrate the epidermal cells, occasionally the subepidermal cells, in search of food. The penetrating tube is slender, but once inside the cell the haustorium becomes a round or pear-shaped enlargement or a branched object with greatly increased absorbing surface.

Conidiophores, growing at right angles from the mycelium, produce the 1-celled conidia in rows or chains of somewhat barrel-shaped hyaline cells, which become oval as they are dislodged from the top of the chain and disseminated by wind. Mildews known only in this imperfect stage are called by the form genus name *Oidium,* for it requires the sexual fruiting bodies, perithecia, to place mildews in their proper genera.

The perithecia (cleistothecia) are round, with a dark, membranous wall, without beak or ostiole, rupturing irregularly to free the asci, and are held in place in the mycelium by appendages. The type of appendage and the development of one or several asci in the perithecium are the chief diagnostic characters differentiating the six powdery mildew genera. Sphaerotheca and Erysiphe both have simple appendages, but the former has one ascus, the latter several. Podosphaera has the appendage tips dichotomously branched and one ascus, whereas Microsphaera has the same type of appendage but several asci.

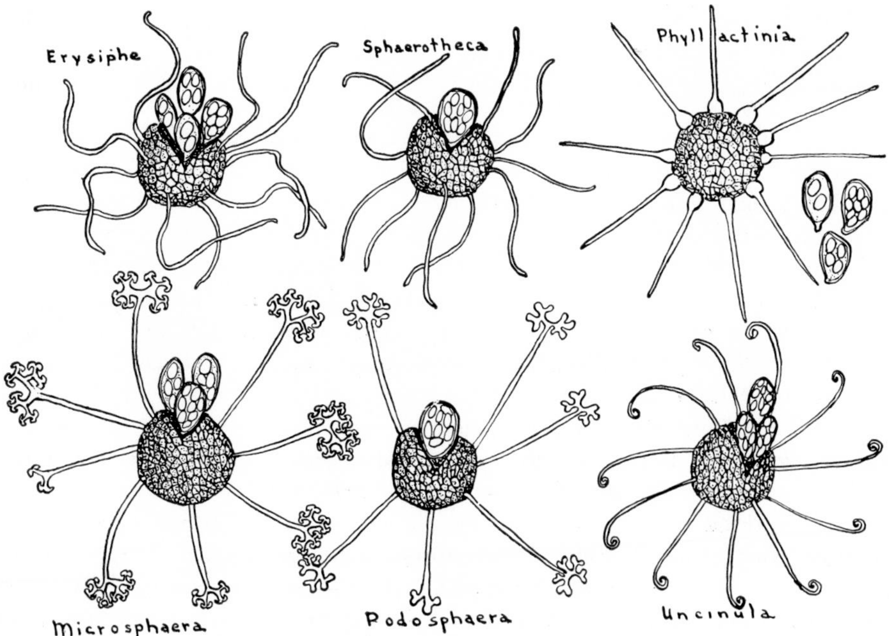

FIG. 74. Powdery Mildews. Perithecia (cleistothecia) of the six genera: *Erysiphe,* simple appendages and several asci; *Sphaerotheca,* same with 1 ascus; *Microsphaera,* dichotomously branched appendages and several asci; *Podosphaera,* same with 1 ascus; *Phyllactinia,* appendages bulbous at base; *Uncinula,* appendages coiled at tip.

Phyllactinia has lance-like appendages swollen at the base, and those of Uncinula are coiled at the tip. Both have more than one ascus.

Powdery mildews are obligate parasites, having no saprophytic growth periods in dead plant parts, although the perithecia carry the fungus through the winter on either living or dead tissue. Sometimes mycelium winters in buds. Symptoms of mildew are dwarfing and stunting, often with a slight reddening and curling of leaves before the white mycelium is noticeable, and sometimes deformation of flower buds, due to excessive respiration and withdrawal of plant foods. Sulfur dust has long been considered a specific remedy and many copper sprays are effective. Even a stream of water will reduce mildew. Some of the newer organic materials are not very effective. In many cases resistant varieties are the best answer, but the presence of physiological races within species makes breeding difficult.

ERYSIPHE

Perithecia globose, or globose-depressed, sometimes concave; asci several, 2 to 8-spored, appendages floccose (cottony), simple or irregularly branched, sometimes obsolete, usually similar to mycelium and interwoven with it; very rarely brown.

Erysiphe aggregata. Powdery Mildew of Alder. Perithecia large, asci with 8 spores, rarely 6 or 7.

Erysiphe cichoracearum. Powdery Mildew of Cucurbits and many ornamentals, many of them composites, perhaps best known to gardeners as the Phlox Mildew. Asci are 2-spored, perithecia rather small, haustoria not lobed. There are various strains, the form on cucurbits not affecting ornamentals. The latter include achillea, anchusa, artemisia, aster, begonia, boltonia, calendula, campanula, chrysanthemum, clematis, coreopsis, cosmos, dahlia, delphinium, eupatorium, gaillardia, golden-glow, goldenrod, helenium, hollyhock, inula, mallow, mertensia, phlox, rudbeckia, salvia, and zinnia, to name a small selection of the 280 or more hosts. Vegetables other than cucurbits—cucumbers, squash, pumpkin, gourds, melons—include lettuce, endive, Jerusalem artichoke, and salsify.

Erysiphe cichoracearum was reported on cucurbits in America in 1890 but did not gain much prominence until 1926 when it suddenly reduced the melon crop in the Imperial Valley of California by 5000 carloads. By 1936 powdery mildew-resistant Cantaloupe 45 had been developed to meet the situation, but in another decade the fungus had produced a different strain to which Cantaloupe 45 was susceptible. Plant breeders can never rest on their laurels because fungi, which are obligate parasites, seldom stay long outwitted. Other varieties—Cantaloupes 5, 6 and 7—have been bred resistant to both strains of cucurbit mildew but undoubtedly the fungus will strike back with a third strain in the course of time.

Sulfur dust gives excellent control of the fungus, but many melons are

FIG. 75. *Erysiphe cichoracearum* on zinnia, upper, and phlox, lower. Note powdery effect caused by conidia on underside zinnia leaf and black perithecia in white mycelium on phlox.

allergic to sulfur. The plant breeders answered that problem by producing melons resistant to sulfur injury. Insoluble copper sprays and dusts are also useful. In California an early lime-sulfur spray followed by spraying with Cuprocide or Burgundy mixture has been tried for early cantaloupes.

Phlox mildew is only too familiar to gardeners. The white coating often appears on variety Miss Lingard in June but on other varieties (at least in the New York City area in a normal season) more prominently in July and August. The mycelium may be present on both leaf surfaces and forms a thick felt on stems. In late summer perithecia are formed in great abundance.

Control. Keep plants well spaced with good air drainage. Dust with sulfur or apply a copper spray at first sign of white growth. My personal solution of the phlox mildew problem is to spray phlox with Triogen, which has a copper base, whenever I have it mixed up for roses. Sulfur dust has the advantage of keeping red spiders in check at the same time. Some phlox varieties are quite resistant to mildew.

Powdery mildew on *zinnias* starts late in the season but should be controlled with sprays or dusts during August and September. Perithecia can be carried in the seed, so all plant refuse should be cleaned up and burned immediately after flowering.

Erysiphe graminis. POWDERY MILDEW OF CEREALS AND GRASSES, economically important on wheat, oats, barley and rye, esthetically important on lawn grasses—Kentucky and Canada blue-grass and redtop. There are many physiological races.

The mildew starts as a white mealy coating on leaves, later turning brown and often studded with tiny brown perithecia. Leaves may turn yellow and be stunted.

Control. Dust lawn grasses with sulfur, destroy wild grasses in damp places from which infection may spread. Correct drainage.

Erysiphe lagerstroemeriae. CRAPE-MYRTLE POWDERY MILDEW on crape-myrtle only, from Maryland to Florida and Texas, the most serious disease of this shrub. The perithecia have been found only in Florida, but presumably it is the same mildew species throughout the host range.

The disease appears on young shoots in early spring, later including leaves and different parts of the inflorescence. Affected parts are soon covered heavily with a white, mealy to dusty growth, young leaves are stunted, often less than one-third normal size, but abnormally thickened; internodes of shoots are short and stems irregular; flower stems are stunted and buds often fail to develop flowers. Infected portions often have a reddish discoloration under the white coating. Diseased leaves and buds drop in a week or two, but stems may sprout again and sometimes produce normal growth in hot weather.

The fungus winters as mycelium in dormant buds, not requiring the rare perfect stage, and in spring covers such buds with a dense white coating of conidia, source of primary infection, which starts as small circular white patches on young leaves. Spores produced in abundance on these patches account for rapid spread of the disease until the midsummer heat.

Control. Spray with commercial lime sulfur at a 1 to 80 dilution when buds burst in spring and repeat two weeks later. Sulfur dust may be used if initial infection is not checked, or wettable sulfur (1 tablespoon per gallon), or copper sprays.

Erysiphe polygoni. POWDERY MILDEW OF LEGUMES, and many other vegetables and ornamentals—about 200 species in 90 plant genera. Appendages are long or short, interwoven with the mycelium, but the perithecia are not immersed in the mycelium. Asci have 4 to 6 spores.

Peas have a white powdery coating over leaves and pods, with the latter often discolored. Leaves are sometimes yellowish and deformed. The disease may be severe in arid sections of Western States, particularly on late home garden varieties.

On beans, the mildew is grayish. It is prevalent in California in cloudy weather or in autumn when humidity increases. Other vegetables infected by this species include lima bean, soybean, cabbage, turnip, radish, and horseradish.

The legume powdery mildew is widespread on lupine and is found on sweet pea, although on this host the most common form is *Microsphaera alni.* Acacia, anemone, candytuft, calendula, California poppy, china aster, clematis, columbine, dahlia, delphinium, erigeron, gardenia, geranium, hydrangea, honeysuckle, locust, matrimony-vine, peony, and tulip-tree are a few other ornamentals which can be affected. Notice that dahlias, delphiniums, and other flowers can have more than one kind of mildew, for they are also in the list under *E. cichoracearum.*

Control. Use sulfur dust or resistant varieties of vegetables.

Erysiphe taurica, on leaves of mesquite.

Erysiphe trina, on coast live oak, in California, causing witches' brooms (but see *Sphaerotheca lanestris* for the common live-oak mildew). Perithecia are small, yellow brown, with appendages lacking or rudimentary; asci have 2, rarely 3, spores.

MICROSPHAERA

Perithecia globose to globose-depressed, appendages branched dichotomously at apex, often ornate; asci several, with 2 to 8 spores.

Microsphaera alni, named for the alder (*Alnus*) on which it is widespread but best known to gardeners as the LILAC MILDEW, also found on many other trees, shrubs, and vines.

This mildew is prevalent on lilac in late summer and fall, sometimes in dry seasons almost completely covering foliage with a thin white coating, but because it comes so late in the season it is not very injurious. Elder, hollies,

New-Jersey-tea, moonseed, mountain-holly, privet, viburnum, euonymus, bittersweet, and trumpet-vine are other occasional hosts.

The lilac or alder mildew is rather common on deciduous azaleas in late summer, forming a very thin, grayish white coating with numerous, prominent, dark perithecia. Blueberries, with varieties Pioneer and Cabot most susceptible,

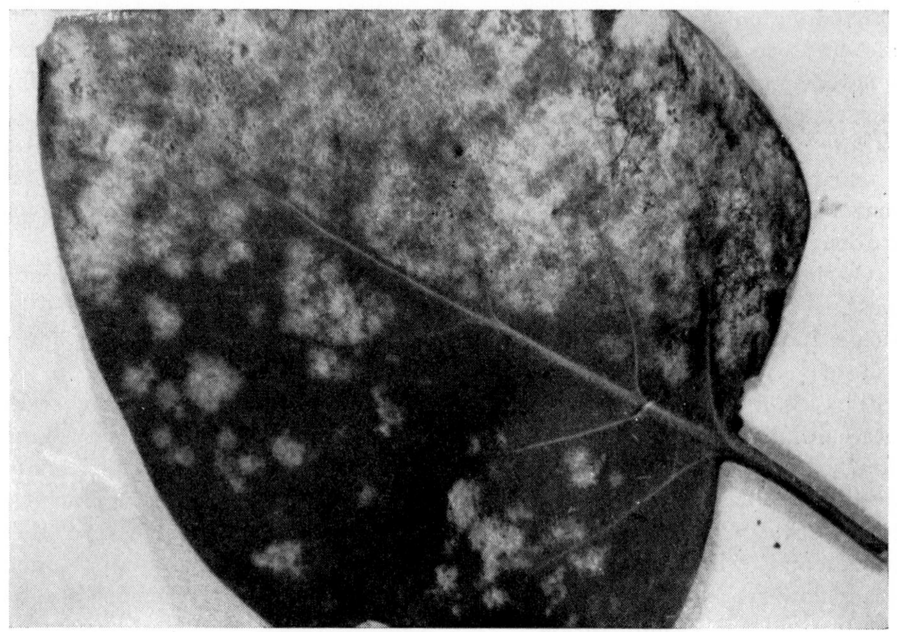

FIG. 76. Lilac Mildew (*Microsphaera alni*).

cranberries, farkleberries, and trailing arbutus are also affected by this mildew.

Among the tree hosts oaks are probably most susceptible, but it would seldom pay to attempt control measures except in nursery rows. On pecans, the white coating starts forming on leaves and nuts in July with occasional premature defoliation and shuck splitting, with shriveled kernels. Most commercial pecan varieties are mildew resistant. Other tree hosts include planes, catalpa, elm, birch, dogwood, American beech, hazelnut, magnolia.

Microsphaera alni is more prevalent than the legume mildew on sweet peas, but it is chiefly a greenhouse problem, in spring when temperature and humidity relations are less uniform. The foliage may be malformed, dropping prematurely or drying out and shriveling.

Control. Dust shrubs with sulfur or apply copper sprays. On lilacs syringing with a hose is helpful. In greenhouses pipes can be painted with sulfur while heat is on. Pecan varieties not resistant to mildew can have two sprays of 6–2–100 bordeaux mixture in June and July.

Microsphaera diffusa, general on snowberry, widespread on wolfberry, coralberry, occasional on black locust, lima bean, kidney bean. Appendages are 2 to 4 times longer than the diameter of the perithecia, with ultimate branches long, forming a narrow fork.

Microsphaera euphorbiae, on lima bean, euphorbia, roselle.

Microsphaera grossulariae. EUROPEAN POWDERY MILDEW on currant, gooseberry. For the important mildew on gooseberry see *Sphaerotheca pannosa.*

Microsphaera vaccinii, probably *M. alni* var. *vaccinii,* reported as widespread on huckleberry, also on lyonia.

OIDIUM

This term is used for mildews known solely from the conidial stage. In some cases the type of conidial fructification may suggest correct genera but until perithecia are found *Oidium* is preferred.

Oidium euonymus-jaonici. EUONYMUS MILDEW, general throughout the South and on the Pacific Coast on *Euonymus japonicus.* The mycelium forms

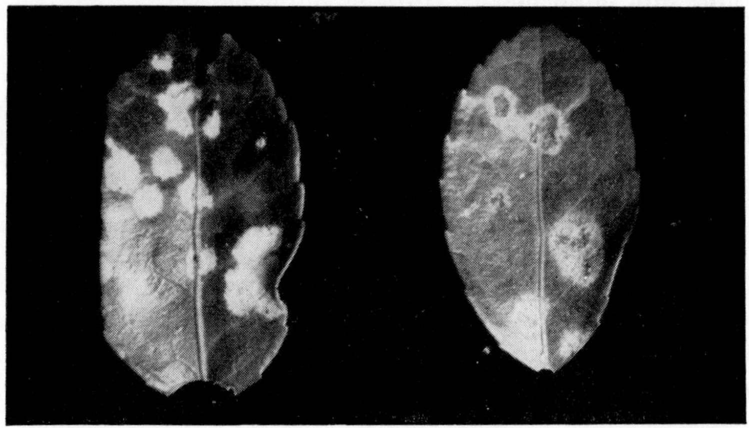

FIG. 77. Euonymus Mildew (*Oidium*) prevalent in the South.

a thick felt on the leaf surface, occasioning some yellowing and defoliation. I have seen this disease rampant in foggy coast towns like Beaufort, S. C., or Mobile, Ala., and equally severe in semi-arid El Paso, Tex.

Control. The washing effect of a water spray applied with pressure, either by adjusting the hose nozzle or putting the thumb over a portion of the orifice, is a deterrent to this mildew. Sulfur dust can also be used.

Oidium obductum, recorded on Oriental plane.

Oidium pyrinum, on crabapple.

Oidium tingitaninum. CITRUS MILDEW, common in Java, Ceylon, and India, but in this country causing only limited injury to tangerine trees in California.

White patches are formed on upper surface of leaves, the tissue underneath first becoming a darker, watery green, but later losing color and turning yellowish.

PHYLLACTINIA

Perithecia are large; appendages are lancelike with a bulbous base. Mycelium does not send haustoria into epidermal cells of host but forms special branches which pass through stomata into intercellular spaces and then each of these intercellular branches or hyphae sends a single haustorium into the adjacent cell.

Phyllactinia corylea. Powdery Mildew of Trees, named for the hazelnut or filbert but also prevalent on many other trees and shrubs, such as amelanchier, ash, barberry, beech, birch, boxwood, catalpa, chinaberry, crabapple, currant, blackberry, raspberry, gooseberry, crape-myrtle, dogwood, buttonbush, chestnut, elm, elder, fringe-tree, hawthorn, hickory, hornbeam, holly, oaks, plane trees, quince, rose, linden, sassafras, tulip-tree, walnut, willow.

Mildew is seldom serious enough on shade trees to warrant control measures, but dusting with sulfur may be advisable in the nursery.

PODOSPHAERA

Perithecia globose, with one, 8-spored ascus; appendages dark brown or colorless, dichotomously branched at tip; rarely an extra set of basal appendages present.

Podosphaera leucotricha. Powdery Mildew of Apple, also crabapple, pear, quince, photinia. First noted in Iowa on seedling apples in 1871, this mildew is widespread on apples. The chief damage is in irrigated regions of the Northwest where twigs, foliage, blossoms, and fruits may be disfigured, stunted, deformed, or killed. In the East the mildew is often present on water sprouts but seldom important except on nursery seedlings.

Gray to white felt-like patches are formed on leaves, often on the underside, which may be crinkled or curled, sometimes folded longitudinally. The foliage is soon covered with masses of powdery spores, turns brittle and dies, resulting in decreased yield. The same powdery growth starts on one-year twigs, but by midsummer is transformed into a brown, felty covering in which minute dark perithecia are embedded in dense aggregations. Infected twigs are stunted or killed. The fungus overwinters as dormant mycelium on twigs or in buds. Such buds produce shriveled blossoms and no fruit, or fruit from infected twigs is stunted or russeted.

Control. Remove mildewed twigs at time of winter pruning. Spray as for scab before blossoms open (pink spray), as last petals fall (calyx spray), 2 weeks after calyx, and 4 weeks after calyx. The first spray is lime sulfur at a 1 to 50 or 1 to 100 dilution, or even weaker in districts where it is injurious; the others are wettable sulfur. Dwarf trees can be dusted with sulfur.

Podosphaera oxyacanthae. Powdery Mildew of Apple and Other Fruits, general on apple, also on amelanchier, apricot, cherry, choke-cherry, crabapple, hawthorn, holodiscus, mountain-ash, nectarine, peach, persimmon, pear, snowberry, spirea. This mildew is more common in the East than *P. leucotricha* but is not often serious enough on apple to call for control measures. Cherry leaves and twigs may be covered with a white coating and remain dwarfed. Spray schedules for brown rot should control cherry mildew.

SPHAEROTHECA

Appendages simple, flexuous, resembling hyphae; only one ascus in a perithecium.

Sphaerotheca castagnei, on buffalo-berry, spirea.

Sphaerotheca humuli. Hop Mildew on hops, fruits—blackberry, dewberry, gooseberry, raspberry, strawberry—rose (but probably not as common as *S. Pannosa*) and many ornamentals including agastache, betony, buffalo-berry, delphinium, epilobium, erigeron, gilia, geranium, gaillardia, geum, hawkweed, hawks-beard, hydrophyllum, kalanchoë, matricaria, meadowsweet, nine-bark, polemonium, phlox, sumac, spirea, tamarisk, vernonia.

This mildew is commercially important on Latham variety of raspberry, coming on the new canes after they are 2 to 3 feet high. The tip leaves are dwarfed, mottled, and distorted, almost as if they had mosaic. The undersurface of leaves appears water-soaked or has the familiar white coating. There is no specific control except to plant for free air circulation.

Sphaerotheca lanestris. Powdery Mildew of Coast Live Oak, on *Quercus agrifolia* in California, reported also on white, southern red, bur and post oaks. The disease is most destructive in the narrow coastal plain of California. The most conspicuous symptom is a powdery white, stunted growth developing from certain terminal or lateral buds. The shoots are swollen, fleshy, with much shortened internodes. Foliage on such shoots is often reduced to pale yellow bract-like leaves which turn brown, dry and shrivel, the whole resembling a witches' broom.

On leaves developing from normal buds and shoots the fungus forms a dense layer on both surfaces, although more abundant on the lower side. Since the grayish white changes to tan and then brown with age, this mildew has been called the brown mildew. Perithecia are formed in the brown felt, abundantly in some years, rarely in others. In southern California the fungus can apparently winter in the conidial state, with widespread leaf and shoot infections coming from wind-borne conidia.

Control is not easy. Spraying with lime sulfur at a 1 to 50 dilution in March and October is fairly effective but lime sulfur may be very injurious at high temperatures and low relative humidity. Wettable sulfur has not been consistently effective. Isothan Q15, 1 pint to 100 gallons, is rather promising.

Removal of witches' brooms by pruning back to normal lateral branches is effective only if the tree is slightly susceptible and conditions for reinfection are unfavorable. Heavy pruning stimulates new growth and increases the amount of mildew. Resistant seedlings are being selected in nurseries. The Holm or Holly Oak is apparently resistant to mildew and well adapted to the coastal region.

Sphaerotheca mors-uvae. AMERICAN POWDERY MILDEW, GOOSEBERRY MILDEW, general on gooseberry, also on currant. In many sections this is the most important gooseberry disease, the limiting factor in production. Fruits dry up with a brown, felty covering. Leaves and canes are stunted with the usual white coating. Perithecia are formed on canes and ascospores are discharged in early May as fruit is set. Conidia for secondary infection are produced within 10 days.

Control. Spray with lime sulfur at a 1 to 50 dilution, plus a spreader such as Spraysoy, immediately after bloom.

Sphaerotheca pannosa var. **persicae.** PEACH MILDEW, general on peach, also on almond, apricot, nectarine, matrimony-vine, and photinia. The mycelium is pannose (ragged) or in dense patches, persistent, usually satiny, shining white, or sometimes grayish or pale brown. The fruits have brown blotches and are scabby and malformed.

Control. Spray with lime sulfur, 1 to 100 dilution.

Sphaerotheca pannosa var. **rosae.** ROSE MILDEW, general on rose and confined to this host. Originally considered the same, it was finally established that the peach variety cannot affect the rose and vice versa. Rose mildew was first described in Germany, in 1819, and is found wherever roses grow. In America powdery mildew has always been a problem with greenhouse roses and is increasingly so with the substitution of aerosol treatments for red spiders and other pests for old-fashioned syringing. Among garden roses mildew is omnipresent in the semi-arid Southwest and along the Pacific Coast. In the East it appears on small-flowered ramblers such as Dorothy Perkins and Crimson Rambler in May and may be serious on hybrid teas in late summer with the advent of cool nights. In the past season or two it has likewise become serious in early summer on many hybrid teas and Floribundas.

The first symptom may be a slight curling of the leaves with the mycelial growth such a light and evanescent weft as to be almost unnoticed. Later the white coating is conspicuous from the chains of conidia produced lavishly over the surface. The coating may cover buds, resulting in no bloom at all or distorted flowers. Leaves often have a reddish or purplish cast under the white mycelium and sometimes turn black. On canes the growth is heavier, more felt-like, especially near thorns. Toward the end of the season perithecia may be found on the canes but they are not common, and I have never seen them on leaves except on a Rugosa rose at Ithaca, N. Y. Mildew is prevalent on soft, succulent young shoots, fostered by an excess of nitrogen.

Control. Sulfur dusts have been standard treatment for garden roses for

FIG. 78. Rose Mildew (*Sphaerotheca pannosa* var. *rosae*). At left, leaves and buds heavily coated with conidia; at right, evanescent thin coating on leaves and over-wintering mycelium forming on cane.

many years. To be effective, dusting must be started at the first sign of mildew, before the mycelium gets too thick and felty. For advanced cases spraying is more satisfactory. Wettable sulfur has been recommended at about 2 table-spoons per gallon with a suitable spreader to wet the felt. Sulfur dusts containing 3 ½% copper or 10% Fermate can be used for dual control of mildew and black spot. Most of the proprietary mixtures now on the market contain too little sulfur (only 10 to 40% instead of 80 to 90%) to give adequate control of mildew. Fermate and some other carbamates seem unsatisfactory.

In my own test garden the beds receiving Fermate and an inadequate amount of sulfur have often had more mildew than the untreated plots, and I have attributed this to the increased succulent growth when Fermate is used as a spray or dust. I get excellent mildew control with Triogen spray, and this does contain Fermate, but the amount of copper is adequate. Copper, an efficient chemical for rose mildew, can be injurious in some formulations.

Recently announced is the possibility of the antibiotic actidione, a by-product of streptomycin, controlling rose mildew. Use of a balanced fertilizer with potash in correct proportion may reduce mildew. Choice of variety is important. Shiny-leaved climbers like Dr. Van Fleet seldom have mildew and the low spreading shrub rose, The Fairy, which looks like a miniature Dorothy Perkins but blooms all summer, is almost mildew-resistant. I have never seen mildew on the hybrid rugosa Vanguard and seldom on that universal favorite, Peace.

Sphaerotheca phytoptophyla, associated with gall mites causing witches' brooms on hackberry. The mycelium is evanescent; perithecia are formed inside loose scales of enlarged buds.

UNCINULA

Perithecia globose, appendages uncinate, slightly coiled at tips; several asci, with 2 to 8 spores.

Uncinula flexuosa. POWDERY MILDEW OF HORSE-CHESTNUT, on *Aesculus* spp.—horse-chestnut and red, yellow, and Ohio buckeyes—widespread in central and eastern states. This mildew gives a very thin coating on leaf surface, supposedly mostly on the underside, although I have seen it on upperside of foliage. Perithecia are numerous, small, barely discernible with the naked eye.

Control. Usually unnecessary except in nurseries. A copper spray used for blotch will also control mildew.

Uncinula circinata, on maple species, Virginia creeper, western soapberry.

Uncinula clintonii, general on American linden.

Uncinula macrospora, general on American and winged elms.

Uncinula necator. POWDERY MILDEW OF GRAPE, general on grapes, common in late summer, of little importance in Eastern United States, but sometimes a major problem in California. Leaves, canes, and young fruits are covered with white patches; growth is often distorted. Late in the season white mycelium disappears and the spots appear brown or black; berries are russeted or scurfy, fail to mature. In eastern grapes the mycelium is largely confined to foliage, mostly on upper surface with numerous dark perithecia.

Control. Keep California grapes covered with a very light coating of sulfur dust (heavy dosage may give burning). Apply it when new shoots are 6 to 8 inches long, when they reach 15 to 18 inches, and when they are 2 to 3 feet long; on late varieties make a fourth application on fruit and in center of vines.

Uncinula parvula, and **U. polychaeta,** widespread on hackberry and southern hackberry.

Uncinula prosopodis, on mesquite.

Uncinula salicis. POWDERY MILDEW OF WILLOW, also pussy willow and poplar, widespread. This may sometimes cause defoliation but is not often serious. It can be controlled with sulfur dust or by spraying with wettable sulfur. The growth is in diffused or circumscribed patches on both leaf surfaces.

ROTS

A rot is a decay or disintegration of plant tissue. It may be a hard dry decay or a soft and squashy one. It may affect root or rhizome, stem, tree trunk, blossom or fruit. Some rots also affect leaves, but diseases primarily of foliage are more often designated leaf spots or blights. Rots caused by bacteria are discussed under Bacterial Diseases.

There are a great many wood rots of trees, recognized by the sporophores or conks of the various species of Fomes, Polyporus and other shelving or bracket fungi. By the time these signs appear it is usually too late to do anything about the disease. The tree-rot fungi enter through unprotected wounds—either pruning cuts or breaks due to wind and icestorms. For proper pruning methods and treatment of wounds, see U.S. Department of Agriculture Farmer's Bulletin 1896, *Care of Damaged Shade Trees,* or *Maintenance of Shade and Ornamental Trees,* by P. P. Pirone, or *Tree Experts Manual,* by Richard R. Fenska.

ACANTHORHYNCHUS

Ascomycetes, Sphaeriales, Sphaeriaceae

Perithecia separate, innate, beaked; spores 1-celled, dark.

Acanthorhynchus vaccinii. BLOTCH ROT OF CRANBERRY. The rot starts as a small, light-colored spot on the berry, spreading to destroy the whole fruit, with dark blotches on the skin. The fungus may attack leaves, but it seldom fruits on them until after they have fallen.

Control. Bordeaux mixture was formerly recommended, but now Fermate at 2 pounds per 100 gallons seems more satisfactory.

ACTINOMYCES (NOW STREPTOMYCES)

One of the soil microbes, intermediate between bacteria and fungi, forming thread-like filaments which break up into bacterial rods, each of which germinates and starts another filament. The most important species, *Actinomyces scabies,* is treated under Scab.

Actinomyces (*Streptomyces*) **ipomoea.** SOIL ROT OR POX OF SWEET POTATOES, general New Jersey to Florida and in the Southwest. Leaves are small, pale green to yellow; plants are dwarfed, make little or no vine growth, and may die before end of the season; the root system is poorly developed with most roots rotted off, or breaking off if plant is pulled from the soil. Small dark lesions are formed on stems below the soil line. Pits with jagged or roughened margins, often coalescing, are formed on mature potatoes. The rot is found in soils at pH 5.2 or above; and is worse in dry soils and seasons.

Control. Apply sulfur to acidify the soil down to pH 5.0.

ALTERNARIA (See under Blights)

Alternaria citri. ALTERNARIA ROT OF CITRUS FRUITS, navel-end rot, black rot, widespread, prevalent in warm, dry sections, but not too serious. In oranges the rot is most common in the Washington Navel variety. It is a dry, firm, black rot at the navel end, often in only one segment, with the fruit coloring prematurely and looking sound on the outside.

In lemons it is a soft, dark internal rot of old or weak fruit in storage. Firm dark brown spots are also formed on the rind. Grapefruit sometimes has a dark, internal storage rot, not readily discernible externally.

Control. There is no chemical treatment after picking that is satisfactory. Produce sound fruit in the orchard; avoid holding too long on the tree; avoid holding weak or old fruit too long in storage; store at low temperatures.

Alternaria mali. FRUIT ROT, widespread storage rot of apple, also quince.

Alternaria radicina. ALTERNARIA BLACK ROT OF CARROTS. This is a soft storage rot of roots held over winter. It may start at the crown, or from some wound on side of the root. Initial infection may be either in field or storage house. A black mycelial weft bearing large brown muriform spores develops over rotted tissue. There is no control except to choose firm, healthy roots for storage.

Alternaria solani. COLLAR ROT OF TOMATO, also fruit rot and early blight, general on tomato, but the collar rot stage is most frequent in the South. See under Blights.

APHANOMYCES

Phycomycetes, Saprolegniales, Saprolegniaceae

Thallus composed of cylindrical branching hyphae without definite constrictions; sporangium cylindrical, threadlike, swarm spores arranged in a single row within and encysting at the mouth. The species are saprophytic or parasitic, live in the soil and cause root rots or damping-off of seedlings.

Aphanomyces cladogamous, reported as causing rootlet necrosis of tomato and probably spinach root rot.

Aphanomyces euteiches. ROOT ROT OF PEAS, also on sweet pea, perennial pea. The fungus is likewise a weak parasite in many nonleguminous roots. The disease was first described in 1925 although it probably existed earlier in various root disease complexes and probably was responsible for giving up many lands formerly devoted to peas for canning. It is considered the most important of the pea root rots, is found in every pea-growing district but is particularly destructive in eastern and central states.

The fungus is parasitic on subterranean parts causing root and stem rot of peas of all ages. Symptoms and crop yield vary with time of infection. If the root system is invaded when only three or four nodes are formed, the plant may wilt and die suddenly; later invasions result in dwarfing and drying out of foliage from the ground upward. When seedlings are pulled out of the ground roots do not break off but come out as a fibrous string or vascular cylinder freed from cortex. The fungus enters only the cortex of roots and base of stem, producing softening and rapid decay of tissue. Large numbers of oospores are formed in the cortex and these may remain viable in the soil for more than one season.

Control. A well-drained soil with low moisture content and use of nitrogenous fertilizers seem to decrease disease. When the soil moisture is at 45 per cent of saturation there is no disease, but at 75 per cent there can be more than 70 per cent infection.

Aphanomyces raphani. Radish Black-Root and damping-off.

ARMILLARIA

Basidiomycetes, Agaricales, Agaricaceae

One of the mushrooms, cap-shaped on a stalk with an annulus or ring but no volva or cup at the base; gills attached to the stem; spores white.

Armillaria mellea. Mushroom Root Rot of trees and shrubs, also known as Armillaria root rot or toadstool disease first described in America in 1887 and known in Europe a hundred years earlier. The fungus is called honey mushroom, honey agaric, oak fungus, or shoestring fungus. Although the honey-

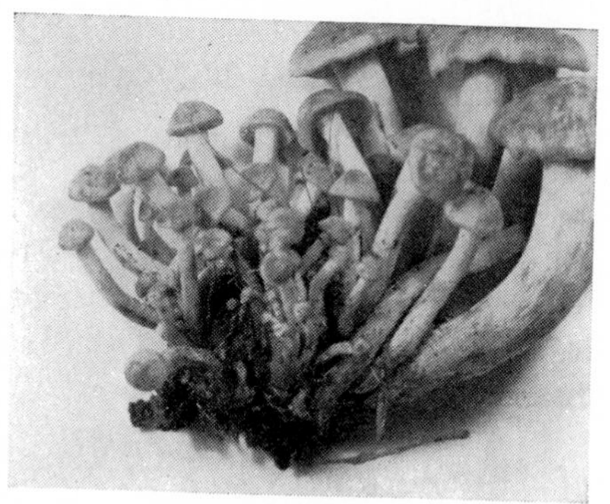

Fig. 79. Mushroom Root-rot Fungus, *Armillaria mellea,* taken at base of rotted oak.

colored toadstools are often seen in the East around rotting tree stumps and may occasionally cause death to weak ornamental trees, the chief damage from the disease is west of the Rocky Mountains, especially in California where most fruit and nut crops, as well as ornamental trees and shrubs are menaced.

The decay is of the roots and root crown. Sheets of tough, fan-shaped mycelium are found between bark and wood, the latter changing to light tan, becoming soft and watery in texture. Clumps of toadstools are often found at base of dead or dying trees, especially in autumn, but do not always appear in dry seasons. They are honey colored or light tan, with a stalk 4 to 6 inches or more long and a cap 2 to 4 inches across, often dotted with brown scales.

Basidiospores formed along the gills are wind borne. They can establish themselves in old stumps and dead trees but cannot infect healthy trees. The latter are infected in the ground by means of brown or black cordlike rhizomorphs, "the shoestrings," which grow out from infected roots a short distance through the rot. On meeting and penetrating a healthy root the fungus progresses along the cambium layer working up to and girdling the root crown. Leaves are dwarfed, turn yellow or fall prematurely; on small trees all foliage may die simultaneously. On conifers, particularly pines, there is an abnormal flow of resin from the root collar.

Trees subnormal in vigor and suffering from drought are most injured. Orchards of citrus and other fruits on lands recently cleared of oaks are liable to enormous damage unless resistant rootstocks are used. The rot is found less on dry hillsides than in valleys near streambeds where flood waters deposit soil and infected debris around root crowns, or in places kept too wet by artificial watering. Ornamental trees and shrubs are often injured when extra soil is added in grading and terracing and then kept too wet by watering the lawn frequently.

The list of susceptible plants is far too long to be given in entirety; a representative selection includes almond, apple, apricot, avocado, cherry, citrus, currant, grape, peach, pear, plum, raspberry; hickory, filbert and walnut; California pepper-tree, oaks, pines, spruce, sycamore; azalea, rhododendron, boxwood, rose; and sometimes even herbaceous plants such as begonia, dahlia, narcissus, peony, rhubarb, strawberry.

Control. Use resistant plants where possible. Of fruits, only French pear, Northern California black walnut, fig, and persimmon are sufficiently resistant to grow safely on infested soil. Some plants can be grafted onto resistant rootstock such as Myrobalan 29. The University of California has prepared a list of resistant or moderately resistant ornamental shrubs. Some on the list are *Acacia decurrens* var. *mollis, A. verticillata, Buxus sempervirens, Ilex aquifolium, Lonicera nitida, Prunus ilicifolia* (hollyleaf cherry), *P. Lyoni* (Catalina cherry), *Pyracantha coccinea* and var. *Lalandii,* but not *P. angustifolia* which is susceptible.

Moderately resistant shrubs include *Abelia grandiflora,* Darwin, Japanese and Mrs. Wilson barberry, Mexican orange (Choisya), *Elaeagnus argentea, Euonymus japonicus,* Japanese privet, *Myrtus communis, Pittosporum tobira,* and *Spiraea prunifolia.*

Mechanical measures are often helpful. Excavate and expose the root crown, remove diseased portions of bark and affected small roots. Paint wounds with a solution made by dissolving one 7-grain tablet of mercuric chloride in a mixture of ½ cup denatured alcohol and 1½ cups water (**caution**—this is a caustic poison; do not mix in a glass container). Leave the treated roots exposed until cool weather in autumn. Trenching or digging a ditch around a plot will restrict the disease temporarily but the roots will grow through the ditch in time.

Of soil disinfectants carbon disulfide is most used, applied in staggered rows in holes 18 inches apart each way and 2 ounces by weight (1 and 3/5 liquid ounces) injected into each hole which should be immediately closed by tamping. Hand applicators are available for injecting the disulfide 6 to 7 inches deep. This treatment is for land where valuable trees have been removed; one cannot go closer to a healthy tree than the edge of the branch spread. After treatment, the land should remain fallow for at least 60 days, and then be ploughed before planting.

ASCOCHYTA (See under Blights)

Ascochyta pinodella. FOOT ROT OF PEAS. Of the three species which make up the Ascochyta blight complex this one is most definitely a foot rot, with infection at the root crown or base of the stem.

ASPERGILLUS

Fungi Imperfecti, Moniliales, Moniliaceae

Conidiophores have a round head at the top with radially arranged bottle-shaped sterigmata that bear conidia in chains; spores are 1-celled, globose to ellipsoid, hyaline. Although usually found in conidial stage, in some cases a sexual fruiting body, cleistothecium, is formed and such species are placed in the order Eurotiales. Bread molds are in the genus Aspergillus.

Aspergillus alliaceus. CLADODE ROT, stem and branch rot, on cacti Cereus and Opuntia. This is a high temperature species. The spores are yellow in mass.

Aspergillus niger. CALYX-END ROT OF DATES; FIG SMUT; BUNCH MOLD OF GRAPES; POMEGRANATE ROT; BLACK MOLD ROT OF PEACH, also market and storage rot of shallot, onions, apple rot, tuber rot of potatoes. The fungus is a weakly parasitic black mold invading ripe tissue through wounds. In dates, the interior of the fruit is filled with a black dusty mass of spores spread to a large extent by the dried fruit beetle.

Control. Practice orchard sanitation; keep decaying fruits cleaned up so insects cannot carry spores.

Aspergillus spp., green and yellow molds causing secondary rots of many fruits and some vegetables in storage.

BOTRYOSPHAERIA (See under Blights)

Botryosphaeria ribis. DOTHIORELLA ROT OF AVOCADO and CITRUS, black fruit rot of pear, nut rot of tung oil. On avocado, this is a soft, rapidly spreading surface rot, starting from small spots when fruit begins to soften. Affected fruits may be covered with decay spots by the time they are usable. The fungus winters in dead twigs, and tipburned leaves.

On lemons and other citrus fruits the rot starts as a discoloration around the button, becoming a brown, leathery and pliable decay. When fruit is entirely involved it becomes olivaceous black. On tung, brown lesions appear on green fruit, which drops prematurely.

Control. Sanitary measures are most hopeful for control, together with fairly low storage temperatures. An oil-bordeaux is suggested for tung trees.

BOTRYOTINIA

Ascomycetes, Helotiales, Sclerotiniaceae

Apothecia as in Sclerotinia, with hyaline, 1-celled, ellipsoidal ascospores, but conidial stage also present with conidiophores of the *Botrytis cinerea* type. Sclerotia hemispherical, attached to epidermis or just beneath it.

Botyotinia convoluta. GRAY MOLD ROT, BOTRYTIS CROWN ROT OF IRIS, on German iris, first recorded in Canada in 1928, and apothecia later produced in culture. The chief diagnostic character is the presence of many shining black sclerotia, much convoluted and agglomerated into large clusters on rotting rhizomes. These are often found in spring on plants which started into the winter apparently healthy, for the fungus is active in cool, wet weather. Conidiophores are brown, formed in fascicles, and bear dense clusters of light brown, ovate or slightly pyriform conidia. They appear in spring growing from or near sclerotia. Affected plants do not start spring growth.

Control. Treat all new rhizomes before planting with a mercury disinfectant: Semesan at 0.25 percent solution for 30 minutes (submerge rhizomes and 3 to 4 inches of leaves), or mercuric chloride at 1 to 1000 dilution for 30 minutes, or calomel (mercurous chloride) 1 ounce to 1 gallon, dipping into the white suspension until there is a heavy coating and planting at once.

BOTRYTIS (See under Blights)

Botrytis allii. GRAY MOLD NECK ROT OF ONIONS, also shallot, garlic, widespread. This is usually found on bulbs after harvest, infection taking place through neck tissue and scales appearing sunken and "cooked." Sclerotia are at first white, then dark, 2 to 4 mm. across. Conidiophores and conidia forming the gray mold are produced directly from mycelium in tissue or from sclerotia.

Control. Artificially cure bulbs after harvest to cause rapid desiccation of neck tissue. Colored varieties keep better than white.

Botrytis byssoidea. MYCELIAL NECK ROT OF ONION. The fungus is much like *B. allii,* but produces more mycelium and less profuse gray mold.

Botrytis cinerea. GRAY MOLD FRUIT ROT, cosmopolitan on peach, cherry, plum, pomegranate, quince, pear, grape, strawberry, pepper, tomato, eggplant, also causing a rot of carrots and lettuce, celery. See under Blights.

Botrytis mali. FRUIT ROT OF APPLE, a decay of ripe fruit, with very small sclerotia formed.

Botrytis narcissicola. See *Sclerotinia narcissicola.*

Botrytis squamosa. SMALL SCLEROTIAL NECK ROT OF ONION. Very thin scalelike sclerotia are formed on dry scales. Decay is slow and does not start until after some weeks in storage.

BRACHYSPORIUM

Fungi Imperfecti, Moniliales, Dematiaceae

Hyphae dark, sterile hyphae lacking; spores dark, with few cross-walls, ovoid.

Brachysporium tomato. FRUIT ROT OF TOMATO.

CATENULARIA

Fungi Imperfecti, Moniliales, Dematiaceae

Hyphae dark; conidiophores simple or sparingly branched with terminal solitary chains of conidia; conidia dark, 1-celled.

Catenularia fuliginea. FRUIT ROT OF DATE.

CEUTHOSPORA

Fungi Imperfecti, Sphaeropsidales, Sphaerioidaceae

Pycnidia in a valsoid stroma; conidia oblong to bacillar, cirrhose (extruded in tendrils); conidophores obsolete or none.

Ceuthospora lunata. BLACK ROT OF CRANBERRY, developing in berries after picking. The fruit turns dark, soft. Spraying for other cranberry diseases largely controls this rot. Pick berries when dry, avoid bruises, keep cool.

CLITOCYBE

Basidiomycetes, Agaricales, Agaricaceae

One of the mushrooms, with gills typically decurrent (running down the stem) cap homogeneous and confluent with fleshy stipe which has neither ring nor cup; spores white, or very lightly colored.

Clitocybe monadelpha, causing rot of privet, apple.

Clitocybe tabescens. MUSHROOM ROOT ROT, CLITOCYBE ROOT ROT of citrus and other fruits and many ornamentals. This root rot is as devastating in Florida as Armillaria rot is in California and very similar, although its importance in the decline of citrus groves has not been long recognized. It is very destructive to Australian-pine (Casuarina), as well as to orange, grapefruit, lemon, tangerine, and lime on rough lemon stock. The disease has been reported on 210 species in 59 plant families, including acalypha, avocado, arborvitae, apricot, castor-bean, cherry-laurel, crape-myrtle, cotoneaster, cypress, dogwood, eugenia, eucalyptus, grape, guava, glory-bush, hamelia, holly, ligustrum, juniper, jasmine, loquat, oleander, poinciana, pomegranate, pear, parkinsonia, palms, rose, viburnum, wax-myrtle.

Symptoms of decline do not ordinarily develop until the pathogen has been working a number of years and has killed a large part of the root system. Oftentimes mushrooms are present at base of trees before tops show more than slight yellowing or lack of vigor, but if soil is removed from the root crown many lateral roots are found dead, and often the taproot is also gone. Infection starts at some point on the lateral roots, spreads to the base of the tree and then to other roots. Sometimes there is gumming at the crown and extending upward on the trunk. Mycelial fans or sheets are present between bark and wood and the clusters of mushrooms developing at the base are similar to those of Armillaria but the black shoestring rhizomorphs are lacking. Instead, there are sometimes black hard stroma-like outgrowths from fissures in bark of infected roots. The fruiting clusters develop in fall, from mid-September to December. The caps are light tan to honey-colored, 2 to 3½ inches in diameter.

Clitocybe root rot is most prevalent on land cleared of oak and other hardwood trees, and also on sandy, well-drained land inclined to periods of drought.

Control. Citrus trees on sour orange stock are quite resistant. Surgical treatment for fruits and ornamental trees is often successful. Remove the soil at least 2 or 3 feet from the trunk, working carefully to avoid injuring healthy roots. Cut off all dead roots flush with the root crown and also remove any infected oak or foreign roots in the vicinity. Cut out dead and infected bark at root crown or base of trunk, being sure to collect all chips (on heavy paper placed under exposed roots) for burning. Paint all exposed surfaces with a pruning wound compound and fill in partially, disinfecting the soil by pouring in 2 to 3 gallons of a 10–10–100 bordeaux mixture. The root crown can be left exposed for aeration and drying or, if too large a proportion of root system has been lost, new roots can be stimulated by mounding the soil around the base to a height of several inches above the partial girdle. The new roots will come from callus formed at margin of living bark.

COLLETOTRICHUM (See under Anthracnose)

Colletotrichum capsici. RIPE ROT OF PEPPER.

Colletotrichum circinans. ONION SMUDGE, surface rot, also on shallot, garlic, leek. Bulb or neck has a dark green or black smudge, often covered with stiff bristles of the acervuli of the fungus. Smudge is more prominent in white onions, being confined to the neck of colored bulbs. The fungus winters on onions, on sets, or in soil, and develops in the field at fairly high temperature and soil moisture. Most of the damage is just before harvest.

There is not much control except sanitation, rotation, and perhaps changing from white to colored onions.

Colletotrichum lilii. Black Scale Rot of Easter Lily, brown scale. The rot was first noticed in Louisiana in 1937, and it immediately threatened the lily industry in that section. Bulbs are brown to nearly black when dug, with outer scales most affected. Young lesions start as irregular light brown areas, then become darker brown and sunken due to collapse of epidermal cells and one or two subepidermal layers. Oldest lesions are nearly black, with tissue dry, shriveled. Stems and roots are not affected. The fungus is a new species with small, gregarious acervuli, many dark brown setae (bristles) and continuous, hyaline conidia.

Control. Treating bulbs for 48 hours in a 1 to 2000 solution of Puratized N5E has been effective and relatively safe. Dusting with Arasan after soaking gives protection against reinfestation.

Colletotrichum nigrum. Fruit Rot of Pepper, probably general on pepper in South and East. The fungus is a wound parasite on pepper pods. The spots are irregular, indefinite, depressed, blackish. Numerous acervuli with stout setae are scattered over the spots.

COLLYBIA

Basidiomycetes, Agaricales, Agaricaceae

Margin of young cap turned in, gills not decurrent, stipe central, no annulus (ring) or volva (cup); spores white or light; species cause wood rots.

Collybia velutipes. Heart Rot, White Sapwood Rot of hardwoods. The fungus is a small toadstool with central stem, base covered with dark brown velvety hairs, cap yellowish or brownish. The disease is a soft, spongy white rot of sapwood of living hardwoods, particularly basswood, horse-chestnut, American elm, and also reported on catalpa. The toadstools are formed in clusters at wounds.

CONIOPHORA

Basidiomycetes, Agaricales, Thelephoraceae

Pileus resupinate, effuse, hymenium with one layer, cystidia lacking; spores dark; wood-destroying species.

Coniophora corrugis, causing sapwood rot of alpine fir.

Coniophora cerebella. Brown Cubical Rot of conifers and sometimes hardwood—on slash, building timbers, and sometimes living trees. The crustlike fleshy fruiting bodies are a little over 2 inches in diameter, olive to brown with whitish margins, and smooth to slightly waxy surface.

CONIOTHYRIUM (See under Cankers)

Coniothyrium diplodiella. WHITE ROT OF GRAPES, appearing spasmodically on grapes but not one of the more important diseases. Small pycnidia appear on outside of fruit cuticle as shiny, rosy points, also on leaves. Infection is usually through wounds. Spots on ripe grapes are grayish, with brown borders.

CORTICIUM

Basidiomycetes, Agaricales, Thelephoraceae

Pileus resupinate, effuse, one hymenial layer; cystidia lacking, spores hyaline. *Corticium vagum* and some other species have been transferred to Pellicularia.

Corticium centrifugum. FISHEYE FRUIT ROT OF APPLE.

Corticium fuciforme. PINK PATCH OF TURF.

Corticium galactinum. WHITE ROOT ROT OF APPLE TREES, also recorded on blackberry, dewberry, dogwood, lychnis, and sumac growing near apples. The disease starts at the collar or on larger roots and advances rapidly outward on smaller roots. The collar may be girdled and killed while distal portions are still alive. A dense weft of white mycelium covers roots and penetrates to wood, causing a white rot. The disease is prevalent on lands recently cleared of oaks and may be a problem in ornamental plantings.

CYLINDROCARPON

Fungi Imperfecti, Moniliales, Tuberculariaceae

Conidia on sporodochia; spores with several cells, like Fusarium but more nearly cylindrical with rounded ends; cosmopolitan, especially in soil, but sometimes pathogenic.

Cylindrocarpon radicicola. SCALE-TIP ROT OF EASTER LILY in Pacific Northwest. Chemical dips are not effective; select healthy stock.

CYLINDROCLADIUM (See under Cankers)

Cylindrocladium scoparium. ROOT ROT OF STRAWBERRY. The same fungus causes crown canker of rose.

DAEDALEA

Basidiomycetes, Agaricales, Polyporaceae

Pileus dimidiate to caplike and stipitate; pores waved, mazelike, or somewhat resembling gills; without cystidia; hymenium labyrinthine.

Daedalea confragosa. WHITE MOTTLED WOUND ROT of hardwoods, also on fir. This is white soft rot, a slash destroyer in eastern hardwood forests but sometimes on living trees, especially willows, near wounds. Annual leathery to rigid conks (fruiting bodies or sporophores) are shelf-shaped, up to 6 inches wide, and may occasionally encircle a small, dead stem. The upper surface is gray to brown, smooth, concentrically zoned. Mouths of tubes on under surface are elongated, wavy in outline.

Daedalea quercina. BROWN CUBICAL ROT of dead timber and HEART ROT of living trees in immediate vicinity of butt wounds, usually on oak, chestnut, sometimes on maple, birch, hickory.

In advanced stages the wood is reduced to a yellow-brown, friable mass, with a tendency to break into small cubes. Conks are corky and shelf-shaped, up to 7 inches wide, grayish to almost black with smooth upper surface and cream to brownish undersurface. Mouths are large, elongated, irregular. The conks are more or less perennial.

Daedalea unicolor. HEART ROT, CANKER of maples and other living hardwoods, including alder, ailanthus, amelanchier, birch, chestnut, and hackberry. Decayed wood is yellow at first, later white and soft. Conks are small, corky, often occurring in clusters, varying from brown to gray.

DALDINIA

Ascomycetes, Sphaeriales, Xylariaceae

Perithecia in a globoid to pulvinate, concentrically zoned stroma, carbonous to leathery, 3 to 5 cm. across; spores 1-celled, dark.

Daldinia concentrica. WOOD ROT of ash, beech, various hardwoods, occasionally on citrus. There is a superficial white rot on dead parts of living trees. On English ash, the decay is called calico wood and is strikingly marked with irregular brown to black bands. Stroma containing sunken perithecia are hemispherical, black, carbonous.

DIAPORTHE (See under Blights)

Diaporthe batatis. DRY ROT OF SWEET POTATO. Imperfect stage of the fungus is *Phomopsis batatae*. If diseased potatoes are planted, the sprouts are affected but the disease shows little in the field. The roots, being infected at the stem end, continue to rot in storage. The potatoes are shrunken, often mummified, covered with papillae which are pycnidia under the skin massed in a coal black stroma.

Control. Use cool storage. Optimum temperature for the fungus is 75° to 90° F.

Diaporthe (*Phomopsis*) **citri.** PHOMOPSIS STEM END ROT, MELANOSE, DECORTICOSIS, SHELL BARK, general on citrus. On fruits the rot is a leathery, pliable, buff to brown area at button end. The melanose is a superficial marking of fruits with yellow or brown, scabby but waxy dots or crusts, often in streaks. Decorticosis or shell bark is found only on lemon trees with variety Eureka more susceptible than Lisbon or Villa Franca. The outer bark dies, loosens, peels off in longitudinal strips. New bark forms below this and the tree may recover only to develop the disease again in four or five years. Some leaves and twigs die and the fungus winters in dead wood.

Control. Lemon trunks can be scraped to remove dead bark and the surface treated with a fungicide—potassium permanganate, 1 pound to 12½ gallons water, or a zinc-copper-lime mixture. For rot and melanose prune out dead wood, spray with bordeaux-oil emulsion.

Diaporthe phaseolarum. Fruit Rot of Pepper and Tomato, also pod blight of lima bean. See under Blights.

DIPLODIA (See under Blights)

Diplodia natalensis. Diplodia Rot, Collar Rot, Fruit Rot, Gummosis general on citrus, sometimes other fruits. Perfect stage of the fungus is *Physalospora rhodina.* On fruit the rot resembles Phomopsis rot in being a leathery pliable decay of the stem end.

Control. Spray young fruit once or twice with 6–6–100 bordeaux mixture, plus 1% oil to check the increase in scales following killing of entomogenous fungi with the copper.

Diplodia opuntia. Cladode Rot of cactus.

Diplodia phoenicum. Leaf and Stalk Rot, Fruit Rot of date palms. The disease is sometimes fatal to transplanted offshoots. Leaves decay and die prematurely; spores are produced in great abundance. Infection is through wounds.

Control. Remove diseased tissue so far as possible and apply copper lime dust.

Diplodia theobromae, perhaps a synonym for *D. natalensis,* cause of stem-end rot of avocado.

Diplodia tubericola. Java Black Rot, general on sweet potatoes, especially in the South. The name was given because the first diseased specimens came from Java. This is strictly a storage rot; the inner part of the tuber is black and brittle, and innumerable pycnidia are produced under the skin, giving it a pimply appearance. The potato is finally mummified.

Control. Use care in handling so skins are not broken or bruised, cure properly after harvest and have suitable temperature in storage house.

Diplodia zeae. Corn Ear Rot, root and stalk rot, seedling blight. This is one of several fungi commonly causing ear rot in corn. The rot is dry, varying from a slight discoloration of kernels to complete rotting of ear. Seedlings and inner tissues of stalks may also have a dry, brown decay.

Control. Treat seed before planting with Semesan Jr., Spergon, or Arasan. Some hybrid corn is already treated when purchased.

ECHINODONTIUM

Basidiomycetes, Agaricales, Hydnaceae

Hymenium in the form of teeth with spiny serrate margins; pileus caplike to crustose.

Echinodontium tinctorium, the Indian paint fungus. BROWN STRINGY ROT or heartwood rot of living conifers—balsam fir, hemlock, Engelmann spruce, Douglas-fir—chiefly in the West, often with large losses in forest stands. Light brown to tan spots are produced in heartwood accompanied by small radial burrows somewhat resembling insect galleries. Rusty streaks follow the grain. In older trees rot can extend entire length of heartwood and into roots.

External signs of decay are hard, woody, hoof-shaped, perennial conks, the upper surface dull black, cracked, undersurface gray covered with coarse teeth, the interior rust or brick red with a pigment used by the Indians for paint. Even one fruiting body is indication of extensive decay.

ENDOCONIDIOPHORA (See under Cankers)

Endoconidiophora fimbriata. SWEET POTATO BLACK ROT, found wherever sweet potatoes are grown; most destructive in storage but present also in seed-bed and field. Round, blackish spots extend into vascular ring or deeper; sprouts are sickly with black cankers below ground, or killed. The fungus winters in storage houses, on weeds, such as wild morning-glory near the field and in soil, and is often spread by the sweet potato weevil. When potatoes are washed before storing, spores are also spread in wash water.

Control. Select sound potatoes for bedding and treat with Semesan Bel before starting in sterilized sand. This organic mercury may be somewhat more injurious than Fermate, Tersan, or other new compounds but seems to be more effective.

FAVOLUS

Basidiomycetes, Agaricales, Polyporaceae

Pileus usually stipitate; lamellae forking irregularly to form elongate, rhomboidal pores.

Favolus alveolaris. HEART ROT OF HICKORY.

FOMES

Basidiomycetes, Agaricales, Polyporaceae

Pileus woody, perennial, with tubes in layers, common cause of wood decays.

Fomes annosus. ROOT AND BUTT ROT, spongy sap rot of conifers, sometimes hardwoods. Infection is through wounds. Thin, tissuelike mycelial felts are formed between bark and wood, which is pinkish to violet in incipient states.

In advanced stages white pockets are formed in wood. Perennial conks are bracket-shaped to flat layers, upper surface zonate, light to dark grayish brown, undersurface beige with small pores.

Infection is sometimes through dead roots from mycelium growing through soil, or sometimes by spores washed by rain or carried by rodents.

Fomes applanatus. White Mottle Rot, widely distributed on hardwoods, maple, beech, alder, acacia, birch, horse-chestnut, hawthorn, hickory, and sometimes on conifers. The rot is generally found on dead timber, but the fungus can attack living trees through wounds and destroy the heartwood for a few feet. In early stages the wood is somewhat bleached, surrounded with a dark brown band.

This shelf fungus is called artist's conk, for the white undersurface immediately turns brown when bruised and can be used for writing or etching pictures. The upper surface is smooth, zoned, gray or gray black. The shelf may be up to 2 feet wide.

Fomes connatus. White Spongy Rot of heartwood of living hardwoods, most prevalent on maples, especially red and sugar maples. Entrance is through wounds or branch stubs but fruiting is usually on basal seams or scars. Conks appear annually but are perennial, small, less than 6 inches wide, hoof-shaped, corky to woody, white to yellowish, the upper surface covered with moss or algal growth. There is usually a limited area of decay.

Fomes everhartii. Yellow Flaky Heart Rot of living hardwoods, including birch and beech but especially oaks. Infection is usually limited to the lower trunk and the flaky character is because the decay is more rapid between rays. There are narrow, dark brown zone lines. Gnarly swellings on the trunk indicate sapwood invasion.

The conks are perennial, hard, woody, shelf-shaped, up to a foot wide, with the yellow brown upper surface becoming black, charred, rough, concentrically grooved with age. The undersurface is reddish brown.

Fomes fomentarius. White Mottled Rot of birch, beech, poplar, maple, and other hardwoods. This "timber" fungus chiefly causes decay of heart and sapwood in dead timber but sometimes attacks living trees. The wood is brownish, firm in early stages of decay, but in advanced decay is yellowish white, soft, spongy, with narrow, dark brown zone lines and small radial cracks filled with yellow mycelium to give a mottled effect. Decay starts in upper part of the bole and progresses downward.

Conks are profuse on dead trees. They are hard, perennial, hoof-shaped, up to 8 inches wide, with a smooth, concentrically zoned upper surface and gray to brown undersurface. The interior is brown, punky, with the tubes encrusted with white.

Fomes fraxinophilus. White Mottled Rot of Ash, a heartwood rot most prevalent on white ash but also occurring on green. Conks are up to a foot wide, with dark rough upper surface, brownish underneath, the first appearing when wood has decayed only a short distance. Infection is usually through branch stubs.

Fomes igniarius. WHITE SPONGY ROT, white trunk rot, white heart rot, on a wide variety of hardwoods but not on conifers. Aspen and birch are particularly susceptible. Decay is mostly confined to heartwood, but in yellow birch living sapwood is killed, causing cankers on the trunk. In an advanced stage the decay is soft, whitish, with fine black lines running through it.

The conks are perennial, hard, woody, thick, usually hoof-shaped, up to 8 inches wide, the upper surface gray to black, becoming rough and cracked with age; undersurface is brown, and the interior rusty brown with many layers of tubes, the oldest stuffed with white. Infection is through branch stubs and open wounds. A single conk may indicate 15 linear feet of rot in the heartwood.

Fomes officinalis. BROWN TRUNK ROT of conifers, chiefly in the West. Heartwood of living trees may be infected.

Fomes pini. RED RING ROT or white pocket rot of conifers, especially of Douglas-fir, larch, pine, spruce, causing heavy forest losses. Decay starts as a purplish or red discoloration of the heartwood, but in an advanced stage there are many soft, white fibrous pockets separated by sound wood. Sporophores vary from shelf to bracket to hoof-shaped, averaging 4 to 8 inches across, rough gray to brownish black with light brown margin on upper surface and gray to brown undersurface. Tube mouths are circular to irregular. On living trees these conks are found at knots or branch stubs.

Fomes pinicola. BROWN CRUMBLY ROT of many conifers and some hardwoods —maple, birch, beech, hickory, peach—usually on dead trees, occasionally in heartwood of living trees. Sporophores are shelf to hoof-shaped, 2 to 10 inches across, sometimes up to 2 feet, upper surface gray to black, often with a red margin, undersurface white to yellow when fresh.

Fomes roseus. BROWN POCKET ROT, cubical rot of heartwood of living conifers, particularly Douglas-fir. Decay originates in upper part of bole. Wood is yellow to reddish brown, soft, breaking into irregular cubes. Woody bracket-like conks, up to 6 inches wide, have black tops and rose undersurface. Infection is through dead branch stubs and broken tree tops.

FUSARIUM

Fungi Imperfecti, Moniliales, Tuberculariaceae

Mycelium and spores generally bright in color. Macroconidia are fusoid, curved, septate, on branched conidia in slimy masses, sporodochia; smaller microconidia are 1- to 2-celled; chlamydospores, resting spores, common. Perfect stage when known is usually in Hypocreales—Nectria, Gibberella. Fusarium species are the cause of many important rots and wilts and of diseases known as yellows, but there are many forms and races, and classification is difficult, with different systems and many synonyms.

Fusarium avenaceum, associated with cereal diseases, also with fruit and storage rots.

Fusarium culmorum, also on cereals, causing storage rot of sweet potato, black root rot of beet seedlings.

Fusarium moniliforme (conidial stage of *Gibberella fujikuroi*) causing ripe rot of figs and carried by the pollinating fig wasp, and root, stalk and pink kernel rot of corn. This species is cosmopolitan as a saprophyte but may have parasitic strains.

Fusarium orthoceras var. **gladioli.** GLADIOLUS YELLOWS, also corm rot. See under Wilts.

Fusarium oxysporum f. **cepae.** BULB ROT of onion, shallot, garlic. In the field there is progressive yellowing and dying back from tip, the roots com-

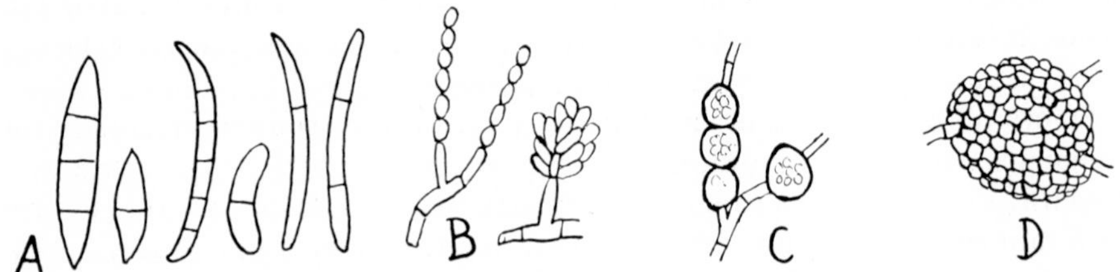

FIG. 80. Forms of *Fusarium*. A, septate macroconidia; B, microconidia in chains or a head; C, chlamydospores; D, sclerotium.

monly turning pink and gradually decaying, the decay often associated with maggot and other insect wounds. In storage the rot is most active at or above room temperature.

Fusarium oxysporum f. **gladioli.** FUSARIUM DRY ROT, BROWN ROT OF GLADIOLUS, a major disease in some sections. Most infection takes place in the field, but subsequent decay appears in storage. Corm lesions are first small, reddish brown, more often on lower half of corm. They enlarge in storage to irregular to circular, sometimes zonate, brown areas which not infrequently advance until the whole corm is a hard, dry, brownish black mummy. Infection comes from old corms, the fungus penetrating through the basal plate and the center of the new corm. The latter is entirely decayed in storage, or the fungus advances from the center to the outside, causing brown to black surface lesions.

Control. Discard corms showing lesions, cure as thoroughly and rapidly as possible, sort again in spring and treat *immediately* before planting with New Improved Ceresan, 1 ounce to 3 gallons for 15 minutes, or Lysol, 4 tablespoons to 3 gallons, for 3 hours, or dust with Arasan. Both Ceresan and Lysol may injure corms somewhat, particularly if left out of moist ground as long as overnight after treating.

Fusarium oxysporum f. **lilii.** FUSARIUM ROT OF LILY, on bulbs, roots, stems of garden and native lilies, on cactus (*Cereus*), corm rot of crocus, freesia. A brown decay at base of scales next to basal plate progresses until the scales fall away; it is more destructive to planting than to larger stock, and to Madonna and some other garden lilies. Infection comes from diseased bulbs or contaminated soil.

Control. Treat bulbs with formalin, 1 to 50 dilution, for 30 minutes (but not scales for propagation, for these are injured). Disinfest soil with formalin or chloropicrin.

Fusarium oxysporum f. **narcissi.** NARCISSUS BASAL ROT, general on hardy varieties, rare on polyanthus varieties. Rot begins at root plate at base of bulbs and spreads through central portions first, extension of the rot being more rapid in affected scales than across to adjacent healthy scales. Rotted tissue is chocolate or purplish brown, the mycelium a delicate weft of white or pink threads. The rot is dry spongy, and often there is little external evidence. It is primarily a storage or transit disease but may occur in the field late in the season. When lightly infected bulbs are planted there is no root development and plants are stunted. Basal rot is spread in hot-water treatment for nematodes unless formalin is added.

Control. New Improved Ceresan, at 2 ounces to 3 gallons of water for a 2 to 5 minute dip immediately before planting, is effective but sometimes injures flowers. Formaldehyde at a 1 to 100 dilution for 30 minutes to 1 hour is also used. Either treatment should be on thoroughly dormant bulbs and planting should follow immediately.

Recent tests include 5-minute after-harvest plus pre-planting dips in phenyl mercuric acetate (Mersolite 8) or Puratized Agricultural Spray. Results are good without the flower injury. Dusting with Arasan or Spergon is not quite so effective in rot control, but the yields are as high.

Fusarium poae. CARNATION BUD ROT. Interior of buds is brown, decayed, often moldy while outer parts are nearly normal. The spores are spread by a mite.

Control. Pick off and burn all infected buds; control mites; avoid excessive humidities.

Fusarium scirpi, causing fruit rot of watermelon, foot rot of euonymus.

Fusarium solani. Fruit rot of peach, citrus, dasheen, xanthosma.

Fusarium solani f. **phaseoli.** ROOT ROT OF PEAS AND BEANS. This is a dry rot, affected plants turning yellow, dying. Use a well-drained soil, crop rotation, and seed treatment.

Fusarium solani f. **pisi.** ROOT ROT OF PEA.

Fusarium sp. BASAL DRY ROT OF GLADIOLUS, a new corm rot, first seen in Michigan in 1931 on corms shipped from Pacific coast. Lesions are irregular, shallow, the tissue hard, rough, somewhat scaly, dark brown to black, sunken, with a sharp line of demarcation. Plants are weak, slow growing, and there is a poor stand.

Control. Dip corms in a suspension of calomel until well coated; discard visibly infected corms.

GANODERMA

Basidiomycetes, Agaricales, Polyporaceae

Ganoderma lucidum, varnish or lacquer fungus. HEART ROT of eastern hardwoods and conifers, especially hemlock, reported also on boxwood, hackberry, citrus. The rot is white, spongy, with black spots scattered throughout. The conks are annual, with a reddish, shiny lacquered upper surface and a short, thick lateral stalk, common on logs, stumps, standing or fallen trees.

GIBBERELLA (See under Blights)

Gibberella zeae (conidial stage *Fusarium graminearum*) CORN ROOT ROT, STALK ROT, EAR ROT, also Fusarium blights or scab of cereals. Corn is attacked at all ages with both roots and kernels rotted. Conidia are pinkish in mass. Perithecia appear on overwintered corn residue.

Control. Treat seed before planting with Spergon, Arasan, or Semesan Jr.; use a long rotation, avoiding wheat and corn in succession; use well-drained soil with sufficient humus and lime.

GLOMERELLA (See under Anthracnose)

Glomerella cingulata. BITTER ROT OF APPLE, also stem rot, canker, dieback of many fruits and ornamentals, berry rot of cranberry, ripe rot of grapes. Bitter rot is a late season disease of apple, often destructive in central and southern states.

The fruits have light brown circular spots which gradually enlarge, and cover rotting flesh which has a bitter taste. Lesions become concave and have concentric rings of pink to dark spore pustules in sticky masses. Spores are splashed by rain or carried by flies and other insects. Eventually apples turn into dry, shriveled mummies, in which the fungus overwinters and where the ascospore stage is produced, although primary infection in spring is usually from conidia. Large limbs have roughened, oval cankers.

Apple varieties vary greatly in resistance and some, like Yellow Newtown, are resistant to the canker but susceptible to fruit rotting. Varieties somewhat resistant include Arkansas, Baldwin, Delicious, Rome Beauty, Stayman Winesap, York Imperial, Transparent, Wealthy, and Winesap.

Control. Use thorough late season sprays. Bordeaux mixture 4–6–100 is standard, but several new fungicides are promising.

On cranberries bitter rot is a soft, brownish yellow discoloration developing late in the season, most serious in a hot July and August. Ripe rot starts on grapes as they mature and gives a bitter taste to pulp. Fermate is probably satisfactory for both grapes and cranberries.

GODRONIA

Ascomycetes, Helotiales, Dermateaceae

Apothecia coriaceous, pitcher-shaped; spores filiform, hyaline.

Godronia cassandrae (*Fusicoccum putrefaciens*). END ROT OF CRANBERRY, general, also ascospore stage on dead branches of leatherleaf (*Cassandra*). The rot starts at either blossom or stem end of berry; fruit is softened, light colored. The rot begins late in the season, especially after picking and packing, and is enhanced by injuries during harvesting and screening.

Control. Sprays immediately preceding and following the blossom period are most important. Bordeaux mixture has been used, but Fermate is replacing it for most cranberry diseases.

GUIGNARDIA (See under Blotch)

Guignardia bidwellii. BLACK ROT OF GRAPES, widespread, principal cause of failure of European grapes in eastern United States, causing more loss than other diseases combined. All parts of the vine are attacked. On leaves reddish

FIG. 81. Black Rot of Grapes.

brown dead spots are sprinkled with black pycnidia. When fruit is half grown rot starts as a pale spot, soon turning brown and involving the entire berry, which shrivels and becomes a black wrinkled mummy, dropping or remaining in the cluster. Some berries shatter if attacked early.

Ovoid conidia and sometimes microconida (spermatia) are formed on leaves, berries, and canes. Ascospores are produced in perithecia in overwintered mummied berries. Primary infection is in spring from either spore form.

Control. In some cases a three-spray schedule is sufficient, using Fermate immediately before, and immediately after, bloom, and 10 to 14 days later, but with severe infection an additional pre-bloom spray and perhaps one when the fruit is about the size of peas could be applied. Bordeaux mixture has been recommended for many years, but Fermate gives excellent control together with increasing yield over vines sprayed with bordeaux.

Guignardia vaccinii. EARLY ROT, scald, blast general on cranberry, sometimes on huckleberry. All aerial plant parts are attacked, but the disease is most destructive to fruit. Young fruit may blast and shrivel but more often rot starts as a light colored soft spot when fruit is half grown. Fruit mummifies, turns black, is covered with small pycnidia. Leaves sometimes have reddish brown spots or may drop prematurely.

Control. Spray with bordeaux mixture or Fermate.

HELICOBASIDIUM

Basidiomycetes, Tremellales, Auriculariaceae

An exposed cottony hymenium or fruiting layer; basidia transversely septate; spores coiled like a watch spring.

Helicobasidium purpureum (sterile stage *Rhizoctonia crocorum*). VIOLET ROOT ROT of potato, sweet potato, asparagus, beet and some ornamentals—ash, catalpa, china-berry, crocus, elm, mulberry, parthenocissus, western soapberry. The fungus invades roots from the soil, turning them violet or reddish. The disease is confined to underground parts unless continuously wet weather allows the reddish purple mycelium to grow up the stem. In this purplish mat, which turns brown with age, are embedded small, darker sclerotia.

HYDNUM (STECCHERINUM)

Basidiomycetes, Agaricales, Hydnaceae

Pileus caplike, with a stipe, or sometimes coral-like, leathery to woody to fleshy; fruiting layer on long, awl-shaped teeth.

Hydnum abietis. BROWN POCKET ROT of heartwood of living firs and western hemlock in Pacific Northwest. Elongated pockets, empty or with white fibers, are separated by firm, reddish brown wood. Sporophores are coral-like, white to cream, soft, up to 10 or 12 inches wide and high, usually on dead trees, sometimes in wounds of living trees. Infection is through wounds and dead branches.

Hydnum erinaceus, hedgehog fungus. WHITE HEART ROT, occasional on living oak. The soft white spongy rot may entirely decompose the tissue, leaving large hollows lined with yellowish mycelium. Sporophores are annual, soft, white, browning with age, globular with a hairy top and long, slender teeth on lower surface.

Hydnum septentrionale. WHITE SPONGY ROT of heartwood of living maples, beech, hickory, and other hardwoods. A zone of brown discolored wood is around the white-rot area and there are fine black zone lines. The fruiting bodies are large, soft, soggy, creamy white, in very large, bracket-like clusters on trunks.

HYPHOLOMA

Basidiomycetes, Agaricales, Agaricaceae

Margin of cap with a curtain-like veil; stipe sometimes with incomplete or vanishing ring; spores purple.

Hypholoma perplexum. Root Rot of currant.

ISARIA

Fungi Imperfecti, Moniliales, Stilbaceae

Conidiophores equally distributed on a synnema, an erect fascicle of hyphae; spores light, 1-celled, not in chains.

Isaria clonostachoides. Fruit Rot of Tomato.

LENTINUS

Basidiomycetes, Agaricales, Agaricaceae

Gills are notched or serrate at edge, decurrent, stipe often lateral or lacking, cap fleshy to leathery; spores white.

Lentinus tigrinus. Sapwood Rot, white mottle butt rot of living hardwoods, associated with fire scars, but more commonly a decay, important in the Mississippi Delta. Fruiting body is white, with cap depressed in center, more or less covered with dark brown hairy scales; rarely developed on living trees.

LENZITES

Basidiomycetes, Agaricales, Polyporaceae

Pores lamellate or resembling gills, pileus shelf-like.

Lenzites betulina. Heart Rot of birch, cypress.

Lenzites saepiaria. Brown Pocket Rot usually of dead sapwood, occasionally a heart rot, rarely on living trees. This is a common destroyer of coniferous slash, is found on telephone poles, other timber in use. Fruiting bodies are long, narrow shelves from cracks in bark, the upper surface a yellow red to dark reddish brown.

MACROPHOMINA

Fungi Imperfecti, Sphaeropsidales, Sphaerioidaceae

Spores, hyaline,1-celled, in pycnidia.

Macrophomina phaseoli (sterile stage *Sclerotium* (*Rhizoctonia*) *bataticola*). Charcoal Root and Stem Rot, also ashy stem blight, of sweet potato and many other plants in warm climates and sometimes in temperate zones. The name comes from the disease on sweet potatoes whose interior turns jet black. The fungus lives in the soil, is particularly prevalent in warm soils and attacks roots and lower stems of a varied list of hosts, including corn, beans, lima beans, soybeans, cowpeas, watermelons, peppers, gourds, strawberries, chrysanthemum, dahlia, marigold, zinnia. In most cases a spore stage is not formed. Mycelium spreads through the soil, and very small black sclerotia which are formed in great abundance on lower stems and roots are carried in irrigation water, crop debris, transported soil. The pycnidial stage is occasionally found on legumes.

Control. Keep plants growing vigorously with proper food and water, control competing weeds, practice general sanitation.

MELANCONIUM

Fungi Imperfecti, Melanconiales, Melanconiaceae

Spores in acervuli, with hairs or setae; conidia dark, 1-celled, globose to oblong.

Melanconium fuligineum. BITTER ROT OF GRAPES, widespread. The disease looks like ripe rot of grapes, caused by Glomerella, but the berry pulp tastes bitter. Sprays for black rot will also control bitter rot.

MERULIUS

Basidiomycetes, Agaricales, Polyporaceae

Hymenium with shallow, netlike pores; cap or pileus waxy.

Merulius tremellosus. WOOD ROT of birch, and other hardwood and coniferous slash in forests.

MONILINIA (See under Blights)

Monilinia fructicola. BROWN ROT OF STONE FRUITS, blossom blight, general on peach, plum, cherry, also on apricot, almond, apple, beach plum, pear, Japanese quince. Brown rot has been known for many years as the most destructive stone-fruit disease in America, causing an annual loss in the peach crop of over five million dollars. This species is more serious east of the Rocky Mountains but *M. laxa* causes a similar rot and blossom blight on the Pacific Coast.

Flowers turn brown prematurely, rot in moist weather; the calyx cup is blackened, and the discoloration may extend down into pedicels. Infrequently there is a leaf and twig blight. Cankers are formed on the larger limbs with exudation of gum.

The fruit rot is the familiar stage, seen in any backyard with a fruit tree, and usually in supplies of fruit purchased for preserving and held over to the next day. The rot starts as a small, circular brown spot, but spreads rapidly to take in the entire fruit. Meanwhile the rotted tissue is covered with gray to light brown spore tufts or cushions (sporodochia), sometimes in concentric rings. Conidia are formed in chains on the sporodochia. The fruit finally shrivels and mummifies, falls to the ground, or remains clinging to the tree.

The fungus and decayed tissue together form a stroma which acts as a sclerotium; and in spring, if the mummy has been kept moist in or on the soil, cup-shaped brown apothecia are produced. Primary infection is either from

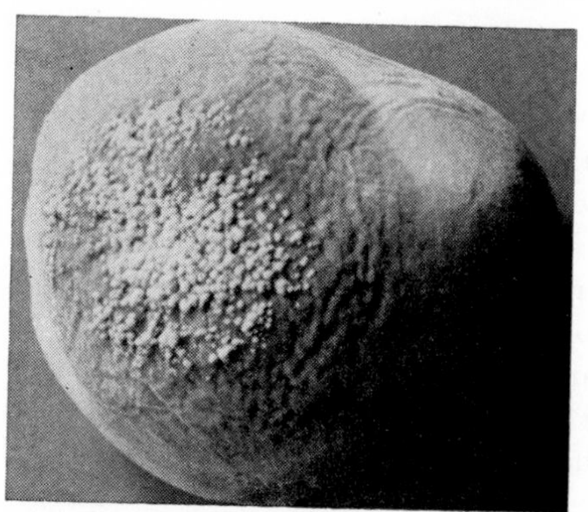

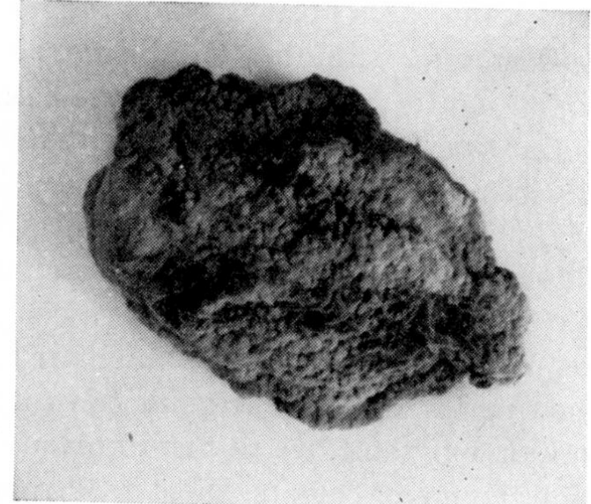

Fig. 82. Brown Rot of Peach. Left, soft brown decayed area with light spore cushions; right, mummied peach covered with dark gray spore masses.

Fig. 83. Brown Rot on Plums.

ascospores, forcibly ejected and carried upward to blossoms by air currents, or from a new crop of conidia formed on mummies hanging on trees. Secondary infection is from conidia windborne from blossom to blossom and later from fruit to fruit with infection often through wounds made by the plum curculio, oriental fruit moth and other insects. Rotting and conidial production continues after picking.

The rot is favored by wet weather, conidia germinating only in a film of water. Acid soil is said to increase apothecial production from mummies on the ground. In a normal season the reduction from blossom blight is not important as some thinning is advantageous, but if blossom infection is not curtailed inoculum is present for the fruit rot which causes such enormous losses.

Control. Sanitary measures are important. In the small garden rake up and burn or bury deeply the fallen mummies; pick mummies from trees; cut out twigs showing gum. Standard control has been wettable sulfur sprays or sulfur dust applied: (1) when shucks are falling; (2) 2 to 3 weeks after shuck fall; (3) 2 to 4 weeks before fruit ripens. For blossom blight a pink bud spray is required and in some seasons more than one spray on the fruit. The newer organic fungicides give good control in many instances, perhaps better than sulfur, but some are rather injurious and it is too early for complete evaluation. Fermate, Parzate, Dithane, Phygon, Bioquin 1, Zerlate are all being tried. Consult your State Experiment Station for latest recommendations for your locality.

Monilinia laxa. BROWN ROT, GREEN AND RIPE FRUIT ROT, blossom blight on almond, apple, apricot, cherry, peach, plum, pear, nectarine, quince, Japanese quince in Pacific Northwest. This is similar to the disease caused by *M. fructicola,* but the blossom and twig blight phase is more important. A dormant spray of copper-lime-monocalcium arsenite-oil is often used, followed by an early bloom spray of 6–8–100 bordeaux mixture, after which sulfurs are used in the spray schedule as with the other brown rot.

Monilinia oxycocci. HARD ROT, TIP BLIGHT OF CRANBERRY. Young growing tips wilt and dry just before blossoming; grayish spore tufts are formed on tips. Fruit is attacked through blossoms or wounds. The berries are yellowish white, firm, leathery, white cottony inside, turning dark and mummifying late in season.

Monilinia vaccinii-corymbosi. BROWN ROT, MUMMY BERRY, TWIG BLIGHT of highbush blueberry, similar to hard rot of cranberry. Varieties Jersey and Rubel are most susceptible with shoot blight sometimes serious on Adams and Cabot.

Control. Spraying seems ineffective. Remove wilted shoots daily before spores are formed. Sweep or rake soil frequently to disturb overwintered mummies and prevent apothecial production. Calcium cyanamide at the rate of 150 pounds per acre applied in spring prevents apothecial formation but must be used with caution.

MUCOR

Phycomycetes, Mucorales, Mucoraceae

Mycelium profusely developed. Sporangiophores erect, simple or branched, all branches terminated by sporangia which are globose to pyriform with a columella and thin wall; gametangia essentially alike, suspensors without definite outgrowths; hyaline chlamydospores are sometimes formed.

Mucor racemosus. STORAGE ROT OF SWEET POTATO, occasional after chilling, fruit rot of citrus. Control with low temperature and a dry atmosphere in the storage house.

MYROTHECIUM

Fungi Imperfecti, Moniliales, Tuberculariaceae

Sporodochia shield-shaped to discoid, dark but with white setae at margin; spores 1-celled, dark.

Myrothecium roridum. RING ROT OF TOMATO, CROWN ROT OF SNAPDRAGON. On greenhouse snapdragons, crowns appear water-soaked then covered with a thin white mycelium and numerous black sporodochia, the epidermis cracking open over infected tissue.

NEMATOSPORA

Ascomycetes, Endomycetales, Saccharomycetaceae

This is a yeast or budding fungus, following after insects; asci, with 8 to 16 spores, are derived directly from vegetative mycelial cells; spores elongate, fusiform to needle-shaped, flagellate.

Nematospora coryli. DRY ROT of pomegranate, citrus; POD SPOT of pepper, bean, CLOUDY SPOT of tomato, KERNEL SPOT of pecan. The yeast is almost always associated with plant bug injury. The western leaf-footed plant bug carries the fungus from pomegranate to citrus. On pomegranates depressed light spots in fleshy covering around seeds are followed by general browning and collapse. In citrus the juice sacs just inside the rind dry out with a brownish to reddish brown stain.

On lima bean the lesions are dark brown, sunken, wrinkled and the fungus is disseminated with seed. Cloudy spot on tomato fruit is associated with pumpkin and leaf-footed plant bugs. Brown areas are formed on pecan kernels.

NEUROSPORA

Ascomycetes, Sphaeriales, Sphaeriaceae (or Fimetariaceae)

Perithecia flask-shaped, membranous, ascospores dark, 1-celled with a gelatinous coating; conidial stage monilioid.

Neurospora sitophila. Ripe Rot of Pear. The fungus is the same one causing the pink bakery mold on bread and there is a luxuriant pink growth on fruit. Conidia are formed in chains.

NIGROSPORA

Fungi Imperfecti, Moniliales, Dematiaceae

All hyphae more or less creeping, conidiophores branched, conidia 1-celled, on cask-shaped stalks.

Nigrospora oryzae. Ripe Fruit Rot of tomato; Dry Ear and Stalk Rot of Corn. Kernels are chaffy, corn cobs easily broken, and stalks break over at any point. Rapid drying checks infection of seed corn.

OMPHALIA

Basidiomycetes, Agaricales, Agaricaceae

Gills decurrent, cap sunken in the center, somewhat funnel-shaped; central cartilaginous stem; spores white.

Omphalia pigmentata and **O. tralucida.** Decline Disease of Date Palms. Growth is retarded, roots decay, leaves die prematurely, fruit is worthless. Deglet Noor variety is most susceptible.

Control. Select thrifty offshoots from healthy plants for new date gardens. Soil can be disinfected with carbon disulfide as for Armillaria rot.

OOSPORA

Fungi Imperfecti, Moniliales, Moniliaceae

Conidia 1-celled, hyaline, globose or suboblong, in chains, arising on the hyphae, which are very short.

Oospora citri-aurantii. Sour Rot of Citrus. This is a soft, putrid slimy rot of fruit, mostly of stored lemons, where it is spread by contact. The mycelium forms a thin, compact, somewhat wrinkled layer over the surface. Fruitflies help spread the rot. Fruit should be stored as short a time as possible and frequent inspections should be made during storage.

Oospora lactis. Sour Rot, Watery Fruit Rot of Tomato, common in transit and market, especially on fruit from the South. There is a velvety or granular coating over the surface or a fluffy growth along margin of cracks, a disagreeable odor and flavor. The rot is common on ripe fruit touching the ground, occasional on green fruit. The fungus is a weak parasite, entering through wounds.

PELLICULARIA (See under Blights)

Pellicularia filamentosa (basidial stage of *Rhizoctonia solani*). Rhizoctonia Disease, Rhizoctoniose, Black Scurf of Potatoes, stem canker and soil rot of beans (see under Blights for Web Blight of Beans and other plants). The sterile stage, *Rhizoctonia solani,* was first named in 1858 in a German textbook and is still the most familiar term for a fungus which apparently has many pathogenic strains, and causes many types of diseases including damping-off of seedlings and brown patch of lawn grasses.

Any housewife has probably seen signs of the disease on potato tubers—the small, brown to black hard flecks, or sclerotia, on the skin which look almost like particles of dirt but do not brush off when potatoes are scrubbed. There may be only one or two sclerotia or they may be numerous enough to nearly cover the whole surface of the tuber.

When such potatoes are planted the growing point may be killed. Some sprouts renew growth after being girdled but this is repeated until they finally die. Larger plants have stems decayed just below the soil line, interrupting the downward transfer of food and resulting in a cluster of green or reddish aerial tubers. Roots may be killed back extensively. There is a high percentage of small tubers and often a brown jelly rot at the stem end.

Under moist conditions a white cobwebby weft of mycelium is formed at base of potato stems and the perfect or basidial stage is produced as a powdery crust on this weft. The fungus winters as mycelium or sclerotia in soil or on tubers. The mycelium has a saprophytic existence in the soil and can grow long distances independent of any living host. Infection is favored by cool temperatures, and the disease is most serious in wet seasons on heavy soils. The yearly average loss for the country is about 10 million bushels, or 2 to 3 percent, but individual losses are often from 5 to 50 percent of the crop.

Control. Use healthy tubers for seed. Rules governing certified seed potatoes limit the amount of Rhizoctonia but allow a small percentage. If infested potatoes must be used choose one of the following treatments:

1. Soak 1½ hours in a 1–1000 solution of mercuric chloride.
2. Dip 5 minutes in acidified mercury, sold as Mercunol.
3. A momentary dip in one of the organic seed treatment chemicals such as Semesan Bel, Spergon or Arasan; or in yellow oxide of mercury (at rate of 1 pound to 15 gallons water).

If the soil is heavily infested use a three-year rotation.

PENICILLIUM (See under Cankers)

Species cause blue, green, occasionally pink molds, including the common blue-green mold on jellies. Some produce antibiotics, *Penicillium notatum* being the one used to get penicillin.

Penicillium digitatum. GREEN MOLD ROT OF CITRUS FRUIT. Olive-green powdery spore masses, forming a dust cloud when disturbed, cover fruit except for a band of white mycelium outside the green area. Avoid injury in harvest and packing. Commercial growers use chemicals in the wash water to prevent decay.

Penicillium expansum. Blue Mold Rot of many fruits—avocado, pear, pomegranate, Japanese persimmon, quince, feijowa, in core cavity of apples. The decay on avocados is slow and often affected portions can be trimmed off.

Penicillium gladioli. Blue Mold Rot, Penicillium Dry Rot of Gladiolus also found in imported bulbs—scilla, tritona, montbretia. This is a storage rot. Light to dark brown sunken lesions appear on any part of corms with border of the decayed area water-soaked and greenish. Small grayish sclerotia are formed, and masses of blue mold under moist conditions.

Control. Rapid drying after harvest, at 80° F. for 10 to 14 days and then storage at a low temperature; avoid wounds, bruises; sort before planting.

Penicillium italicum. Blue Mold Rot, Fruit Rot of Citrus, blue contact mold. It spreads readily from fruit to fruit by contact, through uninjured skin. The mold is blue in the older portion but powdery white at margins.

Penicillium roseum. Fruit Rot of Citrus, dates. This is a pink mold found on lemons but not oranges.

Penicillium vermoeseni. Bud Rot of Palms. The terminal bud is killed and base of leaf stalks rotted. Affected trees of very susceptible *Washingtonia filifera* should be replaced with resistant *Washingtonia robusta,* the Mexican fan palm. Sometimes surgical treatment can remove trunk cankers. See also under Cankers.

PHOLIOTA

Basidiomycetes, Agaricales, Agaricaceae

Spores ochre yellow to rusty brown; gills attached to stipe which has an annulus or ring but not a cup at the base.

Pholiota adiposa. Brown Mottled Heart Rot of maple and other living hardwoods—basswood, birches, poplars, more rarely balsam firs and other conifers. The wood has brown mottled streaks. The sporophores are formed in clusters on trunks, stumps or old logs. They are mushrooms with yellow central stems and caps, a sticky yellowish, slightly scaly upper surface, yellow to brown gills.

PHOMA (See under Cankers)

Phoma apiicola. Phoma Root Rot of Celery, occasionally serious, especially on Golden Self Blanching. This is a black rot of crown or base of leaf stalks near ground level. Plants are stunted; outer leaves or entire plant may be killed, falling over as roots rot off. Spores are produced in tendrils from black pycnidia and spread in rains and irrigation water.

Control. Use fresh soil for the seedbed; rotate crops; use clean seed.

Phoma destructiva. PHOMA ROT OF TOMATO, PEPPER, nearly general, especially in South, but not yet reported from North Central States. Small, irregular dark spots appear in great numbers of leaves. They have zonate markings similar to those of early blight. Severely infected leaves turn yellow, wither.

Fruit spots in field are small, 1/8 inch, slightly depressed, with numerous tiny black pycnidia. After picking and ripening, spots enlarge to 1/2 to 1 1/2 inches, become black and leathery with minute pustules. The fungus can winter in decaying refuse in soil; seedbed infection is common and the disease reaches the field via infected seedlings. Masses of spores produced on leaves are washed to fruits by rain or spread by workers and are also distributed during harvesting and packing.

Control. Locate seedbeds on clean soil, away from land previously growing tomatoes; disinfect seed with mercuric chloride or New Improved Ceresan.

PHYMATOTRICHUM

Fungi Imperfecti, Moniliales, Moniliaceae

Conidia on inflated, spiny apices on erect conidiophores; spores 1-celled, hyaline.

Phymatotrichum omnivorum. PHYMATOTRICHUM ROOT ROT, TEXAS ROOT ROT, cotton root rot. This is the most destructive plant disease in Texas, a limiting factor in gardening and crop production. It occurs through most of the state except the Panhandle, in the Red River Counties of Oklahoma, the southwestern half of Arizona, the southeastern corner of Arkansas and Utah, the southeastern edge of Nevada and California, and in 1947 was reported in the northwest corner of Louisiana near the Arkansas line.

The list of plants—flowers, vegetables, fruits, field crops, trees—which are susceptible is much, much longer than that of plants which are resistant to this omnivorous fungus, so aptly named. At least 1700 plant species are attacked, more than by any other known pathogen. Because of the wide host range and destructiveness the economic losses are enormous, one hundred million dollars a year in Texas alone, with perhaps fifty million in adjacent states.

Crops which are either resistant or escape the disease are the cereals and grasses, annuals grown in winter only, and sweet alyssum, amaranth, sweet basil, beauty-berry, bee-balm, collinsia, diosma, calceolaria, calla lily, California-poppy, candytuft, canna, century plant, agave, cinquefoil, citron, cockscomb, coleus, columbine, corn, cranberry, cucumber, currant, cyclamen, daffodil, dahoon, deutzia, dill, fennel, fern, staghorn, foxglove, freesia, goldentuft, mustang grape, gypsophila, hackberry, hoarhound, hyacinth, iris, lily, nigella, marsh-marigold, mignonette, mints, mimulus, muskmelon, mustard, nasturtium, oak, osage-orange, oxalis, Indian paint-brush, palms, pansy, petunia, phlox, Chinese pink, pitcherplant, pomegranate, poppy, portulaca, primrose, pumpkin, red-cedar, sage, scarletbush, snapdragon, snowdrop, stock, strawberry, strawflower, tuberose, valerian, verbena, violet, wallflower, wandering jew, water-cress, watermelon, yaupon, yucca, zinnia.

Phymatotrichum root rot occurs from July until frost. It kills plants in more or less circular spots, ranging from a few square yards to an acre or more. Death may come within a few days of first wilt symptoms and just preceding the wilt plants actually run a fever, with higher than normal temperature. If plants next to the wilted ones are pulled out these apparently healthy plants will often be found covered with yellow to buff mats of mycelium and under moist conditions spore mats appear on surface of soil around diseased plants. Such mats are 2 to 12 inches in diameter, first snow-white and cottony, later tan and powdery from spores produced in quantities. The fungus spreads through the soil by means of rhizomorphs, smooth, dark brown strands. The rate of spread has been 2 to 8 feet a month in an alfalfa field, 5 to 30 feet a season in a cotton field, or around fruit trees.

Sclerotia are formed along the mycelial strands. These are small, roundish, light at first, then dark and warty. The fungus winters either as sclerotia in soil, and may persist several years in the absence of live hosts, or as dormant mycelium in living roots. The disease is most common and severe on heavy, alkaline soils. Abundant organic material reduces the rot by favoring antagonistic soil saprophytes.

Control. In ornamental plantings replace diseased plants with some of those given in the resistant list. Monocotyledons are generally resistant. In locating new orchards make sure that root rot has not previously been present by growing an indicator crop of cotton for a year. Grow immune crops in rotation with susceptible crops and grow susceptible annuals as winter rather than summer crops. Try heavy manuring.

Ammonium sulfate can sometimes save a valuable individual ornamental tree or shrub already infected with root rot. Prune back the top, make a circular ridge about the plant at the edge of the branch spread, and work one pound of ammonium sulfate into the soil for each 10 square feet of surface within the ridge; then fill the basin with water to a depth of 4 inches. The chemical treatment and watering is repeated in 5 to 10 days, but no more chemical should be applied the same season. Follow through with frequent watering.

PHYSALOSPORA (See under Cankers)

Physalospora mutila. Black Rot of Apple in the West, similar to disease by *P. obtusa* in the East.

Physalospora obtusa. Black Rot of Apple, New York apple tree canker, frog-eye leaf spot, general on apple, crabapple from Atlantic Coast to the Great Plains, also widespread on pear, mountain-ash, peach, quince, currant, and various woody species.

The fungus, in its imperfect state *Sphaeropsis malorum,* was first reported causing apple rot in 1879. The lesions start as small brown spots, frequently at a worm hole, but they darken and turn black as they expand. There is usually one lesion to an apple, often at the calyx end, with concentric zones of black and brown, and minute black pycnidia. The rot eventually takes in the whole fruit which is shriveled and wrinkled and finally mummifies. The pycnidia are black, carbonaceous, and may contain three types of spores—the typical large 1-celled brown spores, large hyaline spores, and 2-celled colored spores. Perithecia, sometimes formed in cankers or on twigs, apparently play little part in the life history, the fungus wintering as dormant mycelium or in the pycnidial state.

Conidia entering through wounds start primary infection in spring on leaves, with the small "frog-eye" leaf spots.

Control. Use the same spray schedule as for apple scab, starting with the petal-fall application. Fermate may replace sulfurs or lime sulfur as used in the past. Bordeaux mixture can cause defoliation. Clean up mummied apples; avoid bruising; cut out cankers.

Physalospora rhodina. Diplodia Rot of Citrus, fig, rubber-tree, pear, possibly apple. The conidial stage is a Diplodia, probably *D. natalensis,* with dark, 2-celled spores.

PHYTOPHTHORA (See under Blights)

Phytophthora cactorum. Stem Rot, Root Rot of tulip, hydrastis, centaurea, peony, clarkia, rhubarb, and tomato; leather rot of strawberries; collar rot of dogwood, walnut, apple, pear; foot rot of lily.

With foot rot, lilies suddenly fall over, wilt and die; the lower part of the stem is shrunken. Plant only healthy bulbs where disease has not occurred previously.

Strawberry leather rot is found mostly in the South. Both green and ripe berries are affected with a brown rot and have a bitter taste. Mulching to prevent contact with the soil is helpful.

See under Blights and Cankers for other manifestations of this fungus.

Phytophthora cinnamomi. Seedling Root Rot, Collar Rot of hardwoods and conifers, decline disease of avocado. Root rot is dry with resin flow in conifers. Infected tissue turns reddish brown except in black walnut where it is black. Conifers show gradual loss of color in needles but in hardwoods there is sudden death of entire seedling.

Phytophthora citrophthora. Brown Rot, Gummosis, Foot Rot of Citrus. Masses of amber gum break out from trunk near crown of tree; the bark is killed above and below ground; foliage turns yellow and the tree may die. The disease is prevalent where excessive water stands around the tree in irrigating or where there is poor drainage. Brown rot of fruit is a decay with no visible surface mold, except in moist air, but a slightly rancid, penetrating odor. Lemons and oranges may be affected on the tree near the ground and there is much loss in storage. This species and others live in soil; spores are splashed up in rainy weather, and are spread in the washing tank.

Control. For gummosis keep tops of first main roots just below soil level; have trees budded so union is 10 to 12 inches above ground; if trees are already planted too deep, pull earth away to tops of main lateral roots and leave in a circular ridge, keeping water away from this basin in irrigating. Clean off diseased bark and paint with a paste made of 1 pound zinc sulfate, ⅕ pound copper sulfate, and 1 pound lime to 1 gallon of water.

To control fruit rot, spray ground and lower branches, up to 3 feet, with 6–6–100 bordeaux mixture just before rains begin. If cyanide fumigation is to be practiced, substitute a copper-zinc-lime spray for the bordeaux. Dithane and Zerlate sprays are promising.

Phytophthora cryptogea. COLLAR AND ROOT ROT of rhododendron, china aster, marigold, gloxinia, zinnia. Stem and roots appear water-soaked, then black from a soft rot. Sterilize soil.

Phytophthora erythroseptica. PINK WATERY ROT OF POTATO, rot of calla lily and golden calla. The rot starts at stem end of potatoes. When tubers are cut flesh turns pink or red, then black. The fungus can exist in soil 4 years.

Phytophthora fragariae. STRAWBERRY RED STELE DISEASE, brown core root rot, a very serious strawberry disease, relatively new to North America, found first in Illinois in 1932, established in Maryland in 1936, and since widespread in northern strawberry sections.

The fungus attacks roots only, destroying fine feeding roots first, then invading central cylinder or stele which turns dark red. New spring leaves on badly infected plants are small, bluish, have short petioles; large leaves from previous season dry up; little or no fruit is produced; many plants die in the first dry period or are stunted.

The fungus is most active in cold wet soil, in rainy periods in late fall, winter except when ground is frozen, and early spring. Zoospores produced on roots in winter and spring are spread by water. Resting spores formed in the red stele carry the fungus in a dormant stage through heat of summer.

Control. Buy clean certified plants; if disease appears plan a rotation of 4 or 5 years. Any plant other than strawberry can be grown. Aberdeen variety is resistant and Temple and Sparkle, good for home and commercial plantings from New Jersey to New England, are fairly resistant.

Phytophthora megasperma. ROOT ROT, occasional on cabbage, cauliflower, brussels sprouts, carrot, artichoke, stock, citrus. Diseased plants wilt suddenly, leaves turn red to purple, underground stems and roots rot. The disease occurs in winter plantings in California, in low, wet, poorly drained areas.

Control. Level properly before planting to avoid waterlogged spots.

Phytophthora palmivora. BUD ROT, leaf drop, wilt of coconut and queen palms, Florida. The fungus is an omnivorous tropical species. In California it causes stem rot of dieffenbachia. Dust cuttings with Fermate, root in clean sand.

Phytophthora parasitica. Brown Rot, Foot Rot, Gummosis on citrus, working with *P. citrophthora;* also tuber rot of potato; on lily, roselle, sempervivum.

Phytophthora richardiae. Root Rot of Calla. The feeder roots are attacked, rotting from tips back to rhizomes, leaving only epidermis as a hollow tube. New roots sent out from rhizomes rot in turn. Leaves yellow and droop, starting with outer leaves; plants do not flower or tip of blossom turns brown. Rot in the rhizome itself is dry, spongy, never wet and slimy.

Control. Clean old rhizomes thoroughly, cut out rotted spots. Treat with New Improved Ceresan, 1 ounce to 3 gallons of water with Dreft added as a spreader, or with a 1 to 50 dilution of formaldehyde or 1 to 1000 dilution of mercuric chloride, for 1 hour. Drain and plant immediately. Grow in sterilized pots rather than benches.

PLECTOSPIRA

Phycomycetes, Saprolegniales, Saprolegniaceae

Sporangium with much inflated branching; swarmspores are formed in basal portion and cut out into a single row in an elongate filamentous apical portion which acts as an exit tube. Swarmspores encyst at the mouth as in Aphanomyces. Oogonium is terminal or intercalary and may be accompanied by as many as 65 antheridia.

Plectospira myriandra. Rootlet Necrosis on tomato. The fungus is weakly parasitic on rootlets.

PLENODOMUS

Fungi Imperfecti, Sphaeropsidales, Sphaerioidaceae

Pycnidia coriaceous or carbonous, more or less sclerotoid. Conidiophores obsolete or none, conidia 1-celled, hyaline.

Plenodomus destruens. Foot Rot of Sweet Potato, one of the more important field diseases and sometimes a storage rot. The base of the stem turns brown from just under the soil surface to 4 or 5 inches above; leaves turn yellow and drop off; vine wilts unless adventitious roots are put out; pycnidia are numerous. The root has a firm brown rot, not affecting the whole root but enough to make it worthless for food. The fungus winters in old plant refuse but not in soil.

Control. Treat seed potatoes with Semesan Bel or other fungicide. More vigorous sprouts are grown under glass than cloth sash and increased vigor decreases foot rot.

PLEOSPORA (See under Leaf Spots)

Pleospora lycopersici. Fruit Rot of Tomato. A firm, dark rot develops in fruit after picking, starting from infections in cracks near stem end of fruit. Progress is most rapid at 65° to 70° F. and is checked by storage at 45° F.

PLEUROTUS

Basidiomycetes, Agaricales, Agaricaceae

Stipe or stem off center or lacking, cap sometimes inverted, gills more or less fleshy and separable into two layers; edge of gills acute; spores white.

Pleurotus ostreatus. White Flaky Sapwood Rot, of maple and other hardwoods, sometimes on living trees. A light colored decay is surrounded by a narrow brown zone. Fleshy, annual conks are shelving, sessile or with a short, stout excentric stalk. The upper surface is smooth, white or grayish, gills extending on to the stalk. Infection is through open wounds.

Pleurotus ulmarius. Brown Heart Rot, sapwood wound rot of elm, maple and living hardwoods. Rot starting in heartwood may extend into sapwood; infected wood separates along annual rings. Annual sporophores have a long excentric stalk, and white to yellow to brown smooth upper surface. They issue from crotches and pruning wounds.

POLYPORUS

Basidiomycetes, Agaricales, Polyporaceae

Pileus tough, thick, with a stipe or shelf-like; pores rounded, small, tubes crowded.

Polyporus abietinus. Pitted Sap Rot, Hollow Pocket, white pocket rot on fir. May attack dead sapwood of living trees in wounds.

Polyporus anceps. Red Ray Rot, on western conifers, causing heart rot of living trees but beneficial as a cause of rapid decay of slash in forests. Fruiting bodies rarely develop on living trees.

Polyporus balsameus. Balsam Butt Rot of living balsam fir, eastern hemlock, northern white-cedar, western red-cedar, also prevalent on dead trees. Advanced decay is brown, brittle, breaking into large cubes, easily crushed to a clay-colored powder. In living trees the rot column is usually only 3 or 4 feet from ground. Sporophores are shelving, up to 2 inches wide, with pale brown upper surface with concentric zones, white underneath.

Polyporus betulinus. Brown Cubical Rot of dead or dying gray and paper birches. Conks have smooth grayish upper surface with incurved margin.

Polyporus gilvus. White Sapwood Rot, prevalent on dead trees, occasional on living trees. Small, annual, yellow to red, brown leathery to corky sporophores, developed in profusion.

Polyporus hirsutus. White Mottled Sapwood Rot, occasional on living trees. Upper surface hairy, gray, brown or yellowish.

Polyporus hispidus. White Spongy Heart Rot of living trees of black ash, oak, maple, birch; does not decay dead trees. Heartwood in upper portion of trunk is reduced to soft spongy yellow or white mass. Shelf sporophores, up to 10 inches wide, have dark brown, coarse, velvety to hairy upper surface

FIG. 84. Sporophore of *Polyporus betulinus,* shelf fungus common on dead birch wood.

and golden brown undersurface, turning dark brown with age. They are formed at branch stubs, frost cracks, or trunk cankers.

Polyporus dryadeus. WHITE ROOT ROT occasional in oaks and conifers in the West. Roots are killed and trees may die. Decayed wood in larger roots is white to cream; bark is loosened and shredded. The decay goes up to the root collar where irregular masses of corky or woody fruiting bodies are formed.

Polyporus pargamenus. WHITE POCKET ROT of dead sapwood in eastern United States but sometimes on living maple and other hardwoods. Sporophore looks like that of *P. abietinus.*

Polyporus squamosus. WHITE MOTTLED HEART ROT on maple, buckeye, birch, occasional on living trees near wounds. Conks are annual, fleshy, white to dingy yellow with a short, thick lateral stalk, upper surface with broad, appressed scales, up to 18 inches wide.

Polyporus sulphureus, sulphur fungus. RED BROWN HEART ROT, brown cubical rot in heartwood of maple and other living hardwoods and conifers, widespread on oak, balsam and Douglas-firs, spruces. The annual, shelf-like fruiting bodies are most conspicuous—soft, fleshy, moist when fresh, with bright orange-red upper surface and brilliant sulfur yellow underneath, formed in overlapping clusters. When old they are hard, brittle, dirty white. Infection is through dead branch stubs and wounds.

Polyporus versicolor, rainbow conk. Sapwood Rot. This is the most common fungus on hardwood slash in woods and sometimes on conifers. The rot is soft, white, spongy. Heartwood of living catalpa may be decayed, the fungus entering through wounds and dead branches. The conks are thin, tough, leathery, annual, up to 2 inches wide with a hairy or velvety surface multicolored white, yellow, brown, gray and black. The undersurface is yellow or white.

PORIA

Basidiomycetes, Agaricales, Polyporaceae

Pileus resupinate, thin, membranous, tubes wartlike, separate.

Poria cocos. Root Rot. On roots of various trees, especially pine, in southeastern United States. Huge sclerotia, weighing up to 2 pounds, are formed; this stage has been known as *Pachyma cocos.*

Poria subacida. Feather Rot, spongy root rot, stringy butt rot of heartwood of living conifers and found on dead hardwood. Decay rarely extends more than 6 to 10 feet in the trunk. Irregular pockets run together forming masses of white fibers, annual rings separate readily. Sporophores are white to straw colored to cinnamon-buff crusts forming sheets several feet long on underside of fallen trunks or on underside of root crotches or exposed roots of living trees.

PYRENOCHAETA (See under Blights)

Pyrenochaeta terrestris. Pink Root of Onions, widespread on onions, garlic, shallot. Roots of affected plants shrivel and turn pink. New roots replacing the old are infected in turn, plants are stunted, bulbs small. The fungus lives in the soil.

Control. Avoid land which has grown any of these three for some years; keep plants growing vigorously. Onions of the Sweet Spanish and Japanese type are less susceptible than Danvers variety.

PYTHIUM

Phycomycetes, Peronosporales (Pythiales) Pythiaceae

Wall of sporangium smooth; discharging swarmspores in imperfectly formed state into thin-walled vesicle which later ruptures to allow spores to escape. Sporangia terminal or intercalary. Species live in moist soil causing damping-off and root rots.

Pythium aphanidermatum. Cotton Leak, Root Rot, Damping-Off of melon, papaya, radish, sugar beet. There is a watery decay with a yellow-brown liquid leaking out when fruit is pressed. Infection is from the soil.

Pythium debaryanum. Damping-Off of Seedlings; Watery Leak of Potatoes. Leak starts as a brown discoloration around a wound and soon spreads to include whole potato which is soft, easily crushed, and drips out a brown liquid with the slightest pressure. Pythium hyphae grow through the soil in great profusion and can enter seedlings either through stomata or unbroken epidermis. See section on Damping-Off.

Pythium ultimum. Damping-Off, Root Rot of many seedlings.

RHIZINA

Ascomycetes, Pezizales, Pezinaceae

Cup-shaped apothecia, with rhizoids below; asci operculate, opening with a lid, 8-spored; spores fusoid, spindle-shaped; paraphyses present.

Rhizina inflata. Seedling Root Rot, Damping-Off. Coniferous seedlings in the Pacific Northwest are sometimes killed in isolated circular patches 2 to 4 feet in diameter, particularly in burned areas. Infected roots are matted together with white mycelium. More or less resinous annual fructifications are formed on the ground. They are irregular, 2 to 3 inches across the undulating brown upper surface with narrow white margin. There is no control, but the disease is minor.

RHIZOCTONIA

Fungi Imperfecti, Mycelia sterilia

Sclerotial form of Pellicularia, Corticium, Macrophomina and Helicobasidium. Young mycelium colorless with branches constricted at points of origin from main axis, but soon colored, a weft of brownish yellow to brown strands, organizing into dense groups of hyphae—sclerotia—made up of short, irregular, angular or somewhat barrel-shaped cells.

Rhizoctonia bataticola. Charcoal Rot. See *Macrophomina phaseoli*.

Rhizoctonia crocorum. Violet Root Rot. See *Helicobasidium purpureum*.

Rhizoctonia solani (*Pellicularia filamentosa*). Brown Patch, root and leaf rot of lawn grasses—redtop, velvet and creeping bent-grass, Kentucky blue-grass,

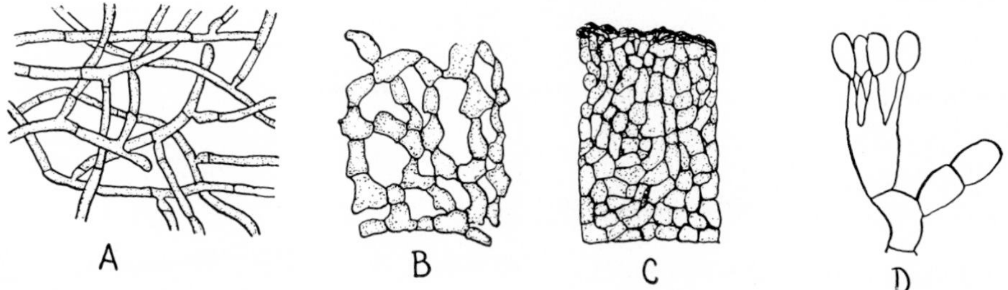

Fig. 85. Forms of *Rhizoctonia solani*. A, young mycelium, constricted at branches; B, loosely formed angular to barrel-shaped colored cells; C, section through sclerotium formed from aggregation of cells in B; D, basidium and spores of Pellicularia, perfect stage of *R. solani*.

infrequently on Canada blue-grass, and Bermuda-grass. The turf shows large brown or blackened areas suggesting sunscald. They are usually somewhat circular varying from a few inches to several feet in diameter with affected grass dark at first then gradually becoming a lighter brown. The disease develops most rapidly during warm humid periods and should not be confused with somewhat similar brown patch caused by chinch bug injury.

Control. Mercury compounds have been used for many years, usually a combination of ⅔ calomel (mercurous chloride) and ⅓ mercuric chloride (available under the trade name of Calochlor) or an organic mercury such as Special Semesan. Newer compounds include Puraturf 177, a cadmium compound; Tersan, tetramethyl thiuram-disulfide; PMAS, a phenyl mercuric acetate complex; and many other new organic materials. The inorganic mercury sprays may at times cause rather severe injury and the newer materials are not yet uniformly effective for brown patch.

Rhizoctonia solani. Root and Stem Rot, Damping-Off. In wet weather cobwebby mycelium develops on lower portions of stems; parts above infection wilt and die, with lower leaves rotting. Seedlings and older plants so rotted include aconitum, abelia, achillea, ageratum, aster, artichoke, begonia, calendula, campanula, clarkia, centaurea, chrysanthemum, columbine, coreopsis, cosmos, carnation, endive, dahlia, delphinium, geranium, iris, lettuce, lupine, orchids, platycodon, salsify, sunflower, tulip.

Control. Spray lower portions of plants thoroughly with bordeaux mixture; avoid excessive use of manure; sterilize soil if necessary.

Rhizoctonia tuliparum. Gray Bulb Rot of Tulips, in northeastern and Pacific states. The most conspicuous sign or symptom of this disease is a bare patch where tulip shoots should be showing in spring. Occasionally an affected bulb will produce some above-ground growth but the plants are slow and often wither and die before flowering. When bulbs are dug they are found to have rotted from the top down, the mycelium has formed felted masses between the scales, and on bulbs and in surrounding soil are masses of brown to black, flattened sclerotia, composed of the yellow brown, irregular thin-walled cells typical of Rhizoctonia. No spore stage is yet known but the fungus lives for years in soil in the sclerotial form attacking bulbs after planting or in very early spring. Occasionally sclerotia are transported on bulbs, but affected bulbs are usually so diseased they are not apt to be sold.

Control. Do not use the same ground for tulips or hyacinths for three or four years, or sterilize soil with formaldehyde.

RHIZOPUS

Phycomycetes, Mucorales, Mucoraceae

Sporangium large, globose, multispored, with a columella and thin wall; sporangiola and conidia lacking. Sporangiophores arise in fasicles from aerial arching stolons which develop rhizoids at points of contact with substratum (Fig. 7).

Rhizopus nigricans, the common black bread mold. SOFT ROT OF SWEET POTATO, FRUIT ROT. The fungus causes a storage rot of sweet potatoes and is a weak parasite on ripe fruit—peach, fig, avocado, citrus, persimmon, pear, strawberry. The rot spreads rapidly; the flesh is soft and watery with an offensive odor. A coarse cottony mold appearing in wounds and on the surface, is covered with sporangia, white when young but black at maturity.

Rhizopus stolonifer. BLACK MOLD of market peas, SOFT ROT of sweet potato, beans, lima beans, cucumber, melons, eggplant, carrot, cabbage, Jerusalem artichoke, potato, onion, amaryllis, lily, tulip.

Control. To prevent storage rot in sweet potatoes, maintain high humidity and a temperature permitting corking over of wounds. Cure at 80° to 85° F. for 10 to 14 days, then store at 55° F. Use proper sanitary measures to prevent build-up of spores. Nancy Hall and Southern Queen are among the more resistant varieties.

ROESLERIA

Ascomycetes, Helotiales

Mycelium inconspicuous; apothecia cup-shaped opening more or less completely, asci disappearing early, leaving persistent mass of spores and paraphyses. Spores hyaline, 1-celled, globose.

Roesleria hypogaea. ROOT ROT of grape.

ROSELLINIA

Ascomycetes, Sphaeriales, Sphaeriaceae

Perithecia smooth, with a papillate ostiole and a subicle or compact mass of mycelium under fruiting layer; paraphyses present; spores olive to brown, 1-celled.

Rosellinia necatrix. DEMATOPHORA ROT, WHITE ROOT ROT of fig, grape, holly osmanthus, privet, poplar, apple, walnut, and other hosts. This is like Armillaria root rot in that all trees in certain areas in an orchard are killed, but there are no rhizomorphs or toadstools formed. A white mycelial growth on surface of affected roots turns black and cobwebby. During wet weather a delicate mold can be seen on surface of bark and on soil around base of tree.

Control. Remove badly affected or dead trees with as much of roots as possible. Remove soil from crowns of lightly infected trees and spray base of trees and surrounding soil with bordeaux mixture.

SCHIZOPHYLLUM

Basidiomycetes, Agaricales, Agaricaceae

Pileus leathery, stipe lateral or none, edge of gills split, spores white.

Schizophyllum commune. WOUND ROT, common on dead parts of living trees—maple, boxelder, almond, acacia, ailanthus, birch, catalpa, hickory, peach, pecan, citrus, fig. Fruiting bodies are small, thin, sometimes lobed, up to 2 inches wide, fan-shaped with gray-white downy upper surface, brownish forked gills on underside, common on fruit trees.

SCLEROTINIA (See under Blights)

Sclerotinia homeocarpa. DOLLAR SPOT, or small brown patch in turf. Spots are not larger than 2 inches in diameter, except where numerous small spots may merge into large irregular areas. Turf is first dark, then a light straw color. The apothecial stage of the fungus is not found in this country.

Control. Some of the newer cadmium compounds, such as Puraturf 177 and Crag Turf Fungicide, seem to be very effective in controlling dollar spot.

Sclerotinia intermedia. STEM ROT, market disease of celery, carrot, salsify.

Sclerotinia minor. STEM ROT of lettuce, celery, carrot, resembling rot caused by *S. sclerotiorum,* but the sclerotia are much smaller.

Sclerotinia (*Botrytis*) **narcissicola.** NARCISSUS SMOULDER. Probably the fungus should be transferred to Botryotinia since there is a conidial stage. The disease is a decay of stored narcissus bulbs and a rot of foliage and flowers in the open, especially during cold wet seasons. Sclerotia are small, black, flattened bodies, up to half an inch long when several grow together, just below outer papery bulb scales. The fungus is inactive in summer but if storage is prolonged into autumn there is a yellowish brown rot. If lightly infected bulbs are planted shoots will be malformed, yellow, and covered with gray spore masses in wet weather.

Control. There is no cure. Inspect every bulb carefully before planting.

Sclerotinia sclerotiorum. DROP, watery soft rot of lettuce, endive. PINK ROT of celery. COTTONY ROT of bean, carrot, parsnip, cabbage and other crucifers, and cucurbits. In lettuce older leaves wilt and fall flat on ground, leaving center leaves erect, but they are soon invaded by mycelium and reduced to a slimy wet mass. In continued moisture a thick, white cottony mold is formed bearing large black sclerotia up to the size of peas. They winter in the soil and send up groups of apothecia in spring. These are brown, cup to saucer-shaped, up to an inch across, on a stalk, and eject spores in a veritable cloud. There is no known conidial stage.

Control. In commercial celery fields deep plowing, or flooding, or treatment with calcium cyanamide is used to prevent apothecial production. Lettuce drop is more prevalent in greenhouses than outside, where ordinary crop rotation gives control.

Sclerotinia sclerotiorum. STEM ROT of pepper, tomato, and many ornamentals—aconite, calendula, chrysanthemum, cynoglossum, dahlia, daisy, hollyhock, delphinium, gazania, lily, peony, snapdragon, sunflower, zinnia, and others. The same sort of cottony mold is formed on ornamentals as on vegetables, but here the sclerotia are quite frequently inside the pith of the herbaceous stem and so are rather long and thin. You can feel them by running

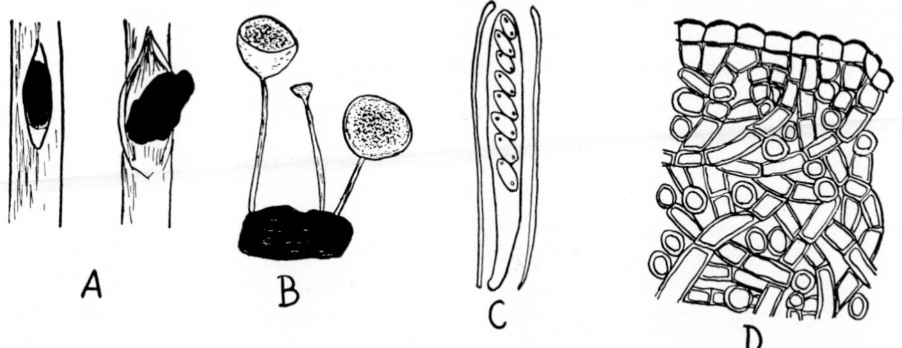

Fig. 86. *Sclerotinia sclerotiorum.* A, sclerotium formed in pith of stem and one falling out from broken stem; B, apothecia produced from sclerotium on ground; C, ascus with paraphyses; D, section through sclerotium, with colorless medulla and dark wall on rind cells.

thumb and finger along the stem and sometimes cottony mycelium and one or two external sclerotia or cracks in the stem indicate their presence. Such sclerotia are very common in peony stems. When sclerotia are formed in flowers the shape corresponds to floral parts. Sunflowers sometimes have very large compound sclerotia.

Control. Cut out affected parts, trying to keep sclerotia from falling out onto the soil. Dusting with sulfur sometimes checks rapid spread of mycelium.

Sclerotinia sclerotiorum. Green Fruit Rot of almond, peach, apricot, also fig, strawberry; Rhizome Rot of ginseng. In almond, young shoots and fruits are killed and wither soon after petals fall. Infection takes place through jackets from apothecia produced under trees where weeds or crop plants have been previously infected with cottony rot. Losses are serious only when there is continuous wet weather during and after blooming.

Control. Spraying for brown rot helps control green rot. Shaking or jarring trees after bloom to remove jackets from young fruits is suggested.

SCLEROTIUM (See under Blights)

Sclerotium cepivorum. White Rot of Onion, shallot, garlic. Affected plants die from a rotting at the neck, at which point there is a surface crust of small black sclerotia and a thin weft of white mycelium. The sclerotia are smaller, and rounder, than those of Botrytis. Roots are often rotted off and sometimes spots in a field covering several square yards are infested.

Control. Dig out all plants in infested spots together with neighboring healthy plants and some soil. Do not replant such a spot to onion or garlic.

Sclerotium delphinii. Crown Rot of Delphinium, iris, ajuga, aconite, phlox, and many, many other ornamentals and some vegetables. Much of the crown rot in the North is attributed to this species but some workers believe it only a strain of *S. rolfsii.* (See under Blights.)

Sclerotium rolfsii. Wet Scale Rot of Narcissus, Crown or Stem Rot of Vegetables and Ornamentals, also known as southern blight, which see. First infection appears in warm humid weather with a sudden wilting and often a falling over of the plant through a rot at the crown. The signs of the

Fig. 87. Crown Rot. Left, sclerotia at base of delphinium stems; right, white fanlike mycelium and sclerotia crowding over iris leaves in wet weather.

fungus are distinctive—a white weft of mycelium at base of the plant and numerous sclerotia, white to tan to reddish tan, either on stem or covering ground near the plant.

Mycelium and sclerotia can follow down through the soil as far as the root system—a foot or more deep, but they are usually in the top 6 inches. The mycelium can spread some distance over the soil to infect nearby plants, and sclerotia can survive in soil more than one year.

Control. In home gardens best control is frequent observation and immediate removal of affected plants and surrounding soil, pouring bichloride of mercury 1–1000 into hole and over crowns of surrounding plants. This does not kill all sclerotia but kills mycelium and stops spread for a single season. Dusting with sulfur temporarily stops mycelial spread. Some organic fertilizers seem to reduce rot. Disinfecting fallow soil with chloropicrin kills most of the sclerotia.

SEAVERINIA

Ascomycetes, Helotiales, Sclerotiaceae

Apothecia shallow cup to disc-shaped, a stroma formed but not definite sclerotia; conidia botryose.

Seaverinia (*Sclerotinia*) **geranii.** Rhizome Rot on geranium only.

STEREUM

Basidiomycetes, Agaricales, Thelephoraceae

Pileus resupinate, consisting of several layers, cystidia lacking; spores dark.

Stereum fasciatum. Brown Crumbly Rot, mostly on slash but sometimes on maple and birch. Thin, leathery, grayish sporophores, undersurface light brown, smooth.

Stereum hirsutum. Wood Rot, Sapwood Wound Rot, occasionally near wounds of living trees—birch, maple, hickory, mountain-mahogany, eucalyptus, peach, and others. Thin, leathery crustlike sporophores have hairy, buff to gray upper surface and are smooth grayish underneath.

Stereum purpureum. Silver Leaf, Sapwood Rot, common on plums and other fruit trees, occasionally on shade and ornamental trees.

The fungus enters through wounds, grows first in heartwood, then kills sapwood and bark; infected branches develop a foliage with a dull leaden or metallic luster, and may die the first season that silvering appears or later. If the disease is not checked, the entire tree may be lost. The sporophores appear after death—resupinate to somewhat shelf-shaped, with faint to dark purple undersurface.

Control. Remove branches and burn at first sign of silvering. Protect trees against wounds, paint pruning surfaces.

Stereum sanguinolentum. Red Heart Rot of slash and living conifers—fir and eastern white pine. Fruiting bodies are small, not over 2 inches wide; upper surface is a silky pale olive-buff; lower surface "bleeds" readily when wounded, dries to grayish brown. They are produced in profusion on dead wood, and occasionally on dead branches of living trees.

STROMATINIA

Ascomycetes, Helotiales, Sclerotiniaceae

Apothecia arising from thin, black, subcuticular, effuse sclerotium or stroma; small black sclerotules are borne free on mycelium, not giving rise to apothecia. There is no conidial stage, and apothecia resemble those of Sclerotinia.

Stromatinia (formerly *Sclerotinia*) **gladioli.** Dry Rot of Gladiolus, also found on imported crocus, freesia, tritonia. Lesions on corms start as reddish specks, with slightly elevated darker borders; with spots enlarging, centers become sunken, dark brown to black with lighter raised edges. They grow together to form irregular areas. On husks the lesions are tobacco brown. Very small black sclerotia are formed on husks, in corm lesions and on dead stems. Plants in field die prematurely due to decay of the leaf sheath. Corms may appear normal when dug and the rot develop in storage. The rot is more prevalent in heavy soils.

Apothecia have been produced artificially by fertilizing receptive bodies on sclerotia with spermatia (microconidia). They are densely crowded, 3 to 7 mm. broad on stipes 6 to 10 mm. high.

Control. Use soil with good drainage. Treat corms before planting with calomel or yellow oxide of mercury at rate of 1 pound to 5 gallons water with a little Dreft added. Dip until they are well coated with the suspension. Cure rapidly after harvest, using artificial heat if necessary.

THIELAVIOPSIS

Fungi Imperfecti, Moniliales, Dematiaceae

Hyphae are dark, distinct from conidia of which there are two kinds: small, cylindric hyaline endogenous spores formed inside hyphae and large, ovate, dark brown exogenous spores; both sets are formed in chains.

Thielaviopsis basicola. Black Root Rot, seedling root rot of tobacco and many vegetables—carrots, beans, peas, corn, onion, okra, tomato, watermelon; and ornamentals—sweet pea, especially begonia, cyclamen, oxalis, lupine, peony, pelargonium, violet, pansy, and others.

There is a blackening and decay of roots. If plants are young they damp-off and die; older plants are stunted, with the decay proceeding until all roots are destroyed. Recent investigation shows that feeding by meadow nematodes may precede black root rot.

The imperfect Thielaviopsis is often accompanied in the soil by an ascomycete, Thielavia, but the genetic connection has not been established. The fungus lives in the soil as a saprophyte. Hyaline conidia produced inside conidioles are forced out through the tip. Larger conidia or chlamydospores are dark, club-shaped with several cells, but breaking up so that each pillbox cell acts as a spore.

The root rot is most destructive in heavy, cold, slightly acid to alkaline soils well supplied with humus. Long wet periods after transplanting are especially favorable to its development. Soils with pH lower than 5.6 or sandy soils low in organic matter are less conducive to disease.

Control. Sterilize soil for seedbeds. Treatment with chloropicrin or D–D-Mixture to kill the nematodes may be most important.

TRAMETES

Basidiomycetes, Agaricales, Polyporaceae

Pileus resupinate to shelving corky; tubes unequally sunken.

Trametes suaveolens. WHITE WOOD ROT of willows, poplars, after wounding. A dry, corky to punky decay with an anise odor begins in lower trunk and progresses upward. Leathery to corky sporophores 6 inches wide are white when young, gray to yellow with age.

TRICHODERMA

Fungi Imperfecti, Moniliales, Moniliaceae

Conidia in heads on conidiophores divided into 2 or 3 tips, a single head on each tip; spores hyaline, 1-celled.

Trichoderma viride. GREEN MOLD ROT, cosmopolitan on narcissus, also on shallot, garlic, occasional on citrus. This fungus has an antibiotic or antagonistic effect on Rhizoctonia, Pythium and other damping-off fungi, also on *Sclerotium delphinii.*

TRICHOTHECIUM

Fungi Imperfecti, Moniliales, Moniliaceae

Conidiophores long, unlike sterile hyphae; spores solitary, 2-celled, hyaline.

Trichothecium roseum. FRUIT, STORAGE ROT on tomato, fig, celery, carrot, occasional on quince and pear. This is a pink mold.

VERTICILLIUM (See under Wilts)

Verticillium lycopersici. COLLAR ROT of tomato in seedbeds. A brown sunken area girdling stem near surface of ground. The leaves may roll up and turn purple or the whole seedling turn yellow and die. Soil should be sterilized before new seedlings are started.

USTULINA

Ascomycetes, Sphaeriales, Xylariaceae

Stroma globoid, pulvinate to cupulate, carbonous, black, somewhat hollow; spores dark, 1-celled.

Ustulina vulgaris. WHITE HEART ROT, a brittle white rot with prominent black zones in butts of living hardwoods, and prevalent on sugar maple sprouts. Black crusts appear on stumps and logs or on flat cankered areas of American beech.

XYLARIA

Ascomycetes, Sphaeriales, Xylariaceae

Stroma is upright, simple or branched; after producing conidia perithecia are formed immersed laterally; spores dark, 1-celled.

Xylaria hypoxylon. Root Rot of hawthorn, gooseberry.

Xylaria sp. Black Root Rot of honey locust, apple. Wood is soft, spongy, dirty white, with narrow conspicuous black zones forming fantastic patterns. Roots are covered with thin compact white mycelium which changes to black incrustations. Fruiting bodies are dark brown to black clubs, one to several inches high, on roots or dead stumps.

RUSTS

Rust fungi belong to the Uredinales, a highly specialized order of the Basidiomycetes. In common with mushrooms they have spores of the sexual stage borne in fours on a club-shaped hypha known as a basidium, but apart from this they differ very decidedly from the woody and fleshy Basidiomycetes. Rusts are obligate parasites; they cannot grow outside a living plant. Many of them are heteroecious, completing their life cycle on two different kinds of plants; but some are monoecious (or autoecious), having all their spore forms on a single host species.

Many rusts show physiological specialization, the existence within a species of numerous races or strains which look alike but attack different varieties of crop plants, thus greatly complicating the problem of breeding for rust resistance.

Rusts with a complete life cycle have five different spore forms, numbered O to IV:

O. *Pycniospores* (spermatia) formed in *pycnia* (spermagonia). The pycnia resemble pycnidia of Ascomycetes and are usually on upper side of leaves. They discharge 1-celled pycniospores with drops of nectar and these function in fertilization.

I. *Aeciospores* (aecidiospores), 1-celled, orange or yellow, formed, often in chains, in a cuplike sorus or *aecium* which has a peridium (wall) opening at or beyond surface of the host.

II. *Urediospores* (uredospores or summer spores or red rust spores), 1-celled, walls spiny or warty, reddish brown, on stalks or in chains in a *uredium* (uredinium or uredosorus) over which the epidermis of the host is broken to free the spores.

III. *Teliospores* (teleutospores, winter spores, black rust spores) 1- or 2-celled, in *telia* (or teleuto sori) either on stalks as in the family Pucciniaceae or sessile, in crusts or cushions, as in Melampsoraceae.

IV. *Basidiospores* (sporidia) on a basidium or promycelium formed by the germinating teliospore.

In heteroecious rusts spore stages O and I are formed on one host and II and III on the other and are so indicated in the information given with each species. Stage IV always follows III on germination. In monoecious rusts all spore forms are on one host, or some are dropped out and we have a short-cycle rust.

Gardeners frequently mistake a reddish discoloration of a leaf, perhaps due to spray injury or weather, or a leaf-spot fungus, for rust, but true rust is told by the presence of the rust-colored spores, which are in powdery pustules, or perhaps gelatinous horns. Any discoloration of host tissue is yellowish, from increased evaporation from broken epidermis. Plants are often stunted.

Losses in food crops due to rust have been enormous since the beginning of history. The Romans had a festival to propitiate the rust gods. Now we try to do it by removing the alternate host—barberry to save wheat, or black currants to save white pine—or by developing more and more resistant varieties for the ever-increasing strains of rust, or by the use of fungicides, classically sulfur, latterly some of the carbamates.

AECIDIUM

This is a form genus, a name applied to the aecial stage where the full cycle is unknown, and O and I the only spore stages. Aecia have a peridium and catenulate spores. There are many species on angiosperms.

APLOPSORA

Pucciniaceae. Teliospores sessile, hyaline, in a single layer; aecia with peridium.

Aplopsora nyssae, on tupelo, II, III.

BAEODROMUS

Pucciniaceae. Spores 1-celled; telia pulvinate, erumpent; chains of spores short.

Baeodromus californicus, on senecio, III.

CAEOMA

Form genus. Aecia with catenulate spores but no peridium.

Caeoma faulliana. Needle Rust on alpine fir. Aecia orange-yellow, on needles of current year.

CEROTELIUM

Pucciniaeae. Spores 1-celled; teliospores in a many-layered mass, sessile, hyaline, not exerted through stomata; aecia with peridium.

Cerotelium dicentrae, O, I on bleeding heart; II, III on Urticastrum.

CHRYSOMYXA

Melampsoraceae. Teliospores in cylindric or branching chains; promycelium exserted; urediospores typically in short chains, uredia without peridium.

Chrysomyxa arctostaphyli, on bearberry, III.

Chrysomyxa cassandrae. SPRUCE NEEDLE RUST, O, I on black, red, blue, Engelmann spruces; II, III on chamaedaphne (bog rosemary). May become epidemic on spruce, causing considerable defoliation.

Chrysomyxa chiogenis, II, III on creeping snowberry; O, I on spruce by inoculation, not found naturally.

Chrysomyxa empetri, II, III on crowberry; O, I on red and white spruce, aecia on upper and lower surfaces of needles.

Chrysomyxa ilicina, II, III on American holly.

Chrysomyxa ledi, O, I on black, red and Norway spruces; II, III on underside of leaves of *Ledum* spp.

Chrysomyxa ledicola, O, I on white, black, red, blue, Engelmann and Sitka spruces; II, III on upper side of leaves of *Ledum* spp. Spruce needles may be so badly discolored trees appear yellowish.

Chrysomyxa piperiana, O, I on Sitka spruce; II, III on underside of leaves of *Rhododendron californicum.*

Chrysomyxa pyrolae, O, I on cones of black, blue, Engelmann, Norway, red and white spruce; II, III on pyrola and moneses. Aecia are on upper side of cone scales; infected cones turn yellow and produce no seed.

Chrysomyxa roanensis, O, I on red spruce; II, III on *Rhododendron catawbiense.*

Chrysomyxa weirii. SPRUCE NEEDLE RUST, III on Engelmann and red spruce. Waxy orange to orange-brown, elongate-elliptical telia occur on 1-year needles, causing yellowish spots. This is the only spore stage known and teliospores can reinfect spruce.

COLEOSPORIUM

Melampsoraceae. Pycnia and aecia are on pines; uredia and telia on dicotyledons. Pycnia subepidermal or subcortical, flattish, linear, dehiscent by a slit; aecia on needles, erumpent, with prominent peridium, spores ellipsoid or globular; uredia erumpent, powdery, without peridia; urediospores globose or oblong, catenulate (in chains) with verrucose (warty) walls; telia indehiscent (remaining closed), waxy gelatinous on germination, spores sessile or obscurely catenulate, 1-celled, smooth but with thick and gelatinous walls.

Coleosporium apocyanaceum, O, I, on loblolly, longleaf and slash pines; II, III on *Amsonia* spp. in the Southeast.

Coleosporium campanulae, O, I on pitch, red and Virginia pines; II, III on campanula, lysimachia, and specularia. Underside of bluebell leaves are covered with orange to reddish brown pustules. Leaves are dry and plants stunted.

Coleosporium crowellii, III, only spore stage known, on needles of piñon and limber pines.

Coleosporium delicatulum. PINE NEEDLE RUST. O, I on 2- and 3-needle pines: II, III on goldenrod and euthamia.

Coleosporium elephantopodis, O, I on 2- and 3-needle pines in the South; II, III on elephantopus.

Coleosporium helianthi. PINE NEEDLE RUST, SUNFLOWER RUST, O, I on pitch and short needle pines; II, III on wild and cultivated sunflower, Jerusalem artichoke, heliopsis. Sunflower leaves with brown rust pustules dry up and fall. Control is not easy but sulfur dust will help, or perhaps spraying with Parzate or Fermate.

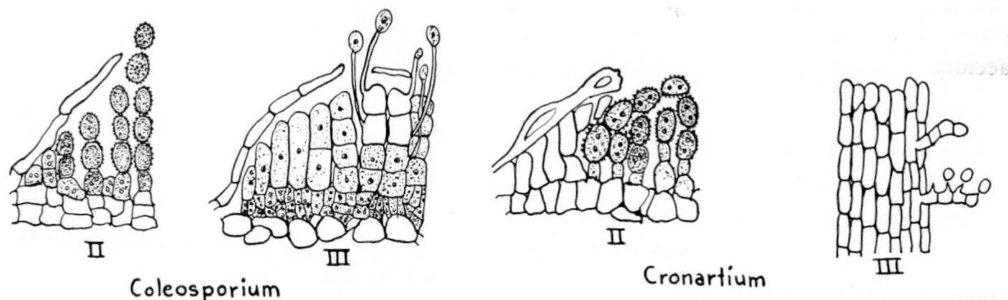

FIG. 88. Pine Rusts. *Coleosporium solidaginis,* uredial (II) and telial (III) stages on aster, teliospores germinating in situ. *Cronartium ribicola,* II and III stages on currant.

Coleosporium inconspicuum, O, I on shortleaf, longleaf, and Virginia pines; II, III on Coreopsis.

Coleosporium ipomoeae, O, I on southern and Chihuahua pines; II, III on moonflower, morning-glory, sweet potato, jacquemontia, quamoclit, most abundant in warmer regions.

Coleosporium jonesii, O, I on piñon pine; II, III on flowering currant, gooseberry.

Coleosporium lacinariae, O, I on loblolly, longleaf, and pitch pines; II, III on liatris.

Coleosporium madiae, on Monterey, Coulter, and Jeffrey pines; II, III on marigold, tarweed and other composites.

Coleosporium minutum, O, I on loblolly and spruce pines; II, III on forestiera.

Coleosporium occidentale, O, I unknown; II, III on senecio.

Coleosporium pinicola, III on Virginia or scrub pine.

Coleosporium solidaginis. NEEDLE BLISTER RUST OF PINE. O, I on all 2- and 3-needle pines in eastern United States; II, III on aster and goldenrod commonly, general on China aster except far South, on golden aster (*Chrysopis*), erigeron, grindelia, seriocarpus and other composites. This is a blister rust on pine needles, with pustules higher than they are long, in clusters or short rows, fairly common on ornamental pines in gardens. The rust winters on aster and related composites. Older needles of young pines may be severely infected, with white aecia conspicuous in spring and early summer. Aster leaves have bright orange-yellow spore pustules on undersurface.

Control. Dust with sulfur early in the season.

Coleosporium sonchi-arvensis, O, I on Scotch pine; II, III on sow-thistle.

Coleosporium terebinthinaceae, O, I on 2- and 3-needle pines, especially in the Southeast; II, III on silphium and parthenium.

Coleosporium vernoniae, O, I on various 2- and 3-needle pines; II, III on ironweed.

Coleosporium viburni, O, I unknown; II, III on *Viburnum* spp.

CRONARTIUM (Causing Blister Rusts)

Melampsoraceae. Heteroecious; pycnia and aecia on trunk and branches of pine; uredia, telia on herbaceous woody dicotyledons.

Pycnia are on stems, caeomoid, forming blisters beneath cortical layer of host, dehiscent by longitudinal slits in the bark; aecia on trunks, erumpent, with peridium sometimes dehiscent at apex but more often splitting circularly or irregularly at side; aeciospores ellipsoid with coarsely warted walls, sometimes with smooth spot on one side.

Uredia are on underside of leaves or on stems of herbaceous hosts; delicate peridium, dehiscent at first by a central pore; urediospores borne singly on pedicels, ellipsoidal with spiny walls; telia erumpent, often coming from uredia; catenulate, 1-celled teliospores often form a much extended cylindric or filiform column, horny when dry.

Blister rusts are characterized by galls which are globose, subglobose or fusiform depending on species. A rust on a pine stem is invariably a Cronartium, although this stage has often gone under the name of Peridermium.

Cronartium cerebrum. EASTERN GALL RUST, **O, I** on pines, especially scrub and shortleaf in the South; II, III on chestnut, tanbark oak. Globose to subglobose galls are formed on pine stems and in spring aecia break through bark of stems in a more or less cerebroid (brainlike) arrangement.

Cronartium coleosporioides (*C. filamentosum*). PAINTBRUSH BLISTER RUST. O, I on lodgepole, ponderosa, and Jeffrey pines, in West; II, III on Indian paintbrush, birds-beak, owls-clover, wood-betony. Slight swellings are formed on twigs, trunks, and branches; many lodgepole pine seedlings are killed.

Cronartium comandrae. COMANDRA BLISTER RUST, O, I on ponderosa, Arizona, and lodgepole pines in the West, and pitch, mountain, jack, loblolly, Austrian, Scotch, and maritime pines in the East; II, III on bastard toadflax (*Comandra* spp.). Destructive effect is limited to the distribution of the toadflax, which is widespread but locally restricted to small areas. Ponderosa pine suffers most severely, with many seedlings and saplings destroyed and occasionally a large tree attacked.

Cronartium comptoniae. SWEET-FERN BLISTER RUST. O, I on 2- and 3-needle pines; II, III on sweet-fern and sweet gale in northern pine regions and south to North Carolina, and on the Pacific Coast. Young trees may be girdled and killed but are fairly safe after attaining a trunk diameter of 3 inches. Losses in nurseries and plantations are high, especially among lodgepole and ponderosa pines.

Affected stems swell slightly near base with long fusiform swellings, or depressed streaks on eastern hard pine; pitch oozes out from insect wounds in these areas. Killing of main stem often results in multiple-stemmed shrub-like trees. Aecia appear on 3-year seedlings, preceded by pycnia the year before, and spores are windborne many miles to infect herbaceous hosts. Sweet gale (*Myrica gale*) has been considered the only alternate host in the West but there is now a report on *Myrica californica,* the Pacific wax-myrtle.

Control. Remove all sweet gale and sweet-fern for several hundred yards around nurseries or pine plantations and allow no large groups of either within a mile.

Cronartium conigenum. PINE CONE RUST, O, I on cones of Chihuahua pine; II, III on oaks in Southwest. Cones develop into large galls producing aecia with distinct erumpent peridium two or three years after infection.

Cronartium fusiforme. SOUTHERN FUSIFORM RUST. O, I, on hard pines in southern states, especially loblolly, slash and pitch pine; II, III on evergreen oaks on underside of leaves. Pine stems have pronounced spindle-shaped swellings, sometimes with witches' brooms. Branch infections that do not reach the main stem are not serious but those that go on to the trunk may kill the tree.

Control. Prune branches yearly before swelling reaches main stem. Spray oaks around nurseries with 8–8–100 bordeaux mixture when leaves are nearly developed. Longleaf and shortleaf pines are resistant.

Cronartium harknessii. WESTERN GALL RUST, O, I on Jeffrey, ponderosa, lodgepole and digger pines; II, III on Indian paintbrush, lousewort, owls-clover, birds-beak, or omitted, with direct infection from pine to pine. A different variety with alternate stage unknown is found on Monterey and knob-cone pines in coastal California.

Galls are globose, with large, confluent aecia; bark sloughs off in large scales; witches' brooms are formed.

Control. Remove trees with galls for a distance of 300 yards around nurseries. Do not ship infected trees from nurseries.

Cronartium occidentale. PIÑON BLISTER RUST, O, I in piñon and Mexican piñon; II, III on currant, gooseberry, flowering currant. This rust so resembles white pine blister rust it cannot be separated from it on the Ribes hosts, but only by the kind of pine attacked. Aecia on Mexican or singleleaf piñon are distinct sori, but are broad layers under bark on piñon.

Cronartium ribicola. White Pine Blister Rust, O, I on eastern white pine from Maine to Virginia and Minnesota, on western white pine in the Pacific Northwest, and on sugar pine in California; II, III on currant, flowering currant, gooseberry.

This dread disease is supposed to have originated in Asia, whence it spread to Europe, there finding eastern white pine introduced from America very susceptible. White pine blister rust was found in Russia in 1854 and by 1900 had spread over most of Europe. It was recorded on *Ribes* sp. at Geneva, New York, in 1906, but is thought to have been there several years previously. In 1909 it was found on pine, at which time it was learned that infected pines from a German nursery had been widely planted throughout the Northeast. The next year the disease reached Vancouver, British Columbia, in a shipment from a French nursery, whence it has spread to Washington, Oregon, northern California and Idaho, and western Montana. Thus from cheap stock brought in for forest planting has come one of our greatest forest hazards. Our present quarantine laws are designed to prevent such introductions.

The western white sugar and whitebark pines are even more susceptible to blister rust than eastern white pine, but in either case robust, dominant trees are more severely attacked, with frail individuals lightly infected. This, however, is partly explained by the vigorous trees having more needles to receive spores. Of the Ribes species black currant is most susceptible and dangerous. Cultivated red currants are somewhat resistant, causing a minimum of pine infection and Viking and Red Dutch varieties are practically immune. Wild gooseberries and skunk currant in the Northeast are highly susceptible, as are western black currant, stink currant, and red flowering currant. The greater the susceptibility of the Ribes species the more spores are produced to inoculate pines, with proportionate damage.

Symptoms and Life History. When a spore arrives on a pine needle from a currant the first sign of infection is a small golden yellow to reddish brown spot. The next season, or possibly in two years, the bark looks yellowish, often with an orange tinge to the margin of the discolored area, and there may be a spindle-shaped swelling. If such symptoms appear early in the season, pycnia are formed in bark by July or August, but if discoloration is delayed until midsummer they appear the next year. These male fruiting bodies are small, honey yellow to brown patches, swelling to shallow blisters and rupturing to discharge drops of a yellowish, sweet liquid. After this is eaten by insects or washed away by rain the lesions turn dark. The next spring or summer aecia push through the bark in the same region. These are white blisters rupturing to free orange-yellow aeciospores which are carried away by wind. The bark then dries out and cracks, with death of cambium and underlying wood. The disease has taken three to six years to reach this stage.

Production of aecia continues yearly until stem is killed beyond the lesion.

Dead foliage assumes a conspicuous red-brown color and this "flag" of brown on a green background is the most conspicuous symptom of blister rust before death of the pine. Infection progresses downward from small to larger branches and into trunk. Swellings are not apparent on stems much over 2 inches in diameter on eastern white pine, but in the West sometimes show up in stems 5 inches through. Larger limbs and trunks sometimes show constriction in the girdled area.

The aeciospores, large, ellipsoidal, with thick, warty walls, are carried by wind great distances to Ribes species (they cannot reinfect pine). They send their germ tubes into a currant or gooseberry leaf through stomata and within 1 to 3 weeks pinhead-size blisters appear in clusters on yellowed leaf tissue. These uredia rupture to release large, ellipsoidal yellow urediospores with thick, colorless walls and short, sharp but sparse spines. The spores are somewhat moist and sticky and are windborne short distances to other near-by Ribes bushes. There may be as many as 7 generations in a summer, or the spores may even remain viable over winter in uredia. This spore stage can only infect currant.

In late summer telia follow uredia in the same or new leaf lesions, appearing as short brown bristles on underside of leaves or looking like a coarse felt. Each felty bristle is composed of vertical rows of broad, spindle-shaped spores which germinate *in situ* (right where they are) to a 5-celled promycelium with each of the four upper cells bearing at the point of a little projection (sterigma) a small, thin-walled round basidiospore. This cannot reinfect currant and soon dies from exposure to the sun unless the wind blows it immediately to a pine needle. The effective range has been considered 900 feet, except for European and western black currants which can spread infection as much as a mile. Recent work indicates that the effective range from red currants to pine is much less than 900 feet, 300 being considered sufficient for eradication in some states and even less may be adequate. The spores from pine to currant, however, can be carried miles, as many as 300.

Control. Eradication of the Ribes host is definitely effective in controlling white pine blister rust. This means complete removal of susceptible black currants (although some breeding is being done for resistant varieties) and local removal of other cultivated and wild currants and gooseberries, up to 300 or 900 feet according to state regulations, taking care to get all the root system capable of resprouting. In some sections 2,4–D or other weedkillers are used.

Blister rust is not often found on ornamental pines in cities because the smoke and fumes are unfavorable to the fungus. Elsewhere valuable ornamentals can be saved by cutting off infected branches and cleaning out trunk infections, stripping off diseased bark and a 2-inch side margin, 4-inch margin at top and bottom, of healthy bark.

Cronartium strobilinum. PINE CONE RUST. O, I on cones of longleaf and slash pines; II, III on evergreen oak. Cones are swollen with a reddish color and 25 to 90 percent may fall.

CUMMINSIELLA

Pucciniaceae. Autoecious; teliospores 2-celled; pycnia and other sori subepidermal.

Cumminsiella sanguinea, O, I, II, III on barberry and mahonia in the West.

ENDOPHYLLUM

Pucciniaceae. Teliospores have form of aeciospores; aecia with cupulate peridium, aeciospores germinating to form a promycelium.

Endophyllum sempervivi, III on houseleek, hen-and-chickens. Succulent leaves may be covered with reddish pustules. This is not common but I have had one serious case. Clean out infected parts; dust with sulfur.

Endophyllum tuberculatum, III on hollyhock and checkermallow.

FROMMEA

Pucciniaceae. Teliospores 2 to many septate; aecia lacking.

Frommea obtusa var. **duchesnea,** O, I, II, III on mock-strawberry.

GYMNOCONIA

Pucciniaceae. Uredia lacking, aecia present but without peridium; teliospores 2-celled, one pore in each cell.

Gymnoconia peckiana. ORANGE RUST OF BLACKBERRY, O, I, III on blackberry, dewberry, black raspberry. Very bright orange spores cover underside of leaves in spring. The mycelium is perennial in the bush so that spraying is useless. It lives throughout the year between cells of the stem, crown, and roots, and each season as new growth begins the fungus invades new tissue. *Infected plants never recover.*

Control. Plant only healthy stock. Remove infected plants showing upright habit of growth, yellow color, and glistening yellowish dots of pycnia, before the orange spore stage is produced. Eldorado varietv is highly resistant.

GYMNOSPORANGIUM

Pucciniaceae. All but one species heteroecious. Pycnia and aecia usually on trees and shrubs of the apple family; telia confined to cedars and junipers except for one species on cypress; uredia wanting. Teliospores thick or thin-walled, various in shape but mostly flat, tongue-shaped, expanding greatly when moistened, usually with 2 cells, sometimes more, walls smooth, 1 to several pores in each cell; pedicel colorless, usually with the outer portion swelling and becoming jelly-like when moistened. Aecia are highly differentiated and conspicuous, with catenulate aeciospores, with verrucose walls, deeply colored.

The life cycle is similar in all juniper leaf rusts. In early summer small, slightly swollen spots appear on leaves of the pomaceous host, then small raised specks in this area on the upper surface. These are the openings of flash-shaped pycnia embedded in leaf tissue. After exuding an orange liquid containing pycniospores the specks are

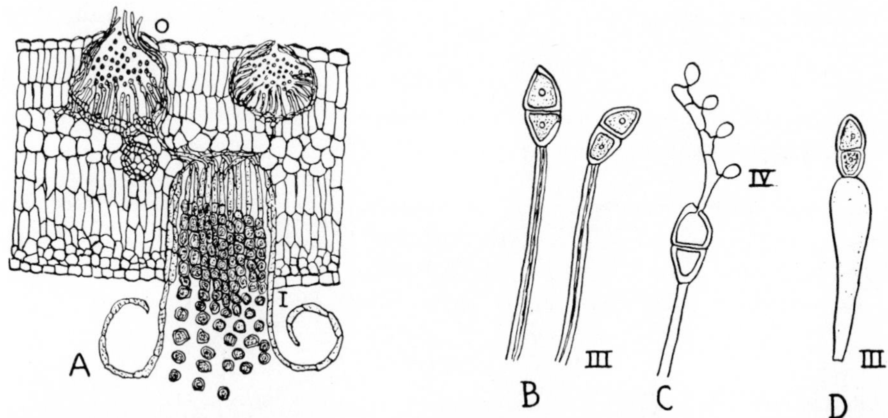

FIG. 89. Cedar-apple Rust, *Gymnosporangium juniperi-virginiani.* A, section through crabapple leaf with pycnia (O) on upper surface and aecium (I) with prominent peridium and aeciospores in chains on undersurface; B, 2-celled teliospores on gelatinous stalks which help form the jelly-like telial horns on cedar galls; C, teliospore germinating with a promycelium and basidiospores. D, teliospore of *G. clavipes,* the quince rust.

black. Later aecia push out on the underside of the same spots as dingy white columns, rostelia, with the outer coating rupturing to release a powdery mass of yellow to brown aeciospores. The ruptured segments sometimes make the open aecium look star-shaped, but in the common cedar-apple rust the aecia are cup-shaped. Aecia are also formed on fruit and tender green stems. Aeciospores released during the summer are windborne to junipers. Mycelium winters in the juniper needle or stem, and in spring galls are started which take a year or more to produce teliospores in cushions or horns.

Gymnosporangium aurantiacum. JUNIPER GALL RUST. III on stems and leaves of common juniper; O, I on mountain-ash.

Gymnosporangium bermudianum, O, I, III on stems of eastern and southern red-cedar in the Gulf States. This is an unusual species in having no alternate host, the aecia preceding telia on small galls.

Gymnosporangium betheli, III on Rocky Mountain juniper; O, I on fruits of hawthorn.

Gymnosporangium biseptatum, III on stems of *Chamaecyparis thyoides;* O, I on amelanchier. Spindle-shaped swellings are formed in stems. If there are many, such trees may die.

Gymnosporangium clavariaeforme, III on common and mountain juniper; O, I on chokeberry, amelanchier, pear, quince. Slender telia 5 to 10 mm. high are produced on long, fusiform swellings on various branches.

Gymnosporangium clavipes. QUINCE RUST. III on eastern red-cedar, dwarf, mountain and prostrate junipers; O, I on fruits and young stems of amelanchier,

FIG. 90. Quince Rust, *Gymnosporangium clavipes,* forming rostelia, aecia with long peridia, on hawthorn hips.

apple, chokeberry, crabapple, hawthorn, mountain-ash, quince, Japanese quince, pear. Short, slight swellings are formed on cedar twigs and branches, many of which die. On main trunk infected areas are black rough patches or rings around the stems. Mycelium is perennial, confined to outer layer of living bark and can sometimes be cleaned out by scraping the bark.

On pomaceous hosts the disease is most frequent on fruits and may cause distortion of fruits, twigs, and buds. Aecia are particularly prominent on hips of English hawthorn with the long whitish peridium around the orange spores.

Gymnosporangium corniculans, III on common juniper and red-cedar; O, I on leaves of amelanchier.

Gymnosporangium cupressi, III on Arizona cypress; O, I on amelanchier.

Gymnosporangium davisii, III on mountain and common juniper; O, I on leaves of red and black chokeberry. Telia are usually on upper surface of needles, sometimes at base of stems.

Gymnosporangium effusum, III on eastern red-cedar; O, I on chokeberry. Fusiform swellings appear on cedar trunk and branches.

Gymnosporangium ellisi. Witches' Broom Rust, III on southern white-cedar (chaemaecyparis) ; O, I on sweet-fern, gale, bayberry, and wax-myrtle leaves, fruits, young stems. Aecia are cluster cups; telia are cylindrical, filiform, 3 to 6 mm. high, appearing on leaf blade or axil the first season after infection, thereafter only on stems, invading inner bark and wood. Witches' brooms are abundant, and even large trees die with heavy brooming.

Gymnosporangium exiguum, on leaves of alligator and Mexican junipers and eastern red-cedar; O, I on leaves, fruits of hawthorn.

Gymnosporangium exterum, III on stems of eastern red-cedar; O, I on gillenia. Flattened telia anastomose over short fusiform swellings with roughened bark on cedars.

Gymnosporangium floriforme, III on red-cedar; O, I on leaves of hawthorn. Cedar galls are small.

Gymnosporangium gobosum. Hawthorn Rust. III general on eastern red-cedar, also on dwarf, prostrate and Rocky Mountain junipers; O, I on leaves of hawthorn, chiefly, also apple, crabapple, pear, mountain-ash. Leaf galls on cedar are very similar to those of common cedar-apple rust but are smaller, seldom over a half inch, nearer mahogany red in color and are not perennial, producing telial horns one season only.

Gymnosporangium hareanum, III on leaves of Chinese juniper; O, I on Chinese flowering quince, pear.

Gymnosporangium harknessianum, III on western juniper; O, I on amelanchier, chiefly on fruits, sometimes stems. Papery margins of aecia are unusually long.

Gymnosporangium hyalinum, III on southern white-cedar; O, I on hawthorn and pear leaves. Slight swellings are formed on small twigs and branches of cedar.

Gymnosporangium inconspicuum, III on Utah juniper; O, I on fruits, chiefly of amelanchier and squaw-apple. Juniper leaves turn yellow; rarely telia appear on branches.

Gymnosporangium japonicum, III, gall on stems of Chinese juniper; O, I on photinia.

Gymnosporangium juniperi-virginianae. Cedar-Apple Rust. III general on red-cedar, eastern and southern, on prostrate and Rocky Mountain junipers; O, I general on apple and crabapple east of Great Plains. The fungus is a native of North America and does not occur elsewhere. It is more important commercially in the apple growing regions of the Virginias and Carolinas and certain states in the Mississippi Valley, but it is generally important on ornamental crabapples in home plantings.

The cedar "apples" or galls vary from $\frac{1}{16}$ inch to over 2 inches across. Leaves are infected during the summer and by the next June a small, greenish-brown swelling appears on upper or inner leaf surface. This enlarges until by autumn the leaf has become a chocolate brown, somewhat kidney-shaped gall covered with small circular depressions. The next spring in moist weather orange telial horns are put forth from the pock-like depressions. The teliospores in horns are enveloped in a gelatinous material which swells vastly, a gall covered with horns sometimes reaching the size of a small orange. They germinate in place to produce the basidiospores which are carried by wind to infect apple or other deciduous host.

By midsummer, apple leaves show yellow areas with amber pustules on upper surface, but after pycnia have exuded drops of sticky liquid they appear as black dots in a rather reddish circle. On the undersurface of these spots small cups are formed, with recurved fimbriate margins. These aecia may also appear near stem end of apples and are common on swollen twigs of crabapple. Spores from these cups are blown back to the cedar in late summer, the entire cycle thus taking two years, 18 to 20 months on the cedar, and 4 to 6 on the apple host.

Chief injury is to the apple host, the rust causing premature defoliation, dwarfing, and poor quality fruit. On very susceptible crabapples, such as Bechtel's crab, repeated infection may cause death of branches or the entire tree. All our native crabapples are susceptible but most foreign crabs are resistant.

Control. Care in planning is most important. Don't let your landscape architect or gardener put cedars and native crabapples or hawthorns close together. Keep them separated as far as possible with a windbreak in between of some tall nonsusceptible host. Some states have laws prohibiting red-cedars within a mile of commercial apple orchards, but for practical garden purposes a few hundred yards is sufficient, the danger markedly decreasing with distance, especially with a house or tree windbreak.

If red-cedars are already planted it is possible in late winter to go over small specimens and remove galls before spore horns are formed. Spraying discourages telial development. Elgetol, a dinitro compound, has been quite successful as an early spring spray on cedars but sometimes injurious. Better results are reported from Bordeaux 180 (12 pounds copper sulfate, 12 pounds lime, 2 pounds monocalcium arsenite, 8 pounds zinc arsenite and 1 pound soybean flour to 100 gallons water).

Fermate in the regular apple spray schedule, used with wettable sulfur or separately at ½ to 1½ pounds per 100 gallons, controls rust. Some apple varieties are fairly resistant: McIntosh, Yellow Transparent, Rhode Island Greening, Red Astrachan, Red Delicious, Northern Spy. A rust-resistant seedling of eastern red-cedar has been found in Virginia and is being developed.

Gymnosporangium juniperinum, III, stem gall on mountain juniper; O, I on Pacific mountain-ash. On smaller branches swellings are subglobose galls

FIG. 91. Cedar-apple Rust. Left, cedar gall in February; right, cedar gall in April or May with gelatinous telial horns protruded.

FIG. 92. Cedar-apple Rust. Leaves of Bechtel's crabapple with dark pycnia in spots on upper surface and aecia in cluster cups on undersurface.

up to ¾ inch in diameter; hemispherical swellings on larger branches are covered with flattened telia.

Gymnosporangium kernianum, III on alligator, Utah, and western junipers; O, I on amelanchier and pear. Telia arise between scale-like leaves on green twigs but mycelium is perennial in stems, causing dense witches' brooms 6 to 18 inches in diameter.

Gymnosporangium libocedri, III on incense cedar; O, I on leaves, fruits of amelanchier and hawthorn, also apple, crabapple, pear, quince, Japanese quince, and mountain-ash. Aecium is a cluster cup on foliage. Peach orchards may be damaged and younger incense cedars have small sprays killed. Telia are always on leaves; witches' brooms and swellings are produced on branches, rarely on trunks. The fungus is said to persist in the mycelial stage up to 200 years.

Gymnosporangium multiporum, III on stems of western, one-seed and Utah juniper between scalelike leaves; O, I unknown.

Gymnosporangium nelsoni, III on one-seed, prostrate, Rocky Mountain, Utah, and western junipers; O, I on hawthorn, quince, Oregon crab, pear, squaw-apple, Pacific mountain-ash. Galls are firm, woody, round, up to 2 inches in diameter.

Gymnosporangium nidus-avis. WITCHES' BROOM RUST. III on eastern and southern red-cedars, on prostrate and Rocky Mountain junipers; O, I on fruit, young stems, leaves of apple, hawthorn, mountain-ash, quince, Japanese quince, amelanchier or serviceberry. Trunks and branches of large trees have both witches' brooms and long, spindle-shaped swellings. Aecia are on both leaf surfaces of alternate hosts.

Gymnosporangium nootkatense. GALL RUST. II, III on Alaska cedar; O, I on mountain-ash, Oregon crabapple. This is the only Gymnosporangium species producing a uredial stage. Uredia are bright orange fading to pale yellow; teliospores appear later in the same pustules; aecium is a cluster cup.

Gymnosporangium speciosum, III on alligator, one-seed and Utah junipers; O, I on leaves of syringa (Philadelphus) and fendlera. Telia are in longitudinal rows on long fusiform swellings on juniper branches which are girdled and die. In severe infections the whole tree dies. Aecia are cluster cups.

Gymnosporangium trachysorum, III on stem of eastern red-cedar; O, I on hawthorn leaves. Swellings on cedar are abruptly fusiform to globoid with prominent telia 6 to 10 mm. high.

Gymnosporangium transformans, III gall on *Chamaecyparis thyoides;* O, I on chokeberry.

Gymnosporangium tubulatum, III on stems of prostrate and Rocky Mountain junipers; O, I on leaves and fruit of hawthorn. Telia are 3 to 4 mm. high on irregular galls on twigs and branches of cedar.

Gymnosporangium vauqueliniae, WITCHES' BROOM RUST. III on one-seed juniper; O, I on *Vauquelinia californica.* This rust is the only Gymnosporangium known to cause witches' brooms on the aecial host, and it also causes slight witches' brooms on green juniper twigs.

HYALOPSORA

Melampsoraceae. Telia on ferns, teliospores several-celled, in epidermis; urediospores of two kinds, with pores.

Hyalopsora aspidiotus. Fir-Fern Rust, O, I on balsam fir; II, III on oak fern (*Phegopteris dryopteris*). Pycnia are slightly raised orange-yellow spots on needles and aecia are yellow to white, columnar, on 2-year needles.

Hyalopsora cheilanthus. Fir-Fern Rust, O, I on balsam fir; II, III on rock brake, parsley fern, cliff brake.

Hyalopsora polypodii. Fir-Fern Rust, general in northern and western states on polypodi fern and woodsia.

KUEHNEOLA

Pucciniaceae. Teliospores in chains, resembling many-celled spores, although 1-celled; wall faintly colored or colorless.

Kuehneola malvicola, II, III on hibiscus and malvaviscus.

Kuehneola uredinia. Yellow Rust, Cane Rust. O, I, II, III on blackberry, dewberry, and raspberry. The disease seems to be increasingly prevalent, especially on the leaves. There is a great difference in varietal susceptibility. Eldorado, Foster, Jumbo, Lawton blackberries are highly susceptible while Nantichoke, Austin Thornless, Boysen Brainerd, Burbank Thornless and others seem resistant. European varieties are generally resistant.

KUNKELIA

Kunkelia nitens. Short-Cycle Orange Rust of Blackberry. I general on blackberry but more common in the South and West, also on dewberry, and black, but not red, raspberry. This is a perennial rust, a systemic disease like that caused by *Gymnosporangium peckiana* but with only the aecial stage present. Undersurface of leaves may be covered with quantities of orange-yellow spores.

MELAMPSORA

Melampsoraceae. Telia more or less indefinite; teliospores sessile, subcuticular or subepidermal, forming crusts of a single layer; aecia when present on leaves with rudimentary peridium; uredia erumpent, pulverulent; spores globoid or ellipsoid, single on pedicels. Species are heteroecious if telia are on woody plants and autoecious if telia are on herbaceous plants.

Melampsora abietis-canadensis. Hemlock-Poplar Rust. O, I on eastern hemlock; II, III on various poplars. Cones have golden powdery masses of spores over the surface, and later shrivel, turn black and hang as mummies; no viable seed are produced. Uredia are golden powdery pustules on undersurface of poplar leaves, but in late summer telia are formed, in orange-yellow crusts which change to black; in spring basidiospores are produced to reinfect hemlock.

Melampsora abieti-caprearum. Fir-Willow Rust. O, I on balsam, white and alpine firs; II, III on willows, widespread. Yellow spots on willow leaves in early summer are followed by dark pustules when the telial stage is produced. There may be some defoliation.

Melampsora albertensis. Douglas-Fir Needle Rust. O, I on Douglas-fir, big-cone spruce; II, III on native poplars. Pycnia are on upper surface of current year needles; aecia, of the caeoma type, are orange yellow on the undersurface. The rust is often epidemic on young trees but with little permanent ill effect.

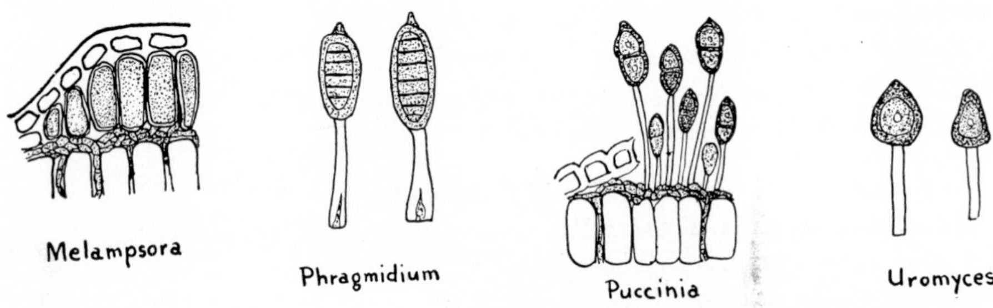

Fig. 93. Rust Teliospores. *Melampsora,* sessile in crust under host epidermis; *Phragmidium,* stalked, with several cells; *Puccinia,* stalked, 2-celled; *Uromyces,* stalked, 1-celled.

Melampsora artica, O, I on saxifrage; II, III on willow.

Melampsora bigelowii. Larch-Willow Rust. O, I on larch; II, III on many species of willow. The damage to larch is insignificant. The fungus can winter on willow as mycelium in catkins, terminal buds and young stems and can maintain itself on willow in the uredial stage without the presence of larches.

Melampsora farlowii. Needle and Cone Rust of Hemlock. O, I unknown; III on hemlock. Reddish slightly raised telia are on undersurface of needles, shoots of the current year and on cones. Young shoots may be twisted and killed. There may be some damage to hemlocks in nurseries and in ornamental hedges.

Control. Spraying weekly during May with summer strength lime sulfur has given control.

Melampsora medusae. Larch Needle Rust. O, I on larch in northeastern states; II, III on native and introduced poplars except far South.

Melampsora occidentalis. Poplar Rust. O, I unknown; II, III on native poplars in West.

Melampsora ribesii-purpureae, O, I on currant, flowering currant, gooseberry; II, III on willow species.

MELAMPSORELLA

Melampsoraceae. Heteroecious on fir, spruce and dicotyledons; pycnia subcuticular, aecia and uredia subepidermal, telia in epidermal cells. Only one species in the United States.

Melampsorella cerastii. Yellow Witches' Broom Rust. O, I on many firs; II, III on chickweed and mouse-ear chickweed.

Infected evergreen branches develop numerous upright lateral shoots from one point, forming a compact witches' broom; twigs are dwarfed and needles turn yellow and drop, leaving brooms bare. The fungus is perennial in stems and new shoots develop with yellow leaves. Pycnia appear in raised orange spots on both surfaces of dwarfed leaves in spring and aecia form in summer on undersurface, in two rows of orange blisters.

Control. The disease is usually not serious enough for special control measures but in forest practice trees with main stem infections should be removed early in life of the stand.

MELAMPSORIDIUM

Melampsoraceae. Heteroecious, on larch and dicotyledonous shrubs and trees. Pycnia are subcuticular; other sori subepidermal.

Melampsoridium betulinum. Birch Leaf Rust. O, I on larch; II, III on various birches. Uredia on underside of birch leaves are small reddish-yellow powdery pustules, followed later in summer by telia, first waxy yellow, then turning dark brown to nearly black.

MILESIA

Melampsoraceae. Heteroecious on firs and ferns. All spores are colorless; urediospores obovate or lanceolate; teliospores in epidermal cells.

Milesia fructuosa, O, I on balsam fir; II, III on *Dryopteris* spp. Aecia are white on current needles, maturing by midsummer.

Milesia marginalis, O, I on balsam fir; II, III on *Dryopteris marginalis.* Pycnia are on both sides of needles, aecia on needles of the current year, maturing by midsummer.

Milesia polypodophila, O, I on balsam fir; II, III on *Polypodium virginianum.* Hyphae are perennial in needles and small stems of balsam fir; aecia on needles 3 to 9 years old.

NYSSOPSORA

Puccinaceae. Autoecious; teliospores with several cells.

Nyssopsora clavellosa, III on *Aralia hispida.*

PERIDERMIUM

A form genus with O, I on Gymnosperms. Aecia have peridia and are cylindric, tongue-like or bullate.

Peridermium ornamentale, O, I on white, alpine, and noble firs.

Peridermium rugosum, O, I on Pacific silver and lowland white firs.

PHRAGMIDIUM

Pucciniaceae. Autoecious. Pycnia subcuticular, other sori subepidermal; aecia caeomoid; teliospores large, conspicuous, of 1 to 10 cells each with 2 or 3 lateral pores; walls somewhat layered, with inner layer colored, outer nearly colorless, smooth or verrucose, pedicel colorless except near spore; often swelling in lower portion. Aecia with catenulate, globoid or ellipsoid verrucose spores; uredia when present circled with paraphyses; urediospores single on pedicels, walls verrucose or echinulate with indistinct scattered pores.

Phragmidium americanum, O, I, II, III on leaves of native and cultivated roses. Teliospores have 8 to 11 cells.

Phragmidium disciflorum. Leaf Rust of Rose. O, I on leaves and stems; II, III on leaves of cultivated roses in **Rosa gallica** group, eastern states to the Rocky Mountains and on Pacific Coast.

This is the common rust of hybrid teas and other roses with large firm leaflets. It is not much of a problem in the East, although sometimes found in New York and New England gardens, but it is a serious menace in the Southwest.

Fig. 94. Rose Rust.

Aecia appear on leaves in spring as small, roughly circular spots, 1/25 inch in diameter, bright orange on the underside of the leaf from the spore masses, and light yellow on the upper surface, sometimes with a narrow, pale green zone. Sometimes the lesions are slightly cup-shaped viewed from the upper surface. Stem lesions are long and narrow.

The summer uredial stage has reddish orange spores in very small spots on undersurface of leaves. This stage may repeat and cause defoliation. Toward fall the telial stage is formed with black pustules of stalked dark spores, rough, with a point and 5 to 9 cells.

The leaf surface must be continuously wet for four hours for rust spores to germinate and enter, and this means liquid water, not high humidity as in mildews. High summer temperatures adversely affect infection, summer urediospores retaining viability for only a week at around 80° F.

Control. Some reports on the use of Fermate for control of rose rust are most enthusiastic; other gardeners feel that even Fermate leaves much to be desired. It is usually used in combination with sulfur, which is more effective than copper in rust control. Removing infected leaves during the season and all old leaves left at time of winter or spring pruning may help some.

Phragmidium montivagum, O, I, II, III on many species roses. Teliospores with 6 to 9 cells.

Phragmidium rosae-acicularis, O, I, II, III on several rose species. Teliospores with 5 to 11 cells, wall chocolate brown, verrucose.

Phragmidium rosae-arkansanae, O, I, II, III, on *Rosa arkansana* and *R. suffulta.* Teliospores with 5 to 8 cells.

Phragmidium rosae-californicae, O, I, II, III on many rose species. Teliospores 8 to 11 cells.

Phragmidium rosicola, III on *Rosa Engelmanni* and *R. suffulta.* Teliospores 1-celled, nearly round.

Phragmidium rubi-idaei. Leaf and Cane Rust of Raspberry, O, I, II, III. Small, light yellow spore pustules appear on young leaves and black teliospores in the same pustules later in the season. On Cuthbert variety the rust may be severe, attacking all leaves, and forming pustules on canes.

Control. There is not much that can be done, but a dormant lime-sulfur spray, 1 to 15 dilution, is helpful, along with cleaning out infected canes at winter pruning.

Phragmidium speciosum, O, I on stems and leaves, III on stems of cultivated and native roses, throughout the United States except the far South.

Phragmidium subcorticinum, O, I on stems; II, III on leaves of roses, commonly on cultivated forms of brier and sweetbrier in all states except the southeast and southwest. Teliospores have 5 to 7 cells with a prominent point, or apiculus.

PHRAGMOPYXIS

Pucciniaceae. Teliospores colored, 2 to many septate; wall 3-layered, the middle layer swelling in water; aecia, uredia and telia with a border of paraphyses.

Phragmopyxis acuminata, O, III on Coursetia.

PHYSOPELLA (Cerotelium or Phakospora)

Melampsoraceae. Only uredia and telia known; in warm climates.

Physopella fici, II, III on common fig and Florida strangler fig, also osage-orange.

Physopella vitis, II on grape.

PILEOLARIA

Pucciniaceae. Autoecious, on members of family Anacardiaceae. Teliospores stipitate, dark, with pores, 1-celled; pycnia subcuticular, uredia present.

Pileolaria patzouarensis, O, I, II, III on sumac.

PUCCINIA

Pucciniaceae. A very large genus, comprising nearly half of all known rusts; autoecious and heteroecious. Teliospores smooth, 2-celled, with apical pores, firm pedicels, colored; Aecia cluster cups with peridium rarely absent. The species given below are only a small selection of the many Puccinias on garden plants; others are listed in the Host Section.

Puccinia andropogonis, with various strains or varieties, O, I on lupine, Indian paintbrush, turtlehead; II, III on andropogon.

Puccinia antirrhini. SNAPDRAGON RUST. II, III general on snapdragon, also linaria; O, I unknown. Pustules on underside of leaves are a chocolate instead of a reddish brown and often in concentric circles. The upper surface of the

FIG. 95. Snapdragon and hollyhock rusts (*Puccinia antirrhini* and *P. malvacearum*) with yellow discoloration of upper leaf surface and spore sori on undersurface.

leaf is yellow in areas of severe infection. Pustules also appear on stems and there is a drying and stunting of the whole plant. There are several strains of this rust with resistant varieties available for the more common strains.

Control. Parzate is now recommended for snapdragon rust, and sometimes Fermate, both being preferable to bordeaux mixture which controls secondary fungi but not the rust. Sulfur dust is still useful, or a rosin lime-sulfur spray (made by adding 1 ounce of rosin soap to a gallon of water and then adding an ounce of lime sulfur, making approximately a 1 to 50 dilution). In greenhouse tests copper-naphthenate applied as an aerosol has controlled snapdragon rust. No spray or dust is very effective once rust has gotten a head start. Resistant varieties are by far the easiest means of avoiding rust.

Puccinia aristidae and varieties, II, III on wild grasses, *Aristides* and *Distichlis;* O, I on eriogonum, greasewood, spinach, western wallflower, garden cress, radish, California bluebell, heliotrope, cleome, primrose, sand-verbena and others.

Puccinia asparagi. Asparagus Rust. II, III general on susceptible varieties; O, I not reported in natural infections.

Asparagus rust reached America in 1896 from Europe and spread with devastating suddenness from Boston and New Jersey plantings to California, reaching there by 1902, one of the fastest cases of disease spread in our history. If tops are attacked several years in succession the root system is so weakened shoots fail to appear in spring or are culls.

The first symptom is a browning or reddening of smaller twigs and needles with the discolored area spreading rapidly until the whole planting looks as if it had ripened prematurely. The reddish color is due to numerous small pustules that give off a dusty spore cloud when touched. These are urediospores which appear in successive generations until autumn, or a spell of drought, when they are replaced by black teliospores either in the same or a new fruiting body. They remain on old stems until spring, germinating then by a promycelium and basidiospores, the latter infecting young shoots as they emerge from the ground.

Control. Resistant varieties have long been the answer to asparagus rust with Mary Washington, or Martha Washington, particularly free from rust and Palmetto somewhat. In the past few years rust appearing on hitherto resistant varieties indicates the fungus has been developing new and hardier strains. Dusting asparagus tops with sulfur is recommended. All volunteer or wild asparagus around the beds should be carefully cleaned up. A parasitic fungus, *Davlucca filum,* aids in control.

Puccinia cannae, II, III on edible canna, garden canna, maranta.

Puccinia caricis var. **grossulariata,** O, I on currant and flowering currant, gooseberry; II, III on *Carex* spp.

Puccinia chrysanthemi. Chrysanthemum Rust, II, general (III is known only in Japan and O, I are unknown). Small blisters of pinhead size appear on underside of leaves and occasionally on upper surface. The spore mass is dark reddish brown and powdery. This rust is more common in greenhouses than outdoors.

Control. Keep tops dry, take cuttings from healthy plants; spray with Fermate or dust with sulfur.

Puccinia coronata. Crown Rust of Oats. O, I on buckthorn and rattan vine; II, III on oats and grasses. Agriculturally this is a most destructive rust, as serious on oats as the leaf rust is on wheat. Control is by using resistant varieties.

Puccinia crandallii, O, I on snowberry, wolfberry, coralberry; II, III on grasses—*Festuca, Poa* spp.

Puccinia extensicola, in many varieties, O, I on aster, goldenrod, erigeron, senecio, lettuce, oenothera, rudbeckia, helenium; II, III on *Carex* spp.

Puccinia flaveriae, III on calendula. Control with Fermate.

Puccinia glumarum. Stripe Rust of Wheat, II, III on wheat, barley, rye, redtop, and many other grasses. Uredial stage is yellow, and pustules are formed in streaklike clusters on leaves; telial stage is in black streaks.

Puccinia graminis. Stem Rust of Grains and Grasses, O, I on barberry and mahonia, especially in north central and northeastern states; II, III on wheat and other cereals and wild and cultivated grasses.

This is the classic example of rust, the one used in school textbooks and the one known through the ages as the major limiting factor in wheat production. Proof of the connection of barberry and wheat in the life cycle was not made until 1864, but long before that farmers had noticed that wheat suffered when barberry plants were near. France in 1660, Connecticut in 1726, and Massachusetts in 1755 enacted laws requiring the destruction of barberry near grain fields.

Puccinia graminis is divided into seven different varieties, with *P. graminis tritici* on wheat, *P. graminis avenae* on oats, *P. graminis secale* on rye and the others on grasses, including redtop, velvet and creeping bent, Bermuda-grass. In addition to varieties there are many physiologic races, more than 180 being attributed to *P. graminis tritici.*

The wheat form of stem rust occurs wherever wheat is grown but is most serious in northern states. Leaf rust (caused by *Puccinia triticina*) is the most destructive form in the southern Great Plains. Stem rust is dependent on weather conditions with epidemics and disastrous losses in certain seasons. The loss depends somewhat on the maturity of the crop when rust strikes, but may be up to one-fourth of the nation's expected yield and higher for individual states.

On grain or grass rust first appears as long narrow streaks on stems, and also on leaf sheaths, leaf bases, and distal part of blade. These streaks are uredial sori, the epidermis being torn back to form a white collar around a dark red powdery mass of 1-celled urediospores. Later the same sori turn black as dark, 2-celled teliospores replace summer urediospores. Stems may be broken at this stage.

The summer spores appear about ten days after infection. This stage can be repeated, the spores reinfecting wheat and, since they are carried by the wind from one plant to another, account for the large outbreaks of disease. In

Mexico and southern Texas this II stage continues on through the winter and causes spring infection without the intervention of barberry. Waves of urediospores coming up from the South can start infection in northern states.

Normally in the North spring infection comes from basidiospores produced on a promycelium put forth by teliospores overwintered in the stem pustules. Pycnia are produced first on the barberry, in reddish lesions on the upper leaf surface, and then cup-shaped aecia filled with a yellowish waxy layer of aeciospores in cluster cup formation appear on the under surface.

Two sexes occur in this rust fungus, designated + and – rather than male or female. A young teliospore contains two nuclei, one + and the other –, but as the spore matures the two fuse into a single nucleus which divides twice in the production of the 4-celled basidium or promycelium. Each cell of the basidium produces a basidiospore and two of these are + and two –. A basidiospore falling on a barberry leaf germinates, sends in an infection thread, develops a feeding mycelium, and finally develops the flask-shaped pycnium, containing pycniospores, which are either + or – according to the sex of the basidiospore that started infection, and also hyphal threads or receptive hyphae which extend out through the mouth of the pycnium. Aided by insects, which are attracted by a sweet nectar, + pycniospores are brought into contact with receptive hyphae of a – pycnium and sexual union takes place, without which there is no further development of the rust.

The binucleate mycelium formed from the fertilized hypha grows through the cells of the barberry leaf and masses together on the underside to produce aecia. The aeciospores, unable to reinfect barberry or mahonia, are windborne to the cereal or grass host, the subsequent mycelium continuing binucleate until the fusion in the teliospore.

Control. Resistant varieties are of primary importance, but it is difficult to maintain these because the sexual process in the rust allows opportunity for the continued development of new strains. Eradication of the barberry not only eliminates the alternate host but the breeding place of new rust strains. Most barberry and mahonia varieties are now under quarantine. The following species and varieties have been designated rust-resistant by the U.S. Department of Agriculture, Bureau of Entomology and Plant Quarantine, and may be shipped interstate under permit: *Berberis beaniana, B. buxifolia, B. candidula, B. circumserrata, B. concinna, B. darwini, B. gagnepaini, B. gilgiana, B. horvathi, B. julianae, B. koreana, B. linarifolia, B. mentorensis, B. potanini, B. sanguinea, B. sargentiana, B. stenophylla, B. thunbergi* and certain horticultural varieties, *B. tricanthophora, B. verruculosa; Mahonia aquifolium, M. bealei, M. dictyota, M. nervosa, M. pinnata, M. repens.*

Sulfur dust, applied by airplane, pays for itself in increased yields in years of heavy rust infestation.

Puccinia helianthi. Sunflower Rust, O, I, II, III general on sunflower, Jerusalem artichoke, and heliopsis. Numerous brownish pustules, in which repeating spores are formed, develop on underside of leaves which may dry and drop.

Puccinia heterospora, III on abutilon, hollyhock, mallow, malvaviscus.

Puccinia heucherae, III on coral-bells, woodland star, saxifrage, bishops-cap, foam-flower.

Puccinia hieracii, O, I, II, III widespread on endive and hawksbeard. Endive leaves are spotted and blighted with the dusty spores and crop is occasionally lost, but no control seems practical in California.

Puccinia malvacearum. HOLLYHOCK RUST, III general on hollyhock, also on mallow, lavatera. This rust is so common and destructive it limits the use of hollyhocks as ornamentals. Stems, leaves, bracts may be attacked with yellow lesions on the upper surface and orange to reddish spore pustules on under surface of leaves and elongated lesions on stems. The spore pustule is sometimes grayish from the production of basidiospores, but no alternate host is known. The fungus winters in pustules in leaves and stems. In severe infections leaves dry and hang down along the stem.

Control. Cleaning up all infected plant parts in fall and again *very* early in spring is most important for infection starts early in the season and once it is under way it is very difficult to stop with a dust or spray. Copper sprays don't help much in control, the use of Fermate is debatable, and sulfur dust does a fair job if started early. Keep infected parts picked off.

Puccinia menthae. MINT RUST, O, I, II, III on mint, also on dittany, horse-mint, mountain-mint, bee-balm, yerba buena, germander. Mint rust is sometimes serious for mint farmers in the Middle West, especially on spearmint. In spring and early summer the disease appears as light yellow to brown raised spots on deformed stems and leaf stalks and sometimes on main veins; golden to dark chocolate brown spots appear in late summer and fall. Leaves dry and oil yield is reduced.

Control. Dust with sulfur and cut early.

Puccinia peridermiospora. ASH RUST, O, I general on ash, east of the Great Plains, also on forestiera; II, III on marsh and cord grasses (*Spartina* spp.). Ash twigs and petioles are swollen and leaves distorted. Cluster cups, aecia, filled with yellow powdery aeciospores are formed on the swellings. In rainy seasons rather serious damage is reported in Massachusetts.

Puccinia phragmitis, O, I on rhubarb; II, III on *Phragmites communis*. The rust with rusty red spore pustules is sometimes seen in California rhubarb plantings but is not serious.

Puccinia poa-sudeticae, II, III on Canada and Kentucky blue-grass; O, I unknown; general east of the Rocky Mountains. The uredia are orange yellow with numerous peripheral paraphyses. Telia are covered rather permanently with epidermis; spores are dark brown with short pedicels.

Puccinia porri, II, III on onion, garlic, shallot. Small red or black pustules may injure garlic leaves, but rust is not serious on onion.

Puccinia rubigo-vera var. **agropyri,** O, I on clematis, aconite, anemone, aquilegia, delphinium; II, III on native grasses.

Puccinia sorghi. CORN RUST, O, I on oxalis; II, III on corn, sweetcorn, general in northeastern and north central states, but not usually serious enough for control measures.

Puccinia triticina. LEAF RUST OF WHEAT, II, III (there is no O, I in nature). This rust is world wide and more serious than stem rust in the southern half of the American wheat belt. It is sometimes epiphytotic with losses up to 30 per cent. The leaf tissue is progressively destroyed through the season, resulting in a reduced number of kernels, shriveled grain, low weight and protein content. The rust pustules breaking through the epidermis greatly increase loss from transpiration. There are many physiological races, each restricted to certain wheat varieties. Orange uredial pustules are followed later by gray telial sori formed under the epidermis. But the urediospores are the effective spore form and can survive winters in the South.

Control by resistant varieties and perhaps sulfur dusting. There is a possibility of the fungus *Darluca filum* helping to keep down infection.

PUCCINIASTRUM

Melampsoraceae. Heteroecious with pycnia and aecia on conifers—firs and spruces; pycnia are subcuticular, other sori are subepidermal, or telia may be intraepidermal; aecia and urediospores are yellow.

Pucciniastrum americanum. LATE LEAF RUST OF RASPBERRY. O, I on white spruce; II, III on raspberry.

Pucciniastrum geoppertianum. FIR-HUCKLEBERRY RUST. O, I on firs; II, III on low and high bush blueberry.

Pucciniastrum hydrangeae, O, I on eastern and Carolina hemlock; II, III on *Hydrangea arborescens* and *H. paniculata.*

Pucciniastrum myrtilli. HEMLOCK RUST. O, I on eastern hemlock; II, III on azalea, rhododendron, lyonia, menziesia, blueberry, cranberry. This is the most common hemlock rust but often only a single leaf or twig is infected. Aecia are formed on current-year needles.

RAVENELIA

Puccinaceae. Autoecious, tropical with only a few species in the United States. Teliospores more or less muriform, many-celled with compound stalks.

TRANZSCHELIA

Pucciniaceae. Teliospores 2-celled, stalked; uredia with pseudo-paraphyses; on Ranunculaceae and *Prunus* spp.

Tranzschelia pruni-spinosae. RUST OF STONE FRUITS. O, I on anemone, hepatica, thalictrum, buttercup; II, III widespread, especially in South and on Pacific Coast, on almond, apricot, cherry, plum, peach, choke-cherry.

Yellow angular spots appear on fruit leaves with powdery spore pustules on underside—reddish on peach, dark brown on almonds. Peach fruit may have round, sunken green spots and oval blisters on twigs in early spring. The disease may cause defoliation especially late in the season. Spring infection in some cases can take place without the alternate host. Urediospores have been found overwintering on old green leaves on sucker shoots in almond orchards and infecting young leaves in spring. Drake variety is most heavily infected, with later varieties escaping.

Control. Spray with lime sulfur at a dilution of 6 to 100 in early fall—October 15 to November 1 in California—or in spring at a 1 to 100 dilution.

TRIPHRAGMIUM

Puccinaceae. Teliospores stalked, with 3 cells forming a triangle, each with a single pore.

Triphragmium ulmariae, O, I, II, III on meadowsweet.

UREDINOPSIS

Melampsoraceae. Telia on ferns, teliospores scattered irregularly in mesophyll, rarely in subepidermal crust and typically several-celled; aecia white.

Uredinopsis macrosperma. Fir-Fern Rust. O, I on various firs; II, III on *Pteridium aquilinum.* Aecia are on 1- to 5-year needles of Pacific silver, white, lowland white, alpine, and noble firs.

Uredinopsis osmundae. Fir-Fern Rust. O, I on balsam fir, widespread; II, III on *Osmunda* spp.

Uredinopsis phegopteridis. Fir-Fern Rust. O, I on balsam fir; II, III on *Phegopteris dryopteris.*

Uredinopsis struthiopteridis. Fir-Fern Rust. O, I on balsam, lowland white, alpine, noble firs; II, III on ostrich fern.

UREDO

Form genus; uredia with or without peridia.

Uredo coccolobae; U. uviferae, on sea grape, Florida.

UROMYCES

Pucciniaceae. Like Puccinia but teliospores with 1 cell, yellow to dark; aecia when present with persistent peridium.

Uromyces betae. Beet Rust, O, I not reported in United States; II, III on beets, swiss chard. Reddish brown powdery pustules are occasionally numerous in late summer or wet seasons. Beets are stunted, swiss chard leaves are unfit for use. Control is seldom attempted, but a dust of 12% Fermate, 48% sulfur, promises well in the West.

Uromyces caryophyllinus. CARNATION RUST, O, I on euphorbia, but not in United States; II, III general on carnation, sweet william, and *Dianthus* spp. This is a serious disease under glass. Chocolate brown pustules varying from 1/16 to 1/4 inch break out on both sides of leaves and on buds and stems. Infected plants are stunted and leaves curl up.

Control. Use surface watering where possible, avoiding syringing; keep greenhouses properly ventilated; use rust-free cuttings; spray with Fermate or dust with sulfur.

Uromyces fabae. PEA RUST, O, I, II, III on pea, peavine, also occasional on broad bean, not very serious.

Uromyces phaseoli var. **typica.** BEAN RUST, O, I, rare on bean; II, III general on kidney bean, widespread but infrequent on lima bean, scarlet runner bean. This is the true bean rust, an old disease reported as far back as 1797, and quite distinct from anthracnose, sometimes called rust. The disease is particularly serious on Kentucky Wonder pole beans.

Rust pustules are formed on leaves, stems and pods, but most frequently on foliage. The reddish brown sori are most numerous on under surface of leaves, with upper surface yellowing, but the pustules are frequently on the upper surface as well. With severe infection nearly all of leaves may drop. In late summer dark telia replace the summer spore stage in the North but in the South the summer urediospores can survive the winter and start early spring infection.

FIG. 96. Bean Rust, *Uromyces phaseoli.*

Rust spores are spread by wind and on tools and clothing. Some cling to the poles and can start a fresh outbreak of rust if poles are not disinfested before using again. There is more than one race of bean rust.

Control. Some varieties are rather resistant—Wisconsin Refugee, Alabama No. 1, special selections of Kentucky Wonder, Florida Belle, Pintos 5 and 14 for dryland West. Sulfur dusting usually gives fair control of bean rust.

SCAB

Diseases characterized by some overgrowth of tissue in a limited area are commonly called scab. The hyperplastic scablike lesions correspond to the necrotic or dead areas of leaf spots or cankers. Various causative organisms are included here, among them Actinomyces, cause of potato scab, which perhaps might more properly be classified under bacterial diseases and Sphaceloma, or its perfect stage Elsinoë, causing citrus, violet, and other scabs but with other species causing spot anthracnoses and included under Anthracnose. Apple scab (due to *Venturia inaequalis*) is of course the most important and best known disease in this category.

ACTINOMYCES (Now Streptomyces)

Actinomycetales, Streptomycetaceae. Intermediate between bacteria and fungi, sometimes considered a ray fungus but often classified under bacteria. A filamentous much-branched mycelium produces conidiospores in chains. All species are soil organisms, and many do a great amount of good in breaking down humus or organic material and releasing the nitrogen. This genus is source of the new drug, Streptomycin.

Actinomyces (Streptomyces) **scabies.** Common Scab of Potatoes, Beet Scab, corky scab, actinomycosis, general on potatoes, widespread on beets, also reported on carrot, parsnip, radish, rutabaga, turnip.

This disease may have been in America as long as potatoes have been grown, but the causal organism was not described until 1890. Scabby potatoes, by lowering the market grade, mean an annual loss of several million dollars. Chief symptoms are the tuber lesions, starting as minute brown specks and progressing to scabs which are warty, or on the surface with corky ridges, or pitted or depressed, with the skin cracking open. Such potatoes can be eaten but have poor customer appeal and are wasteful because of the deep peeling required.

On beets the scabs are similar but more bulging.

The Actinomyces can be found even in virgin soil. It invades young tubers and can sometimes be seen as a grayish coating on freshly dug potatoes. It is most destructive in soils with pH around 5.7, with its activity sharply limited in soils slightly more acid. Although the optimum temperature is 72° to 86° F. it can withstand great extremes of temperature and moisture and can pass through the digestive tract of animals, returning to the field in manure.

Control. Use disease-free tubers for seed if possible; if not, treat 2 hours in formaldehyde (1 pint formalin to 30 gallons of water, or approximately 1 tablespoon to a gallon). Adding sulfur to the soil, from 300 to 2000 pounds per acre, is fairly successful if the soil is somewhat acid to start with. Avoid lime, wood ashes, and manure, all of which give an alkaline reaction. If scab has been present, use a three- or four-year rotation with nonsusceptible crops. Potato varieties Russet Rural, Sebago, Menominee, and Katahdin are moderately scab resistant.

CLADOSPORIUM (See under Blotch Diseases)

Cladosporium carpophilum. PEACH SCAB, freckles, black spot, general on peach, widespread on almond, apricot, cherry, nectarine, plum. Small round olive-black spots appear on infected fruits about six weeks after petals have fallen. These are usually on upper side of fruit and cracking may follow. Twigs show nearly circular yellow brown blotches with gray or bluish borders, cambium may be killed and twigs die. Leaf spots are brown, scattered, with tissue drying and falling out, leaving circular holes.

Control. Use the spray schedule recommended for brown rot in your state, which may be bordeaux mixture in California and wettable sulfur in New York.

Cladosporium cucumerinum. CUCUMBER SCAB, general on cucumber, especially in greenhouses, occasional on muskmelon and winter squash in eastern and central states; first noted in New York in 1887. Leaves may have water-soaked spots and wilt, and stems have slight cankers but most injury is to the fruit. First symptoms, while cucumbers are still small, are gray, slightly sunken spots, sometimes exuding a gummy substance. They darken with age and the collapsed tissue forms a pronounced cavity, lined with a dark-green velvety layer of greenish mycelium, short conidiophores, and dark, 1-celled spores. On leaves, these fruiting fascicles are protruded through stomata. This is a warm weather fungus, with optimum growth at 77° F.

Control. Use a long rotation; treat seed for 5 minutes in mercuric chloride, 1 to 1000 dilution; dust vines with fixed copper, or zerlate combined with rotenone and talc as a diluent (10–15–75).

Cladosporium effusum. PECAN SCAB, leaf spot, general on pecan, hickory. Scab is one of the most important limiting factors in pecan production in the Southeast. All varieties are somewhat susceptible, even those which have been rather resistant in the past, and crop losses may reach 75 to 95 per cent.

The fungus attacks rapidly growing tissues in leaves, shoots, and nuts; mature growth seems immune. On Schley and other highly susceptible varieties primary infection shows in elongated olive brown lesions on veins of underside of leaves. With secondary infection leaves appear almost black, due to coalescing of spots. Defoliation follows. On more resistant varieties, such as Moore and Stuart, infection is delayed until leaves are nearly mature and almost immune, so scab spots are usually confined to nuts.

Spots on nuts are small, black, circular, slightly raised at first, then sunken. On susceptible varieties spots are so close together the whole nut surface turns black. Such nuts drop prematurely or stop growing and remain attached to shoots indefinitely.

Infection is correlated with spring and early summer rainfall, continuous moisture for 6 to 8 hours being required, with first lesions appearing in one or two weeks.

Control. Knock off all old shucks and leaf stems before trees leaf out in spring. If trees are wet after a rain a slight jarring of branches will make diseased material drop. Plow this under deeply or clean up and burn.

Spray with low-lime bordeaux mixture (4–1–100): (1) when leaves are a quarter to half grown and before pollination (April 10 to 20 in Florida); (2) 6–2–100 bordeaux after pollination (when tips of small nuts have turned brown); (3) 6–2–100 bordeaux 3 or 4 weeks after 2; (4) repeat in another 3 or 4 weeks. On varieties Moore and Moneymaker the last two sprays may be sufficient.

Cladosporium pisicola. Scab, black spot of peas. Dark spots, covered with velvety mold, are formed in moist weather on leaves, stems, pods.

ELSINOË (See under Anthracnose)

Elsinoë fawcettii. Sour Orange Scab, Citrus Scab, lemon verrucosis, on citrus fruits, except sweet orange. Lemons, sour orange, King orange, bitter orange, and calamondin are very susceptible; Mandarin and Satsuma oranges, tangerines, and all grapefruit except Royal and Triumph are moderately susceptible. Citrus scab is erratic in its outbreaks, with tender growth most readily infected. Grapefruit and lemons in Rio Grande Valley are less susceptible than in Florida, but Satsumas are more seriously infected in Alabama than in Florida, these differences doubtless being due to climatic conditions when hosts are in a susceptible stage.

An old and important disease, citrus scab has been known in the Orient since ancient times and is believed to have come here with Satsuma orange trees from Japan. It was first noted in Florida in 1885, but the fungus was not classified until 1925, in the form genus Sphaceloma, and transferred to Elsinoë when the connection with the perfect stage was made in Brazil in 1935, even though the Elsinoë stage is not yet known in the United States.

On leaves, minute, semitranslucent spots change to raised excrescences with corky crests, pale yellow to pinkish, then dull olive drab, with a conical depression opposite the crest. Foliage may be distorted, wrinkled, stunted. Fruits have slightly raised scabs or warts with corky crests and are often distorted. Scabs may grow together to form large, irregular patches and on grapefruit they may flake off as the fruit matures with the skin remaining green around such areas.

Spores are spread by wind, rain, dew-drip, and possibly by insects, to infect

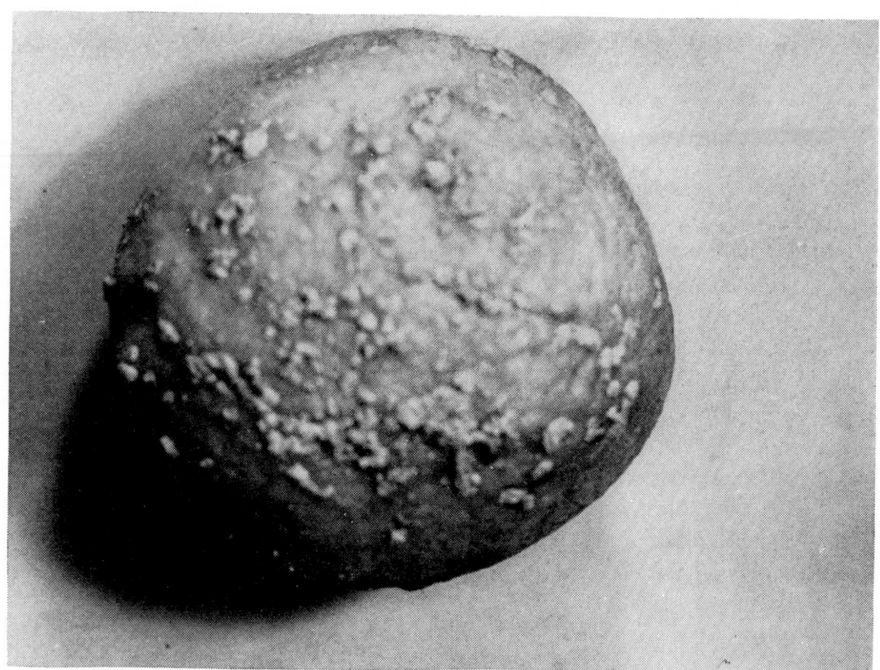

FIG. 97. Sour Orange Scab.

young tender tissue. Young grapefruit, very susceptible right after petal fall, become progressively resistant and are practically immune when fruit reaches ¾ inch in diameter. Leaves become resistant when they are ½ inch across. Temperature range for severe infection is between 59° and 73° F. Excessive nitrogenous fertilization favors the development of scab. The fungus winters on infected leaves, or sometimes fruits.

Control. Spray just before spring growth starts with 6–6–100 bordeaux mixture, if overwintered foliage is heavily infected, or with 3–3–100 for mild infection. In Florida this is usually between January 1 and February 10, and the spray can be combined with an oil emulsion for scale control. Make a second application of 3–3–100 bordeaux when at least two-thirds of the bloom has fallen, or delay the spray two or three weeks to control melanose in the same operation. Other sprays containing equivalent amounts of copper may be substituted for bordeaux mixture.

Remove sour orange and rough lemon trees or topwork them over to commercial varieties.

Elsinoë solidaginis. GOLDENROD SCAB. New growth is affected as it develops with lesions on midrib, veins, petioles, leaf blades, raised on one leaf surface, sunken on the other, with a white to gray center and brown border. The perfect stage of the fungus is formed in these spots.

FUSICLADIUM

Fungi Imperfecti, Moniliales, Dematiaceae

Conidiophores simple or sparsely branched, but with conidia borne only at the tips; spores dark, usually 1-celled.

Fusicladium dendriticum, conidial stage of the apple scab fungus. See *Venturia inaequalis.*

Fusicladium eriobotryae. LOQUAT SCAB, widespread on leaves, stems, fruits of loquat. This is similar to pear and apple scab. Dark velvety spots cause more or less deformation of fruit but the disease is seldom important enough to warrant control measures.

Fusicladium photinicola. CHRISTMASBERRY SCAB, on *Photinia arbutifolia.* Brown velvety spots appear on leaves, flower stalks and green berries, the latter being disfigured when mature.

Control. Prune in winter to remove dead wood and foliage; spray before blossoming with bordeaux mixture.

Fusicladium pyracanthae. PYRACANTHA SCAB, widespread on leaves and fruit. The unsightly black scabs spoil the appearance of bright berries. Control as for Christmasberry scab.

Fusicladium dendriticum. WILLOW SCAB, blight on willow in New England and New York. The perfect stage of the fungus is *Venturia chlorospora* but it is known only in culture in the United States. This is a relatively new disease, first noticed in Connecticut in 1927 and apparently introduced from Europe. It has killed thousands of trees in the Northeast from repeated defoliation.

Young leaves are attacked and often killed in spring, almost within a few hours, and from the leaf blades the fungus enters twigs, kills back young shoots and causes cankers. Olive-green, felty spore masses are formed on the long veins on underside of leaves. Overwintering is as dormant mycelium in twigs infected the previous spring. Defoliation for two or three successive years is fatal.

Another fungus, *Physalospora miyabeana,* is found with the scab fungus, and the two together cause the disease complex known as willow blight (see under Blights). Physalospora usually attacks later in the season than Fusicladium and causes cankers on larger stems.

Control. Remove and destroy dead twigs and branches in the dormant season. Spray with bordeaux mixture just before buds break, when buds are unfolding, when leaves are half grown, when leaves are fully grown, with possibly a fifth spray required 10 days later. Dry lime sulfur, at 3 pounds to 50 gallons of water, can be substituted.

SPHACELOMA (See under Anthracnose)

Sphaceloma hederae. ENGLISH IVY SCAB. Spots on leaves are often numerous, conspicuous, raised, with red brown margins and pale depressed centers.

Conidia are hyaline to colored, continuous to septate, more prominent on underside of leaf.

Sphaceloma mangiferae. MANGO SCAB. Spots most often originate on underside of young mango leaves but become visible above. They are circular to angular, dark brown to black with centers olive buff from conidiophores of the fungus. On mature leaves spots are larger, lightly raised with narrow brown margins and dirty white centers. Stems have irregular grayish blotches and the fruit gray to brown spots with dark margins.

Sphaceloma murrayae. GRAY SCAB OF WILLOW, present in California in 1904 but not properly named until 1943. Spots are only on leaves; they are round, irregular, somewhat raised, grayish white with narrow, dark-brown margins, running together in large patches and leaf portions dropping away. Long narrow patches are also formed along the midrib.

Sphaceloma perseae. AVOCADO SCAB, one of the most important diseases of avocado in Florida, sometimes with nearly 100 per cent infection, also found in Texas. The lesions are mostly initiated on the upper leaf surfaces as very small red spots with a dark olive conidial growth over the scabbed area. Fruit lesions are brown to almost black, up to 1/8 inch in diameter. Highly susceptible varieties are Florida Fuerte, Lulu, Mexican-Guatemalan hybrids, Trapp, and Taylor.

Sphaceloma sp. CAMELLIA SCAB, of several types: (1) brownish discoloration, irregular black spots; (2) circular to irregular, white, slightly raised spots; (3) raised brown to blackened spots on upper surface; (4) large brown spots with grayish centers; (5) water-soaked pustules erupting to corky excrescences on under surface; (6) small, white to gray spots on upper surface.

Sphaceloma violae. VIOLET SCAB, widespread on violet from Connecticut to Mississippi, also on pansy. The disease is serious enough to be nearly a limiting factor in maintaining violet collections. Reddish spots with white centers change to irregular to elongated, raised scabs on leaves and stems, often with much distortion.

Control. Remove and burn old leaves. Spray new growth with bordeaux mixture.

SPONGOSPORA

Phycomycetes, Chytridiales, Plasmodiophoraceae

Spores are united into sponge-like spore balls, essentially solid and lacking a central cavity, but traversed by prominent fissures.

Spongospora subterranea. POWDERY SCAB OF POTATOES, canker, spongy scab, occasional on potato. Indigenous to South America and introduced to Europe more than a century ago, potato scab was not noticed in North America before 1913. Ordinarily not important, it causes economic loss in some seasons.

Slightly raised pimples appear on tubers when they are less than an inch

FIG. 98. Violet Scab, or spot anthracnose.

in diameter. They are varying shades of brown on the surface, faintly purple underneath. The epidermis, not growing as fast as the pimple, breaks and curls back over the pustule which, by this time, is a brown powdery mass of spore balls and decomposed parts of plant tissue. The lesions are often "corked off," but under favorable conditions large, depressed cankers may form.

The fungus winters on stored tubers or in soil, remaining viable for many years. In the presence of a potato tuber and enough moisture, each spore in the ball germinates by swarmspores which stay grouped together in a plasmodium, dissolving the cuticle and killing the cells. When the food supply diminishes the plasmodium again breaks up into spore balls.

Control. Avoid low, soggy ground; if such soil must be used acidify it with sulfur as for common scab.

VENTURIA

Ascomycetes, Sphaeriales, Mycosphaerellaceae

Perithecia setose, often about apex only, papillate, paraphyses absent; spores 2-celled, of unequal size, olive.

Venturia inaequalis (*Fusicladium dendriticum*). APPLE SCAB, scurf, black spot, general on apples except in far South, widespread on most crabapples, also on mountain-ash and hawthorn. Scab is the world's top ranking apple disease and is probably coextensive with the host. In the United States in a favorable year it may take a fourth or more of the crop. The average national loss runs around 8 per cent, or over 10 million bushels of apples yearly. Scab

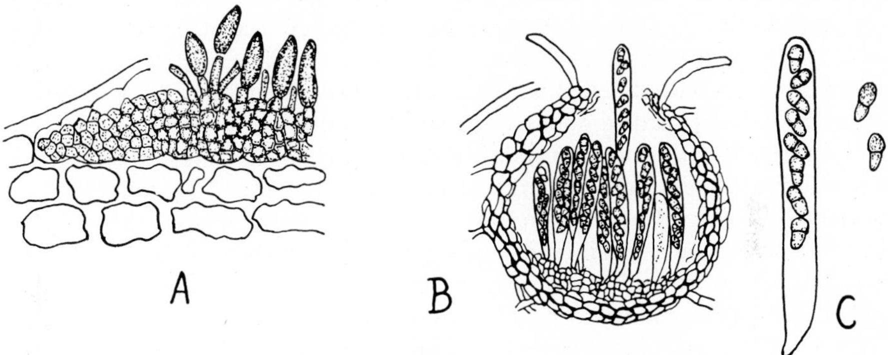

FIG. 99. *Venturia inæqualis* the apple-scab fungus. A, 1-celled dark conidia of Fusicladium stage; B, perithecium with 2-celled ascospores.

is somewhat less important in the South, and is not too much of a problem in irrigated sections of Washington, but important in the humid coastal areas. The pathogen was first described and named by Fries in Sweden in 1819, and was known in New York and New Jersey in 1834, apparently having come here with some European imports.

Symptoms. The first symptom of scab on leaves is a dull, smoky area which changes to an olive drab, moldy spot, ¼ inch or more in diameter without a sharp outline. Sometimes the leaf is slightly raised or domed in the vicinity of the spot; sometimes it turns brown and drops prematurely. Similar spots may be formed on blossom pedicel, calyx, and petals, followed by dropping of young fruit. Scabby lesions sometimes appear on twigs but are less common.

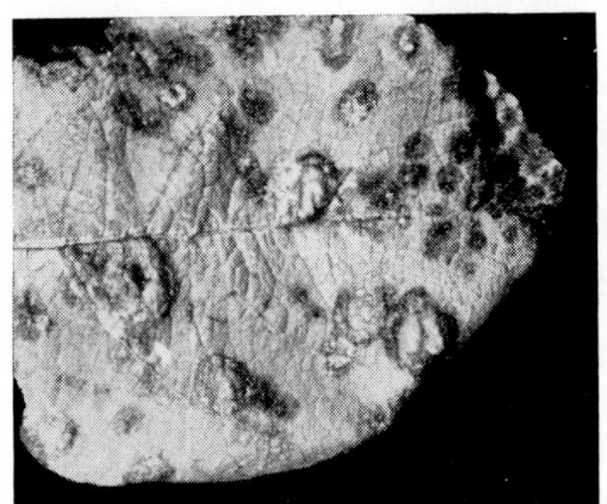

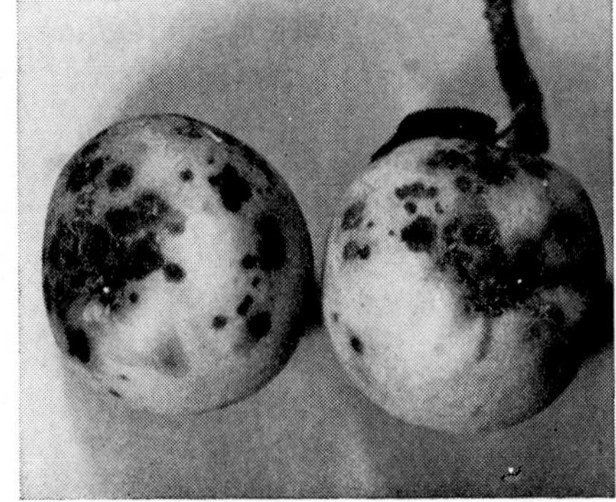

FIG. 100. Apple Scab on Leaf and fruit.

On fruits, spots are small, more or less raised, rounded dark olive areas. As they increase in size the cuticle ruptures to form a white rim around a dark, velvety center, and still later the center may be raised, corky and tan in color, after dark mycelium and spores have disappeared. Lesions are usually most abundant near calyx end of fruit; if they are too numerous the fruit splits.

Life History. The fungus winters in dead fallen leaves, producing there small, dark, flask-shaped perithecia and, toward spring, asci with 8 brown ascospores, unequally 2-celled with the upper cell wider than the lower.

The ascospores mature about the time apple blossoms show pink and are forcibly expelled during warm spring rains. Each ascus elongates, protrudes its tip through the ostiole (mouth) of the perithecium, and explodes its spore content to be carried by wind to blossom, bud, or young leaf overhead. When the spore arrives on a leaf it sends out a germ tube which penetrates the cuticle and develops a layer of branching mycelium just under it. The scab spot is evident in about ten days when brown conidiophores, bearing olive brown, 1-celled, somewhat pointed spores, appear on the surface. Secondary infection occurs when these conidia are carried by rain to new infection courts.

The expulsion of ascospores proceeds in a series of discharges over a rather long period, up to three months, starting in February, on the West Coast, a shorter period in New York, usually beginning in April. Germination and infection take place at 41° to 79° F., with the length of wetting period necessary for infection decreasing as the temperature rises. Ascospore discharge is optimum at a temperature of 50° to 54° F. Secondary infection from conidia continues all season in rainy periods, and even in storage, for scab may show up on apples infected just before picking.

Control. No varieties are immune to scab, and resistance varies with the season and the part of the country. McIntosh apples are particularly susceptible and Baldwins are considered rather resistant but may scab badly in some years. Application of nitrogen increases yield but also susceptibility to scab.

Protective spraying—having a protective chemical layer on blossom, fruit, and foliage at all times when weather makes infection probable—is the only real answer to apple scab. This may mean a dozen or more applications in a wet year and a minimum of five in any season, a program more suited to the commercial grower than the amateur. Timing is all-important and most states have a spray warning service which tells of imminent discharge of ascospores and correlates the spray schedule with the season.

Any spray schedule must be tailored for the locality and the year; the apple grower gets this specific help from his county agent and state experiment station. A typical program calls for Elgetol or other dinitro compound added to the dormant oil spray, or a delayed dormant spray of 1 to 50 lime sulfur, a prepink spray of wettable sulfur or lime sulfur, then Fermate plus wettable sulfur for pink, blossom and calyx sprays and Fermate, or perhaps bordeaux mixture, for three or four cover sprays.

Bordeaux mixture is apt to russet leaves in the early part of the season, and lime sulfur burns in hot weather. Many new materials have been developed and are being tested against apple scab. Fermate has proved its worth, and so has Puratized Agricultural Spray; but the mercury residue from the latter makes it possible only for early eradicant sprays. Phygon controls scab but is sometimes injurious to fruit and foliage. Tag Fruit Fungicide is also helpful as a primary scab spray.

Spraying the ground with an eradicant is another way of fighting scab by preventing discharge of ascospores. Elgetol at the rate of 2 quarts to 100 gallons water can be used to cover the orchard floor very thoroughly, but a few untreated leaves provide plenty of inoculum, for there can be 2 billion spores formed in the leaves under one tree.

Venturia pyrina (*Fusicladium pyrinum*). PEAR SCAB, general on pear, also on quince. This is similar to apple scab and the two species of Venturia are closely related but the pear scab fungus cannot infect apple and vice versa. The pear species overwinters not only in fallen leaves but in affected twigs and the perithecia mature somewhat later than those of apples. Conidia are formed on pear twigs and are washed to leaves and fruit.

Generally speaking, pear scab is not serious except on such varieties as Flemish Beauty, Winter Nelis, and Easter Beurre. In most commercial orchards the schedule followed for pear psylla is sufficient control, with a fungicide at the cluster-bud stage. Fermate and Zerlate may be effective.

SCURF

Two diseases, one of sweet potatoes and one of potatoes, are commonly called scurf.

MONILOCHAETES

Fungi Imperfecti, Moniliales, Dematiaceae

Hyphae dark, spores hyaline, 1-celled, oblong-cylindric, in chains; conidiophores black.

Monilochaetes infuscans. SWEET POTATO SCURF. Small, circular brown or black spots are formed on all underground parts, often forming a uniform patch over the whole potato, or a black patch on red-skinned varieties. The skin cracks and potatoes shrink in storage. The black conidiophores stick up from the surface of the lesions like bristles. The fungus winters on tubers and on decaying vines.

Control. Set only healthy sprouts, grown from potatoes bedded in sand that has not grown sweet potatoes before. Treat sprouts with Fermate or Tersan before planting.

SPONDYLOCLADIUM

Fungi Imperfecti, Moniliales, Dematiaceae

Conidia dark, with several cells, borne in whorls, at sides and tip of conidiophores.

Spondylocladium atrovirens. SILVER SCURF OF POTATO, scab, dry rot, present in almost all potato districts but not too important. Light brown lesions become somewhat blistered, giving the skin a marked silvery appearance. The disease is only skin deep and control measures are seldom used.

SMUTS

Smuts are named for their sooty black spore masses. They belong, like the rusts, to the Basidiomycetes, but their life-history is much less complicated. Vegetative cells of the mycelium round up into thin-walled chlamydospores which germinate with a promycelium and four or more basidiospores at the sides or tip. Smuts in nature are obligate parasites, most of them on grains and grasses, but some on vegetables and ornamentals. Some cause systemic infection, others local infection at each point where a smut spore lands.

Smuts are in the order Ustilaginales in three families, the Ustilaginaceae with basidiospores formed at the side of a 4-celled promycelium, the Tilletiaceae with basidiospores formed at the end of a 1- or 2-celled promycelium, and the Graphiolaceae, false smuts.

BURRILLIA

Tilletiaceae. Spores united into spore balls without a sterile surface layer; on hydrophytes.

Burrillia decipiens. LEAF SMUT of floating heart (Nymphoides).

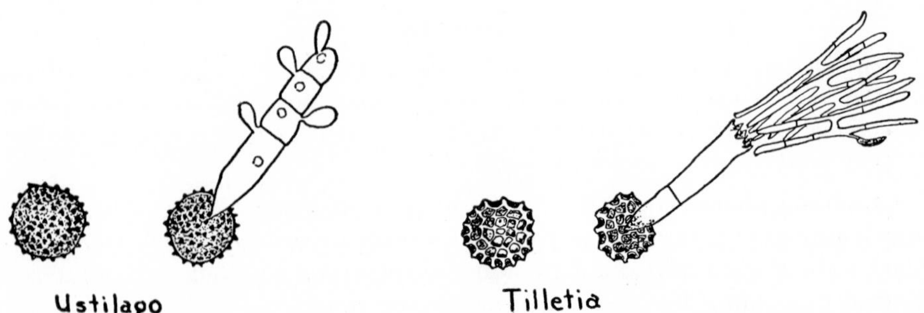

FIG. 101. Smut Spores. *Ustilago,* spiny chlamydospore germinating with promycelium and sporidia formed at sides; *Tilletia,* reticulate chlamydospore with long H-shaped sporidia formed at end of promycelium and sometimes forming small secondary sporidia.

DOASSANSIA

Tilletiaceae. Spores united into groups or balls with a surface layer of sterile cells around a central fertile group.

Doassansia epilobii. Leaf Smut on epilobium.

ENTYLOMA

Tilletiacene. Sori generally in leaves, forming spots that are light in color, giving the name white smut. The true smut spores are colorless to yellow to brown, permanently embedded in host tissue but aerial spores are formed on the surface, giving a white powdery appearance.

Entyloma calendulae. Calendula White Smut. Spots are pale yellow, turning dark brown to black, ¼ inch in diameter. The smut is common but not very serious in commercial plantings around San Francisco. Plant debris should be cleaned up, perhaps the location changed.

Entyloma compositarum. White Smut of boltonia, calendula, erigeron, eupatorium, gnaphalium, golden-glow, helenium, prairie coneflower.

Entyloma dahliae. Leaf Smut of dahlia, a European disease occasionally reported here. It showed up in one location in California where overhead watering was used, but disappeared when the practice was discontinued. Leaves are marked by more or less circular spots, first yellow-green, then brownish and dry. Primary spores germinate in leaves and send projections to the outside where secondary spores are formed to spread the disease. Late planting seems to increase disease incidence.

Entyloma crastophilum. Dark Leaf Smut on redtop, Canada blue-grass, Kentucky blue-grass. Sori in leaves and less frequently in floral bracts are tar-like angular to oblong blisters.

Entyloma polysporum. Leaf Smut of gaillardia, golden-glow, senecio, silphium, sunflower.

GRAPHIOLA

Graphiolaceae. This genus and family is sometimes included in smuts and sometimes not. The sori are erumpent, enclosed in a compact black peridium, on leaves of palms. Sporogenous hyphae are separated by hyphal bundles falling apart after production of spore initials; spores are globose to oblong.

Graphiola phoenicis. False Smut, leaf spot on queen, canary date, Royal and Washington palms and on palmetto. Leaves are yellow-spotted, with small black scabs or warts having a dark, horny outer surface and long flexuous sterile hyphae protruding from an inner membrane containing powdery yellow or light brown spore masses. Badly infected leaves may die.

Control. Cut and burn infected leaves or parts; spray with bordeaux mixture; avoid syringing as much as possible.

MYCOSYRINX

Ustilaginaceae. Spores united in pairs; sori with a double peridium; promycelium septate into 4 cells transversely.

Mycosyrinx osmundae. INFLORESCENCE SMUT, on Osmunda fern.

SOROSPORIUM

Ustilaginaceae. Spores loosely united into balls, but readily separable by pressure.

Sorosporium saponariae. FLOWER SMUT of silene, campion.

THECAPHORA

Ustilaginaceae. Spores firmly united into balls, fertile throughout; promycelium simple, or two-forked, with single apical little spore.

Thecaphora deformans. SEED SMUT of lupine.

TILLETIA

Tilletiaceae. Spores massed in superficial or erumpent sori; promycelium simple with apical whorls of not more than 12 spores.

Tilletia foetida and **T. caries.** BUNT, COVERED SMUT, STINKING SMUT of wheat, one of the major agricultural diseases, especially in the Pacific Northwest, and of historical importance as the first disease controlled by seed disinfection. In 1670 a ship was wrecked off the coast of England and the cargo of wheat salvaged after its salt-water bath was found to produce a bunt-free crop. Liquid seed treatments were used for many years, but now dusts—copper carbonate, New Improved Ceresan, Arasan or Spergon—are standard for farmers, and for seed dealers who treat seed in special machinery at a cost of only a few cents an acre. Bunt fills the wheat heads with black spores before harvest.

Tilletia pallida. HEAD SMUT of velvet and creeping bent-grass.

TUBURCINIA

Tilletiaceae. Spore balls with very inconspicuous sterile spores on surface.

Tuburcinia trientalus. LEAF AND STEM SMUT of starflower.

UROCYSTIS

Tilletiaceae. Spore balls with distinct sterile spores on surface and only a few fertile spores; sori without peridium.

Urocystis agropyri. FLAG SMUT of wheat, redtop and Kentucky blue-grass.

Urocystis anemones. LEAF AND STEM SMUT on anemone, hepatica, and trautveteria. Dark brown powdery pustules are formed in swollen regions of leaf stalks and leaf blades; the epidermis is broken and spore balls are scattered; the smut winters in rootstalks. There is little control except sanitation.

Urocystis carcinodes. SMUT on aconite, baneberry, clematis, and cimicifuga.

Urocystis cepulae. ONION SMUT, general on onion, also on shallot, garlic, chives. This is the most destructive onion disease, found in the Connecticut Valley as early as 1861, and thence spread to all northern onion-growing sections, but chiefly important where onions are grown from seed rather than sets as in most home gardens.

Black, elongated blisters or pustules of spores break out on scales or leaves of young plants. Many plants die, others survive and have black or brown smut pustules on the cured bulbs. Plants are stunted but not rotted, although smut may be followed by secondary rot organisms.

The spores can live in soil for years, but infection is possible only in the young plant, from the second day after seed germination until the seedling is in first leaf, a period of 10 to 15 days. The spore is able to penetrate the onion between root and cotyledon but cannot enter a true leaf, although after entrance it spreads through the seedling until it reaches the leaves to form fruiting pustules just below the epidermis. When this ruptures, spores are dropped to be disseminated by running water, tools, on feet of men and animals, and on roots of transplanted vegetables. Onion smut is confined to states with cool summers, optimum soil temperature for infection being 72° F.

Control. In home gardens start onions from sets or grow seedlings in clean soil and transplant. Farmers apply formaldehyde in the furrow with the seed, a drip method using 1 pint of formalin in 8 to 16 gallons of water or apply Arasan with the fertilizer.

Urocystis colchici. LEAF SMUT of autumn crocus, camassia, Solomon's-seal and false Solomon's-seal.

USTILAGO

Ustilaginaceae. Spores single, not united in balls; powdery sori without a peridium.

Ustilago heufleri. ERYTHRONIUM SMUT. Large dusty pustules lead to cracking and dying of leaves of dogtooth violet.

Ustilago striaeformis. STRIPE SMUT OF WHEAT, also widespread on redtop, creeping bent, Canada, and Kentucky blue-grass. The sori are long, narrow, nearly black stripes in leaves and leaf sheaths. Leaves are shredded after spore dispersal and internodal elongation; development of inflorescence is restricted in many grasses.

Ustilago violaceae. ANTHER SMUT of carnation, dianthus, lychnis, silene.

Ustilago zeae. CORN SMUT, general on corn but most destructive to sweet corn. The average annual loss in this country is 3 to 5 per cent but it can be 100 per cent in any one field. It was described back in 1754 and probably known long before that. There are many physiological races and smut resistance is apt to be correlated with lack of vigor so that it has been hard to breed desirable resistant varieties.

Any above-ground part may be attacked—stalks, prop roots, leaf tassels, husks, and ears. Large boils are formed, at first covered with a greenish white glistening membrane (said to be good eating when boiled or fried). Later the membrane breaks and releases myriads of dark chlamydospores. The plant is often distorted or abnormal.

Infections are local; each boil is formed where a spore lands and there is no systemic growth through the plants as in most smuts. The fungus is not seed borne and germinating seedlings are not affected. Chlamydospores winter in soil, corn debris, or manure, producing sporidia (basidiospores) which infect directly or bud to form secondary sporidia. These are carried by wind

Fig. 102. Corn Smut.

and other agencies to corn plants when they are 1 to 3 feet high and there produce infection hyphae. Mycelia from spores of two sexes are needed for active development. Chlamydospores formed in the first boils provide inoculum for secondary infection of ears.

Corn smut thrives in warm weather, optimum temperature for spore germination being 80° to 92° F. Heaviest infection occurs when scant rainfall in early stages of growth is followed by moderate rainfall as corn approaches maturity. The most vigorous plants are most susceptible but through their rapid growth may escape the most serious effects. Spores retain their viability

5 to 7 years and in passage through an animal into manure, but are killed by the acids in silage.

Control. Seed treatment is not effective. New resistant varieties are in process. Dusting corn with rotenone, DDT, or Ryania to control borers seems to decrease amount of smut. Most reliance in home gardens should be placed on cleanliness, cutting off and burning all smutted parts before the boils break open to release the spores.

SNOWMOLD

Northern lawns and turf of golf greens often show round light patches as the snow melts in early spring. Such a disease is called snowmold and in most of the bulletins on turf has been attributed chiefly to *Fusarium nivale.* In many eastern lawns, however, the organism usually found in connection with snowmold is a Typhula.

FUSARIUM (See under Rots)

Fusarium nivale (perfect stage *Calonectria graminicola*). SNOWMOLD OF TURF GRASSES, most important on golf courses. Irregularly circular patches of dead grass, varying from a few inches to a foot, appear as snow is melting. They are whitish gray, often with a pinkish tinge, and several patches may run together to cover rather large areas. Individual plants have a bleached appearance and feel slimy when wet. Spores are formed in salmon-pink sporodochia over stomata in leaves. They are sickle-shaped, 3-septate. Perithecia are formed on the abundant white mycelial mat.

Abundant moisture in the fall, snow falling on unfrozen ground, deep snow and a prolonged, cold, wet spring are all predisposing factors. The severity of the disease is increased by applying fertilizer late in the fall and by abundant organic matter in the soil. Although Kentucky blue-grass, annual blue-grass, redtop, red fescue, creeping bent, velvet bent, and Colonial bent are all susceptible, there is a difference in grass strains. Metropolitan bent is resistant to this snowmold.

Control. Either mercuric chloride or calomel (mercurous chloride) at the rate of 3 ounces to 1000 square feet and applied in the fall controls Fusarium snowmold.

Sclerotium rhizodes (apparently sclerotial stage of the Rhizoctonia causing brown patch). SNOWMOLD. Leaves are nearly white over their entire length with a row of white to brown sclerotia. When turf is started with rhizomes bearing these snowmold sclerotia, typical summer brown patch develops.

TYPHULA

Basidiomycetes, Agaricales, Clavariaceae

Fruit body erect, simple, like a little club, on a long stipe from a sclerotium; basidia with four sterigmata and simple, hyaline spores.

FIG. 103. Snowmold on lawn in early spring. Light spots are typical of both Typhula and Fusarium molds.

Typhula itoana. SNOWMOLD OF TURF AND LAWN GRASSES, Typhula blight, common in eastern United States. As the snow disappears in spring a felty white mycelial mat is seen over grass and adjacent soil. Plants wither and turn light brown or tan in roughly circular patches, very conspicuous against the spring green of the rest of the lawn. There may be merely dead leaf tissue, or rotting of culm, crown and root tissues. The chief diagnostic character is the presence of very small tawny to hazel brown spherical sclerotia in large numbers over affected parts. These can be made to fruit in the laboratory into rose-colored sporophores up to an inch tall.

Control. The disease gradually disappears as moisture decreases and temperature and sunlight increase, so control seldom seems necessary. Six weeks after very striking cases of snowmold, lawns are uniformly green and show little sign of having been affected. (This is my personal observation in New Jersey; there may be cases where treatment with a mercurial fungicide is required.)

Typhula idahoensis. SNOWMOLD, on wheat and grasses in Idaho and Montana. Sclerotia are chestnut brown and sporophores fawn to wood brown, less than a half inch high.

SOOTY MOLD

Sooty mold is a black coating on surface of leaves or fruit composed of a weft of black, mycelial threads. As here used the term applies to a few saprophytic fungi which live on insect honeydew and harm plants only indirectly. The term is, however, often used for black mildews which are true parasites and for other fungi whose dark mycelium and spores give a sooty appearance to leaves.

CAPNODIUM

Ascomycetes, Dothideales, Capnodiaceae

Mycelium superficial, dark; spores muriform, dark, in perithecium-like conceptacles at tips of branches of a carbonaceous stroma; associated with insect secretion on living plants.

Capnodium citri. SOOTY MOLD on citrus, on honeydew secreted by scale insects, aphids, larvae of whiteflies. Sooty mold is especially abundant following whiteflies in Florida and black scale in California.

A black, velvety membranous coating is formed over leaves, twigs, and fruit. If honeydew is slight the coating appears in spots, but if the insect secretion is abundant the entire surface may be covered by a dense continuous membrane resembling black tissue paper. With age, under dry conditions, it may be blown off in fragments. The black membrane is made up of hyphae which are individually olive green to deep brown, with wide short cells. Branches may crisscross or be cemented together. There are several spore forms: simple conidia which are cut off from upright hyphae, others formed in small, black pycnidia, stylospores in very long flask-shaped conceptacles and muriform brown ascospores formed in perithecia.

Although sooty molds do not obtain food from the plant, the black membrane interferes greatly with photosynthesis and food manufacture. Affected fruit is smaller, with coloring retarded and more likely to decay than normal fruit.

Control is directed against the insects either by spraying with insecticides or using entomogenous fungi and insect parasites. Dusting with sulfur sometimes helps to remove the mold.

Capnodium elongatum. SOOTY MOLD on tulip-tree, oleander, holly-osmanthus, and others. Foliage of tulip-trees very frequently has a black coating, often on honeydew secreted by tulip-tree aphid, sometimes following attacks of tulip-tree scale. A dormant oil spray controls the latter.

Capnodium spp. SOOTY MOLD on gardenia, fig, crape-myrtle and many other plants. Gardenias are especially subject to sooty mold following whiteflies, and crape-myrtle after aphids. A summer oil spray (Volck at a 1 to 50 dilution or weaker) not only helps to control whiteflies but loosens the black coating so that it is fairly readily washed off.

Fig. 104. Sooty Mold following scale on magnolia.

Fig. 105. Sooty Mold on gardenia. Left, mold growing in secretion of whitefly nymphs, seen on underside of leaf; right, sooty layer peeling off after an oil spray.

Fungi Imperfecti, Moniliales, Dematiaceae

Spores dark, muriform, in chains on dark, branched crustose hyphae.

Fumago vagans. Sooty Mold.

VIRUS DISEASES

The word virus means poison or venom. When the word is used in connection with plant disease it means a filterable virus, an infective principle or etiological agent so small it passes through filters which will retain bacteria. Virus diseases range from infantile paralysis to the common cold in man, and from "breaking" of tulip flowers to deadly elm phloem necrosis in plants.

Viruses are obligate parasites in that they are capable of increasing only in the presence of living cells, but the exact nature of a virus particle is not too well known. For many years the argument raged as to whether the virus principle was living or nonliving, biological or chemical. In 1935 a crystalline protein was prepared from tobacco mosaic virus juice, and since then the protein nature of viruses has been accepted by many pathologists. Others still believe in a living organism, and some feel that here is the true borderline, the place where life begins, an agent which acts like a chemical in a test tube but on introduction into a cell acts as a misguided living element.

Virus diseases of plants are very old. Tulip mosaic or breaking of flower color is recorded in a book published in 1576. Many viruses are of great economic importance. Some attack a great many different plants; others are confined to a single host. Symptoms fall into several categories, but a very common feature is loss of color by the suppression of chlorophyll development. Foliage can be mottled green and yellow, *mosaic,* or have yellow rings, *ring spot,* or have a rather uniform yellowing, *yellows.* Stunting is another symptom since the reduction in chlorophyll and of manufactured food leads to reduction in size, shorter internodes, smaller leaves and blossoms, reduced yield. Various distortions of leaves and flowers may occur, and sometimes a hyperplastic growth in the form of witches' brooms or rosettes. Sometimes symptoms are necrotic with death ensuing. Symptoms are often "masked" in periods of hot weather.

Viruses are transmitted from plant to plant by insects, by rubbing or other mechanical means (sometimes handling tobacco and merely touching a healthy plant spreads mosaic), by vegetative propagation, by seeds, in some cases, and rarely in soil. Dodder, that parasitic vine, can transmit a virus through the yellow tendrils linking one plant to another.

Control of virus diseases starts with obtaining healthy seed or plants. "Certified" means that plants have been inspected during the growing period and that the field was free from certain diseases at the dates of inspection. Controlling insect vectors, eliminating weed hosts, roguing or removing a diseased plant before insects can transmit the virus, sometimes heat treatment, and resistant varieties are all ways of eliminating virus diseases.

There are a number of systems of classification of viruses.* One system uses numbers, Pea virus 2, etc., but the binomial system of Francis O. Holmes as given in the 1948 edition of *Bergey's Manual of Determinative Bacteriology* most readily fits into the reference scheme of this book, and so Holmes is followed in all cases where the name is given in Bergey. New or unnamed diseases are given at the end of the alphabetical section. In this system viruses are placed in the order Virales, those affecting plants in the suborder Phytophagineae, which is divided into six families according to the chief symptoms—yellows, mosaic, ring spot, leaf curl, leaf savoying and spotted wilt.

ACROGENUS

Marmoraceae. Spindle-tuber groups, abnormal growth habit of host plants without chlorosis, witches' brooms or galls.

Acrogenus solani, POTATO SPINDLE-TUBER VIRUS, general on all tested varieties of potatoes. Plants are more erect than normal, but spindly, lacking vigor, stems stiff, leaves small, dark green, tubers elongated, pointed at ends, eyes "staring." Symptoms are accentuated by high soil moisture. Transmission is by contaminated knives in cutting tubers, contact between freshly cut seed pieces and by insects, including peach and potato aphids, flea beetles, leaf beetles, tarnished plant bugs, and grasshoppers.

ADELONOSUS

Marmoraceae. Viruses capable of multiplying in living plants but producing no recognizable symptoms except on interaction with other viruses.

Adelonosus lilii, LILY SYMPTOMLESS VIRUS, in Easter lilies (*Lilium longiflorum*) wherever these are grown commercially. There are no symptoms when present alone but in combination with cucumber-mosaic virus necrotic fleck is produced. Transmission is by the cotton aphid, or with difficulty by inoculation of expressed sap.

ANNULUS

Annulaceae. Ringspot group; necrotic or chlorotic spotting with concentric ring lesions and eventual recovery from obvious disease; no vectors known.

Annulus apertus, BROAD-RINGSPOT VIRUS, on tobacco, Wisconsin. Chlorotic or necrotic rings with concentric markings; young leaves puckered at first, somewhat malformed.

* See Common Names of Virus Diseases in Review of Applied Mycology **24**:515–556, 1946; and U. S. Department of Agriculture Plant Disease Reporter Supplements 150, 1944· 154, 155, and 158, 1945.

Annulus delphinii, Delphinium-Ringspot Virus, on perennial delphinium in California, experimentally also on beet, cucumber, cotton, nicotiana, petunia. Faint chlorotic rings and green and yellow centers appear on young leaves and irregular chlorotic spots or rings with yellow bands on mature leaves.

Annulus dubius (*Marmor dubium*), Potato-Mottle Virus, potato virus X, widespread on potato and tomato, experimentally on other solanaceous plants, also on amaranth, chysanthemum, veronica. The virus is present in all known stocks of some potato varieties in the United States. On potato there may be some top necrosis, and yellow cast to foliage; in tomato a mild chlorotic mottling, but if the tobacco-mosaic virus is also present there is a severe systemic necrosis. There are several strains; they are not transmitted by seed.

Annulus orae, Tobacco-Streak Virus, on tobacco, experimentally on some other solanaceous plants but not pepper, tomato, eggplant, or potato.

Annulus tabaci, Tobacco-Ringspot Virus, on tobacco, petunia, potato, cucumber, general, with experimental infection on many plants. Primary rings may be followed by secondary rings on younger leaves. Some varieties show mosaic patterns in young leaves. The virus can be transmitted in about 20 per cent of the seed of diseased petunias.

Annulus zonatus, Tomato-Ringspot Virus, on tomato, tobacco and many other plants experimentally. Systemic infection in tomato produces yellowish green or necrotic ringlike lesions, and stunting.

AUREOGENUS

Chlorogenaceae. Yellow-dwarf group; plants yellowed without typical mosaic mottling; leafhopper vectors.

Aureogenus vastans, Potato Yellow-Dwarf Virus, on potato, daisy, black-eyed Susan, winter cress, red clover in Northeastern United States. In potato, leaves are rolled, yellow, the plant is dwarfed, and stem split showing rusty specks; tubers are small, few, close to stem, often cracked; the flesh is discolored with brown specks. In daisy, first symptom is vein clearing, then young leaves are distorted, thick, stiff, small with short petioles forming a rosette at the crown. Vectors are clover leafhoppers.

CARPOPHTHORA

Chlorogenaceae. Peach X-disease group; rosetting of foliage and sometimes death of host.

Carpophthora lacerans, Peach X-Disease Virus causing peach yellow-red virosis, on peach and choke-cherry. In the past ten years or so X-disease has become a major threat to peach production in northeastern United States and now occurs through the northern half of the country. It is recently reported on sour cherry in Illinois. Peach foliage is normal in spring but by June yellowish areas appear at base of leaves and affected trees look lighter green. Red and yellow spots appear at random on the leaf blade, with the rest of the leaf chlorotic; discolored areas often fall out leaving tattered foliage, which may drop, except from tips of branches. Young trees may die. Fruit shrivels and falls, or ripens prematurely, with a bitter flavor and no viable seed.

On choke-cherry there is conspicuous premature reddening of foliage, fruits have dead embryos. The second and third seasons after infection foliage colors are duller, there are rosettes of small leaves on terminals and death may follow. No insect vector is known. The disease is transmitted from peach to peach or choke-cherry to peach by budding or grafting.

Control. Attempts have been made to eradicate choke-cherry around peach orchards. The virus is inactivated by treating buds in hot water at 125° C., apparently without harm, and buds can be immersed in various chemicals for an hour. Trees can also be immunized by watering with chemical solutions, using some of the quinhydrones used in chemotherapy for the Dutch elm disease, but all this is in an experimental stage.

Carpophthora rosettae, PEACH-ROSETTE VIRUS on peach, plum, experimentally on periwinkle, wild plum, cherry, sand cherry, Ala., Ga., Mo., Okla., Tenn., S. C., W. Va. Peach trees suddenly wilt and die or there is a growth of abnormally short stems bearing dwarfed leaves with clearing and thickening of veins, followed by death in a few months. Transmission is by budding. The virus can be inactivated by heating at 122° F. for 10 minutes, but rosetted trees are sensitive to heat injury.

CHLOROGENUS

Chlorogenaceae. Yellows group; normally dormant and adventitious buds are stimulated to produce numerous slender shoots with long internodes; chlorosis without spotting; invaded parts abnormally erect; flowers often virescent. Hosts are dicotyledons and vectors are leafhoppers.

Chlorogenus callistephi, ASTER-YELLOWS VIRUS, Lettuce white-heart virus, general on aster and on more than 170 species in 38 families of dicotyledonous plants. This virus is general in the United States except that in the Pacific and Mountain states it is replaced by the California aster-yellows virus which differs in its ability to infect celery and zinnia. Aster yellows is the most important disease of China aster, and may be serious on lettuce, endive, carrot, parsley, New Zealand spinach, and other vegetables, but not on legumes—peas, beans—which seem to be immune. Among the ornamentals are anemone, calendula, coreopsis, cosmos, delphinium, daisies, golden-glow, marigold, petunia, phlox, scabiosa, strawflower, and many others.

In most plants vein clearing is followed by chlorosis of newly formed tissues, adventitious growth, erect habit, virescence of flowers. Asters have a stiff yellow growth, with many secondary shoots. They are stunted with shortened internodes with flowers greenish, dwarfed, or none. Transmission is by the six-spotted leafhopper, *Macrosteles divisus,* and two or three other species, by grafting and by dodder, but not by seeds nor through eggs of the insect vector.

FIG. 106. Aster Yellows. Stiff growth, shortened internodes and virescent flowers are special characteristics.

The leafhoppers acquire the virus after feeding for 24 hours and become infectious after an incubation period of 10 days or more.

Chlorogenus callistephi var. **californicus,** CELERY-YELLOWS STRAIN OF ASTER-YELLOWS VIRUS, on most of the same plants and also on celery and zinnia, in California, Colorado, Oregon, Utah, Washington, Wyoming. In celery outer petioles are upright, somewhat elongated, with inner petioles short, chlorotic, twisted, brittle, often cracked, with general yellowing.

Control of aster yellows is directed chiefly against leafhoppers, with DDT quite effective. Asters are frequently grown under cheesecloth, which has at least 22 threads to the inch, or wire screening with 18 wires to the inch. Weeds near the garden which serve as winter hosts should be destroyed.

Chlorogenus persicae, PEACH-YELLOWS VIRUS, little-peach virus, on peach, Japanese plum, and all tested species of Prunus, in eastern United States to North Carolina. Peach yellows first appeared near Philadelphia and may have been introduced on oriental plums. In peach, clearing of veins, production of thin, erect shoots with small chlorotic leaves, premature ripening of fruit is followed by death in a year or two. Japanese plum has systemic infection but no obvious symptoms. Transmission is by the plum leafhopper or by budding. There are several strains of the virus.

Control. Trees and bud sticks can be safely treated with heat sufficient to kill the virus (92° F. for 4 or 5 days or 111° F. for 30 minutes) but cured trees are susceptible to reinfection.

Chlorogenus robiniae, LOCUST WITCHES'-BROOM VIRUS, locust brooming disease virus, from southern Pennsylvania to northeast Georgia, west to Ohio and Tennessee. Vein clearing is followed by reduction in size of new leaves, and growth of spindly shoots to witches' brooms. Roots are more brittle, shorter and darker than normal, with excessive branching rootlets forming root brooms. Transmission is by budding and grafting; no insect vector is known.

Chlorogenus solani, POTATO WITCHES'-BROOM VIRUS, on potato, in many states. Apical leaves are slightly rolled, upright, light green with reddish or yellowing margins; there is proliferation of axial buds, with tendency to bloom and set fruit, and production of aerial tubers and numerous small subterranean tubers, often in a beadlike arrangement, which tend to put out spindle sprouts from most of eyes without a rest period. Such tubers produce dwarfed, very bushy plants with small roundish or heart-shaped leaves.

The insect vector is unknown. The virus can be transmitted by tuber and stem grafts but not by seed.

Chlorogenus vaccinii, CRANBERRY FALSE-BLOSSOM VIRUS, on cranberry in eastern United States. Cranberry flowers are erect, instead of pendent, with calyx lobes enlarged, petals short, streaked with red and green, stamens and pistils abnormal. Flowers may be replaced by leaves or short branches. Axillary buds produce numerous erect shoots forming witches' brooms; diseased fruits are small and irregular. Transmission is by the blunt-nosed leafhopper.

CORIUM

Marmoraceae. Leaf-roll group; thickening and rolling of leaves; leathery foliage; sometimes conspicuous phloem necrosis.

Corium rubi, RASPBERRY LEAF-CURL VIRUS on red raspberry (not on black or purple). Veins are retarded in growth causing downward curling and crinkling of leaves. Foliage is dark green, dry, not wilting readily; leaves are bronzed in late summer with surface glistening. Berries are small and poor; diseased canes are readily winter-killed. Variety Lloyd George is very susceptible. Transmission is by aphids (*Aphis rubicola*).

Corium rubi var. **beta,** a strain that can infect black and purple as well as red raspberries.

Corium ruborum, RASPBERRY DECLINE-DISEASE VIRUS on red raspberry, Oregon. In the Cuthbert raspberry, shoots are retarded in spring, and reddish; in autumn, leaves are rolled downward, fluted along veins, slightly bronzed at margins and crests between veins; internodes are shortened near tips of canes, which are small, weak, not winter-hardy. Roots are small, and feeder rootlets fewer than in healthy plants; fruits are small, irregular, tending to be globose when ripe, worthless. Transmission is by grafting and no insect vector is known.

Corium solani, POTATO LEAF-ROLL VIRUS, on potato, probably wherever it is grown, experimentally on tomato, bittersweet, Jimson weed. Leaves are rigid, thick, leathery and rolled, with excessive starch content. Plants are dwarfed; tubers are few, crisp, with some varieties showing conspicuous net necrosis and spindling sprouts. Transmission is by peach, foxglove, potato and lily aphids, also by grafting. The incubation period in the peach aphid is 24 to 48 hours.

Control. Varieties Katahdin, Sequoia, and Chippewa are free from net necrosis in tubers. In regions where aphids are abundant late in the season early harvest is desirable. Use certified seed potatoes.

Production of certified seed potatoes is an elaborate process. Foundation stock is obtained by tuber-indexing or hill-indexing, an eye from each potato, or a tuber from each hill, being planted early or in the greenhouse. The seed pieces from each potato are planted consecutively in the row and if any plant shows virus symptoms the whole unit is destroyed. Crop from indexed tubers is multiplied the second year in a foundation seed plot, rogued as necessary, grown the third year in a tuber-unit seed plot and certified the fourth year.

GALLA

Chlorogenaceae. Diseases characterized by vascular proliferation.

Galla verrucae, PEACH-WART VIRUS, on peach in Idaho, Oregon, Washington. Foliage is normal, but fruits are blistered, welted, and later have conspicuous, raised warty outgrowths. Affected tissues are light tan to red, rough, cracked and russeted or smooth; gumming often severe. Tissues underlying superficial warts are coarse with gum pockets but not abnormal in flavor. Warts may be hard and bony, or merely tough. Transmission is by budding and inarching.

LETHUM

Lethaceae. Spotted-wilt group; bronzing and necrotic spotting of foliage, streaking of stems, blighting of tips; a single genus with thrips as vectors.

Lethum australiense, Spotted-Wilt Virus on numerous species of many families in higher plants, in the Pacific States and Colorado, Idaho, Texas, Utah outdoors, in eastern and central states in greenhouses and occasionally in the field. It is present outdoors in southern New Jersey on dahlias and tomatoes. Spotted wilt is common on tomato, potato, tobacco, lettuce, pea, and other vegetables and is likewise important on many ornamentals, mostly in California—amaryllis, aster, begonia, calendula, callas, chrysanthemum, dahlia, delphinium, fuchsia, gaillardia, gloxinia, nasturtium, pelargonium, primrose, petunia, salvia, stock, verbena, zinnia, and others.

In tomato there are bronze, ring-like secondary lesions, plants are stunted with some necrosis, and acquire a yellowish mosaic with some leaf distortion. Fruits are often marked with concentric rings of pale red, yellow, or white. Potatoes have zonate, necrotic spots on upper leaves, streaks on stems, which collapse at the top; plants are stunted with yield small. Lettuce is yellowed with retarded growth, brown blemishes on central leaves; affected spots are like parchment but with brown margins. Peas have purplish necrotic spots on stems and leaves following mottling, and circular spots or waxy lines on pods.

Spotted wilt on dahlias appears as yellow ringspots.

On sweet pea, reddish brown to purple streaks may run full length of the stem. Circular to oval leaf spots with diffuse margins are followed by yellowing and death of leaves and shoots. Blossoms sometimes develop a circular pattern in the pigment. Calla lilies have whitish, then brown spots and streaks. Transmission is by onion and flower thrips.

Control. Keep commercial tomato fields isolated from home gardens and planting of ornamentals; keep down weeds; rogue out diseased plants when small. Spotted wilt in calla lilies is carried in infected rhizomes; diseased plants should be destroyed as soon as noticed. Keep sweet peas isolated from other plants susceptible to wilt. Cuttings from upper portions of plants are sometimes healthy.

MARMOR

Marmoraceae. Mosaic group; mottling of foliage, sometimes dwarfing of plants; transmission by aphids.

Marmor abutilon, Abutilon-Mosaic Virus, on flowering maple. Originally the disease came from a single variegated seedling found among green plants of *Abutilon striatum* imported from the West Indies in 1868 and subsequently propagated vegetatively as an ornamental variety. There is a systemic chlorotic mottling, but recovery if variegated leaves are persistently removed. Transmission is by grafting with no insect vector known.

Marmor aevi, Celery-Calico Virus on cucumber, crookneck squash, tomato, celery, *Delphinium chinensis* and larkspur. In celery there is vein clearing, puckering, and downward cupping of younger leaves, green islands in lemon-yellow areas of outer leaves, and green and yellow zigzag bands on leaflets.

On delphinium, basal and middle leaves have orange-amber or lemon-yellow areas, but younger leaves are a normal green; there may be chlorotic ring and line patterns.

Transmission is by many species of aphids—celery, celery-leaf, rusty-banded, cotton, erigeron-root, foxglove, green-peach, and honeysuckle.

Marmor astri, PEACH ASTEROID-SPOT VIRUS, on peach in California. Discrete, chlorotic lesions spread along veins forming star-like spots; some chlorophyll is retained in lesions as leaves turn yellow. Transmission is by grafting; no insect vector is known.

Marmor aucuba, POTATO AUCUBA-MOSAIC VIRUS. Yellow spots appear on lower leaves in some potato varieties but in Irish Chieftain there is a brilliant yellow mottle over the whole plant. Transmission is probably by the peach aphid.

Marmor betae, SUGAR-BEET MOSAIC VIRUS, on beet, spinach. Discrete yellowish secondary lesions are followed by chlorotic mottling, darkening of vascular tissue; leaves bend back near the tips, which sometimes die. In spinach there is dying back from the tips, stunting, chlorotic flecks on young leaves with killing of outer leaves. Transmission is by peach and bean aphids.

Marmor brassicae, TURNIP-MOSAIC VIRUS, on turnip, rutabaga, rape, mustard, cabbage, horse-radish, wallflower, stock. Turnip shows a systemic chlorotic mottling with leaf distortion and stunting of plants. Transmission is by cabbage and peach aphids.

Marmor caricae, FIG-MOSAIC VIRUS, on fig. Systemic chlorotic mottling is accompanied with severe leaf distortion; fruits may have light circular areas, or rusty spots, may be deformed and drop prematurely. Transmission is by budding.

Marmor cepae, ONION YELLOW-DWARF VIRUS. Yellow streaks develop at base of onion leaves, then yellowing, crinkling, and flattening of new leaves; leaves may be prostrate, flower stalks bent, twisted and stunted; plants and bulbs are reduced in size, yield is smaller. Some varieties are relatively tolerant; tree-onions are symptomless. Transmission is by many species of aphids, but chiefly bean, apple grain, and corn leaf aphids.

Marmor cerasi, CHERRY MOTTLE-LEAF VIRUS on sweet cherry, wild cherry in California, Idaho, Oregon, and Washington. Leaves show chlorotic mottling, are puckered, wrinkled, distorted, not perforated. Blossoms are not affected. Fruit is small, hard, insipid, uneven, or delayed in ripening; crop is reduced; branches shortened; tree eventually stunted. Transmission is by budding.

Marmor cruciferarum, CAULIFLOWER-MOSAIC VIRUS on cauliflower, kale, brussels sprouts, cabbage, broccoli, wild mustard, annual stock. Clearing of veins in cauliflower is followed by mild chlorotic mottling, with veins usually banded with dark green, necrotic flecks; midrib is curled, leaves distorted;

plants stunted and terminal head dwarfed. Transmission is by many species of aphids.

Marmor cucumeris, CUCUMBER-MOSAIC VIRUS on cucumber, squash, and melon and a wide range of both dicotyledons and monocotyledons, including spinach, where the disease is known as blight; tomato, where it causes shoestring disease with filiform leaflets; tobacco, petunia, pepper, and many weed hosts wintering on ground cherry, milkweed, pokeweed, catnip, and others.

In cucurbits there is a yellow-green systemic mottling, with leaves small, distorted, curled, plants dwarfed, internodes shortened, few fruits set and those mottled and misshapen, usually called "white pickle." Transmission is by peach, potato, cotton, and lily aphids.

There are many strains of cucumber-mosaic virus. Lily-mosaic strain (*Marmor cucumeris* var. *lilii*) produces a masked infection or chlorotic mottling in lilies unless mixed with the lily symptomless virus, when necrosis is induced. The lima-bean strain (var. *phaseoli*), southern celery mosaic strain (var. *commelinae*), and cowpea strain (var. *vignae*) produce chlorotic mottling in their respective hosts. The strain on zinnia (var. *judicis*) forms local necrotic lesions.

Control. Some resistant varieties are available—Old Dominion, Virginia Savoy, and Bloomsdale spinach; Ohio 31 and Maine No. 2 cucumbers; Geneva Delicata and Shamrock squashes. Keep down weed hosts.

Marmor dahliae, DAHLIA-MOSAIC VIRUS. Tolerant dahlia varieties have inconspicuous mottling or masked symptoms but intolerant varieties show chlorotic mottling of foliage, leaf distortion, dwarfing of all stems and roots, and occasional necrotic streaking of midveins. Transmission is by the peach aphid.

Marmor efficiens, PEA-MOTTLE VIRUS on white clover, pea, in Washington. Pea leaves and stipules have chlorotic spotting or mottling, may be late in opening, and stunted; but the stems, pods, and seed appear normal. If pea-wilt virus is present, severe streak results. No insect vector is known.

Marmor erodens, TOBACCO-ETCH VIRUS on pepper, tomato, tobacco, petunia, Jimson weed, ground cherry. There is a mild-mottling chlorosis, with traces of necrotic etching. Transmission is by peach, lily, bean, and other aphids.

Marmor fastidiens, ALSIKE-CLOVER MOSAIC VIRUS, on pea, except varieties Horal, Perfection and Surprise, and alsike clover. No insect vector known.

Marmor fragariae, STRAWBERRY-CRINKLE VIRUS. Minute chlorotic specks in young strawberry leaves enlarge, with small, necrotic spots in the center; leaves are crinkled, with vein clearing frequent; affected foliage is less uniformly green. Transmission is by the strawberry aphid, which develops in enormous numbers in winter and early spring on the Pacific Coast.

Control. Delay settings of new fields until aphids have disappeared, and start new fields as far from old as possible. Rogue carefully the first season.

Marmor iridis, IRIS-MOSAIC VIRUS, on bulbous iris and babiana in California, Oregon, and Washington. Plants are dwarfed with chlorotic mottling of foliage and breaking of flowers with a darker than normal color. Transmission is by potato and peach aphids.

Marmor lactucae, LETTUCE-MOSAIC VIRUS. Vein clearing, systemic chlorotic mottling, dwarfing, defective heart, sometimes scorching of leaf margins, vein necrosis or necrotic flecking between veins are all symptoms. Transmission is by peach aphid, by *Macrosiphum gei* and through seeds, the latter being the most important source of spring infection.

Marmor laesiofaciens, BEAN MOSAIC VIRUS 4; southern bean mosaic virus 1. Chlorotic mottling or localized necrosis of foliage; pods with dark green blotches or shiny areas, slightly malformed, short, curled at end. Transmission is through seeds.

Marmor leguminosarum, PEA-MOSAIC VIRUS on sweet pea, pea, red clover, broad-bean. In sweet pea flower colors are broken together with systemic chlorosis and chlorotic mottling of foliage. Pea vines are stunted. Transmission is by pea, potato, and bean aphids.

Marmor lineopictum, PRUNUS LINE-PATTERN VIRUS, peach line-pattern virus on Japanese plum, Mahaleb cherry and peach in California, Kentucky, Michigan, Ohio, perhaps other states. In cherry and peach there are light-colored line patterns, or faint chlorotic mottling. Peach foliage may be less glossy than normal. Transmission is by grafting; no insect vector is known.

Marmor mali, APPLE MOSAIC VIRUS. Vein clearing and systemic chlorotic mottling may be followed by necrosis in months of intense sunlight. Transmission is by grafting; no insect vector is known.

Marmor marginans, STRAWBERRY YELLOW-EDGE VIRUS, causing strawberry yellows or xanthosis, prevalent from Puget Sound, Wash., to southern California. In general plants are flat with outer zones of leaves more or less normal, central leaves dwarfed, yellow-edged, deficient in red pigmentation, but symptoms vary with variety and tend to be obscured in warm weather. Plants never recover and all runner plants become infected. Fruit is small, yield reduced. Transmission is by the strawberry aphid. Plants for sale to the public should be grown under rigid state regulation and supervision.

Marmor medicaginis, ALFALFA-MOSAIC VIRUS on alfalfa and potato. The potato-calico strain produces more severe disease in potato, with systemic chlorotic mottling.

Marmor mite, LILY LATENT-MOSAIC VIRUS, on lily, except *Lilium hansoni,* and tulip wherever lilies and tulips are cultivated. In tulip there is systemic chlorotic mottling and flower "breaking" with color removal except in a few varieties which have color intensification. Lilies may have masked symptoms or systemic chlorotic mottling. Transmission is by peach, potato, and tulip-bulb aphids.

Control. If tulips with variegated color are allowed to remain in the garden the virus may be carried to healthy tulips. Spray or dust to control aphids.

Marmor nerviclarens, Cherry Vein-Clearing Virus, on sweet cherry, Oregon and Washington. There is clearing of veins throughout each leaf or in localized areas. Margins of leaves are irregular with most indentation where vein clearing is most conspicuous. Leaves are usually narrow, some with elongated, slot-like perforations, small blisters on lower side of veins and upper surface silvery. Leaves drop and wilt in midsummer and may fold along the midrib. Some branches may show rosetting at end of year-old wood. In advanced disease fruits are pointed, small, flattened on side with swollen ridge. Blossoms are abnormally abundant but crop is reduced. No insect vector is known.

Marmor pelargonii, Pelargonium Leaf-Curl Virus on geranium. Probably general chlorotic spots are small, circular to irregular, sometimes star- or tree-shaped, with brown centers. Severely infected leaves turn yellow and drop; spotted leaves are ruffled, crinkled, malformed, small, sometimes puckered and splitting. Petioles and stems have corky, raised necrotic streaks and tops may die. The disease is most severe in spring, inconspicuous in summer. Transmission is by grafting but not by knife preparing cuttings. No insect vector is known.

Marmor pallidolimbatus, Cherry Banded-Chlorosis Virus, on flowering and Mazzard cherry, Pacific Northwest. In flowering cherry chlorotic bands surround discolored areas on leaves. In Mazzard cherry there is dwarfing of whole plants with chlorotic bands on leaves. The virus is transmitted by budding, even when inserted buds die.

Marmor persicae, Peach Mosaic Virus, on all tested varieties of peach and nectarine, in the Southwest. Spring growth of peaches has short internodes, with sometimes breaking in flower pattern, chlorotic mottling, and distortion of foliage early in the season, masking of leaf symptoms or dropping out of affected areas in midsummer. Fruit is small, irregular in shape, unsalable. Transmission is by budding and other methods of grafting; no insect vector is known.

Marmor phaseoli, Bean-Mosaic Virus, wherever beans are grown. First leaves are crinkled, stiff, chlorotic, later leaves have chlorotic mottling, often with leaf margins rolled down. Symptoms are masked if temperatures are lower than 65° F. or higher than 82° F. Transmission is by bean, potato, cotton, cowpea, spirea, cabbage, turnip and peach aphids, and in seed.

Control. Use mosaic-resistant varieties which include Robust, Great Northern types U.I. 1, 15, 59, 81, 123, Red Mexican U.I. 3 and 34, Wisconsin Refugee, Idaho Refugee, U.S. No. 5 Refugee, Sensation Refugee 1066, and 1071, Medal Refugee, Micheliete, Florida Belle, Florida White Wax, and Logan.

Marmor pisi, Pea Enation-Mosaic Virus, on pea, sweet pea, broad-bean. In peas vein clearing is followed by enlargement and fusion of chlorotic areas which become flaccid, translucent and on lower leaf surface are surrounded by a ridge of proliferated tissue (enations); terminal growth is retarded and distorted; older plants show wrinkling, dwarfing and chlorotic spots; pods are blistered, distorted, mottled. Transmission is by pea and potato aphids with a 12-hour incubation period, not by seeds.

Marmor primulae, PRIMROSE-MOSAIC VIRUS, on primrose in California. Plants are chlorotic, stunted, rugose, with upward, sometimes downward, cupping of leaves. Petioles and peduncles are shortened, flowers are white-streaked; leaves are coarsely mottled with yellow-green, with green islands, and tips of leaves are narrowed. No insect vector is known.

Marmor rosae, ROSE-MOSAIC VIRUS. Usually on greenhouse roses in eastern and central states, on garden roses on Pacific Coast. Chlorotic areas feather away from midribs of leaflets, often with local distortion, sometimes with ring, oakleaf, and watermark patterns. Transmission is by budding and grafting; no insect vector is known. A yellow strain of this mosaic is characterized by brighter and lighter yellow patterns.

Marmor rubi, RED-RASPBERRY MOSAIC, on red and black raspberries, but more important on the latter. Leaves are mottled light and dark green, some varieties are stunted. Stem tips of black raspberries may die, canes stay short, plant is reduced in size and vigor and berries are small and seedy. Symptoms are "masked" in hot weather. Transmission is by two species of raspberry aphids.

Control. Secure healthy plants for setting, and place as far as possible from old patches; inspect and rogue new plantings three times the first year.

Marmor rubiginosum, CHERRY RUSTY-MOTTLE VIRUS, on sweet cherry, in Washington. Chlorotic mottling starts on small basal leaves 4 to 5 weeks after full bloom. Older leaves develop autumnal colors and absciss, with 30 to 70 per cent of foliage being lost, the rest somewhat wilted, with increased mottling and rusty areas. Blossoms are normal but the fruit is small, insipid. Transmission is by grafting.

Marmor scillearum, ORNITHOGALUM-MOSAIC VIRUS on *Ornithogalum thyrsoides,* galtonia, hyacinth, lachenalia. Young leaves are finely mottled with light and dark green, more conspicuously mottled with gray or yellow as leaves mature; flower stalks are boldly marked with light and dark green blotches and there are thin, longitudinal streaks on the perianth segments. The virus is transmitted by cotton, lily, and peach aphids.

Marmor solani, POTATO MILD-MOSAIC VIRUS. Some varieties, as Irish Chieftain, have a mild chlorotic mottling or masked symptoms, others have systemic necrosis. Diseased plants die prematurely in hot weather. Katahdin and Earlaine have pronounced yellow-mosaic patterns if the potato vein-banding virus is present. Transmission is by the peach aphid, and *Aphis abbreviata.*

Marmor trifolii, RED CLOVER VEIN-MOSAIC VIRUS on red clover, sweet pea, and broad-bean. There is yellow color along veins but not mottling. Transmission is by the pea aphid without incubation period or long retention.

Marmor tabaci, TOBACCO-MOSAIC VIRUS, TOMATO-MOSAIC VIRUS on tobacco, tomato, pepper, eggplant, petunia and nearly all solanaceous plants, in fields

FIG. 107. Raspberry Mosaic.

and greenhouses throughout United States. Tomato foliage has a light and dark green mottling, accompanied by some curling and malformation of leaflets. A yellow strain of the virus causes striking yellow mottling of leaves, sometimes stems and fruits and a great reduction in yield. Transmission is by lily, potato, and peach aphids, by grafting, through soil, through handling, and perhaps through newly ripened tomato seed.

The tomato or tobacco mosaic virus is the most resistant and highly infectious of all viruses. It withstands heat, even alcohol and various germicides, and retains infectivity in a dried state for many years. The commonest source of inoculum is smoking tobacco. Gardeners contaminate their hands in smoking and then infect plants as they transplant, disbud, tie, prune, etc., the virus entering through scratches, or broken hairs, and first symptoms appearing in 8 to 10 days. In greenhouses even doorknobs, faucets and flats can be contaminated after handling mosaic plants and remain a source of infection.

Control. Strict sanitation is necessary; wash hands with soap or trisodium phosphate after handling diseased plants or tobacco before touching healthy plants; always wash hands before working with young seedlings; keep down weeds.

Marmor tulipae, TULIP COLOR-ADDING VIRUS on garden tulips, wherever hybrids are grown. There is no obvious effect on the leaves and little interference with growth, but there is a dark striping of flowers by pigment intensification. Transmission is by peach, potato, tulip-bulb, and perhaps geranium aphids.

Marmor umbelliferarum, Celery Mosaic Virus, western celery mosaic virus on celery and celeriac, carrot in California. Young leaflets are mottled green and yellow and in advanced stages are narrow, twisted, and cupped; plants are stunted with central leafstalks shortened and the outer assuming a horizontal position. Transmission is by many species of aphids.

This disease became important about 1930 with yields of commercial growers cut to a third of the normal harvest. In 1936 a host-free period was proclaimed, which meant removal of all vestiges of actively growing celery from all fields within a given area for several weeks. The results have been outstanding and yields are back to normal, or above.

Marmor upsilon, Potato Vein-Banding Virus, Potato Virus Y, on potato, tobacco. On some potato varieties there is leaf drop and necrotic stem-streak; sometimes chlorotic mottling; in other varieties there is no sign of disease. But in combination with strains of the potato mottle virus (*Marmor dubium*) it causes rugose mosaic, a commonly destructive double-virus disease. Rugose mosaic has crinkled, brittle leaves, black lines on veins, and may cause premature death. Transmission is by the peach aphid.

Marmor veneniferum, Rose Streak Virus on rose in eastern United States. Leaves have brownish or reddish ring and veinbanding patterns; stems have ring patterns and sometimes necrotic areas near inserted buds, causing girdling of the stem and wilting of foliage. Transmission is by grafting.

Marmor vignae, Cowpea Mosaic Virus. Clearing of veins is followed by chlorotic mottling, slight convex cupping of leaflets, shortened internodes, abortion of flowers, twisting of petioles, delayed maturity. Plants are malformed, stunted, with reduced yield. The virus is transmitted by potato, pea and cotton aphids.

MORSUS

Chlorogenaceae. Alfalfa-dwarf group; diseases characterized by sudden wilting and death or by gradual decline in vigor with foliage darker green than normal. Vectors are leafhoppers.

Morsus suffodiens, Alfalfa-Dwarf Virus, causing Pierce's Disease of Grape, Anaheim Disease. Dark green color of leaves is retained along veins, but not between them; in late summer of first year there may be dying back of leaf margins and cane tips. Wilting and sudden death comes in summer of second year. Transmission is by budding and root grafting and by many leafhoppers.

Morsus ulmi, Elm Phloem-Necrosis Virus. Phloem necrosis of American elm is now epidemic in the central and lower Ohio River watershed and extends from West Virginia and Georgia to northern Mississippi, eastern Oklahoma,

Kansas, and Nebraska. The origin of the disease is unknown but apparently it has been present since about 1882 and in recent years has destroyed many thousands of valuable elms in Columbus and Dayton, Ohio (more than 20,000 in Dayton alone), in Peoria, Ill., and St. Louis and Kansas City, Mo. Recent evidence points to the leafhopper *Scaphoideus luteolus* as the vector. European and Asiatic elms are resistant, but the American elm may be attacked at any age, with a gradual decline during 12 to 18 months before death, or a sudden wilting, drying and death within 3 or 4 weeks.

The most reliable diagnostic character is a butterscotch yellow, often flecked with brown or black, discoloration of the phloem, shown when the bark is scraped off, and a characteristic odor of wintergreen. The destruction of the phloem causes bark to loosen and fall away when trees die. The roots die first and then the phloem of lower part of trees is killed, followed by wilting and defoliation.

Control. Spraying with DDT, (1) when elm leaves are full grown, (2) 1 to 2 months later when new growth appears, to control the insect vector offers promise, and there is some hope of resistant elms from the many seedlings being grown and inoculated. Communities should interplant existing elms with young elms of resistant types or with some other tree to provide shade when and if the present elms die.

NANUS

Marmoraceae. Dwarf-disease group; plants are dwarfed or have short internodes with adventitious shoots; chlorotic mottling is absent.

Nanus cupuliformis, Strawberry-Stunt Virus, Oregon and Washington. Plants are erect but short, leaves at first folded, later open, dull with a papery rattle, leaflets cupped or with margins turned down; midveins tortuous; petioles half to two-thirds normal length; fruits are small, usually hard and seedy. Virus is transmitted by the strawberry aphid.

Nanus fragariae, Strawberry Witches'-Broom Virus, in western Oregon. Leaves are numerous, light in color with spindly petioles, margins of leaflets are bent down, runners are shortened, plants dwarfed, flower stalks spindly and unfruitful. Transmission is by the aphid *Myzus fragaefolii.*

Nanus holodisci, Ocean Spray Witches'-Broom Virus, on holodiscus, Oregon, Washington. Diseased branches form clusters of thin, wiry shoots with abnormally short internodes, crowded small leaves. Laterals are numerous and more than normally branched. Foliage turns bronze-red early. Transmission is by the spirea aphid and by grafting.

Nanus loganbacci, Loganberry-Dwarf Virus, Oregon, Washington, California. Leaves are small, obovate, rigid, with new canes short and spindly. Young plants have some necrosis along veins, crinkled leaves, and finer veins chlorotic. Flower sepals and petals are small. Fruit is of fair size but drupelets ripen unevenly and tend to fall apart when picked. Transmission is by aphids.

Nanus mirabilis, PEACH PHONY-DISEASE VIRUS. Trees are dwarfed, foliage abnormally green, fruit small, and there are flecks in the wood, especially in roots. The disease is important in commercial peach orchards from South Carolina to Louisiana, having caused the loss of more than a million and a half peach trees. Four species of leafhoppers have been found experimentally to transmit the disease.

Nanus orientalis, RASPBERRY-STREAK VIRUS, or blue-stem or rosette virus, on black raspberry. Plants are stunted, smaller in successive seasons, leaves are usually curled, close together on canes, dark green, often twisted upside down. New canes show bluish violet dots, stripes or spots near the base and sometimes on branches of fruiting spurs. Fruit is small and poor; plants live only 2 or 3 years after infection.

Nanus pruni, PRUNE-DWARF VIRUS on prune and plum, New York. Leaves are small, narrow, rugose, distorted, glazed, internodes short but some branches escape and appear normal. Blossoms are numerous but mature fruits few. Pistils are aborted, petals narrowed. There are no obvious symptoms in Damson and Bradshaw plums. Transmission is by budding and other forms of grafting.

RIMOCORTIUS

Marmoraceae. Rough-bark group; with diseases principally affecting bark.

Rimocortius kwanzani, FLOWERING-CHERRY ROUGH-BARK VIRUS on flowering and Mazzard cherry, Oregon. Trees are dwarfed, deficient in lateral branches, bark is deep brown, roughened, splitting longitudinally; internodes are shortened, bunching the leaves, which are arched downward, with midrib split and cracked on undersurface. Mazzard cherry carries the disease without symptoms and budded stock may transmit it to healthy flowering scions. The virus is transmitted even if the inserted bud dies.

Rimocortius psorosis (*Citrivir psorosis*), CITRUS PSOROSIS VIRUS on orange, lemon, and grapefruit wherever grown. Small, elongated light-colored areas or flecks are formed near small veins on young, tender foliage; leaves are sometimes warped, with clearing of veins and chlorotic line patterns, sometimes concentric. Outer layers of bark scale away, and depressions and deformities appear in bark and wood. Lemons are usually more tolerant than oranges.

There are three strains with somewhat varying symptoms. In some, gum is produced in advance of bark scaling. Yields are reduced and trees are eventually killed. Transmission is by budding, or root grafting, which includes natural grafts from one tree to the next.

Control. Remove trees with advanced infection; remove infected branches of other trees or scrape out the lesions. In California, trees for budwood are regularly inspected and tested for freedom from psorosis. Such trees are registered by the California Department of Agriculture.

Rimocortius pyri, Pear Stony-Pit virus, Oregon, Washington, California. Fruit is deeply pitted and deformed; bark is cracked and resembles oak bark; some leaves have veinlet chlorosis with failure of lateral buds to grow and reduction of foliage. Bartlett and Comice varieties are tolerant, producing sound fruit from infected trees. Transmission is by budding.

RUGA

Rugaceae. Leaf-curl group; development of invaded tissues is suddenly arrested, with leaf curl, enations, and other deformities. Vectors are whiteflies.

Ruga verrucosans (*Chlorogenus eutetticola*). Sugar-Beet Curly-Top Virus on a very wide range of plants in many families of dicotyledons. Curly top is especially important in the commercial sugar-beet industry and thousands of acres have had to be abandoned, but it is also common, west of the Rockies, on many vegetables and ornamentals, including bean, beet, carrot, celery; cabbage and other crucifers; cucumber and other cucurbits; eggplant, New Zealand spinach, and carnation, delphinium, coreopsis, cosmos, petunia, portulaca, poppy, scabiosa, strawflower, zinnia and other flowers.

In beets there is clearing of veins, leaf curling, with sharp protuberances from veins on lower surface of leaf, and increase in number of rootlets. In tomato, where the disease is called western yellow blight or tomato yellows, there is retarded growth, dropping of flowers and buds, rolling, yellowing and thickening of leaves, root decay, and death, or sometimes recovery.

Cucurbits have tips of runners bending upward, yellowing of old leaves, abnormal deep green in tip leaves and stems. In beans, there is a thickening and downward curling of the first true leaf which becomes brittle. The plant stops growing and may die. Older plants survive until the end of the season, showing puckering and downward curling at top of the plant, reduction in size of new leaves and shortened internodes. Ornamentals are usually infected when grown near badly diseased beet fields. Pansies, nasturtium, geraniums, zinnia, etc., are stunted, with leaves mottled and deformed.

Transmission is by the beet leafhopper, *Eutettix tenellus,* and when sugar beets are pulled out swarms of infective hoppers fly out to all neighboring vegetation. The disease is limited to the geographical range of the migratory leafhopper which has its breeding grounds in semiarid areas west of the Rocky Mountains.

In western yellow blight, the disease produced by the virus on tomatoes, seedlings are particularly susceptible, soon turning yellow and dying. Older plants show twisting and upward rolling of leaflets, stiff and leathery foliage, dull yellowing of the whole plant. Branches and stems become abnormally erect and leaf petioles curl downward. Roots and rootlets are killed and few fruits formed. All standard varieties are susceptible, with early varieties killed more quickly.

Control. There are no very satisfactory control methods. Getting rid of weed hosts helps a little, as does varying the time of planting to avoid severe insect attack when tomatoes are small. Shading plants with slats or cloth-covered frames tends to keep insects away. Once an ornamental is infected with curly top there is nothing to do but destroy it. Perhaps spraying or dusting with DDT will give some protection against leafhoppers.

SAVOIA

Savoiaceae. Savoy-disease group; chief symptom crinkling of foliage; vectors are true bugs.

Savoia piesmae, BEET-SAVOY VIRUS on beet in Michigan, Ohio, Minnesota, South Dakota, Wyoming. Leaves are dwarfed, curled down with small veins thickened; roots have phloem necrosis. Transmission by the tingid bug, *Piesma cinerea.*

The following virus diseases are in addition to those named by Holmes in *Bergey's Manual.* They are listed in alphabetical order by hosts.

BEAN YELLOW MOSAIC. **Phaseolus Virus** 2, also causes MILD MOSAIC OF GLADIOLUS, on beans, peas, sweet peas, clovers, gladiolus and freesia. In beans there is a coarse yellow mottle and distortion of leaves, proliferation of stems and shortening of nodes, general stunting, reduced pod production, delayed maturity. In pea and sweet pea there is veinal chlorosis with slight ruffling. Gladiolus flowers are striped or flecked, and young leaves have an angular green mottling; but symptoms are mild compared to those on bean and freesia, which should not be planted near commercial gladiolus fields.

BLUEBERRY STUNT. Bushes are dwarfed, with small leaves, yellowing in summer, brilliant red in fall; berries are small, poor.

CARNATION MOSAIC. Leaves are mottled with light-green, irregular to elongated, blotches. Colored flowers may show somewhat lighter streaks. Transmission is by mechanical contact in cultural practices.

CARNATION STREAK. Yellowish or reddish spots and streaks parallel leaf veins. Lower leaves may turn yellow and die. The streak virus combined with the mosaic virus produce the condition known as yellows with severely spotted foliage. Streak is transmitted by aphids.

CHRYSANTHEMUM STUNT, a new and serious disease first recognized in 1945 and rather generally prevalent on chrysanthemums in greenhouses by 1946. Transmission is by grafts, with symptoms appearing in 3½ to 10 months. Leaves are smaller and paler green than normal, flowers are smaller, with the color bleached in some pink and bronze varieties. There is a tendency to more upright growth. Plants at maturity are about half as tall as healthy plants and blossom 7 to 10 days prematurely. They will flower under a daily light period of 14 hours, a fact which can separate infected from normal plants.

Control. Select healthy plants during two successive flowering periods, control aphids, and reduce handling hazards.

Citrus Quick Decline. Recently important in California in sweet orange trees grown on sour orange stock. The first symptom is the dull, ashen color of top of the tree, followed by curling of leaves lengthwise and upward, then wilting and drying, leaf fall, and death of fibrous roots and disappearance of starch in affected roots and trunk. Orange trees on sweet orange roots can serve as symptomless carriers.

Citrus Stubborn Disease. **Citrivir pertinaciae.** Navel oranges have multiple buds, abnormal branching, acorn shape of fruit, which is sour and bitter at the navel end.

Gladiolus White-Break Mosaic. This is now considered the most serious gladiolus virus disease even though conclusive proof of its virus nature is yet lacking. Leaves sometimes show a streaking or spotting similar to thrips injury. Color breaking in flowers resulting in gray or yellow-green spots on florets, by color transformation in some varieties with thicker petal texture, and color degradation to a lighter than normal hue are all white-break symptoms. Corms may be malformed, warty, constricted into unequal segments.

Control. Remove all diseased plants, most readily detected at flowering.

Lily Rosette, Yellow Flat. **Lilium Virus** 1, on *Lilium longiflorum*. Leaves curl downward, plants are dwarfed, yellowed, mature early. Transmission is by the cotton aphid, not through seed.

Control. Rogue diseased plants as soon as noticed.

Narcissus Mosaic, Yellow Stripe, Gray Disease. Plants are dwarfed. Leaves are streaked pale green, grayish or yellow, often roughed with raised areas near veins and with a peculiar twist in some varieties. Flowers are small, of poor texture, on shorter stems, often with frost-like streaks. Transmission is by aphids, possibly by root contact but not through seeds or soil.

Control. Rogue diseased plants as noticed, with final selection during blooming period.

Narcissus White Streak, Silver Streak. Narrow dark green streaks in leaves become prominently white, gray, or yellowish after flowering. Similar streaks occur on flower stems. There is early maturity.

Pea Streak. **Pisum Virus** 5, on peas, soy bean, clovers. Pea leaflets curl downward, with tendrils distorted, twisted, apical parts rosetted. Transmission is by the pea aphid.

Peony Mosaic, Ringspot. **Paeonia Virus** 1, on peony and petunia. Yellows rings, irregular patches of mottling, or sometimes small necrotic spots are formed. Plants are not dwarfed, and no control is required.

Peperomia Ringspot. Plants are stunted, leaves distorted and disfigured by systemic chlorotic or brown necrotic rings.

Soybean Mosaic. **Soja Virus** 1. Leaves are distorted, stunted, with margins curled downward, surface puckered with dark green, puffy areas between veins; petioles and internodes shortened; pods stunted, flattened, curved; seeds few, small. Transmission is by aphids and in some seed.

WHITE RUSTS

White rusts are all members of a single genus, Albugo, in the Phycomycetes and are apparently obligate parasites like the true rusts. They form a white blister just underneath the epidermis.

ALBUGO (*Cystopus*)

Phycomycetes, Peronosporales, Albuginaceae

Sporangia are borne in chains at apex of a short, clavate, usually unbranched sporangiophore, forming a limited sorus beneath the host epidermis and exposed by its rupture. The mycelium is intercellular except for small, knoblike haustoria. The sporangia dry to a white powder and are disseminated by wind, germinating by swarmspores. Fertilization of a globose oogonium and a clavate antheridium produces a single oospore, also germinating by swarmspores.

Albugo bliti. White Rust, or white blister, on beet, amaranth, globe amaranth. Blister-like white pustules formed in leaves change to reddish brown when mature. Flowers and stems are dwarfed, distorted. The fungus winters in seed coats. Destroy infected plants and debris at end of season. Change location of plantings.

Albugo candida. White Rust of Crucifers on cabbage, chinese cabbage, radish, horse-radish, turnip, water-cress, garden cress, peppergrass, salsify, mustard and arabis, sweet alyssum, boerhavia, draba, hesperis, candytuft, stock, wallflower, and western wallflower.

Blisters appear on any part of host except roots. They vary in size and shape and are often confluent in extended patches. There seem to be two types of infection, general or systemic resulting in stunting of entire plant and formation of pustules on all parts, or local with direct invasion of single leaves, stems or flowers. Upper surface of leaves often has yellow areas with white pustules on the undersurface. The latter are powdery when mature, and the epidermis is ruptured to free chains of sporangia that are carried by wind to moist surfaces. They germinate by 6 to 18 zoospores, swarmspores, which settle down, produce germtubes and enter plants through a stomata.

Stems have localized or extended swellings, sometimes sharp bends, proliferation from lateral buds giving a bushy growth. Various flower parts are deformed with pronounced distortion of flower pedicels. When these thickened parts die, oospores are formed to survive the winter in crop refuse. The disease flourishes in cool, wet weather, for the spores germinate better when slightly chilled.

Control. Remove infected parts of ornamentals as noticed. Clean up all vegetable refuse at end of season and all cruciferous weeds near by. Spraying is usually impractical.

Albugo ipomoeae-panduratae. White Rust, general on sweet potato, also on morning-glory, moonflower, jacquemontia, quamoclit. The disease is usually late on sweet potato, after vines have made their growth, but it is very conspicuous with irregular yellow areas on upper surface and white cheesy pustules on lower surface. Oospores wintering in host tissue are liberated by decay in spring. There are no control measures.

Albugo occidentalis. White Rust of Spinach, a fairly new disease which appeared in Texas in epidemic form in 1937. The white blisters are small, usually on underside of leaves, sometimes on upper. Infected leaves tend to become chlorotic and finally brown.

Albugo platensis. White Rust on trailing four o'clock, common four o'clock and boerhavia.

Albugo portulacae. White Rust on portulaca. Swollen and deformed branches bear white pustules. Shoots tend to become more erect and spindling.

Albugo tragopogonis. White Rust general on salsify, also on antennaria, artemisia, centaurea, feverfew, matricaria, senecio, sunflower.

Light yellow areas appear on leaves. Epidermis, forced into domelike swellings, bursts to show chalk-like sorus of spores. Foliage may die, plants are dwarfed. There is no control.

WILT DISEASES

Wilting means to lose freshness or to become flaccid. Wilting in plants may be temporary, due to too rapid transpiration; or it may be permanent, due to continued loss of water beyond the recovery point. Disease organisms, by reducing or inhibiting water conduction, may cause permanent wilting.

Because wilt diseases are systemic and tied up with the entire vascular system of a plant, they are usually more important, and harder to control, than localized spots or cankers. Oftentimes the fungus is present near the base of a tree while the first symptom is a flagging or wilting or yellowing of a branch way at the top. Many species and forms of Fusarium are responsible for important wilts and "yellows." Verticillium is a common cause of wilt but probably the Dutch elm disease, caused by *Ceratostomella ulmi,* ranks as our major tree wilt.

CEPHALOSPORIUM (See under Leaf Spots)

Cephalosporium diospyri. Persimmon Wilt, a lethal disease of common persimmon. Wilt appears in scattered localities from North Carolina to Florida and west to Oklahoma and Texas, but with most infection in north central Florida and central Tennessee. Spread is rapid and death quick. First notice of the disease was in Tennessee in 1933. By 1938, only 5 per cent of the persimmons in the infected stand were alive. Topmost branches wilt suddenly, then rest of the tree, with defoliation and death. The fungus fruits in salmon-colored spore masses in cracks in dead bark of dying trees, or under bark of dead trees. Fine, blackish-brown streaks are present in five or six outer growth rings of trunk, branches, and roots. No control is known.

CERATOSTOMELLA

Ascomycetes, Sphaeriales, Ceratostomataceae

Perithecia superficial, with long prominent beaks, glabrous; spores hyaline, 1-celled. Some species cause blue-stain in wood, following after beetles. The fungi causing London Plane canker and sweet potato rot have been transferred from Ceratostomella to the closely related Endoconidiophora. The most important species is that causing Dutch elm disease, the conidial stage being a Graphium (Moniliales, Stilbaceae) with hyaline conidia on a coremium or synnema, an erect fascile of hyphae, in a mucous head.

Ceratostomella ulmi (conidial stage *Graphium ulmi*). DUTCH ELM DISEASE on American and European elms, Col., Conn., Del., Ind., Ky., Mass., Md., N. J., N. Y., Ohio, Pa., R. I., Tenn., Va., W. Va., and D. C. This fatal disease is not really of Dutch origin but is so named because it was first investigated in Holland. It was noticed in Europe about 1918, first in France, Belgium, and Holland. It spread throughout central and southern Europe, and then into England and Wales. In many places it virtually exterminated the elms, including those in the famous avenues at Versailles. It is suspected that the fungus came to Europe from Asia during the first World War.

Dutch elm disease was discovered in Ohio in 1930 and in northern New Jersey in 1933. It has spread north into Massachusetts, but an extensive infec-

FIG. 108. Elmwood Avenue after the Dutch elm disease reached town.

tion in Quebec is probably a direct introduction from Europe. In 1948 the disease was found in Denver, Colo., a long jump from the previous western boundary.

The spread of the fungus is linked with the presence of the large and small European bark beetles, *Scolytus scolytus* and *S. multistriatus*. Only the latter is established in this country, having arrived in Boston about 1909. Patient detective work has established the fact that the fungus came here in elm burl logs imported for furniture veneer. After one such infected elm burl was found in Baltimore, in 1934, months of scouting went on in the vicinity of ports of entry, railroad distributing yards, and veneer plants. Such backtracking showed that infected material had come in at four ports of entry and had been carried by 16 railroads over 13,000 miles in 21 states. From this source the disease got its deadly start in at least 13 areas in 7 states.

Elm nursery stock has of course been quarantined and elm burls embargoed, but who would have believed dishes could have anything to do with killing our elms? Dishes have to be crated, however, and several times since 1933 English dishes crated with elm wood carrying bark beetles and Ceratostomella have been intercepted at Quarantine.

All American and European elms are attacked. Asiatic elms, *Ulmus parvifolia,* and *U. pumila* are resistant. A seedling elm, named Christine Buisman for its discoverer, is highly resistant in the Netherlands and is being tested here. Other promising seedlings are now being developed and tested by the U.S. Department of Agriculture.

Symptoms are apparent from the latter part of May until late fall. The acute form of the disease is characterized by sudden and severe wilting. First the young leaves, then all leaves wilt and wither, sometimes so rapidly that they dry, curl, and fall while still green, before they can turn the usual brown of dead leaves. Sometimes terminal twigs are curved into a shepherd's crook.

Chronic disease symptoms are gradual, often taking all summer for complete defoliation. In many cases individual branches or "flags" appear, the yellowed leaves conspicuous against the green of the rest of the tree, but sometimes all leaves gradually turn yellow. In another type of chronic disease trees leaf out late in spring, with sparse, chlorotic foliage and a staghead appearance.

When an affected twig is cut across, the vessels or water-conducting tubes show dark brown or black, being clogged with bladder-like "tyloses" and brown gummy substances. The production of these is stimulated by a toxin secreted by the fungus and carried in the sapstream. It is not dependent on the physical presence of fungus hyphae in all parts of the tree.

The *fungus* lives in the sapwood, fruiting in cracks between wood and loosened bark and in bark beetle galleries under the bark. This fruiting is of the imperfect stage, spores being produced in structures called coremia. These are black stalks about 1 mm. high with enlarged heads bearing vast numbers of minute, egg- to pear-shaped spores embedded in a translucent drop of sticky liquid. Spores in the vessels increase in a yeastlike manner. The perithecial stage has not been found in nature but has been artificially produced in culture by crossing plus and minus strains of the fungus.

Although the smaller European elm bark beetle is chiefly responsible for spread of the disease, at times the native elm bark beetle (*Hylurgopinus rufipes*) is the agent. When the adult beetles emerge from under the bark of dead or dying trees they bring along the sticky spores on their bodies and

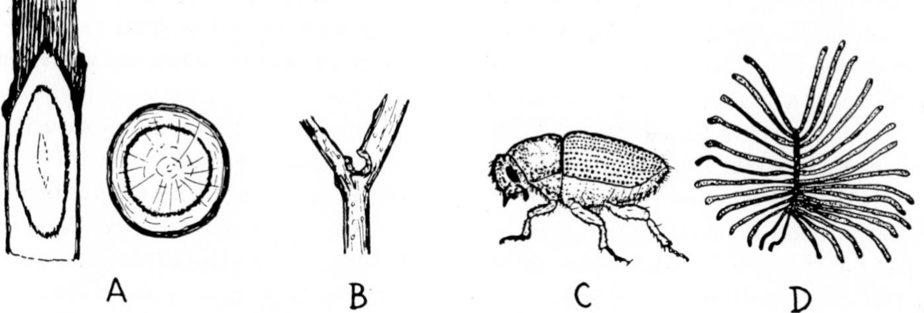

FIG. 109. Dutch Elm Disease. A, branch cut to show discoloration of wood; B, wound in twig crotch due to beetle feeding; C, bark-beetle carrier of the fungus; D, egg and larval galleries of the beetle engraved on sapwood.

deposit these spores as they feed in the crotches of young twigs or leaf axils of near-by healthy trees. So far as we know the only other natural means of infection is by root grafts made when trees are planted so close their roots overlap.

Although they *feed* on healthy wood the beetles *breed* only on weakened or dying wood. The European female tunnels out a brood gallery one or two inches long in the wood and when the larvae hatch they tunnel at right angles. The native beetle makes its egg gallery across the wood. There is a second brood in August and September but the overwintering one, emerging in May, is most to be feared.

Control. 1. ERADICATION. In the first few frantic years an enormous amount of money (more than $26,000,000) was spent on trying to stop the spread of disease by removing and burning diseased trees and while this was undoubtedly helpful it did not stop the spread of the wilt. The Federal government has now left eradication up to the communities and private citizens and is bending its efforts toward research. There is no reason for a town to abandon its cleaning-up program. Any community now free from the disease should attempt to keep a disease-free zone 1000 feet wide around the town, cutting down all affected trees in that area and getting rid of all bark before beetles fly in May. Although beetles may fly a couple of miles to breed, they seldom travel more than a few hundred feet for the spring feeding which spreads the spores. If felled trees cannot have the bark removed at once they can be made safe by spraying with a mixture of 8 pounds technical DDT dissolved in 100 gallons of No. 2 fuel oil, applied to wet the bark surface completely. Within the barrier and in the town trees should be kept vigorous and healthy by pruning all weak and storm-damaged limbs, spraying to control cankerworms, elm leaf beetles, and other foliage pests which weaken the trees.

My own town has consistently carried through a program of immediate removal of diseased elms, pruning and spraying, and has had a remarkably small percentage of Dutch elm disease even though it is in the heart of the region of heavy infection and surrounded by communities which have lost a great many of their elms.

2. ELIMINATING THE CARRIER. Experimental spraying at present is directed toward control of the bark beetles. It can be done with large amounts of DDT, applied in various ways, although the possible effect on plantings underneath the trees and on birds may not be harmless. The U.S. Department of Agriculture has released the following formulae as noninjurious to elm trees and with long-lasting residues.

Formula A. 16 pounds of technical DDT dissolved in 2¼ gallons of benzene and 1 gallon of Velsicol AR–50; add 1 pint of Triton X–100. For use in hydraulic sprayers: dilute with water to 100 gallons for the first treatment; dilute to 200 gallons for the second treatment.

Formula B. 16 pounds technical DDT dissolved in 4 gallons xylene; add 1 pint of Triton X–100. Dilute as given in Formula A.

Formula C. For mist blowers: 20 pounds technical DDT dissolved in a mixture of 5 gallons xylene and 2½ gallons Acme white oil; add 1½ pints of Triton X–100. Dilute with water to 20 gallons for the first treatment; to 40 gallons for the second treatment.

The first treatment is a dormant spray, made for complete bark coverage before elm flowers or leaves appear. The second treatment is made 2½ to 3 months after the first.

The average 50-foot elm tree will require 25 to 30 gallons of spray with hydraulic equipment and 2 to 3 gallons with a mist blower. This means a large amount of DDT per tree, far greater than in usual spraying operations for foliage insects.

3. CHEMOTHERAPY is promising. Chemicals do not cure but often inactivate the toxin so the tree keeps on getting water and survives along with the fungus. A Long Island arborist started treating diseased trees with potassium permanganate nearly 15 years ago and a large percentage of treated trees are still alive. Of course, some elms recover naturally. The Connecticut Experiment Station has been testing many chemicals, the best known to date being oxyquinoline benzoate applied to the soil around a tree with surface injection apparatus. The Rhode Island Experiment Station is also pioneering in chemotherapy.

4. RESISTANT VARIETIES are on the way, but it takes time, and trying to find elms resistant to both Dutch elm disease and phloem necrosis is difficult.

It is impossible for the amateur, and often the expert, to diagnose Dutch elm disease in the field because symptoms can be confused with those of other wilts. If you suspect the disease, take at least six specimens of discolored twigs and branches from different parts of the tree, or slabs of wood cut from the trunk showing discoloration, tie the material from each tree into a separate bundle, mark with your name, and send to Dutch Elm Disease Identification Laboratory, Bureau of Entomology and Plant Quarantine, 503 Main Street, East Orange, N. J. Send a letter giving location of tree and details.

CHALARA

Fungi Imperfecti, Moniliales, Dematiaceae

Conidia endogenous, in simple chains, 1-celled with truncate or cut-off ends, hyaline; hyphae brown to subhyaline.

Chalara quercina. OAK WILT, a very serious disease of oaks in forests, parks, and residential areas of Illinois, Iowa, Minnesota, Missouri, and Wisconsin, apparently present in the Upper Mississippi Valley for nearly 70 years but increasingly important in the past 6 years. The fungus, a new species, was not described until 1943.

First symptoms are slight crinkling and paling of leaves, followed by progressive wilting, bronzing and browning of leaf blades from margins toward midrib and defoliation progressively downward and inward throughout the tree. Red oaks never recover and are usually killed within 4 to 8 weeks after first symptoms, unless infection takes place late in the season. White oaks and bur oaks may persist for several years, with affected branches dying, leaving a staghead effect. All oak species are susceptible.

Infection is apparently through wounds and most often in trees only 30 to 40 feet from a diseased tree but the manner of transmission is not known. Mycelium and very small conidia are found in the xylem, or vessels, and may be carried in the transpiration stream. A toxin typical of wilt diseases is also produced. The fungus winters in stumps of dead trees or in roots, boles, branches, twigs, or leaves of infected white oaks and other oaks not killed as rapidly as red oaks.

Control. No satisfactory method is yet known. If all dead and dying trees in an area are removed, with a 50-foot perimeter of apparently healthy trees also removed the disease can be checked, but this is a most drastic procedure. White oaks can sometimes be saved by cutting out affected branches 4 to 6 feet below the wilted portion.

DEUTEROPHOMA

Fungi Imperfecti, Sphaeropsidales, Sphaerioidaceae

Very minute, almost bacterial-sized spores produced in large numbers in irregular to spherical pycnidia without openings.

Deuterophoma ulmi. Dothiorella or Cephalosporium Wilt of Elms, rather common on American elm, occasional on slippery and Siberian elms in central and eastern United States. The names are confusing. In culture the fungus develops spores as in Cephalosporium and in nature pycnidia are developed, on bark of killed twigs, similar to those of Dothiorella. The fungus, however, has been recently renamed Deuterophoma. Spores are extruded in a sticky mass and are disseminated by wind, rain or possibly insects, and infection is through insect or other wounds on foliage. The mycelium proceeds from leaf petioles into wood where it is confined to the vessels. The foliage wilts and yellows, there is gradual dying back of the crown and a brownish discoloration in outer rings of the wood. Without laboratory diagnosis the disease cannot be positively separated from Dutch elm disease. Older trees die in three to several years after first symptoms, nursery trees in one or two years. Some trees recover and some are infected for many years without much injury.

Control. Prune out infected branches a foot or more below the lowest point of discoloration; burn. A combination insecticide-fungicide spray will reduce the number of leaf infections.

FUSARIUM (See under Rots)

Fusarium orthoceras var. **gladioli.** Fusarium Yellows, a major field disease of gladiolus but somewhat less important now with increased use of resistant varieties. Leaves stop growing, are yellowed in a localized or general blanching, then turn brown and die, often lying on the ground. When the corm is sectioned crosswise a brown discoloration of the core can be seen. The disease is most destructive in dry seasons with high soil temperature, and the fungus can persist in the soil several years.

Control. There are many resistant varieties, including the favorite Picardy. See Michigan Special Bulletin 350 for a long list. Annual treatment of corms with a fungicide will not entirely prevent the disease but is an aid in keeping stock healthy. Small corms for propagating can be soaked for two hours in a 1 to 1000 solution of mercuric chloride, then dipped for one minute in calomel suspension.

Fusarium orthoceras var. **pisi.** Fusarium Wilt of Pea. Plants are stunted, pale yellow-green, with leaves curled downward, stem thickened and brittle near the ground. Plants wilt and die prematurely. The disease may cause more or less circular bare spots in the field, enlarging each year if peas are planted continuously and encouraged by high soil temperature.

Control. Use resistant varieties such as Telephone, Dwarf Alderman, Teton, Asgrow 40.

Fusarium oxysporum f. **apii.** CELERY WILT OR YELLOWS, general in northern celery districts. Plants turn yellow, are stunted; stalks are brittle and taste bitter.

Control. Use a 4- to 5-year rotation. Grow resistant varieties: Forbes Golden Plume, Florida Golden, Green Utah, Paragon, N. Y. 19, Early Green, Sweetheart.

FIG. 110. Fusarium Wilt of Sweet William; healthy plant at rear.

Fusarium oxysporum f. **barbati.** FUSARIUM WILT OF SWEET WILLIAM. New growth is yellowed, plants are stunted, leaves point downward and are tinged with tan as they die. Roots and lower stem are discolored brown. Plant in new or sterilized soil.

Fusarium oxysporum f. **batatas.** SWEET POTATO WILT, STEM ROT, general on sweet potato. This major sweet-potato disease is recognized by dying runners and browning of vascular tissues. Plants are yellowish, lower leaves drop off; base of stem turns dark, with a brown or black layer just under the epidermis. Varieties Yellow Jersey, Red Jersey, and Porto Rico are very susceptible. The somewhat resistant Spanish group includes Dahomey, Red Brazil, Southern Queen, Yellow Strasburg, Key West, Triumph, White Yam.

Control. Do not use same land for sweet potato more than once in three or four years; use disease-free mother potatoes for propagation, and vine-cuttings instead of sprouts for field plantings, or use certified plants. Sterilize suspected soil for bedding. Dip cuttings or sprouts in Spergon or Fermate.

Fusarium oxysporum f. **callistephi.** ASTER WILT, one of the most serious diseases of China aster unless resistant seed is used. Plants wilt, wither, and die at any age from seedlings to full bloom. Older plants are often stunted, with a one-sided development and a brown discoloration of the vascular system. Sometimes all lower leaves are wilted with blackening at base of stem; plants in full bloom may suddenly drop their heads, in contrast to the virus disease, aster yellows, where the plant remains upright, though stunted and yellowed. The fungus is carried in the seed and may persist indefinitely in soil.

Control. Nearly all seedmen advertise wilt-resistant strains. If these are not used seed should be soaked ½ hour in 1–1000 solution of mercuric chloride or Semesan. The latter will not help if the soil is fungus-infested.

Fusarium oxysporum f. **conglutinans.** CABBAGE YELLOWS, FUSARIUM WILT, general on cabbage and other crucifers. This is probably the most destructive disease of crucifers in the Midwest and perhaps other sections. It is serious on cabbage, kohlrabi, and collards, and infects cauliflower, Brussels sprouts, and broccoli moderately in hot, dry seasons.

The fungus, which can live many years in the soil, enters through the roots, usually right after transplanting and at the first hot weather, infection being favored by high temperatures (and also potassium deficiency). Infection advances through the conducting system until the whole plant is killed.

The most striking symptom is the dull yellow to greenish color of the foliage, together with a warping or curling of basal leaves. Leaves die and are shed from the base up, the plant dying of starvation. The woody tissue in the stem is brown, with a water-soaked appearance.

The fungus is spread by means of farm implements, drainage water, wind, animals, infected plant debris, and infected seedlings transplanted into the field. Once the disease is established, general sanitation and crop rotation are of little help in getting rid of a pathogen which can persist so long in the soil.

Control. Do not plant susceptible crucifers in infested soil. There are many resistant varieties, including Jersey Queen, Marion Market, Globe, Wisconsin Golden Acre, Wisconsin All-Season, and Wisconsin Hollander.

Fusarium oxysporum f. **dianthi.** Fusarium Wilt, Stem Rot, Yellows of Carnation, general. The first symptom is a slow withering of shoots often accompanied by change of color from normal deep green to lighter green to pale straw yellow. Plants may appear wilted, especially during the warmer part of the day. Only one side of the plant may be affected, resulting in distortion and tendency to curl. If the stem is split a brownish streak is seen in the vascular system. There may be a dry, shreddy rot of affected wood and cortex. Plants may be infected at any age but succumb faster if attacked when young. The wilt disease does not rot the roots but other root-rot fungi may follow.

Control. Sterilize greenhouse soil and benches; use only healthy plants for cuttings; avoid overwatering. New chemicals for treating soil where plants are growing offer promise.

Fusarium oxysporum f. **lycopersici.** Fusarium Wilt of Tomato, general on tomato, the most damaging tomato disease in many sections, in field and greenhouse. Chief losses are in states where air temperatures are rather high during most of the season, susceptible varieties dying or producing little fruit. Losses go up to 30,000 tons of canning tomatoes, or 10 to 35 per cent of the crop in many states.

In seedlings there is downward curvature of the oldest leaves followed by wilting and death. On older plants the disease is most evident as fruit begins to mature, lower leaves turning yellow, first on one side of the stem, or leaflets on one side of the petiole. One shoot may be killed before the rest of the plant shows symptoms.

The fungus enters through roots and grows into the stem where it produces the toxic substances causing wilting and eventual death. The vascular system in the stem shows a dark brown discoloration. In severe infections the fungus grows into fruits and seed, but such fruits usually drop and seed is not used.

Almost all infection comes from the soil, the Fusarium operating best in light sandy soils and at temperatures between 80° and 90° F.

Control. Start seedlings in clean soil; do not grow in the same land more than once in four years. Marglobe, Pritchard, Rutgers, and Pan America are wilt-resistant varieties, but infestation by the root-knot nematode predisposes even these to wilt.

Fusarium oxysporum f. **niveum.** Watermelon Wilt, general on watermelon and cucumbers, also on winter and summer squash, pumpkin. Symptoms are similar to other Fusarium wilts. Vines turn yellow and wilt about fruiting time, with dark streaks in the stem. The fungus is seedborne, and can remain viable in soil as much as 15 to 18 years.

Control. Use wilt resistant varieties, such as Hawksbury, Improved Kleckly Sweet No. 6, Klondike R 7, Iowa King, Pride of Muscatine.

Fusarium oxysporum f. **pisi.** Near Wilt of Peas, also on soybean, similar to Fusarium Pea Wilt but attacking varieties resistant to that. Do not plant peas in infested land for several years.

Fusarium oxysporum f. **perniciosum.** MIMOSA WILT on mimosa from New Jersey and Maryland to Alabama. This extremely pernicious wilt started about 1930 at Tryon, N. C., and mimosas have wilted and died at a rapid rate ever since. The wilt appeared in one city block at Morganton, N. C., in 1943 and by 1947 trees were dead or dying on 232 blocks.

The first external symptom is wilting of leaves on some of the branches, causing foliage to hang down, then die and drop. Death of the trees follows defoliation from a month to a year after first infection. The trunk has a brown ring of discolored sapwood, usually in the current annual ring, and the color may extend out into the branches. The xylem is plugged with brown, gummy substances.

As with other Fusaria this is a soil fungus entering through the roots. Eradication of diseased trees has not stopped spread of the wilt. Out of a great many seedlings grown from seed collected from Maryland to Louisiana, inoculated several times with the fungus and planted in infested soil, some have remained disease-free for several years. The U.S. Department of Agrictulture hopes to release this resistant stock for propagation in the near future.

PHYTOPHTHORA (See under Blights)

Phytophthora cinnamomi. RHODODENDRON WILT. This is chiefly a wilt of young stock, on grafted plants 2 to 3 years old, seldom on older shrubs, and most severe on *Rhododendron ponticum*. The foliage is first dull yellow, then permanently wilted; roots are decayed; base of stems are brown at soil level and below.

Control. Remove infected stock in frames immediately; avoid excessive irrigation; keep soil acidity at pH 4 to 4.5; provide shade and mulch for young plants.

VERTICILLIUM

Fungi Imperfecti, Moniliales, Moniliaceae

Conidia 1-celled, hyaline, globose to ellipsoid, formed at tips of whorled branches and separating readily from the tips.

Verticillium albo-atrum. VERTICILLIUM WILT of maple, elm, fruit trees and other wood plants, aconite, chrysanthemum, dahlia and other herbaceous perennials, tomato, eggplant and other vegetables, strawberries, raspberries and other bush fruits.

Verticillium wilt is widespread in the United States and particularly important because it attacks so many (more than 150) unrelated plants of value as ornamentals or for food. The fungus was first isolated from potatoes in Germany in 1879, but apparently was present in California about 1850.

Symptoms. Lower leaves turn yellow in early summer and die as the pathogen, starting in the root system, passes slowly up the trunk or stem. Internodes are shortened, the plant is stunted and internally the wood has a characteristic brown discoloration. In annuals an attack is fatal. Perennials may be killed or recover.

Maples and elms are most susceptible among ornamental trees. Maples may have sudden wilting in midsummer, often a large branch or one side of the

FIG. 111. Verticillium Wilt of Aconite (Monkshood).

tree drying while the other side stays fresh. The sapwood of the infected side will have greenish streaks, and sometimes slime flux develops on the bark. In elms the leaves may be smaller than normal, with a drooping flaccidity in hot hours of the day. Later there is a slight yellowing, deepening until the foliage is a striking lemon yellow. Defoliation starts at time of first yellowing and quite often branchlets drop as well as leaves. The disease cannot be told positively from Dutch elm disease without laboratory cultures. Tyloses and gums are formed in the wood as with other toxin-producing fungi.

In fruit trees the disease is often known as black heart, or verticillosis. It is common in apricots, less so in almonds and peaches; branches may drop their leaves and die. In bush fruits the disease is commonly known as blue stem. The symptoms appear late in the season—leaves turning pale, cane tips bending downward, canes taking on a bluish color, lower leaves wilting and drying. Death is often delayed until the season after first infection. Black raspberries are more susceptible than red. Wilt in strawberries is more important in California, large areas having plants collapsing at the beginning of hot weather.

In tomatoes, Verticillium wilt is especially damaging in Utah and California. Yellowing older leaves and wilting of tips during the day are first symptoms, later, the margins of all leaves curl upward, then drop. Plants are stunted, fruit is small.

On herbaceous perennials in eastern gardens I find Verticillium wilt most common on aconite and chrysanthemum with leaves turning dark brown and hanging down along the stem. When the stem is cut across near the base a circle of black dots indicates the fungus in the vessels. Such plants seldom die immediately but flower poorly and gradually peter out. Other ornamental hosts listed, many of them in California, include abutilon, aralia, barberry, begonia, China aster, carnation, dahlia, fremontia, cherry-laurel, marguerite, peony, poppy, snapdragon, stock, and viburnum.

Control. Sometimes it is possible to prune out an infected maple branch and still save the tree, but often the dying tree must be taken out. All tools used in the process should be sterilized before being used on healthy wood and neither maple nor elm should be planted again in the same spot. Cut affected branches of fruit trees back to the trunk; avoid excessive irrigation. Spraying is useless and soil disinfectants are unsatisfactory.

Do not set raspberry plants following potatoes or tomatoes; avoid poorly drained soil; do not transfer plants from any area where wilt has appeared. For tomatoes plan a long rotation, of six to seven years, without peppers, eggplant or potatoes. Home garden soil can be treated with formaldehyde, 1 part to 99 parts water.

Verticillium dahliae, often reported as causing wilt of dahlias and other plants but not clearly differentiated from *V. albo-atrum.*

CHAPTER 5

HOST PLANTS AND THEIR DISEASES

The information telescoped into this section is taken in large part from the records of the Plant Disease Survey as given in the *Plant Disease Reporter* and particularly from the Check List Revision, Diseases of Economic Plants of the United States, by Freeman Weiss, which has been released on the installment plan since 1940. As this manuscript goes to press the Re-Revised Check List is not yet available in book form, but Dr. Weiss has spent many hours correcting mistakes in my list and bringing the names up to date. Indubitably there are many mistakes left, for which I take full responsibility. Where there is a discrepancy in names, e.g., *Ruga verrucosans* versus *Chlorogenus eutetticola* for the virus causing curly top, I have followed the 1948 edition of *Bergey's Manual* for bacteria and viruses and Ainsworth and Bisby's *A Dictionary of the Fungi,* 1945 edition, for the fungi.

The hosts selected for inclusion in this Handbook are those trees, shrubs, vines, flowers, and vegetables likely to be grown in home gardens. Native plants sometimes grown in wild gardens are here, and some trees, like tung-oil, more often grown for profit but most definitely ornamental. Cereals, cotton, and other strictly field crops are omitted. Hosts are listed alphabetically by common names, except where the scientific name means less confusion.

The diseases are those reported from Maine to Florida, from New York to California, and some from Alaska for good measure. Tropical diseases are included only as they affect plants in southern Florida; those of Puerto Rico, the Canal Zone, and Hawaii are omitted for lack of any personal experience with them as well as lack of space.

The geographical distribution of diseases can only be taken as a general guide. It is quite likely that a disease present in New York is also present in New Jersey but has never been officially reported. Or it may be on the official list and inadvertently omitted by me, or reported after my compilation was completed. On the other hand, if a disease is listed for the Pacific Northwest and not from any eastern state it need not worry a New Jersey gardener for the present. Fungi possibly parasitic which are recorded as present on leaves or woody plant parts but not as causing a named disease, have also been omitted.

Diseases listed as "general" are prevalent throughout the host range, "wide-spread" means found over a large area but not prevalent, and "occasional" means of infrequent occurrence. The term "cosmopolitan" indicates universal distribution but not always primary importance, such diseases often being secondary following injuries.

Brief comments, following some of the listings, sort out a few of the more important problems but all specific information is to be found back in Chapter 4. There diseases are grouped according to the names by which they are commonly known, as rot, wilt, blight, black spot, and then by the name of the pathogen, the agent causing the disease. In this Host Section the key word, rot or blight, is given in capitals, followed by the name of the pathogen in bold face. In the disease section (Chapter 4) the pathogens are also listed in bold face, in alphabetical order under each heading of rot or blight, etc., and then the common name of the disease in capitals.

For instance, your acacia seems to be dying and you think maybe it has a root rot; perhaps you can even see objects like toadstools near the base. You look up ACACIA and check through the possibilities until you come to the line: "ROT, Mushroom Root. **Armillaria mellea,** occasional; **Clitocybe tabescens,** Fla."

"Occasional" means that this rot might sometimes be found wherever acacias grow. You live in California so you turn to the section headed ROTS (starting on page 279) and thumb down through the A's until you come to ARMILLARIA. Under the name is the classification of the genus, but you can leave that to the pathologist and go to:

"**Armillaria mellea.** MUSHROOM ROOT ROT of trees and shrubs, also known as Armillaria root rot or toadstool disease ——." You learn that this disease is especially common in California, where you live, and that the honey-colored mushrooms or toadstools are not always present for diagnosis but that black shoe-strings are also tell-tale characters. You conclude this is your fungus and you read on to see what can be done to the soil to prevent a recurrence of the problem. But before you do anything too drastic, you'd better discuss the whole situation with someone at the University of California, for you could be mistaken.

It cannot be expected that a gardener can make accurate diagnosis of disease from reading this Handbook any more than reading a medical book can turn a layman into a doctor. It takes years of experience to recognize diseases on sight, from macroscopic symptoms, and it takes some technical training to recognize diseases by studying the fungus under the microscope and perhaps growing it in culture. For airtight identification of a bacterium or fungus with a new disease not only must the same organism be repeatedly isolated in culture but the disease must be produced in healthy plants by inoculation with the organism grown in culture and finally the fungus, or bacterium, must be reisolated from the artificially infected plant.

In some cases the small number of known diseases for a plant together with their distinctive type and geographical distribution makes layman identification relatively reliable. In other cases specific identification, other than to know that it is a leaf spot, is unnecessary. And in still other cases specimens should be sent to your State Experiment Station for diagnosis. It is my faint hope that the overburdened extension pathologist, receiving some unusual specimen, will find this Host List and the disease descriptions of value in speeding up identifications.

HOST PLANTS

HEADINGS UNDER WHICH DISEASES ARE DESCRIBED

ANTHRACNOSE—dead spots with definite margins, often with pinkish slimy spore masses, on leaves, stems or fruit. SPOT ANTHRACNOSE—small light spots with slightly raised darker borders.

BACTERIAL DISEASES—all types of diseases—galls, blights, rots, leaf spots, caused by bacteria.

BLACK KNOT—black, knotty enlargement of woody tissue.

BLACK LEG—darkening at the base of a plant.

BLACK MILDEW—superficial dark growth caused by parasitic fungi.

BLACK SPOT—definite black lesions on leaves.

BLIGHTS—general killing of leaves, flowers, stems.

BLOTCH DISEASES—superficial dark spots on leaves or fruit often coalescing into irregular areas.

BROOMRAPE—leafless herb parasitic on roots.

CANKERS AND DIEBACKS—localized lesions on stems or trunks, sometimes accompanied by dying back from the top.

CLUB ROOT—distorted, swollen roots.

DAMPING-OFF—sudden wilting of seedlings, or rotting of seeds in soil.

DODDER—parasitic seed plant with conspicuous orange tendrils.

DOWNY MILDEWS—with internal mycelium but fruiting structures protruding to form white, gray or violet patches on leaves.

FRUIT SPOTS—blemishes on fruits.

LEAF BLISTER, LEAF CURL DISEASES—leaf deformities, overgrowths.

LEAF GALLS—leaves enlarged into more or less spherical galls.

LEAF SCORCH—discoloration as if by intense heat.

LEAF SPOTS—delimited dead areas on leaves.

MISTLETOE—semi-parasitic seed plant, forming leafy tufts in trees.

MOLDS—conspicuous fungus growth on leaves, seed, or grafts.

NEEDLE CASTS—conspicuous shedding of evergreen foliage.

NEMATODE DISEASES—root, leaf, stem, and bulb diseases caused by nematodes.

PHYSIOGENIC DISEASES—due to environmental conditions rather than specific organisms.

POWDERY MILDEWS—superficial white felty or powdery growth on leaves and flowers.

ROTS—soft or hard decay or disintegration of plant tissues.

RUSTS—with reddish or rust-colored spore masses.

SCAB—raised or crustlike lesions on leaves or fruit.

SCURF—flaky or scaly lesions.

SMUTS—with sooty black spore masses.

SNOWMOLD—light patches in turf, especially early spring.

SOOTY MOLD—superficial black mycelium growing in insect exudate.

VIRUS DISEASES—mosaics, ring spots, yellows, leaf curl, wilt caused by viruses.

WHITE RUSTS—white blisters in leaves.

WILTS—systemic diseases, interference with vascular system causing wilting and death of leaves and branches, including Dutch elm disease and Fusarium yellows.

ABELIA

NEMATODE, Root Knot. **Heterodera marioni,** Cal., Miss.

PHYSIOGENIC **Chlorosis,** due to soil alkalinity, Tex.

POWDERY MILDEW. **Oidium** sp., Tex.

ROT, Root. **Phymatotrichum omnivorum,** Tex.; **Rhizoctonia solani,** Tex.

ROT, Rootlet. **Pythium** sp.

Generally free from disease; may be top tender in northern winters unless planted in sheltered, well-drained locations.

ABUTILON (Flowering Maple, Indian Mallow and Velvet Leaf)

LEAF SPOT. **Alternaria** sp., Tex., Ill., Ind., N. J., N. Y.; **Cercospora abutilonis,** Ill., Tex.; **Cladosporium herbarum,** N. Y., Kans.; **Colletorichum malvarum,** Iowa; **Phyllosticta althaeina,** Tex.

NEMATODE, Root Knot. **Heterodera marioni,** Ala., Fla.

ROT, Stem. **Macrophomina phaseoli,** Ill.

ROT, Root. **Phymatotrichum omnivorum,** Tex.

RUST. **Puccinia heterospora** (III) ,* Fla. to Ariz.

VIRUS, Mosaic; Infectious chlorosis. **Marmor abutilon,** universal.

WILT. **Verticillium albo-atrum,** N. J.

The leaf spots and rots occur on Indian mallow and velvet leaf. Variegation or mottling in flowering maple is a true mosaic disease, although fostered as a desirable ornamental quality.

ACACIA

CANKER, Twig and Branch. **Nectria** sp., Cal., S. C.

LEAF SPOT, Algal. **Cephaleuros virescens,** Fla.

LEAF SPOT. **Physalospora fusca,** Fla.; **Cercospora** sp., Ga.

NEMATODE, Root Knot. **Heterodera marioni,** occasional.

PHYSIOGENIC **Chlorosis,** due to excess lime, Cal.; **Gummosis,** due to deficient or irregular moisture, Cal.

* Numbers refer to spore stage. See under Rusts.

Rot, Root. **Phymatotrichum omnivorum,** Tex.
Rot, Mushroom Root. **Armillaria mellea,** occasional; **Clitocybe tabescens,** Fla.
Rot, Heartwood. **Fomes applanatus,** Cal.
Rot, Sapwood. **Schizophyllum commune,** Cal.

ACALYPHA (Copper-Leaf)

Downy Mildew. **Plasmopara acalyphae,** Wis.
Leaf Gall. **Synchytrium aureum,** Wis.
Leaf Spot. **Cercospora acalyphae,** N. Y. to Ala., Okla., Tex., Wis.; **Phyllosticta** sp., N. J.; **Ramularia acalyphae,** Tex.
Nematode, Root Knot. **Heterodera marioni,** Md., Ga.
Powdery Mildew. **Erysiphe cichoracearum,** Wis.
Rot, Root. **Phymatotrichum omnivorum,** Tex.; **Rhizoctonia solani,** Ill.
Rot, Mushroom Root. **Clitocybe tabescens,** Fla.

ACANTHOPANAX (5-Leaf Aralia)

Leaf Spot. **Alternaria** sp., Mo.
Rot, Root. **Phymatotrichum omnivorum,** Tex.

ACTINOMERIS (Yellow Ironweed)

Leaf Spot. **Cercospora anomala,** Iowa; **Gloeosporium** sp., W. Va.
Powdery Mildew. **Erysiphe cichoracearum,** Pa. to Va. and Kans.
Rust. **Puccinia verbesinae** (O, I, II, III), Md., Me., Tenn.
Virus, Ring Spot. **Annulus tabaci,** Va.

AFRICAN DAISY (*Arctotis*)

Blotch, Leaf. **Cercospora** sp., Fla.
Nematode, Root Knot. **Heterodera marioni,** Fla.
Rot, Root. **Phymatotrichum omnivorum,** Tex.

AFRICAN-VIOLET (*Saintpaulia*)

Blight, Gray Mold, Leaf Rot. **Botrytis cinerea,** probably cosmopolitan.
Nematode, Leaf. **Aphelenchoides** sp., Cal.; Root Knot, **Heterodera marioni,** Md.
Nematode, Root, **Pratylenchus** sp., Md.
Physiogenic Ring Spot, due to wetting foliage with cold water, general.
Powdery Mildew. **Oidium** sp., occasional in greenhouses.
Rot, Root and Crown. **Pythium ultimum,** Cal.

Bright yellow ring patterns appear on leaves if there is too steep a temperature gradient between leaf and water. Sometimes yellowing is due to too bright sunlight. The cyclamen mite, and not a disease, causes puckering of foliage, abnormal flowers. The root nematode has been found in pots of plants with wilted foliage, flaccid petioles.

AGASTACHE (Giant-Hyssop)

DOWNY MILDEW. **Peronospora lophanthi,** Ill., Iowa, Wis.

LEAF SPOT, Stem Spot. **Ascochyta lophanthi,** Wis.

LEAF SPOT. **Ramularia lophanthi,** Cal., Mont.; **Septoria lophanthi,** Ill., Mo., Ohio, Wis.

POWDERY MILDEW. **Sphaerotheca humili** and var. **fuliginea,** Mo., Wis., Utah, Wash.

RUST. **Puccinia hyssopi** (III), N. Y. to Iowa, Mo., Wis.

VIRUS, Mosaic. Unidentified. Ind.

AGERATUM

BLIGHT, Southern. **Sclerotium rolfsii,** N. J., N. C., probably elsewhere.

ROT, Root. **Pythium mamillatum,** Cal.

ROT, Root and Stem. **Rhizoctonia solani,** Ill., N. J.

RUST. **Puccinia conoclinii** (II, III), Ga., Miss., N. C.; O, I unknown.

AGRIMONY (*Agrimonia*)

DOWNY MILDEW. **Peronospora potentillae,** N. Y., Wis., Iowa.

LEAF SPOT. **Cercospora** sp., Ill.; **Septoria agrimoniae,** Mo., Iowa, Wis.; **Phyllosticta decidua,** N. C., Wis.

POWDERY MILDEW. **Sphaerotheca humuli,** Mass. to N. C., Nebr., Wis.

ROT, Root. **Phymatotrichum omnivorum,** Tex.

RUST. **Puccinia agrimoniae** (II, III), Mo.; **Pucciniastrum agrimoniae** (II, III), general on native species.

VIRUS, Mosaic. Unidentified. N. Y.

AILANTHUS (Tree-of-Heaven)

BLACK MILDEW. **Dimerosporium robiniae,** D. C.

BLIGHT, Twig. **Fusarium lateritium,** Va.

CANKER, DIEBACK. **Nectria cinnabarina,** Kans., N. J., S. C.; **Physalospora obtusa,** Kans., Mich., N. Y.

CANKER, Trunk. **Nectria coccinea,** occasional.

LEAF SPOT. **Cercospora glandulosa,** widespread; **Phyllosticta ailanthi,** Va.; **Gloeosporium ailanthi,** La., W. Va.

ROT, Mushroom Root. **Armillaria mellea,** N. Y.

ROT, Butt. **Daedalea unicolor,** occasional.

ROT, Wound. **Polyporus lacteus; P. versicolor,** occasional on living trees; **Schizophyllum commune.**

WILT. **Verticillium albo-atrum,** N. Y., Pa., Va.

This tree that grows in Brooklyn is well adapted to city smoke and not often troubled by disease. Wilt, however, can be serious and has killed many trees in the Philadelphia area.

ALDER (*Alnus*)

CANKER, DIEBACK. **Nectria coccinea,** N. Y., Pa.; **Solenia anomala,** widespread; **Physalospora obtusa,** S. C., Va.

CANKER, Trunk. **Diatrypella oregonensis,** Ida., Oreg., Wash.; **Hymenochaete agglutinans,** Mich., N. Y., Pa.

HYPERTROPHY, Catkin (see under Leaf blisters). **Taphrina robinsoniana,** widespread; **T. occidentalis,** in West; **T. rugosa,** Ga.

LEAF HYPERTROPHY. **Taphrina macrophylla.**

LEAF SPOT. **Septoria alnifolia,** Cal., Ida.; **Cercospora alni,** Wis.; **Gnomonia alni,** Cal., Oreg.; **Gnomoniella tubiformis,** general.

POWDERY MILDEW. **Erysiphe aggregata,** Mich., N. H., Va.; **Microsphaera alni,** widespread; **Phyllactinia corylea,** general.

ROT, Mushroom Root. **Armillaria mellea,** cosmopolitan.

ROT, Root. **Phymatotrichum omnivorum,** Tex.

ROT, Heart. **Daedalea unicolor; Fomes igniarius; F. pinicola; F. applanatus; Polyporus sulphureus.**

ROT, Sapwood. **Lenzites saepiaria; Polyporus adustus; P. hirsutus; P. versicolor; Schizophyllum commune.**

ROT, Wood. **Fomes scutellatus; Stereum fuscum; S. hirsutum.**

ALLAMANDA

PHYSIOGENIC **Chlorosis** from manganese deficiency in either overlimed or acid, sandy soils, Fla.

ALLIONIA (Trailing Four-O'clock, Umbrellawort)

DOWNY MILDEW. **Peronospora oxybaphi,** Kans., S. Dak.

LEAF SPOT. **Ascochyta oxybaphi,** Iowa, Wis.; **Cercospora oxybaphi,** Iowa, Wis.

ROT, Root. **Phymatotrichum omnivorum,** Tex.

RUST. **Puccinia aristidae,** Ala., Ariz., N. Mex., Tex.

WHITE RUST. **Albugo platensis,** Ala., Ariz., N. Mex., Tex.

ALMOND, Flowering (*Prunus triloba*)

BACTERIAL Fire Blight. **Erwinia amylovora,** Ind.

BACTERIAL Leaf Spot. **Xanthomonas pruni,** N. J.

BLIGHT, Blossom and Twig. **Botrytis cinerea,** N. Y.; **Monilinia fructicola,** Conn., Kans.

POWDERY MILDEW. **Podosphaera oxyacanthae,** Iowa.

ROT, Root. **Armillaria mellea,** Miss.

ALMOND (*Prunus amygdalus*)

ANTHRACNOSE; Kernel Rot. **Gloeosporium amygdalinum,** Cal.

BACTERIAL Shoot Blight. **Pseudomonas syringae,** Cal.

BACTERIAL Crown Gall. **Agrobacterium tumefaciens,** Ala., Ariz., Cal., N. C.
BLIGHT, Blossom; Brown Rot. **Monilinia laxa,** Cal., Oreg.
BLIGHT; Shot-Hole Disease. **Coryneum (Ascospora) carpophilum,** Cal., Ida., Oreg.
CANKER; DIEBACK; Crown Rot. **Phytophthora cactorum,** Cal.; **P. citrophthora,** Cal.
LEAF SPOT; Shot-Hole. **Cercospora circumscissa,** Cal., occasional, Oreg.
NEMATODE, Root Knot. **Heterodera marioni,** Ariz.
PHYSIOGENIC **Little Leaf.** Zinc Deficiency.
POWDERY MILDEW. **Sphaerotheca pannosa,** Cal., rare.
ROT, Mushroom Root. **Armillaria mellea.** Cal., N. C.
ROT, Root. **Phymatotrichum omnivorum,** Ariz., Tex.
ROT, Heart. **Polyporus versicolor,** Oreg.
ROT, Green Fruit. **Sclerotinia sclerotiorum,** Cal.
ROT, Wound. **Schizophyllum commune,** Cal.
RUST. **Tranzschelia pruni-spinosae** var. **discolor** (II, III) ; O and I on Anemone.
SCAB. **Cladosporium carpophilum,** Cal., Oreg.
VIRUS, Calico.
VIRUS, Peach Mosaic. **Marmor persicae.**
VIRUS, Peach Rosette. **Carpophthora rosettae.**
WILT; Blackheart. **Verticillium albo-atrum,** Cal., Ill.

Zinc deficiency shown by little-leaf is not particularly serious in almonds and can be corrected by spraying with zinc sulfate, 25 to 50 pounds to 100 gallons water, in the dormant season. Crown gall and Armillaria rot are decidedly serious, often limiting factors in almond production.

Standard spray schedule in California for control of shot-hole and brown rot has been bordeaux mixture, 10–10–100, in late fall (Nov. 15–Dec. 10) ; in spring just before buds swell; when blossom buds show color; and, in wet seasons when petals have fallen. Bordeaux may cause some injury to almonds with insufficient soil moisture.

Rust may cause some defoliation; spring infection comes from urediospores overwintering on old green leaves on sucker shoots in orchards, so that destruction of anemone, the alternate host, does not help much.

ALOE

ROT, Root. **Pythium ultimum,** Cal.

This commercially important disease of nursery plants of *Aloe variegata* can be controlled by immersing plants in hot water held at 115° F. for 20 to 40 minutes.

ALTERNANTHERA

NEMATODE, Root Knot. **Heterodera marioni,** La.
ROT, Root; Wilt. **Fusarium oxysporum,** N. J.
ROT, Root. **Rhizoctonia solani,** Ill., N. J.

ALYSSUM (Madwort, Yellow-Tuft, Basket-of-Gold)

Club Root. **Plasmodiophora brassicae,** N. J.
Damping-Off. **Rhizoctonia solani,** N. J.

AMARANTH (*Amaranthus*) Love-Lies-Bleeding, Princes-Feather, Josephs-Coat

Damping-Off. **Pythium debaryanum,** Conn.
Nematode, Root Knot. **Heterodera marioni,** Fla., Md.
Virus, Curly Top. **Ruga verrucosans,** Cal., Tex.
Virus, Aster Yellows. **Chorogenus callistephus,** N. Y., Md.
White Rust. **Albugo bliti,** Mass. to Fla., Tex., Neb.

AMARYLLIS (*Amaryllis, Hippeastrum*)

Blight, Gray Mold. **Botrytis cinerea,** chiefly in outdoor plants after chilling.
Blight, Southern; Bulb Rot. **Sclerotium rolfsii,** Fla.
Leaf Scorch; Red Blotch. **Stagonospora curtisii,** widespread.
Leaf Spot. **Cercospora amaryllidis,** Ala., La., probably secondary. **Epicoccum purpurascens,** Cal., probably secondary.
Rot, Seedling Root. **Pythium debaryanum,** Fla., Tex.
Rot, Bulb. **Rhizopus stolonifer.**
Virus, Mosaic. Unidentified, Cal., Fla., Okla., Wis.
Virus, Spotted Wilt. **Lethum australiense,** Cal., Tex.

Although amaryllis is subject to red spotting from various physiological causes, and mite and insect injuries, the fungus red blotch or leaf scorch is fairly common. Leaves and flower stalks have small, red, raised spots in longitudinal lines. Dark reddish spots appear on flower parts and bulb scales. Leaves and stalks may be bent and deformed, and flower stalks dry up before flowering.

AMELANCHIER (Service-Berry, June-Berry, Shadbush)

Bacterial Fire Blight. **Erwinia amylovora,** widespread.
Black Mildew; Witches' Broom. **Apiosporina collinsii,** widespread.
Blight, Leaf. **Fabraea maculata,** widespread.
Blight, Fruit and Leaf. **Sclerotinia gregaria,** Wash.
Canker. **Nectria cinnabarina,** occasional; **Pezicula pruinosa,** widespread.
Powdery Mildew. **Erysiphe polygoni,** occasional; **Phyllactinia corylea,** Wash.; **Podosphaera oxyacanthae,** occasional.
Rot, Brown. **Monilinia fructicola,** Mich., Ohio.
Rot, Fruit. **Monilinia amelanchieris.**
Rot, Wood, Butt. **Daedalea unicolor,** cosmopolitan.
Rust. **Gymnosporangium biseptatum** (I) ; III on Chamaecyparis. Northeastern and Middle Atlantic States. Horned galls, underside leaves.

G. clavariaeforme (I) on leaves, fruits, stems; III on Juniper.
G. clavipes (I) on fruit, stems; III on Juniper.
G. corniculans (I) ; III on Juniper.
G. harknessianum (I) on fruits, Cal., Oreg.; III on Juniper.
G. inconspicuum (I) on fruits; III on Juniper.
G. juvenescens (I) in West; III on Juniper.
G. kernianum (I) on leaves, Ariz., Col., Oreg.; III on Juniper.
G. libocedri (I) on leaves, Cal., Oreg.; III on incense cedar.
G. nelsoni (I) on leaves, fruits; III on Juniper.
G. nidus-avis (I) on leaves, fruits, stems; III on Juniper, Central and Eastern States.

AMORPHA (False Indigo)

Canker, Twig. **Cytospora amorphae.**
Leaf Spot. **Cercospora passaloroides,** Ala., Ill., Nebr., Kans.
Powdery Mildew. **Erysiphe polygoni.**
Rust. **Uropyxis amorphae,** general east of Rocky Mountains.

AMPELOPSIS (*Ampelopsis cordata* and other species)

See Boston Ivy and Virginia Creeper for species now under Parthenocissus.

Canker, Dieback. **Cladosporium herbarum,** N. J.; **Nectria cinnabarina,** occasional.
Downy Mildew. **Plasmopara viticola,** N. Y., Wis.
Leaf Spot. **Guignardia bidwellii; Linospora ampelopsis,** Wis.; **Phleospora ampelopsidis,** Wis.; **Phyllosticta viticola,** widespread.
Powdery Mildew. **Uncinula necator,** widespread.
Rot, Root. **Helicobasidium purpureum,** Tex.

AMSONIA

Leaf Spot. **Mycosphaerella** sp., Ga.
Rust. **Coleosporium apocyanaceum** (II, III) on leaves, Fla., Ga.; O, I on pine. **Puccinia seymouriana** (O, I) ; II, III on Spartina.

ANAPHALIS (Pearl Everlasting)

Leaf Spot. **Septoria margaritaceae,** N. Y., Oreg., Wis.
Rust. **Uromyces amoenus,** Cal., Ida., Mich., Mont., Oreg., Wash., Wyo.

ANCHUSA (Bugloss, Alkanet)

Damping-Off. **Rhizoctonia solani,** Conn.
Rust. **Ruccinia rubigo-vera var. secalis** (O, I), Ind., Mich.; II, III on Secale.
Virus, Mosaic. Unidentified.

ANDROMEDA (Bog-Rosemary)

For cultivated forms, see Leucothoë, Lyonia, Pieris.
BLACK MILDEW. **Dimerosporium clavuligora,** Ala., Ga., Fla.
LEAF GALL; Red Leaf Spot. **Exobasidium vaccinii,** N. C.
LEAF SPOT. **Phyllosticta andromedae,** N. J.
LEAF SPOT, Tar. **Rhytisma andromedae,** N. C.
POWDERY MILDEW, **Microsphaera vaccinii,** Mass. to Ill.

ANEMONE (Cultivated forms, Poppy-Flowered, Japanese)

BLIGHT, Southern. **Sclerotium rolfsii** (incl. *S. delphinii*), Cal., Md., Mass.
LEAF SPOT. **Gloeosporium** sp., N. Y.; **Phyllosticta anemones,** Md.
NEMATODE, Leaf-Blight. **Aphelenchoides olesistus,** Conn., N. Y.
NEMATODE, Root Knot. **Heterodera marioni,** Conn., N. Y.
ROT, collar. **Botrytis cinerea,** N. J., Pa.
RUST. **Tranzschelia cohaesa** (O, I, II, III), Tex.; **T. pruni-spinosae var. discolor** (O, I); II, III on Prunus spp.
VIRUS, Mosaic. Unidentified, Cal.
VIRUS, Aster Yellows. **Chlorogenus callistephus var. californicus,** Cal.

ANEMONE (Native Species)

DOWNY MILDEW. **Plasmopara pygmaea,** widespread.
LEAF GALL. **Synchytrium anemones,** Iowa, Mass., Mich., Minn., Vt., Wis.
LEAF SPOT. **Cercospora pulsatillae,** Col.; **Cercosporella filiformis,** Wis.; **Didymaria didyma,** Iowa, Mich., Wis.; **Phyllosticta anemonicola,** Ill., Mich.; Me., Neb., Va., Wis.; **Ramularia ranunculi,** N. Y., Wis.; **Septoria anemones,** Ill., Iowa, Miss., Mo., Tex., Vt., Wis.; **S. cylindrica,** Mont., Va.; **S. punicea,** Mass., Mich., Miss., Nebr., Kans.
POWDERY MILDEW. **Erysiphe polygoni,** Ill., Iowa, Ind., Mich., Minn., N. Dak., N. J., Wis.
RUST. **Puccinia gigantispora** (O, I, III), Col., Ill., Ida., Mont., N. Dak., Wis., Wyo.; **P. magnusiana** (O, I), N. Y. to Kans., N. Dak.; II, III on Phragmites; **P. anemones-virginianae** (III), Me., to Miss., N. Y. to N. Dak., Nebr.; **P. rubigo-vera** (O, I), N. Y. to Tex; II, III on grasses; **P. pulsatillae** (III), Col., Iowa., N. Dak., S. Dak.; **P. retecta,** Col.
RUST. **Tranzschelia cohaesa** (O, I, II, III), Tex.; **T. pruni-spinosae** var. **typica** (O, I), Kans., Iowa, Neb. to Tex. and Ala.; II, III Prunus; **T. fusca** (O, III), Mass. to Va., Cal. and Northwest; **T. suffusca** (O, III), Col., Iowa, Mont., N. and S. Dak.; **T. tucsonensis** (O, I, II, III), Ariz.
SMUT, Leaf and Stem. **Urocystis anemones,** Me. to Del., Col., Kans., Iowa, Minn., N. Dak., Wis.
SMUT, White. **Entyloma ranunculi,** Wis.

ANGELICA

LEAF SPOT. **Cercospora thaspii,** Ala.; **Fusicladium angelicae,** general; **Gloeosporium angelicae,** S. C.; **Phyllosticta angelicae,** Cal., Wyo.; **Piggotia depressa,** Mont.; **Ramularia angelicae,** Col.; **Septoria dearnessii,** Wis., N. C.

RUST. **Puccinia angelicae** (O, I, II, III), N. Y., Oreg., Pa., Wash.; **P. ellisii,** Cal., Ida., Nev., Oreg., Wash.; **P. ligustici,** Col., Wash.; **P. poromera,** Utah.

ANISE (*Pimpinella*)

LEAF SPOT. **Cercospora malkoffii,** Va.

ROT, Root. **Phymatotrichum omnivorum,** Tex.

ROT, Stem. **Sclerotinia sclerotiorum,** Cal., Tex.

RUST. **Puccinia pimpinellae** (O, I, II, III), Cal.

VIRUS, Western Celery Mosaic. **Marmor umbelliferarum.**

ANISE–TREE (*Illicium*)

BLACK MILDEW. **Lembosia illiciicola,** Ala., Miss.

SOOTY MOLD. **Capnodium footii,** Miss.

ANODA

POWDERY MILDEW. **Oidium erysipheoides,** N. Mex.

RUST. **Puccinia** sp., Tex.

APPLE (*Malus sylvestris*)

ANTHRACNOSE, Northwestern; Black Spot Canker; Fruit Rot. **Neofabraea malicorticis,** prevalent Oreg., Wash., occasional Cal., Ill., Mass., Me., Nebr., Okla.

BACTERIAL Blight, Blast. **Pseudomonas syringae,** Ark.

BACTERIAL Crown Gall. **Agrobacterium tumefaciens,** general.

BACTERIAL Fire Blight. **Erwinia amylovora,** general.

BACTERIAL Hairy Root. **Agrobacterium rhizogenes,** Central States, Ida., N. Y.

BLIGHT, Limb. **Corticium laetum,** La., N. C.; **C. salmonicolor,** Fla., La.

BLIGHT, Thread. **Pellicularia koleroga,** W. Va. and Ind. to Gulf States.

BLIGHT, Southern. **Sclerotium rolfsii,** on seedlings.

BLOTCH, Fruit; Leaf Spot; Twig Canker. **Phyllosticta solitaria,** general except New England and far South; only on nursery stock in Pacific States.

BLOTCH, SOOTY. **Gloeodes pomigena.**

CANKER; DIEBACK. **Botryosphaeria ribis,** East and South; **Cytospora** spp. widespread; **Fusarium** spp., Pacific Northwest, secondary to drouth, winter injury, insect punctures; **Plenodomus fuscomaculans,** Cal., Mich.

CANKER; Fruit Rot. **Glutinium macrosporum,** Oreg.; **Leptosphaeria coniothyrium,** East and Central States, Wash.

CANKER; Leaf Spot. **Monochaetia mali,** N. J.

CANKER; Sapwood Rot. **Hymenochaete agglutinans; Hypoxylon** spp., occasional,

Canker, Bark. **Pezicula** (*Myxosporium*) **corticolum,** Me. to Md., Ill., Mich., Okla., Oreg., S. Dak., also causing fruit rot.

Canker, Blister. **Nummularia discreta,** East of Rocky Mts.

Canker, Branch and Trunk. **Nectria coccinea,** reported from New England to Washington, but possibly mistaken for *N. galligena.*

Canker, European. **Nectria galligena.** East and Central States to N. C. and Miss.; Pacific Coast.

Canker, Perennial. **Neofabraea perennans,** Ida., Mont., Oreg., Wash., also causing bullseye rot of fruit.

Canker, Twig. **Coryneum foliicolum,** widespread; **Gibberella baccata; Nectria cinnabarina,** Northern U. S.

Fruit Spot, Fly Speck. **Leptothyrium pomi,** general.

Fruit Spot, Brooks. **Mycosphaerella pomi,** New England to N. C.

Fruit Spot, Black Pox. **Helminthosporium papulosum.**

Leaf Spot. **Cercospora mali,** Gulf States, N. Y.; **Diaporthe perniciosa,** Ark.; **Illosporium malifoliorum,** Pa. to N. C., Ind.; **Mycosphaerella sentina,** Ill., N. J., Pa.; **Pestalotia** spp., Md. to N. C., Ind., Ida.

Mistletoe. **Phoradendron flavescens,** N. C., Tex.; **P. macrophyllum,** Ariz., N. Mex.

Nematode, Root Knot. **Heterodera marioni,** Miss., Tex., Utah.

Nematode, Root. **Pratylenchus pratensis,** Cal.

Physiogenic Bitter Pit; Baldwin Spot; Stippen; Storage Pit, general in storage.

Black-End, probably drought injury, Ala., Oreg., Wash.

Black-Heart, of wood, perhaps freezing injury, widespread.

Callus-Knot, Graft-Knot, wound overgrowth due to defective union scion and stock, often mistaken for crown gall.

Chlorosis. Iron deficiency, usually, in alkaline soil, West.

Collar Rot. Winter injury.

Cork; Drought Spot; Rosette. Boron deficiency, Northeastern States to Ind., Ky.; Pacific Coast.

Internal Bark Necrosis. Cause unknown, general Pacific Coast.

Internal Breakdown. Overmaturity, delayed cool storage, high temperature, general on certain varieties.

Internal Browning. Accentuated by low storage temperature, characteristic of certain varieties grown in cool, cloudy weather.

Jonathan Spot. Associated with dry weather, delayed storage.

Measles (reddish pimples in bark). Cause unknown, widespread.

Rosette. Boron and zinc deficiency. Occasional in East and Central States, Pacific Northwest.

Scald. Discoloration of fruit skin by volatile respiratory products, general in storage. Controlled by oiled paper wraps.

Soft Scald; Soggy Breakdown. Associated with delayed storage and low temperature.

Stigmonose. Fruit dimpling, distortion from insect punctures, widespread.

Sunburn, of fruit. Heat or light injury.

Sunscald, of bark. Freezing injury of trunk and larger branches on side exposed to sun, chiefly North Central States.

Water-Core. Deficient or irregular water supply, general in arid regions, particularly on Winesap variety.

POWDERY MILDEW. **Podosphaera leucotricha,** general but most common in West; **P. oxyacanthae,** general.

ROT, Black; Frog-Eye Leaf Spot; Twig and Branch Canker. **Physalospora obtusa,** general Atlantic Coast to Great Plains, Cal.

ROT, Black. **Physalospora mutila,** Cal., Mont., Oreg., Wash.; **P. rhodina,** Ky.

ROT, Bitter, of Fruit; Twig and Branch Canker. **Glomerella cingulata,** general, especially in South, rare in West. **G. rubicola,** Ill.

ROT, American Brown. **Monilinia fructicola,** general except far South.

ROT, European Brown; Blossom Blight. **Monilinia laxa,** Oreg., Wash.

ROT, bullseye. **Fusarium** spp., causing moldy core of dropped fruit in Eastern U.S., rot of stored fruit in Pacific Northwest.

ROT, Collar; Fruit, Rot. **Phytophthora cactorum,** widespread.

ROT, Fruit. **Corticium centrifugum,** Pacific Northwest, occasional in East. **Chaetomella** sp., Wash.; **Cladosporium** spp.; **Coniothyrium** sp., Wash.; **Endomyces mali,** Me.; **Epicoccum granulatum,** Wash.; **Gliocladium viride,** Ill.; **Hormodendron cladosporioides,** Wash.; **Pleospora fructicola,** Wash.; **P. herbarum,** Pacific States.

ROT, Fruit; Twig Blight. **Phoma** spp. widespread.

ROT, Heart. **Fomes applanatus; F. fomentarius; F. igniarius; F. pinicola.**

ROT, Mushroom Root. **Armillaria mellea,** general except in New England, prevalent on Pacific Coast; **Clitocybe monadelpha,** Ark., Va.; **C. tabescens,** Fla.

ROT, Root. **Phymatotrichum omnivorum,** Ariz., Ark., N. Mex., Tex.; **Coniocybe nivea,** Mo., N. Y., Pa.

ROT, Black Root. **Xylaria** spp., chiefly in Eastern and Central States.

ROT, Sapwood. **Polyporus** spp., widespread, sometimes on living trees; **Schizophyllum commune,** general except far South.

ROT, Silver Leaf. **Stereum purpureum,** Kans., Me., Minn., N. Y., Pacific Northwest.

ROT, White Root. **Corticium galactinum,** Del. to Va., Ark., Ill.; **Rosellinia necatrix,** Cal.

ROT, Wood. **Poria** spp.; **Stereum** spp., occasional; **Trametes** spp., widespread.

ROT, Wound. **Pleurotus ulmarius,** occasional.

RUST, Cedar and Apple. **Gymnosporangium juniperi-virginianae** (O, I) on leaves, fruit; general east of Great Plains; III on red-cedar and Rocky Mountain juniper.

Rust, Hawthorn. **Gymnosporangium globosum** (O, I) on leaves; III on red-cedar, Me. to Ala., Kans., Nebr.

Rust, Quince. **Gymnosporangium clavipes** (O, I) on fruit; III on common juniper and red-cedar.

Rust. **Gymnosporangium libocedri** (O, I) on leaves, fruit; III on incense cedar, Cal., Oreg.

Rust. **Gymnosporangium nidus-avis** (O, I), leaves, fruit, stems, Ind., Md., Miss., N. J.; III on red-cedar.

Scab. **Venturia inaequalis,** general except far South.

Sooty Mold. **Fumago vagans,** occasional.

Virus, Mosaic. **Marmor mali,** Conn., Cal., Me., Mich., Mo., N. Y., Wash.

If this appalling list of diseases should make you think twice before planting apples in the backyard with the expectation of getting cheap and abundant fruit, that is all to the good. There is no easy, or cheap, road to perfect fruit. Time and again I am called upon to recommend a "tree expert" to spray apple trees, and invariably the homeowner blames his poor fruit on his present arborist. "How many sprays did you have?" I inquire, knowing in advance the answer will be, "Two and that cost me plenty; the fruit should have been fine."

Explanations fall on deaf ears. If we have had a wet season, when commercial growers had to make from twelve to twenty applications to control scab, the backyard gardener still believes a couple of sprays are plenty, if he can only find the right man. When, in *The Gardener's Bug Book,* I attempted a spray schedule for apple insects, listing three sprays as very important, three more as important, and a couple as merely desirable, I was berated from all sides as making life unnecessarily difficult for home gardeners.

I don't want to make life more difficult for home gardeners. All I want to do is to persuade you that if you are not going into fruit growing as a very serious hobby, subordinating business and pleasure to the proper *timing* of treatments, you should relax and grow your apple trees as ornamentals. Prune them properly, get rid of all diseased or weak wood, possibly put on a dormant spray, and then one or two foliage sprays. In lucky seasons there'll be a fair amount of reasonably good fruit; in bad seasons, you can at least make applesauce. Don't be misled by the advertisements on dwarf fruit trees. They are easier to treat, since you can substitute a hand sprayer or duster for power apparatus, but for good fruit proper timing and number of applications are just as important. Frequent dusting with a sulfur-lead arsenate mixture is probably the least arduous method of protecting dwarf trees.

For determined fruit growers, spray schedules are available from any County Agent or Experiment Station, tailored for your section of the country and revised annually to include new materials that have proved their value under local conditions. Scab is the most important apple disease, with blotch, bitter rot, black rot, and rust included in most spray programs. There is a spray warning service in many states, advising farmers when the apple-scab fruiting bodies in old leaves on the ground are ready to shoot their spores and conditions are right for primary infection.

Temperature and length of rainy periods determine amount of scab infection. If the temperature averages 45° F., apple foliage needs to be wet 20 hours for a light primary infection and 41 hours for heavy infection, but if the temperature increases to around 60° F. it only takes 9 hours moisture for light infection, and 20 hours for heavy infection. One-third less time suffices for secondary infection.

Bordeaux mixture will control scab but is apt to russet foliage and sometimes causes severe injury. Lime sulfur is less injurious in cool weather, but burns in hot weather. Compared with wettable or paste sulfur it decreases yield, although it is somewhat more efficient in scab control. Fermate in recent years has given effective control of scab, rust and blotch, and in some instances has had a stimulative effect on the trees. Puratized Agricultural Spray is promising, although it cannot be used late in the season because of its mercury content. Phygon and Bioquin are effective, but occasionally injurious. Other new materials are on the way. But no matter how good the chemical, control will still depend on the ability of the grower to follow a spray schedule accurately.

APPLE–OF–PERU (*Nicandra*)

LEAF SPOT. **Cercospora physaloides,** Ind.
ROT, Root. **Phymatotrichum omnivorum,** Tex.
VIRUS, Mosaic. Unidentified, Ida., Iowa, Ky., Wash., Wis.

APRICOT (*Prunus armeniaca*)

BACTERIAL Canker; Gummosis. **Pseudomonas syringae,** Cal., Ore.
BACTERIAL Crown Gall. **Agrobacterium tumefaciens,** widespread.
BACTERIAL Leaf Spot. **Xanthomonas pruni,** Ill. to Tex., Nebr.
BACTERIAL Fire Blight. **Erwinia amylovora,** Col., Fla., Nebr., Pa., Tex.
BLACK KNOT. **Dibotryon morbosum,** Col., N. Y.
BLIGHT, Shoot; Fruit Spot. **Coryneum carpophilum,** widespread.
BLIGHT, Blossom and Twig; Brown Rot; Green and Ripe Fruit Rot. **Monilinia laxa,** Pacific Coast States.
CANKER, Trunk and Limb Gall. **Monochaetia rosenwaldia,** Cal.
CANKER, Trunk. **Phytophthora cactorum,** Cal.; **P. citrophthora,** Cal.
CANKER, Twig; Dieback. **Cytospora** sp., Ky.; **Valsa leucostoma,** Me., Tex.
DIEBACK; Coral Spot. **Nectria cinnabarina,** Ind.
LEAF CURL. **Taphrina** (?deformans), S. C.
LEAF SPOT. **Cercospora circumscissa,** Tex.; **Coccomyces** sp., Cal., Mass., Tex., Vt.; **Phyllosticta circumscissa,** Cal.
NEMATODE, Root Knot. **Heterodera marioni,** Ariz., Tex.

Powdery Mildew. **Podosphaera oxyacanthae,** Cal., Iowa; **Sphaerotheca pannosa** var. **persicae,** N. Y.

Physiogenic Arsenical Injury, from soil, Cal.

Chlorosis, alkali injury, mineral deficiency, Ariz., Cal.

Xanthema, copper deficiency, Cal.

Gummosis, Sour Sap. Adverse soil and moisture conditions, Ariz., Cal., N. J., Wash.

Little Leaf. ?Zinc deficiency, Cal.

Mottle Leaf. Manganese deficiency, Cal.

Rot, Blossom End; Fruit Spot. **Alternaria** sp., Cal.

Rot, Brown; Blossom Blight. **Monilinia fructicola,** usually on ripe fruit, widespread.

Rot, Green Fruit; Gummosis. **Botrytis cinerea,** Cal.

Rot, Green Fruit; Twig Blight. **Sclerotinia sclerotiorum,** Cal.

Rot, Heart. **Schizophyllum commune,** usually after freezing, Tex., Wash.; **Trametes hispida,** Col.

Rot, Mushroom Root. **Armillaria mellea,** Cal., Tex.; **Clitocybe tabescens,** Fla.

Rot, Root. **Phymatotrichum omnivorum,** Ariz., Okla., Tex. (some resistance to).

Rot, Silver Leaf. **Stereum purpureum,** Cal.

Rust. **Tranzschelia pruni-spinosae** (II, III), Cal., Miss., N. Mex., Tex.

Scab; Freckle; Twig Canker. **Cladosporium carpophilum,** widespread.

Virus, Winters Peach Mosaic, Cal.

Virus, Ring Spot. Undetermined, Col., Wash.

Virus, Yellows. **Chlorogenus persicae,** occasional in East.

Apricots are very susceptible to Armillaria root rot and should be on resistant Myrobalan root stock. Bacterial canker is an epidemic disease in many seasons, with activity starting in late autumn and ceasing in early summer.

Monocalcium arsenite is used effectively in California in controlling blossom and twig blight due to *Monilinia laxa,* and sometimes it is combined with a delayed dormant copper-oil spray, followed by bordeaux mixture at prebloom, early bloom, petal fall, jacket shedding and early fruit stages to prevent rots.

Zinc-coated nails driven into the trunk, or a zinc sulfate spray will check little leaf, and manganese sulfate will control mottle leaf.

ARABIS (Rock-Cress)

Blight, Gray Mold. **Botrytis cinerea,** Wash.

Club Root. **Plasmodiophora brassicae.**

Damping-Off. **Rhizoctonia solani,** N. J.

Downy Mildew. **Peronospora parasitica,** Ala., Col., Ind.

Leaf Spot. **Septoria arabidis,** Tex., Col., Mich.

ROT, Root. **Phymatotrichum omnivorum,** Tex.

RUST. **Puccinia holboelli** (O, III), on numerous native, but not cultivated, species in Rocky Mts. and Pacific States; **P. monica** (O, I), on native species, Wis. to Col., N. Mex., Cal., Wash.; II, III on Koehleria.

WHITE RUST; White Blister. **Albugo candida,** N. Y. to Va., Tex., Col., Wash.

ARALIA (Bristly Sarsaparilla and American Spikenard; see also Hercules Club and Udo)

LEAF SPOT. **Alternaria** sp., N. Y.; **Ascochyta marginata,** Wis.; **Cercospora leptosperma,** Iowa, Mich., N. Y., Wis.; **Phyllosticta decidua,** Wis.; **Ramularia repens,** Wis.

POWDERY MILDEW. **Phyllactinia corylea,** Mich., Nebr.

RUST. **Nyssopsora clavellosa,** Cal., Minn., N. Y., Oreg., Tex.

WILT. **Verticillium dahliae,** N. Y.

ARAUCARIA (Monkey-Puzzle, Norfolk-Island-Pine)

BACTERIAL Crown Gall. **Agrobacterium tumefaciens,** experimental infection, Cal.

BLIGHT. **Cryptospora longispora.**

Pestalotia and one or two other fungi are found on leaves but apparently are not important.

ARBOR-VITAE (*Thuja*)

BLIGHT, Fire. **Cercospora thujina,** on oriental arbor-vitae, Ark., La., Miss., Tex.

BLIGHT, Gray Mold. **Botrytis cinerea,** N. J.

BLIGHT, Leaf. **Didymascella thujina,** Tex., Vt. to Wis.

BLIGHT, Nursery. **Phomopsis juniperovora,** Ind., Ky., Ohio, Pa., Va.

BLIGHT, Twig. **Coryneum berckmanii,** on oriental arbor-vitae, Oreg., Wash.

BLIGHT, Twig. **Phytophthora** sp., N. J.; **Pestalotia funerea,** widespread.

BLIGHT, Snow. **Phacidium infestans,** Northeastern States.

CANKER, Twig. Cypress Canker. **Coryneum cardinale,** Cal.

DAMPING-OFF. **Rhizoctonia solani,** N. Mex., N. Y., Tex., Va.

DIEBACK. **Beltrania rhombica,** Fla.; **Diplodia** sp., Ala., Fla.; **Alternaria** sp., probably secondary, Tex.

NEEDLE CAST; Needle Spot. **Lophodermium thuyae,** Me., N. H., N. Y., Wis.

ROT, Mushroom Root. **Clitocybe tabescens,** Fla.; **Armillaria mellea,** Mich., Miss., N. Y., Tex.

ROT, Root. **Phymatotrichum omnivorum,** Tex.

ROT, Seedling Root. **Fusarium solani,** Tex.

ROT, Wood. **Fomes annosus,** Mich.; **F. roseus,** Me.; **Poria vaporaria, P. weirii,** Great Lakes States; **Lenzites saepiaria,** Minn.; **Schizophyllum commune,** Me.

Oriental arbor-vitae in the South often looks as if it had been blighted by fire, with losses in nurseries somewhat higher than in gardens. A copper spray, applied monthly from June to September, will control the fungus, *Cercospora thujina*. In the Northwest *Coryneum berckmanii* causes discoloration and shedding of branches while *C. cardinale,* the cypress canker fungus, is sporadically injurious.

ARMERIA (*A. maritima*) Sea-Pink, Thrift

RUST. **Uromyces limonii** var. **armeriae** (O, I, II, III), Cal.

ARDISIA

LEAF SPOT, Algal. **Cephaleuros virescens,** Fla.

ARGYREIA

NEMATODE, Root Knot. **Heterodera marioni,** S. C.
ROT, Root. **Phymatotrichum omnivorum,** Tex.

ARNICA

LEAF SPOT. **Ovularia hughesiana,** Mont.; **Phyllosticta arnicae,** Col., Mont., Utah, Wyo.

POWDERY MILDEW. **Erysiphe cichoracearum,** Col.; **Sphaerotheca humuli,** Cal., Wash., Wyo.

RUST. **Puccinia arnicali** (II, III), Alaska to Mont., Cal., Col.; O, I unknown; **Uromyces junci** (O, I), Cal., Col., Mont., Oreg., S. Dak., Wyo.; II, III on Juncus.

ARROW-ARUM (*Peltandra*)

LEAF SPOT. **Cercospora callae,** Ala., Del., Fla., N. Y.; **Colletotrichum** sp., Ala.; **Gloesporium paludosum,** Del., Ind., Mass., N. Y.; **Ramularia** sp., Mich.
RUST. **Uromyces caladii** (O, I, II, III), Ga., N. C., Mass. to Fla., Iowa.

ARROWROOT (*Maranta arundinacea*)

LEAF SPOT. **Glomerella cingulata,** Md., N. J.
RUST. **Puccinia cannae,** Fla.

ARTEMISIA (Wormwood)

BLIGHT, Leaf. **Cercospora olivaceae,** N. Dak., N. J., N. Y.
DOWNY MILDEW. **Peronospora leptosperma,** Iowa, Minn., N. and S. Dak., Wis.
LEAF GALL. **Synchytrium aureum,** Wis.
LEAF SPOT. **Cercospora ferruginea,** N. Y., Wis.
POWDERY MILDEW. **Erysiphe cichoracearum,** Cal., S. Dak.
RUST. **Puccinia absinthii** (O, I, II, III), Cal.; **P. atrofusca** (O, I), N. Dak.; II, III on Carex.; **P. millefolii,** Oreg.
WHITE RUST. **Albugo tragopogonis,** Iowa, Mont., N. and S. Dak., Wis.

ARTICHOKE (*Cynara scolymus*)

BLIGHT, Gray Mold. **Botrytis cinerea,** Cal., N. Y.

BLIGHT, Southern. **Sclerotium rolfsii,** Ga.

LEAF SPOT. **Cercospora obscura,** Cal., Tex.; **Cladosporium** sp., Cal., S. C.; **Ramularia cynarae,** Cal., prevalent.

NEMATODE, Root Knot. **Heterodera marioni,** Cal.

POWDERY MILDEW. **Erysiphe cichoracearum,** Cal., N. J.

ROT, Root. **Phytophthora megasperma,** Cal.

ROT, Root and Stem. **Rhizoctonia solani,** Miss.

ROT, Stem. **Sclerotinia sclerotiorum,** Oreg.

VIRUS, Yellows. Unidentified.

ASCLEPIODORA

LEAF SPOT. **Alternaria fasciculata,** probably secondary, Okla.; **Cercospora asclepiodorae,** Kans.; **Phyllosticta tuberosa,** Okla.

RUST. **Puccinia bartholomaei** (O, I), Okla., Tex., Kans.; II, III on Bouteloua. **Uromyces asclepiadis** (II, III), Kans., N. Mex., Tex.

ASH (*Fraxinus*)

ANTHRACNOSE, Leaf Scorch. **Gloeosporium aridum,** Eastern and Central States.

BLACK MILDEW; Sooty Mold. **Dimerosporium pulchrum.**

BLIGHT, Seedling. **Rhizoctonia solani,** Okla.

CANKER; DIEBACK. **Cytospora annularis,** North Central States; **Diplodia infuscans,** Northeast.

CANKER, Branch. **Dothiorella fraxinicola,** Iowa; **Sphaeropsis** sp., widespread.

CANKER, Branch and Trunk. **Nectria cinnabarina, N. coccinea,** Northeast.

CANKER, Felt Fungus. **Septobasidium** spp.

DODDER. **Cuscuta** sp., occasional.

LEAF SPOT. **Cercospora fraxinites,** Fla., La., Tex.; **C. lumbricoides, C. texensis; Cylindrosporium fraxini,** widespread; **Mycosphaerella effigurata** (*Marssonina fraxini; Piggotia fraxini*). **Mycosphaerella fraxinicola,** widespread east of Rocky Mts.; **Phyllosticta fraxinicola,** East and Central States; **Septoria besseyi; S. leucostoma,** Ind., Mass., Tex.; **S. submaculata,** Mo., Tex.

LEAF SPOT; Twig Blight. **Septoria fraxini,** Mass. to Minn., Fla., La.

MISTLETOE. **Phoradendron flavescens,** South Central to Pacific States.

NEMATODE. **Heterodera marioni,** Ariz., Md., Okla.

POWDERY MILDEW. **Phyllactinia corylea,** Northeast and Central States, Pacific Coast.

ROT, Collar. **Helicobasidium purpureum,** Tex.

ROT, Root. **Phymatotrichum omnivorum,** Ariz., Tex.

ROT, Sapwood. **Lentinus tigrinus,** Miss.

ROT, Trunk. **Ganoderma lucidum,** Miss.

ROT, White Mottled Heart. **Fomes fraxinophilus,** usually on living trees, East and Central States to Great Plains; many other Fomes species.

ROT, Wood. **Daldinia concentrica,** cosmopolitan; **Daedalea** spp.; **Poria** spp.

ROT, Wound. **Polyporus** spp., many.

RUST. **Puccinia peridermiospora** (O, I), general East of Great Plains; II, III on marsh grass (Spartina).

?VIRUS. Witches' broom on Arizona ash, La.

Ash rust has been epidemic in New England in many seasons, causing defoliation and sometimes death of trees. Piggotia leaf spot is common, producing small purplish lesions. Anthracnose can be serious in a wet year. Removal of dead branch stubs, protection of pruning wounds helps to prevent white mottled heart rot.

ASPARAGUS, GARDEN (*Asparagus officinalis*)

ANTHRACNOSE; Canker. **Colletotrichum** sp., Ala., Conn., Ill.

BACTERIAL Soft Rot. **Erwinia carotovora,** general.

BLIGHT, Branchlet; Dieback. **Alternaria** sp., Ill., Mass., N. Y., Okla., S. C.; **Stemphylium botryosum,** secondary.

BLIGHT, Ashy Stem. **Macrophomina phaseoli,** Tex.

BLIGHT, Gray Mold, Shoot. **Botrytis cinerea,** Cal., Ill., Mass., N. Y., W. Va.

DAMPING-OFF, Stem Canker. **Rhizoctonia solani.**

LEAF SPOT. **Cercospora asparagi,** general.

NEMATODE, Root Knot. **Heterodera marioni,** S. C.

ROT, Mushroom Root. **Armillaria mellea.**

ROT, Violet Root. **Helicobasidium purpureum,** Cal.

ROT, Root; Stem Wilt. **Fusarium** spp., general.

ROT, Stem. **Diplodia asparagi; Phytophthora** sp., Cal.

ROT, Watery Soft. **Sclerotinia sclerotiorum,** occasional in South.

RUST. **Puccinia asparagi** (O, I, II, III), general on susceptible varieties.

Rust is the most important asparagus disease, but it is kept to a minimum by use of resistant varieties.

ASPARAGUS FERN (*Asparagus plumosus*)

CANKER, Stem; Blight. **Ascochyta asparaginsa,** Fla., Tex.; **Phoma** sp., Fla.

LEAF MOLD. **Cladosporium** sp., Fla., Miss., Tex.

NEMATODE, Root Knot. **Heterodera marioni,** Fla.

PHYSIOGENIC "Rust." Cause undetermined.

ROT, Root; Wilt. **Fusarium** sp., Fla., Wash.

ASPARAGUS, FLORISTS (*Asparagus asparagoides*)

LEAF SPOT. **Stagonospora smilacis,** Wis.

ROT, stem. **Fusarium** sp., N. J.

SPRENGER ASPARAGUS (*Asparagus sprengeri*)

Bacterial Crown Gall; Fasciation. **Agrobacterium tumefaciens,** Fla., Ore.
Nematode. **Heterodera marioni.**
Rot, Root. **Rhizoctonia solani,** N. Y.

ASPIDISTRA

Blight, Leaf. **Labrella aspidistrae,** Ill., La.
Leaf Spot. **Ascochyta aspidistrae,** Minn., N. J.; **Colletotrichum omnivorum,** Cal., Mo., N. J., Pa., W. Va.

ASTER, CHINA (*Callistephus*)

Anthracnose. **Colletotrichum** sp., Fla.
Blight, Gray Mold; Stem Canker. **Botrytis cinerea,** Cal., Conn., Ill., N. J., N. Y., Pa., Wis.
Blight, Southern. **Sclerotium rolfsii,** Miss., N. C.
Canker, Stem. **Phomopsis callistephi,** Ill., Wis.
Dodder, **Cuscuta** spp., Mass., N. Y., N. J., probably widespread.
Downy Mildew. **Basidiophora entospora,** Fla., Tex.
Leaf Spot. **Ascochyta asteris,** Cal., N. Y., N. Dak., Ohio; **Septoria callistephi,** Ala., Del., Mich., Mo., N. J., N. Y., Ohio, Pa.
Mold, Seed. **Pleospora herbarum,** cosmopolitan; **Alternaria** sp.
Nematode, Root Knot. **Heterodera marioni,** Conn., Fla., Tex., Wash.
Powdery Mildew. **Erysiphe cichoracearum,** Del., Minn., Nebr., N. C., Vt., Wash.; **E. polygoni,** N. J.
Rot, Root. **Phymatotrichum omnivorum,** Tex.; **Pythium ultimum,** Cal., N. Dak.
Rot, Root and Stem. **Rhizoctonia solani,** widespread, chiefly in Northeastern and North Central States.
Rot, Foot; Blackleg. **Phytophthora** sp., Md.
Rust. **Coleosporium solidaginis** (II, III), general, except far South; II, III on 2- and 3-needle pines.
Virus, Spotted Wilt. **Lethum australiense,** Cal.
Virus, Curly Top. **Ruga verrucosans,** Oreg.
Virus, Yellows. **Chlorogenus callistephi,** general, and var. **californicus** in California and perhaps other Western States.
Wilt; Stem Rot. **Fusarium oxysporum** f. **callistephi,** general.
Wilt. **Verticillium** sp., Conn., Mass.

Fusarium wilt and yellows are the two chief aster problems. Wilt resistant varieties take care of the former, but there is no control for yellows except to remove stunted, greenish-yellow plants before leafhopper vectors can spread the virus. Commercial growers use cloth houses to keep out leafhoppers.

ASTER, PERENNIAL (*Aster* spp.)

BACTERIAL Crown Gall. **Agrobacterium tumefaciens,** Conn.
BLIGHT, Gray Mold. **Botrytis cinerea,** Conn., N. J.
DODDER. **Cuscuta** spp., chiefly East and Central States.
DOWNY MILDEW. **Basidiophora entospora,** Ill., Ind., Md., Mo., Nebr., Wis.
LEAF GALL. **Synchytrium nigrescens,** Wis., Central States.
LEAF SPOT. **Alternaria** sp., Mich., Tex., Vt.; **Ascochyta compositarum,** Wis.; **Cercospora asterata,** Ala.; **Cercosporella cana,** Oreg., Wis.; **Discosphaerina pseudimantia** (Placosphaeria?), N. Y., Iowa, N. J., N. Dak.; **Leptothyrium doellingeriae,** N. Y.; **Ovularia asteris,** Wyo.; **O. virgaureae,** Col., Miss., Wis.; **Phyllachora asterigena,** Kans., Nebr.; **Ramularia asteris,** Tex., Mich., Nebr., Wis.; **Septoria asteris,** Tex.; **S. astericola,** Del., Mass., Mich., Ohio, Wis.
NEMATODE, Leaf. **Aphelenchoides** sp., Conn.
NEMATODE, Root Knot. **Heterodera marioni,** Cal., Conn.
ROT, Root. **Phymatotrichum omnivorum,** Tex.
ROT, Stem. **Sclerotinia sclerotiorum,** Conn.
RUST. **Coleosporium solidaginis** (II, III); O, I on 2- and 3-needle pines.
RUST. **Puccinia asteris** (III), general; **P. extensicola** var. **asteris** (O, I); II, III on Carex; **P. grindeliae** (III), Col., Kans., Nev., Wyo.; **P. stipae** (O, I), Col., Iowa, Kans., Nebr., N. and S. Dak.; **Uromyces compactus,** Ariz., N. Mex., Tex.; **U. junci** (O, I), N. H.; II, III on Juncus.
VIRUS, Mosaic. Unidentified, Cal.
VIRUS, Spotted Wilt. **Lethum australiense,** Cal.
WILT. **Verticillium albo-atrum,** Conn.

ASTILBE

POWDERY MILDEW. **Erysiphe polygoni,** Mass.
WILT. **Fusarium** sp., Wash.

AUCUBA

ANTHRACNOSE; Withertip; Leaf Spot. **Gloeosporium cingulata** or **Colletotrichum gloeosporioides,** N. J., Pa.
LEAF SPOT. **Pestalotia aucubae,** N. J.; **Phyllosticta aucubae,** occasional.

AUTUMN CROCUS (*Colchicum autumnale*)

LEAF SMUT. **Urocystis colchici,** Del., N. Y., Ohio., Pa., Wash.

AVOCADO (*Persea americana*)

ANTHRACNOSE; Leaf and Fruit Spot; Dieback. **Glomerella cingulata,** general.
BLACK MILDEW. **Irene perseae,** Fla.
BACTERIAL Fruit Blast; Citrus Blast. **Pseudomonas syringae,** Cal.

BLOTCH; Cercospora Spot; Fruit Spot. **Cercospora purpurea; C. perseae,** Fla.
BLIGHT, Seedling. **Sclerotium rolfsii,** Fla.
CANKER, Branch; Fruit Rot; **Botryosphaeria ribis** var. **chromogena,** Cal.
LEAF SPOT; Algal; Green Scurf. **Cephaleuros virescens,** Fla.
LEAF SPOT; Fruit Spot. **Pestalotia** spp., Fla., Tex.
LEAF SPOT; Smudgy Spot of Twigs. **Helminthosporium** sp., Cal.
NEMATODE, Root Knot. Resistant to.
POWDERY MILDEW. Oidium sp., Fla.
PHYSIOGENIC Carapace Spot, abrasion of young fruits.
End Spot. Desiccation of young fruits.
Little Leaf; Rosette. Zinc Deficiency, Cal., Fla.
Melanorhiza; Asphyxiation. Defective drainage and aeration, Cal.
Mottle Leaf. Nutritional deficiency, Cal.
ROT, Blue Mold. **Penicillium expansum,** Cal.
ROT, Collar; trunk canker. **Phytophthora cactorum,** Cal.; **P. parasitica,** Fla.
ROT, Fruit. **Phytophthora citrophthora,** Cal.; **Rhizopus nigricans,** cosmopolitan; **Alternaria** sp., Cal.
ROT, Stem-End, of Fruit; Dieback. **Diplodia theobromae,** Fla., **Phumopsis** sp., Fla., Tex.
ROT, Root; Decline. **Phytophthora cinnamomi,** Cal.
ROT, Fruit; Bark Disease. **Fusarium** sp., Cal.
ROT, Fruit; Black Spot. **Colletotrichum gloeosporioides,** general.
ROT, Root. **Armillaria mellea,** Cal.; **Clitocybe tabescens,** Fla.; **Phymatotrichum omnivorum.**
SCAB, Fruit and Foliage. **Sphaceloma perseae,** Fla., Tex.
VIRUS, Sun-Blotch. Unidentified. Cal., Fla.

The sun-blotch virus causes yellow depressed streaks in stems, variegated or misshapen leaves, deformed fruits. The disease is transmitted by grafting but not by seed. Scions should be taken from healthy mother trees.

Scab may cause heavy damage in susceptible varieties of West Indian stock; Cercospora blotch, attacking both leaves and fruits, is likewise important. Properly timed bordeaux mixture or other copper sprays will control these, and also anthracnose.

Avocado decline, or root rot, is most serious in wet soils, killing trees if they are waterlogged 6 to 8 days. Soil can be disinfected with ethylene dibromide.

AZALEA (*Rhododendron*)

BLIGHT, Bud and Twig. **Briosia azaleae,** Mass., N. J., N. C.
BLIGHT, Flower; seedling. **Botrytis cinerea** after injuries, cosmopolitan.
BLIGHT, Petal; Flower Spot. **Ovulinia azaleae,** along coast—Md., D. C., Va., N. and S. C., Ga., Fla., Ala., Miss., La., Tex., Cal.
BLIGHT, Shoot. **Monilinia azaleae,** Ga., Mass., N. Y.
BLIGHT, Thread. **Pellicularia koleroga,** La.
DODDER. **Cuscuta** sp.

DAMPING-OFF. **Rhizoctonia solani,** cosmopolitan.
FLOWER SPOT, see Blight, petal.
LEAF GALL; Shoot Hypertrophy. **Exobasidium vaccinii** widespread; **E. azaleae,** on flame azalea; **E. decolorans,** Cal.
LEAF GALL. **Synchytrium vaccinii,** N. J. on swamp azalea.
LEAF GALL; Yellow Leaf Spot. **Exobasidium burtii,** N. J.
LEAF SCORCH. **Septoria azaleae,** Miss., N. J.
LEAF SPOT. **Cercospora rhododendri,** Md.; **Phyllosticta maxima,** Ala.; **Pestalotia macrotricha,** N. J.; **Ramularia angustata,** Miss.; **Septoria solitaria,** Cal., Ore.; **Venturia rhododendri,** La.
LEAF SPOT, Tar. **Melasmia menziesiae,** Wash.
POWDERY MILDEW. **Erysiphe polygoni,** Cal., N. J.; **Microsphaera alni,** Ga., N. J., N. Y., Pa.
ROT, Root. **Phymatotrichum omnivorum,** Tex.
RUST. **Pucciniastrum myrtilli,** Me., Vt. to Pa., Ala.

Azalea flower spot or petal blight devastates bloom of Indian and Kurume azaleas in the South in rainy or foggy weather, but can be controlled by frequent spraying, starting when buds show color. Bud and twig blight has been serious in Massachusetts causing death of some bushes. Leaf galls are unsightly, but not too serious. Leaf scorch may be prevalent in a rainy season, and powdery mildew often appears on deciduous azaleas in late summer.

When azalea foliage turns a general sickly yellow the trouble is generally attributed to unavailability of iron in a too alkaline soil, but a heavy, water-logged soil may produce the same symptoms.

AZARA

ROT, Stem. **Sclerotium rolfsii,** Cal.

BABIANA

VIRUS, Mosaic. **Marmor iridis,** Cal.

BALD CYPRESS (*Taxodium*)

BLIGHT, Twig. **Pestalotia funerea,** Tex.
CANKER, Felt Fungus. **Septobasidium** spp.
ROT, Butt; Heart. **Fomes applanatus,** Fla.; **F. extensus,** Fla.
ROT, Brown Pocket Heart. **Fomes geotropus,** cause of "pecky cypress," Fla. to La.
ROT, Brown Cubical. **Lenzites** sp.
ROT, Wood. **Polyporus** spp., sometimes living trees; **Poria** spp.

BALSAM–APPLE, BALSAM–PEAR (*Momordica*)

ANTHRACNOSE. **Colletotrichum lagenarium,** Ind.
DOWNY MILDEW. **Pseudoperonospora cubensis,** Iowa.
LEAF SPOT; Leaf Blight. **Ramularia momordicae,** Tex.

NEMATODE, Root Knot. **Heterodera marioni,** Fla.
POWDERY MILDEW. **Erysiphe cichoracearum,** Wis.

BALSAM–ROOT (*Balsamorhiza*)

LEAF SPOT. **Septoria** sp., Wash.
NEMATODE, Leaf Gall. **Tylenchus balsamophilus,** Utah.
POWDERY MILDEW. **Erysiphe cichoracearum,** Wyo.
RUST. **Puccinia balsamorhizae** (O, I, II, III), general from Mont. to Col., Cal., Wash.

BAMBOO (*Phyllostachys*)

LEAF SPOT. **Cylindrosporium bambusae,** Ga.
RUST. **Puccinia melanocephala,** Fla., Ga., Tex.
SMUT. **Ustilago shiraiana,** Cal., Fla., La., Tex.

BANANA, DWARF (*Musa cavendishii*)

ANTHRACNOSE. **Gloeosporium musarum,** Fla.
BACTERIAL Leaf Blight. **Pseudomonas solanacearum,** Fla.
NEMATODE, Root Knot. **Heterodera marioni,** Fla.

BANEBERRY (*Actaea*)

LEAF SPOT. **Ascochyta actaeae,** Wis.; **Ramularia actaeae,** Col., Iowa, N. Mex., Vt., Wis.
RUST. **Puccinia rubigo-vera** (O, I), N. Y. to Va., Ill., Wash.; II, III on Agropyron and Elymus.
SMUT, Leaf and Stem. **Urocystis carcinodes,** Ida., Pa., W. Va., Utah.

BAPTISIA (False or Wild Indigo)

LEAF SPOT. **Cercospora velutina,** Kans., Ill., Wis.; **Marssonina baptisiae,** Iowa; **Septoria baptisiae,** S. C.; **Stagonospora baptisiae,** S. C.
POWDERY MILDEW. **Erysiphe polygoni,** prevalent; **Microsphaera alni,** Wis.
RUST. **Puccinia andropogonis** var. **onobrychidis.**

BARBERRY (*Berberis*)

ANTHRACNOSE. **Gloeosporium berberidis.**
BACTERIAL Leaf Spot. **Pseudomonas berberidis,** widespread.
NEMATODE, Root Knot. **Heterodera marioni,** occasional.
POWDERY MILDEW. **Phyllactinia corylea,** occasional.
ROT, Root. **Phymatotrichum omnivorum,** Tex.
RUST, Wheat. **Puccinia graminis,** Me. to Wash., Va. to Col. Japanese barberry is resistant.
RUST. **Cumminsiella sanguinea,** Northern Plains, Rocky Mts., Pacific Coast.
WILT. **Verticillium albo-atrum** and **V. dahliae,** Del., Ohio.

All interstate movement of barberry is under quarantine as of May 1, 1949. Permits are required for most resistant species. See *Puccinia graminis* under Rusts.

BARREN–STRAWBERRY (*Waldsteinia*)

LEAF SPOT. **Ramularia waldsteiniae,** Wis.; **Septoria waldsteiniae,** Mich., N. Y., Vt.

RUST. **Puccinia waldsteiniae,** Mich., N. Y., Vt., Wis.

SMUT. **Urocystis waldsteiniae,** N. Y., Wis.

BASIL (*Ocimum*)

NEMATODE, Root Knot. **Heterodera marioni,** Fla.

BAYBERRY (*Myrica carolinensis*)

LEAF SPOT. **Mycosphaerella myricae,** Ga., Miss.; **Phyllosticta myricae,** N. Y.

RUST. **Gymnosporangium ellisii** (O, I), Mass. to N. Y., Va.; III on Chamaecyparis.

BEAN, KIDNEY, LIMA (*Phaseolus vulgaris, P. limensis*)

ANTHRACNOSE. **Colletotrichum lindemuthianum,** general in East; **G. truncatum,** Va. to Ala., Tex.

BACTERIAL Blight. **Xanthomonas phaseoli,** general in East, rare Pacific Coast.

BACTERIAL Halo Blight; Grease Spot. **Pseudomonas phaseolicola.**

BACTERIAL Northern Wilt. **Corynebacterium flaccumfaciens,** Northeast.

BACTERIAL Southern Wilt. **Pseudomonas solanacearum,** Ala., Fla., Ga., Okla.

BLIGHT, Ashy Stem. **Macrophomina phaseoli,** Southeastern States.

BLIGHT, Gray Mold. **Botrytis cinerea.**

BLIGHT, Pod. **Diaporthe Phaseolorum,** Conn. to Fla., La., Okla. and Ohio on lima bean.

BLIGHT, Southern. **Sclerotium rolfsii,** Va. to Fla., Tex., Ark., Cal.

BLIGHT, Web. **Pellicularia filamentusa** (*Corticium microsclerotia*), Fla., La., Miss., N. and S. C.

BLOTCH, Leaf. **Mycosphaerella cruenta,** N. J. to Fla., Ark., Tex., Wis.

DAMPING-OFF. **Pythium ultimum,** Cal.; **P. debaryanum,** Conn., Del.; **Rhizoctonia** sp.

DOWNY MILDEW. **Phytophthora phaseoli,** on lima bean.

LEAF SPOT. **Cercospora canescens,** Ala., Kans., Mo., N. J., Tex.; **C. phaseolorum; Epiccocum neglectum,** secondary, Md., Miss.

LEAF SPOT, Angular. **Isariopsis griseola,** Me. to Fla., Tex., Okla.; **I. laxa,** Ind., N. J.

LEAF SPOT. **Phyllosticta phaseolina,** N. Y. to Fla., Ind., Tex.; **Stemphylium botryosum,** Wash.; **Stagonospora phaseoli,** Tenn.

NEMATODE, Root Knot. **Heterodera marioni,** Me. to Fla., Ark., Ariz., Cal., Kans., Tex.

NEMATODE, Root. **Pratylenchus pratensis,** Tex.

PHYSIOGENIC Baldhead. Mechanical injury to seed growing point.

Blossom Drop. High temperature, low humidity.

Chlorosis. Copper deficiency, Fla.; Magnesium deficiency, Fla., Mass., Miss., S. C., Va.; Manganese deficiency, Fla.; Zinc deficiency, Fla.

POD SPOT, Yeast Spot. **Nematospora phaseoli,** on lima bean.

POD SPOT; Seed Mold. **Cladosporium herbarum,** on lima bean, Cal., Fla.

POWDERY MILDEW. **Erysiphe polygoni,** East and South, Cal.; **Microsphaera diffusa,** Ga., Md., Ill.; **M. euphorbiae,** Ind.

ROT, Root and Stem. **Pellicularia filamentosa,** general.

ROT, Root. **Fusarium solani** f. **phaseoli,** general; **Phoma terrestris,** secondary, Cal.; **Phymatotrichum omnivorum,** Ariz., Okla.; **Pythium helicoides,** Fla.; **P. rostratum,** Cal.; **P. aphanidermatum,** Cal., Col., Ida., N. Y., Okla., Va.

ROT, Soft. **Rhizopus stolonifer; Sclerotinia minor; S. ricini.**

ROT, Watery Soft; Stem Rot. **Sclerotinia sclerotiorum,** general but especially in South.

ROT, Black Root. **Thielaviopsis basicola,** Ala., Cal.

RUST. **Uromyces phaseoli** var. **typica** (II, III), general.

VIRUS, Bean Mosaic. **Marmor phaseoli,** general, most prevalent Northwest.

VIRUS, Black Root. Necrotic reaction of certain varieties to common mosaic virus.

VIRUS, Cucumber Mosaic. **Marmor cucumeris,** Col. to Ga., Ariz., Mo., Tex.

VIRUS, Southern Bean Mosaic. **Marmor laesiofaciens,** La., Miss.

VIRUS, Bean Yellow Mosaic. *Phaseolus* virus 2, widespread.

VIRUS, Curly Top. **Ruga verrucosans,** Rocky Mt. and Pacific States.

VIRUS, Pod Mottle. **Marmor valvolarum,** S. C.

VIRUS, Ring Spot. **Annulus tabaci.**

WILT, Yellows. **Fusarium oxysporum** f. **phaseoli,** Cal., Col., Ida., Mont.; **F. oxysporum** f. **vasinfectum,** Fla., Ala.

Anthracnose and bacterial blight, often erroneously called "rust" are common and most destructive diseases, best avoided by purchasing healthy seed grown in disease-free arid sections of California and the Northwest. True rust is prevalent in the Southwest and sometimes in the East on susceptible Kentucky Wonder pole beans. Use resistant varieties, and clean and disinfect poles at end of each season.

Downy mildew, common on lima beans in moist summers, can be controlled with copper sprays or perhaps one of the new organic materials. Powdery mildew is not much of a problem in most sections of the country. Resistant varieties are the best solution to mosaic and other virus problems.

Treating seeds with a protectant dust, such as Spergon, before planting is good insurance against damping-off and seedling root rots in cold wet springs, and is particularly important for lima bean seed. Avoiding cultivating or picking beans when foliage is wet will go a long way toward keeping them disease-free.

BEAN, SCARLET RUNNER (*Phaseolus coccineus*)

ANTHRACNOSE. **Colletotrichum lindemuthianum,** N. Y.
BACTERIAL Blight. **Xanthomonas phaseoli,** Ind., N. J.
BACTERIAL Halo Blight. **Pseudomonas phaseolicola,** N. Y.
LEAF SPOT. **Ascochyta boltshauseri,** Oreg.; **Cercospora cruenta,** Ala.
POWDERY MILDEW. **Erysiphe polygoni,** Cal.
ROT, Root. **Fusarium solani** f. **phaseolae,** N. Y.

BEAN, TEPARY (*Phaseolus acutifolius*)

BLIGHT, Southern. **Sclerotium rolfsii,** Ala.
POWDERY MILDEW. **Erysiphe polygoni,** Cal.
ROT, Root. **Fusarium solani,** Cal.; **Phymatotrichum omnivorum,** Tex.
RUST. **Uromyces phaseoli** (II, III), Cal., Tex.
VIRUS, Curly Top. **Ruga verrucosans,** Cal.

BEAN, YARD–LONG or ASPARAGUS (*Vigna sesquipedalis*)

BACTERIAL Spot. **Pseudomonas syringae,** Ind.
LEAF SPOT; Pod Spot. **Cladosporium vignae,** Ind.
LEAF SPOT. **Cercospora cruenta,** Va.
POWDERY MILDEW. **Erysiphe polygoni,** Cal.
VIRUS, Mosaic. Unidentified, Cal.
See also Soybean and Velvetbean.

BEARBERRY (*Arctostaphylos uva-ursi*)

BLACK MILDEW. **Asterina gaultheriae,** Wis.; **Dimerosporium conglobatum,** Me.
LEAF SPOT. **Cercospora gaultheriae,** Wis.
LEAF GALL; Red Leaf Spot. **Exobasidium vaccinii,** widespread.
LEAF GALL; Shoot Hypertrophy. **Exobasidium uvae-ursi,** Mass.
RUST. **Chrysomyxa arctostaphyli** (III), Col., Mont., Utah.

BEAUTY–BUSH (*Kolkwitzia amabilis*)

LEAF SPOT. **Cercospora weigeliae,** Ala.

BEECH, European (*Fagus* spp.)

CANKER, Twig. **Nectria cinnabarina,** after winter injury; **Asterosporium hoffmanni,** Mass.; **Cytospora** sp., N. J.
CANKER, Bleeding; Collar Rot. **Phytophthora cactorum,** southern New England, N. J., N. Y.
ROT, Yellow Sapwood. **Fomes fomentarius,** widespread.
ROT, Wood. **Stereum gausapatum,** Ohio.

BEECH, AMERICAN (*Fagus grandiflora*)

CANKER; Beech Bark Disease. **Nectria coccinea** var. **faginata,** associated with woolly beech scale, destructive northern New England and New York.

CANKER. **Nectria galligena,** New England, N. Y.

CANKER, Bleeding. **Phytophthora cactorum,** Mass., N. Y., R. I.

CANKER, Felt Fungus. **Septobasidium castaneum; S. cookeri,** Fla., Miss., N. C.

CANKER; Dieback. **Cytospora** spp.; **Asterosporium hoffmanni,** New England to Mich., Md.; **Strumella coryneoides,** New England.

LEAF SPOT. **Gloeosporium fagi,** Conn. to Wis.; **Phyllosticta faginea,** Mass. to W. Va.

MISTLETOE. **Phoradendron flavescens,** Southern States.

PHYSIOGENIC Leaf Scorch. Water deficiency, high temperature.

Leaf Mottle. Cause unknown.

POWDERY MILDEW. **Microsphaera alni,** New England to Ill., and Gulf States.

ROT, Mushroom Root. **Armillaria mellea,** occasional.

ROT, Heart; Canker. **Polyporus glomeratus,** New England.

ROT, White Heart. **Fomes applanatus; F. connatus; F. everhartii; F. igniarius,** Lower Miss. Valley; **F. fraxinophilus.**

ROT, Brown Heart. **Fomes pinicola,** N. Y., Vt.

ROT, Sapwood. **Hydnum septentrionale; Ustulina vulgaris,** Northeast; **Fomes fomentarius,** widespread.

ROT, Wood. **Daedalea confragosa, D. quercina,** Conn.; **D. unicolor; Daldinia concentrica** and **D. vernicosa,** general; **Lenzites betulina,** widespread; **Polyporus** spp. with **P. versicolor** sometimes on living trees.

ROT, Wound. **Schizophyllum commune,** cosmopolitan; **Stereum hirsutum; S. purpureum,** widespread.

BEET (*Beta vulgaris*)

BACTERIAL Crown Gall. **Agrobacterium tumefaciens,** occasional.

BACTERIAL Pocket. **Xanthomonas beticola,** occasional.

BLIGHT, Seedling; Root Rot. **Fusarium** spp.

BLIGHT, Southern. **Sclerotium rolfsii,** N. C. to Fla., Tex., Ariz., Cal.

DAMPING-OFF; Crown Rot; Canker. **Pelicularia filamentosa** (*Rhizoctonia solani*), general; **Pythium** spp. cosmopolitan.

DOWNY MILDEW. **Peronospora schactii,** Cal., Oreg., Wash.

LEAF SPOT; Blight. **Cercospora beticola,** general.

LEAF SPOT. **Alternaria** sp., probably secondary; **Septoria betae,** Del., Ind., Mass., Ohio; **Gloeosporium betae,** Miss., Mont.

NEMATODE, Leaf and Stem. **Ditylenchus dipsaci,** Kans.

NEMATODE, Root Knot. **Heterodera marioni,** widespread in South, occasional in North; Root Gall. **H. schactii,** Cal., Col., Ida., Iowa,

NEMATODE, Root. **Tylenchus penetrans,** Utah.

Physiogenic Black Heart; Heart Rot. Boron deficiency, general; phosphorus deficiency occasional, especially in West, and Iowa, Ohio.

Bronzing. Potassium deficiency occasional, Iowa, Ohio, Wash.

Girdle. Strangling constriction of tap root.

Tipburn. Tips blackened on plants with high nitrogen content under low light intensity.

Powdery Mildew. **Erysiphe polygoni,** Cal.

Rot, Black Heart; Seedling Root. **Phoma betae,** general.

Rot, Charcoal. **Macrophomina phaseoli,** Cal.

Rot, Root. **Phytophthora drechsleri,** Cal., Col., Ida.; **Physalospora rhodina,** Ala., Oreg., Utah; **Phymatotrichum omnivorum,** Tex.

Rot, Root and Crown. **Sclerotinia sclerotiorum,** Conn.

Rot, Violet Root. **Helicobasidium purpureum,** occasional.

Rot, Wound, Storage. **Rhizopus** spp., cosmopolitan; **Cylindrocarpon radicicola,** N. Y.; **Penicillium** spp.; **Fusarium** spp.

Rust. **Puccinia aristidae** (O, I), Col., Kans., N. Mex., Utah; II, III on grasses.

Rust. **Uromyces betae** (II, III), Ariz., Cal., N. Mex., Oreg.; O, I, not in U.S.

Scab. **Actinomyces scabies,** widespread from Me. to Va. and west to Cal. and Wash.

Virus, Curly Top. **Ruga verrucosans,** general in West from S. Dak. and Nebr. to Tex., Cal., Wash.

Virus, Mosaic. **Marmor betae; M. cucumeris.**

Virus, Beet Leaf Curl. **Savoia piesmae.** Col., Iowa, Mich., Nebr., Ohio, S. Dak., Wy.

Virus, Yellow Net. Unidentified, Cal.

White Rust. **Albugo bliti,** Iowa, Ohio.

Wilt. **Verticillium albo-atrum,** Col.

Most of these troubles are more important for commercially grown sugar beets, on which crop the virus curly top is particularly serious. Cercospora leaf spot or blight is common on garden beets, though spraying is not often practical. Dusting seeds with Cuprocide or Arasan before planting is good insurance against damping-off and seedling root rots. Internal breakdown, heart rot or black heart due to boron deficiency can be prevented by treating the soil with borax.

BEGONIA

Bacterial Spot. **Xanthomonas begoniae,** Cal., Col., Md., Ga., Mass., N. J., N. Y., Ore., Tex., probably general.

Bacterial Crown Gall. **Agrobacterium tumefaciens,** Conn., Miss., Tex. and probably elsewhere since it is very susceptible to artificial inoculation.

Blight, Gray mold. **Botrytis cinerea,** cosmopolitan.

Leaf Spot; Anthracnose. **Gloeosporium** sp., Fla., La., Mass., Miss.

Leaf Spot. **Cercospora** sp., Fla., Ga., Miss., N. J., Tex.; **Penicillium bacillosporium,** N. Y., Miss., Tex.; **Phyllosticta** sp., N. J., Pa.

Nematode, Leaf. **Aphelenchoides olesistus,** cosmopolitan in greenhouses.

Nematode, Root Knot. **Heterodera marioni,** cosmopolitan, in gardens in the South, greenhouses in the North.

Physiogenic Oedema. A water-soaked spotting, frequent in house plants.

Powdery Mildew. **Erysiphe cichoracearum,** Cal.; **Oidium** sp., Fla., N. C.

Rot, Root. **Armillaria mellea,** Cal.; **Thielaviopsis basicola,** Mass., Ohio.

Rot, Root and Stem. **Pythium** spp., Cal., Mo.; **Rhizoctonia solani,** cosmopolitan.

Rot, Stem. **Sclerotinia sclerotiorum,** Cal.; **Sclerotium rolfsii,** Ill.

Virus, Spotted Wilt. **Lethum australiense,** Cal., Mo.

Wilt. **Verticillium albo-atrum,** Conn., N. Y.

The dry air of the average living room keeps fungus diseases of leaves and flowers at a minimum. Overwatering may foster root rots and physiological oedema. In greenhouses Botrytis blight, bacterial spot, the leaf nematode, and Pythium root and stem rot (of both fibrous and tuberous begonias) may become problems.

BIDENS (Bur-Marigold, Stick-Tight, Tickseed)

Downy Mildew. **Plasmopara halstedii,** Mass. to Ala., Kans. and N. Dak.

Powdery Mildew. **Sphaerotheca humili,** general.

Rust. **Uromyces bidenticola** (O, I, II, III), Cal., Fla., N. Mex.

BIGNONIA (Cross-Vine, Trumpet-Flower)

Black Mildew. **Dimerosporium tropicale,** Miss.; **Meliola bidentata,** S. C. to Tex.

Blight, Gray Mold. **Botrytis** sp.

Leaf Spot. **Cercospora capreolata,** Ala. to Miss.

Nematode, Root Knot. **Heterodera marioni.**

BIRCH (*Betula*)

Canker, Bark Patch. **Solenia ochracea.**

Canker, Trunk. **Hymenochaete agglutinans,** Mich., Pa.; **Nectria coccinea; N. galligena.**

Canker, Twig. **Nectria cinnabarina,** Northeastern States; **Sphaeropsis conglobata,** Ohio.

Dieback. **Melanconis stilbostoma,** Mass. to Ind., on white birch.

Leaf Blister. **Taphrina flava,** Northeast, on gray and paper birches.

Leaf Spot. **Phyllosticta betulina,** N. Y.; **Gloeosporium betularum.**

Powdery Mildew. **Microsphaera alni; Phyllactinia corylea.**

Rot, Heart. **Fomes applanatus; F. connatus; F. fulvus; F. igniarius; F. pinicola; Stereum purpureum; Polyporus hispidus.**

ROT, Root. **Armillaria mellea; Phytophthora cinnamomi,** of seedlings.

ROT, Sapwood. **Polyporus betulinus,** general on gray and paper birches; **P. gilvus,** sometimes on living trees.

ROT, Wood. **Polyporus** spp.; **Stereum fasciatum; S. hirsutum; S. murrayi Daedalea unicolor,** on living trees; other **Daedalea** spp.; **Polyporus tulipiferus.**

ROT, Wound. **Schizophyllum commune.**

RUST. **Melampsoridium betulinum** (II, III) ; O, I on Larch.

?VIRUS, Dieback. Vein clearing and symptoms similar to a virus disease, New England.

BISCHOFIA

LEAF SPOT, Algal. **Cephaleuros virescens,** Fla.

BISHOPS–CAP (*Mitella*)

LEAF SPOT. **Cercospora mitellae,** Mich.; **Phyllostica mitellae,** N. Y., Wis.; **Ramularia mitellae,** Ind., Ill., Mich., N. Y.; **Septoria mitellae,** Mich., Wis.

POWDERY MILDEW. **Sphaerotheca humuli,** Wis.

RUST. **Puccinia heucherae** (III) , widespread.

BITTERSWEET (*Celastrus scandens*)

BACTERIAL Crown Gall. **Agrobacterium tumefaciens,** Conn.

CANKER, Stem. **Glomerella cingulata,** N. H.

LEAF SPOT. **Phyllosticta celastri,** W. Va.; **Ramularia celastri,** general.

POWDERY MILDEW. **Microsphaera alni,** Wis.; **Phyllactinia corylea,** W. Va.

Many other fungi can be found on dead stems and leaves, but are not important pathogens.

BIXA (Annato-Tree)

LEAF SPOT, Algal. **Cephaleuros virescens,** Fla.

LEAF SPOT. **Cercospora bixae; Phyllosticta bixae.**

BLACK BEARBERRY (*Arctous*)

RUST. **Pucciniastrum sparsum** (II, III) .

BLACKBERRY (*Rubus*)

ANTHRACNOSE, Spot. **Elsinoë veneta,** general.

BACTERIAL Crown Gall. **Agrobacterium tumefaciens,** general; **A. rubi.**

BLIGHT, Cane. **Gnomonia rubi,** Md., Me., N. Y., Pa., Vt.; **Leptosphaeria coniothyrium,** N. Y. to N. C.; Wis., Tex., Pacific Northwest.

BLIGHT, Stamen; Dry Berry. **Hapalosphaeria deformans,** Ore., Wash.

BLOTCH, Sooty. **Gloeodes pomigena,** Md. to N. C.; Ind., Tex.

BLOTCH, Leaf. **Mycosphaerella confusa,** Va. to Fla.; Tex., Ill., Ind.

CANKER; Cane Spot. **Ascospora ruborum,** Wash.

CANKER. **Glomerella cingulata,** Md., Va.; **Phomopsis** sp., Wash.

DOWNY MILDEW. **Peronospora rubi,** Md., Wis.

FRUIT SPOT; Fly Speck. **Leptothyrium pomi,** Pa. to N. C.; Ill.

LEAF SPOT, Algal. **Cephaleuros virescens,** Fla.

LEAF SPOT. **Pezizella oenotherae,** also fruit rot, Ohio, Md., Va.; **Phyllosticta** spp., Fla., Ill., N. H.; **Septoria rubi,** Northeast.

POWDERY MILDEW. **Sphaerotheca humuli,** Conn. to Md.; Ill., Minn.; Pacific Northwest.

ROSETTE, Double Blossom. **Cercosporella rubi,** N. Y. to Fla.; Texas, Cal.

ROT, Gray Mold. **Botrytis cinerea,** general on fruit, bud, shoot.

ROT, Root. **Armillaria mellea,** Tex., Wash.; **Phymatotrichum omnivorum,** Tex.

ROT, Root and Collar. **Rhizoctonia solani.**

ROT, White Root. **Corticium galactinum,** near apple trees, Ark., Md., Va.

RUST, Yellow Cane. **Kuehneola uredinia** (O, I, II, III), Me. to Fla., La., Wis.

RUST, Orange. **Gymnoconia peckiana** (O, I, III), Me. to Ga. and west to Pacific; **Kunkelia nitens** (I), general, but probably more common in South.

VIRUS, Blackberry Dwarf. **Nanus loganobacci,** Pacific Coast, on loganberry.

VIRUS, Raspberry Leaf Curl. **Corium rubi,** Mich.

VIRUS, Mosaic. **Marmor rubi,** Mass. to Va., Iowa, Wis., Pacific Northwest.

WILT. **Verticillium albo-atrum.** Cal., Minn., N. Y., Wash.

Sanitation is the best approach to home garden blackberry diseases. Plants with crown gall, orange rust or virus troubles should be removed and burned, replanting with clean stock. Anthracnose and rosette are controlled in the South by cutting off old and new canes right after harvest and elsewhere by a dormant spray. Summer sprays may be needed for cane and leaf spots in some states. Varieties resistant to leaf spot and rust are promised. Fermate is good for cane blight.

BLACKBERRY–LILY (*Belamcanda*)

LEAF SPOT. **Alternaria** sp., Kans., Va.; **Heterosporium iridis,** Cal., Kans., N. Y., Okla., Va., Vt.

BLADDER–SENNA (*Colutea*)

BLIGHT, Twig. **Diplodia colteae,** Pa.

POWDERY MILDEW. **Erysiphe polygoni.**

ROT, Root. **Ganoderma** sp., Okla.

RUST. **Uromyces colutea** (II, III), Kans.

BLEEDING–HEART (*Dicentra spectabilis*)

ROT, Stem. **Sclerotium rolfsii,** N. Y.

ROT, Storage; Wilt. **Sclerotinia sclerotiorum,** Minn.

WILT. **Fusarium** sp., N. J.

BLEPHILIA

LEAF SPOT. **Cercoseptoria blephiliae,** Wis.; **Septoria menthicola.**

RUST. **Puccinia menthae** (O, I, II, III), Ill., Ind., Iowa, Md., Mich., Mo., Tenn., Wis.

BLOODROOT (*Sanguinaria*)

BLIGHT, Gray Mold. **Botrytis cinerea.**

LEAF SPOT. **Cercospora sanguinariae,** Md., Mo., N. Y., Pa., Tex., Wis.; **Gloeosporium sanguinariae,** Ohio, Tex.; **Phyllosticta sanguinariae,** Mo., Tex.

ROT, Root; Root Necrosis. **Pythium paroecandrum,** Va.

BLUEBERRY (*Vaccinium*)

BACTERIAL Crown Gall. **Agrobacterium tumefaciens,** Mass., Miss., Wash.

BLIGHT, Twig; Dieback. **Botrytis** sp., N. J., Wash.; **Diaporthe vaccinii,** Mass., N. J., N. C.

CANKER, Cane. **Physalospora corticis,** Ala., Fla., Miss., N. C.

DODDER. **Cuscuta** sp., Pa.

GALL, Red Leaf. **Exobasidium vaccinii,** general.

Phyllostictina vaccinii, Ga., Miss., Md., N. C.; **Gloeocercospora inconspicua,** Ga., N. C., Md.

LEAF SPOT. **Phyllosticta** spp., Ala., Fla., N. J.; **Septoria difformis,** N. Y.

LEAF SPOT; Double Spot. **Dothichiza caroliniana,** N. C.

LEAF SPOT, Tar. **Rhytisma vaccinii,** widespread.

POWDERY MILDEW. **Microsphaera alni** var. **vaccinii,** widespread.

ROT, Berry; Dieback. **Alternaria** sp., Mass., N. J., N. C.; **Glomerella cingulata,** N. J.

ROT, Brown; Twig Blight. Mummy Berry. **Monilinia vaccinii-corymbosi,** Ind., Me., Mass., N. J., N. Y.

RUST. Witches' Broom. **Pucciniastrum goeppertianum** (III), Me. to Minn.; O, I on fir.

RUST, Leaf. **Pucciniastrum myrtilli** (II, III), Me. to Pa.; Wis.; O, I, spruce.

?VIRUS, Stunt, presumably virus, limiting factor in some districts; known in Mass., Mich., N. C., N. J., N. Y.

Stunt causes dwarfing of bushes, small leaves, yellowing of foliage in summer followed by brilliant reddening towards fall. Berries are small, with unpleasant flavor. Affected bushes should be removed. Fermate is useful against mummy berry.

Physalospora corticis causes extensive cankers and blisters in the South, with highbush varieties Cabot and Pioneer particularly susceptible. Dormant pruning and delayed dormant spraying aids in controlling twig blight, and summer spraying, with bordeaux mixture or Fermate, is used against leaf spots and mummy berry.

BLUE COHOSH (*Caulophyllum*)

Blight, Leaf. **Botrytis** sp., N. J., N. Y.
Leaf Spot. **Cercospora caulophylli,** Vt. to Va., Mo., Wis.

BLUE–CURLS (*Trichostema*)

Leaf Spot. **Septoria trichostematis,** N. Y.

BLUE–EYED–GRASS (*Sisyrinchium*)

Blight, Leaf. **Kellermania sisyrinchii,** Cal., N. Dak., N. Mex.
Nematode, Root. **Pratylenchus pratensis.**
Rust. **Uromyces houstoniatus** (II, III), Me., W. Va.; O, I on houstonia; **U. probus** (I, II, III), Ida., Ore., Utah, Wash.

BLUE LACE–FLOWER (*Trachymene*)

Nematode, Root Knot. **Heterodera marioni,** Fla.
Rot, Root. **Fusarium** sp., Conn., N. J.
Rot, Stem. **Rhizoctonia solani,** N. J.

BOISDUVALIA

Rust. **Puccinia glabella** (II, III), Nev., Ore., Utah; O, I unknown.
P. oenotherae (O, I, II, III), Cal., Ida., Nebr., Ore., Wash.
P. vagans var. **epilobi-tetragoni** (O, I, II, III), Cal., Nev., Ida., Ore., Utah.

BOLTONIA

Leaf Spot. **Septoria erigerontis** var. **boltoniae,** Iowa, Wis.
Powdery Mildew. **Erysiphe cichoracearum,** S. Dak.
Rust. **Puccinia extensicola** var. **asteris** (II, III), Iowa, Nebr., N. and S. Dak.; O, I on Carex.
Smut, White. **Entyloma compositarum,** Wis.

BORAGE (*Borago*)

Leaf Spot. **Ramularia** sp., Cal.

BORRICHIA (*Sea-Oxeye*)

Rust. **Aecidium borrichiae** (O, I), Ala., Fla.; **Puccinia triannulata,** Fla., S. C., Tex.

BOSEA

Nematode, Root Knot. **Heterodera marioni.**

BOSTON IVY (*Parthenocissus tricuspidata*)

DIEBACK. **Cladosporium** sp., N. J.

LEAF SPOT. **Guignardia bidwellii** f. **parthenocissi,** widespread; **Phleospora ampelopsidis,** Iowa; **Sphaeropsis hedericola,** N. J.

The Guignardia leaf spot, caused by a strain of the same fungus which produces black rot of grapes, is common and disfiguring. Control by spraying with bordeaux mixture is nearly as disfiguring and not too effective in a wet season unless timed very carefully. Fermate is somewhat promising, judging by the one season I have tried it.

BOUVARDIA

NEMATODE, Leaf. **Aphelenchoides** sp.

NEMATODE, Root Knot. **Heterodera marioni,** N. Y.

RUST. **Puccinia bouvardiae** (O, I, III), Ariz.

BOYSENBERRY

Subject to most blackberry diseases: anthracnose, crown gall and cane gall, cane canker, dieback, leaf spots, and mosaic. See Blackberry.

BOXELDER (*Acer negundo*)

ANTHRACNOSE; Leaf Blight. **Gloeosporium apocryptum,** widespread.

BLIGHT, Leaf. **Coryneum negundinis,** Mo.

BLIGHT, Twig. **Macroplodia simillima,** Ill., conidial stage of **Physalospora obtusa,** Ga., Ill., Va., Tenn.; **Sphaeropsis albescens,** Iowa, Kans., N. and S. Dak.

CANKER. **Coniothyrium negundinis,** Ill.; **Coryneum septosporioides,** Col.; **Diplodia atrata,** Nebr., W. Va.

CANKER, Felt Fungus. **Septobasidium** spp., N. C.

CANKER, Twig. **Leptothyrium maximum,** Ill.; **Nectria cinnabarina,** widespread; **Phacidium negundinis,** Ill.

LEAF SPOT. **Ascochyta negundinis,** Ill., N. C.; **Cercospora negundinis,** widespread; **Phleospora aceris,** widespread; **Phyllosticta minima,** widepread.

LEAF SPOT, Black-Speckled. **Rhytisma punctatum,** N. Y.

ROT, Root. **Phymatotrichum omnivorum,** Cal., Tex.; **Helicobasidium purpureum,** Tex.

ROT, Sapwood. **Poria pulchella,** Mont.

ROT, Silver Leaf. **Stereum purpureum,** S. Dak.

ROT, White Heart. **Fomes connatus,** sometimes on street trees.

WILT. **Verticillium albo-atrum,** occasional.

BOXELDER, CALIFORNIA (*Acer negundo californicum*)

BACTERIAL Leaf Spot. **Pseudomonas aceris,** Cal.

BLIGHT, Twig. **Cryptodiaporthe lebiseyi,** Cal.

LEAF SPOT. **Phleospora aceris,** Cal., Tex.; **Septoria crassospora,** Cal.

LEAF SPOT, Tar. **Rhytisma acerinum.**

BOXWOOD (*Buxus*)

BLIGHT; Leaf Cast. **Hyponectria buxi,** N. Y., and probably same as *Laestadia buxi* reported from Md., Mass., Miss., N. Y. **Verticillium buxi,** cosmopolitan on dead leaves, is often associated with Hyponectria but connection has not been confirmed.

BLIGHT, Leaf Tip. **Phoma conidiogena,** Md., N. J., N. Y., Okla.

CANKER, "Nectria"; Dieback; Leaf Blight. **Volutella buxi** general on leaves, twigs, branches and considered imperfect stage of **Pseudonectria rouselliana,** but connection not confirmed.

CANKER; DIEBACK. **Fusarium buxicola** (*Nectria desmazierii*), Ala., Md.; **F. lateritium,** Md., S. C., Va., probably secondary infection.

LEAF SPOT. **Phyllosticta auerswaldii,** Md., Mass., N. J., N. Y., Va., Wash. **Colletotrichum** sp., perhaps secondary but associated with a leaf cast; **Macrophoma candollei** prominent, general on dead leaves but following winter injury or disease.

NEMATODE, Root; Root Necrosis. **Pratylenchus** sp., probably a factor in leaf bronzing and dieback, N. Y. to Ala., Tex.

PHYSIOGENIC Winter Injury. Freezing, ice standing on stems, causes bark to slough off stems and dieback to show up any time through the next summer. Sun Scald. Injury in late winter or early spring on boxwood left uncovered all winter, or uncovered too early on a day with bright sun and strong winds.

ROT, Root. **Armillaria mellea,** N. J.; **Fusarium oxysporum** and **F. solani,** Md., perhaps secondary; **Phymatotrichum omnivorum,** Tex.; **Phytophthora parasitica,** Md.; **Pythium** sp., Mass.; **Rhizoctonia solani,** cosmopolitan after nematode injury.

ROT, Heart. **Fomes igniarius,** Va.; **Poria punctata,** Va.

?VIRUS, Mosaic. Variegation. Cause unknown.

Salmon pink pustules appearing on backs of leaves, along twigs or on main stems are usually an indication of *Volutella buxi* and the disease has been commonly called "Nectria Canker" from the probable relation of this imperfect fungus with the perfect fungus, now known as **Pseudonectria rouselliana,** occasionally found on cankered main stems. The disease is supposed to be somewhat tied up with winter injury, the fungus damaging previously weakened bushes, but I frequently find the Volutella stage in epidemic form in late summer on bushes previously green and healthy. The blighting is rapid, and most severe on plants which have not had an annual "housecleaning." It can be checked by a combination of sanitary measures and spraying.

Recent research indicates that much of the unexplained dying back, bronzing and general unhealth of boxwood in some sections is due to a root nematode, related to the meadow or tobacco-root nematode.

BRICKELLIA

DODDER. **Cuscuta exaltata,** Tex.

LEAF SPOT. **Cercospora coleosanthi,** Cal., Col.

ROT, Root. **Phymatotrichum omnivorum,** Tex.

RUST. **Coleosporium aridum** (II), Cal.; **Puccinia kuhniae** (O, I, II, III), Ariz.; **P. subdecora** (O, I, II, III), Col., N. Mex., Utah; **Aecidium aecularium** (O, I), Ariz., Col., N. Mex.

BROCCOLI (See Cabbage)

BRODIAEA

RUST. **Puccinia carnegiana** (O, I, III), Ariz.; **P. dichelostemmae** (O, I, III), Wash., Oreg.; **P. moreniana** (III), Cal.; **P. nodosa** (O, I, II, III), Cal.; **P. pattersoniana,** Ida., Utah, Wash.; II, III on grasses; **P. subangulata** (O, I, III), Cal.; **Uromyces brodiaeae** (O, I, III), Oreg., Cal., Wash.

BROMELIA

LEAF SPOT. **Gloeosporium** sp., Fla., Md.

BROOM (*Genista*)

DIEBACK. **Diplodia** sp., Cal., N. J.

POWDERY MILDEW. **Erysiphe polygoni,** Mo.

RUST. **Uromyces genistae-tinctoriae** (II, III), Cal.

BROOM, SCOTCH (*Cytisus*)

Various fungi are reported on dead twigs and branches but apparently there are no serious diseases.

BROUSSONETIA (Paper-Mulberry)

CANKER; DIEBACK. **Nectria cinnabarina,** Ala., N. Y.

MISTLETOE. **Phoradendron flavescens,** Tex.

NEMATODE, Root Knot. **Heterodera marioni.**

ROT, Root. **Phymatotrichum omnivorum,** Tex.

BROWALLIA

NEMATODE, Root Knot. **Heterodera marioni,** Md.

WILT. **Fusarium** sp., Del.

BRUSSELS SPROUTS (See Cabbage)

BRYONOPSIS

Bacterial Spot. **Pseudomonas lachrymans,** Wis.
Downy Mildew. **Pseudoperonospera cubensis,** Mass., Ohio.

BUCKEYE (*Aesculus*) See also Horse-chestnut

Blotch, Leaf. **Guignardia aesculi,** general.
Canker; Dieback. **Botryosphaeria ribis,** Md., N. Y.; **Cylindrocarpon** spp. Cal.; **Fusarium scirpi,** Cal.; **Cryptodiaporthe aesculi,** Cal.; **Diaporthe eres,** cosmopolitan; **Nectria cinnabarina,** cosmopolitan; **Physalospora obtusa,** N. J., N. Y.
Leaf Spot. **Macrosporium baccatum,** Kans.; **Monochaetia desmazierii,** N. C.; **Mycosphaerella maculiformis,** Cal.; **Septoria glabra,** Ind.
Leaf Blister; Witches' broom. **Taphrina aesculi,** Cal.
Mistletoe. **Phoradendron** spp., Cal.
Physiogenic Leaf Scorch.
Powdery Mildew. **Phyllactinia corylea,** Cal.; **Uncinula flexuosa,** widespread.
Rot, Root. **Phymatotrichum omnivorum,** Tex.; **Armillaria mellea.**
Rot, Heart. **Fomes applanatus** cosmopolitan; **Polyporus squamosus.**
Rust. **Aecidium aesculi,** Ind., Kans., Nebr.

BUCKLEYA

Rust. **Cronartium comandrae** (II, III) ; O, I on pine.

BUCKTHORN, ALDER, COMMON AND YELLOW (*Rhamnus alnifolia, R. cathartica, R. caroliniana*)

Leaf Spot. **Cercospora rhamni,** La., Nebr., N. J., Tex., Wis.; **C. aeruginosa,** Mo., Nebr., S. C.
Powdery Mildew. **Microsphaera alni,** Wis.
Rot, Root. **Phymatotrichum omnivorum,** Tex.
Rust. **Puccinia coronata** (O, I) ; II, III on grasses.

BUCKWHEAT-TREE (*Cliftonia*)

Black Mildew; Black Leaf Patch. **Morenoella cliftoniae,** Miss.
Leaf Spot. **Pestalotia cliftoniae,** Miss.

BUDDLEIA (Butterfly-Bush)

Canker, Stem. **Phoma** sp. (*Phomopsis buddleiae*) , Ariz.
Nematode, Root Knot. **Heterodera marioni,** Miss.
Rot, Root. **Phymatotrichum omnivorum,** Tex.

BUFFALO–BERRY (*Shepherdia*)

LEAF SPOT. **Cylindrosporium shepherdiae,** Utah, Wis.; **Septoria shepherdiae,** Alaska, Mont., Ida., Wis.

POWDERY MILDEW. **Sphaerotheca castagnei,** Mont., Wyo.; **S. humuli,** Col., Mont.

ROT. **Fomes fraxinophilus,** Northern Rockies; **Phymatotrichum omnivorum,** Tex.

RUST. **Puccinia caricis-shepherdiae** (O, I), N. Y. to Col., N. Mex., Wash.; II, III on Carex.

BUGINVILLEA (*Bougainvillea*)

LEAF SPOT. **Cladosporium arthrinioides,** Tex.

VIRUS, Mosaic. Undetermined, Fla.

BUGLE–WEED (*Ajuga*)

BLIGHT, Southern; Crown Rot. **Sclerotium rolfsii** (or *S. delphinii*), Cal., Conn., Kans., N. J., N. Y., probably widespread.

This blight or rot is very common on low-lying *Ajuga reptans,* striking suddenly with the first warm, muggy weather and often killing large patches.

BUMELIA

LEAF SPOT. **Cercospora lanuginosa,** Tex.; **Phyllosticta bumeliifolia,** Ala., Tex.; **P. curtisii,** Fla., Mo., **Septoria bumeliae,** Miss.

ROT, Root. **Helicobasidium purpureum,** Tex.

BUNCH–FLOWER (*Melanthium*)

LEAF SPOT. **Septoria allardii,** Va.

RUST. **Puccinia atropuncta,** N. C., Tenn., Va.

BURNET (*Sanguisorba*)

LEAF SPOT. **Graphium sessile,** N. Y.; **Ovularia bulbigera,** Ill., Alaska.

POWDERY MILDEW. **Sphaerotheca humuli,** Mass., N. Y., Pa., Alaska.

BUTTERFLY–FLOWER (*Schizanthus*)

ANTHRACNOSE. **Colletotrichum schizanthi,** N. Y.

DAMPING-OFF; Root Rot. **Rhizoctonia solani,** N. Y.; **Pythium ultimum,** Mo.

NEMATODE, Root Knot. **Heterodera marioni.**

ROT, Stem. **Sclerotinia sclerotiorum,** Miss., Mo.

VIRUS, Spotted Wilt. **Lethum australiense,** Tex.

VIRUS, Aster Yellows. **Chlorogenus callistephi,** N. J.

BUTTERFLY–PEA (*Clitoria*)

Leaf Spot. **Cercospora clitoriae,** Ala., Fla.
Rot, Root. **Phymatotrichum omnivorum,** Tex.

BUTTERFLY–WEED (*Asclepias*)

Leaf Spot. **Cercospora asclepiadorae,** Ala., Del., Kans., S. C., Tex.; **C. clavata,** general, especially in West; **Phyllosticta tuberosa,** N. J.
Rot, Root. **Phymatotrichum omnivorum,** Tex.
Rust. **Puccinia bartholomaei** (O, I), widespread, especially in West; II, III on Bouteloua; **P. vexans** (O, I), Wis.; II, III on Bouteloua. **Uromyces asclepiadis,** widespread; O, I unknown.
Virus, Cucumber Mosaic. **Marmor cucumeris.**

BUTTON–BUSH (*Cephalanthus*)

Blight, Leaf. **Cercospora perniciosa,** Tex.
Dodder. **Cuscuta gronovii,** N. Y.
Leaf Spot. **Ascochyta cephalanthi,** La., **Coniothyrium cephalanthi,** La. **Phyllosticta cephalanthi,** Tex.; **Ramularia cephalanthi,** Ala., Kans., La., N. Y., Wis.; **Septoria cephalanthi,** Kans., Wis.
Powdery Mildew. **Microsphaera alni,** widespread; **Phyllactinia corylea,** Ind.
Rust. **Puccinia seymouriana** (O, I), New England to Fla., and Central States; II, III on Spartina; **Uredo cephalanthi** (II), Fla.

CABBAGE, and Other Crucifers (*Brassica* spp.)

Includes Brussels Sprouts, Cauliflower, Broccoli, Kale, Kohl-Rabi.

Anthracnose. **Colletotrichum higginsianum,** Fla., on Chinese cabbage.
Bacterial, Black Rot. **Xanthomonas campestris,** general.
Bacterial Leaf Spot; Pepper Spot. **Pseudomonas maculicola,** widespread.
Bacterial Soft Rot; Stump Rot. **Erwinia carotovora.**
Black Leg; Leaf Spot. **Phoma lingam,** general East of Rockies, also Oreg., Wash.
Blight, Southern. **Sclerotium rolfsii,** N. C. to Fla., Tex., occasional.
Blight, Gray Mold. **Botrytis cinerea,** Cal., Fla.
Club Root. **Plasmodiophora brassicae,** general.
Damping-Off; Bottom Rot. **Rhizoctonia solani,** general.
Downy Mildew. **Peronospora parasitica,** general.
Leaf Spot, Black; Brown Rot; Head Browning, of cauliflower. **Alternaria brassicae** and **A. oleracea,** general.
Leaf Spot, Gray; Head Browning. **Alternaria herculea,** general.
Leaf Spot; White Spot. **Cercosporella albomaculans,** Ala., Cal., Ind., Ga., Oreg.

Leaf Spot. **Cercospora** sp., Cal., Del., Fla., Ill., Okla., Miss., N. C.; **Phyllosticta brassicicola,** Cal.

Mold, Leaf. **Heterosporium variabile,** Mont., N. Y.

Mold, Seed. **Stemphylium botryosum,** Pacific States.

Nematode, Root Knot. **Heterodera marioni.**

Nematode, Root. **Pratylenchus pratensis.**

Physiogenic Brown Heart. Probably boron deficiency.

Chlorosis. Magnesium or manganese deficiency.

Oedema. Excessive water tension, or from copper sprays.

Pink Head. Probably genetic.

Tipburn. Potassium deficiency.

Whip-tail.

Powdery Mildew. **Erysiphe polygoni,** Ariz., Cal., Conn., Fla., Md., Oreg., Mass.

Rot, Cottony; Drop. **Sclerotinia sclerotiorum,** Ariz., Mass., N. Y., Tex.

Rot, Root. **Phymatotrichum omnivorum,** Tex.; **Phytophthora megasperma,** Cal.

Rot, Soft; Black Mold. **Rhizopus stolonifer,** occasional.

Virus, Mosaic. **Marmor brassicae; M. cruciferarum.**

Virus, Yellows. **Chlorogenus callistephi,** probably.

White Rust; White Blister. **Albugo candida,** Cal., Ida., Ky., Neb., N. C., Ohio, Tex.

Wilt, Yellows. **Fusarium oxysporum** f. **conglutinans,** general.

A general control program for cabbage and other crucifers calls for choosing varieties resistant to Fusarium yellows, purchasing disease-free seed or having seed hot-water treated against blackleg and black rot organisms, dusting seed for damping-off insurance, starting seedlings in soil free from club root spores, and careful cleaning up of all vegetable refuse at the end of a season.

CACTI (*Cereus* spp.)

Anthracnose. **Mycosphaerella opuntiae,** Tex.

Bacterial Rot. **Erwinia carotovora,** Tex.

Black Spot. **Stevensea wrightii,** Tex.

Nematode, Root Knot. **Heterodera marioni.**

Rot, Stem and Branch. **Aspergillus alliaceus,** Tex.

Rot, Gray Mold. **Botrytis cinerea,** occasional, under damp conditions, indoors.

Rot, Root and Stem. **Fusarium oxysporum,** Ariz., Cal.; **Helminthosporium** sp., Tex.

Rot, **Phymatotrichum omnivorum,** Tex.

Rot, Dry. **Poria** sp., Cal.

Scorch (see under Leaf Scorch). **Hendersonia opuntiae,** Tex.

Stem Spot (see Septoria under Leaf Spots). **Septoria cacticola,** Tex.

GIANT CACTUS (*Carnegiea gigantea*)

BACTERIAL Crown Gall. **Agrobacterium tumefaciens,** Ariz.
BACTERIAL Blight. **Erwinia carnegieana,** Ariz.
ROT, Dry. **Poria carnegieae,** Ariz., Heart Rot. **Fomes robustus,** Ariz.

The bacterial blight or necrosis is now spread over the whole giant cactus area in Arizona with mortality heaviest in magnificent specimens 150 to 200 years old.

PINCUSHION or FISHHOOK CACTI (*Mammilaria* spp.)

ANTHRACNOSE; Zonate Spot. **Gloeosporium cactorum.**
ANTHRACNOSE. **Mycosphaerella opuntiae,** Tex.
NEMATODE, Root Knot. **Heterodera marioni,** Tex.
ROT, Root. **Phymatotrichum omnivorum,** Tex.

PRICKLY PEAR CACTI (*Opuntia* spp.)

ANTHRACNOSE; Zonate Spot. **Gloeosporium cactorum,** Fla., Miss.
ANTHRACNOSE; Black Rot. **Mycosphaerella opuntiae,** Ala., Fla., La., N. Y.; S. C., Tex.
BACTERIAL Rot. **Erwinia aroideae,** Fla., Miss., Okla., Tex.
BLACK MILDEW. **Lembosia cactorum,** Fla.
BLACK SPOT. **Stevensea wrightii,** Fla., Tex.
NEMATODE, Root Knot. **Heterodera marioni,** Miss., Ore.
ROT, Cladode. **Aspergillus alliaceus,** Tex.; **Colletotrichum dematium,** N. Y., Tex.; **Diplodia opuntiae,** Md., Pa., Kans.; **Phoma** sp., Okla.
ROT, Black. **Physalospora obtusa,** N. Y.; **P. rhodina,** Fla.
ROT, Dry. **Phyllosticta concava,** Mo., N. J., Okla., Tex.
ROT, Stem. **Phytophthora parasitica,** N. Y.; **Pythium debaryanum,** Cal.
PHYSIOGENIC Glassiness. Perhaps a form of oedema, water suffusion.
Scab. Cause unknown, occasional in indoor culture.
SPOT, Cladode. **Phyllosticta cacti,** N. Mex.; **Septoria fici-indicae,** Tex.
SCORCH, "Sun Scald." **Hendersonia opuntiae,** Ala., N. J., Kans., Mont., Tex.
VIRUS, Mosaic. Undetermined, Md.

STAR, SEA-URCHIN, BARREL CACTI (*Echinocactus* spp.)

ANTHRACNOSE. **Mycosphaerella opuntiae,** Tex.
BLACK SPOT. **Diplotheca** sp., Tex.
ROT, Root. **Phymatotrichum omnivorum,** Tex.
ROT, Stem. **Aspergillus alliaceus,** Tex.
SCORCH; Scald. **Hendersonia opuntiae,** Tex.

CALADIUM

Bacterial Soft Rot. **Erwinia carotovora,** Fla.
Blight, Southern. **Sclerotium rolfsii,** Fla.
Leaf Spot. **Gloeosporium** sp., Fla.
Nematode, Root Knot. **Heterodera marioni,** Fla., Miss.

CAESALPINIA

Blight, Currant Cane. **Botryosphaeria ribis** in South.

CALCEOLARIA

Physiogenic Necrosis. Boron deficiency, Cal.
Rot, Root. **Pythium ultimum; P. mastophorum.**
Rot, Stem. **Sclerotinia sclerotiorum,** N. Y., Wash.
Virus, Spotted Wilt. **Lethum australiense,** Cal.
Wilt. **Verticillium albo-atrum,** N. Y., Wash.

CALENDULA (Pot Marigold)

Blight, Gray Mold. **Botrytis cinerea,** Mo., N. J., N. Y., Alaska.
Blight, Southern. **Sclerotium rolfsii,** Tex.
Leaf Spot. **Alternaria** sp., N. Y.; **Cercospora calendulae,** Pa., Tex., Va.; **Colletotrichum gloeosporioides,** Va.
Nematode, Root Knot. **Heterodera marioni,** W. Va., Tex.
Powdery Mildew. **Erysiphe cichoracearum,** Cal., N. Y.; **E. polygoni,** Pa.
Rot, Root. **Rhizoctonia solani,** Ind., N. J., N. C., Tex.
Rot, Stem; Wilt. **Sclerotinia sclerotiorum,** Cal., Fla., La., Mo., Ohio, Tex.
Rust. **Puccinia flaveriae** (III), Ill, Ind., Iowa, Kans., Mo., Nebr., Tex.
Smut, White. **Entyloma calendulae,** Cal., N. H., Oreg.; **E. compositarum,** Wash.
Virus, Mosaic. Unidentified, perhaps *Marmor cucumeris.*
Virus, Spotted Wilt. **Lethum australiense,** Cal., Mich., Tex.
Virus, Aster Yellows. **Chlorogenus callistephi,** Conn., Del., Ne., N. J., Pa., Va. and var. **californicus,** Cal.

Fermate gives good control of calendula rust.

CALIFORNIA-BLUEBELL (*Phacelia whitlavia*)

Leaf Spot. **Cylindrosporium phaceliae,** Mont., Tex.
Powdery Mildew. **Erysiphe cichoracearum,** Cal., Mont., N. Mex., Tex.
Rot, Root. **Phymatotrichum omnivorum,** Tex.
Rust. **Puccinia aristidae** (O, I), II, III on wild grasses; **P. phaceliae** (III); **P. rubigo-vera** var. **apocrypta** (O, I), Mont. to Col., Oreg.; also Cal., N. Mex.; II, III on brome grass; **Uredo contraria** (II), Cal.
Virus, Curly Top. **Ruga verrucosans,** Cal.

CALIFORNIA–LAUREL (*Umbellularia*)

Black Mildew. **Asterina anomala,** Cal.

Canker: Dieback. **Nectria cinnabarina; N. coccinea,** Cal.

Rot, Wood. **Fomes** spp.; **Polyporus versicolor,** Cal., Oreg.; **Poria ambigua,** Cal.; **Stereum albobadium,** Cal.; **Schizophyllum commune,** Cal.

CALIFORNIA PEPPER–TREE (*Schinus molle*)

Dodder. **Cuscuta subinclusa,** Cal.

Nematode, Root Knot. **Heterodera marioni,** Tex.

Rot, Root. **Armillaria mellea,** Cal.; **Phymatotrichum omnivorum,** Ariz., Tex.

Rot, Heart. **Fomes applanatus,** Cal.; **Polyporus dryophilus,** Cal.; **P. farlowii,** Ariz., Cal.; **P. sulphureus; P. versicolor,** Cal.

Rot, Wood. **Ganoderma polychromum,** Cal.; **Stereum hirsutum; Trametes hispida,** Cal.

Wilt. **Verticillium** sp., Cal.

CALIFORNIA PITCHER–PLANT (*Darlingtonia*)

Leaf Spot. **Mycosphaerella sarraceniae,** Cal.; **Septoria darlingtoniae,** Oreg.

CALIFORNIA–POPPY (*Eschscholtzia*)

Bacterial Blight. **Xanthomonas papavericola,** Tex.

Mold, Leaf. **Heterosporium eschscholtziae,** Cal.

Nematode, Root Knot. **Heterodera marioni,** Tex.

Powdery Mildew. **Erysiphe polygoni,** Cal.

Rot, Collar. **Alternaria** sp., Tex.

Smut, Leaf. **Entyloma eschscholtziae,** Cal.

Virus, Aster Yellows. **Chlorogenus callistephi,** N. J., N. Y.; also var. **californicus,** Cal.

Wilt. **Verticillium albo-atrum,** Cal.

CALLA, CALLA–LILY (*Zantedeschia aethiopica*)

Bacterial Soft Rot. **Erwinia aroideae,** general; **E. carotovora.**

Blight, Southern. **Sclerotium rolfsii,** Cal., Fla., Oreg.

Leaf Spot. **Alternaria** sp., secondary, Cal., N. J., N. Y.; **Cercospora richardiaecola,** Ala., Miss.; **Gloeosporium callae,** Wash., **Phyllosticta richardiae,** Cal., Fla., Mass., N. J., N. Y., Oreg.

Nematode, Root Knot. **Heterodera marioni,** Cal., Fla.

Rot, Rhizome. **Phytophthora erythroseptica,** Cal.

Rot, Root. **Phytophthora richardiae,** Cal., Fla., Ill., Mass., N. J., N. Y., Ohio, Oreg., Pa., Wash.; **Armillaria mellea,** Cal.

Rot, Dry. **Phoma** sp., Cal., Oreg.

VIRUS, Spotted Wilt. **Lethum australiense,** Cal., Md., N. Y., Oreg., Tex., Wash.

Root rot is controlled by treating rhizomes before planting and growing in pots rather than benches. Specimens showing spotted wilt must be destroyed before thrips spread the virus.

CALLA, GOLDEN, PINK (*Zantedeschia elliottiana, Z. rehmannii*)

BACTERIAL Soft Rot. **Erwinia aroideae,** Cal., Fla.
BLIGHT, Leaf. **Phytophthora erythroseptica,** Cal.
ROT, Root, Seed. **Rhizoctonia solani,** Cal.
VIRUS, Spotted Wilt. **Lethum australiense,** Cal., Md., N. Y., Tex.

CALLA, WILD (*Calla palustris*)

LEAF SPOT. **Cercospora callae,** Mass., N. Y., Wis.; **Marssonina callae,** N. Y.

CALLIANDRA (False Mesquite)

ROT, Root. **Clitocybe tabescens,** on Surinam calliandra, Fla.
RUST. **Ravenelia reticulatae** (II, III), Ariz.

CALLICARPA (Beauty-Berry, French-Mulberry)

BLACK MILDEW. **Meliola cookeana,** Fla., La.
LEAF SPOT. **Cercospora callicarpae,** S. C. to Texas.

CALOCHORTUS (Mariposa-Lily, Globe-Tulip)

RUST. **Puccinia calochorti** (O, I, III), Cal., Oreg., N. Mex.; Wash. to Nebr.

CALYCANTHUS (Sweet-Shrub, Carolina Allspice, Mountain Spicewood)

Various fungi are found on branches but apparently not causing important diseases.

CAMASS (*Camassia*)

BLIGHT. **Botrytis cinerea,** Oreg.
LEAF SPOT. **Septoria chlorogali,** Oreg.
SMUT, Leaf. **Urocystis colchici,** Oreg., Ind.

CAMELLIA (*Camellia japonica* and *C. sasanqua*)

BACTERIAL Crown Gall. **Agrobacterium tumefaciens,** Wash.
BLIGHT, Flower. **Sclerotinia camelliae,** Cal., Ga., Oreg.
BLIGHT, Bud and Flower. **Botrytis cinerea,** general, usually after frost.
DIEBACK; Canker. **Glomerella cingulata** (often reported as *Colletotrichum gloeosporioides* or *Gloeosporium* sp.), widespread; **Phomopsis** sp., Fla.
DODDER. **Cuscuta** sp.

LEAF GALL. **Exobasidium camelliae,** Fla., Ga., La., Miss.

LEAF SPOT, Algal. **Cephaleuros virescens,** Gulf States.

LEAF SPOT; Twig Blight. **Pestalotia guepini,** widespread.

LEAF SPOT. **Phyllosticta camelliae, P. camelliaecola,** Southeast; **Sporonema camelliae,** Ala., Va.

NEMATODE, Root Knot. **Heterodera marioni,** Tex.

PHYSIOGENIC Dieback. Malnutrition, freezing injury, probably other causes. Oedema, Corky excrescences, perhaps confused with scab in some cases, in other cases disturbed water relations. Sunscald.

ROT, Root. **Phytophthora cinnamomi,** in nursery propagating beds, Ala.

ROT, Mushroom Root. **Clitocybe tabescens,** Fla., occasional.

SCAB. **Sphaceloma** sp., causing leaf spots.

VIRUS, Camellia Yellow Spot. Undetermined, Oreg.

VIRUS, Ring Spot. Undetermined, La., S. C.

Flower blight, prevalent in California, now present in Georgia and Oregon, is a potential enemy of camellias elsewhere. Some state quarantines have been set up. Dieback is the subject of much controversy among camellia fans. There are at least two types: one a response to unfavorable environmental conditions, and the other due to one or more fungi. Drastic surgery and a copper spray early in the season to prevent infection through bud-scale scars seem helpful for the latter type of dieback. Physiogenic sunscald is common.

CAMPANULA (Bellflower and Canterbury Bells)

BLIGHT, Southern. **Sclerotium rolfsii,** Ill., N. J.

LEAF SPOT. **Cercoseptoria minuta,** Wis.; **Phyllosticta alliariifoliae,** N. J., N. Y.; **Septoria campanulae,** Ill., Iowa, Kans., Miss., Mo., Wis.

NEMATODE, Root Knot. **Heterodera marioni,** Md.

POWDERY MILDEW. **Erysiphe cichoracearum,** Pa.

ROT, Root. **Fusarium** sp., N. J., N. Y.; **Rhizoctonia solani,** Ill.

ROT, Stem. **Sclerotinia sclerotiorum,** Md., Wash.

RUST. **Aecidium campanulastri** (O, I), Iowa, Minn.; **Coleosporium campanulae** (II, III), N. Y. to Miss., Mo., Wis.; Cal.; O, I on pine; **Puccinia campanulae** (III), Cal., Mont., N. Y., Oreg., Wash.

VIRUS, Yellows. **Chlorogenus callistephi,** Pa.

CAMPHOR-TREE (*Cinnamomum camphora*)

ANTHRACNOSE. **Glomerella cingulata,** Gulf States.

BLACK MILDEW. **Lembosia camphorae,** La.

CANKER; DIEBACK. **Diplodia camphorae, D. tubericola** (probably imperfect stage of **Physalospora rhodina**) widespread.

CANKER; DIEBACK; Leaf Spot. **Gloeosporium camphorae** and **G. ochraceum,** Gulf States.

LEAF SPOT, Algal. **Cephaleuros virescens,** Fla. to La.

PHYSIOGENIC Chlorosis. Manganese deficiency, Fla.

ROT, Root. **Armillaria mellea,** Fla.; **Phymatotrichum omnivorum,** Tex.; **Clitocybe tabescens,** Fla.

CANDYTUFT (*Iberis*)

CLUB ROOT. **Plasmodiophora brassicae,** Mass., N. J.

DAMPING-OFF. **Rhizoctonia solani,** cosmopolitan.

DODDER. **Cuscuta indecora,** Tex.

DOWNY MILDEW. **Peronospora parasitica,** Cal.

NEMATODE, Root Knot. **Heterodera marioni,** Ala.

POWDERY MILDEW. **Erysiphe polygoni,** Cal.

WHITE RUST; White Blister. **Albugo candida,** Cal.

CANNA (*Canna generalis*)

BACTERIAL Bud Rot. **Xanthomonas cannae,** Col., Conn., Ill., Md., Miss., Nebr., N. J., N. C., Ohio, Okla.

BLIGHT, Southern. **Sclerotium rolfsii,** Tex.

LEAF SPOT. **Alternaria** sp., Mich., S. C., Tex.

ROT, Rhizome. **Fusarium** sp., Minn., Mo., Pa.

RUST. **Puccinia cannae** (II, III), Fla., Ohio, Tex.

VIRUS, Canna Mosaic. Unnamed, D. C., Md., N. Y.

Canna mosaic is transmitted by aphids. The President variety seems to be immune.

CANNA, EDIBLE (*Canna edulis*)

RUST. **Puccinia cannae** (II, III), Fla.

CANTALOUPE, See Melon

CAPE–COWSLIP (*Lachenalia*)

VIRUS, Mosaic. **Marmor scillearum,** Ala.

CAPE–HONEYSUCKLE (*Tecomaria*)

LEAF SPOT. **Glomerella cingulata,** Tex.

ROT, Root. **Clitocybe tabescens,** Fla., **Amillaria mellea,** Cal.

CAPE–MARIGOLD, African Daisy (*Dimorphotheca*)

BLIGHT, Gray Mold. **Botrytis cinerea,** Conn., Alaska.

NEMATODE, Root Knot. **Heterodera marioni,** Fla.

ROT, Root. **Pythium ultimum,** Cal.; **Rhizoctonia solani,** Ill.

RUST. **Puccinia flaveriae** (III), Ill., Ind., N. J., Nebr.

VIRUS, Aster Yellows. **Chlorogenus callistephi,** N. J., N. Y.

WILT. **Fusarium** sp., Fla.; **Verticillium albo-atrum,** Iowa, N. Y.

CARAWAY (*Carum*)

NEMATODE, Root Knot. **Heterodera marioni,** Fla.

CARDOON (*Cynara cardunculus*)

LEAF SPOT. **Cercospora obscura,** Cal., Tex.; **Ramularia cynarae,** Cal.
POWDERY MILDEW. **Erysiphe cichoracearum,** Cal.

CARNATION (*Dianthus caryophyllus*)

ANTHRACNOSE. **Colletotrichum** sp., N. J., N. Y., Tex.; **Volutella** sp., Mich., N. J., N. Y., Oreg.
BACTERIAL Crown Gall. **Agrobacterium tumefaciens,** Md.
BACTERIAL Fasciation; Witches' Broom. **Corynebacterium fascians,** Ohio.
BACTERIAL SPOT. **Pseudomonas woodsii,** Mass. to Ga., Ind., Mich., N. Dak., Okla., Oreg., Wash.
BACTERIAL Wilt. **Pseudomonas carophylli,** Ill., Ind., Iowa, Mo., Wash.
BLIGHT; Collar and Branch Rot. **Alternaria dianthi,** general.
BLIGHT, Gray Mold. **Botrytis cinerea,** cosmopolitan in humid weather.
BLIGHT, Southern. **Sclerotium rolfsii,** Fla., Miss., Tex.
BLIGHT, Web. **Pellicularia (Corticium) koleroga,** N. C.
MOLD, Leaf; Fairy Ring. **Heterosporium echinulatum,** occasional, greenhouses; **Cladosporium herbarum,** cosmopolitan.
LEAF SPOT. **Septoria dianthi,** Vt. to S. C., Mich., Miss., Ohio, Cal.
NEMATODE, Root Knot. **Heterodera marioni,** general in South.
PHYSIOGENIC Yellowing, Spotting. Potassium deficiency, N. J., N. Y.
POWDERY MILDEW. **Oidium** sp., Fla., N. C.
ROT, Bud. **Fusarium poae,** Mass. to Va., Kans., Nebr., Wash.
ROT, Root. **Fusarium** spp., general; **Phymatotrichum omnivorum,** Tex.; **Pythium** sp., Ill.
ROT, Root; Wet Stem. **Rhizoctonia solani,** general.
RUST. **Uromyces caryophyllinus** (II, III), general.
SMUT, Anther. **Ustilago violacea,** doubtful reports.
VIRUS, Carnation Mosaic. Unnamed, general in commercial stocks.
VIRUS, Streak. Unnamed, general but less frequent than mosaic.
VIRUS, Yellows. Complex virosis, mosaic and streak together.
WILT. **Fusarium oxysporum, f. dianthi,** probably general.
WILT. **Verticillium dahliae,** N. J.

Commercial carnation growers have plenty of problems. Continuous greenhouse culture, rather than summering outdoors, is suggested for Alternaria blight or branch rot, along with disease-free cuttings and keeping foliage dry. Care in selection of cuttings is likewise best defense against Fusarium and bacterial wilts, although soil treatment with copper 8-quinolinolate and other chemicals is now being tested. Spraying with Fermate controls rust, and virus diseases are reduced by aerosol treatment of aphid vectors.

CAROB, ST. JOHN'S BREAD (*Ceratonia*)

CANKER. **Botryosphaeria ribis,** Cal.
NEMATODE, Root Knot. **Heterodera marioni.**
ROT, Root. **Phymatotrichum omnivorum,** Tex.; **Phytophthora cactorum,** Cal.

CAROLINA MOONSEED (*Cocculus*)

LEAF SPOT. **Cercospora menispermi,** Miss., Tex.
ROT, Root. **Phymatotrichum omnivorum,** Tex.

CAROLINA YELLOW JESSAMINE (*Gelsemium*)

BLACK SPOT. **Asterina stomatophora,** Fla.
LEAF SPOT. **Phyllosticta gelsemii,** N. J.
SOOTY MOLD. **Capnodium grandisporum,** Miss.

CARROT (*Daucus carota* var. *sativa*)

BACTERIAL Blight. **Xanthomonas carotae,** Cal., Ida., Iowa.
BACTERIAL Soft Rot. **Erwinia carotovora,** general.
BLIGHT, Early. **Cercospora carotae,** general.
BLIGHT, Late. **Alternaria dauci,** general.
BLIGHT, Southern. **Sclerotium rolfsii, Ga.** to Fla., Tex., **Cal.**
CANKER, Root; Hairy Root; Scurf. **Rhizoctonia** spp.
DAMPING-OFF. **Pythium** sp., Ida.; **Rhizoctonia solani,** general.
DODDER. **Cuscuta,** sp., Miss., N. Mex., N. Y., Tex., W. Va.
LEAF SPOT. **Ramularia** sp., Kans.; **Alternaria tenuis,** secondary, also seed mold.
NEMATODE, Root Knot. **Heterodera marioni,** general Northeast and South.
PHYSIOGENIC Black Heart. Cause unknown, Wis.
Chlorosis. Magnesium deficiency in acid soil, Mass.
Root Girdle. Cause unknown, Wash.
ROT, Black. **Alternaria radicina,** Ida., Mass., N. Y.; Pa., Wash.
ROT, Black Mold. **Rhizopus** spp.; Blue Mold. **Penicillium** sp.
ROT, Gray Mold. **Botrytis cinerea,** cosmopolitan.
ROT, Dry. **Fusarium** spp., Ida., N. Y. associated with scab.
ROT, Pink Mold. **Tricothecium roseum,** Ind.
ROT, Root. **Helicobasidium purpureum,** Oreg., Wash.; **Phymatotrichum omnivorum,** Ariz., Tex.; **Phytophthora megasperma,** Cal.
ROT, Storage. **Centrospora acerina,** N. Y.
ROT, Watery Soft. **Sclerotinia sclerotiorum,** general; **S. intermedia; S. minor.**
RUST. **Uromyces scirpi** (O, I), Oreg.; II, III on Scirpus.
SCAB. **Actinomyces scabies,** Cal., Mich., Pa., Wash.

VIRUS, Curly Top. **Ruga verrucosans,** Oreg., Utah.

VIRUS, Aster Yellows; Rio Grande Disease. **Chlorogenus callistephi,** Me. to Pa., Ill., and Wyo.; Ida., Oreg., Wash.; La., Tex. and var. **californicus,** Cal.

VIRUS, Western Celery Mosaic. **Marmor umbelliferarum,** Cal.

Carrots in home gardens usually require a deeply dug, friable soil more than treatment for these various diseases. The root-knot nematode is fairly common. If necessary, copper sprays will control leaf spots and blights.

CASSABANANA, CURUBA (*Sicana odorifera*)

ANTHRACNOSE. **Colletotrichum lagenarium,** Fla.

CASHEW (*Anacardium*)

BLIGHT, Southern. **Sclerotium rolfsii,** Fla.

CASSIOPE

LEAF GALL. **Exobasidium vaccinii,** Wash.

CASTOR–BEAN (*Ricinus communis*)

BACTERIAL Crown Gall. **Agrobacterium tumefaciens.**

BACTERIAL Wilt. **Pseudomonas solanacearum.**

BLIGHT, Inflorescence; Gray Mold. **Botryotinia** (*Sclerotinia*) **ricini,** Ga. to Fla. and Tex.; conidial stage *Botrytis* sp.

BLIGHT, Southern. **Sclerotium rolfsii.**

DAMPING-OFF. **Rhizoctonia solani,** Fla., Kans.

LEAF SPOT. **Alternaria** sp., Fla., La., Tex.; **Cercospora canescens,** Ala., Kans., Mont.; **C. ricinella,** Gulf States.

ROT, Root. **Clitocybe tabescens,** Fla.; **Phymatotrichum omnivorum,** Tex.

ROT, Stem. **Phytophthora parasitica.**

CASUARINA (Australian-Pine)

ROT, Root. **Clitocybe tabescens,** Fla.

Australian pine is particularly susceptible to this mushroom root rot. Sometimes trees can be saved by banking clay soil around trunks to stimulate adventitious roots after surgery.

CATALPA

BLIGHT, Southern. **Sclerotium rolfsii,** on seedlings.

DAMPING-OFF. **Rhizoctonia solani,** Nebr.

LEAF SPOT. **Alternaria catalpae,** widespread, perhaps secondary; **Cercospora catalpae,** widespread, Ohio; **Phyllosticta catalpae,** general.

NEMATODE, Root Knot. **Heterodera marioni,** Southern States to Ohio, Okla.

POWDERY MILDEW. **Microsphaera alni** var. **vaccinii,** East Central States; **Phyllactinia corylea,** East to S. C. and Ill.

Rot, Root. **Armillaria mellea,** Wash.; **Phymatotrichum omnivorum; Helicobasidium purpureum,** Ohio; **Thielaviopsis basicola,** of seedlings.

Rot, Heart. **Collybia velutipes,** Ind.; Butt Rot, **Polyporus catalpae,** Kans.

Rot, Sapwood. **Polyporus hirsutus; P. versicolor,** general; **Schizophyllum commune,** Ohio; **Stereum versicolor,** Ohio; **Trametes sepium,** Kans.

Wilt. **Verticillium albo-atrum,** Ill.

Leaf spots may cause some defoliation in a wet season, but in most seasons the expense of spraying may be unjustified on a limited budget.

CATNIP (*Nepeta*)

Bacterial Leaf Spot. **Pseudomonas tabaci,** Wis.

Blight, Southern. **Sclerotium rolfsii,** Tex.

Leaf Spot. **Ascochyta nepetae,** Wis.; **Cercospora nepetae,** Ill., Tex.; **Phyllosticta decidua,** Ill., N. J., Ohio, Wis.; **Septoria alabamensis,** Ala.; **S. nepetae,** Wis.

Rot, Root. **Rhizoctonia solani,** Tex.

Virus, Mosaic. Part **Marmor cucumeris,** part unidentified, Ind., Iowa, Kans., Mich., Wis.

Wilt. **Fusarium** sp., Ga.

CATS–CLAW (*Doxantha*)

Rot, Root. **Phymatotrichum omnivorum,** Tex.

CEANOTHUS (of Western Plains, Pacific Coast)

Bacterial Crown Gall. **Agrobacterium tumefaciens,** Wash.

Leaf Spot. **Cercospora ceanothi,** Kans., Wis.; **Septoria ceanothi,** Ida.; **Cylindrosporium ceanothi,** Pacific Coast.

Rot, Root. **Armillaria mellea,** Cal.

Rot, Sapwood. **Schizophyllum** sp., Cal.

Rust. **Puccinia tripsaci** (O, I), Kans., Nebr., Wis.; II, III on grasses.

CEANOTHUS AMERICANUS (New-Jersey-Tea)

Leaf Spot. **Cercospora ceanothi,** Central States; **Phyllosticta ceanothi,** Miss.

Powdery Mildew. **Microsphaera alni,** widespread.

CEDAR (*Cedrus* spp.)

(Atlas Cedar, *Cedrus atlantica,* Deodar, *C. deodara,* Cedar of Lebanon, *C. libanotica*)

Canker; Dieback. **Sphaeropsis ellisii,** Ala.

Rot, Root. **Armillaria mellea,** Miss.; **Clitocybe tabescens,** Fla.; **Phymatotrichum omnivorum,** Tex.; **Fomes pini,** occasional heart rot.

CELANDINE (*Chelidonium*)

LEAF SPOT. **Septoria chelidonii,** Tex.

ROT, Root. **Phymatotrichum omnivorum,** Tex.

CELERY (*Apium graveolens*)

BACTERIAL Leaf Spot. **Pseudomonas apii,** Conn., Del., Fla., Ind., Mich., Minn., N. Dak., N. Y., Ohio.

BACTERIAL Soft Rot. **Erwinia carotovora,** cosmopolitan.

BLIGHT, Early. **Cercospora apii,** general.

BLIGHT, Late. **Septoria apii,** general; **S. apii-graveolentis,** with small leaf spot, general and more destructive than *S. apii.*

DAMPING-OFF. **Pythium** spp.; **Rhizoctonia** sp.; **Aphanomyces euteiches,** cosmopolitan.

LEAF SPOT. **Phyllosticta apii,** Del., N. J.; **Stemphylium** and **Alternaria** sp., secondary.

NEMATODE, Root Knot. **Heterodera marioni,** Va. to Fla., Cal., occasional in North.

NEMATODE, Stem. **Ditylenchus dipsaci,** Cal.

PHYSIOGENIC Black Heart. Wide fluctuations of soil moisture, general.

Cracked Stem; Stem Canker. Boron deficiency, occasional Fla., Mass., Mich., N. Y.

Hollow Stem. Sometimes from chilling or drought.

Red Root. Associated with acid soils, phosphorus deficiency, Fla.

Brown Stem Discoloration; Growth Crack.

ROT, Brown Spot Disease. **Cephalosporium** sp., Cal.

ROT, Root. **Phoma apiicola,** Cal., Mich., N. Y., Ohio, Wis.

ROT, Petiole Crater Spot, **Rhizoctonia solani,** Cal.

ROT, Pink; Watery Soft Rot. **Sclerotinia sclerotiorum; S. intermedia; S. minor.**

ROT, Gray Mold. **Botrytis cinerea,** cosmopolitan.

ROT, Storage. **Centrospora acerina,** N. Y.; **Typhula variabilis,** N. Y.; **Trichothecium roseum.**

VIRUS, Curly Top. **Ruga verrucosans,** Oreg.

VIRUS, Western Celery Mosaic. **Marmor umbelliferarum,** Cal., Wash.

VIRUS, Southern Celery Mosaic. In part **Marmor cucumeris,** East and South.

VIRUS, Spotted Wilt. **Lethum australiense,** Cal.

VIRUS, Yellows. **Chlorogenus callistephi,** Me., N. Y., Pa., Wis., Wash. and var. **californicus,** Cal.

VIRUS, Calico, Pseudocalico, Crinkle-Leaf, Ring Spot, all unidentified, Cal.

WILT, Yellows. **Fusarium oxysporum** f. **apii,** general.

WILT. **Verticillium albo-atrum,** Cal.

Celery varieties resistant to Fusarium wilt or yellows are on the market. Seed should be treated for leaf blights, unless more than two years old, followed by spraying in seedbed and garden with copper sprays or dusts, or Dithane or Zerlate. Commercial growers in Florida inhibit development of apothecia of the pink-rot fungus by flooding fields or applying calcium cyanamide. Western growers fight mosaic by celery-free periods, and by controlling insect vectors.

CELTUCE

DOWNY MILDEW. **Bremia lactucae,** N. Dak., Pa., Wash.

LEAF SPOT. **Septoria lactucae.**

ROT, Watery Soft; Drop. **Sclerotinia Sclerotiorum,** Mass.

Celtuce is a kind of lettuce and subject to some of the same diseases.

CENTAUREA (Bachelors-Button, Cornflower, Basket-Flower)

BLIGHT, Southern. **Sclerotium rolfsii,** Conn., Md., N. J., Tex.

DODDER. **Cuscuta** sp., Tex.

DOWNY MILDEW. **Bremia lactucae,** Cal.; **Plasmopara halstedii,** Iowa.

NEMATODE, Root Knot. **Heterodera marioni,** Cal., Fla., Ohio.

POWDERY MILDEW. **Erysiphe cichoracearum,** Cal., Conn.

ROT, Root. **Phymatotrichum omnivorum,** Tex.; **Pythium** sp.

ROT, Stem. **Phytophthora cactorum,** N. Y.; **Sclerotinia sclerotiorum,** Cal., Ind., Miss., Mo., Tex.; **Fusarium oxysporum** f. **callistephi,** Mich.; **Rhizoctonia solani,** Ill., Ind., N. Y.

RUST. **Puccinia cyani** (O, I, III), Mass. to N. C.; Ind., Cal., Oreg., Wash.; **P. irrequisita** (II, III), Tex.; O, I unknown.

VIRUS, Aster Yellows. **Chlorogenus callistephi,** widespread, and var. **californicus,** Cal.

WHITE RUST. **Albugo tragopogonis,** Tex.

WILT. **Verticillium albo-atrum,** N. Y.

CENTURY PLANT (*Agave americana*)

ANTHRACNOSE. **Glomerella cingulata** (*Colletotrichum agave*), occasional.

BLIGHT, Gray Mold. **Botrytis cinerea,** occasional after overwatering or chilling.

LEAF Scorch; Leaf Blight. **Stagonospora gigantea,** Tex., N. Mex.

LEAF SPOT. **Coniothyrium concentricum, C. agaves,** common.

LEAF SPOT; Black Patch. **Dothidella parryi,** Tex.

CEPHALOTAXUS (Japanese Yew, Plum-Yew)

BLIGHT, Nursery. **Phomopsis juniperovora.**

CHAMAECYPARIS (White-Cedar, Alaska Yellow-Cedar, also called False-Cypress and Retinospora)

BLIGHT, Tip. **Pestalotia funerea, N. J.**

BLIGHT, Nursery. **Phomopsis juniperovora,** widespread.

PHYSIOGENIC Sun Scorch. Browning foliage from drought, freezing, feeding of spider mites.

ROT, Collar and Root. **Phytophthora lateralis,** Oreg.

ROT, Heart. **Fomes pini,** occasional; **F. subroseus,** N. J.

ROT, Sapwood; Wood. **Hydnum ballouii,** N. J.; **Lenzites saepiaria,** cosmopolitan; **Polyporus** spp., occasional.

RUST, Gall. **Gymnosporangium biseptatum** (III), Me. to N. J.; Ala.; O, I on Amelanchier; **G. nootkatense** (III), Oreg., Wash.; O, I on crabapple, pear, mountain-ash; **G. tranformans** (III), Me. to N. J.; O, I on chokeberry.

RUST; Witches' Broom. **Gymnosporangium ellisii** (III), Me. to Fla. and Ala.; O, I on sweet-fern, bayberry, wax-myrtle.

CHAMAEDAPHNE (Leather-Leaf)

LEAF GALL. **Exobasidium vaccinii,** widespread; **Synchytrium vaccinii,** N. J. north.

LEAF SPOT. **Ascochyta cassandrae,** N. Y. to Wis.

RUST. **Chrysomyxa cassandrae** (II, III), New England to Great Lakes States; O, I on pine.

CHAYOTE (*Sechium edule*)

ANTHRACNOSE. **Colletotrichum lagenarium,** Fla., Tex.

BLIGHT, Southern. **Sclerotium rolfsii,** Tex.

LEAF SPOT. **Cercospora sechii,** Fla., Tex.

NEMATODE, Root Knot. **Heterodera marioni.**

ROT, Fruit. **Glomerella cingulata,** La.

CHECKERMALLOW (*Sidalcea*)

LEAF SPOT. **Ramularia sidalceae,** Col.

RUST. **Endophyllum tuberculatum** (III) Col., Wyo.; **Puccinia interveniens** (O, I) Cal., Mont., Utah; II, III on Stipa; **P. schedonnardi** (O, I, II, III); **P. sherardiana** (O, III), Cal., Col., Nev.

CHERIMOYA (*Annona cherimola* and *A. reticulata,* Custard-Apple)

ANTHRACNOSE, Fruit. **Colletotrichum gloeosporioides,** Fla.

ROT, Mushroom Root. **Clitocybe tabescens,** Fla.

RUST. **Uredo cherimoliae,** Fla.

CHERRY (*Prunus* spp.)

BACTERIAL Crown Gall. **Agrobacterium tumefaciens,** Cal., Tex.

BACTERIAL Fire Blight; Fruit Blight. **Erwinia amylovora.**

BACTERIAL Canker. **Pseudomonas syringae,** Mass. to Mich.; Pacific States.

BACTERIAL Leaf Spot; Black Spot. **Xanthomonas pruni,** N. Y. to Mo., Iowa; Ga., Tex.

BLACK KNOT. **Dibotryon morbosum,** Eastern States.

BLIGHT, Leaf; Shot Hole. **Higginsia hiemalis,** general.

BLIGHT, Shoot; Shot Hole. **Coryneum carpophilum,** Cal., Ida., Oreg., Wash.

BLIGHT, Blossom; Brown Rot. **Monilinia laxa,** general, Pacific States.

BLIGHT, Seedling Twig. **Monilinia seaveri,** Vt. to Ga., Ark, Iowa.

CANKER, Trunk and Collar. **Phytophthora cactorum, P. citrophthora,** Cal.

CANKER, Twig. **Phomopsis padina,** N. Y.; **Valsa leucostoma,** widespread; **Nectria** sp., N. Y.

LEAF BLISTER; Shoot Hypertrophy. **Taphrina farlowii,** Vt. to Fla., Tex.; **Taphrina cerasi,** Me. to N. J., Minn.

LEAF SPOT. **Cercospora circumscissa,** N. J., Ohio, Pa., Tex.; **Alternaria citri** var. **cerasi,** Cal.; **Mycosphaerella cerasella,** Va. to Fla., Miss. **Phyllosticta pruni-avium,** Oreg.; **P. serotina,** widespread; **P. virginiana,** Iowa, Kans.

MISTLETOE. **Phoradendron flavescens.**

NEMATODE, Root Knot. **Heterodera marioni.**

PHYSIOGENIC Chlorosis. Alkali injury, Cal., Tex.

Brown Bark Spot. Arsenical injury, Ida., Mont., Wash.

POWDERY MILDEW. **Podosphaera oxyacanthae,** general.

ROT, Brown. **Monilinia fructicola,** general.

ROT, Fruit. **Alternaria** sp.; **Botrytis cinerea; Glomerella cingulata,** Ind.; **Cladosporium** sp., Cal. to Wash., Ida.

ROT, Root. **Armillaria mellea,** N. Mex., Okla., Oreg.; **Phymatotrichum omnivorum,** Tex.; **Xylaria** sp., Tenn.

ROT, Heart; Wood Rot. **Fomes fomentarius,** Northeast; **Polyporus** spp.; **Poria ambigua,** Cal., **Stereum ramale,** N. Y., Pa.

ROT, Silver Leaf. **Stereum purpureum,** N. Y.

RUST. **Tranzschelia pruni-spinosae** (II, III), Ga., Mass., N. C., Nebr., N. Y., Okla., Tex.; O, I on anemone.

VIRUS, Cherry Banded-Chlorosis. **Marmor pallidolimbatus,** Pacific Northwest.

VIRUS, Cherry Mottle-Leaf. **Marmor cerasi,** Cal., Ida., Oreg., Wash.

VIRUS, Cherry Rusty Mottle. **Marmor rubiginosum,** Wash.

VIRUS, Vein-Clearing. **Marmor nerviclarens,** Cal., Oreg., Wash.

VIRUS, Yellows. Undetermined, Mich., Wis.

VIRUS, Peach X Disease. **Carpophthora lacerans,** on sour cherry.

When there are one or two cherry trees in a home garden it will scarcely pay to spray for disease control unless the trees are small enough to protect with netting against the birds. Most spray schedules are timed primarily for control of brown rot and leaf spot or shot hole, using wettable sulfur, or perhaps Fermate or Phygon at petal fall and shuck stages followed by a copper spray after harvest.

CHERRY, FLOWERING OR ORIENTAL (*Prunus serrulata*)

BACTERIAL Fire Blight. **Erwinia amylovora,** Ga., Ohio.

BACTERIAL Leaf Spot. **Xanthomonas pruni.**

LEAF BLISTER; Witches' Broom. **Taphrina cerasi,** Md., N. J.

LEAF SPOT. **Cercospora circumscissa,** N. Y.; **Higginsia** (*Coccomyces*) **hiemalis,** Mass., N. J.

VIRUS, Vein Clearing. **Marmor nerviclarens,** Ore.

VIRUS, Flowering Cherry Rough Bark. **Rimocortius kwanzani,** Ore.

CHERRY–LAUREL or LAURELCHERRY (*Prunus laurocerasus*)
(including also Catalina Cherry, Holly-leaf Cherry)

BACTERIAL LEAF SPOT. **Xanthomonas pruni,** Ga., Miss., S. C.

BLIGHT, Blossom; Brown Rot. **Monilinia fructicola; M. laxa,** Cal.

LEAF SPOT. **Alternaria** sp., Tex.; **Cercospora circumscissa,** Cal.; **C. cladosporioides,** La., Tex.; **Higginsia** (*Coccomyces*) **lutescens,** Miss.; **Phyllachora beaumontii,** Ala.; **Phyllosticta laurocerasi,** Cal., Fla., N. J.; **Septoria ravenelii,** S. C.

ROT, Mushroom Root. **Clitocybe tabescens,** Fla.

WILT. **Verticillium albo-atrum,** Cal.

CHESTNUT (*Castanea*)
(including Chinquapin)

BLIGHT; Canker. **Endothia parasitica,** general from New England to Ala., also Central States, and locally along Pacific Coast.

BLIGHT, Twig. **Cytospora** sp.; **Phomopsis** sp.; **Diplodia longispora** widespread; **Dothiorella** sp., Cal.

CANKER; DIEBACK. **Botryosphaeria ribis,** occasional; **Cryptodiaporthe castanea,** widespread.

LEAF SPOT. **Marssonina ochroleuca,** general; **Monochaetia desmazierii,** Va., Ohio.

POWDERY MILDEW. **Microsphaera alni; Phyllactinia corylea,** widespread.

ROT, Mushroom Root. **Armillaria mellea,** cosmopolitan.

ROT, Collar; Root Rot. **Phytophthora cinnamomi,** Ark., Ga., La., S. C., Tenn.

ROT, WOOD. There are many heart wood and sapwood rots. **Polyporus versicolor** may attack living trees of Asiatic species.

Listing chestnut diseases may seem somewhat academic, now that Endothia blight has practically eliminated the American chestnut from our landscape. But plant breeders are still making slow progress, crossing native chestnuts with resistant Asiatic varieties.

CHICK-PEA, GARBANZO (*Cicer arietinum*)

NEMATODE, Root Knot. **Heterodera marioni,** Fla.
ROT, Root; Damping-Off. **Pythium ultimum,** Cal.
ROT, Root and Stem. **Rhizoctonia solani,** Cal.
VIRUS, Mosaic. Unidentified, Cal.

CHICORY (See Endive)

CHINABERRY (*Melia azedarach*)

BLIGHT, Limb. **Pellicularia koleroga,** Fla.
CANKER. **Nectria coccinea,** Miss., S. C.
LEAF SPOT. **Cercospora leucosticta,** Gulf States; **C. meliae; Phyllosticta azedarachis,** Ala.
MISTLETOE. **Phoradendron flavescens,** Tex.
NEMATODE, Root Knot. **Heterodera marioni.**
POWDERY MILDEW. **Phyllactinia corylea,** Miss.
ROT, Root. **Helicobasidium purpureum,** Tex.; **Phymatotrichum omnivorum,** Ariz., Tex.
ROT, Wood. **Fomes meliae,** Ala.; **Polyporus versicolor,** Ga.

CHINESE EVERGREEN (*Aglaonema*)

NEMATODE, Banana; Root and Stem Rot. **Pratylenchus musicola,** Fla.
ROT, Root. **Pythium** sp., Fla.

CHINESE LANTERN (*Physalis alkekengi*)

BACTERIAL Wilt. **Pseudomonas solanacearum.**
LEAF SPOT. **Phyllosticta** sp., Conn.
ROT. **Fusarium** sp.
SMUT, White. **Entyloma australe,** Conn., N. Y.
VIRUS, Mosaic.
WILT. **Verticillium** sp., N. Y.

CHINESE TALLOW-TREE (*Sapium sebiferum*)

LEAF SPOT. **Cercospora stillingiae,** La.; **Phyllosticta stillingiae,** La.
ROT, Root. **Clitocybe tabescens,** Fla.; **Phymatotrichum omnivorum,** Tex.

CHINESE WAXGOURD (*Benincasa hispida*)

ANTHRACNOSE. **Colletotrichum lagenarium,** Ind.
DOWNY MILDEW. **Pseudoperonospora cubensis,** Mass.
NEMATODE, Root Knot. **Heterodera marioni,** Fla.

CHIOGENES (Creeping Snowberry)

Rust. **Chrysomyxa chiogenis** (II, III), Mich., N. H., N. Y., Wis.; O, I unknown.

CHIVES (*Allium schoenoprasum*)

Downy Mildew. **Peronospora destructor,** Cal.
See also Onion.

CHIONODOXA (Glory-of-the-Snow)

Nematode, Bulb. *Ditylenchus dipsaci.*

CHLOROGALUM (Soap-Plant)

Leaf Spot. **Heterosporium gracile,** Cal.

CHOKEBERRY (*Aronia*)

Bacterial Fire Blight. **Erwinia amylovora,** Mich., W. Va.

Leaf Spot. **Asoochyta pirina,** Wis.; **Cercospora mali,** Ala.; **C. pyri,** Mich., N. H., Wis.; **Mycosphaerella arbutifolia,** N. Y.; **Phyllosticta arbutifolia,** N. J.

Rot, Brown. **Monilinia fructicola,** Wis.

Rust. **Gymnosporangium clavariaeforme** (O, I), Mass.; III on juniper; **G. clavipes** (O, I), Conn., Me.; **G. davisii** (O, I), Me., Mich., N. H., Wis.; **G. transformans** (O, I), Del., Mass., Me., N. J., Pa.; III on Chamaecyparis.

CHOKE–CHERRY (*Prunus virginiana*)

Bacterial Leaf Spot. **Xanthomonas pruni,** Ill., N. Y., Mont., Wyo.

Black Knot. **Dibotryon morbosum,** general.

Blight, Fruit and Shoot. **Monilinia angustior,** Vt. to Kans., N. Dak.; **M. demissa,** Wash.

Canker. **Cytospora chrysosperma,** Mont.

Leaf Blister; Fruit and Shoot Hypertrophy. **Taphrina confusa,** widespread.

Leaf Spot. **Gloeosporium prunicolum,** N. Y., Wis.; **Lophodermina prunicola; Mycosphaerella cerasella,** Kans.; **Phyllosticta circumscissa; P. serotina,** Nebr., Pa., S. C.; **P. virginiana,** Mont., N. Y. to Kans.; **Septoria pruni,** Mich.

Nematode, Root Knot. **Heterodera marioni.**

Powdery Mildew. **Podosphaera oxyacanthae,** widespread; **Phyllactinia corylea,** Wash.

Rot, Brown Heart. **Fomes fulvus,** N. and S. Dak.

Rust. **Tranzschelia pruni-spinosae** (II, III), Conn. to Ill., Wis.

Virus, Peach X-Disease; Yellow-Red Virosis. **Carpophthora lacerans,** N. H. to Va.; Ill., Wis.; Ida., Oreg., Utah.

Choke-cherries near peach orchards should be eliminated to control the virus disease on peaches.

CHRISTMAS-ROSE (*Helleborus niger*)

BLIGHT, Flower Spot. **Botrytis cinerea,** N. J.; **Gloeosporium** sp., N. J.
LEAF SPOT, Black. **Coniothyrium hellebori,** Md., N. Y., Oreg.
ROT, Stem. **Sclerotium delphinii,** N. Y.

CHRYSANTHEMUM

BACTERIAL Crown Gall. **Agrobacterium tumefaciens,** Conn., N. J., Tex.
BACTERIAL Fascination. **Corynebacterium fascians,** N. J., Mich., N. Y., Ohio.
BACTERIAL Stem Rot. **Erwinia carotovora,** Okla.
BLIGHT, Ray. **Ascochyta chrysanthemi,** Miss., N. J., N. and S. C., Ohio.
BLIGHT, Southern. **Sclerotium rolfsii,** Fla., Va.
BLIGHT, Gray Mold. **Botrytis cinerea,** cosmopolitan.
BLIGHT, Leaf; Blotch. **Septoria leucanthemi.**
DODDER. **Cuscuta** sp., Mich., N. J., N. Y., Tex., Va., Wash.
LEAF SPOT. **Alternaria** sp., Okla., Tex. probably secondary; **Cercospora chrysanthemi,** Ala., La., Md., Pa., Tex.; **Cylindrosporium chrysanthemi,** Mass. to Ala., Kans.; **Phyllosticta chrysanthemi,** Fla., Mass., Miss.; Va.; **Septoria chrysanthemi,** East and Central States to Fla.; Tex., Cal., Col.
NEMATODE, Leaf. **Aphelenchoides ritzema-bosi,** widespread.
NEMATODE, Root Knot. **Heterodera marioni,** N. J. to Fla., Tex., and Kans.; Cal., Wash.
NEMATODE, Root. **Pratylenchus pratensis,** N. J., Tex.
PHYSIOGENIC Crookneck, Occasional in greenhouses, perhaps deficient ventilation.
POWDERY MILDEW. **Erysiphe cichoracearum,** general.
ROT, Charcoal. **Macrophomina phaseoli,** Okla.
ROT, Root and Stem. **Fusarium** sp., Ala., Fla., Ill., N. H., N. J., Ohio, Okla., Tex., Va.; **Rhizoctonia solani,** Ariz., Col., Conn., Ill., Md., N. C., N. J., Tex. **Pythium** sp., N. Dak., Tenn., Tex.
ROT, Root. **Phymatotrichum omnivorum,** Ariz., Tex.
ROT, Stem; Drop; Blossom Rot. **Sclerotinia sclerotiorum,** Ariz., Mich., La., Va.
RUST. **Puccinia chrysanthemi** (II), general; O, I unknown, III known in Japan.
VIRUS, Spotted Wilt. **Lethum australiense,** Cal., Wash.
VIRUS, Stunt. Unidentified, countrywide.
?VIRUS, Mosaic; Dwarf; Yellows. Undetermined.
WILT. **Fusarium oxysporum** f. **callistephi,** Okla.; **Verticillium albo-atrum,** Ill., Ind., Md., Mass., Mich., Minn., N. J., N. Y., Ohio, Pa., Wash.

When garden chrysanthemums have foliage browning and dying progressively up the stem the cause can be leaf nematodes, Septoria leaf spo Verticillium wilt with probabilities, at least in New Jersey, in th Avoidance of overhead watering, never working with plants whe wet, and use of a mulch will reduce the nematode problem and perhaps keep down leaf spots. Spraying with Fermate will control Septoria leaf spot and also rust, although the latter is not a problem in outdoor chrysanthemums in my section. Mildew sometimes appears late in the season and can be controlled with sulfur dust or a copper spray; Fermate is not effective.

Stunt, a virus disease, is the most recent plague of commercial growers, who have learned how to fight leaf nematodes with sodium selenate, Verticillium wilt with "cultured" stock. Parathion sprays also control leal nematodes.

CHRYSOPSIS (Golden Aster)

LEAF SPOT. **Cercospora macroguttata,** Ala., Miss.; **Ramularia chrysopsidis,** N. Y.

POWDERY MILDEW. **Erysiphe cichoracearum,** Mont., Wyo.

RUST. **Coleosporium solidaginis** (II, III), Col., Fla., Nebr.; O, I on pine. **Puccinia grindeliae** (III), Cal., Col., Okla., Utah, Wyo.; **P. stipae** (O, I), Ariz., Col., Fla., Mont., Nebr., Wyo.; II, III on grasses.

CIMICIFUGA (Bugbane, Black Cohosh)

LEAF SPOT. **Ascochyta actaeae,** Conn., N. Y.; **Ectostroma afflatum,** Va.

NEMATODE, Root Knot. **Heterodera marioni,** N. J.

RUST. **Puccinia rubigo-vera** (O, I), N. Y., N. C., Ohio, Pa., Tenn., Va., W. Va.; II, III on grasses.

SMUT, Leaf and Stem. **Urocystis carcinodes,** N. C., N. Y., Ohio, Pa., Tenn., Va.

CINCHONA

LEAF SPOT. **Cercospora cinchonae,** La.

NEMATODE, Root Knot. **Heterodera marioni.**

CINERARIA (*Senecio*)

BLIGHT. **Botrytis cinearea,** Ind., Mo., N. J., Pa., Alaska.

DAMPING-OFF. **Rhizoctonia solani,** Ill., N. Y.

DOWNY MILDEW. **Plasmopara halstedii,** N. Y.

NEMATODE, Root Knot. **Heterodera marioni,** Md.

POWDERY MILDEW. **Erysiphe cichoracearum,** Mass.

ROT, Root. **Pythium** sp., Md.; **P. ultimum,** Cal.

ROT, Stem. **Fusarium** sp., Pa.; **Phytophthora** sp., N. J.; **Sclerotinia sclerotiorum,** Wash.

VIRUS, Mosaic. Unidentified, Wash.

VIRUS, Spotted Wilt. **Lethum australiense,** Cal., Tex., Wash.

VIRUS, Aster Yellows. **Chlorogenus callistephi,** N. Y.

WILT. **Verticillium albo-atrum,** N. J., N. Y., Wash.

CINNAMON–TREE (*Cinnamomum zeylanicum*)

ANTHRACNOSE. **Glomerella cingulata,** Fla.
LEAF SPOT, Algal. **Cephaleuros virescens,** Fla.

CIRSIUM (Plumed Thistle)

LEAF SPOT. **Cercospora** spp.; **Phyllosticta cirsii; Septoria cirsii,** Wis.
POWDERY MILDEW. **Erysiphe cichoraceavum,** general; **Sphaerotheca humuli.**
ROT, Root. **Rhizotonia solani,** Ill.
RUST. **Puccinia cirsii** (O, I, II, III) ; **Uromyces junci** (O, I) .
WHITE RUST. **Albugo tragopogonis,** Tex.

CISSUS

LEAF SPOT. **Cercospora viticola,** La.
RUST. **Aecidium mexicanum** (O, I) , Okla.

CITRUS FRUITS
(Grapefruit, Lemon, Lime, Orange)

ANTHRACNOSE; Withertip; Fruit Spot. **Glomerella cingulata,** general.
ANTHRACNOSE, Lime; Withertip. **Gloeosporium limetticolum,** Fla.
BACTERIAL BLAST; Leaf and Twig Blight; Black Pit. **Pseudomonas syringae,** Cal., after cold, driving rains.
BACTERIAL Canker. **Xanthomonas citri,** formerly present Fla. to Tex., but now eradicated.
BACTERIAL Crown Gall; Branch Knot. **Agrobacterium tumefaciens,** Ariz., Cal.
BLIGHT, Leaf and Stem. **Phytophthora syringae,** Cal.
BLIGHT, Seedling; Fruit Rot. **Sclerotium rolfsii.**
BLIGHT, Thread. **Pellicularia** (*Corticium*) **koleroga,** Gulf States.
BLIGHT, Twig. **Fusarium lateritum,** Cal.
BLOTCH, Sooty. **Gloeodes pomigena.** Gulf States.
CANKER, Felt Fungus. **Septobasidium** spp.
CANKER; Witches' Broom; Branch Knot. **Sphaeropsis tumefaciens,** Fla.
DAMPING-OFF. **Pythium** sp., Cal.; **Rhizoctonia solani,** cosmopolitan.
DODDER. **Cuscuta americana,** Cal., Fla.; **Cassytha filiformis,** Fla., a dodder-like plant.
LEAF SPOT, Algal; Red "Rust." **Cephaleuros virescens,** Gulf States.
LEAF SPOT. **Mycosphaerella lageniformis,** Cal.; **Pleospora** sp., Cal.
LEAF SPOT; Fruit Spot. **Septoria citri,** Cal., Tex.
MISTLETOE. **Phoradendron** sp., Gulf States.
NEMATODE, Root Knot. **Heterodera marioni,** occasional.
NEMATODE, Citrus Root. **Tylenchulus semi-penetrans,** Fla., Cal.

PHYSIOGENIC Bronzing. Magnesium deficiency, Fla.

Chlorosis, Iron deficiency, Ariz., Cal., Fla.; Marl Chlorosis, Manganese deficiency, Fla.

Exanthema. Copper deficiency, augmented by excessive nitrogen fertilization and bad drainage. Cal., Fla.

Greasy Spot; Black Melanose. Cause unknown, Cal., Tex., chiefly on grapefruit.

Gum Spot, of foliage. Probably environmental injuries.

Gummosis, of trunk, branches, fruit. Probably adverse site.

Leprosis. Florida scaly bark, nailhead rust. Cause unknown, Fla.

Mottle Leaf. Zinc deficiency, Ariz., Cal., Fla.

Rind-Oil Spot. Chemical injury from release of oil in rind.

Wilt; "blight"; "leaf curl." Irregular water supply, Fla.

POWDERY MILDEW. **Oidium tingitaninum** and **Oidium** sp., Cal., Fla.

ROT, Black Center; Blossom-End. **Alternaria citri,** widespread.

ROT, Brown. **Phytophthora citrophthora** and other species.

ROT, Cottony Fruit; Twig Blight. **Sclerotinia sclerotiorum,** Cal., Tex.

ROT, Gray Mold; Gummosis; Twig Blight. **Botrytis cinerea,** Cal.

ROT, Green or Blue Mold. **Penicillium** spp., cosmopolitan.

ROT, Fruit. **Aspergillus** spp.; **Fusarium** spp., **Mucor** spp.; **Rhizopus stolonifer; Trichoderma viride,** occasional; **Hendersonula toruloidea,** Cal.

ROT, Diplodia Rot; Twig Blight; Collar Rot; Gummosis. **Diplodia natalensis,** general, perfect stage *Physalospora rhodina.*

ROT, Dothiorella; Bark Canker; Gummosis. **Botryosphaeria ribis,** widespread.

ROT, Melanose; Phomopsis Rot; Decorticosis; Shell Bark; Gummosis. **Diaporthe citri,** general.

ROT, Mushroom Root. **Armillaria mellea,** Cal.; **Clitocybe tabescens,** Fla.

ROT, Root. **Coprinus atramentarius,** secondary; **Fusarium** spp., Ariz., Cal., Fla.; **Macrophomina phaseoli,** Ariz., Cal.; **Phymatotrichum omnivorum,** Tex.; **Poria vaporaria,** Cal.

ROT, Wood. **Daldinia concentrica,** occasional; **Ganoderma lucidum,** Fla.; **Trametes hydnoides; T. hispida; Polyporus** spp.

ROT, Wound. **Schizophyllum commune,** cosmopolitan.

SCAB, Sour Orange; Verrucosis. **Elsinoë fawcetti,** Gulf States.

SOOTY MOLD. **Capnodium** spp. Saprophytic on insect exudate, with indirect effect on leaves, fruit.

VIRUS, Psorosis. Scaly Bark. **Rimocortius psorosis.**

?VIRUS. Quick Decline. Undetermined, Cal.

The importance of citrus diseases varies according to the state and climatic conditions. In California and Arizona brown-rot gummosis, due to *Phytophthora citrophthora* and other species, is found in every citrus section but especially on heavy soils. Shell bark, or dry bark, a disease affecting outer layers of bark of lemon trees, is caused by the same fungus, *Diaporthe citri,* producing melanose in Florida. Armillaria root rot is locally important and often comes from the very susceptible California pepper-tree used around citrus orchards. Mottle leaf, a zinc deficiency, is common in California, and so is psorosis or scaly bark, a virus disease. Recently quick decline, apparently of virus origin, is causing much concern.

In Florida, melanose, which is also Phompsis stem-end rot, is serious, as is sour-orange scab. Mushroom root rot caused by Clitocybe corresponds to the Armillaria root rot of California. Australian-pine around Florida citrus groves is a source of root rot. In Texas, cotton root rot, due to *Phymatotrichum omnivorum,* is important on nursery trees.

Copper compounds are used in most spray schedules, with dithiocarbamates promising for control of brown rot but inferior for melanose. Bordeaux mixture is usually combined with an oil spray to control scale and whiteflies, for the copper kills the Aschersonia species, beneficial fungi which help keep the insects in check.

Several experiment stations are working exclusively on citrus diseases and pests and for commercial growers there is a great deal of specific information available from state and federal sources as well as grower cooperatives. A particularly useful publication is the *Color Handbook of Citrus Diseases,* by L. J. Klotz and H. S. Fawcett, put out by the University of California Press. Here each important disease is pictured in color, with brief descriptions for the grower rather than the scientist.

CLARKIA

ANTHRACNOSE. **Colletotrichum** sp., Pa.

DAMPING-OFF. **Pythium debaryanum,** Cal.; **Rhizoctonia solani,** Conn.

DOWNY MILDEW. **Peronospora arthuri,** Cal.

LEAF GALL. **Synchytrium fulgens,** Cal.

LEAF SPOT; GRAY MOLD; STEM CANKER. **Botrytis cinerea,** Cal., N. Y.

ROT, Stem. **Fusarium** sp., Cal.; **Phytophthora cactorum,** N. Y.

RUST. **Puccinia oenotherae** (O, I, II, III), Cal., Ida., Nev., Oreg., Wash.; **Pucciniastrum pustulatum** (II, III), N. Y., Alaska.

VIRUS, Aster Yellows. **Chlorogenus callistephi** var. **californicus,** Cal.

WILT. **Verticillium albo-atrum,** Cal.

CLAUSENA (Wampi)

LEAF SPOT. **Glomerella cingulata,** Md.

NEMATODE, Root. **Tylenchulus semi-penetrans.**

SCAB, Sour Orange. **Elsinoë fawcetti,** Fla.

CLAYTONIA (Spring Beauty)

DOWNY MILDEW. **Peronospora claytoniae,** Cal., Iowa, Md., Wash.

LEAF GALL. **Physoderma claytonia,** Mich., Wis.

Rust. **Puccinia mariae-wilsoni** (O, II, III), N. H. to Va.; Col., Mo., Utah, Wis., Wash.; **P. agnita** (O, III), Col.; **Uromyces claytoniae** (O, I, III), N. Y.

CLEMATIS

Bacterial Crown Gall. **Agrobacterium tumefaciens,** Minn.

Blight, Leaf. **Phleospora adusta,** Tex.

Leaf Spot. **Ascochyta clematidina,** widespread; **Cercospora rubigo,** Cal., Wash.; **C. squalidula,** widespread; **Cylindrosporium clematidis,** East and South; **Glomerella cingulata,** Fla.; **Phyllosticta clematidis,** Mont., Va.; **Ramularia clematidis,** Mont.; **Septoria clematidis,** Wash.

Nematode, Root Knot. **Heterodera marioni,** widespread.

Powdery Mildew. **Erysiphe polygoni,** widespread.

Rust. **Puccinia rubigo-vera** var. **agropyri** (O, I), on native clematis, Rocky Mts. and Pacific Coast and var. clematidis, Wis.; II, III on grasses; **P. pulsatillae** (III), Cal.; **P. stromatica** (III), Ala.

Smut. **Urocystis carcinodes,** Utah.

CLEOME (Spider-Flower)

Leaf Spot. **Cercospora cleomis,** Mich., N. J.; **C. conspicua,** Okla.; **Heterosporium hybridum,** Iowa, Mont.

Rust. **Puccinia aristidae** (O, I), Ariz., Col., Ind., Mont., Nebr., N. Mex.; II, III on grasses.

CLERODENDRON (Glory-bower)

Leaf Spot. **Septoria phlyctaenioides,** S. Car.

Nematode, Root Knot. **Heterodera marioni,** Md.

CLETHRA (Sweet Pepperbush, White-Alder)

Dodder, **Cuscuta** sp., Fla.

Leaf Gall, red. **Synchytrium vaccinii,** N. J.

Leaf Spot. **Phyllosticta clethricola,** Md., Mass., N. J.

CLINTONIA

Leaf Gall; False Rust. **Synchytrium aureum,** Wis.

Rust. **Puccinia mesomajalis** (III), widespread.

COCCOLOBIS (Sea-Grape, Dove-Plum)

Black Mildew. **Lembosia** spp., Fla.

Rust. **Uredo coccolobae; U. uviferae** (II), Fla.

COCO–PLUM (*Chrysobalanus*)

Leaf Spot, Algal. **Cephaleuros virescens,** Fla.

Leaf Spot. **Cercospora chrysobalani,** Fla.

COCKSCOMB (*Celosia argentia*)

Damping-Off. **Rhizoctonia solani,** Conn.

Leaf Spot. **Cercospora celosiae,** Ala., Okla.; **Phyllosticta** sp., N. J.; **Alternaria** sp., N. J.

Nematode, Root Knot. **Heterodera marioni,** Kans., Ohio, Tex.

Rot, Charcoal. **Macrophomina bataticola,** Tex.

Virus, Curly Top. **Ruga verrucosans,** Cal., Tex.

COFFEE–BERRY (*Rhamnus californica*)

Sooty Mold. **Capnodium** sp., Cal.

Rust. **Puccinia mesneriana** (III) Cal.

COLEUS

Damping-Off; Cutting Rot. **Pythium** spp., Cal., Md.; **Rhizoctonia solani,** Fla., Ill., N. Y., Tex.

Leaf Spot. **Alternaria** sp., N. J.; **Phyllosticta** sp., N. J.; **Botrytis cinerea,** Alaska.

Nematode, Leaf. **Aphelenchoides** sp.

Nematode, Root Knot. **Heterodera marioni,** Ala., Cal., Conn., Md., Mo., N. J., N. Y., Okla.

Rot, Cutting; Gray Mold; Leaf Blight. **Botrytis** sp., Mo., Alaska.

Physiogenic Crinkle. Noninfectious leaf deformity, from genetic factors.

Virus, Mosaic. Unidentified, Ill.

Wilt. **Verticillium** sp., Conn.

COLLARDS (See Cabbage)

Subject to downy mildew and Sclerotinia rot.

COLLINSIA

Leaf Spot. **Septoria collinsiae,** Ill.

Rot, Root. **Pythium mamillatum,** Cal.

Rust. **Aecidium insulum** (O, I), Utah; **Puccinia collinsiae** (O, I, II, III), Cal., Oreg., Utah, Wash.

Smut, White. **Entyloma collinsiae,** Cal., Oreg.

COLLINSONIA (Horse-Balm)

Black Spot, on stem. **Phyllachora** sp., Pa.

COLLOMIA

Powdery Mildew. **Sphaerotheca humuli,** Cal., Col., Ida., Mont., N. Dak., Wash., Wyo.

Rust. **Puccinia giliae** (II, III), Cal., Wash.; O, I unknown; **P. plumbaria** (O, I, III), Nev.; **Uromyces acuminatus** var. **polemonii** (O, I), Col., Nebr., N. Dak.; II, III on marsh grass.

COLTSFOOT (*Tussilago farfara*)

LEAF SPOT. **Mycosphaerella tussilaginis,** N. Y.; **Septoria farfaricola,** Tenn.

COLUMBINE (*Aquilegia*)

BLIGHT, Gray Mold. **Botrytis cinerea; B. streptothrix,** Conn.
DAMPING-OFF, Root Rot. **Rhizoctonia solani,** Ill.
LEAF SPOT. **Ascochyta aquilegiae,** Conn., Ill., Iowa, N. J., N. Y., Pa., Tex., Wis.; **Cercospora aquilegiae,** Kans., Oreg.; **Septoria aquilegiae,** Conn., Ind., Mich., N. Y., Ohio, Va., Vt., Wis.
NEMATODE, Root Knot. **Heterodera marioni.**
ROT, Root. **Phymatotrichum omnivorum,** Tex.; **Pythium mamillatum,** Cal.
ROT, Stem. **Phoma** sp., Pa.; **Sclerotinia sclerotiorum,** Del., Ohio, Pa., Tex.
ROT, Collar, Crown. **Sclerotium rolfsii (S. delphinii),** Del., N. J., Va.
RUST. **Puccinia rubigo-vera** (O, I), Col., Cal., Ida., N. Mex., Oreg., Wyo., Wash.; II, III on grasses.
SMUT, Leaf and Stem. **Urocystis sorosporioides,** Utah.
VIRUS, Mosaic. Unidentified, Iowa, Kans.

COLUMBO (*Frasera*)

BLACK MILDEW. **Asteroma fraserae,** Col., Ida.
LEAF SPOT. **Cercospora fraserae,** Col., Utah; **Marssonina fraserae,** Ida., Wash.; **Phyllosticta fraserae,** Col.
RUST. **Uromyces speciosus** (II, III), Col., N. Mex.; O, I, unknown.

CONFEDERATE–JASMINE (*Trachelospermum jasminoides*)

LEAF SPOT. **Cercospora repens,** La.

CORAL–BERRY (*Symphoricarpus orbiculatus*)

CANKER; Stem Gall. **Phomopsis** sp., Md.
LEAF SPOT. **Cercospora symphoricarpi,** Kans., Nebr., Tex.
POWDERY MILDEW. **Microsphaera alni,** Ind., Ohio, W. Va.; **M. diffusa,** widespread.
ROT, Berry. **Alternaria** sp., Conn.
ROT, Root. **Helicobasidium purpureum; Phymatotrichum omnivorum,** Tex.
RUST. **Puccinia crandallii** (O, I), Kans., Mo., Okla.

COREOPSIS (Tickseed)

BLIGHT, **Botrytis cinerea,** Alaska.
BLIGHT, Southern. **Sclerotium rolfsii,** Fla., Tex.
DODDER. **Cuscuta** sp., N. J.
LEAF SPOT. **Cercospora coreopsidis,** Okla.; **Phyllosticta coreopsidis,** Wis. **Septoria coreopsidis,** Iowa, Wis.

NEMATODE, Root Knot. **Heterodera marioni,** Fla.
ROT, Root and Stem. **Rhizoctonia solani,** Minn., N. Y., Tex.
RUST. **Coleosporium inconspicuum** (II, III), Ga., Md., N. and S. C., Ohio, Tenn., Va., W. Va.; (O, I) on pine.
VIRUS, Curly Top. **Ruga verrucosans,** Cal.
VIRUS, Yellows. **Chlorogenus callistephi,** N. J., N. Y., and var. **californicus.**
WILT. **Verticillium albo-atrum,** La., N. Y.

CORIANDER (*Coriandrum*)

NEMATODE, Root Knot. **Heterodera marioni,** Fla.
ROT, Stem. **Fusarium** sp.

CORN, SWEET (*Zea mays* var. *saccharata*)

BACTERIAL Spot. **Pseudomonas syringae,** Mass.
BACTERIAL Stalk Rot. **Erwinia carotovora,** Fla., W. Va.
BACTERIAL WILT. **Bacterium stewartii,** general but more prevalent in New England and East Central States.
BLIGHT, Leaf. **Helminthosporium turcicum,** Middle Atlantic and Southern States.
LEAF SPOT; Brown Spot. **Physoderma zeae-maydis,** Southern States.
ROT; Black Bundle Disease. **Cephalosporium acremonium,** Mont.
ROT, Ear, Root and Stalk; Seedling Blight. **Diplodia zeae,** Eastern and Central States, from Me. to Va., and to Tex. and S. Dak.
ROT, Fusarium spp., Middle Atlantic and Central States to Texas and Minn.
ROT, Root and Stalk. **Fusarium moniliforme,** cosmopolitan as a saprophyte, occasional parasitic strains.
ROT, Root; Seedling Blight. **Gibberella zeae,** Eastern and Central States, chiefly east of Mississippi River; **Pythium** spp., Ill., Iowa, Ohio, Tex.
ROT, Dry Ear. **Nigrospora oryzae,** Iowa.
RUST. **Puccinia sorghi** (II, III), general, especially in Northeastern and North Central States; O, I on Oxalis.
SMUT. **Ustilago maydis,** general.
VIRUS, Mosaic; Southern Celery Mosaic. **Marmor cucumeris** var. **commelinae,** Fla.
VIRUS, Streak. Cause unknown, Cal.

Smut is the most conspicuous corn disease in home gardens. Formerly the only recommendations were sanitary measures, but recently it has been learned that insecticides directed against the corn borer markedly reduce the amount of smut. Resistant varieties are in the making.

Bacterial wilt or Stewart's Disease seems to be dependent on survival of flea-beetle vectors. If the sum of the mean monthly temperatures, for Dec., Jan., Feb., is above 100, then the insects winter well and wilt may be expected. If the winter index is below 90 wilt will probably be absent. Golden Bantam, which is very susceptible, should be replaced in wilt years by Golden Cross Bantam, Carmel-cross and other resistant varieties.

Treat seed with Arasan, Spergon, or Semesan Jr., to avoid various rots.

CORNCOCKLE (*Agrostemma*)

Leaf Spot. **Marssonina delastrei,** Ill., Ind., Mich., Miss., Mo.; **Septoria lychnidis** var. **pusilla,** N. Dak.; **Gloeosporium** sp., Ind.

Rot, Stem. **Fusarium** sp., Ind.

CORN–MARIGOLD (*Chrysanthemum segetum*)

Leaf Spot. **Septoria chrysanthemi,** N. Y.

Virus, Aster Yellows. **Chlorogenus callistephi,** var. **californicus,** Cal.

CORYDALIS

Downy Mildew. **Peronospora corydalis,** Ind., Mass., Md., Okla., Tex.

Leaf Spot. **Septoria corydalis,** Tex., Wis.

Nematode, Root Knot. **Heterodera marioni,** Fla.

Rust. **Puccinia aristidae** (O, I), Col., Kans., Nebr.; II, III on grasses; **P. brandegei** (III), Col., Wash.

COSMOS

Bacterial Wilt. **Pseudomonas solanacearum,** N. C.

Blight, Southern. **Sclerotium rolfsii,** Miss., doubtless elsewhere.

Canker; Stem Blight. **Diaporthe stewartii,** Conn. to N. J.; Kans., S. Dak., Cal., Tex.

Dodder. **Cuscuta** sp., N. Y.

Leaf Spot. **Cercospora** sp., Tex.; **Septoria** sp., Conn.

Nematode, Root Knot. **Heterodera marioni,** Fla., Md.

Powdery Mildew. **Erysiphe cichoracearum,** Cal., Md., N. C., Nebr.

Rot, Root. **Phymatotrichum omnivorum,** Ariz., Tex.; **Macrophomina phaseoli,** Tex.

Rot, Stem. **Rhizoctonia solani,** Conn., Md., Tex.

Virus, Aster Yellows. **Chlorogenus callistephi,** Del., N. J., N. Y., and var. **californicus,** Cal.

Virus, Curly Top. **Ruga verrucosans,** Cal.

Virus, Mosaic. Unidentified, Fla., Tex.

Virus, Spotted Wilt. **Lethum australiense,** Tex.

Wilt. **Fusarium** sp., N. J.

COTONEASTER

Bacterial Fire Blight. **Erwinia amylovora,** widespread.

Bacterial Hairy Root. **Agrobacterium rhizogenes,** Central States.

Canker; Twig Blight. **Physalospora obtusa,** N. Y. to Ohio, Tex.

Leaf Spot. **Fabraea maculata,** Cal.; **Phyllosticta cotoneastri,** Md., **P. cydoniae,** Miss.

Rot, Root. **Clitocybe tabescens,** Fla.; **Phymatotrichum omnivorum,** Ariz., Tex.

Scab. **Venturia** sp., Wash.

Fire blight is common, as shown by dying back of branches, which should be cut well back of the blighted portion. Scale insects may also cause dieback.

COURSETIA

Rust. **Phragmopyxis acuminata** (O, III) Ariz., Cal.

COWANIA

Rust. **Phragmidium andersoni** (I, II, III), Idaho.

COWPEA (*Vigna sinensis*)

Cowpeas are chiefly of interest to gardeners as a green manure crop, and there is little need of repeating here the long list of possible disases, most of which can be found under Bean. Ashy stem blight or charcoal rot is fairly serious. The root-knot nematode is general, but varieties Iron and Bragham are almost immune. Fusarium wilt, general in the South, is largely controlled by using resistant varieties. Leaf spots are numerous and some may cause defoliation. Rust is widespread on Blackeye and related varieties, but many varieties are resistant.

CRAB, FLOWERING (*Pyrus* spp.)

The diseases to which crabapples may be heir are listed under Apple. Fire blight and scab are both widespread, while the various cedar or juniper rusts are decidedly disfiguring and destructive to most native varieties.

CRANBERRY (*Vaccinium macrocarpon*)

Black Spot. **Mycosphaerella nigromaculans,** Me., Mass., Ore., Wash., Wis.

Leaf Gall, Red. **Synchytrium vaccinii,** Me. to N. J.

Leaf Gall; Shoot Hypertrophy; Rose Bloom. **Exobasidium oxycocci,** Mass., N. H., Oreg., Wash.

Leaf Gall; Red Leaf Spot. **Exobasidium vaccinii,** general.

Leaf Spot; Leaf Smudge. **Venturia** (*Gibbera*) **compacta,** Me. to N. J., Wis., Pacific Northwest.

Powdery Mildew. **Microsphaera alni** var. **vacinii,** Ala., N. J., Ohio.

Rot, Berry; Blotch. **Acanthorynchus vaccinii,** Me. to N. C. and Wis., Pacific Northwest; **Ceuthospora lunata,** Mass., N. J., Oreg., Wash., Wis.; **Curvularia inaequalis.**

Rot, Bitter, of berries. **Glomerella cingulata,** Mass., N. J., N. C., Oreg., Wash., Wis.

Rot, Early; Scald; Blast. **Guignardia vaccinii,** general.

Rot, End. **Godronia cassandrae,** general.
Rot, Fairy Ring. **Psilocybe agrariella** var. **vaccinii.**
Rot, Hard; Twig Blight. **Monilinia oxycocci,** Mass., Me., Oreg., Wash., Wis.
Rot, Storage. **Penicillium** spp., cosmopolitan; **Sphaeronema pomorum,** Mass., N. J.; **Sporonema oxycocci,** Me. to N. J., Wis.; **Melanospora destruens,** Mass., N. J., Wis.; **Gloeosporium minus,** Md., N. J.
Rot, Witches' Broom. **Naevia oxycocci,** Me., Mich., N. H., N. Y.
Rust. **Pucciniastrum myrtilli** (II, III), Oreg., Utah, Wash.; O, I on hemlock.
Virus, Cranberry False-Blossom. **Chlorogenus vaccinii,** Me. to N. J., Mich., Wis., Pacific Northwest.

Fermate has been giving good control of cranberry fruit rots and higher yields than bordeaux mixture. When the flooding water is alkaline there seems to be freedom from false-blossom.

CRAPE-MYRTLE (*Lagerstroemia*)

Blotch, Black Spot. **Cercospora** sp., Fla., Tex.
Blight, Tip. **Phyllosticta lagerstroemia,** La., Tex.
Leaf Spot. **Cercospora lythracearum,** Tex.
Physiogenic Chlorosis. Manganese deficiency, Fla.
Powdery Mildew. **Erysiphe lagerstroemiae,** Md. to Fla. and Tex. **Phyllactinia corylea,** Ala.
Rot, Root. **Clitocybe tabescens,** Fla.; **Phymatotrichum omnivorum,** Tex.
Sooty Mold. **Capnodium** sp., formed in aphid honeydew.

Mildew is general on crape-myrtle with mycelium wintering in dormant buds, and so calling for a lime-sulfur spray (1 to 80 dilution) as buds break. Later sulfur dust or wettable sulfur or copper sprays are useful.

CRASSULA

Anthracnose. **Gloeosporium** sp., N. J.
Leaf Spot. **Phomopsis** sp., Conn.
Rot, Root. **Armillaria mellea,** Cal.; **Pythium** sp., N. J., N. Y.

CREOSOTE BUSH (*Covillea*)

Mistletoe. **Phoradendron californicum,** Tex. to Cal.

CRINUM

Leaf Scorch; Red Blotch. **Stagonospora curtisii,** Cal., N. Y.
Leaf Spot. **Cercospora pancratii,** Ala., Fla., Miss.
Virus, Mosaic. Unidentified, Cal.

CROCUS

Bacterial Scab. **Pseudomonas marginata,** occasional on imported stocks.
Rot, Corm. **Fusarium oxysporum,** various strains, including **lilii,** N. Y., Pa.

Rot, Blue Mold. **Penicillium** sp. in imported stocks.

Rot, Dry. **Stromatinia gladioli,** N. J., N. Y., Wash., probably widespread, frequent on imported stocks.

Virus, Mosaic. May be **Marmor iridis.**

CROTALARIA (*C. retusa,* grown for ornament)

Powdery Mildew. **Microsphaera diffusa,** Md.; **Oidium erysiphoides** var. **crotalariae,** La., Miss. (not a true Oidium).

Wilt, Root Rot. **Fusarium** spp., Ga., Tex.

Crotalaria grown as a cover crop has many other diseases, but *Crotalaria spectabilis* has the virtue of being immune to the root-knot nematode.

CROTON (*Codiaeum*)

Leaf Spot; Stem Spot. **Glomerella cingulata,** widespread.

Rot, Root. **Phymatotrichum omnivorum,** Tex.

CROWBERRY (*Empetrum*)

Rust. **Chrysomyxa empetri** (II), Me., N. H., N. Y.

CROWN-OF-THORNS (*Euphorbia splendens* or *E. milii*)

Wilt. **Verticillium albo-atrum,** N. J.

CRYPTANTHA

Powdery Mildew. **Erysiphe cichoracearum,** Cal., Nev.

Rust. **Puccinia aristidae** (O, I); II, III on native grasses; **P. cryptanthes** (II, III), Cal., Wash.; O, I unknown.

CRYPTOMERIA

Blight, Leaf and Twig. **Phomopsis** sp. = *Diaporthe eres.*

Leaf Spot. **Pestalotia cryptomeriae,** S. C.; **P. funerea,** N. J., perhaps secondary on needles.

CUCUMBER (*Cucumis sativus*)

Anthracnose. **Colletotrichum lagenarium,** general.

Bacterial Wilt. **Erwinia tracheiphila,** general.

Bacterial Spot. **Xanthomonas cucurbitae,** Mass., Mich.

Bacterial Angular Leaf Spot. **Pseudomonas lachrymans,** general.

Bacterial Rot. **Erwinia aroideae; E. carotovorus.**

Blight, Blossom. **Choanephora cucurbitarum,** Fla., Ga.

Blight, Gummy Stem; Black Fruit Rot. **Mycosphaerella citrullina,** widespread, N. Y. to Fla., Tex. and Cal.

Blight, Leaf. **Alternaria cucumerina,** general.

Blight, Southern. **Sclerotium rolfsii,** Va. to Fla., Tex.

Damping-Off. **Rhizoctonia solani,** occasional in greenhouses; **Pythium** spp.

Dodder. **Cuscuta gronovii,** N. Y.

Downy Mildew. **Pseudoperonospora cubensis,** general.

Leaf Spot. **Phyllosticta cucurbitacearum,** Del., Ohio, Tex.; **Septoria cucurbitacearum,** Del., Mass., N. H., Pa.; **Stemphylium cucurbitacearum,** Ind., Ohio.

Mold, Seed. **Alternaria tenuis,** cosmopolitan; **Curvularia trifolii,** N. J.

Nematode, Root Knot. **Heterodera marioni,** general.

Physiogenic Chlorosis. Manganese or nitrogen deficiency.

Powdery Mildew. **Erysiphe cichoracearum,** general.

Rot, Charcoal. **Macrophomina phaseoli,** Ill.

Rot, Fruit. **Fusarium** spp., Tex.; **Phytophthora** sp.; **Rhizopus stolonifer,** occasional.

Rot, Gray Mold. **Botrytis cinerea,** Ill., Ohio, Wash.

Rot, Root. **Fusarium solani,** Conn., Oreg.; **Phymatotrichum omnivorum,** Tex.

Rot, Stem, Fruit. **Sclerotinia sclerotiorum,** occasional.

Scab. **Cladosporium cucumerinum,** general.

Virus, Curly Top. **Ruga verrucosans,** Cal., Ida., Oreg., Tex., Utah.

Virus, Mosaic. **Marmor cucumeris,** general.

Virus, Ring Spot. **Annulus tabaci,** Md., Pa., Va.

Wilt. **Verticillium albo-atrum,** Me., Ohio, Oreg., Wash., Wis.

Starting cucumbers under Hotkaps temporarily circumvents the insects carrying wilt bacteria and mosaic virus. When these covers are removed frequent dusting with rotenone or other contact or stomach poison is in order. DDT is not generally recommended for cucumbers for it injures some varieties. A fixed copper, or Zerlate, or Dithane, can be used with the rotenone in a combination dust to control wilt, leaf spot, downy mildew, and anthracnose when plants are young. When vines are well started copper sprays are alternated with an organic spray. Bordeaux mixture is too injurious to cucumbers if used before plants are about half grown. Treating seed with bichloride of mercury and a two- to three-year rotation controls scab and angular leaf spot.

CUCUMIS ANGURIA (West Indian Gherkin)

Bacterial Angular Leaf Spot. **Pseudomonas lachrymans,** Wis.

Downy Mildew. **Pseudoperonospora cubensis,** Ohio, Tex.

Powdery Mildew. **Erysiphe cichoracearum,** Mass.

CULVERS-ROOT (*Veronicastrum*)

Leaf Spot. **Cercospora leptandrae,** Wis.; **Ramularia veronicae,** Tex.; **Septoria veronicae,** Wis.

Powdery Mildew. **Erysiphe cichoracearum,** Ill.; **Sphaerotheca humuli** var. **fulginea,** Conn., Ill., Iowa, Md., Mich., Mo., Wis.

Rot, Root. **Phymatotrichum omnivorum,** Tex.; **Rhizoctonia solani,** Tex.
Rust. **Puccinia veronicarum** (III), Iowa, Tex., Wis.

CUPHEA

Blight, Gray Mold. **Botrytis cinerea,** occasional in greenhouses.
Leaf Spot. **Septoria maculifera,** N. Y., Pa., Va., W. Va.
Nematode, Root Knot. **Heterodera marioni,** Md.
Powdery Mildew. **Erysiphe polygoni,** Md., Va.
Rot, Root. **Rhizoctonia solani,** Ill.

CURRANT (*Ribes* spp.)

Anthracnose; Leaf, Stem, Fruit Spot. **Pseudopeziza ribis,** or *Drepanopeziza ribis,* general.
Blight, Cane. **Botryosphaeria ribis** var. **chromogena,** general.
Blight, Gray Mold; Fruit and Leaf Spot. **Botrytis cinerea,** Northeast, Oreg., Wash.
Blight, Thread. **Corticium stevensii** (Probably *Pellicularia koleroga*), Fla.
Canker; Cane Knot. **Thyronectria berolinensis,** Conn. to Ind., Kans., Utah.
Canker; Dieback. **Nectria cinnabarina,** Me. to Col., Wash.; **Nectria** sp., Minn., N. Y.
Dieback; Black Pustule. **Phragmodothella ribesia,** Northeastern States, Pacific Northwest.
Downy Mildew. **Plasmopara ribicola,** Wis.
Leaf Spot, Angular. **Cercospora angulata,** N. Y. to Va., Kans., Minn.; **C. ribis,** Ala., Ind., Iowa.
Leaf Spot. **Alternaria** sp., Mich.; **Cylindrosporium ribis,** Wis.; **Mycosphaerella ribis,** Me. to Md., Ark., Oreg., Wash.
Powdery Mildew. **Microsphaera grossulariae,** Mont., Nebr., N. H.; **Sphaerotheca mors-uvae,** Cal., Conn., Mont., Nebr., Oreg., Wash., Alaska; **Phyllactinia corylea,** Mich.
Rot, Berry. **Glomerella cingulata,** Conn.
Rot, Collar. **Fomes ribis,** N. Y. to Ind., Minn., Utah.
Rot, Root. **Armillaria mellea,** Cal., Oreg., Wash.; **Phymatotrichum omnivorum,** Tex.; **Hypholoma perplexum,** N. Y.
Rust, White Pine Blister. **Cronartium ribicola** (II, III), Me. to Va., Minn., Ill.; O, I on white pine; **Puccinia caricis** var. **grossulariata** (O, I); Conn., Ind., Md., N. Y.; II, III on Carex.
Virus, Mosaic. Undetermined, N. Y.
Wilt, **Verticillium** sp., N. Y.

Diseases known as Leaf Crinkle, Witches' Broom and Yellow Leaf are of unknown cause.

Black currant is the most important host of the white pine blister rust. It should be eradicated up to a mile away from pines while 300 to 900 feet is sufficient for red currants. Varieties Viking and Red Dutch are resistant. Bordeaux mixture remains the best treatment for anthracnose and leaf spots, with two sprays often enough. Canes infected with cane blight should be cut out.

FLOWERING CURRANT, Golden and Red

ANTHRACNOSE. **Pseudopeziza ribis,** Minn., Mont.

BLIGHT; Dieback. **Botrytis cinerea,** Ind., Alaska.

CANKER; DIEBACK; Coral Spot. **Nectria cinnabarina,** Alaska, Kans.

CANKER; Cane Dieback. **Botryosphaeria ribis,** Kans.

CANKER; Cane Knot. **Thyronectria berolinensis,** Kans.

DIEBACK; Black Pustule. **Phragmodothella ribesia,** N. Y.

LEAF SPOT. **Cercospora angulata,** Minn.; **C. ribicola,** Oreg., Wash.; **Marssonina ribicola,** Col.; **Mycosphaerella aurea** var. **destruens,** N. Y. to Kans. and S. Dak., Wash.; **M. ribis,** N. Y. to Kans., Minn. and Utah; **Phyllosticta grossulariae,** Ind.; **Septoria sanguinea,** Wash.

ROT, Berry. **Glomerella cingulata,** Conn.

RUST. **Coleosporium jonesii,** Minn., **Cronartium occidentale** (Piñon Blister Rust) Mont. to N. Mex., Cal., Wash.; **C. ribicola,** Me. to Md., Col., Minn.; Pacific States; **Melampsora ribesii-purpureae;** II, III on Willow; **Puccinia caricis** var. **grossulariata** (O, I), N. Y. to Iowa., Cal., Oreg., Alaska; **P. micrantha** (O, I), Nebr., Wyo.; III on Oryzopsis; **P. parkerae** (III), Wash.

CYCAS (Sago-Palm, Fern-palm)

CORALOID ROOTS. **Anabaena cycadearum,** an endophytic alga, Fla.

LEAF SPOT. **Ascochyta cycadina,** Mo., Tex.

A destructive blight of unknown cause has caused trouble in Florida. Pale-green areas appear on pinnae of young leaves which are curled out of flat plane and die back. The disease is apparently systemic and increases annually until death. Eradication of blighted plants is the only control suggested.

CYCLAMEN

BACTERIAL Tuber Rot. **Erwinia carotovora,** Ohio, N. J., N. Y.

BLIGHT; Bud and leaf rot; Petal Spot. **Botrytis cinerea,** cosmopolitan but petal spot symptoms reported in Cal.

BLIGHT, Leaf and Bud. **Glomerella cingulata,** Ind., Mass., Mo., N. J., Ohio, Pa., Va.

LEAF SPOT; White Mold. **Ramularia cyclaminicola,** Cal., Ill., Minn., Ohio.

LEAF SPOT. **Phyllosticta** sp., N. J.

NEMATODE, Leaf. **Aphelenchoides** sp., N. J.

NEMATODE, Root Knot. **Heterodera marioni,** cosmopolitan.

NEMATODE, Root, Meadow. **Pratylenchus pratensis,** Va.

ROT, Root. **Thielaviopsis basicola,** Conn.

STUNT. **Cladosporium cyclaminis,** also spot necrosis on tubers, leaves, Cal., Ill., N. J., N. Y., Ohio, Pa.

WILT. **Fusarium** sp., N. J.

Cyclamen petal spot is controlled in California greenhouses by reducing humidity. At night top ventilators are closed, side ventilators left open and enough heat turned on to dry the air. Avoiding splashing in watering keeps down nematodes, soft rot, and leaf spots, but spraying, perhaps with Fermate, is also recommended. Start seed from healthy plants in new or sterilized soil to avoid stunt.

CYNOGLOSSUM (Hounds-Tongue)

BLIGHT, Southern. **Sclerotium rolfsii,** Fla.

DOWNY MILDEW. **Peronospora cynoglossi,** Md., Ill.

LEAF SPOT. **Cercospora cynoglossi,** Ind.; **Phyllosticta decidua,** Wis.; **Ramularia lappulae,** Wis.

NEMATODE, Root Knot. **Heterodera marioni.**

ROT, Stem. **Sclerotinia sclerotiorum,** Wash.

CYPRESS (*Cupressus*)

BACTERIAL Crown Gall. **Agrobacterium tumefaciens,** Ariz., Cal., Fla.

BLIGHT, Nursery. **Phomopsis juniperovora,** East and South to Tex.

BLIGHT, Twig. **Coryneum berkmanii,** Oreg., on Italian cypress.

BLIGHT, Twig. **Pestalotia funerea,** Cal., Fla., Tex.

BLIGHT, Seedling. **Fusarium solani,** Tex.

CANKER, **Coryneum cardinale,** Cal., chiefly on planted trees but fatal also to native groves of Monterey cypress; sometimes on Italian cypress.

CANKER. **Cytospora cenisia,** Cal., on Italian cypress.

DIEBACK. **Macrophoma cupressi,** Fla., Tex., on Italian cypress; **Sphaeropsis cupressi** on Monterey cypress, Cal.

MISTLETOE, **Phoradendron pauciflorum,** Ariz., Cal., Fla.

NEEDLE CAST. **Lophodermium** sp., N. J.

ROT, Root. **Clitocybe tabescens,** Fla.

ROT, Wood. **Lenzites saepiaria,** cosmopolitan; **Polyporus** spp., Cal.

ROT, Wound. **Hydnum ochraceum,** Cal.; **Polyporus versicolor,** cosmopolitan.

RUST. **Gymnosporangium cupressi** (III) on Arizona cypress, Ariz.; **O, I** on Amelanchier.

Between its discovery in 1927 and 1939 Coryneum canker had killed 30,000 Monterey cypress trees in California. Everyone has cooperated to save the famous native stand on Monterey Peninsula. Cytospora canker is killing trees in a narrow belt along the coast.

CYRILLA (Leatherwood; Swamp Ironwood)

RUST. **Aecidium cyrillae,** La., Miss.

DAHLIA

BACTERIAL Crown Gall. **Agrobacterium tumefaciens,** Conn., Ill.

BACTERIAL Soft Rot. **Erwinia carotovora,** Miss., Wash.

BACTERIAL Stem and Tuber Rot. **Erwinia cytolitica,** N. Y.

BACTERIAL WILT. **Pseudomonas solanacearum,** Del., Miss., N. J., N. C., Okla., Tex.

BLIGHT, Blossom. **Choanephora americana,** Fla.

BLIGHT, Gray Mold. **Botrytis cinerea,** cosmopolitan on bud and flowers.

BLIGHT, Southern. **Sclerotium rolfsii,** Fla., Kans., Miss., N. J., N. C.

LEAF SPOT. **Alternaria** sp., Va. to Ala., Mo., Mich., probably after hopperburn; **Cercospora** sp., Fla., Miss.

NEMATODE, Leaf. **Aphelenchoides ritzema-bosi,** Cal.

NEMATODE, Root Knot. **Heterodera marioni,** N. C. to Ala., Tex., Mo., Ariz., Cal.

POWDERY MILDEW. **Erysiphe cichoracearum,** general, **E. polygoni,** Cal., Del., Ga., Iowa, Mo., N. J., Pa., Va.; **Uncinula** sp., N. C.

ROT, Root. **Armillaria mellea,** Cal.; **Phymatotrichum omnivorum,** Tex.

ROT, Charcoal. **Macrophomina phaseoli,** S. C.

ROT, Stem. **Sclerotinia sclerotiorum,** Cal., Me., N. Y.

ROT, Stem and Root. **Pythium debaryanum,** Conn., Md., Wash.; **P. oedochilum** and **P. ultimum,** Md.; **Rhizoctonia solani,** Md., Miss., N. J., N. C., Wash.

SMUT, Leaf. **Entyloma dahliae,** Cal., N. J., Oreg.

VIRUS, Mosaic, Stunt. **Marmor dahliae,** general.

VIRUS, Ringspot; Spotted Wilt. **Lethum australiense,** Cal., Mich., N. Y., N. J., Tex., Wis.

VIRUS, Streak. Suspected virus, N. Y.

WILT; Root and Stem Rot. **Fusarium** spp., Ariz., Md., Mo., N. H., N. J., N. Y., Ohio; *F. oxysporum* type is associated with wilt, *F. roseum* with tuber rot.

WILT. **Verticillium albo-atrum,** Mich., Mo., N. J., Ohio.

Leafhopper injury, often known as hopperburn, looks like a true disease. Margins of leaves turn brown and there may be general stunting and yellowing. The virus disease, spotted wilt, is correlated in home gardens on the Pacific Coast with growing tomatoes.

Heavy, wet soil contributes to bacterial and fungus rots and wilts. Mildew is prevalent in late summer but is readily controlled with sulfur dust or a copper spray.

DAISY (*Chrysanthemum leucanthemum*)

BLIGHT, Southern. **Sclerotium rolfsii,** Tex.

BLOTCH, Leaf. **Septoria leucanthemi,** Conn., N. Y.

LEAF SPOT. **Septoria chrysanthemi,** Conn., Iowa, N. Y.

NEMATODE, Stem. **Ditylenchus dipsaci,** N. Y.

Rot, Stem. **Fusarium roseum** and **F. solani,** Tex.
Rot, Root. **Phymatotrichum omnivorum,** Tex.
Virus, Potato Yellow-Dwarf. **Aureogenus vastans,** N. Y.
Virus, Aster Yellows. **Chlorogenus callistephi,** Kans., N. J., N. Y.

DALIBARDA

Leaf Spot. **Septoria dalibardae,** Me., Mich., N. H., N. Y., Vt.

DAPHNE

Blight, Twig. **Botrytis** sp., Northeast; Pacific Northwest.
Dieback; Wilt. **Fusarium** sp., N. J.
Leaf Spot; Leaf Drop. **Gloeosporium mezerei,** Wash.
Rot, Collar, Stem. **Phytophthora** sp., N. J.; **Rhizoctonia solani,** N. Y.
Rot, Stem; Wilt. **Sclerotium rolfsii,** Fla.

DATURA

Blight, Southern. **Sclerotium rolfsii,** Fla.
Rot, Root. **Thielaviopsis basicola,** Wis.

DAY-LILY (*Hemerocallis*)

Blight, Gray Mold. **Botrytis** sp., Md.
Blight, Leaf. **Kabatiella** sp., Md., probably secondary.
Leaf Spot. **Cercospora hemerocallis,** Ill.; **Heterosporium gracile,** N. J.
Nematode, Root Knot. **Heterodera marioni.**
Rot, Root. **Sclerotium** sp., Ind.

DECUMARIA

Leaf Spot. **Cercospora decumariae,** Miss.

DELPHINIUM

Bacterial Crown Gall. **Agrobacterium tumefaciens,** Wash.
Bacterial Collar Rot. **Erwinia carotovora,** Cal., N. Y.
Bacterial Foot Rot; Blackleg. **Erwinia phytophthora,** Cal., Minn., N. Y.
Bacterial Leaf Spot; Black Disease. **Pseudomonas delphinii** widespread.
Blight, Gray Mold; Bud Rot. **Botrytis cinerea,** Conn., Mass., Miss., N. Y., W. Va., Wis.
Blight, Southern; Collar and Stem Rot; Crown Rot. **Sclerotium delphinii** and **S. rolfsii,** general.
Canker, Stem. **Diaporthe arctii,** Md., N. C., N. Y., Ohio, Pa.; **Fusarium oxysporum** f. **delphinii,** N. Y.; **Fusarium** spp., Ariz., Fla., Mass., Ohio, Wash. **Phoma** sp., Conn., N. J., N. Y.; **Volutella** sp., Md.

DAMPING-OFF. **Pythium ultimum,** Cal., N. Y., probably cosmopolitan; **Rhizoctonia solani,** cosmopolitan.

LEAF GALL. **Synchytrium aureum,** Iowa.

LEAF SPOT. **Ascochyta aquilegiae,** Conn.; **Cercospora delphinii,** Col., Mo.; **Ovularia delphinii,** Wyo.; **Phyllosticta** sp., N. Y.; **Ramularia delphinii,** Cal., Col., Utah; **Septoria delphinella,** Ill., Kans., Wis.

NEMATODE, Leaf and Stem. **Ditylenchus dipsaci,** Oreg., Wash.

NEMATODE, Root Knot. **Heterodera marioni,** Ariz., N. J., N. Y., Va., Wash.

NEMATODE, Root. **Pratylenchus pratensis.**

PHYSIOGENIC Variegation. Noninfectious seed-transmitted color anomalies.

POWDERY MILDEW. **Erysiphe cichoracearum,** Mass., Minn., N. Y., Wash.; **E. polygoni** general, but some varieties resistant; **Sphaerotheca humuli** var. **fuliginea,** Cal.

ROT, Collar; Leaf Spot. **Diplodina delphinii,** Cal., N. Y.

ROT, Crown. See Southern Blight, above.

ROT, Root. **Phymatotrichum omnivorum,** Tex.

ROT, Stem. **Phytophthora** sp., Minn.; **Sclerotinia sclerotiorum,** Del., Ill., Mass., Mich., Mo., Ohio, Wash.

RUST. **Puccinia delphinii,** Cal.; **P. rubigo-vera** (O, I), Nebr. to N. Mex., Cal.

SMUT, Leaf and Stem. **Urocystis sorosporioides,** Cal., Ky., Va.

SMUT, White. **Entyloma winteri,** Cal.; **E. wyomingense,** Wyo.

VIRUS, Celery-Calico. **Marmor aevi,** Cal., Ida., Wash.

VIRUS, Curly Top. **Ruga verrucosans,** Cal., Wash.

VIRUS, Mosaic. Part **Marmor cucumeris** and part **M. aevi,** Fla., Cal., Ky.

VIRUS, Ring Spot. **Annulus delphinii,** Cal.; perhaps **Annulus tabaci** in Ky., Minn., N. Y., Wash.

VIRUS, Spotted Wilt. **Lethum australiense,** Cal.

VIRUS, Stunt, Witches-broom. Part yellows, or calico and ring spot.

VIRUS, Aster Yellows; Virescence, "greens." **Chlorogenus callistephi** var. **californicus,** Cal., Utah, Wash., ?Ida., ?Ore.

WILT. **Verticillium albo-atrum,** N. Y., Wash.

One of the chief delphinium problems is a condition known as "blacks" which looks like a disease and is often confused with bacterial blackspot but is caused by mites, which stunt and deform the plants and turn buds black.

Crown rot or southern blight is often fatal to delphiniums. When yellowing and wilting appears, check the soil around the crown for reddish sclerotia and white mycelium and take immediate sanitary measures. Many foot, collar, and root rots and stem cankers afflict delphinium. Most growers find that the easiest way to avoid these is to grow fine hybrid delphiniums as biennials, and, where possible, rotating locations, choosing well-drained sites. Aster yellows and other virus diseases are important particularly along the Pacific Coast. Use virus-free planting stock and rogue out all infected individuals. Mildew is common, but readily controlled by dusting with sulfur.

DESERT–CANDLE (*Eremurus*)

Leaf Spot. **Myrothecium roridum,** Ohio.

DESERT–PLUME (*Stanleya pinnata*)

Leaf Spot. **Cercospora nasturtii,** Kans.
Rust. **Puccinia aristidae,** Col., Nev.

DESERT–WILLOW (*Chilopsis*)

Leaf Spot. **Phyllosticta erysiphoides.**
Rot, Root. **Phymatotrichum omnivorum,** Tex.

DEUTZIA

Leaf Spot. **Cercospora deutziae,** Del., Iowa; **Phyllosticta deutziae,** Ala., Iowa, N. J.
Nematode, Root Knot. **Heterodera marioni,** Miss.

DEVILS–CLUB (*Oplopanax horridum*)

Blight, Gray Mold. **Botrytis cinerea,** Alaska.
Leaf Spot. **Cercospora daemonicola,** Oreg.

DEWBERRY (*Rubus*)

Anthracnose. **Elsinoë veneta,** general.
Bacterial, Crown Gall. **Agrobacterium tumefaciens,** general.
Black Mildew. **Irenina sanguinea,** Ala., La.
Blight, Cane; Dieback. **Leptosphaeria coniothyrium,** general; **L. thomasiana,** Oreg., Wash.
Blight, Spur. **Didymella applanata,** Oreg., Wash.
Blight, Stamen; Dry Berry. **Hapalosphaeria deformans.**
Blotch, Sooty. **Gloeodes pomigena.**
Canker; Fruit Rot. **Glomerella cingulata,** Ga., Ill., Md., Miss.
Canker; Cane Spot. **Ascospora ruborum,** Ala., Cal.
Downy Mildew. **Peronospora rubi,** Fla., Md., Wis., Wash.; **P. potentillae,** Conn., Ill.
Fruit Spot; Flyspeck. **Leptothyrium pomi,** N. C.
Leaf Gall, Yellow. **Synchytrium aureum,** Wis.
Leaf Spot; Blotch. **Mycosphaerella confusa,** N. J. to Fla., Tex., Ill.; **Pezizella oenotherae,** Md. to N. C.; **Phyllosticta ruborum,** N. Y.; **P. dispergens,** Ill.; **Septoria rubi,** general.
Powdery Mildew. **Sphaerotheca humuli,** Ill., Minn., Ind., Ohio, Pa., Pacific Northwest.
Rosette; Double Blossom. **Cercosporella rubi,** N. Y. to Ala., La., Miss., Tex.

ROT, Fruit. **Botrytis cinerea; Phyllostictina carpogena,** Md., N. J., N. Y., N. C.

ROT, Collar. **Rhizoctonia solani,** Wash.

ROT, Root. **Armillaria mellea,** Oreg.; **Collybia dryophila,** N. C.; **Corticium galactinum,** Md., Va., Tex.; **Helicobasidium purpureum,** N. C., Tex.; **Phymatotrichum omnivorum,** Tex.

RUST, **Gymnoconia peckiana,** orange rust (O, I, III), Me. to Va., Mo. and Minn.; **Kuehneola uredinis,** yellow rust (O, I, II, III), Me. to Fla., Tex., Kans., Cal.; **Kunkelia nitens,** orange rust (I), Cal., Ore.; Conn. to Fla., Tex., Iowa.

VIRUS, Raspberry Mosaic. **Marmor rubi,** Conn., Mich., N. J., N. Y., Ohio.

VIRUS, Blackberry Dwarf. **Nanus loganobacci,** Oreg., Wash.

VIRUS, Raspberry Leaf-Curl. **Corium rubi,** Mich., Ohio.

WILT. **Verticillium albo-atrum,** Cal., Oreg., Wash.

DIANTHUS (Garden Pinks)

See also Carnation and Sweet William.

BLIGHT; Stem Rot. **Alternaria dianthi,** widespread.

BLIGHT, Gray Mold. **Botrytis cinerea,** Alaska.

BLIGHT, Southern. **Sclerotium rolfsii,** Conn., Fla., N. C., Ill., Tex.

LEAF SPOT. **Ascochyta dianthi,** N. Y., Miss.; **Heterosporium echinulatum,** Cal., N. Y., Oreg.; **Phyllosticta** sp., Wash.; **Septoria dianthi,** Ala., Mich., Miss., N. C., N. Y., N. J.

RUST. **Uromyces caryophyllinus** (II, III).

DICHONDRA

BLIGHT, Southern. **Sclerotium rolfsii,** Cal.

LEAF GALL. **Synchytrium edgertonii,** La.

NEMATODE, Root Knot. **Heterodera marioni,** Cal.

RUST. **Puccinia dichondrae** (I, III), La., Miss., N. C., Tex.

DIEFFENBACHIA

BACTERIAL LEAF SPOT. **Xanthomonas dieffenbachiae,** N. J.

LEAF SPOT; Anthracnose. **Glomerella cincta** (imperfect stage *Colletotrichum* or *Gloesporium* sp.) N. J.; **Cephalosporium dieffenbachiae,** N. Y., Fla.

ROT, Root. **Pythium**sp., Fla., **Rhizoctonia** sp., Fla.

ROT, Stem. **Phytophthora palmivora,** Cal.

Dip cane cuttings in Fermate and root in sterilized sand.

DIERVILLA (Bush-Honeysuckle)

LEAF SPOT. **Cercospora weigeliae,** Me.; **Phyllosticta diervillae,** Tex.; **Septoria diervillae,** New England to Iowa; **Ramularia diervillae,** New England to Wis.; **R. umbrina,** Wis.

NEMATODE, Root Knot. **Heterodera marioni,** Fla.

Powdery Mildew. **Microsphaera alni,** N. J., Wash.
Rot, Root. **Phymatotrichum omnivorum,** Tex.

DILL (*Anethum graveolens*)

Damping-Off. **Rhizoctonia solani,** Ga.
Dodder. **Cuscuta** sp., Ga.
Leaf Spot; Stem Spot. **Phoma anethi,** Conn., Ind., Iowa.
Nematode, Root Knot. **Heterodera marioni,** Fla.
Rot, Root. **Phymatotrichum omnivorum,** Tex.
Rot, Stem. **Sclerotinia sclerotiorum,** Tex.
Virus, Aster Yellows. **Chlorogenus callistephi,** N. Y., Tex.

DITTANY, Stone Mint (*Cunila*)

Leaf Spot. **Septoria cunillae,** Ill.
Rust. **Puccinia menthae** (O, I, II, III), N. Y. to Va., Ark., Ill.

DODECATHEON (Shooting-Star, American Cowslip)

Leaf Spot. **Phyllosticta dodecathei,** Wis.
Rust. **Puccinia melanconioides** (O, I, III), Cal., Oreg.; **P. ortonii** (O, I, II, III), Cal., Oreg., S. Dak., Utah, Wash.; **P. solheimii** (III), Wyo.; **Uromyces acuminatus** var. **steironematis,** Nebr., N. Dak.; II, III on marshgrass.

DOGWOOD (*Cornus*)

Anthracnose, Spot. **Elsinoë corni,** Ga., N. and S. C., Md., Va.
Black Mildew. **Dimerosporium pulchrum** and **Meliola nidulans,** Southeast.
Blight, Flower and Leaf. **Botrytis cinerea,** N. J., N. Y.
Blight, Thread. **Pellicularia koleroga,** La.
Blight, Twig. **Myxosporium everhartii,** Mich., Tenn.; **Cryptostictis** sp., N. J.; **Sphaeropsis** sp., N. Y.
Canker, Crown; Bleeding Canker; Collar Rot. **Phytophthora cactorum,** Mass., N. J., N. Y.
Canker, Felt Fungus. **Septobasidium** spp., Va. to Fla. and La.
Canker, **Botryosphaeria ribis,** Pa.; **Cytospora** sp., Kans., N. J.; **Leptosphaeria** sp., Eastern States to Col.
Leaf Spot. **Phyllosticta globifera,** N. J. to Ind., Tenn.; **Ascochyta cornicola,** Ohio, Wis.; **Cercospora cornicola,** Southern States; **Ramularia gracilipes,** Wis.; **Septoria cornicola,** general, but not reported on pink dogwood; **S. floridae,** Ill.
Physiogenic Scorch. Water deficiency, frequent in Southeast.
Powdery Mildew. **Microsphaera alni,** widespread; **Phyllactinia corylea,** widespread.
Rot, Root. **Armillaria mellea,** N. Y., Wash.; **Clitocybe tabescens,** Fla.; **Phymatotrichum omnivorum,** Tex.; **Corticium galactinum,** Md.

Rot, Wood. **Daedalea confragosa,** Md. to Tenn.; **Fomes scutellatus,** Md.; **Polyporus** spp.; **Poria vaporaria; Stereum purpureum,** N. Y.

The most serious dogwood disease in the East is crown or bleeding canker which attacks trees after transplanting or some injury. In a wet season Botrytis blight is conspicuous as flowers fade and petals rot onto leaves. Septoria leaf spot may cause rather heavy defoliation in a rainy spring or summer. In wet seasons spot anthracnose badly disfigures leaves, twigs, berries.

DWARF DOGWOOD, BUNCHBERRY (*Cornus canadensis*)

Leaf Spot. **Phyllosticta** sp., N. Y.; **Ramularia** sp., N. Y.; **Septoria canadensis,** Wash., Alaska.

Powdery Mildew. **Phyllactinia corylea,** Wash.

Rust. **Puccinia porphyrogenita** (III), general.

PACIFIC DOGWOOD (*Cornus nuttalli*)

Canker, Trunk. **Nectria coccinea.**

Canker, Crown. **Phytophthora cactorum,** Wash.

Powdery Mildew. **Phyllactinia corylea,** general.

Rot, Heart. **Fomes igniarius,** Oreg.

DOLICHOS (Twinflower, Hyacinth-Bean)

Black Mildew. **Parodiella perisporoides,** N. C.

Leaf Spot. **Cercospora canescens,** Fla.

Nematode, Root Knot. **Heterodera marioni,** Fla., S. C.

Powdery Mildew. **Microsphaera euphorbiae,** Ind.

Rot, Root. **Phymatotrichum omnivorum,** Tex.

Virus, Mosaic. Unidentified, Mich.

DORONICUM (Leopards-Bane)

Nematode, Root Knot. **Heterodera marioni,** Cal., Md.

Powdery Mildew. **Erysiphe** sp., Cal.

DOUGLAS–FIR (*Pseudotsuga*)

Bacterial Gall. **Bacterium pseudotsugae,** Cal.

Blight, Brown Felt. **Herpotrichia nigra,** Rockies and Pacific Northwest.

Blight, Gray Mold, Twig; Snow Mold. **Botrytis cinerea,** cosmopolitan.

Blight, Snow. **Phacidium infestans,** Ida.

Blight, Seedling. **Rhizina undulata,** Pacific Northwest.

Canker, Bark. **Chondropodium pseudotsugae,** Oreg.; **Cryptosporium boycei,** Wash., probably secondary; **Aleurodiscus** sp., weakly parasitic.

Canker, Branch, Trunk. **Dasyscypha pseudotsugae,** Cal. to Wash.; **Phomopsis lokoyae,** Pacific Coast.

Canker, Twig. **Cytospora** sp., Col., N. J., Oreg.; **Dasyscypha ellisiana,** Mass., N. C.

Damping-Off. **Pythium ultimum,** Col.; **Rhizoctonia solani,** cosmopolitan. **Fusarium** spp., cosmopolitan.

Dieback; Collar Rot; Seedling Blight. **Sphaeropsis ellisii,** Cal., Kans., N. J., N. Y.

Mistletoe; Witches' Broom. **Arceuthobium douglasii,** Mont. to Col., Oreg., Wash.

Needle Cast. **Adelopus gaumanni,** Pacific States, Northeast; **Rhabdocline pseudotsugae,** probably general in host range. **Rhabdogloeum hypophyllum,** Ariz., N. Mex.

Rot, Root. **Armillaria mellea,** cosmopolitan.

Rot, White Pocket. **Hydnum coralloides,** sometimes on living trees, Pacific Northwest.

Rot, Heart, Sapwood. **Echinodontium tinctorium; Fomes** spp.; **Polyporus** spp.; **Lenzites saepiaria,** widespread; **Poria** spp.; **Stereum** spp.; **Trametes** spp.

Rust. **Melampsora albertensis** (O, I), Mont. to Col., Utah, Wash.; II, III on poplar.

Needle cast, caused by Adelopus, is an endemic disease in the Pacific States, where it is relatively noninjurious, but it is becoming a serious disease on ornamental trees in New England.

DRACAENA

Blight, Tip. **Physalospora dracaenae,** W. Va.; **P. rhodina,** Md.

Leaf Spot. **Glomerella cincta,** general; **Phyllosticta dracaenae,** Ohio, Pa.; **P. maculicola,** N. J.; **Lophodermium dracaenae,** Cal.

Nematode, Root Knot. **Heterodera marioni,** Fla.

Rot, Root. **Phytophthora** sp., N. J.

DRAGONHEAD (*Dracocephalum*)

Blight, Southern. **Sclerotium rolfsii,** Ill., Tex.

Leaf Spot. **Phyllosticta dracocephali,** Tex.; **Septoria dracocephali,** Tex., Wis.

DUTCHMAN'S-BREECHES, SQUIRREL-CORN (*Dicentra*)

Downy Mildew. **Peronospora dicentrae,** Ind., Md., Mich., Mo., N. Y., Va., Wis.

Rust. **Cerotelium dicentrae** (O, I), N. Y. to Md., Kans., S. Dak.; II, III on wood-nettle.

DUTCHMANS-PIPE (*Aristolochia*)

Leaf Spot. **Botrytis cinerea,** Conn., Md.; **Cercospora guttulata,** W. Va., Ill.; **C. serpentariae,** Ala., Conn., Del.; **Gloeosporium** sp., Mass.; **Ovularia aristolochiae,** W. Va.; **Phyllosticta aristolochiae,** N. J.

Rot, Root. **Diplodia radicicola,** Va.

DYSCHORISTE

RUST. **Aecidium tracyanum** (O, I), Fla.

ECHEVERIA

NEMATODE, Root Knot. **Heterodera marioni,** Cal.
RUST. **Puccinia echeveriae** (III), Cal.

ECHINACEA (Purple Coneflower)

LEAF SPOT. **Cercospora rudbeckii,** Iowa; **Septoria lepachydis,** Wis.
VIRUS, Mosaic. Unidentified, N. Y.

EGGPLANT (*Solanum melongena*)

ANTHRACNOSE. **Colletotrichum** spp.; **Gloeosporium melongenae,** N. J. to Fla., Tex., Iowa.
BACTERIAL Soft Rot. **Erwinia carotovora,** N. J.
BACTERIAL Wilt. **Pseudomonas solanacearum,** general.
BLIGHT, Phomopsis; Fruit Rot. **Phomopsis vexans,** general.
BLIGHT, Early. **Alternaria solani,** occasional, N. Y. to Fla., Va., Wis.
BLIGHT, Late. **Phytophthora infestans,** Fla., N. Y.
BLIGHT, Southern. **Sclerotium rolfsii,** Va. to Fla. and Tex.
DAMPING-OFF. **Pythium debaryanum,** Conn., La., N. Y.; **Rhizoctonia solani,** also stem and fruit rot, general.
DODDER. **Cuscuta** sp.
DOWNY MILDEW. **Peronospora tabacina,** S. C.
FRUIT SPOT. **Diplodia natalensis,** Fla.
LEAF SPOT. **Ascochyta lycopersici,** Del., Ill., Ind., N. Y.; **Cercospora melongenae,** Cal.; **Phyllosticta solani,** La.; **Septoria lycopersici,** Ind., Md., N. C., Va.; **Stemphylium solani,** Fla.
NEMATODE, Root. **Pratylenchus pratensis,** Tex.
NEMATODE, Root Knot. **Heterodera marioni,** general in Southeast.
POWDERY MILDEW. **Erysiphe cichoracearum,** N. J., Va.
ROT, Charcoal. **Macrophomina phaseoli,** N. J.
ROT, Cottony Leak. **Pythium aphanidermatum,** Cal., Fla.
ROT, Fruit. **Colletotrichum truncatum,** Miss.; **Phytophthora parasitica,** Fla., Ind.; **Rhizopus stolonifer,** Cal., Ind., Tex.
ROT, Gray Mold. **Botrytis cinerea,** Cal., Conn., Mass., N. J., Va., Wash.
ROT, Root. **Phymatotrichum omnivorum,** Tex.
ROT, Stem. **Sclerotinia sclerotiorum,** Cal., Fla., Ind., La., Oreg., Tex.
?VIRUS, Bunchy Top. Suspected virus, Tex.
VIRUS, Curly Top. **Ruga verrucosans,** Oreg., Tex., Wash.
VIRUS, Cucumber Mosaic. **Marmor cucumeris.**
VIRUS, Yellows. Unidentified, Fla., La., Okla., S. C., Tex.

WILT. **Fusarium** sp.; **Verticillium albo-atrum,** general.

Phomopsis blight and Verticillium wilt are the two most important eggplant diseases. Treat seed before planting and, for wilt, use a long rotation that does not include tomatoes, potatoes, or raspberries. Copper sprays or dusts are used for blight.

ELAEAGNUS (Russian Olive, Silverberry)

BACTERIAL Hairy Root. **Agrobacterium rhizogenes,** Central States.

BLIGHT, Southern. **Sclerotium rolfsii,** Tex.

CANKER, **Nectria cinnabarina,** Cal.; **Fusarium** sp., Wyo.; **Phytophthora** sp., Ill.

LEAF SPOT. **Cercospora carii,** Tex.; **C. elaeagni,** Tex.; **Phyllosticta argyrea,** Md.; **Septoria argyraea,** Iowa, N. and S. Dak., Nebr.; **S. elaeagni,** Kans.

POWDERY MILDEW. **Phyllactinia corylea,** Oreg.

ROT, Root. **Phymatotrichum omnivorum,** resistant or only slightly susceptible to.

RUST. **Puccinia caricis-shepherdiae** (O, I), Northern Plains; II, III Carex; **P. coronata** var. **elaeagni** (O, I), N. Dak.; II, III Calamagrostis.

ELDER (*Sambucus*)

BLIGHT, Thread. **Pellicularia koleroga** (*Corticium stevensii*), La.

BLIGHT, Web. **Corticium microsclerotia** (*Pellicularia filamentosa*), Fla.

CANKER, Branch. **Cytospora sambucicola,** Ill.; **C. chrysosperma.**

CANKER, Twig; Dieback. **Diplodia** spp.; **Nectria cinnabarina,** widespread; **N. coccinea,** Md., Mich., Wash.; **Sphaeropsis sambucina.**

LEAF SPOT. **Ascochyta wisconsina,** Wis., N. Y.; **Cercospora catenospora,** Ala., Kans., Miss.; **C. depazeoides,** Me. to Ala., Kans., N. and S. C., Tex., Wash.; **Cercosporella prolificans,** N. Mex.; **Phyllosticta sambuci,** Mo., N. Y., Wis.; **Ramularia sambucina,** Mo., N. Y., Wis.; **Mycosphaerella** sp., N. Mex.; **Septoria sambucina,** Vt. to Fla., Tex., Cal., Wash., Wis.

POWDERY MILDEW. **Microsphaera alni; M. grossulariae,** widespread; **Phyllactinia corylea,** Mich.; **Sphaerotheca humuli,** Mass.

ROT, Root. **Helicobasidium purpureum,** Tex.; **Phymatotrichum omnivorum,** Tex.; **Xylaria multiplex,** Tex.

ROT, Heart, Wood. **Fomes igniarius,** Idaho; **Hymenochaete agglutinans,** Wyo.; **Polyporus** spp.

RUST. **Puccinia bolleyana** (O, I), Mass. to Ind., Mich.

WILT. **Verticillium albo-atrum.**

ELEPHANTS–EAR (*Colocasia*)

BACTERIAL Soft Rot. **Erwinia carotovora,** Fla.; **E. aroideae,** Fla.

NEMATODE Root Knot. **Heterodera marioni,** Fla.

ROT, Black. **Diplodia** sp., Fla., S. C.

ROT, Powdery Gray. **Fusarium solani,** Fla.

ELM (*Ulmus*)

BACTERIAL Wetwood; Slime flux. **Erwinia nimipressuralis.**

BLACK SPOT. **Gnomonia ulmea,** general.

BLIGHT, Twig. **Septogloeum parasiticum,** Mich.; **Phomopsis oblonga,** Mass.

CANKER, Bleeding. **Phytophthora cactorum,** R. I.

CANKER, Branch. **Botryosphaeria ribis.**

CANKER, Pit. **Phytophthora inflata,** Conn., Mass.

CANKER, Twig; DIEBACK. **Apioporthe apiospora,** Iowa; **Coniothyrium** spp., Ill., Mass., Mich.; **Cytospora ludibunda,** Conn., Pa.; **Nectria coccinea,** N. J., N. Y.; **N. cinnabarina,** coral spot, widespread; **Phoma** sp.; **Phomopsis** sp., Northeastern States to S. C., Ill., Minn.; **Sphaeropsis** sp., Conn. to Miss.

DAMPING-OFF. **Rhizoctonia solani,** cosmopolitan, especially in nurseries; **Pythium** sp., Great Plains States.

DUTCH ELM DISEASE—see under Wilts.

LEAF BLISTER. **Taphrina ulmi,** Conn. to Miss., Mo., Wis.

LEAF SPOT; Twig Blight; Anthracnose. **Gloeosporium inconspicuum,** Mass. to Va., Ga., Kans., Minn., Okla., Tenn., Tex.

LEAF SPOT. **Cercospora sphaeriaeformis,** La., Tex.; **Cylindrosporium tenuisporium,** Tex.; **Coryneum tumoricola,** N. Y.; **Monochaetia desmazierii,** Ga.; **Phyllosticta confertissima,** Pa.; **P. melaleuca,** Miss., Wis.; **Mycosphaerella ulmi,** Mass. to Ala.; **Septogloeum profusum,** Ala.; **Coniothyrium ulmi,** W. Va.

MISTLETOE. **Phoradendron flavescens,** Ind., Tex.

NEMATODE, Root Knot. **Heterodera marioni,** Okla., Tex.

POWDERY MILDEW. **Microsphaera alni,** Ill., Iowa, Miss., Ohio; **Phyllactinia corylea,** N. C. to Tex., Iowa; **Uncinula macrospora,** widespread.

ROT, Root. **Helicobasidium purpureum,** Tex.; **Phymatotrichum omnivorum,** Tex.; **Xylaria** spp.

ROT, Heart. **Collybia velutipes,** widespread; **Daedalea confragosa,** widespread; **Fomes** spp.; **Ganoderma curtisii,** N. Y.

ROT, Wood. **Daldinia concentrica,** widespread; **Lenzites saepiaria,** Ind., Mass., Md.; **Pleurotus ostreatus,** widespread; **Polyporus** spp.; **Schizophyllum commune,** cosmopolitan; **Ustulina vulgaris,** Md.

VIRUS, Phloem Necrosis. **Morsus ulmi,** Ala., Ark., Ga., Ind., Ill., Iowa, Kans., Ky., Miss., Mo., Nebr., Ohio, Okla., Tenn., W. Va.

VIRUS, Mosaic. Undetermined, Ohio.

WILT; Dutch Elm Disease. **Ceratostomella ulmi,** Col., Conn., Ky., Ind., Md., Mass., N. J., N. Y., Ohio, Pa., R. I., ?Tenn., Va., Vt., W. Va., D. C.

WILT, **Deuterophoma ulmi** (*Cephalosporium* sp.)

WILT. **Verticillium** sp., Me. to Va., Oreg., Wis.

"Shall we lose the American elm as we did the chestnut?" is a question not yet answered. Certainly many towns and cities have witnessed stark tragedy in the past twenty years, with phloem necrosis raging along the Ohio River watershed, killing upwards of 75 per cent of the elms in some sections, and Dutch elm disease taking its toll of thousands and thousands and thousands of elms in the East. Certainly also this is no time to admit we are licked and stop trying to protect the elms we have to the best of our ability, or to stop planting new elms, for that is the surest way to provide an elm-less future. With resistant varieties coming along, chemotherapy, control of insect vectors, and sanitary measures available, town officials should not stand idly by and let the rest of the elms die just because disease has gotten a headstart.

The latest advance in chemotherapy, announced at the end of 1949, is the suppression of wilt symptoms by soil treatment with chemicals, urea, salicylate and azo dye, combined with low magnesium lime. The mixture is available for limited use under the name of Carolate, and is promising as a conditioner for healthy elms and those showing not more than 5 per cent wilt.

Verticillium and Deuterophoma wilts may be confused with Dutch elm disease, with accurate diagnosis possible only by laboratory cultures. Black spot causes some defoliation in a wet season.

EMILIA (Tassel-Flower. Floras-Paintbrush)

RUST. **Puccinia emiliae,** Fla.
VIRUS, Mosaic. **Marmor cucumeris,** in part.
VIRUS, Spotted Wilt; Yellow Spot. **Lethum australiense,** Cal.

ENCELIA

RUST. **Puccinia enceliae** (O, I, II, III), Cal.

ENDIVE, ESCAROLE, WITLOOF CHICORY (*Cichorium*)

BACTERIAL Center Rot. **Pseudomonas cichorii,** Ariz., Fla., Mont., Tex., Wash.
BACTERIAL Soft Rot. **Erwinia carotovora,** Mass., N. Y.
BLIGHT, Southern. **Sclerotium rolfsii,** Fla., Tex.
DAMPING-OFF; Bottom Rot. **Rhizoctonia solani,** Conn., Fla., N. Y., Tex.
DOWNY MILDEW. **Bremia lactucae,** Fla., Pa.
LEAF SPOT. **Alternaria** sp., Conn., Fla., N. Y.; **Cercospora cichorii,** Tex.; **Marssonina panattoniana,** Tex.
NEMATODE, Root Knot. **Heterodera marioni,** Tenn.
PHYSIOGENIC Brown Heart; Canker. Boron deficiency, in part. N. J., N. Y.
PHYSIOGENIC Tipburn. High temperature and excessive transpiration.
POWDERY MILDEW. **Erysiphe cichoracearum,** Ida., N. J.
ROT, Watery Soft. **Sclerotinia sclerotiorum,** Ark., Ariz., Cal., Fla., La., Mont., Pa., Tex.
ROT, Root. **Pythium debaryanum,** Conn., Fla.; **Phoma** sp.
ROT, Gray Mold. **Botrytis cinerea,** Cal., Fla., N. Y., Pa.
RUST. **Puccinia hieracii** (O, I, II, III), Cal., Conn., Mass., N. Y.
VIRUS, Mosaic. Unidentified, Fla.

VIRUS, Spotted Wilt. **Lethum australiense,** Cal.
VIRUS, Aster Yellows. **Chlorogenus callistephi,** Col., Ill., Ind., N. J., N. Y., Tex., Wis. and var. **californicus,** Cal.

Control aster yellows with DDT to kill leafhopper vectors. Or use a pyrethrum or rotenone and sulfur dust.

ENGELMANNIA (Engleman Daisy)

LEAF GALL. **Synchytrium taraxaci,** Tex.

ENGLISH DAISY (*Bellis perennis*)

BLIGHT, Gray Mold. **Botrytis cinerea,** Alaska.
LEAF SPOT. **Cercospora** sp., Minn.
NEMATODE, Root Knot. **Heterodera marioni,** Fla.
ROT, Root. **Phymatotrichum omnivorum,** Tex.; **Pythium mastophorum,** Md.
VIRUS, Aster Yellows. **Chlorogenus callistephi,** N. J., N. Y.

ENGLISH IVY (*Hedera helix*)

BACTERIAL SPOT. **Xanthomonas hederae,** Ga., Ill., Md., N. J., N. Y., Va., Wash.
DODDER. **Cuscuta** sp., Ariz., N. J.
LEAF SPOT; Stem Spot; Anthracnose. **Amerosporium trichellum,** Mass. to S. C.; Tex., Okla., Oreg., Wash.
LEAF SPOT. **Glomerella cingulata,** Conn., Md.; **Phyllosticta concentrica,** Mass. to Ala., Tex., Nebr.; **P. hederae,** Del., N. Y.; **P. hedericola,** Cal., Conn., Miss., N. J., N. Y., Oreg.; **Ramularia hedericola,** Tex.
MOLD, Leaf. **Cladosporium brunneolum,** Cal.
PHYSIOGENIC Winter Injury. Sunburn, freezing.
POWDERY MILDEW. **Erysiphe cichoracearum,** Okla.
ROT, Root. **Rhizoctonia solani,** Conn.
SCAB; Spot Anthracnose. **Sphaceloma hederae,** Cal., N. C., Va.
SOOTY MOLD. Common under trees, on insect exudate.

Leaf spots are not often important in the garden, but browning of foliage from winter injury is conspicuous in early spring. English ivy used as a ground cover is often black with sooty mold growing in honeydew dropped from aphids in trees overhead. Dodder sometimes gets a stranglehold and is extraordinarily difficult to eliminate.

EPHEDRA

RUST, Witches' broom. **Peridermium ephedrae** (O, I), Tex. to Utah and Cal.

EPIGAEA (Mayflower, Trailing Arbutus)

LEAF SPOT. **Cercospora epigaeae,** N. Y., N. C., Wis.; **Phyllosticta epigaeae,** Mass., N. Y.
POWDERY MILDEW. **Microsphaera alni** var. **vaccinii,** Conn. to Va. and Wis.

EPILOBIUM (Willow-Herb; Fireweed)

Downy Mildew. **Plasmopara epilobii,** Ill., N. Y.

Leaf Spot. **Cercospora montana,** widespread; **Discosia bubakii,** N. Y., Wis.; **Phyllosticta chamaeneri,** Oreg.; **P. wyomingensis,** Wyo.; **Ramularia cercosporoides,** Mont., Tex., Wash., Wyo.; **R. karstenii,** Col.; **R. punctiformis,** Wis.; **Septoria epilobii,** Cal., Del., Ill., Vt., Wis.

Nematode, Root Knot. **Heterodera marioni.**

Powdery Mildew. **Sphaerotheca humuli,** widespread; **Erysiphe polygoni,** Wash., **Microsphaera** sp., Ill.

Rot, Root. **Phymatotrichum omnivorum,** Tex.

Rust. **Puccinia epilobii** (III), Mich., Wyo.; **P. extensicola** var. **oenotherae** (O, I), Col.; **P. gigantea** (III), Ida., Mont., Tex., Wash., Wyo.; **P. scandica** (III), Utah, Wash., Wyo.; **P. oenotherae** (O, I, II, III), Cal.; **P. vagans** (O, I, II, III), N. Dak. to N. Mex., Cal.; **P. veratri** (O, I), N. H., Mont. to Wash.; **Pucciniastrum pustulatum,** Northeastern States to Pacific Northwest.

Smut, Leaf. **Doassansia epilobii,** Col., N. H.

ERANTHEMUM

Leaf Spot. **Phyllosticta** sp., N. J.

ERIGERON (Fleabane)

Blight, Gray Mold. **Botrytis cinerea,** Alaska.

Downy Mildew. **Basidiophora entospora,** La., Ill.; **Plasmorpara halstedii,** Md., Iowa.

Leaf Gall. **Synchytrium erigerontis,** La.

Leaf Spot. **Cercospora cana,** La.; **Cercosporella colubrina,** Wash.; **Septoria erigerontis,** Me. to Md., Nebr. and Mich.

Powdery Mildew. **Erysiphe cichoracearum,** Col., Mich., Mont., N. Mex., Pa., S. Dak., Wyo.; **Phyllactinia corylea,** Wash.; **Sphaerotheca humuli,** Ind., Ky.

Rot, Stem. **Sclerotium rolfsii,** Ill.

Rust. **Puccinia cyperi** (O, I), Mo.; II, III on sedge; **P. extensicola** var. **erigerontis** (O, I), East, South; **P. grindeliae** (III), Col., Utah, Nev., Wyo.; **P. stipae** (O, I), Col., Wyo.; **Coleosporium solidaginis** (II, III), Cal., Alaska; O, I on pine.

Smut, White. **Entyloma compositarum,** Mich., N. Dak., Utah, Wash., Wis., Wyo.

Virus, Aster Yellows. **Chlorogenus callistephi,** Kans., Md., Miss., N. J., N. Y., Okla.

Virus, Mosaic. Unidentified, Ind.

Wilt. **Verticillium albo-atrum,** Mass.

ERIOGONUM (Buckwheat Vine)

Downy Mildew. **Peronospora** sp., Cal.
Leaf Spot. **Gloeosporium eriogoni,** Col.; **Cercospora eriogoni,** Cal.
Powdery Mildew. **Erysiphe cichoracearum.**
Rust. **Puccinia aristidae** (O, I), Ariz.; II, III on grasses; **Uromyces intricatus,** Ariz., Cal.

ERIOPHYLLUM

Rust. **Puccinia eriophylli** (II, III), Wyo., Oreg. to Cal.; **Uromyces junci** (O, I); II, III on Juncus.

ERYTHRINA (Coral-Tree, Red Cardinal)

Blight, Thread. **Pellicularia** (*Corticium*) **koleroga,** Fla.
Nematode, Root Knot. **Heterodera marioni.**
Rot, Root. **Phymatotrichum omnivorum,** Tex.
Wilt, **Verticillium** sp., Cal.

ERYTHRONIUM (Dog-Tooth Violet, Trout Lily)

Black Spot. **Asteroma tenerrimum** var. **erythronii,** Ida., Mont., Wash.
Blight. **Botrytis** sp., Ill., N. Y., Vt., Wash.
Blight, Leaf. **Ciborinia gracilis,** Ill., Nebr.; **C. erythronii,** N. Y.
Rust. **Uromyces heterodermus** (O, III), Cal., Col., Ida., Mont., Oreg., Utah, Wash., Wyo.
Smut, Leaf. **Urocystis erythronii,** Conn., N. Y.; **Ustilago heufleri,** Del., Md., Mich., Mo., N. J., N. Y., Pa.

EUCALYPTUS (Gum-Tree, Blue Gum)

Bacterial Crown Gall. **Agrobacterium tumefaciens.**
Canker, Felt Fungus. **Septobasidium curtisii,** N. C.
Leaf Spot. **Mycosphaerella molleriana; Phyllosticta extensa.**
Rot, Mushroom Root. **Clitocybe tabescens,** Fla.; **Armillaria mellea,** Cal.
Rot, Heart. **Fomes applanatus,** Cal.
Rot, Butt, Root. **Polyporus schweinitzii; P. sulphureus.**
Rot, Wood. **Polyporus gilvus; P. hirsutus; P. versicolor; Stereum hirsutum.**

Many other fungi may be found on leaves, twigs, and branches but are not reported as causing specific diseases.

EUCHARIS (Amazon Lily)

Blight, Gray Mold, **Botrytis cinerea,** Fla.
Leaf Scorch; Red Blotch. **Stagonospora curtisii,** Cal.

BLACK SPOT. **Asterinella puiggarii,** Fla.
LEAF SPOT. **Pezizella oenotherae,** N. Y.
ROT, Root. **Clitocybe tabescens,** Fla.

EUONYMUS

ANTHRACNOSE. **Gloeosporium frigidum,** Ark., La., Miss., Tex.; **G. griseum,** Gulf States, N. J., N. Y.

BACTERIAL Crown Gall. **Agrobacterium tumefaciens,** Conn., Miss., N. J., Mich., S. C., Tex.

BLIGHT, Thread. **Pellicularia** (*Corticium*) **koleroga,** La.

LEAF SPOT. **Cercospora destructiva,** Va. to Tex.; **C. euonymi,** Pa. to Wis.; **Exosporium concentricum,** Va. to S. C., Gulf States; **Phyllosticta euonymi,** N. Y. to Miss. and Tex.; **P. pallens,** Tex.; **Septoria euonymi,** Miss., Va.; **S. atropurpurei,** Ill.; **S. euonymella,** S. C.; **Ramularia euonymi,** Cal., Iowa, Kans., Mo.; **Marssonina thomasiana,** Ohio to Wis., Mo.

NEMATODE, Root Knot. **Heterodera marioni,** Md.

POWDERY MILDEW. **Microsphaera alni,** N. J. to S. Dak. and South; **Oidium euonymijaponici,** N. J., Iowa, Gulf States, Pacific Coast.

ROT, Root. **Phymatotrichum omnivorum,** Tex.

ROT, Foot. **Fusarium scirpi,** N. J.

The Oidium mildew is prevalent and disfiguring on *Euonymus japonicus* throughout the South and in California. Crown gall is rather common, at least in New Jersey, with conspicuous knobs along the vines, but it is not often fatal.

EUPATORIUM (Mist-flower; White Snakeroot; Joe-Pye Weed, Boneset)

BLIGHT, Gray mold; Canker. **Botrytis cinerea,** N. J.

DOWNY MILDEW. **Plasmopara halstedii,** N. Y. to Md., Kans., Mo., Tex., Wis., W. Va.

LEAF SPOT. **Ascochyta compositarum,** W. Va., Wis.; **Cercospora ageratoides,** Ala., Miss., N. J., Tex., W. Va.; **C. eupatorii,** N. Y.; **C. perfoliata,** Ill., Mich., Wis.; **Phyllosticta decidua,** Wis.; **P. eupatorina,** Ill., N. J.; **Septoria eupatorii,** Ill., Miss., Md., N. J., Tex.; **S. eupatoriicola,** Ill.

NEMATODE, Root Knot. **Heterodera marioni,** Ala.

POWDERY MILDEW. **Erysiphe cichoracearum,** general in East and Central States to Tex. and Minn.

ROT, Root. **Phymatotrichum omnivorum,** Tex.

ROT, Stem. **Sclerotium rolfsii,** Conn., Ill., Md., N. J., Tex.; **Rhizoctonia solani.**

RUST. **Puccinia conoclinii** (II, III), Md. to Fla. and Ala., La., Tex., Ariz., Ill.; O, I, unknown. **P. eleocharidis** (O, I), widespread in Eastern and Central States to Ala., Miss., Tex., Wyo.; II, III on Eleocharis; **P. tolimensis** (III), N. Y.

SMUT, White. **Entyloma compositarum,** Ill., Iowa, Miss., W. Va., Wis.
VIRUS, Yellows. Apparently distinct from aster yellows, Central States.
WILT, **Fusarium** sp., N. J.

The blue eupatorium or mist-flower so common in gardens does best if it is separated each spring. If it grows in too compact, humidity-holding clumps southern blight or stem rot and Botrytis blight may get started. The latter causes a girdling canker toward the base of the stem, followed by wilting of the whole plant.

EUSTOMA (Prairie Gentian, Texas Bluebell)

BLIGHT, Stem. **Alternaria** sp., Tex.; **Sclerophoma eustomonis.**
LEAF SPOT. **Cercospora eustomae,** Col., Nebr., Tex.; **C. nepheloides,** Cal., Tex.; **Phyllosticta** sp., Tex.
ROT, Root. **Fusarium solani,** Tex.

EXACUM

BLIGHT; Stem Canker. **Botrytis cinerea,** Kans.

FARKLEBERRY, SPARKLEBERRY (*Vaccinium arboreum*)

LEAF GALL. **Exobasidium vaccinii,** Ala., Fla.
LEAF SPOT. **Ophiodothella vaccinii,** Md. to Ga., Tex.; **Pestalotia vaccinicola,** Fla.; **Phyllosticta vaccinii,** Ala., Fla., Miss., Tex.; **Septoria albopunctata,** Fla., S. C., Tex.
POWDERY MILDEW. **Microsphaera alni** var. **vaccinii,** Mass. to Ga., Ill.
ROT, Root. **Phymatotrichum omnivorum,** Tex.

FEIJOA

ROT, Fruit. **Botrytis cinerea,** Cal.; **Colletotrichum gloeosporioides,** Cal.; **Penicillium expansum,** Cal.
ROT, Root. **Phymatotrichum omnivorum,** Tex.

FENNEL (*Foeniculum*)

BACTERIAL, Soft Rot. **Erwinia carotovora,** Ill.
DAMPING-OFF; Stem Pitting. **Rhizoctonia solani,** Ga., N. J.
NEMATODE, Root Knot. **Heterodera marioni,** Fla.
ROT, Gray Mold. **Botrytis cinerea,** N. Y.
ROT, Root. **Phymatotrichum omnivorum,** Tex.
ROT, Stem. **Sclerotinia sclerotiorum,** Ill., N. J., Tex.

FERNS

BIRDS-NEST-FERN (*Asplenium*)

LEAF SPOT. **Cercospora** sp., Fla.
NEMATODE, Leaf. **Aphelenchoides olesistus,** Conn., N. J., N. Y., Pa.

BLADDER–FERN (*Cystopteris*)

LEAF BUSTER. **Taphrina cystopteridis,** Kans., Ind., Wis.

RUST. **Hyalospora polypodii** (II, III), general in Northern and Western States; O, I, unknown; **Uredinopsis ceratophora** (II, III), Ind., N. Y., Wis.; O, I, unknown; **U. glabra** (II, III), N. Mex.

BOSTON–FERN (*Nephrolepis*)

ANTHRACNOSE; Tip Blight. **Glomerella nephrolepis,** N. Y., Ohio.

DAMPING-OFF. **Rhizoctonia solani,** Fla.

LEAF SPOT. **Cercospora** sp., Ind.; **Cylindrocladium pteridis,** Fla.

BRAKE–FERN (*Pteris*)

BLIGHT, Tip. **Phyllosticta pteridis,** Miss., N. J.

DAMPING-OFF. **Completoria complens,** N. Y.; **Pythium intermedium,** N. Y.

NEMATODE, Leaf. **Aphelenchoides olesistus,** Conn., N. J., N. Y.

RUST. **Hyalopsora cheilanthis** (II, III), Iowa, Mich., Mont., Wis.; **Milesia darkeri** (II, III), Cal., Oreg.

BRACKEN (*Pteridium*)

LEAF SPOT; Tar Spot; Black Mildew. **Catacauma flabellum,** Ga., Md., N. J., Pa., S. C., Tenn., W. Va., Wis.

LEAF SPOT; Tar Spot, Leafroll Disease. **Cryptomycina pteridis** (imperfect form *Gloeosporium*) Me. to N. C., Ala., Cal., Ga., Ida., Miss., Mont., Iowa, Oreg., Wash., Wis.

LEAF SPOT. **Phyllosticta pteridis,** Me., N. J.

RUST. **Uredinopsis aspera** (II, III), Cal.; **U. macrosperma** (II, III), Ala., Cal., Fla., Ga., Ida., Miss., Mont., N. Mex., Oreg., Wash., Wis.; **U. virginiana** (II, III), N. Y. to N. C., Tenn.; Ga. to Tex.

SCURF, Canker. **Rhizoctonia** sp., Oreg.

CHRISTMAS–FERN (*Polystichum*)

LEAF BLISTER. **Taphrina faulliana,** Oreg.; **T. polystichi,** Me. to N. C. and Tenn.

LEAF SPOT. **Cylindrocladium pteridis,** Fla.

NEMATODE, Leaf. **Aphelenchoides olesistus,** Oreg.

RUST. **Milesia polystichi** (II, III), Ida., Mont., Oreg., Wash.; O, I, unknown. **M. vogesiaca** (II, III), Oreg.

HOLLY–FERN (*Cyrtomium*)

BLIGHT, Gray Mold. **Botrytis cinerea,** Alaska.

DAMPING-OFF, of prothallia. **Completoria complens,** N. Y.

LADY–FERN and SILVERY SPLEENWORT (*Athyrium*)

BLIGHT, Gray Mold. **Botrytis cinerea,** Alaska.
LEAF SPOT. **Septoria asplenii,** Mich.
RUST. **Uredinopsis copelandii** (II, III), Cal.; O, I, unknown; **U. longimucronata** (II, III), Me. to Pa., Wis., Cal., Ida., Mont., Oreg., Wash.; O, I on fir.

MAIDENHAIR FERN (*Adiantum*)

LEAF SPOT. **Mycosphaerella** sp., Fla.

OSMUNDA (Cinnamon, Interrupted and Royal Fern)

LEAF SPOT. **Gloeosporium osmundae,** Mich.
RUST. **Uredinopsis osmundae** (II, III), Northeastern and Great Lakes States to Fla. and Ala.; O, I on balsam fir.
SMUT, inflorescence. **Mykosyrinx osmundae,** N. Y., Mich., Wis.

OSTRICH–FERN (*Pteretis*)

LEAF BLISTER. **Taphrina struthiopteridis,** Wis.
RUST. **Uredinopsis struthiopteridis** (II, III), N. Y., Vt., Wis.; O, I on fir.

POLYPODY (*Polypodium*)

LEAF SPOT. **Alternaria polypodii,** N. Y.; **Cercospora phyllitidis,** Fla.; **Phyllosticta** sp., Va.
NEMATODE, Leaf. **Aphelenchoides olesistus.**
RUST. **Milesia laeviuscula** (II, III), Cal., Oreg., Wash., Alaska; O, I, unknown. **M. polypodophila** (II, III), Conn., Me., Mass., N. H., N. Y., Pa., Tenn., Vt.

SENSITIVE FERN (*Onoclea sensibilis*)

DODDER. **Cuscuta gronovii,** N. Y.
LEAF BLISTER. **Taphrina hiratsukae,** N. Y., Pa.
RUST. **Uredinopsis mirabilis** (II, III), Me. to Va., Nebr. and Minn. O, I on balsam fir.

WALKING–FERN (*Camptosorus*)

LEAF SPOT. **Cercospora camptosori,** Wis.

WOOD–FERN, SHIELD–FERN (*Dryopteris*)

LEAF BLISTER. **Taphrina californica,** Cal.; **T. filicina,** N. Y.; **T. lutescens,** Me., Minn., N. Y., Wis.; **T. fusca,** N. H., Vt., W. Va.; **T. gracilis,** N. Y.
LEAF SPOT. **Cylindrocladium pteridis,** Fla.; tar spot, **Cryptomycina pteridis,** Fla.

LEAF NEMATODE. **Aphelenchoides olesistus.**

RUST. **Hyalopsora aspidiotus** (II, III), Me. to N. C., Wash., Wis.; O, I on fir. **Milesia dilatata** (II, III), Oreg.; O, I, unknown; **M. fructuosa** (II, III), Me., Mass., N. Y., Vt.; O, I, balsam fir; **M. marginalis** (II, III), Mass., N. H., N. Y.; O, I on fir; **Uredinopsis atkinsonii** (II, III), Me. to Miss., Nebr., N. Dak.; O, I on fir; **U. phegopteris** (II, III), Me., N. H., Wis.; O, I, fir.

WOODSIA (Rock-Fern)

RUST. **Hyalopsora polypodii** (II, III), Mich., Ida.; O, I unknown.

WOODWARDIA (Chain-Fern)

RUST. **Uredinopsis arthurii** (II, III), Vt. to Ala., Ind. and Mich.; O, I unknown.

FEVERFEW (*Chrysanthemum parthenium*)

POWDERY MILDEW. **Erysiphe cichoracearum,** N. Y.

ROT; Root and Stem. **Rhizoctonia solani,** Wash.

FIG (*Ficus carica*)

ANTHRACNOSE. **Colletotrichum gloeosporioides,** N. C. to Tex.

BACTERIAL Crown Gall. **Agrobacterium tumefaciens,** Tex.

BLOTCH, LEAF. **Cercospora fici,** N. C. to Fla., Tex.

BLIGHT, Limb. **Corticium salmonicolor,** Gulf States.

BLIGHT, Thread, Leaf. **Pellicularia** (*Corticium*) **koleroga,** Fla., La., Miss.

BLIGHT, Twig. **Fusarium lateritium,** Cal.

BLIGHT, Southern. **Sclerotium rolfsii,** Fla.

CANKER; DIEBACK. **Botryosphaeria ribis; Diplodia sycina,** N. C., Oreg.; **Nectria cinnabarina,** Tex.; **Megalonectria pseudotrichia,** La., Tex.; **Physalospora rhodina,** Ala., Fla., Tex.; **Sclerotinia sclerotiorum,** Cal., Tex.

LEAF SPOT. **Mycosphaerella bolleana,** N. C. to Tex.; **Alternaria** sp., Cal.; **Cladosporium** sp., La.

NEMATODE, Root Knot. **Heterodera marioni,** Southern States to Cal.

NEMATODE, Root. **Pratylenchus musicola; P. pratensis,** Cal.

PHYSIOGENIC Little Leaf. Zinc deficiency, Cal.

ROT, Fruit. **Aspergillus niger,** black mold, Cal., Wash.; **Diplodia natalensis,** Tex.; **Fusarium** sp., Ala., N. C.; **Fusarium moniliforme,** Cal.; **Oospora** sp., sour rot, Tex.; **Rhizopus nigricans,** Cal., Gulf States; **Tricothecium roseum,** Gulf States.

RUST. **Physopella fici** (II), N. C. to Tex.

SOOTY MOLD. **Capnodium** sp., Tex.; **Fumago vagans,** Gulf States.

VIRUS, Fig-Mosaic. **Marmor caricae,** Cal., Tex.

FIG, FLORIDA STRANGLER (*Ficus aurea*)

ANTHRACNOSE. **Colletotrichum gloeosporioides,** Fla.

BACTERIAL Crown Gall. **Agrobacterium tumefaciens,** Fla.

LEAF SPOT. **Ophiodothella fici,** Fla.; **Phlyctaena ficuum,** Fla.; **Phyllosticta physopellae; P. roberti,** Fla.

NEMATODE, Root Knot. **Heterodera marioni.**

ROT, Fruit. **Fusarium moniliforme,** Cal.

RUST. **Physopella fici** (II, III), Fla.

FIGWORT (*Scrophularia*)

DOWNY MILDEW. **Peronospora sordida,** Cal., Ill., N. Y., Va. to Kans.

LEAF SPOT. **Cylindrosporium scrophulariae,** Ill., Okla., Pa.; **Mycosphaerella** sp., Kans.; **Septoria scrophulariae,** Cal., Oreg.; N. Y. to Miss., Col., Wash.

FILBERT. See Hazelnut

FIR (*Abies*)

BLACK MILDEW. **Dimerosporium abietis,** Ida., Oreg., Wash.

BLIGHT, Brown Felt. **Herpotrichia nigra,** on high western firs.

BLIGHT, Snow. **Phacidium infestans,** on snow-covered seedlings in Northeastern States; **P. balsameae; P. abietinellum.**

BLIGHT, Needle; Tar Spot. **Lophodermium piceae** widespread, weakly parasitic.

BLIGHT, Needle Tip. **Rehmiellopsis balsameae,** Northeast; **Cenangium abietis,** Mich.

CANKER. **Cytospora pinastri,** Me., Wis.; **Cryptosporium macrospermum,** New England; **Dasyscypha resinaria,** Minn.; **Gloeosporium balsameae,** Wis.; **Phomopsis boycei,** Ida., Mont.; **Phoma abietina,** Ida., Mont., Wash.; **Scoleconectria balsamea,** Mich., Minn., N. Y., Pa.; **S. scolecospora,** widespread; **Scleroderris abieticola,** Oreg.; **Sphaeropsis abietis,** Mich.

MISTLETOE, Dwarf; Witches' Broom. **Arceuthobium campylopodium,** widespread in West.

NEEDLE CAST. **Bifusella abietis,** Ida., Mont., Wash.; **B. faullii,** Me., Mich., N. H.; **Hypodermella mirabilis,** Mich., N. Y.; **H. nervata,** Me., N. H., Vt.; **Lophodermium autumnale,** Mich.; **L. lacerum,** N. H., N. Y., Pa., Vt.

ROT, Mushroom Root. **Armillaria mellea,** general.

ROT, Heart. **Stereum sanguinolentum,** widespread on standing trees; **Polyporus sulphureus,** general.

ROT, Trunk, Butt, Wood. **Fomes** spp.; **Echinodontium tinctorium; Hydnum balsameum; Polyporus** spp.; **Poria subacida.**

RUST, Fir-Fern. **Milesia fructuosa** (O, I), Me., N. H., N. Y., on new needles; II, III on *Dryopteris spinulosa;* **M. marginalis** (O, I), Mass., on new needles; II, III on *Dryopteris marginalis;* **M. polypodophila** (O, I), Me., N. Y., N. H., on 3- to 9-year needles; II, III on Polypodium; **Hyalopsora aspidiotus** (O, I), northern host range on 2-year needles; II, III on *Dryopteris linnaeana;* **Uredinopsis mirabilis** (O, I) general on new needles; II, III on *Onoclea sensibilis;* **U. osmundae** (O, I) on new needles; II, III on *Osmunda* sp.; **U. struthiopteridis** (O, I), Mich., on new needles; II, III on *Pteris struthiopteris;* **U. phegopteris** (O, I), new needles; II, III *Dryopteris linnaeana.*

RUST, Fir-Fireweed. **Pucciniastrum pustulatum** (I), widespread; II, III on Epilobium.

RUST, Fir-Huckleberry. **Pucciniastrum goeppertianum** (I), widespread on western firs; II, III on Vaccinium.

RUST, Fir-Willow. **Melampsora abieti-capraearum** (I), widespread on new needles; II, III on willow.

RUST, Needle. **Caeoma faulliana,** Oreg.; **Peridermium ornamentale,** Ida., Mont., Oreg., Wash.; **P. rugosum.**

RUST; Witches' Broom. **Melampsorella cerastii** (I), general; II, III on chickweed.

Despite this long list of possibilities the gardener should not have much trouble with ornamental firs. Rehmiellopsis tip blight yellows needles of new growth and causes twig dieback of native balsam firs and white and Colorado firs in the Northeast, but it can be controlled by spraying with bordeaux mixture. This will also aid in the control of needle cast diseases. Avoid bark and branch injuries to prevent cankers. Rust is taken care of, if necessary, by eliminating the proper alternate host, but only an expert mycologist can identify the many different rust species.

FLAX, FLOWERING (*Linum*)

DAMPING-OFF. **Rhizoctonia solani,** Ill.

NEMATODE, Root Knot. **Heterodera marioni,** Cal.

ROT, Stem. **Sclerotinia sclerotiorum,** Cal.

FOAM–FLOWER (*Tiarella*)

RUST. **Puccinia heucherae** (III), Conn. to N. C. and Tenn., Col., Mich., Wis.; Cal., Ida., Mont., Oreg., Wash., Alaska.

FORESTIERA (Swamp Privet)

MISTLETOE. **Phoradendron flavescens,** Tex.; **P. villosum,** Oreg., Cal.

POWDERY MILDEW. **Microsphaera alni,** Ill., Tex.

RUST. **Coleosporium minutum** (II, III), Fla., Tex.; O, I on pine; **Puccinia peridermiospora** (O, I), Fla., Tex.; II, III on marsh grass.

FORGET–ME–NOT (*Myosotis*)

BLIGHT, Gray Mold. **Botrytis cinerea,** cosmopolitan.

DOWNY MILDEW. **Peronospora myosotidis,** Ill., Mich., Miss., Wis.

ROT, Crown. **Sclerotinia sclerotiorum,** Ill., Wash.

RUST. **Puccinia eatoniae** var. **myosotidis** (O, I), Ill., Ind., Miss., Mo., N. C., Wis.; II, III on grass.

?VIRUS, Chlorosis. Suspected aster yellows.

FORSYTHIA

BACTERIAL Crown Gall. **Agrobacterium tumefaciens,** Miss., N. J., Tex.

BLIGHT, Blossom, Twig. **Sclerotinia sclerotiorum,** N. C.

BLIGHT, Southern. **Sclerotium rolfsii,** Ga.

CANKER, Stem Gall. **Phomopsis** sp., Ky.

LEAF SPOT. **Alternaria** sp., Iowa; **Phyllosticta discincola,** Md.; **P. forsythiae,** Conn.; **P. terminalis,** Fla., Tex.

ROT, Root. **Phymatotrichum omnivorum,** Tex.

FOUQUIERIA (Ocotillo, Coachwhip Cactus)

ROT, Root. **Phymatotrichum omnivorum,** Tex.

RUST. **Aecidium cannonii** (O, I), Ariz.

FOUR-O'CLOCK (*Mirabilis*)

LEAF SPOT. **Cercospora mirabilis,** Tex.

NEMATODE, Root Knot. **Heterodera marioni,** Fla.

ROT, Root. **Phymatotrichum omnivorum,** Tex.

RUST, **Aecidium mirabilis** (O, I), Ariz., N. Mex.; **Puccinia aristidae** (O, I); II, III on wild grasses.

VIRUS, Curly Top. **Ruga verrucosans,** Cal.

WHITE RUST. **Albugo platensis,** Tex.

FOXGLOVE (*Digitalis*)

ANTHRACNOSE. **Colletotrichum fuscum,** Conn., Mass., Oreg.

LEAF SPOT. **Phyllosticta digitalis,** N. Y., Tex.; **Ramularia variabilis,** Oreg.

NEMATODE, Stem and Leaf. **Ditylenchus dipsaci,** Conn.

NEMATODE, Root Knot. **Heterodera marioni,** Cal.

ROT, Root and Stem. **Rhizoctonia solani,** N. J.; **Fusarium** sp., Cal., N. H.

ROT, Stem; Wilt. **Sclerotinia sclerotiorum,** N. Y.; **Sclerotium rolfsii,** Ind., N. J., Tex.

WILT. **Verticillium albo-atrum,** N. Y.

FREESIA

BACTERIAL Scab. **Pseudomonas marginata,** Wash.

LEAF SPOT. **Heterosporium iridis,** Conn.

NEMATODE, Root Knot. **Heterodera marioni,** Cal.

ROT, Root, Corm; Wilt. **Fusarium** spp., Cal., Fla., Tex.

Rot, Dry. **Stromatinia gladioli,** N. J., N. Y.
Rot, Blue Mold. **Penicillium** sp.
"Rust." Cause unknown, but not true rust, Cal.
Virus, Mosaic. **Marmor iridis,** Cal.

Fusarium corm rot causes wilting and death. Corms should be inspected before planting and all those showing pinkish lesions should be discarded.

FREMONTIA

Leaf Spot. **Hendersonia fremontiae,** Cal.; **Septoria angularis.**
Rot, Stem. **Phytophthora cactorum,** Cal.
Wilt. **Verticillium albo-atrum,** Cal.

FRINGE-TREE (*Chionanthus*)

Leaf Spot. **Cercospora chionanthi,** N. J. to N. Car., W. Va.; **Phyllosticta chionanthi,** N. J.; **Septoria chionanthi; S. eleospora,** S. C., Tex.
Powdery Mildew. **Phyllactinia corylea,** Md.
Rot, Wood. **Daedalea confragosa,** Md.

FRITILLARIA

Leaf Spot. **Phyllosticta fritillariae,** Cal.
Rust. **Uromyces miurae** (III), Wash.
Virus, Mosaic. Undetermined.

FROEHLICHIA

Leaf Spot. **Cercospora crassoides,** Wis.
Nematode, Root Knot. **Heterodera marioni,** Fla.
White Rust. **Albugo froehlichiae,** Nebr., Tex.

FROSTWORT (*Crocanthemum*)

Leaf Spot. **Cylindrosporium eminens,** Wis.

FUCHSIA

Blight, Gray Mold. **Botrytis cinerea,** W. Va., Alaska.
Dieback. **Phomopsis** sp., Va.
Leaf Spot. **Septoria** sp., Okla.
Nematode, Root Knot. **Heterodera marioni,** Cal., Md., Oreg.
Rot, Rootlet. **Pythium rostratum** and **P. ultimum,** Cal.
Rust. **Uredo fuchsiae** (II), Ohio.
Virus, Spotted Wilt. **Lethum australiense,** Cal.
Wilt. **Verticillium** sp., Cal.

Verticillium wilt is common in garden plantings of fuchsia in California.

GAILLARDIA

LEAF SPOT. **Septoria gaillardiae,** Iowa, Okla., Tex.

POWDERY MILDEW. **Erysiphe cichoracearum,** Mont., Tex.; **Sphaerotheca humuli** var. **fuliginea,** Mont., Wash., Wyo.

ROT, Root. **Phymatotrichum omnivorum,** Tex.

RUST. **Puccinia gaillardiae** (O, I), Cal.; II, III unknown.

SMUT, White. **Entyloma polysporum,** Minn., Kans., Nebr.

VIRUS, Spotted Wilt. **Lethum australiense,** Cal.

VIRUS, Aster Yellows. **Chlorogenus callistephi** var. **californicus,** Cal

GALAX

BLACK SPOT. **Clypeolella leemingii,** Md. to Ga., Tenn.

LEAF SPOT. **Pezizella oenotherae,** N. C., Tenn.; **Phyllosticta galacis,** N. C., Va., W. Va.; **Laestadia galactina,** N. C.

GALIUM (Bedstraw, False Babys-Breath)

DOWNY MILDEW. **Peronospora calotheca,** Iowa, N. Dak., Wis.

LEAF SPOT. **Cercospora galii,** Ala., Iowa, N. H., N. Y., Oreg., Alaska; **Pseudopeziza repanda,** Cal., Conn., Ga., Ill., Iowa, N. Dak., N. Y., Oreg., Wis.; **Septoria cruciatae,** Ind., Mich., N. J., N. Y., Wis., W. Va.

POWDERY MILDEW. **Erysiphe cichoracearum,** Cal., Mont., Oreg., Pa., Wash.; **E. polygoni,** Kans.

ROT, Root. **Phymatotrichum omnivorum,** Tex.

RUST. **Puccinia difformis** (O, I, III), Ohio to Kans.; Mont., Pacific Coast; **P. punctata** (O, I, II, III), Conn., N. C., Miss., N. Dak. to Cal., Wash.; **P. punctata** var. **troglodytes,** II, III, Conn. to Mo. and S. Dak., Wash.; **Uromyces galii-californici** (II, III), Cal.; O, I, unknown.

GALTONIA (Summer Hyacinth)

VIRUS, Mosaic. **Marmor scillearum.**

GARDENIA (Cape-Jasmine)

BACTERIAL Leaf Spot. **Pseudomonas gardeniae,** N. J.; **Phytomonas** (*Xanthomonas?*) **maculifolium-gardeniae,** Cal.

BLIGHT; Bud Rot. **Botrytis cinerea,** chiefly in greenhouse; outdoors, Cal.

CANKER, Stem Gall. **Phomopsis gardeniae,** Cal.

LEAF SPOT, Algal. **Cephaleuros virescens,** Gulf States; **Phyllosticta** sp., Miss., N. J., Tex.; **Rhizoctonia** sp., N. J.; **Mycosphaerella gardeniae.**

NEMATODE, Root Knot. **Heterodera marioni,** general.

PHYSIOGENIC Bud Drop. Excessive soil moisture and temperature fluctuation.

Physiogenic Chlorosis. Decrease in soil temperature; unfavorable pH.
Powdery Mildew. **Erysiphe polygoni,** Tex.
Rot, Root. **Phymatotrichum omnivorum,** Tex.
Sooty Mold. **Capnodium** sp., Gulf States.

In the Deep South gardenia foliage is almost always disfigured with sooty mold growing in whitefly honeydew, unless the insects are controlled. Gardenias are difficult house plants, frequently dropping their buds in uneven humidity and temperature relations. Substituting the more resistant veitchii variety for susceptible Belmont and Hadley is one way of avoiding Phomopsis canker. The other is care in handling and potting plants, since the fungus enters only through wounds.

GARLIC (*Allium sativum*)

Subject to diseases of Onion, which see. White rot is recently serious in Louisiana; pink root is a common problem.

GARRYA (Silk-Tassel Bush)

Leaf Spot. **Cercospora garryae,** Cal., Tex.; **Phyllosticta garryae,** Cal., Tex.
Rot, Root. **Phymatotrichum omnivorum,** Tex.

GAULTHERIA (Wintergreen, Checkerberry)

Black Mildew. **Meliola nidulans,** Cal.
Leaf Gall, Red. **Synchytrium vaccinii,** N. J.
Leaf Spot. **Cercospora gaultheriae,** N. J., Wis.; **Discosia maculicola,** N. J.; **Mycosphaerella gaultheriae,** Cal., Oreg., Wash., Me. to Md.; **Phyllosticta gaultheriae,** Me. to Va., Cal. to Wash.; **P. shallon,** Wash.; **Pestalotia gibbosa,** Cal., Oreg., Wash.; **Schizothyrium gaultheriae,** Me. to Va. and Wis.; **Venturia gaultheriae,** Mass., N. J., N. Y., Wis.
Powdery Mildew. **Microsphaera alni,** Md.

GAURA

Downy Mildew. **Peronospora arthuri,** Kans., Nebr.
Leaf Gall. **Synchytrium fulgens,** Tex.
Leaf Spot. **Cercospora gaurae,** N. Y., Okla., Tex.; **Septoria gaurina,** Ill., Kans., N. Dak., Nebr., N. Mex., Okla., Tex.; **S. oenotherae,** Tex.
Powdery Mildew. **Erysiphe polygoni,** Col., Tex.
Rot, Root. **Phymatotrichum omnivorum,** Tex.
Rust. **Puccinia extensicola** var. **oenotherae** (O, I), Col., Nebr., Tex.; II, III on Carex; **Uromyces plumbarius** (O, I, II, III), N. Y. to Va., Mont. to Miss., N. Dak., Wis., Tex.
Virus Aster yellows. **Chlorogenus callistephi** var. **californicus,** Cal.

GENTIAN (*Gentiana*)

Blight; Stem canker. **Botrytis cinerea,** N. Y.

Leaf Spot. **Asteromella andrewsii,** Del., Ill., Iowa, Nebr., N. J., Pa., W. Va., Wis. (probably conidial stage of **Mycosphaerella andrewsii**), Del., N. Dak., Wis.; **Cercospora gentianae,** N. Dak., N. Y., Vt.

Rot, Root. **Fusarium solani,** Md.

Rust. **Puccinia gentianae** (O, I, II, III), N. Y. to Ind., Nebr., Minn., Western States to Cal., Wash., Alaska; **P. haleniae,** Wyo.; **Uromyces gentianae** (II, III), Col., Iowa, Nev., N. Mex., Wash., Wyo., N. C., Vt.; O, I, unknown.

GERANIUM, FLORISTS (*Pelargonium*)

Bacterial Crown Gall. **Agrobacterium tumefaciens,** Mass., Md.

Bacterial Fasciation. **Corynebacterium fascians,** Mass., Ohio.

Bacterial Leaf Spot. **Pseudomonas erodii,** Ala., Fla., Miss., Mo., Tex., occasional in North; **Xanthomonas pelargonii,** Mass. to Va., Miss., Ohio, Col., Wash.

Blight, Blossom; Gray Mold; Cutting Rot. **Botrytis cinerea,** cosmopolitan.

Leaf Spot. **Alternaria** sp., cosmopolitan but probably secondary; **Ascochyta** sp., Conn., N. J.; **Cercospora brunkii,** mostly in South (Fla., Tex.), sometimes Md., Ohio, N. H.; **Pleosphaerulina** sp., Pa.

Mold, Leaf. **Botryosporium pulchrum,** occasional in greenhouses.

Nematode, Leaf. **Aphelenchoides** sp., N. Y.

Physiogenic Oedema, Dropsy. Intumescence. Excessive soil moisture and retarded transpiration.

Rot, Stem, Cutting; Blackleg. **Pythium** spp., cosmopolitan; **Rhizoctonia solani,** cosmopolitan; **Fusarium** sp., Ind., N. Y., Wash.

Rot, Root. **Thielaviopsis basicola,** Conn.

Virus, Curly Top. **Ruga verrucosans,** Cal.

Virus, Leaf Curl; Crinkle. **Marmor pelargonii,** probably general.

Virus, Mosaic. **Marmor cucumeris,** Fla., Ind., Minn., N. J., N. Y., Pa., Wash.

Virus, Spotted Wilt. **Lethum australiense,** Cal., Tex.

Wilt. **Verticillium albo-atrum,** Cal., N. Y.

The dry air of the average home makes foliage diseases due to pathogenic organisms unlikely, but sometimes a water-logged soil and cloudy weather, with less rapid evaporation, lead to the condition known as oedema, small swellings in the leaves, and corky ridges on petioles. Botrytis blight and bacterial leaf spots may be expected in greenhouses unless plants are spaced widely, given proper air circulation, overhead watering kept at a minimum, and all infected plant parts speedily removed. Start cuttings in fresh or sterilized sand to avoid blackleg and other cutting rots. Control virus diseases by roguing.

GERANIUM (Cranesbill)

BACTERIAL LEAF SPOT. **Pseudomonas erodii,** Fla., Ill., Ind., Ore., Tex.; **Xanthomonas geranii,** N. Y.

BLACK SPOT; Black Leaf Speck. **Stigmatea geranii.**

DOWNY MILDEW. **Plasmopara geranii,** N. J. to Fla., Kans., Tex., Mass. to Iowa; Mont., Utah, Wis.

LEAF GALL. **Synchytrium geranii,** La., Okla., Tex.

LEAF SPOT. **Botrytis cinerea,** Kans., Mo.; **Cercospora geranii,** Col., Kans., Iowa, Mo., Mont., N. Y., Tex., Utah, Wis.; **Cylindrosporium** sp., La.; **Dilophosphora geranii,** Wis.; **Pestalozziella subsessilis,** Miss., Mo., N. J., Wis.; **Phyllosticta geranii,** La., Tex.; **Ramularia geranii,** Cal., La., Wash., Wyo.; **Septoria expansa,** Kans., Tex.; **Venturia glomerata,** Cal.; **V. circinans,** Alaska.

POWDERY MILDEW. **Erysiphe polygoni,** Col., Ill., Ind., Ohio, Pa., W. Va., Wis., Wyo.; **Sphaerotheca humuli,** Cal., Mo., Minn., Nebr., Pa., Utah, Wash.

ROT, Root. **Phymatotrichum omnivorum,** Tex.

ROT, Rhizome. **Seaverinia** (*Sclerotinia*) **geranii,** Wis., N. Y.

RUST. **Puccinia leveillei** (III), Col., Mont., Utah, Wash., Wyo.; **P. polygoni-amphibii** (O, I), Conn. to Wis., Mo., Minn., Mont., Kans., Tex.; II, III on Polygonum; **Uromyces geranii** (O, I, II, III), Me., Wyo., Alaska.

VIRUS, Mosaic. **Marmor cucumeris,** Fla.

GERBERA (Transvaal Daisy)

BLIGHT, Gray Mold. **Botrytis cinerea,** Fla., N. Y.

LEAF SPOT; Stem Rot. **Gloeosporium** sp., N. Y.

NEMATODE, Root Knot. **Heterodera marioni,** Ala., Cal., Md., N. C., N. Y.

POWDERY MILDEW. **Erysiphe cichoracearum,** Cal., Okla.

ROT, Root, Stem. **Phytophthora cryptogea** and **P. drechsleri,** Cal., N. J., N. Y.

ROT, Crown. **Sclerotinia sclerotiorum,** Md., N. Y.

GEUM (*Avens*)

DOWNY MILDEW. **Peronospora potentillae,** Cal., Ill., Ind., Iowa, Kans., Neb., Wis.

LEAF GALL. **Synchytrium aureum,** Wis.

LEAF SPOT. **Cercospora gei,** Wis.; **Cylindrosporium gei,** N. H., Wis.; **Marssonina adunca,** Mont., Wash.; **Phyllosticta** sp., Wis., W. Va.; **Ramularia gei,** Wis., Mo.; **Septoria gei,** Ill., Mich., Nebr., Ohio.

NEMATODE, Root Knot. **Heterodera marioni,** Cal.

POWDERY MILDEW. **Erysiphe polygoni,** Alaska; **Sphaerotheca humuli,** Ind., Md., Nebr., N. Dak., Ohio, Wis.

ROT, Root. **Phymatotrichum omnivorum,** Tex.

SMUT, Leaf. **Urocystis waldsteiniae,** Mont., Wash.

RUST. **Puccinia sieversii** (III).

GILIA

LEAF SPOT. **Ramularia giliae,** Oreg.
NEMATODE, Root Knot. **Heterodera marioni,** Cal.
NEMATODE, Root. **Pratylenchus pratensis,** Tex.
POWDERY MILDEW. **Sphaerotheca humuli,** Cal., Tex., Wash.
ROT, Root. **Phymatotrichum omnivorum,** Tex.
RUST. **Puccinia aristidae** (O, I), Ariz., Col.; **P. giliae** (II, III), Ariz., Cal., Col., Neb., Oreg., Wash.; O, I, unknown. **P. plumbaria** (O, I, III), Cal., Col., Nev., Utah, Wyo.; **P. yosemitana** (I, III), Cal., Col.
VIRUS, Aster Yellows. **Chlorogenus callistephi** var. **californicus,** Cal.

GILLENIA (American Ipecac)

RUST. **Gymnosporangium exterum** (O, I), Ind., Ky., Mo., N. C., Tenn., Va.; III on red-cedar.

WILD GINGER (*Asarum*)

LEAF SPOT. **Ascochyta versicolor,** Ida.; **Laestadia asarifolia,** S. C.
ROT, Rhizome. **Sclerotinia sclerotiorum,** N. Y.
RUST. **Puccinia asarina,** Cal., Ida., Oreg., Wash.

GINKGO (Maidenhair-Tree)

LEAF SPOT. **Phyllosticta ginkgo,** Pa.
NEMATODE. Root Knot. **Heterodera marioni,** Miss.
ROT, Root. **Phymatotrichum omnivorum,** Tex.
ROT, Sapwood. **Polyporus hirsutus, P. lacteus, P. tulipiferous, P. versicolor,** sometimes on living trees.
ROT, Wound. **Fomes meliae,** Md.

GINSENG (*Panax*)

BLIGHT. **Alternaria panax,** general, Me. to N. C. and Mo., Minn.; **Botrytis cinerea,** N. Y. to N. C., Mich., Wash.
DAMPING-OFF. **Pythium debaryanum,** N. Y.; **Rhizoctonia solani,** Ark., Ind., Mich., N. J., N. Y., Wash.
LEAF SPOT. **Septoria** sp., Minn.; **S. araliae,** Wis.; **Colletotrichum dematium,** secondary, N. Y. to N. C.; Mo., Minn.
NEMATODE, Root Knot. **Heterodera marioni,** Conn., Mich., N. Y., Ohio, Pa., Wis.
PHYSIOGENIC Papery Leaf. Moisture deficiency, sunscald.
ROT, Rhizome. **Sclerotinia sclerotiorum,** white rot, Mich., N. Y., Ohio, Pa., Wis.; **S. smilacina,** black rot, Mich., Minn., N. Y., Wis.

Rot, Root. **Armillaria mellea,** Wash.; **Fusarium scirpi,** N. Y. to Ala., Mo., Wis., Wash.; **Thielaviopsis basicola,** Ill., Mich., N. J., N. Y., Ohio; **Ramularia** spp., Mich., N. Y., Oreg., Wash., Wis.

Rot, Stem, Root; Downy Mildew. **Phytophthora cactorum,** Conn. to N. C.; Iowa and Mich.; Wash.

Rust. **Puccinia araliae** (III), Mass., Pa.

Wilt. **Verticillium albo-atrum,** Ind., Ky., Mich., N. J., N. Y., Ohio, Pa., Tenn., Wis.

GLADIOLUS

Bacterial Leaf Blight. **Xanthomonas gummisudans,** N. Y. to Mo. and N. Dak., Wash.

Bacterial Scab; Neck Rot; Leaf Spot. **Pseudomonas marginata,** general.

Bacterial Soft Rot. **?Erwinia carotovora,** Mich.

Blight, Leaf and Flower Spot; Corm Rot; **Botrytis gladioli** or **B. gladiolorum?** on West Coast or **B. cinerea,** Cal., Fla., Mich., N. J., N. Y., Oreg., Wash., Wis., Alaska.

Blight, Leaf and Stem Spot. **Stemphylium** sp., Fla., Mich., N. J., N. Y.

Blight, Brown Spot; Leaf and Flower Spot. **Curvularia lunata,** N. Y. to Fla.; Ala., Mich., Miss., Wis.

Blight, Southern. **Sclerotium rolfsii,** Fla.

Leaf Spot. **Alternaria** spp., cosmopolitan; **Cladosporium herbarum,** cosmopolitan, but secondary; **Heterosporium** sp., Md.

Nematode, Root Knot. **Heterodera marioni,** N. C. to Fla. and Tex.; Cal.

Physiogenic "Rust," Spot Necrosis. Sun on water drops? Occasional.

Rot, Basal. **Fusarium oxysporum** f. **gladioli,** general except New England and Pacific Northwest; Basal Dry Rot, **Fusarium** sp., Mich.

Rot, Corm, in storage. **Penicillium gladioli,** general in North from Mass. to Col. and Wash.; occasional south to Tex. and Cal.

Rot, Dry; Corm, Leaf, Stalk Rot. **Stromatinia gladioli,** general.

Rot, Hard; Leaf spot. **Septoria gladioli,** general.

Rot, Root, Leaf-Base. **Rhizoctonia solani,** Ill., N. J., N. Dak., Tex.

Virus, Mosaic. There are two types: Mild Mosaic due to strain of yellow bean mosaic virus, and White-Break Mosaic, caused by suspected but unproved virus, N. Y. to Ill., Cal., and Wash.

Wilt, Yellows, Corm Rot. **Fusarium orthoceras** var. **gladioli,** N. Y. to Fla., Tex. and Minn., Cal.

The backyard gardener with a few rows of gladiolus probably uses DDT for thrips and forgets about diseases, but for the serious grower diseases are becoming increasingly important. Control starts with choosing varieties resistant to Fusarium yellows, treating corms before planting to take care of dry and hard rots, scab, and, perhaps, field spraying for the relatively new Botrytis, Stemphylium, and Curvularia leaf blights or spots. The latter suddenly flared up in Florida in 1947, causing disastrous losses in commercial fields. Mild mosaic is spread from beans to gladiolus by aphids, so they should be widely separated in the garden. Roguing infected individuals is the only way to keep down white-break mosaic. Botrytis blight has become a limiting factor in the Northwest.

GLOBE AMARANTH (*Gomphrena*)

Leaf Spot. **Cercospora gomphrenae,** Ga., Okla., Tex.
Nematode, Root Knot. **Heterodera marioni,** Fla.
Virus, Curly Top. **Ruga verrucosans,** Tex.
White Rust. **Albugo bliti,** N. Mex.

GLOBE-MALLOW (*Sphaeralcea*)

Powdery Mildew. **Erysiphe polygoni,** Ida.
Rust. **Puccinia interveniens,** Ida., Wash.; **P. schedonnardi,** Ariz., N. Mex.; **P. sherardiana,** Ariz., Cal., Col., Ida., Nebr., N. Mex., Tex., Utah.

GLOBE THISTLE (*Echinops*)

Rot, Crown. **Sclerotium rolfsii,** Conn.

GLORY-BUSH (*Tibouchina*)

Rot, Root. **Clitocybe tabescens,** Fla.

GLOXINIA (*Sinningia*)

Physiogenic Dieback; Wilt. Boron deficiency, Cal.
Rot, Bud. **Botrytis cinerea,** Cal.
Rot, Leaf. **Cladosporum herbarum,** N. J.
Rot, Root and Crown. **Phytophthora cryptogaea,** Cal.; **Pythium ultimum,** Cal.
Rot, Crown. **Sclerotinia sclerotiorum,** Cal.
Virus, Spotted Wilt. **Lethum australiense,** Cal., Mo., Tex.

GNAPHALIUM

Canker, Stem. **Phoma erysiphoides,** Tex., Wis.
Downy Mildew. **Plasmopara halstedii,** Ala., Miss.
Leaf Spot. **Cercospora gnaphaliacea,** Miss., Kans.; **C. gnaphalii,** Cal., Tex.; **Cylindrosporium gnaphalicola,** Ala., Tex.; **Septoria cercosperma,** Tex.
Nematode, Root Knot. **Heterodera marioni.**
Rot, Root. **Phymatotrichum omnivorum,** Tex.
Rust. **Puccinia gnaphalii** (II, III), Ala., La., N. and S. C.; O, I, unknown; **P. investita** (O, I, III), Ariz., Cal., Conn., Mass., N. Y., Pa., Tenn., W. Va., Wis.

SMUT, White. **Entyloma compositarum,** Ala., Md.

VIRUS, Aster Yellows. **Chlorogenus callistephi** var. **californicus,** Cal.

GOATS–BEARD (*Aruncus*)

LEAF SPOT. **Cercospora** sp., Oreg.; **Ramularia ulmariae,** Alaska.

GODETIA

DAMPING-OFF. **Rhizoctonia solani,** Ill.

DOWNY MILDEW. **Peronospora arthuri,** Cal.

NEMATODE, Root Knot. **Heterodera marioni.**

ROT, Root. **Pythium ultimum,** Mo.; **Phytophthora cryptogea.**

RUST. **Puccinia oenotherae** (O, I, II, III), Cal., Oreg., Nev., Wash.; **P. vagans** (O, I, II, III), Cal.; **Pucciniastrum pustulatum** (II, III), Alaska; O, I on fir.

VIRUS, Aster Yellows. **Chlorogenus callistephi** var. **californicus,** Cal.

GOLDEN–CHAIN (*Laburnum anagyroides*)

BLIGHT, Twig. **Fusarium** sp., Md., Ohio; **F. lateritium,** N. J.

LEAF SPOT. **Cercospora laburni,** Okla.

GOLDEN–CLUB (*Orontium*)

BLIGHT, Leaf. **Botrytis streptothrix,** N. J.

LEAF SPOT. **Phyllosticta orontii,** N. J., Tex.; **Mycosphaerella** sp., N. J.; **Ramularia orontii,** N. J.; **Volutella diaphana,** N. J.

GOLDEN–EYE (*Viguiera*)

POWDERY MILDEW. **Erysiphe cichoracearum,** Utah.

ROT, Root. **Helicobasidium purpureum,** Tex.

RUST. **Puccinia abrupta** (II, III), Ariz., Tex.; **P. turgidipes** (II, III), Ariz., Cal.

SMUT, White. **Entyloma compositarum,** Utah.

GOLDEN–GLOW (*Rudbeckia laciniata*)

BLIGHT, Southern. **Sclerotium rolfsii,** Fla.

DOWNY MILDEW. **Plasmopara halstedii,** Iowa, Nebr., N. C., N. Dak., Wis.

LEAF GALL. **Synchytrium aureum,** Ill., Wis.

LEAF SPOT. **Cercospora rudbeckiae,** N. Y.; **Phyllosticta rudbeckiae,** Iowa, N. Y., Wis.; **Ramularia rudbeckiae,** Vt. to Miss., Col. and Ida.; **Septoria rudbeckiae,** Kans., Nebr., Wis.

POWDERY MILDEW. **Erysiphe cichoracearum,** general.

ROT, STEM. **Sclerotinia sclerotiorum,** Conn.

RUST. **Puccinia extensicola** (O, I), Mo., S. Dak.; **Uromyces perigynius** (O, I), Md. to Mo. and Mont.; II, III on Carex. **U. rudbeckiae** (III), Md. to Miss., N. Mex. and Mont.

Smut. **Entyloma compositarum,** Iowa, Mo., Ohio, Wis.

Virus, Mosaic. Unidentified, Ind.

Virus, Aster Yellows. **Chlorogenus callistephi,** N. Y.; and var. **californicus,** Cal.

Powdery Mildew is the most general and conspicuous disease of goldenglow, coating the foliage with white in late summer.

GOLDEN–LARCH (*Pseudolarix*)

Canker. **Dasyscypha willkommii,** Mass.

GOLDENRAIN–TREE (*Koelreuteria*)

Canker. **Nectria cinnabarina,** Cal., Conn.

Leaf Spot. **Cercospora** sp., Fla.

Rot, Root. **Phymatotrichum omnivorum,** Tex.

Wilt. **Verticillium** sp., N. J.

GOLDENROD (*Solidago*)

Anthracnose, Spot. **Elsinoë solidaginis,** Fla., Ga., S. C.

Black Knot. **Gibberidia heliopsidis,** Conn., Mo., N. Dak., N. Y.

Blight, Thread. **Pellicularia** (*Corticium*) **koleroga,** La.

Black Spot, Black Scurf. **Asteroma solidaginis,** Iowa.

Canker, Stem. **Botryosphaeria ribis.**

Dodder. **Cuscuta** spp., occasional in East and Central States southward.

Downy Mildew. **Basidiophora entospora,** Ill., Wis.; **Plasmopara halstedii,** Ill., Wis.

Leaf Spot. **Ascochyta compositarum,** Wis.; **Cercospora parvimaculans,** Wis.; **C. stomatica,** Iowa, Wis.; **C. virgaureae,** N. J. to Ala., Kans., Wis.; **Colletotrichum solitarium,** Kans., Nebr., Wis.; **Macrophoma gallicola,** blister gall; **M. sphaeropsispora,** Cal.; **Phyllosticta gallicola,** blister gall, Col.; **P. solidaginicola,** Ill., Wis.; **Ramularia spp.,** Ill., Wis., Wyo.; **Septoria** spp.

Mold, Leaf. **Cladosporium astericola,** Wis.

Nematode, Root. **Pratylenchus pratensis,** Fla.

Powdery Mildew. **Erysiphe cichoracearum,** general; **Phyllactinia corylea,** Wash.; **Sphaerotheca humuli** var. **fuliginea,** Ind.; **?Uncinula** sp., N. Y.

Rust. **Coleosporium delicatulum** (II, III), Me. to Va., Kans.; O, I on pines; **C. solidaginis** (II, III), general; O, I on 2- and 3-needle pines. **Puccinia extensicola** var. **solidaginis** (O, I), general; II, III on Carex; **P. virgaureae** (III), Ill., N. H., Mass., Mich., N. Y.; **P. stipae** (O, I), Col., Mont., Nebr., N. Mex., N. Dak.; II, III on Stipa; **P. grindeliae** (III), Ill., Wis. to Cal., Wash.; **Uromyces perigynius** (O, I), Me.; II, III on Carex; **U. solidaginis** (III), Col., Ida., Mont., Oreg., Wash., Wyo.

Smut, inflorescence. **Thecaphora cuneata,** Kans.

Virus, Mosaic. Unidentified, N. Y.

GOLDEN-SEAL (*Hydrastis*)

BLIGHT, **Alternaria** sp., Mich., N. Y., Ohio.

BLIGHT, Leaf. **Botrytis** sp., Conn. to N. C., Ind., Wash., Wis.

NEMATODE, Root Knot. **Heterodera marioni,** Mich., Ohio, Wash.

ROT, Root. **Rhizoctonia solani,** N. C.

ROT, Stem. **Phytophthora cactorum,** N. C.

VIRUS, Mosaic. Unidentified.

WILT. **Fusarium** sp., Ill., N. Y., Ohio, Wash.

GOLDTHREAD (*Coptis*)

LEAF SPOT. **Mycosphaerella coptis,** Me., N. Y., Vt.; **Septoria coptidis,** Ida., Mich., N. Y., Vt., Wis., Wash.; **Vermicularia coptina,** N. Y.

GOOSEBERRY (*Ribes grossularia*)

ANTHRACNOSE. **Pseudopeziza ribis,** general.

BLIGHT, Cane. **Botryosphaeria ribis,** N. J., Va.; **Leptosphaeria coniothyrium,** Ind., Mo.

BLIGHT, Thread. **Corticium stevensii = Pellicularia koleroga,** Fla.

DIEBACK; Coral Spot. **Nectria cinnabarina,** Minn.

DIEBACK. **Physalospora obtusa,** N. Y. to Va., Kans.; **Phragmodothella ribesia,** Oreg.; **Botrytis cinerea,** Conn., Oreg., Wash.

DODDER. **Cuscuta** sp., Minn., N. Y.

DOWNY MILDEW. **Plasmopara ribicola,** Minn., Oreg., Wis., W. Va.

LEAF SPOT. **Marssonina grossulariae,** Ohio, Wis.; **Mycosphaerella ribis,** Mass. to Va., Kans., Minn., Oreg., Ala.; **Phyllosticta grossulariae,** Wis., Conn., N. J., Wash.; **Ramularia** sp., Mich.

NEMATODE, Bud, Leaf. **Aphelenchoides ribes,** one report, Cal., but chiefly known in England.

POWDERY MILDEW. **Sphaerotheca humuli,** Minn.; **S. mors-uvae,** general; **Microsphaera grossulariae,** Cal.; **Phyllactinia corylea, N. Y.**

ROT, Root. **Armillaria mellea,** Oreg., Wash.; **Dematophora** sp.; **Xylaria hypoxylon,** Oreg.

RUST. **Puccinia caricis** var. **grossulariata** (O, I), leaves, fruit, Me. to Md., Miss., Kans., Idaho; II, III on Carex; **P. caricis uniporula,** Iowa, Md., N. Y., Wis.; **Cronartium occidentale,** Ariz., Col., Utah; **C. ribicola,** white pine blister rust (II, III)—European varieties are resistant; **Coleosporium jonesii** (II, III), Col., Mo., Minn., N. Mex., Wis., Wyo.

SCAB; Spot Anthracnose. **Sphaceloma ribis,** Wash.

VIRUS, Mosaic. Unidentified, Ill., N. Y.

Powdery mildew caused by *Sphaerotheca mors-uvae* is the most important gooseberry disease, but seems to be readily controlled by a lime-sulfur spray immediately after bloom, followed by bordeaux mixture for leaf spots.

GORDONIA (Franklinia and Loblolly Bay)

Black Mildew. **Meliola cryptocarpa,** Fla., La.
Leaf Spot. **Phyllosticta gordoniae,** Fla.

GOURD (*Lagenaria, Luffa,* and *Trichosanthes*)

Anthracnose. **Colletotrichum lagenarium,** Conn., Ill., Ind., Minn., Nebr.
Bacterial Angular Leaf Spot. **Pseudomonas lachrymans,** Wis.
Blight, Thread. **Pellicularia** (*Corticium*) **koleroga,** Fla.
Downy Mildew. **Pseudoperonospora cubensis,** Conn., Fla., Mass., N. C., Ohio.
Fruit Spot. **Stemphylium** sp., N. Y.; **Macrophoma trichosanthis,** Ala.; **Phoma subvelata,** Tex.
Leaf Spot. **Cercospora cucurbitae,** Ala., Ind.
Nematode, Root Knot. **Heterodera marioni,** Ala., Fla., Ohio.
Powdery Mildew. **Erysiphe cichoracearum,** Conn., Wis.
Rot, Root. **Phymatotrichum omnivorum,** Tex.
Virus, Mosaic. **Marmor cucumeris,** Ind., N. Y.

GOUANIA

Rust. **Puccinia invaginata** (II, III), Fla.

GRAPE

Anthracnose, Spot; Bird's Eye Rot. **Elsinoë ampelina,** widespread.
Bacterial Crown Gall. **Agrobacterium tumefaciens,** widespread.
Blight, Shoot. **Sclerotinia sclerotiorum,** Cal.
Blotch, Leaf. **Briosia amphelophaga,** Tex.
Canker; Deadarm; Branch Necrosis. **Cryptosporella viticola,** widespread.
Downy Mildew. **Plasmopara viticola,** general, serious in East.
Fruit Spot; Fly Speck. **Leptothyrium pomi,** Pa., W. Va.
Leaf Spot. **Mycosphaerella personata** (conidial stage *Isariopsis clavispora*), widespread; **Septoria ampelina,** N. Y., Tex., Va.
Nematode Root Knot. **Heterodera marioni.**
Nematode, Root. **Pratylenchus pratensis,** Cal.; **P. musicola,** Cal.
Physiogenic. Sulphur dioxide injury. Skin blanching, Cal.
Physiogenic Shot Berry. Defective pollination.
Physiogenic Ring Mildew; Fruit Blemish. Cause unknown.
Powdery Mildew. **Uncinula necator,** general.
Rot, Black Mildew. Measles. Secondary effect of wood rotting fungi in trunk.
Rot, Bitter. **Melanconium fuligineum,** widespread, as secondary fungus after black rot.
Rot, Black. **Guignardia bidwellii,** general.

ROT, Fruit. **Alternaria** sp., Cal.; **Aspergillus niger,** black mold, Cal., Oreg.; **Glomerella cingulata,** ripe rot, widespread; **Botrytis cinerea,** gray mold, Cal., Oreg.; **Cladosporium** sp., green mold; **Pestalotia** sp.; **Phoma** spp.
ROT, Root. **Armillaria mellea,** Ark., Cal., Mo., Tex., Wash.
ROT, Root. **Clitocybe tabescens,** S. C. to Tex., Okla.; **Roesleria hypogaea,** N. Y. to Va., Mo., Iowa; **Rosellinia necatrix,** Ala., Ind., Mich., N. Y., Ohio.
ROT, Charcoal. **Macrophomina phaseoli,** Tex.
ROT, White; Dieback. **Coniothyrium diplodiella,** Mass. to Fla. and Tex.
ROT, Wood. **Schizophyllum commune,** Va.; **Stereum** spp.
RUST. **Physopella vitis** (II), Fla., S. C.
VIRUS, Pierce's Disease, or Anaheim, California Vine or Emperor Disease. **Morsus suffodiens** (alfalfa dwarf virus).

Black rot is the most destructive grape disease in most sections of the country, often causing total loss of fruit in home gardens. Fermate is replacing bordeaux mixture in the spray schedule and helps to control downy mildew as well as rot. Bordeaux mixture, however, is somewhat superior for downy mildew and is needed where powdery mildew is prevalent.

Pierce's disease has destroyed many vineyards in California. The virus is transmitted by grafting and also by spittle bugs.

GRAPEFRUIT. See Citrus Diseases

GRAPE–HYACINTH (*Muscari*)

ROT, Dry. **Sclerotium** sp., Mo., Wash.
SMUT, Flower. **Ustilago vaillantii,** Wash., Mass.

GRASS. See Lawn Grasses

GRASS–OF–PARNASSUS (*Parnassia*)

POWDERY MILDEW. **Erysiphe polygoni,** N. Y.
RUST. **Puccinia parnassiae** (III), Utah.

GREASEWOOD (*Sarcobatus*)

RUST. **Puccinia aristidae** (O, I), Nebr. to Cal., Wash.; II, III on *Aristida;* **P. luxuriosa** (O, I), Mont. to Ariz., Cal., Oreg.

GREVILLEA (Silk-Oak)

DIEBACK; Gum Disease. **Diplodia** sp., Fla.
LEAF SPOT, Algal. **Cephaleuros virescens,** Fla.
ROT, Root. **Phymatotrichum omnivorum,** Ariz.

GRINDELIA (Gum-Plant)

Leaf Spot. **Cercospora grindeliae,** Cal., Tex., Wis.; **Septoria grindeliae,** Col., Kans., Tex.; **S. grindeliicola,** Wis.

Powdery Mildew. **Erysiphe cichoracearum,** Minn. to N. Mex., Cal., Mont.

Rust. **Coleosporium solidaginis** (II, III), Cal., Col., Wash., Wis.; O, I on pine; **Puccinia extensicola** var. **solidaginis** (O, I), Kans., Nebr., Tex.; II, III, Carex; **P. grindeliae** (III), Nebr. to Tex., Cal., Mont.; **P. stipae** (O, I), Col., Kans., Nebr., N. and S. Dak.; II, III on Stipa and other grasses; **Uromyces junci** (O, I); II, III on Juncus.

Smut, Inflorescence. **Thecaphora californica,** Utah, Cal.; **T. cuneata,** Col., Kans., Nebr., N. Mex.

GROUND–CHERRY, HUSK–TOMATO (*Physalis*)

Bacterial Angular Leaf Spot. **Pseudomonas angulata,** Ky.

Bacterial Wildfire. **Pseudomonas tabacum,** Pa.

Blight, Southern. **Sclerotium rolfsii,** Fla.

Leaf Spot. **Alternaria solani; Cercospora diffusa,** Ill., Kans., Wis.; **C. physalicola,** Conn. to Ga., Tex.; **Leptosphaeria physalidis,** Ky.; **Septoria** sp., Nebr.; **Stemphylium solani,** Fla.

Nematode, Leaf and Stem. **Ditylenchus dipsaci,** Cal.

Nematode, Root Knot. **Heterodera marioni,** Ala., Fla.

Rot, Root. **Phymatotrichum omnivorum,** Tex.

Rust. **Aecidium physalidis,** Wis. to Tex., N. Mex., Col.; **Puccinia physalidis,** Col., Iowa, Minn., Nebr., Wis.

Smut, White. **Entyloma australe,** Conn., N. Y., Mass. to Miss., N. Mex. and N. Dak.

Virus, Curly Top. **Ruga verrucosans,** Cal.

Virus, Mosaic. Part **Marmor cucumeris** and part **M. tabaci.**

GROUND–CHERRY, Purple Flowered (*Quincula*)

Leaf Spot. **Cercospora physalidis,** Kans.

Rust. **Puccinia aristidae,** Col.

GROUND–SMOKE (*Gayophytum*)

Leaf Spot. **Cercospora gayophyti,** Cal.

Rust. **Puccinia vagans** (O, I, II, III), N. Dak. to N. Mex., Cal., Wash.

Smut, Seed. **Ustilago** sp., Cal., Nebr., Oreg., Utah.

GUAVA (*Psidium*)

Anthracnose; Leaf and Fruit Spot; Ripe Rot. **Glomerella cingulata,** Fla.

Blight, Thread. **Pellicularia koleroga** (*Corticium stevensii*), Fla.

LEAF SPOT, Algal; Green Scurf. **Cephaleuros virescens, Fla.**
LEAF SPOT. **Cercospora psidii,** Fla.
NEMATODE, Root Knot. **Heterodera marioni,** Fla.
ROT, Root. **Clitocybe tabescens,** Fla.
ROT, Wound. **Polyporus versicolor,** Fla.

GYPSOPHILA (Babys Breath)

BACTERIAL Fasciation. **Corynebacterium fascians,** Ohio.
BACTERIAL Root Gall. **Agrobacterium gypsophilae,** N. J.
BLIGHT, **Botrytis cinerea,** N. J.
DAMPING-OFF. **Pythium debaryanum,** Conn.; **Rhizoctonia solani,** Conn.
NEMATODE, Root Knot. **Heterodera marioni,** Fla.
VIRUS, Aster Yellows. **Chlorogenus callistephi,** N. J., and var. **californicus,** Cal.

HACKBERRY, SUGARBERRY (*Celtis*)

BLIGHT. **Cylindrosporium defoliatum,** Tex.
CANKER, Felt Fungus. **Septobasidium burtii,** Tex.
DOWNY MILDEW. **Pseudoperonospora celtidis,** Md., Ga.
LEAF SPOT. **Cercosporella celtidis,** Ala., Tex., Central States; **Cylindrosporium celtidis,** Ala.; **Phleospora celtidis,** Mass. to Tex.; **Phyllosticta celtidis,** general; **Septogloeum celtidis,** N. Y.
MISTLETOE. **Phoradendron** spp., Gulf States.
POWDERY MILDEW. **Sphaerotheca phytoptophyla,** Central States to Kans., associated with gall mites and witches' brooms; **Uncinula parvula,** widespread; **U. polychaeta,** South.
ROT, Root. **Armillaria mellea,** occasional; **Phymatotrichum omnivorum,** Tex.; **Poria ambigua,** Tex.
ROT, Wood. **Daedalea ambigua,** sometimes on living trees; **Fomes** spp.; **Ganoderma lucidum; Polyporus** spp.; **Stereum fuscum,** cosmopolitan.

Hackberry witches' brooms, so prominent in a winter landscape, are caused by gall mites in association with the powdery mildew fungus. There is no real control, except to cut off unsightly branches. Chinese hackberry and southern hackberry are less susceptible.

HALESIA (Snowdrop-Tree; Silver-Bell)

LEAF SPOT. **Cercospora halesiae,** Tenn.
ROT, Wood. **Polyporus halesiae,** Ga.

Other fungi are reported on twigs and branches but not as causing specific diseases.

HAMELIA (Scarlet-Bush)

ROT, Root. **Clitocybe tabescens,** Fla.

HARBINGER–OF–SPRING (*Erigenia*)

RUST. **Puccinia erigeniae** (O, I, III), Ohio.

HARDENBERGIA

NEMATODE, Root Knot. **Heterodera marioni.**

HAWKBIT (*Leontodon*)

RUST. **Puccinia hieracii** (O, I, II, III), Me., N. H.
VIRUS, Aster Yellows. **Chlorogenus callistephi,** Me., N. Y.

HAWKS–BEARD (*Crepis*)

LEAF SPOT. **Cercospora stromatis,** Col.; **Phyllosticta eximia,** Col.; **Ramularia crepidis,** N. Mex.

POWDERY MILDEW. **Erysiphe cichoracearum,** Nebr., Pa.; **Sphaerotheca humuli,** Wyo.

RUST. **Puccinia crepidis-montanae** (O, I, II, III), Col., Ida., Mont., Oreg., Utah, Wash., Wyo.; **P. hieracii,** N. Dak. to Col., Wash.; **P. stipae** (O, I), Mont. to Utah, Wash.; II, III on grasses.

HAWKWEED (*Hieracium*)

BLIGHT, Stem. **Phoma hieracii,** Tex.

DOWNY MILDEW. **Bremia lactucae,** Wis.

LEAF SPOT. **Cercospora hieracii,** Ala., N. C.; **Phyllosticta decidua,** Wis.; **Septoria cercosperma,** Tex.; **S. hieracicola,** N. Y.

POWDERY MILDEW. **Erysiphe cichoracearum, Pa.,** Tex.; **Sphaerotheca humuli** var. **fuliginea,** Ill.

ROT, Root. **Phymatotrichum omnivorum,** Tex.

RUST. **Puccinia extensicola** var. **hieraciata** (O, I), Wis., Pa. to Ill.; Cal., Mont., Oreg.; II, III on Carex; **P. fraseri** (III), Mont., Nebr., N. Y., N. H., Pa., Tenn., Va., W. Va.; **P. hieracii** (O, I, II, III), Tex.; Me. to Va.; Ill., Wash., Fla., Col., Fla.; **P. maculosa,** Oreg., Tex., Wash.

HAWTHORN (*Crataegus*)

BACTERIAL Fire Blight. **Erwinia amylovora,** widespread, especially on English hawthorn.

BLIGHT, Leaf. **Fabraea maculata** (*Entomosporium maculatum*), East and Central States southward.

BLIGHT, Leaf; Fruit Spot. **Monilinia johnsonii,** N. Y. to Minn.

BLIGHT, Seedling. **Sclerotium rolfsii,** Fla.

CANKER, Felt Fungus. **Septobasidium** spp., Southeast and Gulf States.

Leaf Spot. **Cercospora confluens** and **C. apiifoliae,** Tex.; **Cercosporella mirabilis,** Col., N. Y., Wis.; **Cylindrosporium brevispina,** Cal. to Mont., Wash.; **C. crataegi,** W. Va.; **Gloeosporium crataegi,** Wash.; **Hendersonia crataegicola,** Ala., Tex.; **Phyllosticta** spp., widespread; **Septoria crataegi,** Mich. to N. Dak.

Mistletoe. **Phoradendron flavescens,** Tex.

Powdery Mildew. **Podosphaera oxyacanthae,** East and Central States; **Phyllactinia corylea,** general.

Rot, Gray Mold, on fruit. **Botrytis cinerea,** Mass.

Rot, Root. **Armillaria mellea,** Okla.; **Phymatotrichum omnivorum,** Tex.; **Xylaria hypoxylon,** Ind., Ohio.

Rot, Wood. **Daedalea confragosa,** cosmopolitan; **Polyporus versicolor,** sometimes on living trees; **Fomes** spp.

Rust. **Gymnosporangium betheli** (O, I), on fruits, N. Dak. to Wash., Col., N. Mex.; III on juniper; **G. clavipes,** quince rust (O, I), fruits, stems, general east of Rocky Mts.; III on juniper; **C. exiguum** (O, I), on leaves, fruits, Tex.; III on juniper; **C. floriforme** (O, I), leaves, S. C. to Fla.; III on red-cedar; **G. globosum,** hawthorn rust (O, I), leaves, Me. to N. Dak., Ga., Tex; III on juniper; **G. hyalinum** (O, I), leaves, Atlantic Coast, N. C. to Fla.; III, unknown; **G. libocedri** (O, I), leaves, fruit, Pacific Coast; III on Libocedrus; **G. nelsoni** (O, I), leaves, fruits, Wyo.; III on juniper; **G. trachysorum** (O, I), leaves, Atlantic and Gulf Coasts, Pa. to La.; III on red-cedar; **G. tubulatum** (O, I), leaves, Northern Rocky Mts. to Oreg., Wash.

Scab. **Venturia inaequalis,** widespread.

Leaf blight, beginning in a moist spring, causes spotting and defoliation in August and September. Spraying with bordeaux mixture, starting in May, gives excellent control, although sometimes a slight reddish spotting of foliage. Rusts are common on hawthorn and particularly so in the Central States, where junipers should be at least a half mile away to prevent infection.

When branches die back from fire blight cut well below the blighted portion.

HAZELNUT, FILBERT (*Corylus*)

Bacterial Blight. **Xanthomonas corylina,** Oreg., Wash.

Bacterial Crown Gall. **Agrobacterium tumefaciens,** Wash.

Bacterial Leaf Spot. **Pseudomonas colurnae,** Ill.

Canker; Twig Blight. **Apioporthe anomala,** Eastern and Central States; **Hymenochaete agglutinans,** Me.

Leaf Curl. **Taphrina coryli,** Pa., Wis.

Leaf Spot. **Cylindrosporium vermiformis,** Wis.; **Gloeosporium coryli,** Me. to N. J., Pa., Oreg., Wash.; **Phyllosticta coryli,** widespread; **Septogloeum profusum,** Ind., Mass., Miss.; **Septoria corylina,** widespread.

Physiogenic Bitter Pit; Brown Stain. Cause unknown, Pacific Northwest.

Physiogenic Shrivel. Sterility, failure of embryo to develop.

Powdery Mildew. **Phyllactinia corylea,** Pacific Northwest; **Microsphaera alni.**
Rot, Root. **Armillaria mellea,** Pacific Coast.

Bacterial blight often kills young trees in Washington and Oregon, but a copper dust will reduce bud and twig infection. Powdery mildew is important in the Northwest.

HEATH (*Erica*)

Powdery Mildew. **Erysiphe polygoni,** Cal.
Rot, Collar. **Phytophthora cinnamomi,** N. Y.
Rust. **Pucciniastrum ericae** (II), Cal.

HEATHER (*Calluna*)

Pseudophacidium (*Hypoderma?*) **callunae** on stems and leaves, Oreg., Wash.

HEBE

Leaf Spot. **Septoria exotica,** Cal.

HELENIUM (Sneezeweed)

Leaf Spot. **Cercospora helenii,** Ala., Tex.; **Septoria helenii,** Iowa, Pa., Tex.
Powdery Mildew. **Erysiphe cichoracearum,** Col., Oreg., Tex., Utah, Wash., Wis., Wyo.
Rot, Root. **Phymatotrichum omnivorum,** Tex.
Rust. **Puccinia conspicua** (O, I), Ariz., Col., N. Mex.; II, III on Koeleria; **P. extensicola** var. **solidaginis** (O, I), Nebr., Col., Tex.; II, III on Carex.
Smut. **Entyloma compositarum,** Tex., Wis.; **E. polysporum,** Mont.
Virus. Aster Yellows. **Chlorogenus callistephi** var. **californicus,** Tex., Cal.

HELIOPSIS

Black Knot; Black Patch. **Gibberidia heliopsidis.**
Leaf Spot. **Phyllosticta pitcheriana,** N. Y.; **Septoria helianthi,** Ind.; **S. heliopsidis,** Wis.
Powdery Mildew. **Erysiphe cichoracearum,** Iowa, Minn., Nebr., N. Dak., N. Mex., Wis.
Rot, Root. **Phymatotrichum omnivorum,** Tex.
Rust. **Coleosporium helianthi** (II, III), N. C.; O, I on pine. **Puccinia batesiana** (O, I, III), Del., Pa., Iowa, Kans., Md., Minn., Nebr., Wis.; **P. helianthi** (O, I, II, III), Ind., Minn., N. C., Pa., Va.
Virus, Mosaic. Unidentified.

HELIOTROPE

Blight, Shoot; Leaf Spot. **Botrytis cinerea,** cosmopolitan.
Leaf Spot. **Cercospora heliotropii.**

NEMATODE, Root Knot. **Heterodera marioni,** Mass., Wash.
RUST. **Puccinia aristidae** (O, I), Ariz., Cal., Nev.
WILT. **Verticillium albo-atrum,** Md.

HEMLOCK (*Tsuga*)

BLIGHT, Needle. **Didymascella tsugae,** Mass., N. H., Wis.
BLIGHT, Twig. **Botrytis** sp., N. J.
CANKER, Twig. **Cytospora** sp., Md., Va.; **Dermatea balsamea,** Ga., N. Y., Tenn., Va.
CANKER, Stem Girdle, of saplings. **Hymenochaete agglutinans,** Pa.
ROT, Seedling Root. **Cylindrocladium scoparium,** N. J.; **Rhizina undulata,** N. Y.
ROT, Root. **Armillaria mellea,** Mass. to Pa., Mich.
ROT, Sapwood. **Coniophora puteana,** widespread; **Ganoderma lucidum,** New England to Ind.
ROT, Wood. **Fomes** spp.; **Polyporus** spp., general.
RUST, Needle, Cone. **Melampsora abietis-canadensis** (O, I), New England to Pa.; II, III on poplar; **M. farlowii** (III), New England to N. C., Wis.; **Pucciniastrum hydrangeae** (O, I), Ind., Md., Pa., Tenn.; II, III on *Hydrangea arborescens;* **P. myrtilli** (O, I), Me. to Ala., Ind., Wis.; II, III on Ericaceae.

HEMP (*Cannabis*)

BLIGHT, Southern. **Sclerotium rolfsii,** S. C., Tex.
BLIGHT, Gray Mold. **Botrytis cinerea,** Oreg., Va.
BROOM RAPE. **Orobanche ramosa,** Cal., Ill, Ky., Wis.
CANKER, Stem Wilt. **Botryosphaeria marconii,** Md., Va.
CANKER; Stem Rot. **Gibberella quinqueseptata; G. saubinetii,** Ind., Va.
LEAF SPOT. **Cylindrosporium** sp., Md.; **Septoria cannabis,** Md. to Ky., Iowa, Minn., Fla., Tex.
NEMATODE, Root Knot. **Heterodera marioni,** Tenn.
ROT, Root. **Hypomyces cancri,** Md.; **Phymatotrichum omnivorum,** Ariz., Tex.
ROT; Stem Wilt. **Sclerotinia sclerotiorum,** Mont.
ROT, Charcoal. **Macrophomina phaseoli,** Ill.

HEPATICA (Liverleaf)

DOWNY MILDEW. **Plasmopara pygmaea,** Iowa, Ill., N. Y., Pa., Wis.
LEAF SPOT. **Septoria hepaticae,** Mich., N. C.
RUST. **Transzchelia pruni-spinosae** (O, I), Mass. to Md., Minn., Tenn.; II, III on Prunus.
SMUT, Leaf and Stem. **Urocystis anemones,** N. Y. to Ind., Mo., Minn., Wis.

HERCULES–CLUB (*Xanthoxylum*)

Leaf Spot. **Cercospora xanthoxyli,** Fla., Ga., Tex.; **Septoria pachyspora,** Tex.
Mistletoe. **Phoradendron flavescens,** Tex.
Rust. **Puccinia andropogonis** var. **xanthoxyli** (O, I), Tex.

HESPERIS (Dames-Rocket)

Club Root. **Plasmodiophora brassicae,** N. J.
Downy Mildew. **Peronospora parasitica,** N. Y., Pa.
Virus, Mosaic. Probably **Marmor brassicae,** Oreg.
White Rust; White Blister. **Albugo candida,** N. Y.

HEUCHERA (Alum-Root, Coral-Bells)

Leaf Spot. **Cercospora heucherae,** Ind., Ohio, Pa., Va., W. Va., Ill., Ind., Iowa, Wis.; **Phyllosticta excavata,** Ida.; **Ramularia mitellae,** Wash.; **Septoria heucherae,** Ind.
Leaf Nematode. **Aphelenchoides** sp., Cal.
Powdery Mildew. **Erysiphe cichoraceaeum,** Cal.; **Sphaerotheca humuli,** var. **fuliginea,** Mont., N. Mex.; **Phyllactinia corylea,** Mont.
Smut, Leaf and Stem. **Urocystis lithophragmae,** Utah.

HIBISCUS (Arborescent Forms, Rose-of-Sharon, Confederate-Rose, Shrub-Althaea)

Anthracnose. **Colletotrichum gloeosporioides,** Fla.; **C. hibisci,** Fla., Tex.
Bacterial Leaf Spot. **Pseudomonas syringae,** Cal.
Blight, Gray Mold. **Botrytis cinerea,** Md.
Blight, Blossom. **Choanephora infundibulifera,** Fla.
Blight, Southern. **Sclerotium rolfsii,** Tex.
Blight Thread, Web. **Pellicularia** (*Corticium*) **koleroga,** Fla.; **Corticium microsclerotia** = *Pellicularia filamentosa,* Fla.
Damping-Off. **Rhizoctonia solani,** Tex.
Dieback. **Fusarium lateritium,** Fla., La., N. Y.
Leaf Spot. **Alternaria tenuis,** Ind.; **Cercospora hibisci,** Fla., Okla., Tex.; **Phyllosticta hibiscina,** La.
Nematode, Root Knot. **Heterodera marioni,** Miss., Tex.
Rot, Root. **Clitocybe tabescens,** Fla.; **Phymatotrichum omnivorum,** Tex.
Rot, Stem. **Fusarium** sp., Fla.; **Phytophthora parasitica,** Tex.
Rust. **Kuehneola malvicola** (II, III), Gulf States.

HICKORY (*Carya*)

Bacterial Crown Gall. **Agrobacterium tumefaciens,** Md., Kans.
Blotch, Leaf. **Mycosphaerella dendroides,** widespread East and South.

Canker; Bark Patch. **Aleurodiscus candidus,** Mo., Ohio, Pa.; **Solenia ochracea,** Mass.; **Septobasidium** spp., felt fungus, Southeast.

Canker. **Nectria galligena,** Eastern States; **Strumella coryneoidea,** Pa.

Leaf Spot. **Gnomonia caryae,** widespread; **Marssonina juglandis** (conidial stage of *Gnomonia leptostyla*), N. J., N. C. to Iowa; **Microstroma juglandis,** witches' broom; **Monochaetia desmazierii,** Md. to N. C., Tenn.; **Septoria caryae,** Del.; **S. hicoriae,** Tex.; **Phyllosticta** spp., widespread.

Mistletoe. **Phoradendron flavescens,** Ind., Tex.

Physiogenic Rosette. Zinc deficiency, Southeast.

Powdery Mildew. **Phyllactinia corylea,** Wis.; **Microsphaera alni,** cosmopolitan.

Rot, Heart. **Favolus alveolaris,** Va., Vt.; **Fomes applanatus,** cosmopolitan; **F. pinicola,** Wis.; **F. igniarius,** cosmopolitan; **Steccherinum** (*Hydnum*) **septentrionale,** sometimes on living trees.

Rot, Root. **Armillaria mellea,** cosmopolitan.

Rot, Wood. **Daedalea** spp.; **Fomes** spp.; **Polyporus** spp.; **Ganoderma curtisii,** Lower Mississippi; **Stereum hirsutum; Trametes rigida.**

Rot, Wound. **Schizophyllum commune,** cosmopolitan.

Scab; Leaf Spot. **Cladosporium effusum,** general.

Of the various leaf spots on hickory, that caused by **Gnomonia caryae** is the most destructive. Zerlate and Parzate were effective for control, in a recent test of organic fungicides, but Fermate was useless. Strumella canker may injure hickories, but is more commonly found on oak. Witches' brooms appear on shagbark hickory, with no recommended control measures.

HIPPEASTRUM. See Amaryllis

HOARHOUND (*Marrubium*)

Leaf Gall. **Synchytrium marrubii,** Tex.

Leaf Spot. **Cercospora marrubii,** Okla., Tex.

Nematode, Root Knot. **Heterodera marioni,** Ala.

HOLLY (*Ilex*)

(Includes American and English Holly, Chinese, Japanese; **Inkberry, Yaupon**)

Anthracnose. **Gloeosporium** sp., Tex.

Black Mildew. **Morenoella** (*Lembosia*) spp., Miss.

Black Spot. **Microthyriella cuticulosa,** Ga., Miss.; **Asterina** spp., black patch, Gulf States.

Blight, Web, of cuttings. **Rhizoctonia solani,** Md.

Canker; Dieback. **Diaporthe eres,** Oreg., Wash.; **Diplodia** sp., Md.; **Nectria coccinea,** W. Va.; **Phomopsis** sp.; **Physalospora ilicis,** on twigs.

Canker, Felt Fungus. **Septobasidium** spp., Fla., La., N. C.

Dodder. **Cuscuta exaltata,** Tex.

LEAF SPOT. **Cercospora ilicis,** N. J. and Gulf States; **C. pulvinula,** N. J., Tex.; **Englerulaster** (*Asterina*) **orbicularis,** N. J. to Fla.; **Gloeosporium aquifolii,** N. J., Wash.; **Macrophoma phacidiella,** N. J.; **Phyllosticta concomitans,** La.; **P. terminalis,** Miss.; **Septoria ilicifolia,** N. J.

LEAF SPOT, Tar. **Phacidium curtisii,** Mass. to W. Va., Fla., Tex.; **Rhytisma ilicinicolum,** Va. to Ga., Tenn.; **R. velatum,** Ga., Miss., S. C.

PHYSIOGENIC Leaf Blotch. Purplish blotches associated with soil deficiencies and drought or winter injury.

PHYSIOGENIC Chlorosis. Mineral deficiency induced or accentuated by soil alkalinity.

POWDERY MILDEW. **Microsphaera alni,** Ala., Ill., N. C.; **Phyllactinia corylea.**

ROT, Root. **Clitocybe tabescens,** Fla.; **Phymatotrichum omnivorum,** Tex.

ROT, Wood. **Daedalea confragosa,** Md.; **Polyporus** spp.; **Stereum** spp., Md.; **Ustulina vulgaris,** Md.

RUST. **Chrysomyxa ilicina** (II, III), Tenn., W. Va.

SCAB. **Cladosporium** sp., Oreg.

SOOTY MOLD. **Capnodium elongatum,** Gulf States; **Fumago** sp., Wash.

WILT; Dieback. **Fusarium solani** var. **martii,** N. J.

None of these diseases is as important to the average gardener as the holly leaf miner. Spraying is necessary to control that insect but seldom obligatory for the various leaf spots. The most common leaf discoloration is a purplish blotch due to environment rather than a fungus. Tar spot, caused by *Phacidium curtisii,* can be conspicuous. Proper growing conditions with correct soil acidity are more important than fungicides. Pick off occasional spotted leaves, prune out blighted branches.

HOLLYHOCK (*Althaea rosea*)

ANTHRACNOSE. **Colletotrichum malvarum,** N. Y. to Miss., Iowa, Tex.

BACTERIAL Hairy Root. **Agrobacterium rhizogenes,** Wis.

BACTERIAL WILT. **Pseudomonas solanacearum,** N. Y., W. Va.

BLIGHT, Southern. **Sclerotium rolfsii,** Ark.

BLIGHT, Web. **Rhizoctonia microsclerotia** = *Pellicularia filamentosa,* Tex.

CANKER, Branch. **Nectria cinnabarina,** Okla.

LEAF SPOT. **Alternaria** spp., secondary, Conn. to N. C., Nebr., Minn.; **Ascochyta althaeina,** Ind., Md., N. J., N. Y., Pa., W. Va.; **Cercospora althaeina,** East and Central States to Ala., Tex., S. Dak.; **C. kellermanii,** Ind., Minn., Mo., Md., N. J., Ohio; **Myrothecium roridum,** Md.; **Septoria malvicola,** Mich., Minn., N. Y., Ohio, Okla., Vt., Wis.

LEAF SPOT; Stem Canker. **Phyllosticta althaeina,** Ala., N. J., N. Y., Ohio, Pa., W. Va.

NEMATODE, Root Knot. **Heterodera marioni,** Fla., Kans., Miss., Okla., Tex.

NEMATODE, Root. **Pratylenchus pratensis,** Tex.

POWDERY MILDEW. **Erysiphe cichoracearum,** Cal., Miss.; **E. polygoni,** Iowa.

Rot, Crown. **Phytophthora megasperma,** Md., Va.; **Sclerotinia sclerotiorum,** Mont., N. J.

Rot, Root. **Phymatotrichum omnivorum,** Ariz., Tex.

Rust. **Puccinia malvacearum** (III), general; **P. heterospora** (III), Cal., Kans., Miss., Tex.; **P. lobata,** Ariz., N. Mex., Tex.; **P. schedonnardi** (O, I), Kans., Miss., Nebr., N. Dak.; **P. sherardiana** (O, III), Cal.; **Endophyllum tuberculatum** (III), Col., Kans., Nebr., Okla.

Rust is by far the most generally destructive disease of hollyhocks, disfiguring foliage in most seasons and in some causing nearly all leaves to shrivel and die. Control is difficult. I have not yet found anything better than sulfur dust, starting applications very early in the season, combined with removal of infected leaves.

HOLODISCUS (Rock-Spirea, Ocean Spray)

Canker, Twig; Coral Spot. **Nectria cinnabarina.**

Leaf Spot. **Cylindrosporium ariaefolium,** Oreg.; **Rhapalidium cercosporelloidis,** Ida.; **Septogloeum schizonoti,** Wash.

Powdery Mildew. **Podosphaera oxyacanthae,** Ida.; **Phyllactinia corylea,** Wash.

Virus, Ocean Spray Witches' Broom. **Nanus holodisci,** Oreg., Wash.

HOMALOMENA

Leaf Spot. **Glomerella cincta,** N. J.

HONESTY (*Lunaria*)

Club Root. **Plasmodiophora brassicae,** N. J.

Leaf Spot. **Alternaria** sp., Mass.; **Helminthosporium lunariae,** Mass.

HONEY LOCUST (*Gleditsia*)

Bacterial Hairy Root. **Agrobacterium rhizogenes,** Central States.

Canker; Wilt. **Thyronectria austro-americana,** Mass.; **T. denigrata,** Mass. to S. C., La., and Nebr.

Canker, Felt Fungus. **Septobasidium curtisii,** Ark., La.

Canker. **Dothiorella** sp., Miss.

Leaf Spot. **Cercospora condensata,** Ill. to Kans., Nebr., Wis.; **C. olivacea,** Ill., Iowa to Miss.

Leaf Spot, Tar. **Linospora gleditsiae,** S. and N. C. to Nebr., Tex.

Mistletoe. **Phoradendron flavescens,** Ind., Tex.

Powdery Mildew. **Microsphaera alni,** widespread.

Rot, Crown. **Phytophthora citrophthora,** Cal.

Rot, Root. **Phymatotrichum omnivorum,** Okla., Tex.

Rot, Heart. **Fomes** spp., some on standing trees.

Rot, Wood. **Daedalea ambigua, D. elegans; Ganoderma curtisii** and **G. lucidum** sometimes on living trees in South; **Polyporus** spp. sometimes living trees; **Xylaria mali,** Va.

Rot, Wound. **Schizophyllum commune,** cosmopolitan.

Rust. **Ravenelia opaca** (III), Ill.

Virus, Robinia Brooming; Witches' Broom. **Chlorogenus robiniae,** Ohio, Ky.

HONEYSUCKLE (*Lonicera*)

Bacterial Crown Gall. **Agrobacterium tumefaciens,** Conn.

Bacterial Hairy Root. **Agrobacterium rhizogenes,** Central States.

Blight, Leaf. **Herpobasidium deformans** (*Glomerularia lonicerae*), Conn., Iowa, N. Y., Wis.

Blight, Thread. **Pellicularia koleroga,** La.

Blight, Twig. **Phoma mariae,** Mass., Conn., N. Y.

Leaf Spot. **Cercospora antipus,** Mich. to Mont., Tex.; **C. varia,** Tex.; **Guignardia lonicerae,** Cal.; **Kabatia lonicerae,** Cal.; **Lasiobotrys affinis,** Cal., Pacific Northwest; **Leptothyrium periclymeni,** widespread; **Marssonina lonicerae,** Cal.; **Septoria sambucina,** Mont., Wis.

Nematode, Root Knot. **Heterodera marioni,** on *L. nitida* only.

Powdery Mildew. **Microsphaera alni,** general; **Erysiphe polygoni,** Cal., Wyo.

Rot, Root. **Phymatotrichum omnivorum,** Tex.

Rust. **Puccinia festucae** (I), Iowa; II, III on Festuca but not in America.

HOP (*Humulus*)

Anthracnose; Leaf Spot. **Colletotrichum** sp.; **Glomerella cingulata,** Ind., Kans., Md., N. Y., Oreg., Wash., Wis.

Bacterial Crown Gall. **Agrobacterium tumefaciens,** Cal., Okla., Oreg., Wash.

Downy Mildew. **Pseudoperonospora humuli,** Cal., N. Y., Oreg., Wash., Wis.

Leaf Spot. **Cercospora** sp., Nebr.; **Cylindrosporium humuli,** N. Y. to N. C., Iowa, Wis.; **Phyllosticta decidua,** Iowa, Wis.; **P. humuli,** Iowa, Mass., Mich.; **Mycosphaerella erysiphina,** Cal.; **Septoria humuli,** N. H.; **S. lupulina,** Kans.

Nematode, Root Knot. **Heterodera marioni,** Cal.

Powdery Mildew. **Erysiphe cichoracearum; Sphaerotheca humuli,** general.

Rot, Root. **Armillaria mellea,** occasional.

Rust. **Aecidium** sp., Wash.

Virus, Mosaic. Unidentified.

Wilt. **Verticillium albo-atrum,** Me., Ohio, Oreg., Wis.

HOP-HORNBEAM, IRONWOOD (*Ostrya*)

Canker. **Nectria** spp., N. Y., W. Va.; **Strumella coryneoidea,** Northern Appalachians; **Aleurodiscus griseo-canus,** on bark of living trees, Iowa, Mo.

CANKER, Felt Fungus, **Septobasidium** spp., Tenn., W. Va.
LEAF BLISTER; Witches' Broom. **Taphrina virginica,** widespread.
LEAF SPOT. **Cylindrosporium dearnessi,** Va.; **Gloeosporium robergei,** Pa., Wis.
POWDERY MILDEW. **Microsphaera alni,** widespread; **Phyllactinia corylea,** widespread; **Uncinula macrospora,** Mich., Wis.
ROT, Root. **Armillaria mellea,** cosmopolitan.
ROT, Wood. **Daedalea confragosa,** cosmopolitan; **Fomes** spp.; **Pleurotus similis,** N. Y.; **Poria** spp.; **Polyporus** spp.; **Stereum** spp.

HOP–TREE (*Ptelea*)

LEAF SPOT. **Cercospora afflata,** Ind., Mo.; **C. pteleae,** Tex.; **Phleospora pteleae,** Tex.; **Phyllosticta pteleicola,** Ill.; **Septoria pteleae,** Ind., Wis.
RUST. **Puccinia windsoriae** (O, I), N. Y. to Ala., Kans., II, III on grasses.

HORNBEAM (*Carpinus*)

BLIGHT, Twig. **Fusarium lateritium,** Ala.
CANKER, Bark. **Pezicula carpinea,** Mass. to Ohio; **Solenia ochraceae,** Mich.
CANKER, Felt Fungus. **Septobasidium curtisii,** widespread.
CANKER, Trunk. **Nectria galligena,** Conn., N. Y.
LEAF BLISTER. **Taphrina australis,** Ala.
LEAF SPOT. **Gloeosporium robergei,** N. Y., Pa., W. Va., Wis.; **Gnomoniella fimbriata** Northeast; **Septoria carpinea,** Wis.
POWDERY MILDEW. **Microsphaera alni,** Mass. to Iowa; **Phyllactinia corylea,** widespread.
ROT, Sapwood. **Polyporus adustus,** N. Y.; **P. gilvus,** Ind., Mo., N. Y.; **P. versicolor,** cosmopolitan.
ROT, Wood. **Stereum sericeum,** cosmopolitan.

HORSE–CHESTNUT (*Aesculus hippocastanum*)

See Buckeye for other species

BLOTCH, Leaf. **Guignardia aesculi,** general.
BLIGHT, Leaf. **Glomerella cingulata,** Conn., Md., N. Y.
?CANKER. **Diplodia aesculi,** N. Y.
LEAF SPOT. **Septoria hippocastani,** Pa., Vt.
PHYSIOGENIC Scald; Scorch. Response to drought and heat.
POWDERY MILDEW. **Uncinula flexuosa,** widespread.
ROT, White Sapwood. **Collybia velutipes,** R. I.

In a wet season, leaves are blotched, turn brown, and drop from the Guignardia fungus; in a dry season, leaves look scorched or blotched, turn brown, and drop from drought and heat. The minute black fruiting bodies of the fungus distinguish the parasitic from the physiogenic disease.

HORSE GENTIAN (*Triosteum*)

Leaf Spot. **Cladosporium triostei,** Ill., Iowa, Mo., Nebr., W. Va., Wis.; **Cylindrosporium triostei,** Kans., Wis.

Powdery Mildew. **Phyllactinia corylea,** Mich.

Rust. **Aecidium triostei,** Mo.

HORSE-RADISH (*Armoracia*)

Bacterial Crown Gall. **Agrobacterium tumefaciens,** N. J., N. Y.

Bacterial Leaf Spot. **Xanthomonas campestris** var. **armoraciae,** Conn., Ill., Iowa, Me., Mo., S. Dak., Va.

Bacterial Soft Rot. **Erwinia carotovora,** in stored roots, Conn., N. Y.

Club Root. **Plasmodiophora brassicae,** Ill.

Downy Mildew. **Peronospora parasitica,** Ala., Ill., N. J.

Leaf Spot. **Alternaria brassicae,** Conn. to Del., Ill., Iowa; **A. oleracea,** Conn. to Del., Mo., Nebr., Tex.; **Cercospora armoraciae,** general; **Phyllosticta decidua,** Tex., Wash., Wis.; **P. orbicula,** N. Y.; **Ramularia armoraciae,** general.

Nematode, Root Knot. **Heterodera marioni,** Ill., Miss., Okla.

Powdery Mildew. **Erysiphe polygoni,** Cal.

Rot, Collar, Root. **Pellicularia filamentosa,** Ill., Mich., Minn., N. J., N. Y., Tex., Wash.

Rot, Root. **Penicillium hirsutum,** blue mold; **Phymatotrichum omnivorum,** Tex.; **Thielaviopsis basicola,** Kans., N. J.

Virus, Curly Top. **Ruga verrucosans,** Cal., Oreg., Wash.

Virus, Mosaic. Unidentified, but part turnip mosaic; **Marmor brassicae,** nearly universal.

White Rust. **Albugo candida,** probably general.

Wilt. **Verticillium albo-atrum,** Mich., Wash.

HOSTA (Plantain-Lily, Funkia)

Leaf Spot. **Alternaria** sp., N. Y.; **Phyllosticta** sp., N. J.

Rot, Crown. **Botrytis cinerea,** Alaska, N. J.; **Sclerotium delphinii,** Conn., Minn., N. J., N. Y.; **S. rolfsii,** Md.

HOUSTONIA (Bluets)

Downy Mildew. **Peronospora calotheca,** Ill.; **P. seymourii,** Ala., Ark., Ill., Iowa, Miss., Tex.

Leaf Spot. **Cercospora houstoniae,** Del.; **Septoria** sp., Tex.

Rot, Root. **Phymatotrichum omnivorum,** Tex.

Rust. **Puccinia lateritia,** Tex.; **Uromyces houstoniatus** (O, I), Mass. to Miss., Mo., Ill., Wis.; Kans., Tex.; II, III on blue-eyed-grass; **Uromyces peckianus** O, I), Ala., Miss., Tex.; II, III on grasses.

HUCKLEBERRY (*Gaylussacia*)

Blight, Leaf. **Guignardia vaccinii,** Md.

Leaf Gall; Shoot deformity. **Exobasidium vaccinii; Synchytrium vaccinii,** red leaf, N. J.

Leaf Spot. **Ophiodothella vaccinii,** Tex.; **Rhytisma vaccinii,** tar spot.

Nematode, Root Knot. **Heterodera marioni,** Okla.

Powdery Mildew. **Microsphaera alni,** var. **vaccinii,** widespread.

Rust. **Pucciniastrum myrtilli** (II, III), New England to Va., Wis.; O, I, on hemlock.

HUISACHE, SWEET ACACIA (*Acacia farnesiana*)

Rot, Mushroom Root. **Clitocybe tabescens,** Fla.

Rust. **Ravenelia australis,** Tex.; **R. hieronymi,** witches' broom, **R. siliquae,** N. Mex., Tex.

HYACINTH (*Hyacinthus*)

Bacterial Soft Rot. **Erwinia carotovora,** cosmopolitan.

Bacterial Yellows. **Xanthomonas hyacinthi** occasional in imported bulbs, Mass., Mich., Minn., N. J., Wash.

Nematode, Bulb; Ring Disease. **Ditylenchus dipsaci,** N. J., Wash.

Rot, Gray Mold. **Botrytis** sp., N. C., after frost injury.

Rot, Bulb. **Fusarium** sp., Col., Mo., N. J., R. I., Wash.; **Penicillium** spp., blue mold, cosmopolitan; **Sclerotinia bulborum,** black slime, formerly reported on imported bulbs but no present records.

Virus, Mosaic. In part **Marmor scillearum,** general.

HYDRANGEA

Bacterial Wilt. **Pseudomonas solanacearum,** N. Y.

Blight, Gray Mold. **Botrytis cinerea,** cosmopolitan, common on *Hydrangea opuloides* after frost injury.

Blight, Southern. **Sclerotium rolfsii,** Fla.

Leaf Spot. **Ascochyta hydrangeae,** Alaska, N. J.; **Cercospora arborescentis,** Ill., Okla.; **C. hydrangeae,** Md., Va. to Fla., Ala., Tex.; **Colletotrichum** sp., Md., N. J.; **Phyllosticta hydrangeae,** Ind.; **Septoria hydrangeae,** Conn., Miss.

Nematode, Root Knot. **Heterodera marioni,** Tex.

Nematode, Stem. **Ditylenchus dipsaci.**

Physiogenic Chlorosis. Iron deficiency, excess lime.

Powdery Mildew. **Erysiphe polygoni,** general.

Rot, Wound. **Polyporus versicolor,** Conn., Md., Iowa.

Rust. **Pucciniastrum hydrangeae** (II, III), Pa. to N. C., Ark., Ill.; O, I on hemlock.

HYDROPHYLLUM (Water-Leaf)

DOWNY MILDEW. **Peronospora hydrophylli,** Md., Ill., Iowa, N. Y., Wash., Wis.

LEAF SPOT. **Ascochyta hydrophylli,** Oreg.; **Gloeosporium hydrophylli,** N. Y.; **Ramularia hydrophylli,** Wash.; **Septocylindrium hydrophylli,** N. Y.; **Septoria hydrophylli,** N. Y.

POWDERY MILDEW. **Erysiphe cichoracearum,** occasional; **E. polygoni,** Ida., Wash.; **Sphaerotheca humuli,** Ohio, N. and S. Dak.

RUST. **Puccinia hydrophylli** (III), Cal., Col., N. Y. to Nebr., N. Dak., Utah; **P. rubigo-vera** var. **apocrypta** (O, I), Mont. to Col., Utah and Wash., Cal., N. Y. to Nebr., N. Dak.; II, III on grasses.

HYMENOCALLIS (Spider-Lily)

LEAF SPOT. **Cercospora pancratii,** Fla., La., Tex.

LEAF SCORCH. **Stagonospora curtisii,** Cal., Tex.

VIRUS, Mosaic. Unidentified, Cal.

HYMENOPAPPUS

DOWNY MILDEW. **Plasmopara halstedii,** Okla.

ROT, Root. **Phymatotrichum omnivorum,** Tex.

RUST. **Puccinia grindeliae** (O, III), Okla.

HYSSOP (*Hyssopus*)

NEMATODE, Root Knot. **Heterodera marioni,** Mich.

IMPATIENS (Garden Balsam, *I. balsamina* and Sultan, *I. sultani*)

BACTERIAL WILT. **Pseudomonas solanacearum,** Wis.

DAMPING-OFF. **Pythium** sp., Wash.; **Rhizoctonia solani,** Fla.

LEAF SPOT. **Cercospora fukushiana,** Kans., Fla.; **Septoria noli-tangeris; Phyllosticta** sp., N. J.

ROT, Stem. **Sclerotium rolfsii,** Ill.

WILT. **Verticillium albo-atrum,** N. Y.

INDIA–HAWTHORN (*Raphiolepis*)

BLIGHT, Southern. **Sclerotium rolfsii,** Fla.

INDIAN CUCUMBER–ROOT (*Medeola*)

LEAF SPOT. **Phyllosticta medeolae,** N. Y.

INDIGO (*Indigofera*)

ROT, Root. **Phymatotrichum omnivorum,** Tex.

RUST. **Ravenelia laevis,** Tex.; **Uromyces indigoferae** (II, III), Fla., Tex.

INDIGO BUSH, FALSE INDIGO (*Amorpha* spp.)

Leaf Spot. **Cylindrosporium passaloroides,** widespread.
Powdery Mildew. **Erysiphe polygoni,** Wyo.
Rust. **Uropyxis amorphae,** general.

INULA (Elecampane)

Leaf Spot. **Ramularia** sp., Mich.
Powdery Mildew. **Erysiphe cichoracearum,** N. Y., Wis.
Rust. **Puccinia hieracii,** Wis.

Inula is very susceptible to powdery mildew, which coats the leaves white by late summer.

IRESINE (Blood-Leaf)

Nematode, Root Knot. **Heterodera marioni,** Md., Fla.
Rot, Root. **Helicobasidium purpureum,** Tex.; **Rhizoctonia solani,** Ill.
Smut, Inflorescence. **Thecaphora iresine,** Ind.

IRIS

Bacterial Soft Rot. **Erwinia carotovora,** general.

Bacterial Leaf Spot. **Bacterium tardicrescens,** Mass. to Ala., Ind., Minn.

Blight, Blossom. **Botrytis cinerea,** Mass., Oreg.; **Glomerella cingulata,** flower spot, Md.

Blight, Leaf; Ink Disease of bulbs. **Mystrosporium adustum,** N. C., Oreg., Va. on bulbous iris.

Blight, Southern; White Rot. **Sclerotium rolfsii,** N. Y. to Fla., and Tex.

Damping-Off; Root Rot. **Rhizoctonia solani,** occasional.

Leaf Spot; Blight. **Didymellina macrospora** (conidial stage *Heterosporium iridis,* often reported as *H. gracile*) general; **Alternaria iridicola,** Ill., Wis., Mont., Wash.; **Ascochyta iridis,** Md., N. Y.; **Mycosphaerella** sp., N. Mex.; **Phyllosticta iridis; Cladosporium herbarum,** secondary; **Kabatiella microsticta,** secondary.

Nematode, Bulb. **Ditylenchus iridis,** Fla., N. Y., N. and S. C., Oreg., Va., Wash.

Nematode, Root-Plate. **Aphelenchoides parietinus,** Wash., Mich., N. Y., N. C., Tex., on bulbous iris.

Nematode, Root Knot. **Heterodera marioni,** N. C.

Rot, Crown. **Sclerotium delphinii,** Conn., Mass., N. Y. and N. J., probably general in North but may be only a form of *S. rolfsii;* see above under blight.

Rot, Gray Mold, Crown. **Botryotinia convoluta,** Minn., N. J., N. Y., Wis.

Rot, Basal, Dry. **Fusarium** sp., Ariz., Cal., N. C., N. Y., Oreg., Va., Wash.

Rot, Bulb. **Sclerotium tuliparum,** N. J.; **Penicillium** spp., blue mold, general.

Rust. **Puccinia iridis** (II, III), Cal., Ind., La., N. C., Col., Ida., N. Mex.; **P. sessilis** (O, I), Me. to Ind., Nebr. and Minn.; II, III on Phalaris.
Virus, Mosaic. **Marmor iridis,** general.

The most common disease of bearded iris in home gardens is bacterial soft rot, following the iris borer. Shallow planting in full sun and wide spacing keep down rot to some extent, but whenever division and transplanting are necessary the rhizomes should be treated before replanting in clean soil. Sanitary measures will be sufficient control of Didymellina and bacterial leaf spots in normal summers, but sometimes spraying with bordeaux mixture will be required.

Crown rot or southern blight gets started when iris is crowded and somewhat shaded. If growth is too rank it may be advisable to cut foliage back somewhat after flowering, to admit light and air to the crown and reduce humidity. The disease has been controlled in Wedgewood iris by soaking the bulbs in Tersan.

IRONWEED (*Vernonia*)

Downy Mildew. **Plasmopara halstedii,** Kans., Mo.
Leaf Spot. **Cercospora noveboracensis,** Mo.; **C. occulta; C. vernoniae,** Ala., La., Nebr., Wis., W. Va.
Powdery Mildew. **Erysiphe cichoracearum,** general; **Sphaerotheca humuli** var. **fuliginea,** Mo.
Rot, Root. **Phymatotrichum omnivorum,** Tex.
Rust. **Puccinia vernoniae,** N. Y. to Miss., Tex., N. Dak.

IVESIA

Rust. **Phragmidium horkeliae,** Utah; **P. ivesia,** Cal.; **P. jonesii,** Nev., Oreg., Utah.

IXIA

Rot, Corm. **Fusarium orthoceras** var. **gladioli** in commercial stocks; **Sclerotium** sp.
Virus, Mosaic. **Marmor iridis,** Cal.

IXORA

Nematode, Root Knot. **Heterodera marioni,** Fla.
Rot, Root. **Clitocybe tabescens,** Fla.

JACARANDA

Rot, Mushroom Root. **Clitocybe tabescens,** Fla.

JACK BEAN, SWORD BEAN (*Canavalia*)

Leaf Spot. **Cercospora ternateae,** Ala.; Pod Spot. **Vermicularia** sp., Ala.
Nematode, Root Knot. **Heterodera marioni,** resistant to.

JACK-IN-THE-PULPIT (*Arisaema*)

BLIGHT, Leaf and Stalk. **Streptotinia arisaemae** (Conidial stage *Botrytis streptothrix*), Ill., Iowa, Md., N. Y., Pa., Wis.
LEAF SPOT. **Cladosporium** sp., Va.; **Volutella** sp.
RUST. **Uromyces caladii,** N. Y. to Fla., Miss., Tex., Nebr., N. Dak.

JACQUEMONTIA

LEAF SPOT. **Cercospora alabamensis,** Miss.
NEMATODE, Root Knot. **Heterodera marioni,** Ala.
RUST. **Coleosporium ipomoeae,** La.
WHITE RUST. **Albugo ipomoeae-panduratae,** Ala.

JACQUINIA

BLACK SPOT. **Asterella paupercola,** Fla.

JAMESIA (Cliffbrush)

BLIGHT. **Ovularia edwiniae,** Col.

JASMINE (*Jasminum*)

BACTERIAL Crown Gall. **Agrobacterium tumefaciens,** Md.
BLIGHT, Blossom Blight. **Choanephora infundibulifera,** Fla.
BLIGHT, Southern. **Sclerotium rolfsii,** Fla.
CANKER; Stem Gall. **Phomopsis** sp., Fla.
LEAF SPOT, Algal; Green Scurf. **Cephaleuros virescens,** Fla.
LEAF SPOT. **Colletotrichum gloeosporioides,** Fla., Tex.
NEMATODE, Root Knot. **Heterodera marioni,** Fla.
ROT, Root. **Clitocybe tabescens,** Fla.
?VIRUS. Infectious chlorosis or variegation, graft transmitted.

JERUSALEM ARTICHOKE (*Helianthus tuberosus*)

BACTERIAL Spot. **Pseudomonas helianthi,** Ill.
BLIGHT, Southern. **Sclerotium rolfsii,** Fla., La., Miss., S. C., Tex.
DOWNY MILDEW. **Plasmopara halstedii,** N. J. to Kans., S. Dak., Vt.
LEAF SPOT. **Cercospora helianthi,** Kans.
NEMATODE, Root Knot. **Heterodera marioni,** Cal., Fla., Md., N. Y., S. C., Tenn.
POWDERY MILDEW. **Erysiphe cichoracearum,** Mass. to Tex., N. Dak., Wash.
ROT, Root. **Phymatotrichum omnivorum,** Tex., Ariz.
ROT, Soft. **Rhizopus stolonifer,** Minn.
ROT, Wilt. **Sclerotinia sclerotiorum,** Mass., Minn., Wash.
RUST. **Coleosporium helianthi** (II, III), Ala., Ill., Minn., N. Y., N. and S. Dak., Okla., Pa., Tenn., Va.; **Puccinia helianthi** (O, I, II, III), Me. to Ga., Tex., N. Dak.; **Uromyces junci,** Nebr., N. Dak.

JERUSALEM–CHERRY (*Solanum pseudocapsicum* and other species, including False Jerusalem-Cherry, Bitter Nightshade, Bittersweet)

BACTERIAL Crown Gall. **Agrobacterium tumefaciens,** Conn.

DODDER. **Cuscuta gronovii,** N. Y.

LEAF SPOT. **Alternaria solani; Mycosphaerella solani,** Ohio; **Ascochyta lycopersici,** N. Y., Ohio; **Cercospora dulcamarae,** Mich., N. Y., Wis.; **Phyllosticta pseudocapsici,** La.; **Stemphylium solani,** Fla.

NEMATODE, Root Knot. **Heterodera marioni,** Cal., Md., Oreg.

VIRUS, Mosaic. Unidentified, probably **Marmor tabaci.**

VIRUS, Tip Blight. **Lethum australiense,** Oreg.

WILT. **Verticillium albo-atrum,** N. Y.

JETBEAD (*Rhodotypos*)

ANTHRACNOSE, **Gloeosporium** sp., Ill.

BLIGHT, Twig; Coral Spot. **Nectria cinnabarina,** Mass.

LEAF SPOT. **Ascochyta rhodotypi,** Ill.

JOBS–TEARS (*Coix lachryma-jobi*)

?VIRUS. Chlorotic Streak. Unidentified.

JUNIPER, RED–CEDAR (*Juniperus*)

BACTERIAL Crown Gall. **Agrobacterium tumefaciens,** Miss., Fla.

BLACK MILDEW. **Apiosporium pinophilum,** Oreg.; **Dimerium juniperi,** Cal.

BLIGHT, Brown Felt. **Herpotrichia nigra,** Northern Rockies to Pacific Northwest.

BLIGHT, Leaf. **Chloroscypha juniperina,** Iowa; **Pestalotia funerea,** secondary, cosmopolitan.

BLIGHT, Nursery. **Phomopsis juniperovora,** Mass. to Fla., Kans., Minn.

CANKER. **Coryneum cardinale,** Cal.; **Lagenula nigra,** N. Y., gall.

DIEBACK. **Sphaeropsis** sp.; **Physalospora** spp.

MISTLETOE. **Phoradendron juniperina,** Southwest.

NEEDLE CAST; Leaf Spot. **Lophodermium juniperinum,** widespread, secondary; **Cercospora sequoiae** var. **juniperi** = ***Exosporium?,*** Conn., Wis.

PHYSIOGENIC Dieback. Winter injury, etc.; common in ornamentals.

ROT, Root. **Clitocybe tabescens,** Fla.; **Phymatotrichum omnivorum,** Okla., Tex.

ROT, Heart. **Fomes juniperinus,** Pa. to Ky., Tenn.; **F. earlei,** Southwest; **F. subroseus,** general; **F. texanus,** Ariz., N. Mex., Tex.

ROT, Wood. **Lenzites saepiaria,** occasionally on living trees; **Coniophora corrugis,** Pacific Northwest; **Daedalea juniperina,** S. C. to Ark.

RUST. **Gymnosporangium aurantiacum** (III), gall on stems, leaves, Col., Me., Mich.; O, I on mountain-ash; **G. betheli** (III), on stems, N. Dak. to Okla.,

N. Mex., Wash.; O, I on hawthorn; **G. bermudianum** (III), gall on stems, Gulf States; **G. exiguum** (III), on leaves, Okla., Tex.; O, I on hawthorn; **G. clavariaeforme** (III), gall on stems, Me. to Ala., west to Mont.; O, I on Amelanchier, chokeberry, quince, pear; **G. clavipes** (III), quince rust, on stems Me. to Ill., Mont.; O, I on Amelanchier, hawthorn, quince, apple; **G. corniculans** (III), gall on stems, Me., Mich., N. Y., Wis.; O, I on Amelanchier; **G. davisii** (III), leaf gall, Me., Wis.; O, I on chokeberry; **G. effusum** (III), gall on stems, N. Y. to S. C.; O, I on chokeberry; **G. exterum** (III), gall on stems, Ky.; O, I, Gillenia; **G. floriforme** (III), gall on leaves, stems, S. C. to Fla., Okla., Tex.; O, I on hawthorn; **G. globosum,** hawthorn rust (III); O, I on hawthorn, apple, pear, mountain-ash; **G. harknessianum** (II) on western juniper; O, I on Amelanchier.

RUST, Cedar-Apple. **Gymnosporangium juniperi-virginianae** (III), gall on leaves of red-cedar and prostrate and Rocky Mountain junipers, general; O, I on apple, crabapple.

RUST. **G. inconspicuum** (III), Cal., Col., Utah, O, I on Amelanchier; **G. juniperinum** (III), gall on stems, Col. to Pacific Northwest; O, I on mountain-ash; **G. juvenescens** (III), gall on stems, witches' brooms, Minn., Nebr., Wis.; O, I on Amelanchier; **G. japonicum** (III), Conn., Mass., N. J., Wash.; O, I on Photinia; **G. kernianum,** witches' broom, Ida., Oreg. to Ariz., N. Mex.; O, I Amelanchier, pear; **G. multiporum** (III), Col. to N. Mex., Cal.; O, I unknown; **G. nelsoni** (III), gall on stems, Mont., S. Dak.; O, I on hawthorn, crabapple, mountain-ash, quince, Amelanchier; **G. nidus-avis** (III), gall on stems, witches' brooms, East and South; O, I on Amelanchier, apple, hawthorn, mountain-ash, quince; **G. speciosum** (III), gall on stems, Ariz., Col., Nev., N. Mex.; O, I on Fendlera, Philadelphus; **G. trachysorum** (III) on stems; Fla., La., Miss., S. C.; O, I on hawthorn; **G. tubulatum** (III), gall on stems, S. Dak. to Oreg., Wash.; O, I on hawthorn; **G. vauqueliniae** (III), on one-seed juniper; O, I on Vauquelinia, causing witches' brooms.

Of this lengthy list of juniper rusts the three common apple rusts are most important in the garden, not so much for the damage to this host as for the harm to the deciduous fruit or ornamental. These three are the cedar-apple rust (*Gymnosporangium juniperi-virginianae*), the hawthorn rust (*G. globosum*) and the quince rust (*G. clavipes*). The latter is perennial in juniper and may produce spores each spring for as long as twenty years.

Spraying junipers at the proper time in spring inhibits the development of the spore horns from the galls and in this way protects apples, crabapples, hawthorns, etc. Elgetol is effective but sometimes injurious to the cedars and a special "Bordeaux 180" has been suggested. See under Rusts for details. Spraying the apple hosts with Fermate is also satisfactory. If you have only a few small red-cedars it is quite feasible to cut out the galls in late winter. Or you can eliminate red-cedars, replacing them with forms not susceptible to these three rusts.

KALANCHOË

BACTERIAL Crown Gall. **Agrobacterium tumefaciens,** experimental infection, but very susceptible.
POWDERY MILDEW. **Sphaerotheca humuli** var. **fuliginea,** Md., N. J.
ROT, Crown, Stem; Wilt. **Phytophthora cactorum,** N. J., N. Y.
The crown rot or wilt is fostered by excessive soil moisture.

KENTUCKY COFFEE-TREE (*Gymnocladus*)

LEAF SPOT. **Cercospora gymnocladi,** North Central States; **Marssonina** sp., Nebr.; **Phyllosticta gymnocladi,** Ill.
ROT, Root. **Phymatotrichum omnivorum,** Okla., Tex.
ROT, Wood. **Polyporus pulchellus,** Ind., Mich.

KERRIA

BLIGHT, Leaf and Twig. **Coccomyces kerriae,** widespread Eastern States to Iowa, Tex.
BLIGHT, Twig. **Phomopsis japonica,** Ohio, N. J., Tex.
CANKER; Coral Spot. **Nectria cinnabarina,** Oreg., Wash.
LEAF SPOT. **Septoria** sp., Md., N. J.
ROT, Root. **Phymatotrichum omnivorum,** Tex.

KIDNEY VETCH (*Anthyllis*)

BLIGHT, Leaf and Stem. **Fusarium** sp., N. C.
LEAF SPOT. **Phyllosticta** sp., N. C.

KNIPHOFIA (formerly Tritoma, Poker-Plant, Red-Hot-Poker, Torch-Lily)

LEAF SPOT. **Alternaria** sp., Ala.
NEMATODE, Root Knot. **Heterodera marioni,** Cal.

KRIGIA (Dwarf Dandelion)

DOWNY MILDEW. **Bremia lactucae,** Miss., Mo., Okla., Wis.
LEAF SPOT. **Mycosphaerella krigiae,** Ill., Wis.; **Septoria krigiae,** Ky., N. Y., Wis.
ROT, Root. **Phymatotrichum omnivorum,** Tex.
RUST. **Puccinia extensicola** var. **hieraciata** (O, I), Iowa, Wis.; II, III on Carex; **P. hieracii** (O, I, II, III), N. C.; **P. maculosa** (III), Ill., Mich., Miss., Mo., Pa., Tenn.

KUDZU-VINE (*Pueraria*)

BACTERIAL Halo Blight. **Pseudomonas phaseolicola,** Conn. to Fla., La., Ind.
BACTERIAL Blight. **Pseudomonas syringae,** N. Y.
BLIGHT, Web. **Rhizoctonia microsclerotia,** Ga., Miss.

DAMPING-OFF. **Rhizoctonia solani.**

LEAF SPOT. **Alternaria** sp., secondary; **Mycosphaerella** (*Cercospora*) **puerari-cola,** Miss.

NEMATODE, Root Knot. **Heterodera marioni,** Cal., Ga., Tex.

ROT, Root. **Phymatotrichum omnivorum,** Tex.

ROT, Stem. **Fusarium** sp.; **Macrophomina phaseoli,** Ga.

KUHNIA (False Boneset)

LEAF SPOT. **Pleospora compositarum,** N. Mex., Tex.

ROT, Root. **Phymatotrichum omnivorum,** Tex.

RUST. **Puccinia kuhniae,** Ind. to Ala., Nebr., N. Dak., Mont., Fla., Tex.

KUMQUAT (*Fortunella*)
(See also Citrus)

BACTERIAL Canker. **Xanthomonas citri,** Ala., Eradicated?

LEAF SPOT. **Cephaleuros virescens,** algal spot, Gulf States; **Phyllosticta citricola,** Miss.

NEMATODE, Root. **Tylenchulus semi-penetrans,** Fla.

ROT, Black. **Alternaria citri,** Cal.

ROT, Stem-End. **Diaporthe citri,** Cal.

LANTANA

BLACK MILDEW. **Meliola cookeana,** Fla.

LEAF SPOT. **Alternaria** sp., Tex.

NEMATODE, Leaf. **Aphelenchoides** sp., N. J.

NEMATODE, Root Knot. **Heterodera marioni,** widespread.

ROT, Root. **Phymatotrichum omnivorum,** Tex.

RUST. **Puccinia lantanae** (III), Fla.

WILT. **Fusarium** sp., N. J.

LAPPULA

DOWNY MILDEW. **Peronospora myosotidis,** Mont.

RUST. **Puccinia mertensiae** (III), Utah.

SMUT. **Entyloma serotinum,** Utah.

LARCH (*Larix*)

BLIGHT, Seedling; Girdle; Smother. **Thelephora caryophyllea,** Ida., Mont.

BLIGHT, Needle. **Hypodermella laricis,** Great Lakes, Pacific Northwest; **Lophodermium laricis,** Ida.; **L. laricinum,** Mont. to Oreg.; **Meria laricis,** Ida.

CANKER. **Aleurodiscus amorphus,** Northwest; **Dasyscypha willkommii,** European larch canker, Mass.

DAMPING-OFF. **Rhizoctonia solani,** cosmopolitan.

Mistletoe, Dwarf. **Arceuthobium campylopodum** f. **laricis,** Mont. to Oreg., Wash.; **A. pusillum,** Northeast.

Rot, Heart. **Fomes annosus,** widespread; **F. officinalis,** in West; **F. pini,** red ring, general; **F. pinicola,** widespread; **F. subroseus,** widespread.

Rot, Root. **Armillaria mellea,** cosmopolitan.

Rot, Seedling. **Botrytis douglasii,** gray mold, Northwest; **Cylindrocladium scoparium; Phytophthora cinnamomi.**

Rot, Sapwood. **Lenzites saepiaria,** sometimes living trees.

Rot, Wood. **Polyporus** spp.; **Poria subacida,** cosmopolitan; **Stereum,** widespread.

Rust. **Melampsora bigelowii** (O, I), Northern U. S. to Col., Oreg.; II, III on willow; **M. medusae** (O, I), Wis.; II, III on poplar; **Melampsoridium betulinum** (O, I), Wis.; II, III on birch.

The European larch canker kills young trees in Massachusetts. Japanese larch is relatively resistant.

LARKSPUR (See Delphinium)

Crown Rot or Southern Blight is prevalent on annual larkspur.

LAUREL (See California-Laurel, Cherry-Laurel, Mountain-Laurel)

LAUREL, SWEET BAY (*Laurus nobilis*)

Anthracnose. **Gloeosporium nobili,** N. J.

LAURESTINUS (*Viburnum tinus*)

Downy Mildew. **Plasmopara viburni,** Ga.

Leaf Spot, algal. **Cephaleuros virescens,** Fla., La.

Leaf Spot. **Hendersonia tini,** La.; **Leptosphaeria tini,** La.

Nematode, Root Knot. **Heterodera marioni,** Cal.

Wilt. **Verticillium albo-atrum,** Oreg.

LAVATERA (Tree-Mallow)

Anthracnose. **Colletotrichum malvarum,** Cal., Tex.

Rot, Root. **Phymatotrichum omnivorum,** Tex.

Rust. **Puccinia malvacearum** (III), Cal.

Virus, Variegation. **Marmor abutilon.**

LAVENDER (*Lavandula*)

Leaf Spot. **Septoria lavandulae,** Ohio, Okla.

Nematode, Root Knot. **Heterodera marioni.**

Rot, Root. **Armillaria mellea,** Tex.

LAWN OR TURF GRASSES

(Including Bermuda-Grass, *Cynodon dactylon,* Bent-Grasses, *Agrostis canina; A. palustris, A. tenuis;* Canada and Kentucky Blue-grass, *Poa compressa* and *P. pratensis;* and Redtop, *Agrostis alba*).

Anthracnose. **Colletotrichum graminicolum,** N. Y. to Ky., Tex. and N. Dak. on Kentucky blue-grass; Ill., Iowa, Md., Ohio, Pa. on redtop.

Blight, Leaf. **Helminthosporium stenacrum,** Oreg. on bent; **H. cynodontis,** Fla., Ga., N. C., Va. on Bermuda-grass; **H.** sp., Fla., Ga., Okla., Tex.; **Piricularia grisea,** Tex. on bent.

Blight, Southern. **Sclerotium rolfsii,** Fla., N. J.

Blotch, Purple Leaf. **Septoria macropoda,** general on blue-grass.

Damping-Off. **Cladochytrium graminis,** on bent-grass.

Dodder. **Cuscuta** sp., Mo.

Downy Mildew. **Sclerospora farlowii,** Okla. on Bermuda-grass.

Ergot. **Claviceps purpurea,** N. Y. to Ky., Tex., N. Dak., Mont., Okla., Wis. on blue-grass; bent, Oreg.; **C. microcephala,** Md., Mich., Ohio.

Leaf Spot; Brown Stripe. **Scolecotrichum graminis,** N. Y. to Iowa, Mont., Alaska, Oreg., Wash. on blue-grass, widespread on redtop.

Leaf Spot, Black Spot. **Phyllachora graminis,** N. Y.

Leaf Spot, Copper Spot. **Ramulispora sorghi.**

Leaf Spot; Gray Leaf Speckle. **Septoria triseti,** Oreg., Wash. on redtop, bent; **Selenophoma donacis,** Northwest.

Leaf Spot; Red Eye-Spot. **Mastigosporium rubricosum,** Md., Oreg., Wash. on bent; Oreg., Wyo. on redtop.

Leaf Spot, Tan. **Ovularia pulchella,** Oreg., Utah on bent; **Septoria oudemansii,** N. Dak., Oreg. on blue-grass.

Leaf Spot; Zonate Eye-Spot. **Helminthosporium giganteum,** Conn. to Va., Tex., Fla. on blue, bent and Bermuda-grass.

Leaf Spot. **Ascochyta graminicola,** N. C., N. Dak.; **Cercospora seminalis,** Tex.; **Cercosporella poagena; Cylindrosporium glyceriae,** N. Y.; **Macrophoma** sp., Oreg.; **Helminthosporium vagans,** general; **H.** spp.; **Septoria cynodontis,** Tex.; **S. calamagrostis,** Oreg.; **Phaeoseptoria** sp., Oreg.; **Placosphaeria graminis, Phyllachora graminis,** N. Y.; **Stagonospora intermixta,** Miss.; **Septogloeum oxysporum,** Wyo.

Mold. **Cladosporium herbarum; Fusarium heterosporum.**

Powdery Mildew. **Erysiphe graminis,** general.

Rot; Large Brown Patch. **Rhizoctonia solani** (*Pellicularia filamentosa*), widespread, more important on bent than blue-grass.

Rot; Dollar Spot. Small Brown Patch. **Sclerotinia homeocarpa,** Mass., Pa., R. I., Minn.

Rot; Banded Sclerotial Disease. **Corticium sasakii,** Ala., La., Miss. on Bermuda-grass.

ROT; Pink Patch. **Corticium fuciforme.**

ROT, Root. **Pythium debaryanum; P. ultimum; Fusarium** spp.

RUST, Crown. **Puccinia coronata** (II, III), Ala., Kans., Mo., Oreg., Pa., Wis., Fla., Ga., Ky., La.

RUST, Stem; Wheat rust. **Puccinia graminis,** Ill., Ind., Md., Mich., N. C., Oreg., Ohio, Pa., Wis.

RUST. **Puccinia poae-sudeticae,** yellow leaf, Ala., Col., Md., Mich., Minn., N. Dak.; Me. to N. C., Oreg.; Pa., Tenn., Wash., Wyo.; **P. rubigo-vera,** N. Y. to N. C., Cal., Mont., Utah; **P. glumarum,** stripe rust, Mont.; **P. cynodontis** on Bermuda grass, Gulf States.

RUST. **Uromyces jacksonii** (II, III), Oreg.; **U. dactylidis,** Ind., Mich., S. Dak., Vt.

SMUT, Flag. **Urocystis agropyri,** Wis.

SMUT, Head. **Tilletia pallida,** Oreg.

SMUT, Stripe. **Ustilago striaeformis,** widespread; **U. cynodontis** on Bermuda grass in South.

SMUT, Inflorescence. **Sorosporium syntherisme,** Cal.

SNOWMOLD, Blight. **Fusarium nivale,** Mich., Minn., Oreg., Wash.; **Sclerotium rhizodes,** white tip, Conn., Mass., N. J., Pa., Wis.; **Typhula itoana,** Mass., Minn., N. J., N. Y., Pa.; **T. idahoensis,** Ida.

The possibility of any large proportion of these diseases appearing on the average suburban lawn is remote. In my garden-visiting I see snowmold occasionally, meaning every few years, after a winter when the snow cover has been rather continuous. Light tan, circular areas appear in March, but usually the grass recovers by itself about as well as if chemically treated.

Large brown patch (due to Rhizoctonia or Pellicularia—see under Rot) is fairly general and appears in humid weather in summer with patches of grass looking scalded and sometimes with a light weft of mycelium in the morning dew. Dollar spot or small brown patch, due to *Sclerotinia homeocarpa,* starts with spots only two inches across, but several dead areas may run together. Pink patch, caused by *Corticium fuciforme,* is a spot where the dead grass is bright pink with coral-red masses of mycelium becoming gelatinous in wet weather. Helminthosporium leaf blight and leaf spots are serious in warm, humid weather.

There are many promising new fungicides; cadmium compounds are alternated with organic mercuries in some turf-management schedules. Resistant varieties of grass, like blue-grass B 27, are being developed. In my experience, gardeners and insects, to say nothing of dogs, are more harmful than fungi to the average lawn. When grass has been growing lushly and there is a sudden spell of hot, dry weather, mowing too close will almost surely result in a burn resembling brown patch. Grass clippings, which normally can be left on the lawn, will cause new grass to die out in humid weather. Chinch-bug injury is sometimes mistaken for brown patch, and so is the burn that comes from fertilizers or weed killers applied in hot weather.

LEADTREE (*Leucaena*)

Rust. **Ravenelia leucaenae** (II, III), Tex.

LEATHERWOOD (*Dirca*)

Rust. **Puccinia extensicola** var. **hydnoidea** (I), Me. to Minn., Mo., Ala.; II, III on Carex.

LEBBEK (*Albizzia lebbek*)

Leaf Spot, Algal. **Cephaleuros virescens,** Fla.

LEDUM (Labrador-Tea)

Anthracnose, Spot. **Elsinoë ledi,** Me. to Minn., Pacific States.
Leaf Gall. **Exobasidium vaccinii,** Alaska, Oreg., Wash.; **E. ledi,** Ida.
Leaf Gall; Red Leaf. **Synchytrium vaccinii,** Me.
Leaf Spot. **Cryptostictis arbuti,** Cal., Oreg.
Rust. **Chrysomyxa ledi** (II, III), Northern United States; O, I on spruce; **C. ledicola** (II, III), Northern United States, Me. to Wash., Alaska.

LEEK (See Onion)

LEMON. See Citrus Fruits

LEMON–GRASS (*Cymbopogon*)

Leaf Spot; Eye-Spot. **Helminthosporium sacchari,** Fla.

LETTUCE (*Lactuca sativa*)

Anthracnose. **Marssonina panattoniana,** N. Y. to Fla., Tex., Mich., Cal., Oreg., Wash.
Bacterial Marginal Leaf Blight. **Pseudomonas marginalis,** Kans., Mo., N. J., N. Y.
Bacterial Soft Rot. **Erwinia carotovora,** cosmopolitan in market.
Bacterial Rosette. **Pseudomonas rhizoctonia,** N. Y., Pa.
Bacterial Rot. **Pseudomonas viridilivida,** ?Del., La., N. H., Va., Wash.
Bacterial Wilt. **Xanthomonas vitians,** N. J., N. Mex., N. Y., Pa., S. C., Va.
Blight, Southern. **Sclerotium rolfsii,** Cal., Fla., N. and S. C., Tex., Va.
Damping-Off; Root Rot; Stump Wilt. **Pythium** spp., cosmopolitan.
Downy Mildew. **Bremia lactucae,** general.
Leaf Spot. **Alternaria** sp., Fla., La., Ohio, Okla., Tex., Wash., occasional in Northeast; **Cercospora longissima,** Fla., Ill., Ind., Tex., Va., Wis.; **Septoria**

lactucae, occasional in East and Central States to Fla., Col., Minn.; **Stemphylium botryosum,** secondary, and seed mold, Fla., Ky., N. Y.

NEMATODE, Root Knot. **Heterodera marioni,** general, Va. to Fla.

PHYSIOGENIC Tipburn. High temperature and excessive transpiration.

?PHYSIOGENIC Brown Blight. Cause unknown, Ariz., Cal.

POWDERY MILDEW. **Erysiphe cichoracearum,** Cal., Mich.

ROT, Bottom; Damping-Off. **Rhizoctonia solani,** general.

ROT, Watery Soft; Drop. **Sclerotinia sclerotiorum,** widespread; **S. minor,** in transit and market.

ROT, Gray Mold. **Botrytis cinerea,** chiefly in greenhouses, sometimes in gardens from plants started indoors.

ROT, Root. **Fusarium** sp., Ky., Ohio; **Phymatotrichum omnivorum,** Ariz., Tex.

RUST. **Puccinia extensicola** var. **hieraciata** (O, I), Ind., Minn., N. Dak., Wis.; II, III on Carex; **P. hieracii** (II).

VIRUS, Big Vein. Unidentified. Ariz., Cal., Col., Ill., Mo., N. J., N. Y.

VIRUS, Mosaic. **Marmor lactucae,** general.

VIRUS, Spotted Wilt. **Lethum australiense,** Cal., Tex.

VIRUS, Aster Yellows; White Heart; Rio Grande Disease. **Chlorogenus callistephi,** Northeast and Central States to Miss. and Tex., Col., Ida., Ore., Wyo.; var. **californicus,** Cal.

WHITE RUST. **Albugo** sp., Tex.

Nonparasitic tipburn is the most general of lettuce diseases, prevalent at high temperatures when the soil is deficient in moisture. One or two new hot-weather varieties are quite resistant to tipburn.

Seed treatment with Spergon, Arasan or Semesan helps to prevent damping-off. Bottom rot and Drop are not so serious when plants are spaced well apart in a well-drained soil. Big Boston variety with its heavy base in contact with the ground is more likely to succumb to bottom rot than an upright form.

Aster yellows is increasing in the Northeast, with no practical control except to reduce the leafhopper vectors and wild weed hosts around the garden. DDT dust can be used up to three weeks before harvest.

LEUCOJUM (Snowflake)

LEAF SCORCH; Red Blotch. **Stagonospora curtisii,** Cal.

ROT, of bulb scales. **Botrytis** sp., Oreg.

LEUCOTHOË

CANKER, Felt Fungus. **Septobasidium** spp., Fla.

LEAF Gall. **Exobasidum vaccinii,** Mass., Miss., N. C.

LEAF SPOT, Black. **Asterina diplodioides,** Ala.

LEAF SPOT. **Cercospora kalmiae,** N. J.; **C. leucothoës,** N. J., N. Y.; **Cryptostictis** sp., N. J.; **Lophodermium orbiculare,** N. C., Tenn.; **Mycosphaerella** sp., R. I.; **Pestalotia leucothoës,** N. J.; **Phyllosticta terminalis,** N. Y. to Fla.; **Ramularia andromeda,** N. J.

LEWISIA

Rust. **Uromyces unitus,** Cal., Mont., Wash.

LIATRIS (Gay-Feather)

Dodder. **Cuscuta glomerata,** Okla.

Leaf Spot. **Phyllosticta liatridis,** Wis.; **Septoria liatridis,** Minn., N. Dak., Tex., Wis.

Nematode, Root Knot. **Heterodera marioni.**

Rot, Root. **Phymatotrichum omnivorum,** Tex.

Rot, Stem. **Sclerotinia sclerotiorum,** N. Y.

Rust. **Coleosporium laciniariae** (III), Ark., Tex., N. J. to Fla.; O, I on pines; **Puccinia liatridis** (O, I), Kans., Ind., N. Dak., Nebr., Mont., Wis. to Col.; II, III on grasses.

Wilt. **Verticillium albo-atrum,** N. J.

LIGUSTRUM (See Privet)

LILAC (*Syringa vulgaris*)

Anthracnose, Shoot Blight. **Gloeosporium syringae,** Conn., Mass.

Bacterial, Crown Gall. **Agrobacterium tumefaciens.**

Bacterial Blight, Twig Canker. **Pseudomonas syringae,** Northeastern States to Ala., Ill., Pacific Coast.

Blight, Blossom, Shoot. **Phytophthora cactorum,** Iowa, Md., Mass., Minn., N. J.

Blight, Gray Mold. **Botrytis cinerea,** Pacific Northwest; Northeast.

Blight, Thread. **Pellicularia koleroga** (*Corticium stevensii*), Fla., Miss., N. C.

Blight, Leaf. **Heterosporium syringae,** N. J.; **Cladosporium herbarum,** secondary? cosmopolitan.

Blight, Shoot. **Phytophthora syringae,** Md., N. Y.; **Sclerotinia sclerotiorum,** Wash.

Canker; Stem Girdle. **Hymenochaete agglutinans,** Conn.

Dieback. **Physalospora obtusa,** Mass. to Va., Ohio.

Leaf Spot. **Cercospora lilacis,** widespread; **Macrophoma halstedii,** Conn., N. J., N. Y.; **Phyllosticta porteri,** Ill.; **P. syringae,** Wash.; **P. syringella,** N. Y., Wis.; **Pleospora herbarum,** secondary, Md.

Physiogenic Blight. Graft incompatibility of lilac scion on privet stock.

Powdery Mildew. **Microsphaera alni,** general.

Rot, Root. **Phymatotrichum omnivorum,** Ariz., Tex.; **Thielaviopsis basicola,** Conn.; **Armillaria mellea,** Cal., Miss.

Rot, Wood. **Polyporus gilvus,** Md.; **P. versicolor,** Mo., N. C., N. Y.

?Virus, Mosaic, Ring Spot. Unidentified, Mich., Minn.

Powdery mildew is the most general and conspicuous disease of lilacs but it comes from midsummer to autumn, too late in the season to materially damage the bushes. It can be controlled by persistent dusting with sulfur, or with a copper spray, wherever the time and expense are justified. In wet weather bacterial and Phytophthora blights may be important. Prune out blighted twigs, and perhaps spray with a weak bordeaux mixture.

LILY (*Lilium*)

BACTERIAL Soft Rot. **Erwinia carotovora,** Ga., Mass., N. J., W. Va.

BLIGHT, Botrytis; Leaf Spot. **Botrytis elliptica,** general; **B. cinerea,** general.

BLIGHT, Southern. **Sclerotium rolfsii** and **S. delphinii,** cosmopolitan.

BLIGHT, Bud. **Sporotrichum** sp., Va.

CANKER, Stem. **Rhizoctonia solani,** Cal., Oreg., Wash.

DAMPING-OFF. **Pythium debaryanum,** Ind.; **Rhizoctonia solani,** cosmopolitan.

LEAF SPOT. **Cercospora** sp., Fla.; **Cercosporella lilii,** Conn., N. Y.; **Ramularia** sp., Wash.

MOLD, Leaf and Bulb. **Cladosporium** sp., cosmopolitan.

NEMATODE; Bunchy-Top; Dieback. **Aphelenchoides olesistus,** Oreg., Wash.

NEMATODE, Root Knot. **Heterodera marioni,** Fla.

PHYSIOGENIC Limber Neck. N. Y.

PHYSIOGENIC Chlorosis, Iron deficiency, N. Y.

ROT, Basal. **Fusarium oxysporum** f. **lilii,** general.

ROT, Black Scale. **Colletotrichum lilii,** La., Miss.

ROT, Charcoal. **Macrophomina phaseoli,** Cal.

ROT, Dry; Blue Mold, of bulb scales. **Penicillium** spp.

ROT, Stem, Foot. **Phytophthora cactorum,** Md., Mich., Minn.; **Rhizoctonia tuliparum,** Wash.; **Sclerotinia sclerotiorum,** Conn., Fla., Wash.

ROT, Stem, Top. **Phytophthora parasitica,** Ind., Md., N. J., N. Y.

ROT, Soft, of bulbs. **Rhizopus stolonifer** and **Rhizopus** spp., cosmopolitan.

RUST. **Puccinia sporoboli** (O, I), on *Lilium umbellatum,* Nebr., N. Dak.; II, III on Sporobolus; **Uromyces holwayi** (O, I, II, III), Me. to N. J., Nebr., Mich., Minn., Cal., Ida., Oreg., Wash.

VIRUS, Mild Mosaic, Mottle. **Marmor mite,** general and also **M. cucumeris,** lily mosaic strain.

VIRUS Necrotic Fleck. Combination of symptomless virus **Adelonosus lilii** and **Marmor cucumeris,** on Easter lilies (*L. longiflorum*).

VIRUS, Rosette, Yellow Flat. Lilium virus 1, Cal., La., Md., Mo., N. J., N. Y.

VIRUS suspected, Yellow Top. Unidentified, Ala., Fla., La.

Garden lilies are particularly subject to Botrytis blight and mosaic. Madonna lilies are most susceptible to blight, which often starts as a reddish brown, oval leaf spot, progressing in wet weather until all leaves are blackened and hanging down along the stem. Despite the success of Fermate with some other Botrytis diseases lily growers believe that copper sprays are somewhat more effective on lilies.

The only sure way to be free from mosaic and other virus diseases is to grow lilies from seed in an isolated portion of the garden, far removed from other lily plantings. It is difficult to purchase virus-free stock. Mosaic in mild or masked form is present in much commercially grown material, particularly in Easter lilies, and when these varieties are introduced into home plantings severe mosaic may show up on garden varieties. Neither control of the aphid vectors nor roguing of diseased individuals can be relied on to entirely eradicate lily viruses.

LILY–OF–THE–VALLEY (*Convallaria*)

BLOTCH. **Ascochyta majalis,** Mass., Pa.

BLIGHT, Gray Mold, Rhizome Rot. **Botrytis paeoniae** (*B. cinerea* f. *convallariae*), Ill., Me., Pa.

BLIGHT, Southern. **Sclerotium rolfsii,** Md.

LEAF SPOT. **Gloeosporium convallariae,** N. Y.; **Kabatiella microsticta,** Md.; **Phyllosticta** sp., N. J., N. Y.

NEMATODE, Root. **Pratylenchus pratensis,** occasional in imported pips, associated with forcing failures.

LINARIA (Blue Toadflax; Butter-and-Eggs)

ANTHRACNOSE. **Colletotrichum vermicularioides,** Mass., N. J., N. Y., Tex., Wis.

BLIGHT, Southern. **Sclerotium rolfsii,** Tex.

DOWNY MILDEW. **Peronospora linariae,** Fla., Mass., Okla., Wis.

LEAF SPOT. **Alternaria** sp., Mich.; **Septoria linariae,** Wis.

NEMATODE, Root Knot. **Heterodera marioni.**

NEMATODE, Stem and Leaf. **Ditylenchus dipsaci,** N. Y.

ROT, Root. **Phymatotrichum omnivorum,** Tex.; **Rhizoctonia solani,** Ill.; **Thielaviopsis basicola,** Conn.

ROT, Stem. **Sclerotinia sclerotiorum,** Ariz.

VIRUS, Aster Yellows. **Chlorogenus callistephi** var. **californicus,** Cal.

LINDEN, BASSWOOD (*Tilia*)

ANTHRACNOSE; Leaf Spot. **Gnomonia tiliae** (Conidial stage *Gloeosporium tiliae*), Conn. to Va., Iowa, Minn.

BLIGHT, Leaf. **Cercospora microsora,** general.

CANKER, Bark. **Aleurodiscus griseo-canus,** Iowa, Mo., Pa.

CANKER, Trunk and Branch. **Nectria** spp., N. Y., Pa., Va.; **Strumella** sp., N. J.

CANKER; Dieback. **Nectria cinnabarina,** widespread.

LEAF SPOT. **Phlyctaena tiliae,** N. Y.; **Phyllosticta praetervisa,** Wis.

MISTLETOE. **Phoradendron flavescens,** South.

POWDERY MILDEW. **Microsphaera alni,** Minn.; **Phyllactinia corylea,** Minn.; **Uncinula clintonii,** general.

ROT, Heart. **Daedalea confragosa,** Vt.; **Fomes** spp.; **Steccherinum** (*Hydnum*) **septentrionale,** Ala., Mich.; **Pholiota adiposa,** Mass., Pa., Tenn.

ROT, Root. **Phymatotrichum omnivorum,** Tex.; **Ustulina vulgaris.**

ROT, Sapwood. **Collybia velutipes,** occasional; **Pleurotus ostreatus,** cosmopolitan.

ROT, Wood. **Daldinia concentrica,** Minn., N. Y.; **Lenzites betulina,** N. Y., Vt.; **Schizophyllum commune; Stereum** spp.; **Trametes mollis,** Vt.

SOOTY MOLD. **Fumago vagans.**

WILT. **Verticillium albo-atrum.**

Anthracnose and Cercospora leaf blight are common diseases, but in most seasons control, aside from cleaning up and burning fallen leaves, is not practical. Where injury has been severe in previous years spray with bordeaux mixture as buds are opening, repeating in ten days.

LINNAEA (Twin-Flower)

BLACK MILDEW. **Halbaniella linnaeae,** N. Y.

LEAF SPOT, Tar. **Phyllachora wittrockii,** Mich., Mont., N. Mex., N. Y.

LEAF SPOT. **Septoria breviuscula,** N. Y.; **Venturia dickei,** Ida., Mich., Mont., N. Mex., N. Y., Oreg., Wash., Wis.

LIONS–EAR (*Leonotis*)

LEAF SPOT. **Cercospora leonotidis,** La.

RUST. **Puccinia leonotidis** (O, I, II, III), Fla.

LIPPIA (Fog-Fruit and Lemon-Verbena)

ANTHRACNOSE, Spot. **Sphaceloma lippiae,** Ind.

BLACK MILDEW. **Meliola lippiae,** Fla.

BLIGHT, Southern. **Sclerotium rolfsii,** Cal.

LEAF SPOT. **Cercospora lippiae,** widespread; **Cylindrosporium lippiae,** Tex.

NEMATODE, Root Knot. **Heterodera marioni.**

ROT, Root. **Phymatotrichum omnivorum,** Tex.

LITHOCARPUS (Tanbark-Oak)

BLIGHT, Leaf. **Pestalotia castagnei,** Cal.

ROT, Wood. **Poria** spp.; **Stereum hirsutum.**

RUST. **Cronartium quercuum** (II, III), Cal.; O, I on pine.

LITHOPHRAGMA (Woodland-Star)

RUST. **Puccinia heucherae** (III), Cal., Utah, Wash.

SMUT, Leaf and Stem. **Urocystis lithophragmae,** Utah.

LITHOSPERMUM (Gromwell, Puccoon)

POWDERY MILDEW. **Erysiphe cichoracearum,** Pa.

RUST. **Aecidium hesleri,** Tenn.; **Puccinia rubigo-vera** var. **apocrypta** (O, I), Nebr., N. and S. Dak.

LITSEA (Pond Spice)

LEAF SPOT. **Cercospora olivacea,** Ga.

LOBELIA (Cardinal-Flower and Edging Lobelia)

BLIGHT, Gray Mold. **Botrytis cinerea.**

DAMPING-OFF. **Pythium debaryanum,** Mass., N. Y.

LEAF SPOT. **Cercospora lobeliae,** Ala., Kans., Ill., Ind., Md., Tex.; **C. lobeliicola,** Ill., Iowa, Pa., Tenn., Tex., Va., Wis.; **Phyllosticta bridgesii,** Ind.; **Septoria lobeliae,** Me. to Va., Tex., Wis.

NEMATODE Root Knot. **Heterodera marioni,** Nebr., N. Y.

ROT, Root. **Phymatotrichum omnivorum,** Tex.; **Rhizoctonia solani.**

RUST. **Puccinia lobeliae** (III), Ark., Mich., Wis., N. Y. to N. C., Tex., Wash.

SMUT, Leaf. **Entyloma lobeliae,** Me. to Pa., Mo., Wis.

VIRUS, Curly top. **Ruga verrucosans,** Tex.

VIRUS, Spotted Wilt. **Lethum australiense,** Tex.

LOCUST (*Robinia*)

Chiefly Black Locust, *Robinia pseudoacacia*

BLIGHT, Seedling; Leaf. **Alternaria** sp., N. C. to Ala., Mo.; **Fusicladium robiniae,** Md. to Ala., Mo., Wis.

CANKER; Twig blight. **Aglaospora anomala,** Me. to Ga.; **Fusarium sarcochroum,** Iowa; **Diaporthe oncostoma,** N. Y. to Ga., Ill.

DAMPING-OFF. **Rhizoctonia solani,** Me. to Ala., Nebr., Tex.; **Pythium** spp., Nebr., Tex.

LEAF SPOT. **Cladosporium epiphyllum,** Tenn., W. Va.; **Cylindrosporium solitarium,** Tex.; **Gloeosporium revolutum,** N. J.; **Phleospora robiniae,** N. Y. to Ohio; **Phyllosticta robiniae,** La.

MISTLETOE. **Phoradendron flavescens,** N. C.

NEMATODE, Root Knot. **Heterodera marioni,** Okla.

PHYSIOGENIC Chlorosis. Iron deficiency, Nebr., Tex.

PHYSIOGENIC Little Leaf. Zinc deficiency, Cal.

POWDERY MILDEW. **Erysiphe polygoni,** Cal.; **Microsphaera diffusa,** Ill., N. C.; **Phyllactinia corylea,** N. Mex.

ROT, Root. **Armillaria mellea; Phymatotrichum omnivorum,** Okla., N. Mex.; **Pythium myriotylum,** N. C.

ROT, Heart. **Fomes applanatus; F. igniarius; F. rimosus; Polyporus robiniophilus,** Pa. to Va., Mo., Mich.; **P. sulphureus.**

ROT, Seedling Stem. **Phytophthora cinnamomi,** Md.; **Rhizoctonia** sp.

ROT, Wood. **Daedalea unicolor,** Wis.; **Poria** spp.

VIRUS, Brooming Disease; Witches' Broom. **Chlorogenus robiniae,** Pa. to Ga., Ark. and Nev.

WILT. Seedling, Top. **Phytophthora parasitica.**

WILT. **Verticillium albo-atrum,** Ill.

The virus brooming disease is found from southern Pennsylvania and Ohio southwest to Arkansas. A profusion of short branches forms a broomlike growth, most common on highway trees after pruning. Some trees die, some recover; there is no effective control.

LOGANBERRY (See Blackberry)

LOMATIUM (Biscuit-Root)

DOWNY MILDEW. **Plasmopara nivea,** Mont.

LEAF SPOT. **Phyllachora** sp., Wash.

RUST. **Puccinia asperior,** Cal., Oreg., Wash.; **P. jonesii** var. **typica** (O, I, III), Kans., Nebr., Utah, Wash.; **P. ligustici,** Ida., Wash.

LOOSESTRIFE, MONEYWORT (*Lysimachia*)

LEAF GALL. **Synchytrium aureum,** Wis.

LEAF SPOT. **Cercospora lysimachiae,** N. J.; **Cladosporium lysimachiae,** Mass.; **Ramularia lysimachiae,** Wis.; **Septoria conspicua,** Iowa, N. Y., Vt.

NEMATODE, Root Knot. **Heterodera marioni,** Tex.

ROT, Crown, Stem. **Sclerotium delphinii,** Kans.

RUST. **Coleosporium campanulae** (II, III), Tenn.; O, I on red pine; **Puccinia limosae** (O, I), Mass. to N. C., Ill., Mich., Nebr.

LOOSESTRIFE, Fringed (*Steironema*)

LEAF SPOT. **Cylindrosporium steironematis,** N. Y.; **Mycosphaerella** sp., N. Y.; **Phyllosticta lysimachiae,** N. Y.; **P. steironematis,** N. Y., Pa., Wis.; **Ramularia lysimachiae,** N. C., Wis.; **Septoria conspicua,** Me. to Miss., Col., Ill., Iowa, N. Dak., Wis.; **S. lysimachiae,** Mich., N. Y.

RUST. **Puccinia dayi,** N. Y. to W. Va., Ill., Mich., Mont., Wis.; **P. distichlidis** (O, I), Col., N. Dak.; II, III on marsh grass; **Uromyces acuminatus** var. **steironematis,** Conn. to Col., S. Dak., N. Dak.

LOQUAT (*Eriobotrya*)

ANTHRACNOSE; Flower Blight; Withertip. **Colletotrichum gloeosporioides,** Cal., Fla., Tex.

BACTERIAL Fire Blight. **Erwinia amylovora,** Gulf States, Ariz., Cal.

BLIGHT, Leaf; Blotch. **Fabraea maculata,** Fla.

LEAF SPOT, Algal. **Cephaleuros virescens,** Fla.

LEAF SPOT. **Phyllosticta eriobotryae,** Fla.; **Pestalotia** sp., secondary?

ROT, Root. **Armillaria mellea,** Cal.; **Clitocybe tabescens,** Fla.

ROT, Crown. **Phytophthora cactorum,** Cal.

SCAB. **Fusicladium eriobotryae,** on leaves, stems, fruit, Gulf States.

LOTUS (*Nelumbium*)

LEAF SPOT. **Alternaria nelumbii,** Md., N. J., N. Y., Okla., Pa., Tex.; **Cercospora nelumbonis,** Ind., Tex.

LUCUMA (Egg-Fruit)

ANTHRACNOSE; Fruit Spot. **Colletotrichum gloeosporioides,** Fla.
RUST. **Acrotelium lucumae** (II, III), Fla.

LUDWIGIA

LEAF SPOT. **Cercospora ludwigiae,** Ala.; **Pezizella oenotherae,** Va.; **Phyllosticta ludwigiae,** N. Y., Wis.; **Septoria ludwigiae,** Md., Miss., Pa.
RUST. **Puccinia jussiaeae** (O, I, III), Del. to Fla., Miss., La., Tex., Cal., Ohio, Wis.

LUPINE (*Lupinus*)

BLIGHT, Gray Mold. **Botrytis cinerea,** Mass., Mont.
BLIGHT, Leaf. **Hadrotrichum globiferum,** Cal., Col., Oreg., Wash., Wyo.
BLIGHT, Southern. **Sclerotium rolfsii,** probably general.
BLIGHT; Stem Necrosis. **Ascochyta** sp., Wis., Conn.
DAMPING-OFF. **Rhizoctonia solani,** Conn., Tex.
DOWNY MILDEW. **Peronospora trifoliorum,** Wis.
LEAF SPOT. **Alternaria** sp., Mass.; **Cercospora longispora,** Fla., Mo., N. Y., Wis.; **C. lupini,** Fla., Oreg., S. C.; **C. lupinicola,** Tex.; **Cylindrosporium lupini,** Cal., Wash.; **Mycosphaerella pinodes,** Wis.; **Ovularia lupinicola,** Wash.; **Phoma lupini,** also stem spot, Col. to N. Mex., Cal.; **Phyllosticta ferax,** Cal. to Wash., Wyo., S. Dak. to Col.; **P. lupini,** Cal.; **Ramularia lupini,** Tex.; **Septogloeum lupini,** Mich., Cal.; **Septoria lupinicola,** Wis.; **Stictochorella lupini,** Cal., Wash.
NEMATODE, Root Knot. **Heterodera marioni,** widespread.
NEMATODE, Root. **Pratylenchus pratensis,** Cal.
POWDERY MILDEW. **Microsphaera** sp., **Erysiphe polygoni,** widespread.
ROT, Root. **Armillaria mellea,** Cal.; **Thielaviopsis basicola,** Iowa, Wis.
ROT, Charcoal. **Macrophomina phaseoli,** Cal.
ROT, Stem. **Pythium debaryanum,** Tex., Cal.
RUST. **Puccinia andropogonis** var. **onobrychidis;** O, I, Mich., Minn., Wis., Wyo., N. Y. to Col.; II, III on Andropogon; **Uromyces lupini** (O, I, II, III), Cal., Oreg., Wash., Nebr., Mont.; **U. occidentalis** (II, III), on native lupine, Mont. to N. Mex., Cal., Wash.
SMUT. **Sorosporium astragali,** Wyo.; **Thecaphora** sp., on seed, Col., Wyo.
VIRUS, Ring Spot. Unidentified, Wash.
VIRUS, Spotted Wilt. **Lethum australiense,** Tex.

These diseases are of lupines grown as ornamentals. Lupines as ground covers and soil preservers have their own troubles. In gardens powdery mildew is prevalent, but readily controlled with dusting sulfur. Leaf spots are not often serious enough to call for control other than removing infected leaves.

LYCHNIS (Evening Campion, Rose Campion)

BLIGHT, Shoot and Flower. **Botrytis cinerea,** Alaska.

BLIGHT, Southern. **Sclerotium rolfsii,** Tex.

LEAF SPOT. **Alternaria dianthi,** Alaska; **Leptothyrium lychnidis,** Ala.; **Phyllosticta lychnidis,** Iowa, Tex.; **Septoria lychnidis,** Mass.

MOLD, Leaf. **Heterosporium** sp.

ROT, Root. **Phymatotrichum omnivorum,** Tex.; **Rhizoctonia solani,** Ill.; **Corticium galactinum,** Md.

RUST. **Puccinia arenariae,** Pa.; **Uromyces suksdorfii,** Utah; **U. verruculosus,** Ind., Mich., N. Y., Tex.

SMUT, Anther. **Ustilago** sp., Minn., Wis., Wyo.

LYCIUM (Wolfberry, Desert-thorn)

LEAF SPOT. **Cercospora lycii,** Okla.

POWDERY MILDEW. **Oidium** sp., La.

ROT, Root. **Phymatotrichum omnivorum,** Tex.

RUST. **Aecidium lycii** (O, I), Ariz.; **Puccinia globosipes** (II, III), Utah to N. Mex., Cal.; **O, I** unknown; **P. tumidipes** (II, III), Tex. to Ariz., Utah.

LYCORIS

LEAF SCORCH. **Stagonospora curtisii,** Cal.

NEMATODE, Bulb. **Ditylenchus dipsaci,** N. C., Va.; **Aphelenchoides** sp., N. C., Va.

NEMATODE, Root. **Hoplolaimus** sp., N. C.

LYONIA (Male-berry, Fetter-bush, Stagger-bush)

BLACK SPOT. **Asterina lepidigena,** Fla.

DODDER. **Cuscuta compacta,** Fla.

LEAF GALL; Shoot Hypertrophy. **Exobasidium vaccinii,** Mass. to Fla., Ala.

LEAF SPOT, Tar. **Rhytisma andromedae,** widespread; **R. decolorans,** Miss.

POWDERY MILDEW. **Microsphaera alni** var. **vaccinii.**

RUST. **Pucciniastrum myrtilli** (II, III), Del. to Ala., Ark.; O, I on hemlock.

LYSILOMA

ROT, White Pocket Heart. **Fomes extensus,** Fla.

RUST. **Ravenelia annulata** (II, III), Fla.; **R. lysilomae.**

LYTHRUM (Purple Loosestrife)

LEAF GALL. **Synchytrium lythrii,** La.

LEAF SPOT. **Cercospora lythri,** Wis.; **Mycosphaerella lythracearum,** Miss.; **Pezizella oenotherae,** N. Y., Mich.; **Septoria lythrina,** Kans., N. Y., Wis.

ROT, Root. **Rhizoctonia solani,** Ill.

MAACKIA

ROT, Root. **Phymatotrichum omnivorum,** Tex.

MADRONE (*Arbutus menziesii*)

ANTHRACNOSE, Spot. **Sphaceloma mattirolanum,** Cal.

CANKER, Trunk. **Phytophthora cactorum,** Cal., Wash.

LEAF GALL; Red Leaf Spot. **Exobasidium vaccinii,** Cal., Oreg., Wash.

LEAF SPOT. **Ascochyta hanseni,** Cal.; **Cryptostictis arbuti,** Cal., Oreg.; **Didymosporium arbuticola,** Oreg.; **Mycosphaerella arbuticola,** Cal., Oreg., Wash.; **Phyllosticta fimbriata,** Oreg.

LEAF SPOT, Tar. **Rhytisma arbuti,** Col., Oreg., Wash.

RUST. **Pucciniastrum sparsum,** Cal., Oreg., Wash.

MAGNOLIA

(Saucer, Southern and Mountain Magnolia, Sweet-bay, Cucumber-tree)

BLACK MILDEW. **Irene araliae,** Miss.; **Meliola amphitrichia,** Gulf States; **M. magnoliae; Trichodothis comata,** Gulf States.

BLIGHT, Seedling. **Rhizoctonia solani,** N. J.

BLIGHT, Thread. **Pellicularia** (*Corticium*) **koleroga,** on *M. grandiflora.*

CANKER, Felt Fungus. **Septobasidium curtisii,** on sweetbay, Fla.

CANKER, Twig Blight. **Nectria coccinea,** W. Va.

LEAF SPOT, Algal; "Red Rust." **Cephaleuros virescens,** Fla.

LEAF SPOT. **Alternaria tenuis,** Tex.; **Cladosporium fasciculatum,** Ga. to Tex.; **Cercospora magnoliae,** N. J.; **Colletotrichum** sp., Fla., Ga., S. C.; **Coniothyrium olivaceum,** Tex.; **Epicoccum nigrum,** Tex.; **Exophoma magnoliae,** Fla., Tex.; **Glomerella cingulata; Hendersonia magnoliae,** Va.; **Micropeltis alabamensis,** Ala.; **Phyllosticta cookei,** Gulf States, N. J., N. Y., W. Va.; **P. glauca,** N. C. to Fla., Ala.; **P. magnoliae,** N. J., N. Y. to Gulf States; **Septoria magnoliae,** S. C. to Tex.; **S. niphostoma,** N. and S. C.

NEMATODE, Root Knot. **Heterodera marioni,** Ga., Tex.

NEMATODE, Root. **Pratylenchus pratensis.**

POWDERY MILDEW. **Microsphaera alni,** Md., Pa.; **Phyllactinia corylea,** Ohio, Pa.

ROT, Heart. **Fomes fasciatus** and **F. geotropus,** on living trees.

ROT, Root. **Phymatotrichum omnivorum,** Tex.

ROT, Wood. **Daldinia concentrica,** cosmopolitan; **Fomes** spp.; **Poria** spp.; **Stereum** spp.

These various leaf spots are nothing to be alarmed about. Only one, the Phyllosticta, is general on *Magnolia soulangeana*. The spotting on *M. grandiflora* may be considerable but seldom causes premature defoliation. Glomerella spots are dark brown to black with yellow border. In the Gulf States lichens appear as small round gray spots on leaves and the parasitic alga Cephaleuros often forms a velvety coating with hairlike outgrowths.

MAHONIA (Oregon-Grape)

LEAF SPOT. **Phyllosticta berberidis,** Wash.; **P. japonica,** Conn.; **P. mahoniaecola,** Ala., N. Y., Wash.; **P. mahoniana,** Ala.

NEMATODE, Root Knot. **Heterodera marioni.**

PHYSIOGENIC Scald. In eastern states winter injury to foliage is often severe.

ROT, Root. **Phymatotrichum omnivorum,** Tex.

RUST. **Cumminsiella sanguinea** (O, I, II, III), common Western Great Plains to Pacific; **C. texana; C. wootoniana** (II, III), Ariz., N. Mex.; **Puccinia graminis** (O, I), Cal., Mich., rare; **P. koeleria** (O, I), Col., Ida., Mont., Oreg.; II, III on Koeleria; **P. oxalidis** (O, I), N. Mex.; II, III on Oxalis.

Rust due to Cumminsiella is usually inconspicuous but in a wet season there is a general blighted effect. Mahonia, like barberry, is under wheat-rust quarantine. See **Puccinia graminis,** under Rusts, for a list of varieties that can be shipped under permit.

MAIANTHEMUM

BLIGHT. **Botrytis** sp., N. Y.

LEAF SPOT. **Ramularia rubicunda,** Cal., Mich., N. Y., Ohio, Pa., Wis.; **Sphaeropsis cruenta,** Wash.

RUST. **Puccinia sessilis** (O, I), Mass., Mich., Minn., N. Y., Pa., Wis.; II, III on Phalaris; **Uromyces acuminatus** var. **magnatus** (O, I), Mich., N. Y., Wis.; II, III on marsh grass.

MALACHRA

LEAF SPOT. **Cercospora malachrae,** Tex.

MALACOTHRIX

LEAF GALL. **Synchytrium innominatum,** Cal.

RUST. **Puccinia harknessii,** Cal., Ill.; **P. hieracii** (O, I, II, III), Cal.

MALLOTUS

LEAF SPOT. **Cercospora malloti,** Miss.

MALLOW (*Malva*)

LEAF SPOT. **Alternaria** sp., Mich.; **Colletotrichum malvarum,** N. Dak.
POWDERY MILDEW. **Erysiphe cichoracearum.**
ROT, Root. **Phymatotrichum omnivorum.**
RUST. **Puccinia heterospora,** Kans., Tex.; **P. malvacearum,** Cal., Col., Oreg., W. Va., general.
VIRUS, Curly Top. **Ruga verrucosans,** Cal.
VIRUS, Spotted Wilt. **Lethum australiense,** Cal.

MALVASTRUM (False-Mallow, Bush-Mallow)

ROT, Root. **Phymatotrichum omnivorum,** Tex.
RUST. **Puccinia interveniens** (O, I), Cal.; III on Stipa; **P. schedonnardi** (O, I), Mont., N. Dak. to N. Mex.; II, III on wild grasses; **P. sherardiana** (O, III), Mont., N. Dak. to Tex., N. Mex.; **P. heterospora,** Tex.

MALVAVISCUS

BLIGHT, Twig. **Sclerotinia sclerotiorum,** Tex.
ROT, Collar. **Helicobasidium purpureum,** Tex.
ROT, Root. **Clitocybe tabescens,** Fla.; **Phymatotrichum omnivorum,** Tex. but *M. grandiflorus* is resistant.
RUST. **Kuehneola malvicola** (II, III), Tex.; **Puccinia heterospora** (III), Tex.

MANGO (*Mangifera indica*)

ANTHRACNOSE; Flower and Twig Blight; Fruit Rot. **Glomerella cingulata,** general.
BLIGHT, Twig. **Phomopsis** sp., Fla.
LEAF SPOT, Algal; Green Scurf. **Cephaleuros virescens,** general.
LEAF SPOT. **Phyllosticta mortoni,** Fla., Tex.; **Septoria** sp., Fla.
PHYSIOGENIC Little Leaf. Zinc deficiency.
POWDERY MILDEW. **Oidium mangiferae,** Cal.
SCAB, Spot Anthracnose. **Sphaceloma** sp., Fla.
SOOTY MOLD. **Capnodium** spp., general.
ROT, Tuber. **Aspergillus niger,** Cal.; **Diplodia theobromae,** Cal.
ROT, Wood. **Stereum albobadium,** Fla.; **Trametes hynoides,** Fla.

MANIHOT (Cassava, Manioc)

ANTHRACNOSE; Withertip. **Gloeosporium** sp. and **G. manihotis,** Fla. to Tex.
LEAF SPOT. **Cercospora caribaea,** Fla., Tex.
NEMATODE, Root Knot. **Heterodera marioni,** Fla.
ROT, Root. **Phymatotrichum omnivorum,** Tex.; **Rhizoctonia solani,** Fla.

MANZANITA (*Arctostaphylos*)

LEAF GALL; Shoot Hypertrophy. **Exobasidium vaccinii-uliginosi,** Oreg., Wash.; **E. oxycocci,** Cal.; **E. vaccinii,** Col., Pacific States.

LEAF SPOT. **Cryptostictis arbuti,** Oreg.; **Phyllosticta amicta,** Cal., Oreg.

MISTLETOE. **Phoradendron villosum,** Cal., Oreg.

ROT, Heart. **Fomes arctostaphyli,** Cal.

RUST. **Pucciniastrum sparsum,** Ala., Cal., Oreg.

MAPLE (*Acer*)

ANTHRACNOSE. **Gnomonia veneta,** occasional.

ANTHRACNOSE; Leaf Blight. **Gleosporium apocryptum,** general.

BACTERIAL Crown Gall. **Agrobacterium tumefaciens,** nursery plants.

BACTERIAL Leaf Spot. **Pseudomonas aceris,** on Japanese maple, Cal.

BLIGHT, Seedling; Smother. **Thelephora terrestris.**

BLIGHT, Twig. **Macroplodia simillima,** on silver, sugar maple; **Phoma fumosa,** occasional; **Phomopsis lobiseyi,** Iowa, Cal.; **Sphaeropsis albescens,** widespread; **S. malorum; Steganosporium piriforme,** Kans., Minn., N. J., N. Y., Mass., Va., Wash., W. Va.

CANKER, Bark. **Aleurodiscus acerina,** widespread; **Pezicula acericola; Dermatea acerina,** occasional.

CANKER, Bleeding. **Phytophthora cactorum,** R. I., Mass., N. J.

CANKER, Basal, Crown. **Phytophthora cinnamomi,** N. J., especially on Norway maple.

CANKER, Felt Fungus. **Septobasidium fumigatum,** Ky. on silver maple.

CANKER; Dieback. **Cytospora** sp.; **Physalospora obtusa,** occasional; **Valsa sordida,** occasional.

CANKER, Trunk. **Nectria galligena,** widespread, especially on mountain, red and sugar maples; **N. coccinea; N. cinnabarina,** widespread.

LEAF BLISTER. **Taphrina** spp., scattered.

LEAF SPOT, Tar. **Rhytisma acerinum,** general on red and silver maples, rare on Norway and sycamore, rare on Pacific Coast.

LEAF SPOT; Black Speckled Tar Spot. **Rhytisma punctatum,** on all species except silver; rare in East, abundant on Pacific Coast.

LEAF SPOT; Leaf Blight. **Phleospora aceris,** general.

LEAF SPOT. **Phyllosticta minima,** general on silver, sugar maples; **Phoma palmatum,** N. Y., Pa.; **Cladosporium** sp., **Coniothyrium** sp., **Cristulariella** sp., on Norway maple.

MISTLETOE. **Phoradendron flavescens,** occasional in South.

NEMATODE, Root Knot. **Heterodera marioni,** Oreg.

PHYSIOGENIC Leaf Scorch. Common on street and lawn trees, associated with drouth, frost, sunburn.

POWDERY MILDEW. **Phyllactinia corylea,** Mass., Wis.

Rot, Heart. **Daedalea unicolor,** occasional in living trees; **D. quercina; Ganoderma lucidum,** widespread; **Fomes applanatus; F. fomentarius; Steccherinum** (*Hydnum*) **septentrionale; Polyporus adustus; P. hirsutus; P. hispidus; P. pargamenus; P. squamosa; P. sulphureus,** sometimes on living trees with wounds; **Pholiota adiposa; Poria subacida; Stereum fasciatum.**

Rot, Root. **Armillaria mellea.**

Rot, Wound. **Pleurotus ulmarius; P. ostreatus; Schizophyllum commune; Stereum hirsutum.**

Wilt. **Verticillium albo-atrum,** perhaps also **V. dahliae,** widespread in cultivated trees, especially Norway maple.

Verticillium wilt is probably the most destructive maple disease and seems to be particularly prevalent in street trees. The wilting may be confined to a single branch, which sometimes can be cut out to save the rest of the tree, or it may kill the whole tree. In removing the dead tree care should be taken to remove all the roots, but even with that precaution it would be wiser to use some tree other than maple for replacement.

Leaf scorch is a very common foliage trouble, most pronounced on sugar maple, due to evaporation of water in hot, dry, windy weather faster than it can be drawn up from the roots. All measures promoting general health are useful, and sometimes judicial pruning of the top, to reduce the total transpiration surface, gives good results. The fungus anthracnose or leaf blight causes similar symptoms in an over-wet season, but not often enough to make annual spraying economical. Black tar spots on leaves are conspicuous but not very important. Several species of the leaf blister Taphrina sometimes cause early defoliation, but again the expense of spraying is not ordinarily warranted. Chemotherapy seems to have been successful in some cases of bleeding canker.

MARANTA (*Calathea*)

Leaf Spot. **Glomerella cincta,** N. J.; **Phyllosticta** sp., N. J.

MARGUERITE (*Chrysanthemum frutescens*)

Bacterial Crown Gall. **Agrobacterium tumefaciens,** Iowa, Md., N. J., N. Y., Va.

Nematode, Root Knot. **Heterodera marioni,** Fla., Miss., Ohio, Tex., Wash.

Powdery Mildew. **Erysiphe cichoracearum,** N. J.

Virus, Aster Yellows. **Chlorogenus callistephi** var. **californicus,** Cal.

Wilt. **Verticillium albo-atrum,** N. J.

MARIGOLD (*Tagetes*)

Blight, Head. **Botrytis cinerea,** Conn., N. J., Pa.; **Helminthosporium** sp., flower spot.

Blight, Southern. **Sclerotium rolfsii,** Fla., N. J., Va.

LEAF SPOT. **Alternaria** sp., secondary?; **Cercospora** sp., Conn., Fla.

NEMATODE, Root. **Aphelenchoides tagetae,** Md.

NEMATODE, Root Knot. **Heterodera marioni.**

ROT, Charcoal. **Macrophomina phaseoli,** Okla.

ROT, Root. **Pythium ultimum,** Cal.; **Rhizoctonia solani,** Tex.

ROT, Stem; Wilt. **Sclerotinia sclerotiorum,** N. Y.; **Phytophthora cryptogea,** N. Y.

RUST. **Coleosporium madiae** (II, III), Cal.; O, I on Monterey pine; **Puccinia tageticola** (II, III), Tex.

VIRUS, Mosaic. **Marmor cucumeris,** Fla.

VIRUS, Aster Yellows. **Chlorogenus callistephi,** Conn., N. J., N. Y., Pa., Wis. and var. **californicus.**

WILT; Stem Rot. **Fusarium** sp., Cal.

WILT. **Verticillium albo-atrum.**

Marigolds are easy to grow, without paying too much attention to disease. Fading flower heads should be cut off into a paper bag before the gray mold of Botrytis blight gets started.

MARSH–MARIGOLD (*Caltha palustris*)

LEAF GALL. **Synchytrium aureum,** Wis.

LEAF SPOT. **Cercospora calthae,** Wis.; **Cylindrosporium** sp., N. Y.; **Fabraea rousseauana,** Cal., Wis.; **Ramularia calthae,** N. Y., Wis.

POWDERY MILDEW. **Erysiphe polygoni,** Mich., Ohio, Wis.

RUST. **Puccinia areolata** (O, I, II, III), Cal., Col., Wash.; **P. gemella** (III), Cal., Ida., Mont., Oreg., Wash.; **P. calthae** (O, I, II, III), N. Y. to N. J., Ind., and N. Dak.; **P. calthicola** (O, I, II, III), N. Y. to Iowa and Minn.; **P. treleasiana** (III), Col., Nev., Utah, Wash., Wyo.

MATRICARIA (False-Chamomile)

NEMATODE, Root Rot. **Heterodera marioni,** Cal.

POWDERY MILDEW. **Erysiphe cichoracearum,** Wash.; **Sphaerotheca humuli,** Wash.

VIRUS, Aster Yellows. **Chlorogenus callistephi** var. **californicus,** Cal.

WHITE RUST. **Albugo tragopogonis,** Cal., N. Dak., Oreg.

MATRIMONY–VINE (*Lycium halimifolium*)

LEAF SPOT. **Alternaria** sp., Iowa; **Cercospora lycii,** Iowa; **Phyllosticta lycii,** Ohio, N. Y.

POWDERY MILDEW. **Erysiphe polygoni,** widespread; **Microsphaera diffusa,** Ohio, Pa., Utah; **Sphaerotheca pannosa,** Ida., Wash.

RUST. **Puccinia tumidipes** (II, III), N. Y. to Ala., Tex., S. Dak.; **P. globosipes** (II, III), Pa.

MARITIUS–HEMP (*Furcraea gigantea*)

NEMATODE, Root Knot. **Heterodera marioni,** Md.

MAURANDIA

LEAF SPOT. **Septoria antirrhinorum,** Tex.

MAY–APPLE (*Podophyllum*)

BLIGHT, Gray mold. **Botrytis cinerea,** N. J.
BLIGHT, Leaf. **Septotinia podophyllina,** Del., Md., Mo., N. J., N. Y., Va., W. Va.
LEAF SPOT. **Cercospora podophylli,** Ill.; **Glomerella cingulata,** Del.; **Pezizella oenotherae,** Va.; **Phyllosticta podophylli,** N. Y. to Ala., Ark., Wis.; **Septoria podophyllina,** N. Y., Mo., Wis. to Miss.
RUST. **Puccinia podophylli,** general (O, I, III).

MEADOW–BEAUTY (*Rhexia*)

LEAF SPOT. **Cercospora erythrogena,** Ala., Del., Miss., Tenn.; **Colletotrichum rhexiae,** Del.; **Phyllosticta rhexiae,** Fla.

MEADOW–RUE (*Thalictrum*)

DOWNY MILDEW. **Phytophthora thalictri,** Wis., Conn., N. Y.
LEAF SPOT. **Ascochyta clematidina** f. **thalictri,** Wis.; **Cercospora fingens,** Wis., Ill.; **Cercosporella filiformis,** Wis.; **Cylindrosporium thalictri,** Ind., Kans., Wis.; **Gloeosporium thalictri,** Wis.; **Mycosphaerella thalictri,** N. J., N. Y., Vt., Wis.; **Septoria thalictri,** Kans.
POWDERY MILDEW. **Erysiphe polygoni,** Mass. to Pa., Ill., and N. Dak.
RUST. **Puccinia cockerelliana** (O, I), Col.; II, III on Festuca; **P. rubigovera** (O, I), Northeastern and North Central States to Col. and Mont.; **P. septentrionalis** (O, I), Alaska, ?Cal.; II, III on Polygonum; **Tranzschelia pruni-spinosae** (O, I), Col., Ind., Iowa, Kans., Nebr., N. and S. Dak., Ohio, Pa.; II, III on Prunus; **T. thalictri** (O, III), Eastern and Central States to Miss.; Cal., N. Mex., Ida.
SMUT, Leaf and Stem. **Urocystis sorosporioides,** Ariz., Mass., N. Y., Utah.
SMUT, White. **Entyloma thalictri,** Conn., Ill., Ind., N. Y., Wis.

MEADOWSWEET (*Filipendula*)

LEAF SPOT. **Cylindrosporium** sp., Conn.; **Septoria ulmariae,** Conn.
POWDERY MILDEW. **Sphaerotheca humuli,** Ind., N. Y., Vt.
RUST. **Triphragmium ulmariae** (O, I, II, III), Ind.

MEDLAR (*Mespilus germanica*)

BACTERIAL Fire Blight. **Erwinia amylovora,** N. Y.
LEAF SPOT. **Fabraea maculata,** Cal.

MELON, MUSKMELON, CANTALOUPE (*Cucumis melo*)

ANTHRACNOSE. **Colletotrichum lagenarium,** general, in East and South.

BACTERIAL Angular Leaf Spot. **Pseudomonas lachrymans,** Cal., Del., Iowa, Md., Mich., N. J., Pa.

BACTERIAL Wilt. **Erwinia tracheiphila,** general East of Rocky Mts.; Ariz. to Ida., Wash.

BLIGHT, Gummy Stem. **Mycosphaerella citrullina,** Del., Mass., N. J., N. Y., Tex.

BLIGHT, Leaf; Black Mold. **Alternaria cucumerina,** general.

BLIGHT, Southern. **Sclerotium rolfsii,** Fla., Ohio, Tex., Va.

DAMPING-OFF. **Rhizoctonia solani,** Cal., Ga., N. J., also fruit rot, Fla., Tex.; **Pythium debaryanum,** Cal., Conn., Iowa, N. J., N. Y.

DODDER. **Cuscuta arvensis,** Md.

DOWNY MILDEW. **Pseudoperonospora cubensis,** general.

LEAF SPOT. **Cercospora** sp., Col., Ga., Tex.; **C. citrullina; C. cucurbitae,** Del., Ind., Tex.; **Septoria cucurbitacearum,** Del., Mass., Mich., N. H., N. Y., Pa., Vt., Wis.

NEMATODE, Root Knot. **Heterodera marioni,** N. J. to Fla., Cal.

POWDERY MILDEW. **Erysiphe cichoracearum,** general.

ROT, Charcoal. **Macrophomina phaseoli,** Oreg., Tex., Cal.

ROT, Fruit. **Fusarium** spp., general in market; **Monilia sitophila,** Ind., N. Y.; **Mucor** sp., N. Y.; **Penicillium** spp., blue mold; **Phytophthora** sp.; **Rhizopus stolonifer,** cosmopolitan; **Trichoderma viride,** green mold, Minn.; **Tricothecium roseum,** pink mold, occasional in market.

ROT, Root; Cottony Leak. **Pythium aphanidermatum.**

ROT, Root. **Phymatotrichum omnivorum,** Tex.; **Pythium periploccum,** Cal.

ROT, Stem. **Sclerotinia sclerotiorum,** Ark., Mass., Tex.

SCAB. **Cladosporium cucumerinum,** occasional East and Central States.

VIRUS, Curly Top. **Ruga verrucosans,** Ariz., Cal., Ida., Oreg., Tex., Wash.

VIRUS, Mosaic. **Marmor cucumeris,** and special cantaloupe strain.

VIRUS, Ring Spot. **Annulus tabaci,** N. C., Pa., Va.

WILT. **Fusarium oxysporum** f. **melonis,** general.

Melons belong to the cucurbit family and in general have the same diseases as cucumbers. Downy mildew is a problem on the moist East Coast and powdery mildew may be a limiting factor in California and the arid Southwest. Although there are varieties resistant to powdery mildew, different physiological races of the fungus keep things complicated. Sulfur dust should not be used for mildew except on sulfur-resistant varieties of melon. Variety Iroquois is resistant to Fusarium wilt. The mosaic virus is transmitted both by seed and aphids. Purchase virus-free seed, eliminate weeds, and keep down insects so far as possible. Sulfur dust, used for mildew on sulfur-resistant varieties, is a help in insect control.

MELOTHRIA

Downy Mildew. **Pseudoperonospora cubensis,** Ga., Ohio.
Nematode, Root Knot. **Heterodera marioni,** Fla.
Powdery Mildew. **Erysiphe cichoracearum,** Wis.

MENTZELIA (Blazing Star)

Leaf Spot. **Phyllosticta mentzeliae,** Kans., Tex.; **Septoria mentzeliae,** Kans., Wash., Tex.
Rot, Root. **Phymatotrichum omnivorum,** Tex.; **Rhizoctonia solani,** N. J.
Rust. **Puccinia aristidae** (O, I), Ariz., Col.; II, III on grasses; **Uredo floridana,** Fla.

MENZIESIA

Leaf Gall. **Exobasidium vaccinii,** Pacific Northwest; N. C., Va., W. Va.
Leaf Spot, Tar. **Rhytisma** sp.; **Melasmia menziesii,** Mont. to Oreg., Wash.
Rust. **Pucciniastrum myrtilli** (II, III), W. Va.; O, I on hemlock.

MERTENSIA (Bluebells, Virginia-Cowslip)

Downy Mildew. **Peronospora** sp., Mont.
Leaf Spot. **Septoria poseyi,** Oreg.
Powdery Mildew. **Erysiphe cichoracearum,** Ala., Col., Mont., Utah, Wyo.
Rot, Stem. **Sclerotinia sclerotiorum,** Col.
Rust. **Puccinia mertensiae,** Col., Utah, Wyo.; **P. rubigo-vera** var. **apocrypta** (O, I), N. and S. Dak.
Smut, Leaf. **Entyloma serotinum,** Ind., Iowa, Md., Va., Wyo.

MESEMBRYANTHEMUM (Fig-Marigold)

Nematode, Root Knot. **Heterodera marioni,** Ala., Tex.

MESQUITE (*Prosopis*)

Bacterial Crown Gall. **Agrobacterium tumefaciens.**
Blight, Leaf. **Cercospora prosopidis; Scleropycnium aureum,** Ariz., Tex.
Leaf Spot. **Napicladium prosopodium,** Tex.; **Phyllosticta juliflora,** Tex.; **Gloeosporium leguminum,** also pod spot, Tex.
Mistletoe. **Phoradendron californicum** and **P. flavescens,** Tex.
Powdery Mildew. **Uncinula prosopodis,** Tex.
Rot, Heart. **Polyporus texanus,** Cal., Tex.; **Schizophyllum commune.**
Rot, Root. **Phymatotrichum omnivorum,** Tex.
Rust. **Ravenelia arizonica** (II, III), Tex. to Cal.; **R. holwayi** (O, I, II, III), Tex. to Cal.

MIGNONETTE (*Reseda*)

Damping-Off, Root Rot. **Rhizoctonia solani,** Conn.
Leaf Spot. **Cercospora resedae,** Mass. to Miss., Mo., Iowa.
Nematode, Root Knot. **Heterodera marioni,** Fla.
Wilt. **Verticillium albo-atrum,** N. Y.

MIKANIA (Climbing Hempweed)

Leaf Spot. **Cercospora mikaniae,** Miss.; **Septoria mikanii,** Conn., Tex.
Rust. **Puccinia spegazzinii,** Ala., Fla., Miss., N. C.

MILKWORT (*Polygala*)

Anthracnose. **Gloeosporium ramosum,** Ind., N. J., Wis.
Leaf Spot. **Cercospora grisea,** Miss., N. J., Va.; **Septoria consocia,** Ind., Mich.; **S. polygalae,** N. Y.
Rust. **Aecidium renatum,** N. Mex.; **Puccinia andropogonis** var. **polygalina** (O, I), Iowa, Mich., Wis.; II, III Andropogon; **P. pyrolae** (III), Conn., Me., Mich., N. H., N. Y., Wis.

MIMOSA SPP. (Leguminosae)

Leaf Spot. **Cylindrosporium** sp., Tex.
Rot, Root. **Phymatotrichum omnivorum,** Tex.
Rust. **Ravenelia dysocarpae** (III), Ariz.; **R. fragrans,** II, III, Ariz., Tex.

MIMOSA, SILK–TREE. (*Albizzia julibrissin*)

Canker, Dieback. **Nectria cinnabarina,** D. C., N. C., Va.
Wilt. **Fusarium oxysporum** f. **perniciosum,** N. J., Md. to Ala.

The mimosa wilt is one of the most devastating tree diseases on record. Between 1930, when trees started to die at Tryon, N. C., and 1947, it had spread to 82 counties in 6 states. In one North Carolina town wilt appeared in 1943 in one city block and in four years had killed trees on 232 blocks. The fungus is in the soil, with no possibility of control by spraying, but some resistant seedlings are being propagated. Out of 1437 seedlings 20 have survived after living with the disease eight years (up to 1949).

MIMULUS (Monkey-Flower)

Blight, Gray Mold. **Botrytis cinerea,** Alaska.
Leaf Spot. **Cercospora mimuli,** Mo., **Ramularia mimuli,** N. Y., Cal., Ohio, Wyo.; **Septoria mimuli,** Pa. to Miss., Mo., Neb.
Powdery Mildew. **Erysiphe cichoracearum,** Cal., Pa., Utah.
Virus, Aster Yellows. **Chlorogenus callistephi** var. **californicus.**

MINT (*Mentha*)

ANTHRACNOSE, Spot; Leopard Spot Disease. **Sphaceloma menthae,** Ind., Mich.
CANKER, Stem. **Fusarium** sp., Mich., Wash.
LEAF SPOT. **Cercospora menthicola,** Ill., Tex.; **Phyllosticta decidua,** occasional, Me. to Ohio, Iowa, Wis.; **Ramularia menthicola,** Cal., Me., Mont., Oreg., Wash., Wis., Wyo.; **R. variata,** Wis.; **Septoria menthicola,** Wis.
POWDERY MILDEW. **Erysiphe cichoracearum,** Col., Iowa, Utah, Wash.; **E. polygoni,** Tex.; **Sphaerotheca humuli,** Wash.
RUST. **Puccinia angustata** var. **typica** (O, I), Cal., S. Dak., Wis.; II, III on Scirpus, Eriophorum; **P. menthae** (O, I, II, III), East and Central States to Texas and Pacific Coast.
WILT. **Verticillium albo-atrum,** Ind., Mich., Oreg.

Rust (*Puccinia menthae*) is serious in mints grown commercially, in greenhouses or in the field. Overwintering spores can be killed by treating rhizomes with hot water. Spot anthracnose is largely controlled in the field by thorough coverage when mint is plowed under in the fall. Mint in the backyard garden is usually too prolific for worry about disease.

MISTLETOE (*Phoradendron*)

BLIGHT, Twig. **Nectria cinnabarina,** Tex.
BLIGHT, Leaf. **Sphaeropsis visci,** S. C., Tex., Fla.
CANKER, Felt Fungus. **Septobasidium pseudopedicellatum,** Fla.
DODDER. **Cuscuta exaltata,** Tex.
LEAF SPOT. **Exosporium phoradendri,** Tex.
RUST. **Uredo phoradendri,** Cal., Oreg.

If you treasure the mistletoe in your trees for Christmas greens you will be sorry to note it has a few diseases, but if you treasure your trees and consider mistletoe a pest, then you'll wish the above list were longer.

MOCK–CUCUMBER (*Echinocystis*)

ANTHRACNOSE. **Colletotrichum lagenarium,** Fla.
DOWNY MILDEW. **Pseudoperonospora cubensis,** Ohio.
LEAF SPOT. **Cercospora echinocystis,** N. J. to Ky., Wis.; also Fruit spot, Fla., Mich.; **Septoria** spp.
POWDERY MILDEW. **Erysiphe cichoracearum,** Wis.
VIRUS, Curly Top. **Ruga verrucosans,** Cal.
VIRUS, Mosaic. **Marmor cucumeris.**
WILT. **Fusarium** sp., Fla.

MOCK–STRAWBERRY (*Duchesnea indica*)

LEAF SPOT. **Pezizella oenotherae,** Va.
DOWNY MILDEW. **Peronospora potentillae,** N. C.
RUST. **Frommea obtusa** var. **duchesnea** (O, I, II, III), N. H. to Fla., Ky.

MONARDA (Horse-Mint, Bee-Balm, Wild-Bergamot)

BLIGHT, Southern. **Sclerotium rolfsii,** Tex.

LEAF GALL. **Synchytrium holwayi,** Iowa, Wis.

LEAF SPOT. **Cercospora** sp., Okla.; **Phyllosticta decidua,** Kans., Nebr., Okla., Tex., Wis.; **P. monardae,** Kans.; **Ramularia brevipes,** Ala., Tex.; **R. variata,** Wis.

RUST. **Puccinia angustata** (O, I), Nebr., Wis.; **P. menthae** (O, I, II, III), general from Me. to Miss.; Tex., Ida.

VIRUS, Mosaic. Unidentified.

MONARDELLA

LEAF SPOT. **Phyllosticta monardellae,** Cal.

RUST. **Puccinia menthae** (O, I, II, III), Cal., Nev., Oreg., N. Mex., Utah.

MONESES

RUST. **Chrysomyxa pyrolae** (II, III), Col., Me., Mich., Mont., N. Mex., Wash., Wyo.; O, I on spruce.

MONKSHOOD, ACONITE (*Aconitum*)

BACTERIAL Leaf Spot. **Pseudomonas delphinii,** Me.

DOWNY MILDEW. **Plasmopara pygmaea,** Alaska.

NEMATODE Root Knot. **Heterodera marioni,** N. Y., Vt.

ROT, Root. **Phymatotrichum omnivorum,** Tex.; **Rhizoctonia solani,** Conn., N. J.

ROT, Stem. **Sclerotinia sclerotiorum,** Col.; **Sclerotium rolfsii** (*S. delphinii*), Conn., Del., Minn., N. J., N. Y.

RUST. **Puccinia rubigo-vera** (O, I), Col.; II, III on Elymus, Festuca; **Uromyces lycoctoni** (O, I, II, III), Cal., Col., Tex., Utah, Wyo.

SMUT, Leaf and Stem. **Urocystis carcinodes,** Utah; **U. sorosporioides,** Utah.

VIRUS, Mosaic Unidentified.

WILT. **Verticillium albo-atrum,** Mass., N. J., N. Y., Ohio.

Verticillium wilt is doubtless more general in monkshood than the official reports, for I have seen it in nearly every garden. The leaves dry along the stem, flowers are poor, and when the stem is cut across the blackened bundles are readily seen. The clumps do not die immediately but peter out over a period of years.

MONKSHOOD VINE (*Ampelopsis aconitifolia*)

DIEBACK; **Tuberculaa nigricans,** N. H., Tex.

MONSTERA

LEAF SPOT. **Macrophoma philodendrii,** Fla., Mich.

MONTIA (Indian-Lettuce)

SMUT, Seed. **Ustilago claytoniae,** Wash.

MOONFLOWER (*Calonyction*)

LEAF SPOT. **Phyllosticta** sp., N. J.
NEMATODE, Leaf. **Aphelenchoides** sp., N. J.
NEMATODE, Root Knot. **Heterodera marioni,** N. and S. C.
RUST. **Coleosporium ipomoeae** (II, III), Ala., N. and S. C., Tex.; O, I on pine.
WHITE RUST. **Albugo ipomoeae-panduratae,** Fla.

MOONSEED (*Menispermum*)

LEAF SPOT. **Cercospora menispermi,** N. Y. to Va., Kans., Wis.; **Colletotrichum sordidum,** Wis.; **Phyllosticta menispermicola,** Ill.; **Septoria abortiva,** Ill., Kans.
POWDERY MILDEW. **Microsphaera alni,** widespread.
SMUT, Leaf. **Entyloma menispermi,** Pa. to Va., Kans., N. Dak.

MORNING-GLORY (*Ipomoea*)

BLIGHT, Southern. **Sclerotium rolfsii,** Tex.
BLIGHT, Thread. **Pellicularia koleroga** (*Corticium stevensii*).
CANKER, Stem. **Vermicularia ipomoearum,** N. Y., Pa.
LEAF SPOT. **Alternaria** sp., Va.; **Cercospora alabamensis,** Ala., Fla., N. J.; **C. ipomoeae,** Ala., Kans., Mo., Ohio; **C. viridula,** Ill., Nebr., N. J., N. C., Tex., Va.
NEMATODE, Root Knot. **Heterodera marioni,** Ala., Okla.
ROT, Root. **Phymatotrichum omnivorum,** Tex.
RUST. **Puccinia crassipes** (I, III), Fla., Ga., La., S. C.; **Coleosporium ipomoeae** (II, III), N. J. to Fla., Tex., Kans.; O, I on pine.
?VIRUS, Mosaic. Suspected virus, Fla.
WHITE RUST. **Albugo ipomoeae-panduratae,** N. J. to Ariz., Nebr.

MOTHERWORT (*Leonurus*)

LEAF SPOT. **Ascochyta leonuri,** La.; **Dimerosporium hispidulum,** Tex.; **Phyllosticta decidua,** Ohio, Tex., Wis.; **Septoria lamii,** Pa.
VIRUS, Mosaic. Unidentified, Ind.

MOUNTAIN-ASH (*Sorbus*)

BACTERIAL Fire Blight. **Erwinia amylovora,** widespread.
BACTERIAL Crown Gall. **Agrobacterium tumefaciens,** Conn., N. J.
BLIGHT, Leaf. **Fabraea maculata,** Alaska, Wis., Minn., W. Va.

Blight, Twig. **Phomopsis** sp., Mass.; **Valsa leucostoma,** Ohio, W. Va.

Canker, Blister. **Nummularia discreta,** Iowa, Mass.

Canker; Dieback. **Cytospora chrysosperma,** Minn., Mont., Nebr., N. J., Wash.; **C. leucostoma,** Mont.; **C. massariana,** Idaho; **C. microspora,** Mont.

Canker, Branch; Fruit Rot. **Glomerella cingulata,** Ind.

Canker, Trunk; Black Rot. **Cytospora rubescens; Physalospora obtusa,** Ind., Mich., Ohio, Conn. to Va.

Leaf Spot. **Graphium sorbi,** N. Y., Wis.; **Phyllosticta globigera,** Ida., Wash.; **P. sorbi; Septoria sorbi,** Iowa; **S. sitchensis,** Ida.

Rot, Root. **Armillaria mellea,** N. J.

Rot, Heart. **Polyporus hirsutus,** Mich., Wash.; **P. versicolor,** Wis.

Rust. **Gymnosporangium aurantiacum** (O, I), Me. to N. J., Wis.; III on juniper; **G. globosum** (O, I), Northeast; III on red-cedar; **G. juniperinum** (O, I), Mont. to Col., Wash.; **G. nelsoni,** Mont., Wash., Wyo.; **G. nootkatense,** Wash.; **G. libocedri** (O, I), Oreg.; III on Libocedrus.

Scab. **Venturia inaequalis,** Ill., Minn., N. Y., Wash.

Mountain-ash is quite susceptible to fire blight, but usually affected branches can be pruned out. Rust may show on the foliage in midsummer, and, if the mountain-ash is more desirable than the junipers near by, the latter can be eradicated. Fertilizing will help the tree recover after a bout with Cytospora cankers but may increase susceptibility to fire blight.

MOUNTAIN–HOLLY (*Nemopanthus mucronata*)

Leaf Spot. **Ramularia nemopanthus,** N. H., N. Y., Vt., Wis.

Leaf Spot, Tar. **Rhytisma ilicis-canadensis,** Me. to Pa., Mich.

Powdery Mildew. **Microsphaera alni,** N. Y., Wis.

MOUNTAIN–LAUREL (*Kalmia latifolia*)

Blight, Flower. **Ovulinia azaleae,** S. C., Ala.

Blight, Leaf. **Phomopsis kalmiae,** N. Y. to N. C.

Canker, Felt Fungus. **Septobasidium** sp., Tex., Ala.

Leaf Spot. **Cercospora kalmiae,** N. Y. to N. C.; **C. sparsa,** Miss., Pa., S. C., Tex.; **Venturia** (*Coleroa*) **kalmiae,** N. Y.; **Mycosphaerella colorata** (*Phyllosticta kalmicola*), Conn. to Ala., Ind., Mich., Tex.; **Septoria angustifolia,** Mass. to Ala., Ohio; **S. kalmicola,** N. C., Pa.

Physiogenic Chlorosis. Iron deficiency?

Rot, Root. **Phymatotrichum omnivorum,** Tex.; **Corticium galactinum,** near apple trees.

Phomopsis leaf blight and Mycosphaerella or Phyllosticta leaf spot are common and rather disfiguring in bushes in shade or under tree drip. In light cases, removal of spotted leaves is sufficient; in stubborn cases at least three sprays of bordeaux mixture, or less disfiguring proprietary copper sprays, will be needed, starting when new growth is fairly well out.

MOUNTAIN–MAHOGANY (*Cercocarpus*)

Rot, Wood. **Stereum hirsutum,** Oreg.

Various fungi on dead leaves, twigs and branches.

MOUNTAIN–MINT (*Pycnanthemum*)

Leaf Gall. **Synchytrium cellulare,** Wis.

Leaf Spot. **Cercoseptoria blephiliae,** Wis.; **Cercosporella pycnanthemi,** Ala.

Rust. **Puccinia angustata,** Ind.; **P. menthae,** Mass. to Va.; Iowa to Ala.; Cal., Tex., Okla., N. Dak.

MOUNTAIN–SORREL (*Oxyria*)

Rust. **Puccinia oxyriae** (II, III), Cal., Col., Ida., Oreg., Utah; O, I, unknown.

Smut, Floral. **Ustilago vinosa,** Cal., Col., Wash., Wyo.

MULBERRY (*Morus alba*)

Bacterial Hairy Root. **Agrobacterium rhizogenes,** Nebr.

Bacterial Leaf Spot. **Pseudomonas mori,** general.

Blight, Berry; Popcorn Disease. **Ciboria carunculoides,** N. C. to Fla., Tex.

Blight, Twig. **Myxosporium diedickei,** Tex., Wash.

Canker; Twig Blight. **Cytospora** sp., N. J., Tex.; **Dothiorella** sp., **D. mori; Fusarium lateritium** var. **mori,** widespread; **Nectria** sp., widespread.

Leaf Spot. **Cercospora moricola,** Pa. to Fla., Nebr., Tex.; **Cercosporella mori,** Nebr., Okla., Tex.; **Mycosphaerella mori,** widespread.

Nematode, Root Knot. **Heterodera marioni,** N. J., N. C., Okla.

Powdery Mildew. **Phyllactinia corylea,** Ohio; **Uncinula geniculata,** N. Y. to Kans., Ala. on red mulberry.

Rot, Root. **Armillaria mellea,** Del., N. C., Okla.; **Helicobasidium purpureum,** Tex.; **Phymatotrichum omnivorum,** Tex.

Rot, Heart. **Polyporus farlowii,** Ariz., N. Mex.; **P. hispidus,** Conn.

Rot, Wood. **Schizophyllum commune; Stereum cineracens.**

Bacterial leaf spot damages nursery trees having overhead irrigation and Cercosporella leaf spot sometimes defoliates older trees.

MULLEIN (*Verbascum*)

Downy Mildew. **Peronospora sordida,** N. J.

Leaf Spot. **Cercospora verbascicola,** Tex.; **Phyllosticta verbascicola,** Tex.; **Ramularia variabilis,** N. Y. to Miss., Tex., Wash.; **Septoria verbascicola,** Tex., N. Y. to Ala., Mo., Tex.

Nematode, Root Knot. **Heterodera marioni.**

Powdery Mildew. **Oidium** sp., N. J.

Rot, Root. **Phymatotrichum omnivorum,** Tex.

MUSK–ROOT (*Adoxa*)

LEAF GALL. **Synchytrium anomalum,** Iowa.

LEAF SPOT. **Phyllosticta adoxae,** Col.

RUST. **Puccinia adoxae** (III), Col., Utah, Wyo.; **P. argentata** (O, I), Iowa, Minn., Wis.; II, III on Impatiens.

MUSTARD GREENS (*Brassica hirta*)

BACTERIAL Soft Rot. **Erwinia carotovora,** Okla.

CLUB ROOT. **Plasmodiophora brassicae,** Cal.

DAMPING-OFF. **Rhizoctonia solani,** cosmopolitan.

DOWNY MILDEW. **Peronospora parasitica.**

LEAF SPOT. **Alternaria oleracea,** Cal.; **Cercospora** sp.; **Cercosporella albo-maculans,** Cal.; **Ramularia armoraciae,** Mich.; **Septoria brassicae,** W. Va.

NEMATODE, Root Knot. **Heterodera marioni,** Fla., Tex.; **H. schachtii,** Utah.

POWDERY MILDEW. **Erysiphe polygoni.**

ROT, Crown; Drop. **Sclerotinia sclerotiorum,** Tex.

RUST. **Puccinia aristidae,** Col.

VIRUS, Mosaic. **Marmor brassicae.**

WHITE RUST; White blister. **Albugo candida,** general.

WILT, **Fusarium** sp.

MYRTLE (*Myrtus communis*)

LEAF SPOT. **Pestalotia decolorata,** La.

ROT, Stem. **Sclerotium rolfsii,** Fla.

NANDINA

ANTHRACNOSE. **Glomerella cingulata,** Tex.

LEAF SPOT. **Cercospora nandinae,** Ala.

NEMATODE, Root Knot. **Heterodera marioni,** N. C.

ROT, Root. **Phymatotrichum omnivorum,** Tex.

NARCISSUS (Daffodil)

BLIGHT, Leaf; Fire. **Botrytis** (*Sclerotinia*) **polyblastis; B. cinerea.**

LEAF SCORCH. **Stagonospora curtisii,** general, especially in eastern and southern bulb districts.

LEAF SPOT, Ramularia; White Mold. **Ramularia vallisumbrosae,** Oreg., Wash.

NEMATODE, Bulb; Scale necrosis. **Aphelenchoides** sp., Fla., Ga., N. and S. C.

NEMATODE, Brown Ring Disease; Leaf "Spikkel." **Ditylenchus dipsaci,** in all narcissus areas.

NEMATODE, Root. **Pratylenchus pratensis,** Ohio.

ROT, Basal. **Fusarium oxysporum** f. **narcissi,** general on hardy varieties.

ROT, Neck; Smoulder. **Sclerotinia narcissicola,** N. J., N. Y., Oreg., Va., Wash., probably general in northern bulb districts, but not on Polyanthus narcissus.

ROT; Large Scale Speck. **Sclerotium** sp., Md., Mo., N. C., N. Y., Oreg., Va., Wash.

ROT; Small Scale Speck; Neck Rot. **Sclerotium** sp., common, especially in South.

ROT, Root and Bulb. **Armillaria mellea,** Cal., Oreg., Wash.; **Aspergillus** spp., black mold; Penicillium, blue mold, in wounds; **Trichoderma viride,** green mold in scales, cosmopolitan after injury; **Rhizopus stolonifer,** soft rot, cosmopolitan after sun scald.

ROT, Root. **Cylindrocarpon radicicola,** secondary, N. C., N. Y., Oreg., Va., Wash.

ROT, Leaf and Stem. **Gloeosporium** sp., La., N. C.

ROT, Wet Scale. **Sclerotium rolfsii,** Cal., Fla., N. Y., Va.

VIRUS, Mosaic; Yellow Stripe; Gray disease, general.

VIRUS, White Streak. Probably general.

Control of narcissus diseases rests with the grower, who should supply the gardener with sound, healthy bulbs. In most cases this is done; yet on rare occasions I have found an almost total loss from smoulder, a disease which must have gotten to the garden via infected bulbs. Inspect all bulbs very carefully before planting, making sure there are no black sclerotia present. Do not plant any bulbs with basal rot—chocolate brown at base of scales—for once the Fusarium is in the soil it is hard to get rid of.

NASTURTIUM (*Tropaeolum*)

BACTERIAL Leaf Spot. **Pseudomonas aptata,** Me., Minn., Miss., N. J., Pa., Va.

BACTERIAL Wilt. **Pseudomonas solanacearum,** Fla., Md., N. J., N. C., Va.

BLIGHT, Gray Mold. **Botrytis cinerea,** Alaska.

DODDER. **Cuscuta** sp., Mo., N. H.

LEAF SPOT. **Cercospora tropaeoli,** Ala.; **Heterosporium** sp., Cal.; **Pleospora** sp. (Conidial stage *Stemphylium* or *Alternaria*), Miss., N. J., Ohio.

NEMATODE, Root Knot. **Heterodera marioni,** N. J.; Root Gall. **H. schachtii.**

RUST. **Puccinia aristidae** (O, I), Utah; II, III on grasses.

VIRUS, Curly Top. **Ruga verrucosans,** Cal., Tex.

VIRUS, Spotted Wilt. **Lethum australiense,** Cal., Md., Tex.

VIRUS, Yellows. **Chlorogenus callistephi** var. **californicus,** Cal.

Compared to the almost inevitable affliction of black aphids nasturtium diseases pale into insignificance.

NECTARINE (*Prunus persica* var. *nectarina*)

BACTERIAL Leaf Spot. **Xanthomonas pruni,** Okla.

BACTERIAL Crown Gall. **Agrobacterium tumefaciens,** Mo.

LEAF CURL. **Taphrina deformans,** Wash.

LEAF SPOT; Shot Hole. **Ascospora carpophilum,** Cal., Wash.

NEMATODE. Root Knot. **Heterodera marioni,** Cal.
POWDERY MILDEW. **Podosphaera oxyacanthae,** Ida., Wash.
ROT, Brown; Twig blight. **Monilinia laxa,** Cal., Wash.; **M. fructicola,** Conn., N. Y.
SCAB. **Cladosporium caropophilum,** Conn., Del., Ill., N. Y.
VIRUS, Rosette. **Carpophthora rosettae.**
VIRUS, Yellows. **Chlorogenus persicae.**
VIRUS, Yellow-red Virosis. **Carpophthora lacerans.**

NEMOPHILA (Baby Blue-Eyes)

POWDERY MILDEW. **Erysiphe cichoracearum,** Cal., Nev., Tex., Wash.

NERINE

LEAF SCORCH; Red Blotch. **Stagonospora curtisii,** Cal.

NEW ZEALAND SPINACH (*Tetragonia expansa*)

LEAF SPOT. **Helminthosporium** sp., Tex.; **Cercospora tetragoniae,** Ind., Mass.
NEMATODE, Root Knot. **Heterodera marioni,** Tex.
VIRUS, Curly Top. **Ruga verrucosans,** Cal.
VIRUS, Mosaic, Del., and Rosette, Ind. Unidentified.
VIRUS, Aster Yellows. **Chlorogenus callistephi.**

NICOTIANA (Flowering Tobacco)

DOWNY MILDEW. **Peronospora tabacina,** Cal., Tex.
LEAF SPOT. **Alternaria longipes,** Tex.
NEMATODE, Root Knot. **Heterodera marioni,** Fla.
POWDERY MILDEW. **Oidium** sp.
ROT, Root. **Phymatotrichum omnivorum,** Tex.
VIRUS, Curly Top. **Ruga verrucosans,** Tex.
VIRUS, Mosaic. **Marmor tabaci** (experimental infection).
VIRUS, Ring Spot. **Annulus tabaci.**

NINEBARK (*Physocarpus*)

LEAF SPOT. **Cercospora spiraeae,** Ind.; **Marssonina neilliae,** Cal., Wis.; **Phyllosticta opulasteris,** Ida.; **Ramularia spiraeae,** Mich., N. Y., Wis.
POWDERY MILDEW. **Sphaerotheca humuli,** Mass. to Wis.

NOTHOSCORDUM (False Garlic)

RUST. **Uromyces hordeinus,** Kans., Okla., Tex. (O, I); II, III on Festuca; **Uromyces primaverilis** (O, I, III), Ill., Mo., Tex.
VIRUS, Mosaic. Unidentified. La.

NYMPHOIDES (Floating-Heart)

RUST. **Puccinia scirpi** (O, I) ; II, III on Scirpus, Fla.

SMUT, Leaf. **Burrillia decipiens,** N. J.

OAK (*Quercus*)

ANTHRACNOSE, Leaf and Twig Blight. **Gnomonia veneta,** East and Central States to Ga., Kans.; also on coast live oak, Oreg.

BLIGHT; Twig Canker. **Coryneum kunzei,** Iowa, Mass.; **Diplodia longispora,** N. J., N. Y., Ohio.

BLIGHT; Leaf. **Gloeosporium quernum,** Cal.

BLOTCH, Purple Leaf. **Morenoella quercina,** Ga., N. C.

CANKER, Bark. **Aleurodiscus oakesii,** N. Y. to Ill., Iowa, Cal.; **A. candidus; A. acerinus; Dichaena quercina,** N. J.

CANKER, Bleeding. **Phytophthora cactorum,** Cal., Fla., N. C.

CANKER, Trunk. **Nectria galligena; Strumella coryneoides,** Minn., Mo., Pa.

CANKER, Twig. **Physalospora glandicola,** Md.; **P. obtusa,** Minn., Va.; **P. rhodina,** Va.; **Pseudovalsa longipes,** Iowa.

LEAF BLISTER. **Taphrina caerulescens,** Northeast to Central and Gulf States; **T. rubeobrunnea,** N. Y.

LEAF SPOT. **Cylindrosporium microspilum,** Mo.; **Dothiorella phomiformis,** Mass. to Va., Mo.; **Gloeosporium septorioides,** Ill., Md., Mo., N. Y., Wis.; **G. umbrinellum; Leptothyrium dryinum,** Ga., N. Y., Wis.; **L. californicum,** on coast live oak, Cal.; **Marssonina martini,** N. Y. to Iowa, Wis.; **M. quercus,** Md., Mo.; **Microstroma album,** downy spot, W. Va.; **Monochaetia desmazierii,** Eastern States to S. C., Ark., Ill.; **Phyllosticta tumericola,** associated with insect galls; **P. livida,** Cal.; **Septogloeum quercum,** Wis.; **Septoria quercus,** Ill.; **S. quercicola,** Cal.

MISTLETOE. **Phorodendron flavescens,** N. C. to Fla., Tex.; **B. villosum,** Cal., Oreg. in live oak.

PHYSIOGENIC Chlorosis. Iron deficiency, in pin oaks, particularly.

POWDERY MILDEW. **Erysiphe trina,** witches' broom in live oak; **Microsphaera alni,** widespread; **Phyllactinia corylea,** N. J. to Ga., Miss.; **Sphaerotheca lanestris,** "brown mildew," serious on coast live oak, Ala., Cal., Miss.

ROT, Heart. **Daedalea quercina,** widespread; **D. confragosa,** Me., N. Y.; **Fistulina hepatica,** Va.; **Fomes applanatus,** East and Central States, Ariz., Cal.; **F. everhartii,** Mich., Minn., Cal.; **F. igniarius,** wound; **Hydnum erinaceous,** East to Gulf States; **Polyporus hispidus,** Conn., Va.; **Stereum** spp.

ROT, Mushroom Root. **Armillaria mellea,** widespread; **Clitocybe tabescens,** Okla.

ROT, Wood. **Daldinia vernicosa,** East and Central States; **Lenzites betulina,** cosmopolitan; **Polyporus sulphureus** and many other species, sometimes on living trees.

RUST, Leaf. **Cronartium quercuum** (*C. cerebrum*) (II, III), widespread; O, I on pines.

WILT. **Chalara quercina,** Mo. to Minn., Wis.

WILT, Seedling. **Phytophthora cinnamomi,** Md.

Chalara oak wilt is the most serious disease in the Upper Mississippi Valley, most serious on red and black oaks, with trees usually dying the first summer that symptoms—leaf crinkling, bronzing, defoliation—appear. Anthracnose is general, most severe on white oak, defoliating in wet seasons. Leaf blister is more serious in the South, where it sometimes causes defoliation. Powdery mildew, due to *Sphaerotheca lanestris,* is important in California where it produces witches' brooms on live oaks.

Oaks are frequently invaded by the honey mushroom, *Armillaria mellea,* sometimes called the oak fungus and causing "shoestring" root rot. Strumella canker causes sunken areas and swellings on trunks. Frequent in forest trees, it is sometimes found in ornamentals.

OCOTILLO (*Fouquieria splendens,* Coach-Whip)

RUST. **Aecidium cannonii** (O, I), Ariz.

OENOTHERA (Evening-Primrose)

DODDER. **Cuscuta arvensis,** Okla.

DOWNY MILDEW. **Peronospora arthuri,** Mass. to Miss., Kans., Mont., Nebr., Okla., S. Dak.

LEAF GALL. **Synchytrium fulgens,** Ala., Kans., La., Miss., N. C., Okla., Tex.

LEAF SPOT. **Alternaria tenuis,** N. J.; **Cercospora oenotherae,** Ala., Kans., Tex., W. Va.; **C. oenotherae-sinutae,** Ala., N. C.; **Pezizella oenotherae,** Ga., Md., Ohio, N. C.; **Pestalotia oenotherae,** Ohio, Okla.; **Septoria oenotherae,** Me. to Fla., N. and S. Dak., Okla.

POWDERY MILDEW. **Erysiphe polygoni,** general.

ROT, Root. **Phymatotrichum omnivorum,** Tex.; **Rhizoctonia solani,** Tex.

RUST. **Aecidium anograe,** Nebr.; **Puccinia aristidae** (O, I), Ariz., Nev.; II, III on grasses; **P. extensicola** var. **oenotherae** (O, I), Me. to Ala., Col., N. Dak., Tex., Ga.; II, III on Carex; **P. oenotherae** (O, I, II, III), Col., Cal. to Mont., Wash.; **Uromyces plumbarius** (O, I, II, III), general.

VIRUS, Mosaic. Unidentified.

OKRA (*Hibiscus esculentus*)

BLIGHT, Blossom. **Choanephora cucurbitarum,** Fla., Ga., Tex.

BLIGHT, Southern. **Sclerotium rolfsii,** Ala.

FRUIT SPOT; Pod Spot. **Colletotrichum gloeosporioides,** Fla., Pa.; **Ascochyta abelmoschi,** Ga., Md., N. J., N. Y.

Leaf Spot. **Alternaria** sp., Fla., Ohio, Pa., S. C., Utah; **Cercospora hibisci,** N. C. to Fla., Tex.; **C. malayensis,** Va. to Fla., Tex., Okla.; **Phyllosticta hibisina,** Ala., Ill., N. J.

Nematode, Root Knot. **Heterodera marioni,** general in South.

Powdery Mildew. **Erysiphe cichoracearum,** Conn., N. J., N. C., Pa.

Rot, Charcoal. **Macrophomina phaseoli,** Tex.

Rot, Pod. **Botrytis** sp., N. Y.

Rot, Root. **Phymatotrichum omnivorum,** Ariz., Tex.; **Rhizoctonia solani,** Ala., Fla.; **Thielaviopsis basicola,** N. J.

Rot, Stem. **Sclerotinia sclerotiorum,** Mass.

Virus, Ring Spot. **Annulus tabaci,** Ga. Va.

Wilt. **Fusarium oxysporum,** Conn. to Fla., Tex., Ariz.; **Verticillium albo-atrum,** widespread.

OLEANDER (*Nerium*)

Bacterial Gall. **Pseudomonas tonelliana,** Ariz., Cal., Conn.

Canker; Witches' Broom. **Sphaeropsis** sp., Fla.

Leaf Spot. **Alternaria** (*Macrosporium nerii*), Cal., Gulf States; **Cercospora neriella,** Ala., La.; **C. repens,** Tex.; **Gloeosporium** sp., N. J.; **Phyllosticta nerii,** Mich., Gulf States; **Septoria oleandrina,** Fla., La.

Rot, Root. **Clitocybe tabescens,** Fla.; **Phymatotrichum omnivorum,** Tex.

Scab; Spot Anthracnose. **Sphaceloma oleanderi,** La.

Sooty Mold. **Capnodium elongatum,** Gulf States.

OLIVE (*Olea*)

Anthracnose. **Gloeosporium olivarum,** Cal.

Bacterial Olive Knot. **Pseudomonas savastanoi,** Cal.

Black Spot. **Asterina oleina,** Fla., Ga.

Leaf Spot; Peacock Spot. **Cyclonium oleaginum,** Cal.

Cercospora sp., also fruit spot, Cal.

Physiogenic Bitter Pit; Dry Rot of Fruit. Associated with over-nutrition.

Chlorosis; Dieback. Boron deficiency.

Exanthema; Dieback. Deficiency of organic matter; poor drainage, Cal.; Copper deficiency.

Soft Nose, Blue Nose. Variety Sevillano, possibly related to water supply.

Nematode, Root Knot. **Heterodera marioni,** Cal.

Nematode, Root. **Pratylenchus musicola,** Cal.

Rot, Root. **Armillaria mellea,** Cal., Tex.; **Phymatotrichum omnivorum,** Tex.

ONCOBA

Rot, Root. **Phymatotrichum omnivorum,** Tex.

ONION (*Allium cepa*)

BACTERIAL Soft Rot. **Erwinia carotovora; Pseudomonas alliicola,** Mass., N. Y., Wash.

BLIGHT, Southern. **Sclerotium rolfsii,** Ala., Cal., Ga., Okla., Tex.

BLOTCH, Purple. **Alternaria porri** (*Macrosporium*).

DAMPING-OFF. **Pythium** spp., Ida., Mass., N. Y.; **Rhizoctonia solani,** occasional.

DODDER. **Cuscuta** spp., Cal., Del., Ida., Ill., N. Y.; **C. gronovii,** N. Y.

DOWNY MILDEW. **Peronospora destructor,** general.

LEAF SPOT. **Heterosporium allii,** Cal., Col., Wash.; **Phyllosticta allii,** Ill.

NEMATODE, Bulb; Bloat. **Ditylenchus dipsaci.**

PHYSIOGENIC Blast, of Inflorescence. Cause indefinite.
Blight. Texas foliage disease.
Chlorosis. Mineral deficiency.
Scale. High Temperature.

ROT, Pink Root. **Pyrenochaeta terrestris,** widespread.

ROT, Neck; Gray Mold. **Botrytis** spp., N. H. to Fla.; **B. allii,** common; **B. byssoidea,** Conn., Ida., Ill., Ind.; **B. cinerea; B. squamosa,** Fla., Ida., Ill., Ind., La., Me.

ROT, Basal; Pink Root. **Fusarium** spp.

ROT, Black Stalk. **Stemphylium botryosum.**

ROT, Charcoal. **Macrophomina phaseoli,** Cal., Tex.

ROT, Dry. **Diplodia natalensis,** Tex.

ROT, Root. **Thielaviopsis basicola,** Tex.

ROT, Smudge. **Colletotrichum circinans.**

ROT, Soft. **Rhizopus stolonifer,** after sun scald or freezing; **Sclerotinia sclerotiorum.**

ROT, White. **Sclerotium cepivorum,** Cal., La., N. J., N. Y.

RUST. **Puccinia asparagi,** Cal., Conn., Iowa, Kans., Minn.; **P. porri** (II, III), Cal. Conn., Nebr.

SMUT. **Urocystis cepulae,** general.

VIRUS, Aster Yellows. **Chlorogenus callistephi,** widespread, common in Cal., Ida., Tex.

VIRUS, Yellow Dwarf. **Marmor cepae.**

Smut is the most general onion disease, but it seldom afflicts onions grown from sets, the usual method for a small garden. Growing colored instead of white onions avoids smudge, and neck rots to some extent. Sweet Spanish onions are resistant to pink root and yellow dwarf. If the pink-root fungus (*Pyrenochaeta terrestris*) has become established in the soil, onions should not be grown in that space for several years. Dithane dust is rather successful in control of downy mildew, and Dithane spray controls purple blotch.

ONOSMODIUM (Marbleseed)

Rust. **Puccinia rubigo-vera** var. **apocrypta** (O, I), Col., Kans., Nebr., N. Dak.

OPUNTIA (See Cacti)

ORANGE (See Citrus Fruits)

ORCHIDS (Imported species)

Anthracnose; Leaf and Stem Spot. **Colletotrichum** spp. and **Gloeosporium** spp., general. *Glomerella cincta* and *G. cingulata* are doubtfully distinguishable stages of *Colletotrichum cinctum* and *Gloeosporium gloeosporioides.*

Bacterial Soft Rot. **Erwinia carotovora,** N. Y.

Bacterial Leaf Spot; Bud Rot. **Phytomonas cattleyae,** Cal.

Blight, Gray Mold; Flower Spot. **Botrytis cinerea,** occasional.

Blight, Sobralia. **Glomerella cincta.** See above.

Leaf Spot. **Cercospora** spp.; **Chaetodiplodia** sp.; **Phyllosticta** spp.; **Physalospora** spp., also stem decay; **Selenophoma,** N. J., N. Y.; **Volutella albido-pila.**

Nematode, Root. **Pratylenchus pratensis,** Md.

Rot, Leaf. **Pythium splendens,** N. Y.

Rot, Root. **Rhizoctonia solani,** Okla.

Rot, Stem. **Sclerotium rolfsii.**

Rust. **Uredo behnickiana** (II), N. J., N. Y.; **U. epidendri** (II); **U. guacae,** Fla.; **U. nigropuncta** (II), Fla.

Virus, Mosaic. Suspected virus. Cal., Ill., N. J., N. Y., Ohio.

ORCHIDS (Native species)

Leaf Spot. **Cercospora cypripedii,** N. Y., Wis.; **Fusicladium aplectri,** Del.; **Mycosphaerella cypripedii,** N. Y.; **Phyllosticta aplectri,** Del.; **Septoria calypsonis,** Mich.

Rust. **Aecidium graebnerianum,** Cal., Mont., Oreg., Wash.; **Pucciniastrum goodyerae** (II, III), Cal., Col., N. Mex., Oreg., Wash.

OSAGE–ORANGE (*Maclura pomifera*)

Blight, Leaf. **Sporodesmium maclurae,** Mo., S. C., Tex.

Leaf Spot. **Cercospora maclurae,** Ala.; **Ovularia maclurae,** Ala., La., Tex.; **Phyllosticta maclurae,** Mo., N. J.

Mistletoe. **Phorodendron engelmanni,** Tex.; **P. flavescens,** Tex.

Rot, Root. **Phymatotrichum omnivorum,** Tex.

Rust. **Physopella fici,** S. C. to Fla., Tex.

OSIER (*Salix viminalis* and *S. purpurea*)

Canker, Blister. **Cryptomyces maximus.**
Leaf Rust. **Melampsora abieti-capraearum,** N. Y., Pa.

OSMANTHUS FRAGRANS (Sweet Olive)

Black Leaf Spot. **Asterina** sp., Miss.

HOLLY–OSMANTHUS (*O. ilicifolius*)

Leaf Spot. **Phyllosticta oleae,** Tex.; **P. sinuosa,** Tex.
Rot, Root. **Phymatotrichum omnivorum,** Tex.; **Rosellinia necatrix,** Cal.
Sooty Mold. **Capnodium elongatum,** Tex.; **Fumago salicina,** Tex.

OSMANTHUS AMERICANUS (American Devilwood)

Black Mildew. **Lembosia oleae,** Miss.; **Meliola amphitricha,** Fla. to Miss.
Black Spot. **Asterina asterophora,** Fla., Ga.; **A. discoidea,** Fla., Ga.; **A. purpurea,** Fla.
Leaf Spot. **Phyllosticta oleae,** Fla., N. C.; **P. sinuosa; P. terminalis,** Fla.

OSMARONIA (*Osoberry*)

Leaf Spot. **Cylindrosporium nuttallii,** Cal. to Wash.; **Gloeosporium osmaroniae,** Wash.
Powdery Mildew. **Phyllactinia corylea,** Oreg.

OSMORHIZA (Sweet-Root)

Leaf Gall. **Urophlyctis pluriannulata,** Mont.
Leaf Spot. **Cercospora osmorhizae,** Ill., Ohio, Wis.; **Fusicladium angelicae,** Wash.; **Phleospora osmorhizae,** N. Y., Iowa, Wis.; **Ramularia reticulata,** Wis., Va.; **Septoria aegopodii,** N. Y., N. Dak., Ohio, Wis.

OWLS–CLOVER (*Orthocarpus*)

Leaf Spot. **Ascochyta garrettiana,** Oreg., Utah.
Rust. **Cronartium coleosporioides** (II, III), Col., Ida., Utah; O, I on pine.

OXALIS

Leaf Spot. **Cercospora oxalidiphila,** Wis.; **Phyllosticta guttulatae,** Vt. to N. J., Ind.; **P. oxalidis,** Tex., Wis.; **Ramularia oxalidis,** N. H., Nebr., N. Mex., Pa., Tenn., Vt.; **Septoria acetosella,** N. Y.
Nematode, Root Knot. **Heterodera marioni.**
Rot, Root. **Thielaviopsis basicola, Conn.**
Rust. **Puccinia oxalidis** (II, III), Fla., Ga., La., Miss., N. Mex., S. C., Tenn., Tex., Wis.; O, I on Mahonia; **P. sorghi** (O, I), Kans., Ind., Iowa, Mich., Miss., N. and S. Dak., Okla., Tex.; II, III on corn and Euchlaena.

Smut, Seed. **Ustilago oxalidis,** Conn. to Miss., Tex., Ohio, Wis.
Virus, Curly Top. **Ruga verrucosans,** Tex.

OXYDENDRUM (Sourwood, Sorrel-Tree)

Blight, Twig. **Sphaerulina polyspora,** N. C.
Leaf Spot. **Cercospora oxydendri,** Ala., Miss., Tex., W. Va.; **Mycosphaerella caroliniana,** Ga., N. C., Tex., W. Va.
Rot, Root. **Phymatotrichum omnivorum,** Tex.
Rot, Wood. **Poria punctata; Godronia rugosa.**

PACHISTIMA

Leaf Spot. **Mycosphaerella pachystimae,** Ida.

PACHYSANDRA (Japanese Spurge)

Blight, Leaf. **Volutella pachysandrae** (conidial stage of *Pseudonectria pachysandricola*), Conn. to Va.; **Volutella** sp.
Leaf Spot. **Gloeosporium** sp., Va.; **Phyllosticta** sp., N. Y. to N. C.; **P. pachysandrae.**
Nematode, Root Knot. **Heterodera marioni.**

Volutella leaf blight is fairly common after injury, when the pachysandra is near a path, or when there is too much moisture from plants crowded too close together or an accumulation of leaves from trees overhead. Pinkish spore pustules appear on stems and large brown areas in leaves. Laborious cleaning out of infected plants plus a spray of Bordeaux mixture controls the disease, but it is easier to prevent it by keeping plants well thinned.

PACIFIC WAX–MYRTLE (*Myrica californica*)

Leaf Spot. **Phyllosticta myricae,** Cal.
Rust. **Cronartium comptoniae** (II, III), Oreg.

PAINTED–CUP, INDIAN PAINT–BRUSH (*Castilleja*)

Powdery Mildew. **Erysiphe polygoni,** Col., Wash.; **Sphaerotheca humuli** var. **fuliginea,** Col., Wash., Wis.
Rust. **Cronartium coleosporioides** (II, III), Cal., Col., N. Mex., Utah, Wyo., Wash., S. Dak. to Tex.; O, I on 2- and 3-needle pines; **Puccinia andropogonis** var. **micropuncta** (O, I), Cal., Iowa, Mont., N. Mex., Wis.; II, III on Andropogon; **P. castillejae** (II, III), Cal., Utah; O, I unknown.

PALMETTO, CABBAGE PALM (*Sabal*)

Black Mildew. **Meliola palmicola,** Gulf States.
Canker, Felt Fungus. **Septobasidium sabalis,** La.
Leaf Spot. **Helminthosporium apiculiferum,** La., Miss.; **Mycosphaerella serrulata,** Fla., S. C.; **Phyllosticta palmetto,** La., Miss.

SMUT, False. **Graphiola phoenicis,** Fla., Miss.; **G. thaxteri,** Fla.
Many other fungi on dead leaves, leaf stalks, and trunks.

PALMS

(See *Arecastrum, Arenga, Caryota, Cocos, Phoenix, Roystonea, Washingtonia,* below)

ARECASTRUM (Queen Palm, *Cocos plumosa,* or Plumy Coconut)

CANKER; Gummosis. **Dothiorella** sp., Cal.; **Penicillium vermoeseni,** Fla.
LEAF SPOT. **Glomerella cincta,** N. J.; **Septoria cocoina.**
ROT, Bud; Wilt. **Phytophthora palmivora,** Fla.
SMUT, False. **Graphiola phoenicis,** Fla.

ARENGA (Sugar Palm)

SMUT, False. **Graphiola phoenicis,** occasional.

CARYOTA (Fishtail Palm)

BLIGHT, Leaf and Stem. **Glomerella cingulata.**

COCOS (Coconut)

BLIGHT, Thread. **Pellicularia** (*Corticium*) **koleroga,** Fla.
LEAF SCORCH; Leaf-Bitten Disease; Stem Bleeding. **Ceratostomella paradoxa,** Fla.
LEAF SPOT, Gray; Leaf Break. **Pestalotia palmarum,** probably secondary, Fla.
ROT, Bud; Leaf Drop; Wilt. **Phytophthora palmivora,** Fla.
WILT. **Pythium** sp., Fla.

PHOENIX DACTYLIFERA (Date)

BLIGHT, Inflorescence; Fruit Rot. **Fusarium** spp., Ariz.
FRUIT SPOT; Brown Spot. **Helminthosporium molle,** Ariz.; **Alternaria** sp.; **A. stemphyloides,** Ariz., Cal., Tex.
LEAF SCORCH; Black Heart; Bud Rot. **Ceratostomella paradoxa.**
LEAF SPOT. **Exosporium palmivorum,** Gulf States.
NEMATODE, Root Knot. **Heterodera marioni,** Cal.
PHYSIOGENIC Black Nose. Fruit checking, cracking, due to rain and high humidity.
ROT; Decline Disease. **Omphalia pigmenta; O. tralucida,** Cal.
ROT, Fruit. **Aspergillus niger,** Cal., Wash.; **Catenularia fuliginea,** Ariz., Cal.; **Penicillium roseum,** Cal., Ariz.; **Pleospora herbarum.**
ROT, Leaf; Stalk; Shoot and Fruit Blight. **Diplodia phoenicum,** Ariz., Cal.; **Phomopsis phoenicola.**
ROT, Root Necrosis. **Ceratostomella radicicola.**

ROT, Wood. **Poria** spp., Ariz., Cal.
SMUT, False. **Graphiola phoenicis,** widespread.

PHOENIX CANARIENSIS (Canary Date)

CANKER. **Penicillium vermoeseni,** Cal.
LEAF SPOT. **Alternaria** sp., Fla.; **Exosporium palmivorum,** Fla., La., Tex.
NEMATODE, Root Knot. **Heterodera marioni,** Ariz.
ROT, Root. **Armillaria mellea,** Cal.
SMUT, False. **Graphiola phoenicis,** widespread.

ROYSTONEA (Royal Palm)

ANTHRACNOSE. **Colletotrichum gloeosporioides,** Fla., Tex.
LEAF SPOT. **Alternaria** sp., Fla.; **Diplodia** sp., Fla.; **Epicoccum neglectum,** Fla.; **Helminthosporium** sp., stripe, Fla.
LITTLE LEAF. Cause unknown, Fla.
NEMATODE, Root Knot. **Heterodera marioni,** Fla.
SMUT, False. **Graphiola phoenicis,** Fla.
WILT. **Phytophthora palmivora,** Fla.

WASHINGTONIA (Washington Palm)

LEAF SPOT. **Auerswaldia** sp., Cal.; **Cercospora** sp., Fla.; **Colletotrichum** sp., Fla.; **Cylindrocladium macrosporium,** Fla.; **Phoma palmicola,** Tex.
NEMATODE, Root Knot. **Heterodera marioni,** Ariz., Fla.
ROT, Bud. **Phytophthora** sp., Ariz.; **Penicillium vermoeseni,** Cal.
ROT, Root. **Clitocybe tabescens,** Fla.; **Phymatotrichum omnivorum,** Tex.
SMUT, False. **Graphiola phoenicis,** Fla., Tex.
WILT. **Pythium** sp., Fla.

The Penicillium disease—canker, bud or leaf rot—causes serious losses in ornamental palms in California. *Washingtonia robusta* is resistant and can be substituted for *W. filifera.*

PALO VERDE (*Cercidium*)

MISTLETOE. **Phoradendron californicum,** Tex. to Cal.
ROT, Root. **Phymatotrichum omnivorum,** Tex. to Cal.

PAMPAS-GRASS (*Cortaderia*)

LEAF SPOT. **Helminthosporium** sp., Ga.; **Hendersonia culmiseda,** Oreg.; **Phoma terrestris,** Ky.; **Phyllosticta** sp., Ky.

PANDANUS (Screw Pine)

LEAF SPOT. **Heterosporium iridis,** Iowa; **Macrophoma pandani,** Cal., Fla.; **Melanconium pandani,** Fla., Md.; **Phomopsis** sp., N. J.; **Pestalotia palmarum,** Fla.; **Volutella mellea,** N. Y.

PANSY (*Viola tricolor*)

ANTHRACNOSE. **Colletotrichum violae-tricoloris,** Me. to Fla., Ind., and Mich., Wash., Pa.

BLIGHT, Gray Mold. **Botrytis cinerea,** Alaska, La., N. J., probably general.

BLIGHT, Southern. **Sclerotium rolfsii,** Fla., Va.

DAMPING-OFF; Root Rot. **Pythium** spp., Cal., Conn., Mo., N. J.; **Rhizoctonia solani,** Del., Ill., Minn., N. Y.

DOWNY MILDEW. **Peronospora violae,** Ala., Ill., Miss., Nebr.

LEAF SPOT. **Alternaria violae,** N. J., N. Y., Pa.; **Cercospora violae,** Conn., Ind., Mich., N. Y., Tex., Wis.; **Phyllosticta rafinesquii,** Ala., Ill.; **P. violae,** Mich.; **Ramularia agrestis,** Oreg.; **R. lactea,** Wash.

NEMATODE, Root Knot. **Heterodera marioni,** N. Y., Tex.

POWDERY MILDEW. **Sphaerotheca humuli,** var. **fulginea,** Kans., Wash.

ROT, Root, Wilt. **Aphanomyces** sp., Md.; **Fusarium oxysporum,** Conn., Mich., Nebr., N. J., N. Y., Ohio, Tex.; **Thielaviopsis basicola,** Conn.

RUST. **Puccinia ellisiana** (O, I), Kans., Nebr.; II, III on Andropogon; **P. violae** (O, I, II, III), Conn., Fla., Kans., N. J., N. Dak., S. C.; **Uromyces andropogonis** (O, I), Conn.; II, III on Andropogon.

SCAB; Spot Anthracnose. **Sphaceloma violae,** Md., N. J.

SMUT, Seed. **Urocystis kmetiana,** Ark., Mo., Tenn.

VIRUS, Curly Top. **Ruga verrucosans,** Cal., Oreg., Tex.

PAPAYA, PAWPAW (*Carica*)

BLIGHT, Flower. **Choanephora americana,** Fla.

LEAF SPOT, Black. **Mycosphaerella caricae,** Fla.; Target. **Phyllosticta caricae-papayae,** Fla.

LEAF SPOT. **Pucciniopsis caricae,** Fla.

POWDERY MILDEW. **Erysiphe cichoracearum,** Cal., Fla.

ROT, Fruit, Leaf and Stem. **Colletotrichum gloeosporioides,** Fla., Tex.

ROT, Fruit. **Diplodia** spp., Tex.; **Fusarium** sp., Cal., Tex.

ROT, Root. **Phymatotrichum omnivorum,** Tex.; **Pythium aphanidermatum,** Cal., Fla.

ROT, Stem. **Sclerotium rolfsii,** Tex.

Pucciniopsis leaf spot and Colletotrichum fruit rot are said to be the two most important papaya diseases in Florida. Spraying with bordeaux mixture controls leaf spots.

PARKINSONIA

LEAF SPOT. **Cylindrosporium parkinsoniae,** Tex.; **Phyllosticta parkinsoniae,** Tex.

MISTLETOE. **Phoradendron californicum,** Cal., Tex.

ROT, Root. **Clitocybe tabescens,** Fla.; **Phymatotrichum omnivorum,** Ariz., Tex.

PARSLEY (*Petroselinum*)

Bacterial Soft Rot. **Erwinia aroideae,** Cal.; **E. carotovora,** Fla.
Blight, Leaf. **Alternaria dauci,** Conn.; **Septoria petroselini,** Cal., Conn., N. J., N. Y.
Blight, Gray Mold. **Botrytis cinerea,** Alaska.
Damping-Off; Root Rot. **Pythium** sp., N. J.; **Rhizoctonia solani,** N. J., N. Y.
Dodder. **Cuscuta,** Tex.
Leaf Spot. **Cercospora petroselini,** N. J.
Nematode. **Ditylenchus dipsaci,** Cal.
Nematode, Root Knot. **Heterodera marioni,** Fla., Ga., Kans., Tex., Va.
Rot, Root. **Phymatotrichum omnivorum,** Tex.
Rot, Stem. **Sclerotinia sclerotiorum,** Conn., Ga., La., N. Y., Pa., Tex., Va.
Virus Curly Top. **Ruga verrucosans,** Cal.
Virus, Yellows. **Chlorogenus callistephi,** Col., N. Y., Tex.

PARSNIP (*Pastinaca sativa*)

Bacterial Crown Gall. **Agrobacterium tumefaciens,** Va.
Bacterial Soft Rot. **Erwinia carotovora,** occasional in storage.
Leaf Spot. **Alternaria** sp., N. J.; **Cercospora pastinacea,** general; **C. pastinacina,** Cal., Ind., Mich., N. Y.; **Cylindrosporium pastinacae,** Utah, Wis.; **Ramularia pastinacae,** Ind., Mass., N. Y., N. Dak., Ohio.
Nematode, Root Knot. **Heterodera marioni,** Kans., N. J. and southward.
Physiogenic Heart Rot. Boron deficiency, N. Y.
Rot, Gray Mold. **Botrytis cinerea,** occasional.
Rot, Black Mold. **Rhizopus** spp., occasional in storage.
Rot, Root. **Phymatotrichum omnivorum,** Ariz., Tex.; **Rhizoctonia solani,** black scurf, N. C., Tex.
Rot, Watery Soft. **Sclerotinia sclerotiorum,** Cal., Ind., La.
Scab. **Actinomyces scabies,** Wash.
Virus, Mosaic. Undetermined, Oreg., Utah.
Virus, Aster Yellows. **Chlorogenus callistephi,** Me., N. Y., Pa., S. Dak., Tex., Wash., Wis., and var. **californicus,** Cal.

Ramularia leaf spot or blight may give some trouble but not usually enough to warrant control measures. One grower mows off tops in late summer, forcing new tops free from disease.

PARTRIDGE–BERRY (*Mitchella*)

Black Mildew. **Meliola mitchellae,** Ala., Fla., Miss., Pa.
Rot, Stem. **Sclerotium rolfsii,** Md.

PASSION–FLOWER, MAYPOP (*Passiflora*)

Blight, Southern. **Sclerotium rolfsii,** Fla.

Leaf Spot. **Colletotrichum gloeosporioides,** Fla., also stem spot; **Cercospora biformis,** Ark., N. C.; **C. fuscovirens,** Me. to Mo., Tex.; **C. regalis,** Tex.; **C. truncatella,** S. C., Tex.; **Gloeosporium fructigenum,** La.; **Phyllosticta** sp., N. J.

Nematode, Root Knot. **Heterodera marioni.**

Rot, Root. **Phymatotrichum omnivorum,** Tex.

Rot, Collar, **Sclerotinia** sp., Cal.

PAULOWNIA (Empress-Tree)

Leaf Spot. **Ascochyta paulowniae,** Md.; **Phyllosticta paulowniae,** Ala., Md., N. Y.

Rot, Root. **Phymatotrichum omnivorum,** Tex.

Rot, Wood. **Polyporus spraguei,** Ala.; **P. versicolor,** Md.

PAWPAW (*Asimima*)

Blotch, Leaf. **Phleospora asiminae,** Ohio to Kans.

Leaf Spot. **Cercospora asiminae,** widespread; **Phyllosticta asiminae,** widespread.

PEA (*Pisum sativum*)

Anthracnose, Leaf and Pod Spot. **Colletotrichum pisi,** Conn., Ga., Iowa, Me., Minn., N. Y., Wis.

Bacterial Blight. **Pseudomonas pisi,** general, especially East and South.

Blotch, Leaf. **Septoria pisi,** widespread but infrequent.

Blight, Seedling; Leaf Spot. **Alternaria** sp., Del., N. H.

Blight, Stem; Charcoal Rot. **Macrophomina phaseoli,** Tex.

Blight, Foot Rot. **Mycosphaerella pinodes,** widespread.

Blight, Southern. **Sclerotium rolfsii,** Fla.

Damping-Off; Root and Pod Rot. **Pythium** sp.

Dodder. **Cuscuta** sp., Mo.

Downy Mildew. **Peronospora pisi,** general, especially in North Central and Pacific Coast States.

Leaf Spot. **Ascochyta pisi,** general, rare in Northwest. **Pleospora hyalospora,** Miss.; **Cercospora pisa-sativae,** Ga.; **Septoria flagellifera,** Minn., N. and S. Dak., Wis.; **Stemphylium polymorphum,** Me.

Nematode, Root Knot. **Heterodera marioni,** Ariz., Cal., Fla., N. and S. C., Tex., Utah, Wis.

Physiogenic Chlorosis. Manganese or zinc deficiency, Fla., Tex., Wash.
Intumescence, Pod Swellings. Cal., N. J., Wash.
Seed Spotting. Cause unknown, Conn., Ida., Me., Mont., Okla., Va., Wis.

Powdery Mildew. **Erysiphe polygoni,** general.

Rot, Black Mold. **Rhizopus stolonifer,** cosmopolitan.

Rot, Foot. **Aphanomyces euteiches,** general, except in North; **Ascochyta pinodella,** Conn., N. J. to Fla., Col., Minn., Mont., Oreg., Utah, Wash.

Rot, Gray Mold. **Botrytis cinerea,** occasional, Ida., Me., Wash.

Rot, Root. **Fusarium solani** f. **pisi,** N. Y. to Fla.; **Fusarium** spp. wilt, Minn., Wis.; **Pellicularia filamentosa** (*Rhizoctonia solani*), stem canker, damping-off, general; **Phoma** sp., N. J., Wis.; **Pyrenochaete terrestris,** Iowa; **Phymatotrichum omnivorum,** Tex.; **Phytophthora** sp., Cal., Conn.; **Thielaviopsis basicola,** Ark., Cal.

Rot, Stem; Wilt. **Sclerotinia sclerotiorum,** Cal., Del., Fla., Ida., Mont., N. J., Pa., Tex., Va., Wash.

Rust. **Uromyces fabae** (O, I, II, III), Cal., Ida., Me., Mass., Minn., Nebr., N. Dak., Wash., Wyo.

Scab; Black Spot. **Cladosporium pisicola,** Cal., Oreg., Utah.

Virus, Pea-Mosaic. **Marmor leguminosarum;** and Pea Enation-Mosaic, **Marmor pisi,** general.

Virus, Pea-Mottle. **Marmor efficiens,** Wash.

Virus, Pea-Wilt. **Marmor repens,** Col., Ida., Wash.

Virus, Spotted Wilt. **Lethum australiense,** Cal., Wis.

Wilt. **Fusarium orthoceras** var. **pisi,** Mass. to Va., Ill., Minn.; Cal., Col., Ida., Mont., Oreg., Wash.; **F. oxysporum** f. **pisi,** N. H. to S. C., Ill., Minn., Neb., Cal., Col., Ida., Mont., Oreg., Wash.

Seed treatment with Spergon, or Arasan, to prevent damping-off and root rots, pays off in increased yields. Resistant varieties are the answer to Fusarium wilt. Telephone, Dwarf Alderman, Teton, Asgrow 40, Alaska, are among the wilt-resistant garden peas. Clean seed, preferably grown in the West, is the best way to avoid bacterial blight. A well-drained, fertile soil, 3 to 5 year rotation, and cleaning up or plowing under pea refuse immediately after harvest all help to produce healthy peas. Rhizoctonia root rot may make growing peas almost hopeless in home gardens.

PEACH (*Prunus persica*)

Bacterial Shoot Blight; Gummosis. **Pseudomonas syringae,** Cal., Ore.

Bacterial Crown Gall. **Agrobacterium tumefaciens,** general.

Bacterial Hairy Root. **Agrobacterium rhizogenes,** Central States.

Bacterial Leaf Spot. **Xanthomonas pruni,** East and Central States.

Blight; Shot-Hole Disease; Pustular Spot. **Coryneum carpophilum** (conidial stage of *Ascospora*), general, especially in West.

Blight, Leaf. **Fabraea maculata,** Cal., N. J.

Blight, Twig. **Coniothyrium** sp., Tex.; **Cyphella marginata,** Oreg.; **Nectria cinnabarina,** Ala.

Canker, Crown. **Phytophthora citrophthora,** Cal.

CANKER, Stem. **Phoma persicae,** East and South; **Phytophthora cactorum,** Ark., Cal.

CANKER, Dieback; Gummosis. **Botryosphaeria ribis,** Fla., Ga.; **Valsa cincta** and **V. leucostoma,** widespread East and Central States; **Fusicoccum persicae,** Ga., La., Pa.; **F. amygdali,** Mass., N. J., N. Y.

DAMPING-OFF. **Rhizoctonia solani,** Ark., Conn.

LEAF CURL. **Taphrina deformans,** general.

LEAF SPOT, Shot-Hole. **Cercospora circumscissa,** general.

LEAF SPOT. **Cercospora consobrina,** Ill., La.; **Phyllosticta circumscissa,** widespread; **P. persicae,** Md., Nebr., Ohio; **Mycosphaerella persica,** frosty mildew, widespread.

NEMATODE, Root Knot. **Heterodera marioni,** N. C. to Kans., Fla., Cal.

PHYSIOGENIC Chlorosis. Iron or magnesium deficiency, Southwest.

Little Leaf. Zinc deficiency, Cal.

Gummosis. Winter injury, bad drainage.

POWDERY MILDEW. **Podosphaera oxyacanthae,** general; **Sphaerotheca pannosa,** general.

ROT, Brown. **Monilinia fructicola,** general.

ROT, Brown; Blossom and Twig Blight. **Monilinia laxa,** Pacific Coast States.

ROT, Bud and Twig Blight. **Fusarium lateritium,** Cal., Ga., Kans.

ROT, Fruit. **Aspergillus niger,** black mold, cosmopolitan; **Botrytis cinerea,** gray mold, cosmopolitan; **Trichothecium roseum,** pink mold, widespread; **Choanephora persicaria,** in market, N. Y.; **Diplodia natalensis,** gumming disease, Ala., Fla., Tex.; **Fusarium** spp., Cal., Ill., N. Y., Tex.; **Glomerella cingulata,** occasional; **Rhizopus nigricans,** cosmopolitan.

ROT, Root. **Armillaria mellea,** cosmopolitan; **Clitocybe monadelpha,** Ark., Fla., Mo., Okla.; **C. tabescens,** Fla.; **Phymatotrichum omnivorum,** Ariz., N. Mex., Tex.; **Ganoderma curtisii,** N. C., Va.

ROT, Heart. **Fomes applanatus,** Conn., N. J.; **F. connatus,** Conn.; **F. pinicola; F. subroseus,** Oreg., W. Va.; **Lenzites saepiaria.**

ROT, Seedling Stem. **Sclerotium rolfsii,** South.

ROT, Silver Leaf. **Stereum purpureum,** occasional.

ROT, Wood, Sapwood. **Polyporus hirsutus** and **P. versicolor,** cosmopolitan; **P. lacteus,** N. C.; **Stereum hirsutum,** Oreg.

RUST. **Tranzschelia pruni-spinosae** var. **discolor** (II, III), general; O, I on anemone, hepatica.

SCAB. **Cladosporium carpophilum,** general.

SOOTY MOLD, Fruit stain. **Fumago vagans,** cosmopolitan.

VIRUS, Peach Asteroid Spot. **Marmor astri,** Cal.

VIRUS, Peach Line-Pattern Virosis. **Marmor lineopictum,** Cal., Ky., Mich., Ohio.

VIRUS, Peach Mosaic. **Marmor persicae,** Ariz., Cal., Col., N. Mex., Okla., Tex., Utah.

VIRUS, Phony Peach. **Nanus mirabilis,** Ala., Ark., Fla., Ga., La., Miss., Mo., S. C., Tenn., Tex.

VIRUS, Peach Red-Suture. Prunus virus 4, Mich., Md.

VIRUS, Peach Rosette. **Carpophthora rosettae,** Ala., Ga., Mo., Okla., S. C., Tenn., W. Va.

VIRUS, Peach-Wart. **Galla verrucae,** Ida., Oreg., Wash.

VIRUS, Peach Yellow Bud Mosaic. **Inops consilii.**

VIRUS, Peach Yellows. **Chlorogenus persicae,** Eastern U. S., to S. C.

VIRUS, Peach X-Disease; Yellow-Red Virosis. **Carpophthora lacerans.**

Brown rot is the No. 1 peach enemy, and spray schedules are built around this, although they start with a dormant spray of lime sulfur, bordeaux mixture, Fermate or Elgetol to control leaf curl. Wettable sulfur is the standard spray for brown rot but Phygon and other organic fungicides are used somewhat. Get the latest advice and spray schedule from your county agent.

Peach foliage is very sensitive to arsenicals and, where lead arsenate is combined with the fungicide, directions should be most carefully followed as to amounts and the addition of lime or zinc sulfate for safety. Never allow a spray prepared for shade trees to touch peach foliage.

For a few small peach trees dusting will be simpler, and a mixture of 80 parts fine dusting sulfur and 20 parts of lime is recommended by some State Experiment Stations for control of brown rot.

PEANUT (*Arachis hypogaea*)

BACTERIAL WILT. **Pseudomonas solanacearum,** Ala., Fla., N. C., Va.

BLIGHT, Stem. **Diaporthe sojae,** Va., W. Va.

BLIGHT, Seedling. **Rhizoctonia** spp., N. C. to Fla., Cal., Okla., Tex.

BLIGHT, Southern; Stem and Nut Rot. **Sclerotium rolfsii.**

LEAF SPOT. **Alternaria** sp., Fla., Mo., N. J., N. Mex., S. C.; **Ascochyta** sp., Ark.; **Phoma** sp., Mo., Va.; **Phyllosticta** sp., Ala., Ark., Miss.; **Pleospora** sp., Ark., Okla.; **Stemphylium** sp., N. Dak.

LEAF SPOT; Brown Halo Spot. **Mycosphaerella arachidicola,** general; **M. berkeleyi** (*Cercospora personata*), general.

NEMATODE. **Heterodera marioni,** Cal., Fla., Ga., N. C., but usually resistant.

NEMATODE, Root. **Aphelenchoides parietinus,** Miss.

PHYSIOGENIC Chlorosis. Mineral deficiency, excess lime, Fla., Tex.

Necrotic Spot. Perhaps nutritional deficiency.

"Pouts," Stunting, Chlorotic spotting, caused by thrips, N. C., Tex.

ROT; Black Mold, of Pods. **Cladosporium herbarum,** cosmopolitan.

ROT, Blue Mold, of Pods and Nuts. **Penicillium** sp.

ROT, Gray Mold, Leaf. **Botrytis cinerea,** Conn., Miss., Tenn.

ROT, Charcoal. **Macrophomina phaseoli.**

ROT, Root. **Curvularia inaequalis,** S. C.; **Helminthosporium** sp., Okla.; **Phymatotrichum omnivorum,** Ariz., Tex.; **Pythium** sp., Cal., Ga., N. C.; **Thielaviopsis basicola,** N. C.

ROT, Seed. **Rhizopus** spp.; **Trichoderma viride,** S. C.

ROT, Stem, Pod. **Fusarium** spp., also root rot, wilt; **Physalospora rhodina,** Fla., Ga.

RUST. **Puccinia arachidis** (II), occasional in Fla., Ga., Tex.

VIRUS, Stunt. Unidentified, Tex.

Treat seed before planting with Arasan or 2% Ceresan. Dust with sulfur to control leaf spot. Rotate crops to avoid southern blight and bacterial wilt.

PEAR (*Pyrus*)

ANTHRACNOSE, Northwestern; Black Canker. **Neofabraea perennans,** Oreg., Wash.

BACTERIAL Fire Blight. **Erwinia amylovora,** general on *Pyrus communis* but Kieffer and other crosses between common and sand pears are resistant.

BACTERIAL Crown Gall. **Agrobacterium tumefaciens,** general.

BACTERIAL Blossom and Twig Blight; Canker. **Pseudomonas syringae,** Ark., Cal.

BACTERIAL Fruit Rot. **Erwinia carotovora,** Mass.

BLIGHT, Leaf. Fruit Black Spot. **Fabraea maculata,** general.

BLIGHT, Thread. **Pellicularia koleroga** (*Corticium stevensii*) N. C. to Fla., Tex., W. Va.

BLIGHT, Twig. **Corticium salmonicolor,** Fla., La.; **Fusarium** spp., occasional; **Phomopsis ambigua,** widespread; **Valsa leucostoma,** Wash.

BLOTCH, Sooty. **Gloeodes pomigena,** Eastern States to Okla., Tex.

CANKER, Bark. **Helminthosporium papulosum,** Miss.; **Phomopsis mali,** Cal.; **Myxosporium corticolum** (*Pezicula corticola*), N. Y. to Mich., Miss., Oreg.

CANKER. **Cytospora** spp., Oreg., Va., Wash.; **Nectria cinnabarina,** coral spot, dieback; **N. galligena,** trunk canker; **Nummularia discreta,** Del., Iowa.

FRUIT SPOT; Flyspeck. **Leptothyrium pomi,** Eastern States.

LEAF SPOT. **Cercospora minima,** Fla. to Tex.; **C. pyri,** Mich.; **Coniothyrium pyrina,** Mass. to Ala.; Tex., Iowa; **Coryneum foliicolum,** Ind.; **C. microstictum; C. longistipitatum,** Fla., N. J.; **Hendersonia cydoniae; H. foliorum,** Tex.; **Phyllosticta pyrorum,** Ill., Miss., S. C.; **P. solitaria,** Md.; **Septoria piricola** (*Mycosphaerella sentina*), ashy fruit spot, widespread in East.

MISTLETOE. **Phoradendron flavescens,** Ariz., N. Mex., Tex.

NEMATODE, Root Knot. **Heterodera marioni,** Cal.

NEMATODE, Root. **Pratylenchus pratensis,** Cal.

PHYSIOGENIC Bitter Pit. Moisture deficiency. Pacific States, N. Y.

Black End. Oriental pear rootstocks on poor soil.

Brown Bark Spot. Undetermined. Pacific Northwest, Fla., Ind.

Brown Blotch of Fruit, especially Kieffer pear. Undetermined, East.

Chlorosis. Mineral deficiency, alkalinity. Pacific States, Tex.
Cork, Drought Spot. Boron deficiency, Tex.
Exanthema. Copper deficiency, Cal., Fla.
PHYSIOGENIC Little Leaf; Rosette. Zinc or boron deficiency, Cal., Fla.
Marginal Leaf Blight; Leaf Scorch. Calcium or potassium deficiency, Ida., Wash.
Stigmonose. Insect punctures during growth, widespread.
Target Canker, Measles. Undetermined, Cal., Ga., N. Y., Va., Wash.

POWDERY MILDEW. **Podosphaera leucotricha,** Col., Oreg., Wash.; **P. oxyacanthae,** N. J.

ROT, Bitter; Twig and Branch Canker. **Glomerella cingulata,** widespread, but not destructive.

ROT, Black; Canker; Leaf Spot. **Physalospora obtusa,** widespread.

ROT, Brown, **Monilinia fructicola,** Eastern States.

ROT, Brown, Blossom blight. **Monilinia laxa,** Pacific States.

ROT, Blossom and Twig Blight; Gray Mold. **Botrytis cinerea.**

ROT, Collar. **Phytophthora cactorum,** widespread; **P. citrophthora,** Cal.

ROT, Fruit. **Alternaria** sp., black mold; **Aspergillus** sp., cosmopolitan; **Botryosphaeria ribis,** Va.; **Cephalosporium carpogenum,** Oreg., Wash.; **Trichothecium roseum,** occasional, pink mold; **Cladosporium** sp., occasional; **Gloeosporium** sp., widespread; **Neurospora sitophila,** ripe rot, N. C.; **Penicillium** sp., blue mold, widespread; **Phoma exigua; P. mali,** Wash.; **Rhizopus nigricans,** black mold, cosmopolitan; **Pleospora fructicola,** Wash.; **Sclerotinia sclerotiorum,** Cal., Wash.; **Sporotrichum malorum,** storage rot, Oreg., Wash.

ROT, Heart. **Fomes igniarius; F. pinicola; Polyporus** spp.

ROT, Root. **Armillaria mellea,** widespread; **Xylaria** sp., Ida., Ind.

ROT, Silver Leaf. **Stereum purpureum.**

ROT, Trunk. **Schizophyllum commune,** sometimes on living trees, cosmopolitan; **Sterum hirsutum.**

RUST. **Gymnosporangium clavipes** (O, I), chiefly on fruit, La., Tex.; **G. clavariaeforme** (O, I), on leaves, fruit, S. C.; **G. kernianum,** Ariz.; **G. libocedri** (O, I), leaves, fruit, Cal., Oreg.; **G. nelsoni,** leaves, fruit, Ariz., Col.; **G. nootkatense** (O, I), on Asiatic pear, Alaska.

SCAB. **Fusicladium pyrinum,** conidial stage of **Venturia pyrina,** general; **Sphaceloma pirinum,** spot anthracnose, Oreg., Wash.

VIRUS, Stony Pit. **Marmor pyri,** Pacific Coast States.

Fire blight is the limiting factor in pear production. Many orchards have been abandoned in many sections of the country because of this devastating disease. Kieffer pears and some Asiatic pears are resistant and are being used in breeding with desirable eating pears. Varieties Old Home, Orient, and Richard Peters are blight-resistant. In addition to pruning blighted twigs, cutting out cankers, a blossom spray of a weak bordeaux mixture (2–6–100) or a 20–80 copper lime dust is frequently recommended. The pear scab fungus is closely related to that causing apple scab but is not ordinarily so destructive. Pears take about the same spray schedule as apples, but the program is directed more for the control of insects. The blisters caused by blister mites and blackening associated with pear psylla are often mistaken for diseases. Fabraea leaf blight and Mycosphaerella leaf spot sometimes cause defoliation. They are most damaging to Kieffer pears and in nursery stock.

PEA–TREE (*Caragana*)

BACTERIAL Hairy Root. **Agrobacterium rhizogenes,** Ky. to Nebr., Okla.
BLIGHT, Leaf. **Ascochyta** sp., Ohio.
BLIGHT, Pod. **Botrytis cinerea,** Mass.
LEAF SPOT. **Phyllosticta gallarum,** Alaska.
ROT, Seedling Root. **Rhizoctonia solani,** N. Dak.

PEAVINE, VETCHLING (*Lathyrus*)

BLIGHT. Stem and Pod Spot. **Ascochyta lathyri,** Wash.
LEAF SPOT. **Alternaria tenuis,** secondary; **Cercospora lathyri,** Wash.; **Phleospora reticulata,** Me.; **Phyllosticta orobella,** Mass., N. Y.; **Septoria astragali,** Mass., Vt.; **S. emaculata,** N. Y., Wis.
POWDERY MILDEW. **Erysiphe polygoni,** Wash.; **Microsphaera alni,** Ill., Mich., N. Y., Ohio, Wis.
RUST. **Uromyces fabae** (O, I, II, III), general.

PECAN (*Carya illinoensis*)

ANTHRACNOSE, Nursery Blight. **Elsinoë randii,** Southeast and Gulf States.
BACTERIAL Crown Gall. **Agrobacterium tumefaciens,** widespread.
BLIGHT, Leaf. **Septoria caryae,** Del.; **S. hicoriae,** Tex.
BLIGHT, Thread. **Pellicularia** (*Corticium*) **koleroga,** Fla., N. C.
BLOTCH, Leaf. **Mycosphaerella dendroides,** South.
CANKER, Stem. **Microcera coccophila,** La., Tex.
CANKER, Dieback. **Botryosphaeria berengeriana,** Ariz., S. C. to La.
LEAF SPOT, Algal. **Cephaleuros virescens,** Fla.
LEAF SPOT, Brown. **Cercospora fusca,** prevalent through pecan belt.
LEAF SPOT; Downy Spot. **Mycosphaerella caryigena,** Ga. and Fla. to Tex.
LEAF SPOT; Liver Spot. **Gnomonia caryae** var. **pecanae** (*Leptothyrium caryae*).
LEAF SPOT; Vein Spot. **Gnomonia nerviseda** (*Leptothyrium nervisedum*), Ariz., La., Miss.
LEAF SPOT. **Microstroma juglandis,** Ga. to Tex.; **Pestalotia uvicola,** Fla., Tex.; **Myriangium tuberculans,** black spot on bark, Ga., Miss.
MISTLETOE. **Phoradendron flavescens,** widespread in South.
NEMATODE Root Knot. **Heterodera marioni.**

PHYSIOGENIC Leaf Scorch. Low fertility and soil moisture capacity.
Little Leaf; Rosette. Zinc deficiency, Southeast.
Sand Burn, of Seedlings. High temperature, occasional in South.
POWDERY MILDEW. **Microsphaera alni,** occasional.
ROT, Heart. **Schizophyllum commune,** after drought injury, Okla.
ROT, Root. **Helicobasidium purpureum,** Tex.; **Phymatotrichum omnivorum.** Ariz., Tex.
SCAB. **Cladosporium effusum,** general.
VIRUS. Bunch Disease. Undetermined, La., Miss., Okla., Tex.

A representative spray program calls for four applications of bordeaux mixture: (1) when leaves are half-grown, 4–1–100 bordeaux, to control scab, downy spot, nursery blight; (2) 6–2–100 bordeaux, for scab, blight, blotch, brown leaf spot, downy spot; applied about the time tips of small nuts have turned brown; (3) three weeks later, 6–2–100 bordeaux; for same diseases and powdery mildew; (4) three weeks after, 3, 6–2–100 bordeaux for scab, nursery blight, and powdery mildew. Nicotine sulfate and lead arsenate are combined in the sprays as needed for insects. Zinc sulfate can be added to the last three sprays, at the rate of 2 pounds per 100 gallons, to control rosette, a serious nutritional disease; but more lasting results come from applying it to the soil, at 5 to 10 pounds per tree.

In Arizona severe infection with Phymatotrichum root rot has come where trees are intercropped with lucerne, which provides a rapid transit medium for the fungus. Getting rid of the lucerne and treating with ammonium sulfate saves some trees. See under Rots.

PENSTEMON (Beard-Tongue)

LEAF SPOT. **Cercospora penstemonis,** Ala., Kans., Ind., Mont., N. and S. Dak., Nebr., Okla., Tex., Wis.; **Cercosporella nivosa,** Col., Ida., Ohio, Wash.; **Phyllosticta antirrhini,** Ill.; **Septoria penstemonis,** Cal., Ill., Me., Mich., Miss., Mo., N. Y., Tex., Wash., Wis.
LEAF SPOT; Stem Spot. **Ascochytella penstemonis,** Cal.
NEMATODE, Root Knot. **Heterodera marioni.**
ROT, Crown, Stem. **Sclerotium rolfsii,** Conn., Ill., N. J., Mass., Tex.
ROT, Root. **Phymatotrichum omnivorum,** Tex.
RUST. **Puccinia andropogonis** var. **penstemonis** (O, I), Ala., Ga., Kans., Ill., Iowa, Miss., Mo., N. and S. Dak., Nebr., N. Y., Okla., Pa., Wis.; **II, III** on Andropogon; **P. penstemonis** (III), Ariz., Cal., Oreg., Wyo.; **P. confraga** (III), Ariz.; **P. palmeri** (O, I, III), Ariz., Cal., Ida., Mont. to N. Mex., Wash.

PEONY (*Paeonia*)

ANTHRACNOSE. **Gloeosporium** sp., Kans., Ill., Mass., Md., N. C., N. J., **Pa.,** Va.
BACTERIAL Crown Gall. **Agrobacterium tumefaciens,** Mich., Md.

BLIGHT, Early; Bud Rot. **Botrytis paeoniae,** general.

BLIGHT, Late; Gray Mold. **Botrytis cinerea,** also leaf rot, general.

BLIGHT, Southern. **Sclerotium rolfsii,** Miss., Tex.

BLIGHT, Tip; Crown Rot. **Phytophthora cactorum,** Conn., Ill., Ind., Kans., N. J., N. Y., Ohio.

BLOTCH, Leaf, Stem; Measles. **Cladosporium paeoniae,** general.

CANKER; Stem wilt. **Coniothyrium** sp., Cal., on tree peonies.

LEAF SPOT. **Alternaria** sp., occasional in Northeastern and Central States; **Cercospora paeoniae,** Ill.; **C. variicolor,** Pa. to N. C., Nebr., Wis.; **Cryptostictis paeoniae,** Ill.; **Pezizella oenotherae,** Md., Pa.; **Phyllosticta** spp., N. J., Pa., Va.; **Septoria paeoniae,** also stem canker, Me., Mich., Minn., N. J., N. Y., Oreg., R. I., Wash., Wis.

NEMATODE, Leaf and Stem. **Ditylenchus dipsaci,** N. J., Wash.

NEMATODE, Root Knot. **Heterodera marioni,** N. Y. to N. C., N. D., Okla.

POWDERY MILDEW. **Erysiphe polygoni,** Tex.

ROT, Root. **Armillaria mellea,** Cal., Iowa, Mich., Oreg.; **Fusarium** sp., Col., Ind., Mo., Nebr., N. J., Okla.; **Phymatotrichum omnivorum,** Ariz., Tex.; **Rhizoctonia solani,** Conn., Ill., Minn., N. Y., Pa., Va.; **Thielaviopsis basicola,** Conn.

ROT, Stem; Wilt. **Sclerotinia sclerotiorum,** Ill., Md., Minn., N. J., N. Y., Okla., Ohio.

VIRUS, Ring Spot, Mosaic. Paeonia virus 1, Mass. to Va., Cal., Kans., Mich., Wash.

?VIRUS. Crown Elongation Disease. Cause unknown.

?VIRUS. Le Moine Disease. Unidentified.

WILT. **Verticillium albo-atrum** or **V. dahliae,** Ill., Kans., Md., N. Y., Ohio.

Botrytis blight is doubtless the best known peony disease. Young shoots are rotted at base in spring, young buds turn black, or flowers are blasted. Cutting down all tops *at ground level* in fall, and spraying with bordeaux mixture in spring, starting when reddish shoots first show, are necessary precautions. And never mulch with manure so the shoots have to push through it in spring. If used at all, apply it in a wide circle around the bush, but never touching stems.

Other diseases depend somewhat on location. Anthracnose, blotch, and sometimes leaf spot are serious on occasion. In humid New Jersey summers I frequently find *Sclerotinia sclerotiorum* killing stalks, and filling the pith with very large sclerotia. A white cottony growth on stems identifies this disease, which calls for prompt removal of infected parts, before sclerotia fall to the ground. Plants that are sickly-looking sometimes have nematode galls on the roots, particularly in sandy locations. Lack of bloom may be due to too-deep planting, growing in shade, Botrytis blight, or nematodes.

PEPEROMIA

VIRUS, Ring Spot. Undetermined.

Plants are stunted, leaves distorted and disfigured by systemic chlorotic or brown necrotic rings. Transmitted by grafting; no insect vector known.

PEPPER (*Capsicum frutescens*)

ANTHRACNOSE; Fruit, Leaf, and Stem Spot. **Colletotrichum piperatum,** Mass. to Fla., Tex., Ill.; **Glomerella cingulata,** fruit rot, Conn. to Fla., Tex., Kans., N. Y., Ohio.

BACTERIAL Soft Rot. **Erwinia aroideae; E. carotovora,** Conn., Fla., La., Mich., Mo., Tex., occasional in market.

BACTERIAL SPOT; Fruit and Stem Spot; Seedling Blight. **Xanthomonas vesicatoria,** general in South and East.

BACTERIAL WILT. **Pseudomonas solanacearum,** Pa. to Fla.

BLIGHT, Fruit Rot. **Phytophthora capsici,** Cal., Col., Fla.

BLIGHT, Southern. **Sclerotium rolfsii,** N. C. to Fla.

DAMPING-OFF; Stem and Root Rot. **Pythium** spp., cosmopolitan; **Rhizoctonia solani,** cosmopolitan.

DODDER. **Cuscuta** sp., Ga., N. J., Va.

DOWNY MILDEW. **Peronospora tabacina,** Ga., N. and S. C., Tex.

LEAF SPOT. **Ascochyta capsici,** Wash., N. Y. to Fla.; **Cercospora capsici,** frog-eye; stem-end rot; **Stemphylium solani,** Fla.

MOLD, Leaf. **Cladosporium herbarum,** Cal., Ga., Tex.; seed mold, **Stemphylium botryosum,** Conn., Fla.

NEMATODE, Root Knot. **Heterodera marioni,** general in South.

PHYSIOGENIC Blossom-end Rot. Hot dry weather following rainy.
Sunscald. High temperature.

ROT. **Alternaria** sp., general after sunscald and blossom-end rot.

ROT, Blossom. **Choanephora cucurbitarum,** Fla., N. C.

ROT, Charcoal. **Macrophomina phaseoli,** Cal., Ga., Kans., N. Y.

ROT, Fruit. **Colletotrichum capsici; C. nigri,** Fla., Ga., N. J., Tex.; **Diaporthe phaseolorum,** Miss., Mo.; **Phoma destructiva,** Ala., Del., Fla., Ga., Miss., N. Y.; **Phytophthora parasitica,** Ill., Ind.; **Rhizopus stolonifer,** Fla., Tex., Wash.; **Sclerotinia sclerotiorum,** also stem rot, Cal., Conn., Fla., Mass.

ROT, Gray Mold. **Botrytis cinerea,** occasional in market; stem canker in field, Cal., Conn., N. J., Pa., Wash.

ROT, Pod. **Curvularia lunata,** Fla.; **Nematospora coryli,** yeast spot after plant bug injury.

VIRUS, Calico. **Marmor medicaginis.**

VIRUS, Curly Top. **Ruga verrucosans,** Ariz., Cal., Ida., N. Mex., Oreg., Tex., Wash.

VIRUS, Mosaic. **Marmor cucumeris, Marmor tabaci.**

VIRUS, Ring Spot. **Annulus tabaci,** Col., Del., Md., N. J., N. Y.

VIRUS, Spotted Wilt. **Lethum australiense.**

VIRUS, Tobacco Etch. **Marmor erodens.**

WILT. **Verticillium** sp., Cal.

To control bacterial spot and anthracnose, soak seed 5 minutes in mercuric chloride, 1 tablet to 3 pints water, rinse 15 minutes, then dry and dust with Arasan or Semesan to control damping-off. Rotate crops, avoiding land growing potatoes, tomatoes, eggplant or pepper the previous year and do not grow immediately adjoining other solanaceous crops. Soil should be well-drained but provided with plenty of humus to avoid blossom-end rot, not too much nitrogen, and a liberal supply of superphosphate. To avoid sunscald on fruits keep them shaded by controlling leaf spots on foliage, probably by copper sprays. For virus diseases be sure seed is healthy; don't start plants in greenhouses with petunias or Jerusalem cherries and don't use tobacco around the plants, either smoking, or as ground stems for a mulch.

PEPPER–GRASS, GARDEN CRESS (*Lepidium*)

CLUB ROOT. **Plasmodiophora brassicae,** N. J.

DAMPING-OFF. **Pythium debaryanum,** Tex.; **Rhizoctonia solani,** Tex.

DODDER. **Cuscuta arvensis,** Okla.

DOWNY MILDEW. **Peronospora lepidii,** S. Dak., Tex., Fla.; **P. parasitica,** Iowa, Kans., N. Dak., Tex., Wis.

LEAF GALL. **Synchytrium lepidii,** La.

LEAF SPOT. **Alternaria brassicae,** N. Y.; **Cercospora,** sp., N. J.; **Cylindrosporium capsellae,** Ind., Wis.; **Septoria lepidiicola,** Nebr., Md., Tex., Wis.

NEMATODE, Leaf and Stem. **Ditylenchus dipsaci,** N. Y.

ROT, Root. **Pyrenochaeta terrestris,** N. and S. Dak.; **Phymatotrichum omnivorum,** Tex.

RUST. **Puccinia aristidae** (O, I), Col., Ky., Mont., Tex.; **P. holboelli** (O, I, III), Mont., Wyo.; **P. monoica** (O, I), Wyo.

WHITE RUST; White blister. **Albugo candida,** general.

PEPPER–VINE (*Ampelopsis arborea*)

LEAF SPOT. **Cercospora arboreae; Guignardia bidwellii,** Miss., N. J.

PERSIMMON, Native and Japanese (*Diospyros*)

ANTHRACNOSE; Fruit, Twig Blight. **Gloeosporium diospyri,** East and South to Kansas.

BACTERIAL CROWN GALL. **Agrobacterium tumefaciens,** Cal.

BLIGHT, Thread. **Pellicularia koleroga,** Fla., on Japanese persimmon.

BLIGHT, Twig. **Phomopsis diospyri,** Fla., S. C.; **Physalospora obtusa,** Gulf States.

BLOTCH, Leaf. **Mycosphaerella diospyri,** Gulf States.

DIEBACK. **Diplodia natalensis,** Ala., Tex.

FRUIT SPOT; Fly Speck. **Leptothyrium pomi, Fla.**

LEAF SPOT, Algal. **Cephaleuros virescens,** Fla.

LEAF SPOT. **Cercospora fuliginosa,** Del. to Gulf States; **C. diospyri; Macrophoma diospyri,** also fruit spot; **Pestalotia** sp., Gulf States; **Phyllosticta biformis,** Tex.; **Ramularia** sp., Fla.

LEAF SPOT, Tar. **Melasmia falcata,** Oreg.

NEMATODE. **Heterodera marioni,** Tex.

POWDERY MILDEW. **Podosphaera oxyacanthae,** Ind.

ROT, Fruit. **Alternaria** sp., occasional on Japanese persimmon; **Botrytis cinerea,** gray mold; **Penicillium expansum,** blue mold, cosmopolitan; **Physalospora obtusa,** Gulf States, black rot, also twig blight; **Rhizopus nigricans,** Tex.

ROT, Root. **Phymatotrichum omnivorum,** Tex.

SCAB. **Fusicladium levierii,** Conn., Fla.

WILT. **Cephalosporium diospyri,** Ala., Fla., Ga., N. and S. C., Miss., Okla., Tenn., Tex.

Persimmon wilt started in Tennessee in 1933 and at the end of five years only 5 per cent of the persimmons in that native stand were alive. The disease is now present from the Carolinas south to Florida and west to Texas. Oriental persimmons are resistant, but death of our American persimmons is a great loss to wildlife.

PETASITES (*Butter-Bur*)

LEAF GALL. **Synchytrium aureum,** Wis.

LEAF SPOT. **Ramularia variegata,** Wis.; **Stagonospora petasitidis,** Wis.

RUST. **Puccinia conglomerata,** Mich., Minn., N. Y., Wis.

PETUNIA

BACTERIAL Wilt. **Pseudomonas solanacearum,** Fla.

BLIGHT, of old flowers. **Choanephora conjuncta,** Ga.

BLOTCH, Leaf. **Cercospora petuniae,** Fla., Okla.

DAMPING-OFF. **Rhizoctonia solani,** Fla., N. J., N. Y., N. C., Okla., Pa., Tex.

DODDER. **Cuscuta** spp., Md., N. J., N. Y., Okla., Tex., W. Va.

LEAF SPOT. **Ascochyta petuniae,** Tex.

NEMATODE, Root Knot. **Heterodera marioni,** general in South; occasional in greenhouses in North.

POWDERY MILDEW. **Oidium** sp., Cal., N. Y., Va., but rare.

RUST. **Puccinia aristidae** (O, I), Ariz.

ROT, Stem; Wilt. **Fusarium** sp., Wash.; **Sclerotinia sclerotiorum,** Wash.; **Stemphylium botryosum,** secondary, black stem, Tex.

VIRUS, Curly Top. **Ruga verrucosans,** Cal., Oreg.

VIRUS, Mosaic. **Marmor tabaci,** sometimes, **M. cucumeris,** general.

VIRUS, Ringspot. **Annulus tabaci,** Va.

VIRUS, Spotted Wilt. **Lethum australiense,** Cal.
VIRUS, Aster Yellows. **Chlorogenus callistephi,** Mich., Cal.
WILT. **Verticillium** sp., Cal.

The cause of fasciation is undetermined, but it is possibly due to the bacterium *Corynebacterium fascians.*

Dodder is common on petunias, reported in window boxes, lawn tubs, etc., as well as in a garden bed. Plants started in greenhouses may get infected with cucumber or tobacco mosaic. Smoking around petunias, or a tobacco-stem mulch, provides another source of infection.

PHILADELPHUS (Mock-orange; incorrectly called Syringa)

BLIGHT, Flower and Shoot. **Botrytis cinerea,** cosmopolitan.
BLOTCH, Sooty. **Sarcinella heterospora,** Fla.
LEAF SPOT. **Ascochyta philadelphi,** N. Y.; **Ramularia philadelphi,** Tex., Wash.; **Septoria philadelphi,** Ida., Iowa, Mont.
NEMATODE, Root Knot. **Heterodera marioni.**
POWDERY MILDEW. **Phyllactinia corylea,** Mont., Wash.
ROT, Root. **Phymatotrichum omnivorum,** Tex.
RUST. **Gymnosporangium speciosum** (O, I), Col., N. Mex., Utah; **III** on juniper.

PHILIBERTIA

POWDERY MILDEW. **Phyllactinia corylea,** Fla.
RUST. **Puccinia bartholomaei** (O, I), Ariz.; **P. obliqua** (III), Ariz., Cal., Fla., N. Mex., Tex.

PHILODENDRON

LEAF SPOT. **Colletotrichum philodendri,** N. J.
?PHYSIOGENIC. Leaf Scorch, Mo.

PHLOX

BACTERIAL Crown Gall. **Agrobacterium tumefaciens,** N. J.
BLIGHT, Southern, and Stem or Crown Rot. **Sclerotium rolfsii,** and **S. delphinii,** Conn., Fla., Ill., Md., N. J., N. Y., Ohio, Tex. Va.
BLIGHT, Stem. **Pyrenochaeta phlogis,** N. Y.
CANKER, Stem. **Colletotrichum** sp., Fla.
DOWNY MILDEW. **Peronospora phlogina,** Iowa, Wis.
LEAF SPOT. **Ascochyta phlogis,** var. **phlogina,** N. Y., Mass., Tex.; **Cercospora omphakodes,** N. Y. to Iowa, Wis.; **C. phlogina,** Miss., N. Y., Va.; **Macrophoma cylindrospora,** Cal.; **Phyllosticta** sp., Wash.; **Ramularia** sp., Wash.; **Septoria** spp.; **Volutella phlogina,** La.

NEMATODE, Leaf. **Aphelenchoides** sp., Md.

NEMATODE, Leaf and Stem. **Ditylenchus dipsaci,** Cal., Conn., Md., N. Y., Ohio, Wash.

NEMATODE, Root Knot. **Heterodera marioni,** Kans., Md., Mass., N. J., Ohio, Tex., Wash.

PHYSIOGENIC Leaf Drop; Blight; "Rust." Cause unknown but possibly inability of old stems of some varieties to provide adequate water.

POWDERY MILDEW. **Erysiphe cichoracearum,** general; **Sphaerotheca humuli,** Kans., N. H., N. Y., Ohio, Wash.

ROT, Charcoal. **Macrophomina phaseoli,** Ill.

RUST. **Puccinia douglasii** (O, I, III), N. J., Pa.; on *Phlox subulata,* and other species, Col., Mont., Nebr., N. Mex., Oreg., Utah, Wash., Wyo., but not on perennial summer phlox.

RUST. **Uromyces acuminatus** var. **polemonii** (O, I), Ill., Iowa, Minn., Miss., S. Dak., Wis.

VIRUS, Mosaic. Undetermined, suspected virus, Md., N. C., N. Y.

VIRUS, Aster Yellows. **Chlorogenus callistephi,** N. J., N. Y., Pa., and var. **californicus,** Cal.

WILT. **Verticillium albo-atrum,** N. Y., Minn.

Gardeners are always talking about "rust" on phlox, and yet the true rusts are not often found on perennial summer phlox. They are talking about a physiological condition which cannot be corrected by spraying and seems to be related to water conduction in stems of some varieties of phlox. Powdery mildew is general, but fairly readily controlled with sulfur dust or copper sprays unless plants are shaded and crowded, with little air circulation.

PHOENIX–TREE (*Firmiana simplex*)

BLIGHT, Web. **Corticium microsclerotia,** Fla.

PHOTINIA (Christmas-Berry, Toyon, *Heteromeles arbutifolia*)

BACTERIAL Fire Blight. **Erwinia amylovora,** Cal.

BLIGHT, Leaf. **Fabraea maculata,** Cal.

LEAF SPOT. **Cercospora heteromeles,** Cal., Tex.; **Lophodermium heteromeles,** Cal.; **Phyllosticta heteromeles,** Cal., Tex.; **Septoria photiniae,** Cal.

ROT, Root. **Phymatotrichum omnivorum,** Tex.

RUST. **Gymnosporangium japonicum** (O, I); III on juniper.

SCAB. **Fusicladium photinicola,** on leaves, berries, Cal.

PHOTINIA (Oriental species, *P. glabra, P. serrulata*)

ANTHRACNOSE. **Gloeosporium** sp., Miss.

LEAF SPOT. **Pestalotia** sp., N. J.; **Septoria photiniae,** Pa.

POWDERY MILDEW. **Podosphaera leucotricha,** Cal.; **Sphaerotheca pannosa,** Oreg.

PHYLLODOCE (Mountain-Heath)

Blight, Brown Felt. **Herpotrichia nigra,** Ida.

Leaf Gall; Witches' Broom. **Exobasidium vaccinii-uliginosi,** Oreg.

Sooty Mold. **Antennaria rectangularis,** Alaska.

PHYSOSTEGIA (False Dragonhead)

Blight, Southern. **Sclerotium rolfsii,** Va. to Okla., Kans.; **S. delphinii,** Conn., N. J., N. Y., Wis.

Downy Mildew. **Plasmopara cephalophora,** Wis.

Leaf Spot. **Septoria physostegiae,** Ill., Wis.

Rot, Stem. **Sclerotinia sclerotiorum,** Me.

Rust. **Puccinia physostegiae** (III), Ind., N. H., Mont., N. Y.

PIERIS (Commonly, but incorrectly, called Andromeda)

Dieback. **Phytophthora** sp.

Leaf Spot. **Pestalotia** sp., Conn., N. J.; **Phyllosticta andromedae,** N. J.; **P. maxima,** Conn., N. J.

PINE (*Pinus*)

Blight, Brown Felt. **Herpotrichia nigra,** Northeastern States on snow-buried foliage, at high altitudes. **Neopeckia coulteri,** Mont., Cal.

Blight, Gray. **Hypoderma lethale,** on hard pines, New England to Fla., La.

Blight, Needle. **Hendersonula pinicola,** N. C., Tenn.; **Pullaria pullulans,** after insect injury; **Septoria spadicea,** N. H., N. Y., Vt.

Blight, Seedling. **Botrytis cinerea,** cosmopolitan; **Cylindrocladium scoparium,** N. J.; **Fusarium** spp.; **Phytophthora cactorum,** Northeast; **Rhizina undulata,** Minn., Me., Cal.; **Thelephora terrestris,** Me., N. H., Northern Rocky Mts., seedling smother.

Blight, Snow. **Phacidium infestans,** in northeastern nurseries.

Blight, Twig. **Diplodia pinea** (*Sphaeropsis ellisii*), New England to Tenn., Nebr.; **Cenangium ferruginosum,** Me., N. J., N. Y., Ohio, Pa., Mont. to Oreg., Wash.

Canker. **Atropellis** spp.; **Caliciopsis pinea,** New England to S. C., Tenn.; **Dasyscypha ellisiana; D. pini,** on 5-needle pines, Pacific Northwest, Mich.; **Nectria** spp., New England to N. C., Iowa; **Tympanis** sp., Northeast to Mich., Ohio.

Damping-Off. **Rhizoctonia solani,** cosmopolitan; **Pythium** spp., cosmopolitan.

Needle Cast. **Bifusella linearis,** Me. to N. C., Minn., Ida., tar spot; **B. striiformis,** Cal.; **Cytospora pinastri,** Me., N. J.; **Elytroderma deformans,** also witches' broom, chiefly in West, but on white pine in Southeast; **Hypoderma desmazierii; H. hedgecockii,** Southeast; **H. pedatum,** Cal.; **H. pini,** Cal., Nev.;

Hypodermella spp., Great Lakes States, Cal., Col. to Ida., Mont., Oreg.; tar spot, **Lophodermium nitens; L. pinastri,** widespread; **Systremma acicola,** brown spot of hard pines in South.

Rot, Root. **Armillaria mellea,** widespread; **Phymatotrichum omnivorum,** Tex.

Rot, Heart, Wood. **Fomes** spp., general; **Lentinus lepideus,** widespread; **Polyporus** spp., widespread.

Rust, White Pine Blister. **Cronartium ribicola** (O, I), swellings on trunk and branches of eastern white pine, from New England to Va. and Minn., and on western white pine in Pacific Northwest, on sugar pine, Cal.; II, III on gooseberry, currant.

Rust, Comandra Blister. **Cronartium comandrae** (O, I), swellings in twigs, trunks of hard pines; II, III on bastard toadflax.

Rust, Sweet-fern Blister. **Cronartium comptoniae,** swellings on trunk and branches of 2- and 3-needle pines from Northeastern to Central and Great Lakes States; II, III on sweet-fern and sweet gale.

Rust, Lodgepole Pine Blister. **Cronartium coleosporioides** (O, I), swellings on twigs, branches, trunk cankers, Rocky and Western Mts.; II, III on painted-cup, birdbeak, owls-clover, wood-betony.

Rust, Piñon Blister. **Cronartium occidentale** (O, I), mountain regions in West; II, III on painted-cup.

Rust, Cone. **Cronartium conigenum,** hypertrophy of cones, especially in South; II, III on oak; **C. strobilinum;** II, III on evergreen oaks.

Rust, Fusiform. **Cronartium fusiforme,** swellings in trunk, branches in South; II, III on evergreen oaks.

Rust, Eastern Gall. **Cronartium quercuum,** galls on trunk, branches, and witches' brooms on 2- and 3-needle pines East to Rocky Mts., especially Southeast; II, III on oak, rarely chestnut.

Rust, Western Gall. **Cronartium harknessii,** galls on branches, trunks, also witches' brooms, on hard pines throughout West.

Rust, Needle. **Coleosporium apocynaceum** (O, I), Southeast; II, III on Amsonia; **C. campanulae** (O, I), Northeast to Ind., N. C.; II, III on bellflower, loosestrife, Venus-looking-glass; **C. crowellii** (III) on piñon and limber pines, Ariz., Col., N. Mex.; **C. delicatulum** (O, I), New England to Fla. and west to Great Plains; II, III on goldenrod; **C. elephantopodis** (O, I), N. J. to Fla., Tex.; II, III on Elephantopus; **C. helianthi** (O, I), N. Y. to Ga., Ohio; II, III on sunflower; **C. inconspicuum** (O, I), Md. to Ga., Tenn., Ohio; II, III on Coreopsis; **C. ipomoeae** (O, I), N. J. to Fla., Ill., Ariz.; II, III on morning-glory; **C. jonesii** (O, I), Ariz., Col., N. Mex.; II, III on currant and gooseberry; **C. laciniariae,** N. J. to Fla.; II, III on Liatris; **C. madiae** (O, I), on Monterey, Coulter and Jeffrey pines; II, III on tarweed and other composites; **C. minutum** (O, I), on loblolly and spruce pines; II, III on Forestiera; **C. pinicola,** Del. to N. C., Tenn.; **C. senecionis** (O, I); II, III on Senecio; **C. solidaginis** (O, I), on all 2- and 3-needle pines in Eastern U. S.; II, III on aster, goldenrod and other composites; **C. sonchi-arvensis** (O, I), on Scotch pine; II, III on sowthistle; **C. terebinthinaceae** (O, I), Southeast; II, III on Parthenium and Silphium; **C. vernoniae** (O, I), on 2- and 3-needle pines, East and South; II, III on ironweed.

Little Leaf Disease. Cause unknown, on shortleaf and loblolly pine in South.

White pine blister rust is, of course, our foremost disease of pines, and full details are given under Rusts. Black currants should be banned entirely in infected areas, but red currants are relatively safe and can be grown up to 900 feet from pines, and probably 300 feet is a safe enough area for eradication.

Of the other possible rusts on various pines the only one I have met very often in gardens is the aster rust (*Coleosporium solidaginis*), which may be slightly disfiguring to the needles but not very damaging to general health. When rusts become important, eliminate the near-by weed hosts.

Brown needles may be due to one of the needle blight or needle cast fungi but frequently to winter drying. New shoots of Austrian pine turn brown from Diplodia tip blight, which should not be mistaken for the very common discoloration and distortion caused by the pine shoot moth.

PINEAPPLE (*Ananas comosus*)

Nematode, Root. **Heterodera marioni,** Fla.

Rot, Leaf Base, Soft; White Leaf Spot. **Ceratostomella paradoxa,** Fla.

Wilt. Toxic effect of mealybug feeding.

PIPSISSEWA (*Chimaphila*)

Leaf Spot. **Mycosphaerella chimaphilina,** N. Y., Oreg., Pa., Wash.; **Septoria chimaphilae,** Del.

Rust. **Pucciniastrum pyrolae** (II, III), N. Y. to N. C., Tenn., Wis., Cal., Mont., Oreg., Wash.

PISTACHE (*Pistacia*)

Blight, Thread. **Pellicularia koleroga** = *Corticium stevensii,* Fla., Tex.

Leaf Spot. **Cercospora** sp., Md.; **Phyllosticta lentisci,** Tex.

Nematode, Root Knot. **Heterodera marioni,** Cal.

Rot, Root. **Phymatotrichum omnivorum,** Ariz., Cal., Tex.

Rot, Sapwood. **Pleurotus ostreatus,** Cal.; **Schizophyllum commune,** Cal.

PITCHER–PLANT (*Sarracenia*)

Blight, Southern. **Sclerotium rolfsii,** Tex.

Leaf Spot. **Colletotrichum gloeosporioides,** N. J., Tex.; **Helminthosporium sarraceniae,** secondary; **Mycosphaerella sarraceniae,** Ga., Me., Mich., Minn., Miss., N. Y., Pa., S. C.; **Pestalotia aquatica,** Minn., Md., Tex.

Rot, Root. **Pythium graminicola,** N. C.; **Rhizoctonia solani.**

PITHECELLOBIUM (Blackbead)

BLIGHT, Twig. **Phomopsis** sp.

RUST. **Ravenelia gracilis** (O, I, II, III), Tex.; **R. siderocarpi** (II, III), Tex.; **R. pithecolobii** (II, III), Fla.

PITTOSPORUM

BLIGHT, Southern; Wilt. **Sclerotium rolfsii.**

BLIGHT, Thread. **Pellicularia koleroga** = *Corticium stevensii.*

LEAF SPOT, Angular. **Cercospora pittospori,** Fla., La., S. C. to Tex.; **Phyllosticta** sp., Ala.

NEMATODE, Root Knot. **Heterodera marioni,** Fla.

ROT, Root. **Phymatotrichum omnivorum,** Tex.

ROT, Foot. **Diplodia** sp., Fla.

VIRUS, Mosaic. Undetermined, Cal.

?VIRUS. Variegation. The variegated forms of *Pittosporum tobira* may be due to a virus; graft transmission has been reported in France.

PLANE–TREE, SYCAMORE (*Platanus*)

(American sycamore, *P. occidentalis;* California sycamore, *P. racemosa,* London plane, *P. acerifolia,* and Oriental plane, *P. orientalis*)

ANTHRACNOSE; Leaf and Twig Blight. **Gnomonia veneta,** general.

BLIGHT, Leaf. **Phleospora multimaculans,** Tex.

BLIGHT, Twig; Canker. **Massaria platani,** widespread.

CANKER STAIN; London Plane Blight. **Endoconidiophora** (*Ceratostomella*) sp. (*E. fimbriata?*), Del., Ky., Md., Miss., N. C., N. J., Pa., Va., W. Va.

LEAF SPOT. **Mycosphaerella** (*Cercospora*) **platanifolia,** N. C. to Ga., La., Iowa; **M. stigmina-platani,** N. C.; **Phyllosticta platani,** Ala., Kans., Mass., Md., Va.; **Septoria platanifolia,** Ga., Md., S. C., W. Va.; **Stigmella platani-racemosae,** Cal.

MISTLETOE. **Phoradendron flavescens,** Ariz., Cal., Tenn., Tex.

PHYSIOGENIC Rosy Canker. Illuminating gas in soil, N. J., Md., N. Y.

POWDERY MILDEW. **Microsphaera alni,** widespread; **Oidium obductum,** Pa., Va., W. Va.; **Phyllactinia corylea,** Ind.

ROT, Root. **Armillaria mellea,** Md., Tex., W. Va.; **Phymatotrichum omnivorum,** Tex., Ariz.; **Phytophthora cinnamomi,** Md.

ROT, Heart, Trunk. **Fomes** spp., **Steccherinum** (*Hydnum*) **erinaceus,** sometimes on living trees.

ROT, Wood. **Daedalea** spp., widespread; **Stereum** spp., widespread; **Polyporus** spp.

The canker stain of London plane and American sycamore flared up in epidemic form around Philadelphia in 1935, killing thousands of street and ornamental trees from Newark to Baltimore in the next few years. Eventually we learned that the fungus was spread in pruning and in the tree paint, so present recommendations call for no pruning except in winter, and a wound dressing fortified with a special fungicide (see under Cankers).

Every few years, in a season of frequent rainfall and high humidity, an epidemic of anthracnose occurs on sycamore and oak. When the disease has been serious in former years a dormant lime-sulfur spray and a couple of foliage sprays, with bordeaux mixture, should give control. That is an expensive program for the average homeowner. It may be a comfort to know that your trees will probably survive even if heavily defoliated in one season, and we seldom have two excessively wet springs in succession.

PLATYCODON (Balloon-Flower)

BLIGHT. **Phytophthora cactorum?** Minn.

ROT, Root. **Phymatotrichum omnivorum,** Tex.; **Rhizoctonia solani,** Conn., Pa.

PLUM (*Prunus domestica*)

BACTERIAL Fire Blight. **Erwinia amylovora,** occasional, Oreg., Wash.

BACTERIAL Leaf Spot; Black Spot. **Xanthomonas pruni,** Eastern and Southern States to Wis., Tex.

BACTERIAL Shoot Blight; Gummosis. **Pseudomonas syringae,** Cal.

BLACK KNOT. **Dibotryon morbosum,** widespread except far West.

BLIGHT, Blossom and Twig. **Monilinia laxa,** Cal., Oreg., Wash.; **Botrytis cinerea,** on blossoms.

BLIGHT, Twig. **Diplodia** spp., secondary.

BLOTCH, Leaf. **Phyllosticta congesta,** Ga., Tex.

CANKER. **Phytophthora cactorum,** Cal., Ind.; **Valsa leucostoma,** dieback, widespread.

LEAF CURL; Witches' broom. **Taphrina** spp., **T. pruni,** plum pockets, widespread.

LEAF SPOT; Shot Hole. **Cercospora circumscissa,** Cal., Fla., Mass., Tex., Wash.; **Coryneum carpophilum,** Cal. to Ida., Wash.; **Higginsia prunophorae,** widespread.

NEMATODE, Root Knot. **Heterodera marioni,** Fla.

PHYSIOGENIC Brown Bark Spot. Cause unknown.

Chlorosis. Alkaline Soil, Cal., Idaho.

Exanthema. Copper deficiency, Cal., Fla.

Gum Spot. Drought Spot. Moisture irregularity.

ROT, Brown, Blossom Blight. **Monilinia fructicola,** general.

ROT, Fruit. **Alternaria** sp., Oreg.; **Botrytis cinerea,** Cal., Wash.; **Cladosporium** sp., Ida., Oreg.

ROT, Heart. **Fomes applanatus,** Oreg.; **F. fulvus,** widespread; **Lenzites saepiaria,** Pacific Northwest; **Polyporus hirsutus; P. versicolor,** widespread.

ROT, Silver Leaf. **Stereum purpureum,** Wash.
RUST. **Tranzschelia pruni-spinosae** (II, III), widespread, especially in South, and Pacific Coast States.
SCAB. **Cladosporium carpophilum,** widespread.
VIRUS, Diamond Canker. Undetermined, Cal.
VIRUS, Cherry Vein-Clearing. **Marmor nerviclarens,** Oreg., Wash.
VIRUS, Plum or Prune-Dwarf. **Nanus pruni,** N. Y.
VIRUS, Peach Line Pattern. **Marmor lineopictum,** Cal., Ky., Mich., Ohio.
VIRUS, Peach-Yellows. **Chlorogenus persicae,** occasional in East.
WILT; Seedling Black Heart. **Verticillium albo-atrum,** Cal.

Plums are even more subject to brown rot than peaches. In fact, if you don't do something about it, preferably sulfur sprays or dusts, pretty soon you have no plums at all, as my own backyard can testify. Black knot is sometimes conspicuous on the twigs, but diseased portions can be pruned out and a dormant lime-sulfur spray applied.

Also like peaches, plum foliage is subject to arsenical injury, and Japanese plums are injured by both copper and lead arsenate.

PLUMERIA (*Frangipani*)

RUST. **Coleosporium domingense** (II, III), Fla.

PODOCARPUS

ROT, Root. **Clitocybe tabescens,** Fla.

POINCIANA

ANTHRACNOSE. **Gloeosporium** sp., Fla.
BACTERIAL Crown Gall. **Agrobacterium tumefaciens,** Fla.
ROT, Root. **Clitocybe tabescens,** Fla.; **Phymatotrichum omnivorum,** Tex.
RUST. **Ravenelia humphreyana** (II, III), Fla.

POINSETTIA (*Euphorbia pulcherrima*)

BACTERIAL Canker; Leaf Spot. **Corynebacterium poinsettiae,** Md., N. J., N. Y., Pa.
BLIGHT, Tip; Stem Canker. **Botrytis cinerea,** Mo., Tex., Wash.
LEAF SPOT. **Cercospora pulcherrima,** Tex.
NEMATODE, Root Knot. **Heterodera marioni,** N. Y.
PHYSIOGENIC Chlorosis. Possibly due to cloudy weather.
ROT, Root. **Clitocybe tabescens,** Fla.; **P. omnivorum,** Ariz., Tex.; **Rhizoctonia solani,** Fla., Ill., N. J., Tex.
ROT, Stem; Wilt. **Fusarium** sp., Fla., N. J.; **Pythium debaryanum,** Okla.; **P. ultimum,** N. J.; **Phytophthora** sp., N. J.; **Sclerotinia sclerotiorum,** Wash.
RUST. **Uromyces proëminens** var. **poinsettiae** (O, I, II, III), Miss., Okla., Tex.
SCAB; Spot Anthracnose. **Sphaceloma poinsettiae,** Fla.

POLEMONIUM (Jacobs-Ladder, Greek-Valerian)

Leaf Spot. **Cercospora omphakodes,** Pa.; **Septoria polemonii,** Mo., Wis.; **S. polemoniicola,** Conn., Ind., Mo.

Powdery Mildew. **Erysiphe cichoracearum,** Utah; **Sphaerotheca humuli,** Wash.

Rust. **Puccinia gulosa** (III), Cal.; **P. polemonii** (III), Cal., Ida., Ind.; **Uromyces acuminatus** var. **polemonii** (O, I), Ill., Ind., Iowa, Wis.

Wilt. **Fusarium** sp., N. J.; **Verticillium albo-atrum,** N. J.

POMEGRANATE (*Punica granatum*)

Anthracnose Fruit Spot. **Colletotrichum** sp., Fla.

Blight, Thread. **Pellicularia koleroga** (*Corticium stevensii*), Fla.

Blotch, Leaf; Fruit Spot. **Mycosphaerella** (*Cercospora*) **lythracearum,** Fla. to Miss., Tex.

Nematode, Root Knot. **Heterodera marioni,** Miss.

Rot, Fruit. **Alternaria** sp., Cal.; **Aspergillus niger,** Ariz., Cal., Tex.; **Botrytis cinerea,** gray mold, cosmopolitan; **Nematospora coryli,** dry rot, Cal.; **Penicillium expansum,** blue mold, cosmopolitan.

Rot, Root. **Clitocybe tabescens,** Fla.; **Phymatotrichum omnivorum,** Tex.

POPLAR, ASPEN, COTTONWOOD (*Populus*)

Blight, Shoot. **Didymosphaeria populina** (conidial stage *Napicladium tremulae*), Northeast to Wis.

Canker. **Botryosphaeria ribis** var. **chromogena,** widespread, especially in South.

Canker; Dieback. **Cytospora chrysosperma** (conidial stage of *Valsa sordida*), especially in West, prevalent on ornamental poplars: **Valsa nivea.**

Canker, Branch and Trunk. **Dothichiza populea,** most serious on Italian and Chinese varieties.

Canker, Trunk. **Hypoxylon pruinatum,** Northeast and Great Lakes States; **Nectria cinnabarina; N. galligena,** New England and Great Lakes.

Leaf Blister, Yellow. **Taphrina aurea,** New England to Great Lakes, Pacific Coast; **T. johansonii,** catkin deformity, widespread.

Leaf Spot, Black; Ink Spot. **Ciborinia bifrons,** in Northeast and **C. confundens** (*Sclerotinia bifrons* of Seaver & Shope), in West.

Leaf Spot. **Marssonina** spp., widespread; **Mycosphaerella** (*Septoria*) **populicula; M. populorum** (*Septoria musiva*), also twig canker. **Phyllosticta alcides,** Ala.

Physiogenic Chlorosis. Iron deficiency, Wyo.

Powdery Mildew. **Uncinula salicis,** widespread.

Rot, Root. **Armillaria mellea,** occasional.

ROT, Heart. **Daedalea** spp., sometimes on living trees; **Fomes igniarius,** widespread; **Pholiota adiposa** and **P. destruens,** New England States.

ROT, Wood. **Collybia velutipes,** sometimes living trees, Rocky Mt. States; **Fomes** spp.; **Polyporus** spp.; **Lenzites saepiaria,** widespread, sometimes on living trees.

ROT, Wound. **Schizophyllum commune,** cosmopolitan.

RUST, Leaf. **Melampsora abietis-canadensis** (II, III), on native and introduced poplars New England to Great Plains; O, I on hemlock; **M. albertensis** (II, III), on native poplars, Cal., Mont., N. Mex.; O, I on Douglas-fir; **M. medusae,** on native and introduced species through U. S. except far South; O, I on larch; **M. occidentalis** (II, III), on native poplars Mont. to Cal., Wash.; O, I unknown.

Cytospora canker is rather common on poplars lacking in vigor, but the Rio Grande cottonwood in the West is resistant. Avoid wounding, prune out twigs that have died back and promote better growing conditions. Dothichiza canker may kill Lombardy poplars. Seriously diseased trees should be destroyed. Leaf spots and scab are seldom serious enough to call for treatment.

POPPY (*Papaver*)

BLIGHT, Bacterial. **Xanthomonas papavericola,** Conn., Me., Mo., N. J., N. Y., Ohio, Oreg., Va.

BLIGHT, Gray Mold. **Botrytis cinerea,** Md., Wis.

LEAF SPOT; Pod Spot. **Cercospora papaveri,** Ala., Fla., Tex.; **Septoria** sp., Iowa.

NEMATODE, Leaf. **Aphelenchoides** sp., N. J.

NEMATODE, Root Knot. **Heterodera marioni.**

POWDERY MILDEW. **Erysiphe polygoni,** Oreg.

ROT, Root and Stem; Damping-Off. **Rhizoctonia solani,** Kans., Ida., Ind., Me., N. J., N. Y.

SMUT, Leaf. **Entyloma fuscum,** Iowa, Me., Tex.

VIRUS, Curly Top. **Ruga verrucosans,** Tex.

VIRUS, Spotted Wilt. **Lethum australiense,** Col.

WILT. **Verticillium albo-atrum,** N. Y.

Bacterial blight, showing as water-soaked black spots on all plant parts, kills poppies when the stems are girdled. Use general sanitary precautions, and collect seed from healthy plants only.

POPPY–MALLOW (*Callirhoë*)

LEAF SPOT. **Cercospora althaeina,** Kans., Ill., Nebr., Wis.

RUST. **Endophyllum tuberculatum** (III), Kans., Ind., Nebr., Okla., Tex.

RUST. **Puccinia interveniens** (O, I), Nebr., Tex., N. Y.; II, III on Stipa; **P. schedonnardi,** Col., Kans., Nebr., Okla., Tex., Utah.

WILT. **Verticillium albo-atrum,** N. Y.

PORTULACA

DAMPING-OFF. **Rhizoctonia solani,** Ill.

NEMATODE, Root Knot. **Heterodera marioni,** Ala.

VIRUS, Curly Top. **Ruga verrucosans,** Cal.

WHITE RUST. **Albugo portulacae.**

POTATO (*Solanum tuberosum*)

ANTHRACNOSE; Black Dot Disease. **Colletotrichum atramentarium,** probably general after wilt; **Gloeosporium** sp., Ind., Ohio.

BACTERIAL Blackleg. **Erwinia phytophthora,** general, especially in North; **Erwinia atroseptica.**

BACTERIAL Ring Rot. **Corynebacterium sepedonicum,** all states except far South and West.

BACTERIAL Soft Rot. **Erwinia carotovora; Erwinia aroideae.**

BACTERIAL Wilt. **Pseudomonas solanacearum,** chiefly in the South.

BLIGHT, Early. **Alternaria solani,** general.

BLIGHT, Late. **Phytophthora infestans,** general, common in Northeast, Middle Atlantic and N. Central States, occasional in Gulf and Western States.

BLIGHT, Southern. **Sclerotium rolfsii,** N. C. to Fla., Ariz., Okla.

BLOTCH, Leaf. **Cercospora concors,** Ga., Ind., Mich., N. Y.

CANKER. **Phoma** sp., on stems, Me. to N. J., Mich., Cal.

DODDER. **Cuscuta** sp., Del., Nebr., N. J., Wash.

LEAF SPOT. **Ascochyta lycopersici,** Oreg.

NEMATODE, Golden. **Heterodera rostochiensis,** L. I., N. Y.

NEMATODE, Root Knot. **Heterodera marioni,** general Va. to Fla. and Cal.

NEMATODE, Meadow. **Pratylenchus pratensis,** Miss., S. C., Va.

NEMATODE; Tuber Necrosis. **Ditylenchus destructor,** Ida.

PHYSIOGENIC Blackheart. Oxygen deficiency.

Blackening after cooking. Drought, heat, deficient light or potassium deficiency during growth, partly genetic, mostly Middle Atlantic and Central States.

Blackening before cooking. Mechanical Injury.

Chlorosis; Tip Blight. Boron deficiency.

Chlorosis, Leaf Drop. Magnesium deficiency in sandy soils, Me. to S. C.

Checking. Partly fertilizer injury.

Giant Hill, oversized late plants, few tubers. Genetic factors.

Glassy End. Starch deficiency; high water content.

Growth cracks. Fluctuating moisture.

Hollow Heart. Excessive soil moisture and fertility.

Hopperburn. Marginal necrosis, from leafhoppers, general.

Knobbiness. Fluctuations in soil moisture.

Lenticel enlargement. Wet soil or oxygen deficiency.

Mahogany browning. Low temperature or manganese toxicity.

Marginal bronzing. Potassium deficiency.

Psyllid yellows. Insect injury. N. Dak. to Cal., Ida.

Scald, Tuber Injury. Overheating, sunburn, frequent in South.

Tipburn. Abrupt transition from cool, moist to hot, dry weather, general.

POWDERY MILDEW. **Erysiphe cichoracearum,** Ky., N. J.; **Oidium** sp., Md., N. J., Pa.

ROT, Charcoal. **Macrophomina phaseoli,** Cal., Ga., Ill., Okla., Tex.

ROT, Gray Mold. **Botrytis cinerea.**

ROT, Pink, Watery. **Phytophthora erythroseptica,** Ida., La., Mass., Me., Okla.

ROT, Root. **Armillaria mellea,** Cal., Mich., Oreg., Wash., Wyo.; **Phymatotrichum omnivorum; Helicobasidium purpureum.**

ROT, Silver Scurf. **Spondylocladium atrovirens,** general, less frequent in South.

ROT, Stem. **Sclerotinia** sp., Fla., Me., S. C.

ROT, Stem; Rhizoctoniose, Black Scurf. **Rhizoctonia solani** (*Pellicularia filamentosa*), general.

ROT, Tuber. **Aspergillus niger; Gliocladium roseum,** secondary, occasional, Me.; **Penicillium** sp., blue mold; **Phoma tuberosa,** Me.; **Phomopsis tuberivora,** Wash.; **Phytophthora drechsleri,** Ida.; **Rhizopus** spp., Cal., Ida., Ohio, Tex., Wash.; **Trichothecium roseum,** pink mold, Ida., Minn.; **Xylaria apiculata.**

ROT, Watery Leak. Chiefly **Pythium debaryanum,** in West; **Pythium** spp., Cal., Col., Fla.

SCAB. **Actinomyces** (*Streptomyces*) **scabies; Spongospora subterranea,** powdery scab.

VIRUS, Apical Leaf Roll. Solanum virus 17.

VIRUS, Aster Yellows. **Chlorogenus callistephi** var. **californicus.**

VIRUS, Aucuba Mosaic. **Marmor aucubae,** Me., Md.

VIRUS, Calico. **Marmor medicaginis** var. **solani.**

VIRUS, Crinkle, Mild Mosaic. **Marmor solani,** general.

VIRUS, Curly Dwarf, Complex.

VIRUS, Leaf Roll. **Corium solani,** general.

VIRUS, Leafrolling Mosaic. Solanum virus 11.

VIRUS, Potato Virus X; Potato Mottle; Interveinal Mosaic; Latent Mosaic. **Annulus dubius.**

VIRUS, Net Necrosis. Potato leaf roll virus plus potato virus A.

VIRUS, Purple Top Wilt. Eastern strain of aster yellows virus.

VIRUS, Ringspot. In part tobacco mosaic, **Annulus tabaci.**

VIRUS, Rugose Mosaic, Potato Virus Y. **Marmor upsilon.**

?VIRUS, Spraing. Concentric necrosis.

VIRUS, Spindle Tuber. **Acrogenus solani,** general.

VIRUS, Veinal Mosaic, Mild Mosaic; Potato Virus A. **Marmor solani.**

VIRUS, Witches' Broom. **Chlorogenus solani,** Northeast and North Central States.

VIRUS, Yellow Dwarf. **Aureogenus vastans,** East and North Central States.

WART, Potato. **Synchytrium endobioticum,** Md., Pa., Va. See under Leaf Galls with other Synchytriums.

WILT; Stem-end Rot. **Fusarium** spp.; **F. oxysporum; F. solani** var. **eumartii; F. solani** f. **radicicola** (jelly-end rot in West); **F. avenaceum,** probably general; **F. caeruleum,** dry rot; and many other species.

If this enumeration of diseases should lead you to believe that potato growing is a highly specialized business you are quite right. You can get a lot more return on small garden space with a variety of other vegetables than by attempting potatoes which are cheaper grown in quantity. If you still want to try potatoes, use certified seed, resistant varieties where possible, spray for late blight with Dithane or bordeaux mixture, adding DDT to take care of the insects spreading virus diseases, and keep your fingers crossed!

POTENTILLA (Cinquefoil)

DOWNY MILDEW. **Peronospora potentillae,** N. J.

LEAF SPOT. **Marssonina potentillae,** Cal., Col., Mass., Mich., N. Mex., Wis.; **Fabraea dehnii,** N. Y., Vt.; **Phyllosticta anserinae,** Ill.; **Ramularia arvensis,** Wis.

POWDERY MILDEW. **Erysiphe polygoni,** Col.; **Sphaerotheca humuli,** Col., Wis.

RUST. **Phragmidium andersonii** (I, II, III), general.

PRENANTHES (Rattlesnake Root)

DOWNY MILDEW. **Bremia lactucae,** Iowa, Mass., Minn.

LEAF GALL. **Synchytrium aureum,** Wis.

LEAF SPOT. **Laestadia prenanthis,** Ala.; **Septoria nabali,** N. Y. to Iowa, Wis., Me. to Va.; **Cercospora brunnea,** Ark., N. C., Wis.; **C. prenanthis,** Ala., Kans., Ind.; **C. tabacina,** Wis.

POWDERY MILDEW. **Erysiphe cichoracearum,** Ill., Md., N. C., Pa.; **Sphaerotheca humuli,** N. Y. to Ala., Ill., Minn., Ohio, Pa.

RUST. **Puccinia atropuncta** (O, I), Pa., Va.; II, III on Amianthium; **P. extensicola** var. **hieraciata** (O, I), Ill., Minn., N. Y., Va., Wis.; II, III on Carex; **P. insperata** (I, II, III), Oreg.; **P. orbicula** (O, I, II, III), Me. to Tenn. and N. Dak.

PRICKLY-ASH (*Xanthoxylum americanum*)

CANKER, Stem. **Diplodia natalensis,** Texas.

LEAF SPOT. **Cercospora xanthoxyli,** Ind., Tex.; **Septoria pachyspora,** Iowa, Nebr.

POWDERY MILDEW. **Phyllactinia corylea,** widespread.

ROT, White Heart. **Fomes igniarius.**

RUST. **Puccinia andropogonis** var. **xanthoxyli** (O, I), Kans., Iowa, Mo., Nebr., Tex., Wis.; II, III on *Andropogon* spp.

PRICKLY-POPPY (*Argemone*)

DOWNY MILDEW. **Peronospora arborescens,** Tex.

LEAF SPOT. **Alternaria lancipes,** Kans., Tex.; **Gloeosporium argemonis,** Kans., Tex.; **Septoria argemones,** Nebr., Okla., Tex.

ROT, Root. **Phymatotrichum omnivorum,** Tex.

RUST. **Aecidium plenum** (O, I), Tex.

PRIMROSE (*Primula*)

BACTERIAL Leaf Spot. **Pseudomonas primulae,** Cal.

BLACK SPOT. **Asteroma garrettianum,** Col., Utah.

BLIGHT, Gray Mold. **Botrytis cinerea,** frequent in greenhouses, occasionally in open.

LEAF SPOT. **Ascochyta primulae,** Wis.; **Cercosporella primulae,** Wash.; **Colletotrichum primulae,** Fla.; **Mycosphaerella** sp., Ariz.; **Ramularia primulae,** Cal., Conn., Del., N. Y.

NEMATODE, Leaf and Stem. **Ditylenchus dipsaci,** Md., Pa.

NEMATODE, Root Knot. **Heterodera marioni,** occasional in greenhouse.

PHYSIOGENIC Chlorosis. Mineral deficiency, occasional in greenhouse.

POWDERY MILDEW. **Erysiphe polygoni,** Conn., N. J., Va.

ROT, Root. **Pythium irregulare,** Cal.; **Rhizoctonia solani,** Fla., Ill., Tex.

ROT, Stem. **Alternaria** sp., Conn.; **Sclerotinia sclerotiorum,** in pots *Primula malachoides,* Md.

RUST. **Uromyces apiosporus,** Cal., Nev.; **Puccinia aristidae,** Maine.

VIRUS, Mosaic. **Marmor primulae** and also **Marmor cucumeris.**

VIRUS, Spotted Wilt. **Lethum australiense,** Cal.

VIRUS, Aster Yellows. **Chlorogenus callistephi** var. **californicus,** Cal.

PRIVET (*Ligustrum*)

ANTHRACNOSE; Canker; Dieback. **Glomerella cingulata,** general, especially on common privet.

BACTERIAL Crown Gall. **Agrobacterium tumefaciens,** occasional.

BLIGHT, Leaf. **Ramularia** sp., N. J.

BLIGHT, Thread. **Pellicularia** (*Corticium*) **koleroga,** Fla.

LEAF SPOT. **Cercospora adusta,** Del. to Ala., Tex.; **C. ligustri,** Gulf States; **Exosporium concentricum,** Tex.; **Phyllosticta ovalifolii,** Md., Miss., Tex.

LEAF SPOT, Algal. **Cephaleuros virescens,** Gulf States.

NEMATODE, Leaf. **Aphelenchoides** sp.

NEMATODE, Root Knot. **Heterodera marioni,** in South.

POWDERY MILDEW. **Microsphaera alni,** Ind., N. J., Ohio.

ROT. **Rosellinia necatrix,** Cal.; **Fomes applanatus,** collar rot.

ROT, Root. **Armillaria mellea,** Miss., Tex.; **Clitocybe monadelpha,** Ark.; **C. tabescens,** Fla.; **Phymatotrichum omnivorum,** Ariz., Okla., Tex.

ROT, Wood. **Stereum hirsutum; Polyporus versicolor,** cosmopolitan, wound rot.

SOOTY Mold. Common after whiteflies in South.

?VIRUS. Variegation, graft transmitted.

PRUNELLA (Self-Heal, Heal-All)

BLACK KNOT, Tar Spot. **Gibberidea abundans,** Me., Wash.

BLIGHT, Southern. **Sclerotium rolfsii,** Tex.

LEAF SPOT. **Linospora brunellae,** Ida., Wash.; **Phyllosticta brunellae,** Tex.; **Ramularia brunellae,** Ill., Ind., N. Y., Ohio, Tex., Va., Wis.; **Septoria brunellae,** general.

POWDERY MILDEW. **Erysiphe cichoracearum,** Pa.; **Sphaerotheca humuli** and var. **fuliginea,** Ill., Ind., Md., Miss., Wash., Wis.

ROT, Root. **Pythium palingenes,** Va.

PUMPKIN (See under Squash)

PYRACANTHA (Firethorn)

BACTERIAL Fire Blight. **Erwinia amylovora,** widespread.

BLIGHT, Twig. **Diplodia crataegi.**

BLIGHT, Leaf. **Fabraea maculata,** La.

CANKER. **Botryosphaeria ribis,** Miss.

CANKER, Felt Fungus. **Septobasidium cokeri,** on scale insects on bark.

ROT, Root. **Armillaria mellea,** Cal.; **Phymatotrichum omnivorum,** Tex.

SCAB. **Fusicladium pyracanthae,** widespread.

Fire blight is the most common disease. It infects all species but some are relatively resistant. Scab is often disfiguring on berries.

PYRETHRUM (*Chrysanthemum cinerariaefolium, C. coccineum*)

BACTERIAL Fasciation. **Corynebacterium fascians,** Conn., Md.

BLIGHT, Gray Mold. **Botrytis cinerea.**

NEMATODE, Root Knot. **Heterodera marioni,** Fla., Miss., Md., Ohio, Tex., Wash.

ROT, Root. **Phymatotrichum omnivorum,** Tex.; **Pythium** sp., Col.; **Rhizoctonia solani,** N. J.

ROT, Stem. **Sclerotinia sclerotiorum,** Va.

QUAMOCLIT

NEMATODE Root Knot. **Heterodera marioni,** Ala.

ROT, Root. **Phymatotrichum omnivorum,** Tex.

RUST. **Coleosporium ipomoeae,** Ill., S. C., Tenn.
WHITE RUST. **Albugo ipomoae-panduratae,** N. Mex., Miss.

QUINCE (*Cydonia oblonga*)

ANTHRACNOSE, Northwestern. **Neofabraea malicorticis,** on fruit, Oreg., Wash.
BACTERIAL Fire Blight. **Erwinia amylovora,** general.
BACTERIAL Crown Gall. **Agrobacterium tumefaciens,** widespread.
BACTERIAL Hairy Root. **Agrobacterium rhizogenes,** Me. to N. C.; Pacific Coast.
BLIGHT, Leaf; Black Spot. **Fabraea maculata,** general.
BLIGHT, Thread. **Pellicularia** (*Corticium*) **koleroga,** N. C., Gulf States.
BLIGHT, Dothiorella Twig. **Botryosphaeria ribis,** Tex.
CANKER, Trunk. **Nectria galligena,** Oreg.; **Nectria perennans,** perennial canker, Oreg.
CANKER; Twig Blight. **Valsa leucostoma.**
FRUIT Spot. **Leptothyrium pomi,** Mo.; **Mycosphaerella pomi,** Northeast to Ohio.
LEAF SPOT. **Phyllosticta** sp.
NEMATODE, Root Knot. **Heterodera marioni,** Tex.
POWDERY MILDEW. **Phyllactinia corylea,** Va.; **Podosphaera leucotricha,** Cal., Wash.; **P. oxyacanthae,** N. Y., W. Va. to Ind.
ROT, Fruit. **Alternaria mali,** Ind.; **Botrytis cinerea,** occasional on fruit; **Trichothecium roseum,** pink mold, occasional; **Penicillium expansum,** cosmopolitan; **Phoma cydoniae,** pale rot, Ill., Mich.; **P. mali,** Ind.
ROT, Black; Canker; Leaf Spot. **Physalospora obtusa,** Eastern Central States to Ala., Tex.
ROT, Brown. **Monilinia fructicola,** Eastern States, Miss., Oreg.; **M. laxa,** also blossom and twig blight. Pacific Coast.
RUST. **Gymnosporangium clavariaeforme** (O, I), leaves, fruits, stems, Conn., Me., N. H.; III on juniper; **G. clavipes,** orange rust, quince rust; (O, I), fruits, stems; III on juniper, red-cedar; **G. libocedri** (O, I), fruit, stems, Oreg.; III on incense-cedar; **G. nelsoni** (O, I), leaves, stems, Ariz., Col.; III on juniper; **G. nidus-avis** (O, I), on leaves, fruits, stems, Conn., N. Y.; III on red-cedar and juniper.
SCAB. **Venturia pirina,** Conn.

Quinces are subject to fire blight; infected branches should be cut out with the usual precautions. For leaf blight, spray when blossoms show pink, again when the last of the petals are falling (calyx spray), and perhaps twice more at 2-week intervals with 1 to 40 lime sulfur or 6–16–100 bordeaux mixture. Brown rot is not very important on quince. To prevent rust remove near-by susceptible junipers or spray them in spring as spore horns are developing on galls. See under Rusts.

QUINCE, FLOWERING (*Chaenomeles japonica, C. sinensis*) (Japanese Quince, Chinese Quince)

BACTERIAL Crown Gall. **Agrobacterium tumefaciens.**

BACTERIAL Fire Blight. **Erwinia amylovora,** occasional.

BLIGHT, Leaf. **Fabraea maculata,** Ala., Conn., N. Y.

BLIGHT, Twig. **Phoma** sp., Md., Tex.; **Botryosphaeria ribis,** Ala., Tex.

CANKER, Felt Fungus. **Septobasidium burtii.**

LEAF SPOT. **Cercospora cydoniae.**

ROT, Brown. **Monilinia fructicola,** also leaf blight; **M. laxa,** also blossom and twig blight, Cal.

NEMATODE, Root Knot. **Heterodera marioni.**

RUST, Quince. **Gymnosporangium clavipes** (O, I), on stems; **G. libocedri** (O, I), on leaves.

RABBITBRUSH (*Chrysothamnus*)

LEAF SPOT. **Phleospora bigeloviae,** Cal.

POWDERY MILDEW. **Erysiphe cichoracearum.**

RUST. **Puccinia extensicola solidaginis** (O, I), N. Mex. and Cal.; **P. grindeliae** (III), Mont. to N. Mex., Cal.; **P. stipae** (O, I), Mont. to N. Mex., Cal.; II, III on Stipa and other grasses.

SMUT, Inflorescence. **Thecaphora pilulaeformis,** Ariz.

RADISH (*Raphanus sativus*)

BACTERIAL Black Rot. **Xanthomonas campestris.**

BACTERIAL Spot. **Xanthomonas vesicatoria** var. **raphani,** Ind.

BACTERIAL Soft Rot. **Erwinia carotovora,** cosmopolitan.

BLOTCH; Black Pod. **Alternaria raphani,** N. J., Ohio, Pa.

CLUB ROOT. **Plasmodiophora brassicae,** occasional in North, Mass. to N. J., Minn., Wash.

DAMPING-OFF. **Pythium debaryanum,** Mass., Minn., N. J., W. Va.; **Rhizoctonia solani,** cosmopolitan.

DOWNY MILDEW. **Peronospora parasitica,** Northeast and Central States, Cal., Miss., Tex.

LEAF SPOT. **Alternaria brassicae,** Cal., Conn., Mich.; **A. oleracea,** Conn., N. J.; **Cercospora cruciferarum,** Ala., Ill., Mo., Tex.; **C. atrogrisea,** N. J.

NEMATODE, Leaf and Stem. **Ditylenchus dipsaci,** N. Y.

NEMATODE, Root Knot. **Heterodera marioni.**

POWDERY MILDEW. **Erysiphe polygoni,** Cal., Mo., Tex.

ROT, Pod. **Phoma** sp., Fla.

Rot, Root. **Ascochyta** sp.; **Phymatotrichum omnivorum,** Tex., general; **Pythium aphanidermatum,** black root, Ind., Kans., Mass.

Rust. **Puccinia aristidae,** Ariz., Col.

Scab. **Actinomyces** (*Streptomyces*) **scabies,** Ind., Mich., N. J., Ohio, Tex., Wis.

Virus, Curly Top. **Ruga verrucosans.**

Virus, Mosaic. **Marmor brassicae.**

White Rust; White Blister. **Albugo candida,** general.

Radishes are so easily grown in most home gardens—at least during their brief spring season—that not many of us worry about disease control. Seed can, however, be treated with Fermate, Arasan, or Semesan as a protection against damping-off and black root.

RAIN–LILY (*Cooperia*)

Rust. **Puccinia cooperiae** (O, I, II, III), Tex.

RANUNCULUS (Buttercup, Crowfoot)

Blight, Gray Mold. **Botrytis cinerea,** Cal., N. Y., Wis.

Downy Mildew. **Peronospora ficariae,** occasional, Mass. to Md., Iowa, Minn. also Cal.

Leaf Gall. **Synchytrium anomalum,** Iowa; **S. aureum,** Cal., Ill., Wis.

Leaf Spot. **Ascochyta infuscans,** Wis.; **Cercospora ranunculi,** Iowa, Wis.; **Cylindrosporium ficariae,** Wash.; **Didymaria didyma,** Ill., Ind., Iowa, Mass., Mich., Miss., N. Y., Wis.; **Fabraea ranunculi,** Cal., Nebr., N. Y., Wis.; **Ovularia decipiens; Ramularia aequivoca,** Ill., Iowa, Oreg., Wis.; **Septocylindrium ranunculi,** Ill., N. Y., Wash., Wis.; **Septoria** spp.

Nematode, Leaf and Stem. **Ditylenchus dipsaci.**

Powdery Mildew. **Erysiphe polygoni,** frequent in Eastern and Central States; **Sphaerotheca humuli,** Col.

Rot, Root. **Phymatotrichum omnivorum,** Tex.

Rot, Stem. **Sclerotinia** sp., Ariz., Cal.; **Pythium** sp., Cal.; **Sclerotium rolfsii,** Cal.

Rust. **Puccinia andina** (III), Ill., Ind.; **P. eatoniae** var. **ranunculi** (O, I), Conn. to S. C., Miss., N. Dak., also Cal., Col.; II, III on Sphenopholis; **P. ranunculi** (III), Ariz., Col., Utah, Wash., Wyo.; **P. rubigo-vera** (O, I), Wis. to Tex., Cal., Wash.; III on Hordeum and Poa; **Uromyces alopecuri** (O, I), Col., Tex.; **U. dactylidis** (O, I), Mass.; **U. jonesii** (O, I, III), Cal., Col., Mont., Wyo.

Smut, Leaf. **Entyloma microsporum,** Ill., Ind., Iowa, Ky., Va., Wis.; **Doassansia ranunculina,** Ind., Wis.

Smut, Leaf and Stem. **Urocystis anemones,** Ill., Utah, Wyo.

Virus, Curly Top. **Ruga verrucosans.**

Virus, Yellows. **Chlorogenus callistephi** var. **californicus,** Cal.

RASPBERRY (Rubus)

ANTHRACNOSE; Dieback; Gray Bark. **Gloeosporium allantosporum,** Oreg., Wash.

ANTHRACNOSE, Spot. **Elsinoë veneta,** general but less common on red than black raspberry.

BACTERIAL Crown Gall. **Agrobacterium tumefaciens,** general; **A. rubi,** cane gall.

BACTERIAL Fire Blight; Flower and Twig Blight. **Erwinia amylovora** on black raspberry, Pa.

BLACK SPOT. **Stigmatea rubicola,** Mont., N. Mex., N. Y., Vt., Wis.

BLIGHT, Spur. **Didymella applanata,** general.

BLIGHT, Cane. **Leptosphaeria coniothyrium,** general; **L. thomasiana,** Oreg.; **Physalospora obtusa,** Iowa, Md., Mich., Mo., N. Dak.; **Phoma** sp., N. J.

CANKER; Cane Spot. **Ascospora ruborum,** Mass., Oreg., Wis.

CANKER; Dieback. **Glomerella cingulata,** Ark., Ky., Md., Mich., Mo., N. J., Ohio, R. I., W. Va.; **G. rubicola,** white bud, Ill., N. J., W. Va.; **Macrophoma rubi,** Ill.

DODDER. **Cuscuta gronovii,** Conn., Ill., Wis.

DOWNY MILDEW. **Peronospora rubi,** Wash.

FRUIT SPOT, Fly Speck. **Leptothyrium pomi,** Mass., Ind., Ky.

LEAF SPOT. **Sphaerulina rubi** (*Septoria darrowii*), Pa. to Tex., Wis.; **Mycosphaerella confusa,** Ga.; **M. rubi,** also cane spot, general; **Pezizella oenotherae,** Md., Mo., Va.

PHYSIOGENIC Chlorosis. Iron deficiency, in West.

POWDERY MILDEW. **Phyllactinia corylea,** Mich.; **Sphaerotheca humuli,** Mich., N. Y., Ohio.

ROSETTE, Double Blossom. **Cercosporella rubi,** Ky., Ill., Md., N. Y., Pa.

ROT, Fruit. **Botrytis cinerea,** gray mold, cosmopolitan; **Rhizopus nigricans,** black rot, cosmopolitan; **Alternaria,** sp., Mass.

ROT, Root. **Armillaria mellea,** Oreg., Wash.; **Rhizoctonia solani,** Col., Ida., Wash.

RUST, Leaf. **Phragmidium rubi-idaei** (O, I, II, III), Cal., Mass., Oreg., Wis.

RUST, Orange. **Kuehneola uredinis** (O, I, II, III), Ill., Pa., Del. to Wis.

RUST, Orange. **Gymnoconia peckiana** (O, I, III), on black raspberry, Northeast to Minn., Pacific Northwest.

RUST. **Pucciniastrum americanum** (II, III), Northeast to N. C., Ill., Idaho; O, I on spruce.

VIRUS, Raspberry Leaf Curl. **Corium rubi,** general.

VIRUS, Raspberry Mosaic. **Marmor rubi,** general.

VIRUS, Raspberry Streak. **Nanus orientalis.**

WILT. **Verticillium albo-atrum,** Mass. to N. J., Ohio, Oreg., Wash.

Virus diseases are important on raspberries and cannot be controlled by spraying. Mosaic has two forms, green mosaic being more common on black raspberries and yellow mosaic infecting red varieties more frequently. There are two forms of leaf curl, one attacking only red raspberries and the other present on both red and black. Mild and severe forms of streak appear only on black raspberry. Purchase healthy plants for setting; plant, if possible, 500 feet away from old patches, and inspect at least three times the first year, roguing all diseased plants, after first searing them with a blow torch or flame thrower so aphids will not carry virus to near-by healthy bushes.

Plants seldom recover from Verticillium wilt and never from orange rust, which is systemic. The nonsystemic leaf and yellow rusts are not very important. Crown gall is important on red raspberries; if infected plants are found raspberries should not be replanted in the same soil for some years. Bordeaux mixture has been recommended for anthracnose and spur-blight, but Fermate is now said to give excellent control of the latter.

RATIBIDA (Prairie Coneflower)

Downy Mildew. **Plasmopara halstedii,** Iowa.

Leaf Spot. **Cercospora ratibida,** Kans., Wis.; **Physalospora lepachydis,** Mont.; **Ramularia rudbeckiae,** Ida.; **Septoria lepachydis,** Kans., Wis.; **S. infuscata,** Wis.; **S. rudbeckiae,** N. Mex., N. Dak.

Powdery Mildew. **Erysiphe cichoracearum,** N. Dak., Tex.

Rot, Violet Root. **Helicobasidium purpureum,** Tex.

Rust. **Uromyces perigynius** (O, I), N. Dak. Tex.

RATTAN VINE (*Berchemia scandens*)

Rust. **Puccinia coronata** (O, I), Va. to La.; II, III on oats and wild grasses.

REDBUD (Judas-Tree, *Cercis*)

Canker; Dieback. **Botryosphaeria ribis,** Del., Md., N. J., N. C., Tex., Va., a serious disease.

Dodder. **Cuscuta exaltata,** Tex.

Leaf Spot. **Mycosphaerella cercidicola,** general; **Cercosporella chionea,** Ill., Ind., Kans., N. C.; **Phyllosticta cercidicola,** Ind., W. Va.

Rot, Root. **Phymatotrichum omnivorum,** Tex.

Rot, Sapwood. **Polyporus adustus; P. versicolor.**

RED BAY, SWAMP BAY (*Persea borbonia*)

Black Mildew. **Irenopsis martiniana,** Ala., Miss., Tex.; **Lembosia rugispora,** Miss., N. C.; **Meliola amphitricha,** Fla., Miss.; **Englerula carnea,** Fla.

Black Spot. **Asterina delitescens,** Va. to Fla., Tex.

Leaf Spot. **Cercospora purpurea,** Ga. to Fla., Miss.; **Phyllosticta micropuncta.**

LEAF SPOT, Algal. **Cephaleuros virescens,** Gulf States.
ROT, Wood. **Polyporus hirsutus; P. mutabilis.**

RED–CEDAR (See Juniper)

RHABDADENIA

LEAF SPOT, Algal; Green Scurf. **Cephaleuros virescens,** Fla.
LEAF SPOT. **Cercospora** sp., Fla.

RHODODENDRON

BLIGHT, Flower and Twig. **Botrytis** sp. and **B. cinerea,** seedlings, N. J., Wash.
BLIGHT, Bud and Twig. **Briosia azaleae,** Mass. to N. C. and Tex., Pacific Coast.
BLIGHT, Gray. **Pestalotia macrotricha,** after winter injury, widespread.
CANKER; Dieback. **Botryosphaeria ribis,** N. J., Mass.; **Gloeosporium** sp., N. Y.; **Phomopsis** sp., twig canker, N. J.; **Phytophthora cactorum,** Mass. to N. J., Ohio.
DAMPING-OFF. **Rhizoctonia solani,** Conn., N. J., Ohio.
FLOWER SPOT. **Ovulinia azaleae,** S. C. See also Azalea.
LEAF GALL; Shoot Hypertrophy. **Exobasidium vaccinii,** widespread; **E. vaccinii-uliginosii,** white leaf, witches' broom.
LEAF SPOT, Yellow. **Exobasidium burtii,** N. J., especially on *R. ponticum.*
LEAF SPOT. **Cercospora** sp., N. Y. to Fla., Cal., Oreg.; **Coryneum rhododendri,** N. C., Tenn., Wash.; **C. triseptatum,** Tenn.; **Cryptostictis mariae,** Tenn., Pacific Coast; **Diplodina eurhododendri,** Cal.; **Gloeosporium rhododendri,** Md.; **G. ferrugineum,** N. C.; **Hendersonia concentrica,** N. C., Tex., W. Va.; **Laestadia rhodorae,** N. Y.; **Lophodermium melaleucum,** N. C., Tenn.; **L. rhododendri,** N. Y. to N. C., Tex., Pacific Coast; **Monochaetia** sp., N. Y., Tenn., Wash.; **Mycosphaerella** sp., N. C., N. Y., Wash.; **Pestalotia** sp., N. C., N. J., N. Y., Tenn.; **Phyllosticta maxima** and other species, N. C., N. J., N. Y., Oreg., Pa., W. Va.; **Physalospora rhododendri,** Pa., Tenn., Va.; **Septoria rhododendri,** Me., Mass., Tex.; **Venturia rhododendri,** Va.
LEAF SPOT, Tar. **Melasmia rhododendri,** Alaska.
PHYSIOGENIC Chlorosis. Mineral deficiency, usually iron, widespread.
Sunscald; Windburn. Severe winter injury in exposed locations, especially with drying winds in early spring.
Black Walnut Wilt. Toxicity from walnut roots to shrubs near-by.
POWDERY MILDEW. **Microsphaera alni,** Md., N. J., N. Y.
ROT, Root and Collar. **Phytophthora cryptogaea,** N. J.; **P. cinnamomi,** Md., N. Y., N. J., Pa.
ROT, Root. **Armillaria mellea,** N. J., N. Y., Wash.; **Phymatotrichum omnivorum,** Tex.
ROT, Trunk. **Fomes applanatus,** N. Y.; **Stereum rugosum,** Tenn.; **Polyporus caesius,** Ala., Va.

Rust. **Chrysomyxa roanensis** (II, III), N. C., Tenn.; O, I on spruce; **C. piperiana** (II, III), Cal., Oreg., Wash.; **Pucciniastrum myrtilli** (II), Conn., N. J., R. I.

Wilt. **Phytophthora cinnamomi** (*P. cambivora*), N. J., N. Y., Pa.

Most rhododendron leaf spots are not worth worrying about. Some come in after winter injury, some are definitely parasitic but not particularly serious. I find a Phyllosticta leaf spot on *R. carolinianum* that is rather disfiguring, but not more so than the spray it would take to control it. Lacebug injury is much more important than the leaf spot, and so is response to unfavorable environment. Winter wind and sun will turn exposed foliage brown in any year, but sometimes cold March winds follow a February warm spell and then dying of leaves, twigs, and branches is extensive. Don't cut back too soon; wait until new growth starts and you can be sure where to cut. Usually the actual branch killing is less than dead leaves indicate. Even if rhododendrons have to be cut almost to the ground, they will grow up again rather speedily.

If aluminum sulfate is used for acidifying soil, be cautious and do not use too much. Sulfur is somewhat safer, though slower. Rhododendrons can be injured by an accumulation of wet matted leaves around the trunk, though greatly benefited by a mulch of peat moss or oak leaves which do not mat.

Three species of Phytophthora may infect rhododendrons. *Phytophthora cactorum* causes dieback of tips and *P. cryptogea* a rot at the crown of established garden shrubs, while *P. cinnamomi* is a nursery problem, producing wilt of young seedlings or grafted plants.

RHUBARB (*Rheum rhaponticum*)

Anthracnose. **Colletotrichum erumpens,** Ill., Mo., Pa., W. Va., Wis.

Bacterial Soft Rot. **Erwinia carotovora,** occasional, in market.

Bacterial Crown Gall. **Agrobacterium tumefaciens,** Iowa.

Bacterial Crown Rot. **Bacterium rhaponticum,** Okla.

Blight, Southern. **Sclerotium rolfsii,** Fla., Miss., Tex., Va.

Damping-Off, Crown Rot. **Pythium** spp., Cal., Md.

Downy Mildew. **Peronospora rumicis,** Cal.

Leaf Spot. **Ascochyta rhei,** eastern and central states to Miss., Kans.; **Alternaria** sp., Cal., Minn., Nebr., N. J., Pa.; **Cercospora** sp., Del., Md., Nebr.; **C. rhapontici,** Ill.; **Cladosporium** sp., Cal., Wash.; **Macrophoma** (*Phyllosticta*) **straminella,** general; **Ramularia rhei,** Cal.

Nematode Root Knot. **Heterodera marioni,** Cal., Md., Okla., Utah.

Physiogenic Crack Stem; Black Tip. Boron deficiency, Wash.

Rot, Gray Mold. **Botrytis cinerea,** occasional.

Rot, Root. **Armillaria mellea,** Cal., Tex.; **Phymatotrichum omnivorum,** Ariz., Tex.; **Pythium** sp., Cal.; **Phytophthora** spp. and **P. cactorum,** crown rot, Cal., Mo., Okla., Pa.; **P. parasitica,** Ill., Kans., La., Md., Mo., N. Y., Tex., Va.; **Rhizoctonia solani,** Cal., Conn., Ill., Minn., Mo., N. Y.. Okla., Tex., Wash.

RUST. **Puccinia phragmites** (O, I), Cal., Minn., Neb.; II, III on *Phragmites.*
VIRUS, Mosaic. Unidentified, Cal., Ill., N. Y., Pa., Wash.
?VIRUS, Ring Spot.

Macrophoma or Phyllosticta leaf spot is common but seldom calls for control measures beyond removal of old stalks in late fall. Plants showing crown rot should be dug and burned. From Pennsylvania south grow in raised beds.

RIBBON–BUSH (*Homalocladium platycladum*)

LEAF SPOT, Algal; Green Scurf. **Cephaleuros virescens.**
POWDERY MILDEW. **Erysiphe polygoni,** N. Y., Pa., Wis.

RICE–PAPER PLANT (*Tetrapanax papyriferum*)

NEMATODE, Root Knot. **Heterodera marioni,** Fla.

ROCK–JASMINE (*Androsace*)

DOWNY MILDEW. **Peronospora candida,** Kans.
LEAF SPOT. **Mycosphaerella primulae,** N. Mex.

ROMANZOFFIA

RUST. **Puccinia romanzoffiae** (III), Oreg.

ROSARY–PEA (*Abrus precatorius*)

Resistant to Root-Knot Nematode, **Heterodera marioni.**

ROSE (*Rosa*)

ANTHRACNOSE, Spot. **Sphaceloma rosarum,** Me. to Fla., Tex. to Kans.; Pacific Coast States.
BACTERIAL Crown Gall. **Agrobacterium tumefaciens,** general.
BACTERIAL Hairy Root. **Agrobacterium rhizogenes,** Pa., Tex., Md., Va.
BACTERIAL Shoot Blight. **Pseudomonas syringae,** Ark.
BLACK SPOT. **Diplocarpon rosae,** general.
BLIGHT, Cane. **Physalospora obtusa,** Conn. to Ala., Kans., Tex.; **Gloeosporium** spp., widespread.
BLIGHT, Blossom. **Botrytis cinerea,** also bud and twig, cosmopolitan; **Dothiorella** sp., La., Va.
BLIGHT, Southern. **Sclerotium rolfsii,** Fla., Kans., Tex.
CANKER, Brand. **Coniothyrium wernsdorffiae,** Minn., N. Y., Pa., also reported from Col., Ind., Miss., Tex. but perhaps mistaken for *C. fuckelii.*
CANKER, Brown. **Cryptosporella umbrina,** Mass. to Fla., Tex., Nebr. and Mich., Cal., Ida.
CANKER, Common, Graft. **Leptosphaeria coniothyrium** (*Coniothyrium fuckelii*).

CANKER, Basal, Crown. **Cylindrocladium scoparium,** Mass. to Ga., Tex. and Ill.

CANKER, Graft. **Coniothyrium rosarum,** Cal., Iowa, Mass., Minn., N. J., Pa.

CANKER; Dieback. **Botryosphaeria ribis** var. **chromogena,** Ala., Md., Tex., Va.; **Cryptosporium minimum,** Oreg., Pa.; **Diplodia** spp., probably secondary; **Griphosphaeria corticola** (*Coryneum microstictum*), N. H. to Ala., N. Dak.; Pacific Northwest; **Nectria cinnabarina,** Mass. to Va., Wash.; **Cytospora** sp., Ky., Pa., Va., Wash.

DIEBACK. **Didymella sepincoliformis,** Md.; **Glomerella cingulata,** Md., N. J., Va.; **Macrophoma** sp., Tex., Va.

DODDER. **Cuscuta indecora** and **C. paradoxa,** Tex.

DOWNY MILDEW. **Peronospora sparsa** (chiefly under glass), Me. to Fla., and Iowa; Cal.

LEAF SPOT. **Alternaria circinans,** Ala., Tex., Va.; **Cercospora puderi,** Fla., Ga.; **Mycosphaerella rosicola** (*Cercospora rosicola*), general except possibly far South where *M. rosigena* is reported; **Monochaetia compta,** Iowa; **Septoria rosae,** Miss., N. J., S. C.

MOLD, Black, of Grafts. **Chalaropsis thielavioides,** Ill., N. Y., Pa., on understocks from Oreg., Wash.

MOLD, Leaf and Bud. **Cladosporium** sp., Md., Minn., Miss., Tex.

NEMATODE, Root Knot. **Heterodera maroni,** Conn. to Fla., Mich., Nebr., Tex. to Cal., mostly on greenhouse roses in North.

PHYSIOGENIC Chlorosis. Mineral deficiency in alkaline soil, Nebr., Tex.

POWDERY MILDEW. **Sphaerotheca pannosa** var. **rosae,** general, and **S. humuli** not readily distinguished; **Phyllactinia corylea,** Wash.

ROT, Root. **Armillaria mellea,** Cal., Miss., Oreg., Tex., Wash.; **Clitocybe tabescens,** Fla.; **Fusarium** spp., occasional, especially in South; **Phymatotrichum omnivorum,** Ariz., Tex.; **Ramularia macrospora,** Md.

RUST. **Phragmidium americanum** (O, I, II, III), leaves of cultivated and native roses, Me. to N. C., Tex., N. Dak.; **P. disciflorum** (O, I), on leaves, stems; II, III leaves of cultivated roses of *R. gallica* group, Eastern States to Rocky Mountains, Pacific Coast; **P. speciosum** (O, I), leaves, stems; II, III stems of cultivated and native roses except far South; **P. subcorticinum** (O, I on stems); II, III leaves of cultivated roses of brier and sweetbrier groups from all States, and Alaska except Southeast and Southwest.

RUST, on Native Roses. **Phragmidium montivagum,** S. Dak. to N. Mex., Wash.; **P. rosae-acicularis** (O, I, II, III), Mich. to Col., Cal.; **P. rosicola** (III), Col., Mont., Nebr.; **P. rosae-arkansanae** (O, I, II, III), Ill. to Cal., Col.; **P. rosae-californicae** (O, I, II, III), Ariz., Cal., Oreg.

?VIRUS, Crinkle. Virus-like but not known to be transmissible, mostly in understock, sometimes in garden roses.

VIRUS, Mosaic. **Marmor rosae,** usually on greenhouse roses in Eastern and Central States, sometimes on garden roses.

VIRUS, Streak. **Marmor veneniferum,** Md., N. J., N. Y., Tex., Va.
WILT. **Verticillium** sp., Ark., N. Y.; **V. albo-atrum,** Cal., N. J., Ill.

Pedicel Necrosis (collapse of flower stem), Rough Bark and Speckle are diseases of unknown cause.

Black spot, brown canker, powdery mildew, and rust are probably the most important diseases of garden roses. Black spot is almost inevitable except in some dry Western States and shows up even there when overhead watering is substituted for the usual irrigation. Rust and mildew are more of a problem in the Southwest, although recently mildew seems to be getting the upper hand even in Eastern gardens. My personal explanation is that this is partly due to the switch from the older sulfur and copper fungicides to Fermate, which is very effective for black spot, fairly so for rust, but has no effect on mildew. The proprietary combination sprays and dusts usually include some sulfur with the Fermate but not nearly enough to control mildew. In greenhouses recent increase in powdery mildew is attributed to use of aerosols instead of syringing for red spiders. Syringing increases black spot, but it does keep mildew from getting much of a start.

Brown canker and other cane diseases are controlled by cutting out infected canes at spring pruning, remembering always to cut *close* to a bud (not only then but in gathering summer flowers, or cutting off faded blooms), a dormant lime-sulfur spray immediately after pruning, and the regular spray or dust schedule for black spot through the season.

Roses are sensitive to many chemicals. Copper sprays in cold weather produce red spots on foliage; sulfur in hot weather may give a brown marginal burn; Phygon sometimes makes faint white specks in petals and a black discoloration on leaves; DDT sometimes gives an orange cast to leaves in addition to the yellowing caused by red spiders it encourages, and so on. It is important to distinguish spray injury from black spot and not increase the dosage of the chemical just because you think you are not getting disease control.

ROSE ACACIA (*Robinia hispida*)

LEAF SPOT. **Alternaria fasciculata,** N. Dak.
ROT, Root. **Phymatotrichum omnivorum,** Tex.

ROSELLE (*Hibiscus sabdariffa*)

ANTHRACNOSE. **Colletotrichum gloeosporioides,** Fla.
BLIGHT, Gray Mold. **Botrytis cinerea,** Md.
BLIGHT, Southern. **Sclerotium rolfsii,** Tex.
DAMPING-OFF. **Rhizoctonia solani,** Tex.
LEAF SPOT. **Cercospora hibisci,** Tex.
NEMATODE, Root Knot. **Heterodera marioni,** Tex.
POWDERY MILDEW. **Microsphaera euphorbiae,** Ala., Fla.

Rot, Root. **Phymatotrichum omnivorum,** Tex.
Rot, Stem. **Fusarium** sp., Fla.; **Phytophthora parasitica,** Tex.

ROSE–GENTIAN (*Sabatia*)

Anthracnose. **Gloeosporium** sp., Okla.
Leaf Spot. **Cercospora sabbatiae,** Del., Miss., N. C., Okla., Tex.

ROSE–MALLOW (*Hibiscus palustris*)

Bacterial Crown Gall. **Agrobacterium tumefaciens,** Miss.
Dieback. **Colletotrichum hibisci,** N. J., N. Y., Tex.
Leaf Spot. **Ascochyta abelmoschi,** Ark.; **Cercospora kellermanii,** Ind.; **Phyllosticta hibiscina; Septoria** sp., N. J.
Rot, Root. **Phymatotrichum omnivorum,** Tex.
Rust. **Puccinia schedonnardi** (O, I), Conn. to Ala., Nebr., Tex.; II, III on Muhlenbergia, Sporobolus.

ROSEMARY (*Rosmarinus*)

Rot, Root. **Phymatotrichum omnivorum,** Ariz.

ROUGE–PLANT (*Rivina humulis*)

Leaf Spot. **Cercospora flagellaris,** Fla., Tex.
Rot, Root. **Helicobasidium purpureum,** Tex.
Rust. **Puccinia raunkiaeri** (O, I, II, III), Fla., Tex.

RUBBER–PLANT (*Ficus elastica*)

Anthracnose, Leaf Spot. **Glomerella cingulata,** general.
Bacterial Crown Gall. **Agrobacterium tumefaciens.**
Leaf Spot. **Alternaria** sp., Ind., Tex.; **Leptostromella elastica,** Northeastern States, Tex.; **Mycosphaerella bolleana,** Ga.; **Phyllosticta roberti,** Gulf States, Md.; **Stemphylium elasticae,** probably secondary; **Phyllachora** (*Trabutia*) **ficuum,** black spot.
Nematode, Root Knot. **Heterodera marioni.**

RUDBECKIA (Black-Eyed Susan, Coneflower, Golden-Glow)

Blight, Southern. **Sclerotium rolfsii,** Fla., N. J.
Downy Mildew. **Plasmopara halstedii,** Iowa, N. C., N. D., Nebr., N. Y., Wis.
Leaf Gall. **Synchytrium aureum,** Ill., Wis.
Leaf Spot. **Cercospora rudbeckiae,** N. Y.; **C. tabacina,** Wis., Ill., N. Y.; **Phyllosticta rudbeckiae,** Iowa, N. Y., Wis.; **Ramularia rudbeckiae,** Vt. to Miss., Col., Ida., Mont., Va., Vt., W. Va.; **Septoria rudbeckiae,** Del., Kans., Nebr., Wash., Wis.
Powdery Mildew. **Erysiphe cichoracearum,** general.
Rot, Root. **Phymatotrichum omnivorum,** Tex.

Rot, Stem. **Sclerotinia sclerotiorum,** Conn.

Rust. **Aecidium batesii** (O, I), Nebr.; **Puccinia extensicola** (O, I), Md., S. Dak.; **P. rudbeckiae** (III), Tex.; **Uromyces perigynius** (O, I), Md. to Mont.; II, III on Carex; **U. rudbeckiae** (III), Mont., Md. to Miss., N. Mex., Tex.

Smut, White. **Entyloma compositarum,** Iowa, Mo., Ohio, Wis.

Virus, Mosaic. Unidentified, Ind., Ill.

Virus, Yellow Dwarf. **Aureogenus vastaus,** N. Y.

Virus, Yellows. **Chlorogenus callistephi.**

Wilt. **Verticillium albo-atrum,** N. Y.

RUELLIA

Leaf Spot. **Cercospora consociata,** Ala., Ill., Miss., Mo.

Rot, Root. **Phymatotrichum omnivorum,** Tex.

Rust. **Puccinia ruelliae** (O, I, II, III), Md. to Fla., Kans., Tex.; **Uromyces ruelliae** (O, I, II, III), Tex.

RUMEX (Garden Sorrel)

Leaf Gall. **Synchytrium anomalum,** Iowa.

Leaf Spot. **Cercospora acetosellae,** La., N. J.; **Phyllosticta** sp., N. Y.; **Gloeosporium rumicis,** N. Y., Tex.; **Septoria pleosporioides,** Tex.

Nematode, Root Knot. **Heterodera marioni,** Fla.

Nematode. **Ditylenchus dipsaci,** N. Y.

Rust. **Puccinia acetosae** (II, III), Me. to Fla.

Virus, Yellows. **Chlorogenus callistephi,** var. **californicus,** Cal.

RUE–ANEMONE (*Anemonella thalictroides*)

Leaf Spot. **Cercospora caulophylli,** Mo.

Rust. **Puccinia rubigo-vera,** Ind., Iowa, Mo.

Smut, Leaf and Stem. **Urocystis anemones,** N. Y.

RUTABAGA (See Turnip)

SAFFLOWER, False Saffron (*Carthamus tinctorius*)

Anthracnose; Blight. **Gloeosporium carthami,** Ind., Tex., Va.

Leaf Spot. **Alternaria** sp., Ind.; **Septoria carthami,** Ind., Tex.

Nematode, Root Knot. **Heterodera marioni,** Fla.

Rust. **Puccinia carthami** (II, III), Col., Mass., Mont., Nebr., N. Dak.

Rot, Stem; Wilt. **Sclerotinia sclerotiorum,** Ind., N. Dak., Va.

SAGE (*Salvia officinalis*)

Blight, Southern. **Sclerotium rolfsii,** Ill.

Damping-Off; Root Rot. **Rhizoctonia solani,** Conn., Ill.

Leaf Spot. **Cercospora salviicola,** W. Va.

SAGE–BRUSH (*Artemisia tridentata*)

Blight, Gray Mold. **Botrytis cinerea,** Alaska.
Blight, Stem. **Sclerotium** sp., Oreg.
Canker, Stem Gall. **Syncarpella tumefaciens,** Cal., Mont., Nev.
Dodder. **Cuscuta** sp., Tex.
Downy Mildew. **Peronospora leptosperma,** Cal., Kans., Iowa, N. Dak., Wis.
Leaf Spot. **Cercospora ferruginea,** Wis.; **C. olivacea,** N. Y.; **Cylindrosporium artemisiae,** Wash., Wis.; **Gloeosporium heterophyllum,** Cal.; **Phyllosticta raui,** Mont.; **Ramularia artemisiae,** N. Y., Wis.; **Septoria artemisiae,** Wash.
Nematode, Root Knot. **Heterodera marioni,** Ala.
Powdery Mildew. **Erysiphe cichoracearum,** Wis. to N. Mex., Cal., Wash.
Rot, Root. **Phymatotrichum omnivorum,** Tex.
Rust. **Puccinia absinthii** (O, I, II, III), Wis. to Tex., Cal., Wash.; **P. atrofusca,** Iowa to Tex., Cal., Oreg.; II, III on *Carex* sp.; **P. millefolii** (III), N. Dak. to Tex., Cal., Wash., Alaska; **Uromyces oblongisporus** (III).

ST. ANDREWS CROSS (*Ascyrum hypericoides*)

Leaf Spot. **Cladosporium gloeosporioides,** Ala.
Rust. **Uromyces hyperici** (O, I, II, III), Miss., N. J., Tex.

ST. JOHNSWORT (*Hypericum*)

Black Knot. **Gibberidea heliopsidis,** Md.
Leaf Spot. **Cercospora hyperici,** Ill.; **Cladosporium gloeosporioides,** N. Y., Ala., N. J., Wis.
Nematode, Root Knot. **Heterodera marioni,** Fla., Md.
Powdery Mildew. **Erysiphe cichoracearum.**
Rust. **Uromyces hyperici** (O, I, II, III), N. C., Ill., N. Y., Wis., Me. to Ala., Iowa.

SALAL (*Gaultheria shallon*)

Anthracnose, Spot. **Elsinoë ledi.**
Black Mildew. **Meliola nidulans,** Cal.
Leaf Spot. **Mycosphaerella gaultheriae,** Alaska, Cal., Oreg., Wash.; **Pestalotia gibbosa,** Cal., Oreg., Wash.; **Phyllosticta gaultheriae,** Cal. to Wash.; **P. shallon,** Wash.

SALPIGLOSSIS (Painted-Tongue)

Nematode, Root Knot. **Heterodera marioni,** N. Y.
Nematode, Root. **Pratylenchus pratensis,** N. Y.
Wilt. **Fusarium** sp.; **Verticillium albo-atrum,** N. Y., Cal.
Virus, Yellows. **Chlorogenus callistephi,** Cal.

SALSIFY (*Tragopogon porrifolius*)

BACTERIAL Soft Rot. **Erwinia carotovora,** Conn.

BLIGHT, Leaf. **Sporodesmium scorzonerae,** Ala., Md., N. Y., Pa., Va., W. Va.

LEAF SPOT. **Cercospora tragopogonis,** Mont., Okla.; **Stemphylium botryosum,** N. Y.

NEMATODE, Leaf and Stem. **Ditylenchus dipsaci,** Cal.

POWDERY MILDEW. **Erysiphe cichoracearum,** general.

ROT, Root. **Phymatotrichum omnivorum,** Tex., Ariz.; **Rhizoctonia solani,** Wash.

VIRUS, Curly Top. **Ruga verrucosans,** Oreg.

VIRUS, Yellows. **Chlorogenus callistephi,** Md., N. Y., Pa., Wis., also var. **californicus,** Cal.

WHITE RUST. **Albugo tragopogonis,** general.

WILT. **Verticillium albo-atrum,** N. Y.

BLACK SALSIFY (*Scorzonera hispanica*)

NEMATODE, Root Knot. **Heterodera marioni,** Fla.

WHITE RUST. **Albugo tragopogonis,** Cal.

VIRUS, Yellows. **Chlorogenus callistephi** var. **californicus.**

SALVIA

DAMPING-OFF. **Pythium debaryanum,** Ohio; **Rhizoctonia solani,** Conn., Ill., N. J., Ohio.

DOWNY MILDEW. **Peronospora swinglei,** Kans.

LEAF SPOT. **Cercospora salviicola,** Okla., Tex.; **Ramularia salviicola,** Okla.

NEMATODE, Leaf. **Aphelenchoides** sp.

NEMATODE, Root Knot. **Heterodera marioni,** Ariz., N. J.

POWDERY MILDEW. **Erysiphe cichoracearum,** Cal.

ROT, Charcoal. **Macrophomina phaseoli,** S. C.

ROT, Root. **Phymatotrichum omnivorum,** Tex.

ROT, Stem. **Sphaeropsis salviae,** Miss.

RUST. **Aecidium subsimulans,** Ariz.; **Puccinia ballotaeflorae** (II, III), Tex.; O, I, unknown; **P. caulicola** (O, I, II, III), Iowa to Tex.; N. Mex.; **P. farinacea** (O, I, II, III), Ala., Ariz., Kans., Miss., Mo., Nebr., Okla., Tex.; **P. salviicola** (O, I, II, III), Fla., Tex.; **P. vertisepta** (O, I, III), Ariz., N. Mex.

VIRUS, Aster Yellows. **Chlorogenus callistephi** var. **californicus,** Cal.

SANCHEZIA

ROT, Mushroom Root. **Clitocybe tabescens,** Fla.

SAND-MYRTLE (*Leiophyllum*)

LEAF GALL. **Exobasidium vaccinii,** N. C., N. J.

SAND–VERBENA (*Abronia*)

Downy Mildew. **Peronospora oxybaphi,** Tex.

Leaf Spot. **Heterosporium abroniae,** Cal., Tex.

Rust. **Puccinia aristidae** (O, I), Ariz., Cal., Col., N. Mex.; II, III on **Aristida, Distichlis.**

SAND–VINE (*Gonolobus*)

Black Mildew. **Meliola bidentata,** N. C.

Downy Mildew. **Plasmopora gonolobi,** Md. to Fla., Tex.

Leaf Spot. **Septoria** sp., La.; **Cercospora gonolobi,** Okla.; **C. vincetoxici,** Tex.

Rust. **Puccinia obliqua** (III), Gulf States to S. C., Ky., Okla.; **Uromyces asclepiadis** (II, III), W. Va., Ind.

SANDWORT (*Arenaria*)

Leaf Spot. **Hendersonia tenella,** Tex.

Powdery Mildew. **Erysiphe polygoni,** Cal.

Rot, Root. **Phymatotrichum omnivorum,** Tex.

Rust. **Puccinia arenariae** (III), Cal., Fla., Mont., N. Y., Tex., Wis.; **P. tardissima,** Col., N. Mex., Utah, Wyo.; **Uromyces silenes,** Col., Utah.

Smut, Anther. **Ustilago violacea,** Me., N. H., N. Y., Vt.

SANSEVIERIA (Bow-String Hemp)

Bacterial, Soft Rot. **Erwinia aroideae; E. carotovora.**

Leaf Spot. **Fusarium moniliforme,** Fla., Mo., Wash.; **Gloeosporium sansevieriae,** Fla., Wash.

Nematode, Root Knot. **Heterodera marioni,** Fla.

SASSAFRAS

Canker, Branch, Trunk. **Nectria** sp., Conn. to W. Va., Miss.

Canker; Dieback. **Physalospora obtusa,** N. Y. to Ga.

Leaf Spot. **Septoria** sp., N. Y.; **Actinothyrium gloeosporioides,** Ill.; **Phyllosticta illinoensis,** Ill., Mass.; **P. sassafras,** N. Y. to Ga., Tex., Ill.

Mistletoe. **Phoradendron flavescens,** Tex.

Powdery Mildew. **Phyllactinia corylea,** Mich.

Rot, Root. **Armillaria mellea,** Pa.

Rot, Heart, Trunk. **Daedalea confragosa,** Ind., N. Y.; **Fomes igniarius,** Ohio, Va.; **F. ribis,** Mo.

Rot, Wood. **Daldinia vernicosa; Hymenochaete agglutinans,** Va.; **Hypoxylon** spp., N. Y. to Ga.; **Polyporus** spp., sometimes on living trees; **Poria ferruginosa; Schizophyllum commune,** N. Y.; **Trametes sepium,** Ind.

?Virus, Mosaic. Suspected virus.

?VIRUS, Yellows, suspected virus, Tex.
WILT. **Verticillium** sp., Ill.

Compared with the ravages of Japanese beetles, diseases of sassafras are scarcely worth mentioning and seldom call for control measures. The undetermined yellows disease produces fasciation of tops, leafroll and dwarfing of leaves.

SATUREIA (Basil Weed)

LEAF SPOT. **Phyllosticta decidua,** N. Y.
RUST. **Puccinia menthae** (O, I, II, III), Mass. to Va., Col., Wis.

SAXIFRAGE (*Saxifraga*)

LEAF SPOT. **Cercosporella saxifragae,** Wis.; **Phyllosticta saxifragarum,** Wyo.; **Septoria albicans,** Wis.; **Ramularia** sp., Alaska.
POWDERY MILDEW. **Spharotheca humuli,** N. Y., Alaska, and var. **fuliginea,** Col., Pa., Wyo.
ROT, Gray Mold. **Botrytis cinerea,** Alaska.
RUST. **Melampsora arctica** (O, I), Col., Alaska; II, III on Salix; **Puccinia heucherae** (III); Mont. to N. Mex., Ida., Wash., Wyo.; N. Y. to Ill., Minn., Alaska; **P. pazsckei** (III), Ida., Mont., Wash., **P. turrita** (III), Col., Utah.

SCABIOSA

BLIGHT, Southern. **Sclerotium rolfsii,** Fla.
POWDERY MILDEW. **Erysiphe polygoni.**
ROT, Root. **Phymatotrichum omnivorum,** Tex.
ROT, Stem. **Sclerotinia sclerotiorum,** N. Y.
VIRUS, Curly Top. **Ruga verrucosans,** Cal.
YELLOWS. **Chlorogenus callistephi,** Conn., N. J., N. Y., Va.; also var. **californicus,** Cal.

SCARBOROUGH–LILY (*Vallota speciosa*)

LEAF SCORCH. **Stagonospora curtisii,** La.

SCILLA (Squill)

NEMATODE, Bulb. **Ditylenchus dipsaci,** Va.
ROT, Blue Mold. **Penicillium gladioli,** on imported bulbs.
SMUT, Flower. **Ustilago vaillantii,** Mass., Wash.
VIRUS, Mosaic. **Marmor scillearum,** N. Y.

SEA–KALE (*Crambe maritima*)

LEAF SPOT, Black. **Alternaria oleracea,** Va.
WILT; YELLOWS. **Fusarium oxysporum** f. **conglutinans,** Ind.

SEDUM (Stonecrop, Live-For-Ever)

Blight, Southern. **Sclerotium rolfsii,** Kans., N. J., Va.

Leaf Spot. **Septoria sedi,** Ill., Iowa, Me., N. Y.; **Pleospora** sp., N. Y.

Nematode, Root Knot. **Heterodera marioni.**

Rot, Stem. **Colletotrichum** sp. (*Vermicularia beneficiens*), Va., N. Y.; **Phytophthora** sp., N. Y.; **Rhizoctonia solani,** Ill., N. J.

Rust. **Puccinia rydbergii** (III), Utah; **P. umbilici** (III), Col., Wyo.

SEMPERVIVUM (Houseleek, Hen-and-Chickens)

Rot, Leaf and Stem. **Phytophthora parasitica,** N. Y.

Rot, Root. **Pythium** sp., Iowa.

Rust. **Endophyllum sempervivi** (III), Mass., N. J., N. Y.

SENECIO (Groundsel)

(See Cineraria for Florist's Senecio, *S. cruenta*)

Leaf Gall. **Synchytrium aureum,** Wis.

Leaf Spot. **Cercospora senecionicola,** Wis.; **C. senecionis,** Tex.; **Gloeosporium senecionis,** Cal.; **Phyllosticta garrettii,** Oreg., Utah, Wyo.; **Ramularia filaris,** Col., Mont.; **R. pruinosa,** Col., Wyo.; **R. senecionis,** Cal., Col.; **Septoria cacaliae,** Ala., Ind., Tex.; **S. senecionis,** Cal., Wis.

Nematode, Leaf. **Aphelenchoides** sp.

Powdery Mildew. **Erysiphe cichoracearum,** Ida., Minn., Nebr., Va., Wash.; **Sphaerotheca humuli,** Col., Mont., Utah, Wyo.

Rot, Root. **Phymatotrichum omnivorum,** Tex.; **Rhizoctonia solani,** Ill., N. J.

Rot, Stem. **Phytophthora** sp., N. J.; **Sclerotinia sclerotiorum,** La.

Rust. **Coleosporium occidentale** (II, III), Cal., Col., Ida., Mont., Oreg., Wash., Wyo.; O, I unknown; **C. senecionis** (II, III), Col., R. I.; **Puccinia angustata** var. **eriophori** (O, I), Conn., Iowa, Minn., N. H., Utah, Vt.; II, III, Eriophorum and Scirpus; **P. expansa,** Cal., Utah, Wash., Wyo.; **P. recedens,** Conn. to N. C., Tenn., Iowa, N. Dak. to Oreg., Wash.; **P. extensicola** var. **hierciata** (O, I), Nebr., N. Mex., Tex.; II, III, Carex; **P. stipae** (O, I), Col., Wyo., Nebr.; II, III, Stipa; **P. subcircinata** (O, I, III), Nebr., Nev., N. Dak., Ida., Utah, Wash., N. Mex.; **Baeodromus californicus** (III), Col.

Smut, White. **Entyloma compositarum,** Kans., Md., Nebr., Pa., Tex., Wis.

Virus, Aster Yellows. **Chlorogenus callistephi** var. **californicus.**

White Rust. **Albugo tragopogonis,** Cal., Col., Ind., Mo., Mont., Nev., Utah, Wash.

Wilt. **Fusarium** sp., N. J.; **Verticillium albo-atrum,** Wash.

SENNA (*Cassia*)

Dieback. **Diplodia natalensis,** Tex.

Nematode, Root Knot. **Heterodera marioni,** Cal., Tex.

Rot, Root. **Phymatotrichum omnivorum,** Tex.; **Clitocybe tabescens,** Fla.

SEQUOIA (Redwood and Giant Sequoia)

BLIGHT, Seedling. **Botrytis douglasii.**

BLIGHT, Needle. **Chloroscypha chloromela** and **Mycosphaerella sequoiae** on redwood; **Cercospora sequoiae,** Md., Pa.; and **Pestalotia funerea,** Tex., on giant sequoia.

BLIGHT, Twig. **Phomopsis juniperovora** on giant sequoia.

BURLS, GALLS on trunk. Cause unknown.

CANKER, Bark. **Dermatea livida.**

ROT, Root. **Armillaria mellea.**

ROT, Trunk; Heart. **Fomes annosus; Ganoderma sequoiae; Poria sequoiae.**

ROT, Wood. **Hymenochaete tabacina; Lenzites saepiaria; Merulius hexagonoides; Polyporus** spp.; **Schizophyllum commune; Stereum** spp.

SERIOCARPUS (White-Topped Aster)

RUST. **Coleosporium solidaginis** (II, III), Conn.; **Puccinia extensicola** var. **solidaginis** (O, I), N. C., Ind., Tenn.

SESUVIUM

NEMATODE, Root Knot. **Heterodera marioni,** Ala., Fla.

RUST. **Puccinia aristidae** (O, I), Tex.; II, III, grasses.

SESAME (*Sesamum*)

BACTERIAL Leaf Spot. **Pseudomonas sesami,** Kans., Tex.

BACTERIAL Wilt. **Pseudomonas solanacearum,** Ariz.

LEAF SPOT. **Cercospora sesami,** Fla., Ga., S. C.

ROT, Charcoal. **Macrophomina phaseoli,** Cal., Tex.

SHALLOT (*Allium ascalonicum*)

BACTERIAL Soft Rot. **Erwinia carotovora,** Ga., La., Tex.

BLIGHT, Southern. **Sclerotium rolfsii,** La., Ga., Tex.

BLOTCH, Purple. **Alternaria porri,** La., Tex., Conn.

CANKER, Dry Rot. **Helminthosporium allii,** La., N. Mex., Tex.

DODDER. **Cuscuta** sp., Wis.

DOWNY MILDEW. **Peronospora destructor,** Cal., Conn., La.

NEMATODE, Stem. **Ditylenchus dipsaci,** Cal.

ROT, Bulb. **Fusarium oxysporum** f. **cepae,** Ida.

ROT, Charcoal. **Macrophomina phaseoli,** Tex.

ROT, Mold. **Aspergillus niger,** black mold, Cal., Ohio, Tex.; **Penicillium** sp., blue mold, Cal., Tex.; **Stemphylium botryosum,** seed mold, black stalk and tip blight; **Trichoderma viride,** green mold, cosmopolitan.

ROT, Neck; Gray Mold. **Botrytis allii,** Cal., La., Tex.

ROT, Pink Root. **Fusarium solani,** Conn., Tex.; **Pyrenochaete terrestris,** Col., La., N. Mex., N. Y.

ROT, White. **Sclerotium cepivorum,** La., Oreg., Va.

RUST. **Puccinia porri** (II, III), Cal., Conn., N. Y., Wash.

SMUT. **Urocystis cepulae,** Mass. (leek is resistant).

SMUDGE. **Colletotrichum circinans,** Ill., La., Wis.

VIRUS, Mosaic, unidentified.

VIRUS, Chlorosis. Aster yellows?

WILT. **Fusarium** sp.

Shallots and garlic are grown commercially in Louisiana, where pink root is prevalent. Louisiana Pearl with vigorous root system is less injured than other varieties. Losses from white rot are heavy when plants are set late, but September setting may give a good crop.

SHASTA DAISY (*Chrysanthemum maximum*)

LEAF BLOTCH. **Septoria leucanthemi,** Cal., Oreg.

LEAF SPOT. **Cercospora chrysanthemi,** Okla.

NEMATODE, Root Knot. **Heterodera marioni,** Fla., Md., Miss., Ohio, Tex., Wash.

ROT, Root. **Pythium** sp., N. J.

ROT, Stem. **Rhizoctonia solani,** Md.; **Sclerotinia sclerotiorum,** Mont., Wash.; **Fusarium roseum** and **F. solani,** Tex.

SHORTIA (Oconee-Bells)

LEAF SPOT. **Pezizella oenotherae,** N. and S. C.

ROT. **Sclerotium** sp., S. C.

SIDA

BLIGHT, Southern. **Sclerotium rolfsii,** Fla.

LEAF SPOT. **Cercospora sidicola; Colletotrichum malvarum,** Kans., Utah; **Phyllosticta spinosa,** Kans.; **Ramularia sidarum,** Fla.

NEMATODE, Root Knot. **Heterodera marioni,** Ala., Miss.

ROT, Root. **Phymatotrichum omnivorum,** Tex.

RUST. **Puccinia heterospora,** Fla. to La., Mo., Ind.; **P. lobata,** Ariz., Cal., N. Mex., Tex., Utah; **P. schedonnardi,** Fla.

VIRUS, Mosaic. **Marmor abutilon,** Fla.

SILENE (Cushion Pink and Campion)

LEAF SPOT. **Marssonina delastrei,** Wis.; **Septoria silenicola,** Nebr., Ida., Iowa, Md., Mont., Pa., Utah, Wis.

RUST. **Uromyces silenes** (O, I, II, III), Pa., Cal., Iowa, Kans., Mont., Wash.; **U. suksdorfii,** Cal., Ida., N. Mex., Utah, Wash.

SMUT, Flower. **Sorosporium saponariae,** Col., Nev., Utah; **Ustilago violacea,** anther smut, Cal., Mont., N. H., Tex., Va., Wash., Wyo.

SILK–TASSEL BUSH (*Garrya*)

Leaf Spot. **Cercospora garryae,** Cal., Tex.; **Phyllosticta garryae,** Cal., Tex.
Rot, Root. **Phymatotrichum omnivorum.**

SILPHIUM (Rosinweed, Compass Plant)

Downy Mildew. **Plasmopara halstedii,** Ill., Iowa, Wis. to Ark., Kans., Minn.
Leaf Spot. **Ascochyta compositarum,** Wis.; **Cercospora silphii,** Iowa, Wis.; **Septoria silphii,** Iowa, Wis.
Powdery Mildew. **Erysiphe cichoracearum,** Conn.
Rust. **Coleosporium terebinthinaceae** (II, III), Pa. to Ala., Tex., Kans.; **Puccinia silphii,** N. C. to Ala., N. Dak., Tex.; **Uromyces silphii** (O, I), Ohio to Kans.; II, III on Juncus.

SKULLCAP (*Scutellaria*)

Leaf Spot. **Cercospora scutellariae,** Ill., Miss., Mo., Tex.; **Phyllosticta decidua,** Tex., Wis.; **Septoria scutellariae,** Me. to Iowa, Cal., Col., Miss., Okla.
Powdery Mildew. **Erysiphe galeopsidis,** Mich., N. Y., Ill., Ind., Iowa, Kans., Ohio, Wis.; **Microsphaera** sp., Ill.
Rot, Root. **Rhizoctonia solani,** Tex.; **Phymatotrichum omnivorum,** Tex.
Rot, Stem. **Botrytis cinerea,** Wash.

SKUNK–CABBAGE (*Symplocarpus foetidus*)

Blight, Leaf. **Botrytis** sp., Conn., Ill., N. J., N. Y.
Leaf Spot. **Cercospora symplocarpi,** Mass. to Va., Ind., Wis.; **Septoria spiculosa,** Md., N. Y., Pa., Wis.

SMELOWSKIA

Rust. **Puccinia aberrans** (O, III), Col., Mont., Nebr., Utah, Wash.; **Puccinia holboelli,** Nev.; **Puccinia monoica,** (O, I), Col., Wyo.

SMILACINA (False Solomons-Seal)

Leaf Spot. **Cercosporella idahoensis,** Ida.; **Cylindrosporium smilacinae,** Col., Oreg., Utah; **Heterosporium asperatum,** Wyo.; **Phleospora vagnerae,** Mont.; **Ramularia smilacinae,** Mont., Wyo., Wash.; **Septoria smilacinae,** general; **Sphaeropsis cruenta,** Cal., N. Mex.
Rot, Rhizome. **Stromatinia smilacinae,** N. Y.
Rust. **Puccinia sessilis,** Kans., Iowa., Ida., N. Y., Okla., Pa.; **Uromyces acuminatus,** Col., Minn., Mont., Nebr., Wis.
Smut, Leaf. **Urocystis colchici,** Mont.

SMILAX

Leaf Spot. **Ascochyta confusa,** N. Y., Wis.; **Cercospora smilacina,** Conn. to Fla., Tex.; **C. smilacis,** Conn. to Fla., Tex., Nebr.; **Colletotrichum smilacis,**

Ill.; **Cylindrosporium smilacis,** Ala.; **Dothiorella smilacina,** Mass. to La., Tex.; **Mycosphaerella smilacicola,** Ga., S. C.; **Pestalotia clavata,** N. Y. to Ala., La.; **Phyllosticta subeffusa,** Kans., Ill., W. Va.; **Ramularia subrufa,** Iowa, Miss., Nebr., Wis.; **Septogloeum subnudum,** Ill., Wis.; **Septoria smilacis,** W. Va.; **Sphaeropsis cruenta,** Iowa; **Stagonospora smilacis,** Conn. to Md., N. Dak., Tex.

Powdery Mildew. **Phyllactinia corylea,** Mich.

Rust. **Aecidium smilacis** (O, I), N. and S. C.; II, III, unknown; **Puccinia amphigena** (O, I), Kans., N. Dak., Nebr., Okla.; **P. macrospora** (O, I), N. J., Kans.; **P. smilacis** (II, III), Mass. to Fla.

SMOKE–TREE (*Cotinus coggygria*)

Leaf Spot. **Cercospora rhoina,** Ala.; **Pezizella oenotherae,** N. J.; **Septoria rhoina,** Northeast.

Wilt. **Verticillium albo-atrum,** Ill., N. J., N. Y.

SMOKE–TREE (*Dalea spinosa*)

Leaf Spot. **Cercospora daleae,** Kans.

Mistletoe. **Phoradendron californicum,** Cal. to Tex.

Rot, Root. **Phymatotrichum omnivorum,** Tex.

Rust. **Puccinia andropogonis** var. **onobrychidis** (O, I).

SNAPDRAGON (*Antirrhinum*)

Anthracnose. **Colletotrichum antirrhini,** general in Eastern and Southern States to Col., and Tex.

Bacterial Crown Gall. **Agrobacterium tumefaciens,** N. Y.

Blight, Gray Mold. **Botrytis cinerea.**

Blight, Southern; Stem Rot. **Sclerotium rolfsii** (including **S. delphinii**), Cal., Fla., Miss., N. J., N. Y., Tex.

Damping-Off; Root Rot. **Pythium** spp., cosmopolitan; **Rhizoctonia solani,** also collar rot.

Dodder. **Cuscuta** sp., Wash.

Downy Mildew. **Peronospora antirrhini,** Cal., Okla., Oreg., Pa.

Leaf Spot; Stem Rot; Canker. **Phyllosticta antirrhini,** general in Eastern and North Central States, also Tex., Wash.

Nematode, Root Knot. **Heterodera marioni,** general in South from Md. to Fla.

Nematode, Root. **Pratylenchus pratensis.**

Physiogenic. Fasciation. Cause unknown, probably genetic. Occasional wherever grown.

Tip Blight. Cause unknown, Md., Okla., Va. In California caused by feeding injury from peach aphid.

Powdery Mildew. **Oidium** sp., Mass., N. Y., Pa.

Rot, Root. **Phymatotrichum omnivorum,** Tex.; **Thielaviopsis basicola,** Conn., N. J.

Rot, Stem; Wilt. **Fusarium** sp., perhaps secondary, Conn., Fla., Ga., Okla., Tenn., Wash.; **Myrothecium roridum,** Tex.; **Phoma** sp., Conn., Ind., Mass., Mich., N. Y., Ohio, Va.; **Phytophthora cactorum,** Cal., Ill., Minn., N. J., N. Y.; **P. cryptogea,** Cal., Okla.; **Sclerotinia sclerotiorum,** Cal., Ind.; **S. minor,** Conn.

Rust. **Puccinia antirrhini** (II, III), general; O, I, unknown.

Virus, Mosaic. In part **Marmor cucumeris** and part unidentified, Fla., Kans., N. Y., Ohio, Pa.

Virus, Ring Spot. Unidentified, Okla.

Wilt. **Verticillium albo-atrum,** Cal., Conn., Mass., Me., Minn., N. J., N. Y., Pa.

Rust is the most generally important disease and can be prevented to a large extent by purchasing rust-resistant seed, although not all such seed is resistant to all strains of rust. Fermate and Parzate, especially the latter, are recommended for rust control, but once the disease is established in epidemic form it is difficult to get it subdued.

Seedlings planted out from greenhouses sometimes bring along anthracnose which spreads to other plants in wet weather. Bordeaux mixture is useful for this and Phyllosticta leaf spot.

SNOWBERRY (*Symphoricarpos*)

Anthracnose. **Glomerella cingulata,** widespread, Ind., Mass., Mich., N. Y., Pa.

Anthracnose, Spot. **Sphaceloma symphoricarpi,** Me. to Md., Ark., Minn., Cal., Col., Oreg.

Bacterial Crown Gall. **Agrobacterium tumefaciens,** Md.

Leaf Spot. **Ascochyta symphoricarpophila,** N. Y.; **Cercospora symphoricarpi,** Mont., S. Dak.; **Phyllosticta symphoricarpi,** N. Y., N. Mex., Wash.; **Septoria signalensis,** Wyo.; **S. symphoricarpi,** N. Dak. to Col., Cal., Wash.

Powdery Mildew. **Microsphaera diffusa,** general; **Podosphaera oxyacanthae,** Wash.

Rot, Berry. **Alternaria** sp., Col., Conn., Mass., N. Y.; **Botrytis cinerea,** Conn., Mass., N. Y.

Rot, Collar. **Fomes ribis,** Kans., Mont.

Rust. **Puccinia crandallii** (O, I), N. Dak. to Mo., Cal., Wash.; II, III on Festuca, Poa; **P. symphoricarpi** (III), Mont. to Cal., Col., Wash.

SNOWDROP (*Galanthus*)

Blight, Botrytis. **Botrytis galanthina,** disease not reported here but sclerotial stage of fungus found in imported bulbs, along with another type, **Sclerotium** sp.

SNOW-ON-THE-MOUNTAIN (*Euphorbia marginata*)

BLIGHT. **Botrytis cinerea,** N. J.
LEAF SPOT. **Alternaria** sp., Kans., Tex.; **Cercospora euphorbiicola,** Nebr.; **C. pulcherrimae,** Okla.; **Phyllosticta** sp., N. J.
RUST. **Puccinia panici,** Miss. to Tex., Col., S. Dak.; II, III on Panicum.

SOAPBERRY, SOUTHERN (*Sapindus saponaria*)

BLACK MILDEW. **Meliola sapindacearum;** and **M. sapindii.**
BLIGHT, Thread. *Corticium stevensii* = **Pellicularia koleroga,** Fla.
LEAF SPOT; Dieback. **Glomerella cingulata,** Fla.; **Phyllosticta sapindi,** Fla.

SOAPBERRY, WESTERN (*Sapindus drummondii*)

BLIGHT, Leaf. **Cylindrosporium griseum,** Okla., Tex.
LEAF SPOT; Dieback. **Glomerella cingulata,** Tex.; **Mycosphaerella sapindi,** Mo.
MISTLETOE. **Phoradendron flavescens** and var. **macrophyllum,** Ariz., N. Mex., Tex.
POWDERY MILDEW. **Uncinula circinata,** Tex.
?VIRUS, Mosaic. Suspected virus, Tex.
This is one of the few plants reported resistant to Texas root rot.

SOAPWORT (*Saponaria*)

LEAF SPOT. **Alternaria saponariae,** also stem spot, Conn. to Md., Ind., Minn.; **Cylindrosporium officinale,** Ind.; **Phyllosticta tenerrima,** N. J.; **Septoria noctiflorae,** Ill.
RUST. **Puccinia aristidae,** Col.

SOLOMONS-SEAL (*Polygonatum*)

LEAF SPOT. **Sphaeropsis cruenta,** Conn., Ida., Ind., Iowa, Va., Wis.; II, III on Phalaris; **Colletotrichum liliacearum,** probably cosmopolitan.
ROT, Rhizome. **Stromatinia smilacinae.**
RUST. **Puccinia sessilis** (O, I), Ala., Conn., Iowa, N. Y., Ohio, Pa., Wis.; **Uromyces acuminatus** var. **magnatus,** Ill., Iowa, Minn., Nebr., N. and S. Dak.
SMUT, Leaf. **Urocystis colchici,** Iowa.
VIRUS, Mosaic. Unidentified, Me.

SOPHORA JAPONICA (Japanese Pagoda-Tree)

BLIGHT, Twig. **Nectria cinnabarina,** Conn., N. Y.
DAMPING-OFF. **Rhizoctonia solani,** Conn.
DIEBACK. **Diplodia sophorae,** Ohio.
POWDERY MILDEW. **Microsphaera alni,** Conn.
ROT, Root. **Phymatotrichum omnivorum,** Tex.

SOPHORA SPP. (Mescalbean, Silky Sophora, Vetchleaf Sophora)

Leaf Spot. **Phyllosticta sophorae,** Tex., on mescalbean.
Mistletoe. **Phoradendron flavescens,** Tex., on mescalbean.
Nematode, **Heterodera marioni,** Md. on vetchleaf sophora.
Rot, Root. **Phymatotrichum omnivorum,** Tex.
Rust. **Uromyces hyalinus,** S. Dak. to Tex., Ariz., Wyo., on silky sophora.

SOYBEAN (*Soja max*)

Anthracnose. **Glomerella glycines,** N. C., Mich. to Fla., Nebr., Tex.
Bacterial Blight. **Pseudomonas glycinea,** East and South to Tex., Minn.
Bacterial Pustule; Pustular Spot. **Xanthomonas phaseoli** var. **sojense,** general.
Bacterial Wild Fire. **Pseudomonas tabaci,** Md. to Ala., La., Neb.
Bacterial Wilt. **Pseudomonas solanacearum,** N. C.
Blight, Gray Mold, Leaf Spot, Shoot. **Botrytis cinerea.**
Blight, Pod and Stem. **Diaporthe sojae,** N. Y., Mich. to Ga., La., Kans.
Blight, Ashy Stem, Charcoal Rot. **Macrophomina phaseoli,** N. J. to S. C., Tex., Nebr.
Blight, Southern. **Sclerotium rolfsii,** Va. to Fla., Tex., Iowa.
Damping-Off; Root Rot. **Pythium** spp., Ill., Iowa, Minn., Mo., N. C., N. Dak.
Downy Mildew. **Peronospora manshurica,** East and South to La., Iowa.
Leaf Spot; Brown Spot. **Septoria glycines,** Ark., Del., Ind., Iowa, Md., N. C., Wis.
Leaf Spot. **Alternaria** sp., widespread but secondary; **Cercospora canescens** (cruenta?), Ala., Ill., Md., Miss., N. C., W. Va.; **C. sojina,** frog-eye, Iowa, N. Y., Mich. to Fla., Okla.; **Helminthosporium vignae,** zonate spot, N. C.; **Mycosphaerella cruenta,** Ga., Miss.; **Myrothecium roridum,** La.; **Phyllosticta glycinea,** Ill., Md., N. C., Va.; **P. phaseolina,** Ga., N. C.; **Pleosphaerulina sojaecola,** Md., N. J., N. Y., Wis.
Nematode, Stem. **Ditylenchus dipsaci,** N. Y.
Nematode, Root Knot. **Heterodera marioni,** Va. to Fla., Tex.
Physiogenic Yellowing. Potassium deficiency.
Baldhead. Loss of seedling growing point.
Powdery Mildew. **Erysiphe polygoni,** Del., Iowa, N. and S. C.; **Microsphaera** sp., N. C.
Rot, Root; Stem Canker. **Pellicularia filamentosa** (*Rhizoctonia solani*), Ariz., Col.
Rot, Root. **Phymatotrichum omnivorum,** Tex.
Rot, Seed. **Fusarium scirpi** f. **tracheiphilum; Nematospora coryli,** yeast spot, N. and S. C., Va.
Virus, Bud Blight; Streak; Leatherneck. **Annulus tabaci.**
Virus, Curly Top. **Ruga verrucosans,** Oreg., Wash.
Virus, Mosaic. Soja virus 1.

WILT; Fusarium Blight. **Fusarium oxysporum.**

Don't be misled by the numerous diseases. Edible soybeans are well suited to home garden culture, and I get an excellent crop in my own backyard with no control measures other than dusting seed with Spergon before planting. Commercial growers find a number of diseases of economic importance: bacterial pustule, the various blights, some leaf spots, downy mildew and wildfire, virus diseases. U.S.D.A. Farmers' Bulletin 1937 gives details and suggestions on resistant varieties.

SPARAXIS (Wandflower)

VIRUS, Mosaic. **Marmor iridis,** Cal., Oreg.

SPECULARIA (Venus Looking-Glass)

DODDER. **Cuscuta** sp., Tex.

LEAF Gall. **Synchytrium** sp.

LEAF SPOT. **Cercospora speculariae,** La.; **Septoria speculariae,** Va., Kans., Pa. to Ala., Tex., Wis.

ROT, Root. **Phymatotrichum speculariae,** Tex.

RUST. **Coleosporium campanulae** (II, III), N. C.

SMUT, Seed. **Ustilago speculariae,** Okla.

SPHACELE

RUST. **Uredo sphacelicola** (II), Cal.

SPICEBUSH (*Benzoin aestivale*)

LEAF SPOT. **Phyllosticta linderae,** Del., Ind.; **P. lindericola,** W. Va.

MISTLETOE. **Phoradendron flavescens,** Eastern States.

ROT, Root. **Phymatotrichum omnivorum,** Tex.

SPIDER–LILY (*Hymenocallis*)

LEAF SPOT. **Cercospora pancratii,** La., Fla., Tex.; **Stagonospora curtisii.**

VIRUS, Mosaic. Unidentified, Cal.

SPIDERLING (*Boerhaavia*)

BACTERIAL Leaf Spot. **Xanthomonas campestris,** Tex.

LEAF SPOT. **Ascochyta boerhaaviae,** Tex.; **Cercospora boerhaaviae,** Tex.

NEMATODE, Root Knot. **Heterodera marioni,** Fla.

ROT, Root. **Phymatotrichum omnivorum,** Tex.

WHITE RUST. **Albugo platensis,** Ariz., Fla., N. Mex., Tex.

SPINACH (*Spinacea oleracea*)

ANTHRACNOSE. **Colletotrichum spinaciae,** Conn., La., Miss., N. J., N. Y., Tex., Va.

BACTERIAL Soft Rot. **Erwinia carotovora.**

DAMPING-OFF; Root Rot. **Rhizoctonia** sp., general; **Pythium** sp., pre-emergence seed decay.

DOWNY MILDEW. **Peronospora effusa,** general.

LEAF SPOT. **Stagonospora spinaciae,** S. Dak.; **Cercospora beticola,** Ga., Ill., Iowa, Mass., N. Y., Tex., widespread; **Heterosporium variabile,** pinhead "rust"; **Phyllosticta chenopodii,** Del., N. J., N. Y.

MOLD, Leaf. **Cladosporium macrocarpum,** Del., Okla., Pa., Tex.

MOLD, Seed. **Pleospora herbarum** (*Stemphylium botryosum*); **Alternaria** sp., also secondary leaf spot.

NEMATODE, Root Knot. **Heterodera marioni,** Ga., Ind., S. C., Va.

PHYSIOGENIC Yellows. Nutrient deficiency.

ROT, Root; Crown Wilt. **Fusarium solani; F. oxysporum; F. spinaciae; Phytophthora** sp., Ind., N. J., N. Y.; **P. megasperma,** Cal., N. C.; **Sclerotinia sclerotiorum,** Ga., N. Y.

ROT, Root. **Phymatotrichum omnivorum,** Tex.; **Pyrenochaete terrestris,** Iowa.

RUST. **Puccinia aristidae** (O, I), Ariz., Cal., Oreg., Wash.

SMUT, Leaf. **Entyloma ellisii,** N. J.

VIRUS, Curly Top. **Ruga verrucosans,** Cal., Oreg., Tex., Utah, Wash.

VIRUS, Mosaic. **Marmor cucumeris,** in part.

VIRUS, Spotted Wilt. **Lethum australiense.**

VIRUS, Aster Yellows. **Chlorogenus callistephi.**

WHITE RUST. **Albugo occidentalis,** Ark., Okla., Tex.

WILT. **Verticillium** sp., N. Y.

Downy mildew is the outstanding spinach disease. All varieties are susceptible. Dithane Z–78 or Parzate give, in some places, best control and yield. Avoid mosaic by planting Old Dominion or Virginia Blight Resistant. Variety Bloomsdale Longstanding is very susceptible to white rust, while Virofly is somewhat resistant. Arasan, red copper oxide, or zinc oxide are suggested for seed treatment before planting.

SPIRAEA (Oriental Flowering Spirea)

BACTERIAL Fire Blight. **Erwinia amylovora,** Md., N. J., N. C., Va.

BACTERIAL Hairy Root. **Agrobacterium rhizogenes,** Iowa.

LEAF SPOT. **Cylindrosporium filipendulae,** Iowa.

NEMATODE, Root Knot. **Heterodera marioni,** Fla., Miss.

POWDERY MILDEW. **Microsphaera alni,** Conn.; **Podosphaera oxyacanthae,** widespread.

ROT, Root. **Phymatotrichum omnivorum,** Ariz., Tex.

SPIRAEA (Native Hardhack, Meadowsweet)

BLIGHT, Seedling; Stem Girdle. **Thelephora terrestris.**

CANKER. **Cryptodiaporthe macounii,** N. Y.

LEAF SPOT. **Cercospora rubigo,** Cal., Kans., Oreg., Wis.; **Phleospora salicifoliae,** N. Y. to Kans., Wash.

Powdery Mildew. **Podosphaera oxyacanthae,** widespread; **Sphaerotheca castagnei,** Pa.; **S. humuli,** Conn., Mich., N. Y., Pa.

SPRUCE (*Picea*)

Blight, Brown Felt. **Herpotrichia nigra,** Mont., Northern Rocky Mts., Pacific Northwest.

Blight, Snow. **Phacidium infestans,** Northeastern States.

Blight, Twig. **Ascochyta piniperda,** N. C., Me.

Canker; Twig Blight. **Cytospora kunzei,** Northeast to Ill., Minn., N. Y.; **C.** spp., Mass. to N. J., Ill.

Damping-Off. **Cylindrocladium scoparium,** N. J.; **Phytophthora cinnamomi,** Va.

Mistletoe; Witches' Broom. **Arceuthobium campylopodum,** N. Mex., Rocky Mts.

Needle Cast; Tar Spot. **Lophodermium piceae,** Cal., Mass., Mich., Oreg.; **L. septata,** Oreg.; **Rhizophaera kalkhoffii,** Conn., N. Y.

Rot, Collar. **Diplodia pinea,** N. J., N. Y.

Rot, Heart. **Fomes annosus,** Cal. to Wash.; **F. pini,** widespread; **F. pinicola,** widespread; **F. roseus; F. subroseus,** widespread; **Polyporus** spp.

Rot, Root. **Armillaria mellea.**

Rust, Cone. **Chrysomyxa pyrolae,** Me., N. Y., Pa., Vt.

Rust, Needle. **Chrysomyxa cassandrae** (O, I), Minn., Mich., N. Y., Wis.; **C. empetri; C. ledicola** (O, I), Col., Idaho; **C. chiogenis; C. ledi,** New England to Great Lakes; **C. piperiana** (O, I); II, III on *Rododendron californicum;* **C. roanensis** (O, I), N. C., Tenn.; II, III on *Rhododendron catawbiense;* **C. weirii,** Tenn., W. Va.

Rust, Witches' Broom. **Melampsorella cerastii,** Me., N. Y., N. and S. Rocky Mts., Ida., Mont., Wash., Wyo.

Cytospora canker frequently kills lower branches of ornamental spruces. There is little control except to remove affected portions.

SPURGE, CYPRESS (*Euphorbia cyparissias*)

Leaf Spot. **Cercospora euphorbiae,** Tex.

Rot, Root. **Phymatotrichum omnivorum,** Tex.

Rust. **Melampsora euphorbiae** (O, I, II, III), Me. to Pa., Ind., Wis.

Personally I'd welcome a lot more diseases of cypress spurge, which is a fine ground cover in its place, but impossible to keep in bounds.

SPURGE, FLOWERING (*Euphorbia corollata*)

Leaf Spot. **Cercospora euphorbiae,** Kans., Tex.; **C. heterospora,** Wis.; **Phyllosticta** sp.

Powdery Mildew. **Microsphaera euphorbiae,** Md. to Ga., Ind., Wis.

Rot, Root. **Phymatotrichum omnivorum,** Tex.

Rust. **Puccinia panici** (O, I), Ohio to Ala., Tex., Minn.; II, III on Panicum.

SPURGE, PAINTED, Mexican Fireplant (*Euphorbia heterophylla*)

RUST. **Uromyces proëminens** (O, I, II, III), Ind. to Fla., Tex., Kans.

SMUT, Stem. **Tilletia euphorbiae,** La.

SQUASH and PUMPKIN (*Cucurbita*)

ANTHRACNOSE. **Colletotrichum lagenarium,** N. J., N. Y., Conn., Kans., Md., Tex.

BACTERIAL Spot. **Xanthomonas cucurbitae,** Conn., Ga., Ill., Ind., Mass., Md., Mich., Wis.

BACTERIAL Soft Rot. **Erwinia carotovora,** cosmopolitan.

BACTERIAL Wilt. **Erwinia tracheiphila,** general.

BLIGHT, Blossom. **Choanephora cucurbitarum,** also brown rot of fruit, Me. to Fla., Mich., Okla., Tex.

BLIGHT, Gummy Stem. **Mycosphaerella citrullina,** also black fruit rot, Conn., Fla., Ga., Mass., Mich., N. J., N. Y.

BLIGHT, Leaf. **Alternaria cucumerina,** Del., Minn., N. C., N. J., N. Y., Utah.

BLIGHT, Southern. **Sclerotium rolfsii,** Ala., Fla., Ga.

DAMPING-OFF. **Pythium debaryanum,** Conn., Wis.

DOWNY MILDEW. **Pseudoperonospora cubensis,** Me. to Ala., La. and Tex., Cal., Iowa.

LEAF SPOT. **Ascochyta** sp.; **Cercospora cucurbitae,** Del., N. J., Wis., Ala.; **Gloeosporium** sp., Ill.; **Phyllosticta cucurbitarum,** Ind., N. Y.; **P. orbicularis,** Del., N. Y., Pa.; **Septoria cucurbitacearum,** Mass., N. Y., Wis.; **Stemphylium cucurbitacearum,** Ind., Ohio.

MOLD, Seed. **Alternaria tenuis,** cosmopolitan; **A. radicina,** occasional; **Curvularia trifolii,** Conn.

NEMATODE, Root Knot. **Heterodera marioni,** Cal., Fla., Tex.

PHYSIOGENIC Blossom-End Rot. Common on summer squash when hot dry weather follows a cool, rainy spell.

Chlorosis. Nutrient deficiency: manganese—interveinal chlorosis; nitrogen—leaf yellowing and chlorosis of bud end of fruit.

Bronzing, marginal, and leaf necrosis; fruit deformities. Potassium deficiency.

POWDERY MILDEW. **Erysiphe cichoracearum,** general.

ROT, Blossom-End Root Rot. **Phythium aphanidermatum,** Ariz., Cal., Md.

ROT, Charcoal. **Macrophoma phaseoli,** Oreg., Tex.

ROT, Fruit. **Alternaria** sp., Mass., N. H., Oreg., Vt., Wash.; **Diplodia natalensis,** Tex.; **Fusarium** spp., Col., Conn., Mass., Tex., W. Va.; **F. solani** f. **cucurbitae,** Cal., N. Y., Oreg.; also root and stem rot; **Phytophthora cactorum,** Ariz.; **Pythium ultimum,** Cal.; **Rhizopus stolonifer,** general in storage after injury; **Sclerotinia sclerotiorum,** Ida., Mass., Me., N. H., N. Y., Wash. Also stem rot; **Trichothecium roseum,** pink mold, Mass.

SCAB; Storage Rot. **Cladosporium cucumerinum,** Md., Mass.

Virus, Curly Top. **Ruga verrucosans,** Cal., Ida., N. Mex. Oreg., Utah, Wash.
Virus, Cucumber Mosaic. **Marmor cucumeris,** in part, with one or more strains known as squash mosaic, cucurbit ring mosaic, western cucumber mosaic.
Virus, Ring Spot. **?Annulus tabaci.**
Virus, Aster Yellows. **Chlorogenus callistephi,** Me.
Wilt. **Fusarium oxysporum** f. **niveum,** Cal., Ill., Mich., Wis.; **Phytophthora capsici,** Col.; **Verticillium albo-atrum,** Oreg.
Wilt, Anasa. Feeding injury from the squash bug.

Compared to home-garden losses caused by the squash vine borer, diseases seem rather unimportant, although they can be serious. Fungicide-insecticide combinations should be used with caution. Some squash varieties are injured by sulfur dusts and some are very sensitive to DDT. In general, diseases and control measures are the same as for other cucurbits.

SQUAW–APPLE (*Peraphyllum*)

Leaf Spot. **Septoria peraphylli,** Utah.
Rust. **Gymnosporangium inconspicuum** (O, I), Col.; III on juniper; **G. nelsoni** (O, I), on leaves, fruit, Col., Utah.

SQUAW–BUSH (*Condalia*)

Mistletoe. **Phoradendron californicum,** Cal.

SQUIRREL–CORN (*Dicentra*)

Downy Mildew. **Peronospora dicentrae,** Ind., Md., Mo., N. Y., Va., Wis.
Rust. **Cerotelium dicentrae** (O, I), Kans., N. Y. to Md., S. Dak.; II, III on wood-nettle.

STACHYS (Betony, Hedgenettle, Woundwort)

Leaf Gall. **Synchytrium stachydis,** La.
Leaf Spot. **Cercospora stachydis,** Iowa, Me.; **Cylindrosporium stachydis,** Ill.; **Ovularia bullata,** Cal.; **O. stachydis-ciliatae,** Wash.; **Phyllosticta decidua,** Mass., Wis.; **P. palustris,** Ohio, Ill.; **Ramularia stachydis,** Oreg.; **Septoria stachydis,** Cal., Ill., Miss., N. Y., Wis.
Nematode, Root Knot. **Heterodera marioni.**
Powdery Mildew. **Erysiphe galeopsidis** (*E. cichoracearum?*), Ohio to Col., Mont., N. Y. to Ind., Wis.; **Sphaerotheca humuli,** Cal.
Rust. **Puccinia pallidissima,** Tex.
Virus, Spotted Wilt. **Lethum australiense.**

STAPHYLEA (Bladdernut)

Blight, Twig. **Hypomyces ipomoeae,** Mass.; **Coryneum microstictum,** Mass.
Leaf Spot. **Mycosphaerella staphylina,** Ga.; **Ovularia isarioides,** N. Y. to Mo., Iowa; **Septoria cirrhosa,** Mo.

STARFLOWER (*Trientalis*)

LEAF GALL. **Synchytrium aureum,** Pa.
LEAF SPOT. **Cylindrosporium magnusianum,** Cal., Mass., Mich., N. Y., Wis.; **Septoria increscens,** Cal., Me., Mich., N. Y., Vt., Wis.
RUST. **Puccinia karelica** (O, I), N. Y., Wis.; II, III on Carex.
SMUT, Leaf and Stem. **Tuburcinia trientalis,** Oreg., Wash.

STAR-GRASS, Gold (*Hypoxis*)

LEAF SPOT. **Cylindrosporium guttatum,** Wis.; **Septoria hypoxis,** Pa.
RUST. **Uromyces affinis,** Conn., Mo., Miss.; **U. necopinus,** N. Y.
SMUT, Floral. **Urocystis hypoxis,** Conn., Mass.

STAR-OF-BETHLEHEM (*Ornithogalum*)

BLIGHT, Southern. **Sclerotium rolfsii,** Cal.
LEAF SPOT. **Didymellina ornithogali,** Ill., Pa., Wash.; **Septoria ornithogali,** Conn., Mass.
VIRUS, Mosaic. **Marmor scillearum; Marmor tulipae** experimentally.

STATICE (Sea-Lavender, *Limonium*)

LEAF SPOT. **Alternaria** sp., Conn.; **Cercospora** sp., Tex.; **Fusicladium staticis; Phyllosticta** sp., Conn.; **P. staticis,** N. Y.
NEMATODE, Root Knot. **Heterodera marioni.**
RUST. **Uromyces limonii** (O, I, II, III), Me. to Miss. and Tex., Cal., N. Mex.
VIRUS, Aster Yellows. **Chlorogenus callistephi** var. **californicus,** Cal.

STENANTHIUM

RUST. **Puccinia atropuncta** (II, III), Ga.; **P. grumosa,** Oreg.

STEPHANOMERIA (Wire Lettuce)

LEAF SPOT. **Cercospora calvicarpa,** Cal.
RUST. **Puccinia harknessii** (O, I, III), Mont. to N. Mex., Cal., Wash.

STERNBERGIA (Fall-Daffodil)

LEAF SCORCH; Leaf Spot. **Stagonospora curtisii,** Cal.

STEVIA (*Piqueria trinervia*)

DAMPING-OFF. **Rhizoctonia solani,** Ill.
VIRUS, Yellows. **Chlorogenus callistephi,** Mich., N. J.

STILLINGIA (Queens Delight)

DODDER. **Cuscuta** sp., Okla.
LEAF SPOT. **Cercospora stillingiae,** Tex.

ROT, Root. **Phymatotrichum omnivorum,** Tex.
RUST. **Uromyces graminicola,** Okla.; II, III on Panicum.

STOCK (*Matthiola*)

ANTHRACNOSE. **Colletotrichum gloeosporioides,** Tex.
BACTERIAL Rot. **Xanthomonas incanae,** Cal., Tenn.
BLIGHT, Gray Mold. **Botrytis cinerea,** Tex.
CLUB ROOT. **Plasmodiophora brassicae,** N. J.
DAMPING-OFF. **Pythium** spp.; **Rhizoctonia solani,** cosmopolitan.
LEAF SPOT. **Myrothecium roridum,** Tex.
NEMATODE, Root Knot. **Heterodera marioni,** Tex.
ROT, Crown; Wilt. **Sclerotinia sclerotiorum,** Cal., Mich., Pa.
ROT, Root. **Fusarium** sp., Del., N. J.; **Phymatotrichum omnivorum,** Tex.; **Phytophthora megasperma,** Cal.
VIRUS, Curly Top. **Ruga verrucosans.**
VIRUS, Mosaic. **Marmor brassicae** (*M. matthiolae*) ; Flower breaking, **M. cruciferarum,** Cal.
VIRUS, Spotted Wilt. **Lethum australiense,** Tex.
WILT. **Fusarium oxysporum;** f. **mathioli,** Ariz., Cal.

STOKESIA (Stokes-Aster)

BLIGHT, Head. **Botrytis cinerea,** N. Y.
LEAF SPOT. **Ascochyta** sp., Iowa, Pa.
VIRUS, Mosaic. Unidentified, Iowa.

STRANVAESIA

ROT, Root. **Clitocybe tabescens,** Fla.
BACTERIAL Fire Blight. **Erwinia amylovora,** N. J.

STRAWBERRY (*Fragaria*)

ANTHRACNOSE. **Colletotrichum fragariae,** Fla.
BACTERIAL Soft Rot. **Erwinia carotovora,** Mass.
BLIGHT, Gray Mold. **Botrytis cinerea,** general on fruit.
BLIGHT, Leaf. **Dendrophoma obscurans,** angular leaf spot, Mass. to Fla., Mich., Minn., Nebr., Oreg., Tex.
BLIGHT, Southern. **Sclerotium rolfsii,** Ala., Fla., N. C., Tex.
DOWNY MILDEW. **Peronospora fragariae,** Iowa.
LEAF SCORCH. **Diplocarpon earliana,** general.
LEAF SPOT. **Cercospora** sp., La.; **Gloeosporium** sp., Ill., Mass., Mich., Pa.; **Mycosphaerella fragariae,** common leaf spot and black seed, general; **M. louisianae,** purple spot, La., Miss.
NEMATODE, Spring Dwarf. **Aphelenchoides fragariae** from Cape Cod, Mass. to Norfolk, Va.

NEMATODE, Crimp; Summer Dwarf. **Aphelenchoides besseyi,** chiefly in Southeast from Va. and Ark. southward, but also Ill., Del., D. C., and Cal.

NEMATODE, Leaf and Stem. **Ditylenchus dipsaci,** Cal.

NEMATODE, Root. **Pratylenchus pratensis.**

NEMATODE, Root Knot. **Heterodera marioni,** general in South from N. C. to Fla., Tex.

PHYSIOGENIC Black Root. Winter injury, defective drainage, soil toxins, widespread.

Variegation, of Leaf. Chlorophyll deficiency, especially in Blakemore, Progressive, and related varieties, general.

POWDERY MILDEW. **Sphaerotheca humuli,** general, but not prevalent in South.

ROT, Crown. **Sclerotinia sclerotiorum,** Md. to Fla., Tex.

ROT, Fruit. **Penicillium** spp., secondary; **Pezizella oenotherae,** tan rot, Me. to Fla., Okla.; **Phytophthora cactorum,** leather rot, Ala., Ark., Ky., Ill., La., Md., Miss., Mo., Tenn., Va.; **Rhizopus stolonifer,** black rot, leak, cosmopolitan; **Rhizoctonia solani,** hard brown rot, widespread; **Sphaeropsis** sp., Cal., Col., Ill., Iowa, Minn.

ROT, Red Stele Root Disease; Brown Core. **Phytophthora fragariae,** Me. to Va., Ark., Cal., Ky., Ind., Mich., Ohio, Oreg., Tenn., Wash., Wis.

ROT, Root. **Cylindrocladium scorparium,** Oreg., Tenn. and associated with black root, **Leptosphaeria coniothyrium; Fusarium** spp.; **Olpidium brassicae,** Wash.; **Pythium** spp.

VIRUS, Strawberry-crinkle. **Marmor fragariae,** Cal., Ida., Oreg., Wash.

VIRUS, Leafroll. Unidentified, Md., N. J., N. Y., Vt.

VIRUS, Stunt. **Nanus cupuliformis,** Ida., Oreg.

VIRUS, Witches' Broom. **Nanus fragariae,** Ida., Mont., Oreg.

VIRUS, Yellow Edge; Yellows; Xanthosis. **Marmor marginans,** Pacific Coast, occasional in N. E. and Middle Atlantic States.

WILT. **Verticillium albo-atrum,** Cal., N. Y.

A relatively new disease, red stele, is becoming of first importance on strawberries. The roots rot and above-ground parts are stunted or wilted. There are some resistant varieties, as Aberdeen, Temple, Pathfinder, and Sparkle. Spring and summer dwarf nematodes also cause stunting, crinkling, as do some of the virus diseases. The best control is purchase of healthy plants, preferably certified. Leaf spots, leaf blights, leaf scorch can be taken care of with bordeaux mixture if necessary, but some varieties are resistant to some foliage diseases. Mulching helps to prevent fruit rots.

U. S. Department of Agriculture Farmers' Bulletin 1891 gives an excellent discussion of Diseases of Strawberries.

STRAWBERRY–TREE (*Arbutus unedo*)

CROWN GALL. **Agrobacterium tumefaciens,** Cal.

LEAF SPOT. **Septoria unedonis,** Oreg.

STRAWFLOWER (*Helichrysum bracteatum*)

NEMATODE, Root Knot. **Heterodera marioni,** Fla.
ROT, Stem. **Fusarium** sp., Fla.
VIRUS, Curly Top. **Ruga verrucosans,** Cal., Oreg., Wash.
VIRUS, Yellows; Bunchy Top. **Chlorogenus callistephi,** East and Central States; also var. **californicus,** Cal.
WILT. **Verticillium albo-atrum,** Cal.
In some seasons Verticillium wilt appears in California in epidemic form.

STREPTANTHERA

VIRUS, Mosaic. **Marmor iridis,** Cal.

STREPTOPUS (Twisted Stalk)

LEAF SPOT. **Cercospora streptopi,** Wash.; **Septoria streptopidis,** Mont.
SMUT, Leaf. **Tuburcinia clintoniae,** Wis.

STYRAX (Snowbell)

NEMATODE, Root Knot. **Heterodera marioni,** Md.

SUMAC (*Rhus*)

CANKER; Dieback. **Cryptodiaporthe aculeans,** N. Y. to Ga., Miss., Mo.; **Physalospora** sp.
DODDER. **Cuscuta exaltata,** Tex.
LEAF BLISTER. **Taphrina purpurascens,** widespread.
LEAF SPOT. **Pezizella oenotherae,** Ga., N. J., Md., Va., W. Va.; **Phyllosticta** sp., Minn.; **Phleospora** (*Cylindrosporium*) **irregularis,** widespread; **Septoria rhoina,** Vt. to Kans., Fla., Mich., Minn., N. J.
POWDERY MILDEW. **Sphaerotheca humuli,** widespread.
ROT, Root. **Phymatotrichum omnivorum,** Tex.; **Armillaria mellea,** Cal.; **Corticium galactinum,** white root, near apple trees, Va.
ROT, Wood. **Polyporus hirsutus,** sometimes on living shrubs; **P. poculum,** W. Va.; **Poria cocos,** Fla.; **Schizophyllum commune,** widespread; **Stereum** spp.
RUST. **Pileolaria effusa** (O, III), Ariz.; **P. patzouarensis** (O, I, II, III), Col., N. Mex., Okla.
WILT. **Verticillium albo-atrum,** Mass.

SUNFLOWER (*Helianthus*)

BACTERIAL Blight. **Pseudomonas helianthi,** Ill.
BACTERIAL Crown Gall. **Agrobacterium tumefaciens,** experimental.
BACTERIAL Wilt. **Pseudomonas solanacearum,** Fla.
BLACK KNOT, Black Patch. **Gibberidea heliopsidis,** Ga., Ill., Miss., Mo., N. C., Va., Wis.

BLIGHT, Gray Mold; Bud Rot. **Botrytis cinerea,** Cal., Oreg.

BLIGHT, Southern. **Sclerotium rolfsii,** La., Tex.

DODDER. **Cuscuta** sp., Okla., Tex., Wash.

DOWNY MILDEW. **Plasmopara halstedii,** N. Y. to Md. and to Kans., Ill., Mont., Tex., chiefly in Central States.

LEAF SPOT. **Ascochyta compositarum,** Wis.; **Cercospora helianthi,** Kans., Ill., Mo., Ohio, Tex., Wis.; **C. pachypus,** Ala., Kans., Okla., Tex.; **Colletotrichum helianthi,** Wis.; **Phyllosticta helianthi,** Wis.; **Septoria helianthi,** general in Middle West and from Conn. to Miss., N. Mex., Okla.

NEMATODE, Leaf Gall. **Tylenchus balsamophilus,** Wash.

NEMATODE, Root Knot. **Heterodera marioni,** Ala., Tex., Fla., W. Va.

ROT, Charcoal. **Macrophomina phaseoli,** Md.

ROT, Root. **Armillaria mellea,** Oreg.; **Phymatotrichum omnivorum,** Tex.; **Helicobasidium purpureum,** violet root, Tex.; **Rhizoctonia solani,** Ill., Md., Nebr., N. Y., Wis.

ROT, Stem; Wilt. **Sclerotinia sclerotiorum,** widespread.

RUST. **Puccinia helianthi** (O, I, II, III), general; **P. massalis** (O, I, II, III), N. Mex., Tex.; **Uromyces junci** (O, I), Nebr., Okla., Cal., Kans., N. and S. Dak., Wyo.; II, III on Juncus; **U. silphii** (O, I), N. Y., Ill., Mo., Tenn., Wis.; **Coleosporium helianthi** (II, III), N. Y. to Fla., La., Ind., Okla.; II, III on pine.

WHITE RUST. **Albugo tragopogonis,** Ill., Mo., Wis.

SMUT, Leaf. **Entyloma polysporum,** Mont.

VIRUS Mosaic. Unidentified.

SWEET ALYSSUM (*Lobularia maritima*)

CLUB ROOT. **Plasmodiophora brassicae,** N. J.

DODDER. **Cuscuta** sp., Tex.

DAMPING-OFF. **Pythium ultimum,** N. J.; **Rhizoctonia solani,** N. J., N. Y., Va.

DOWNY MILDEW. **Peronospora parasitica,** Cal., N. J.

NEMATODE, Root Knot. **Heterodera marioni.**

VIRUS, Yellows. **Chlorogenus callistephi,** N. J.

SWEET-FERN (*Comptonia*)

RUST, Blister. **Cronartium comptoniae** (II, III), Me. to Minn., N. C. to Ohio; O, I on pine; **Gymnosporangium ellisii** (O, I), N. J.; II, III on *Chamaecyparis.*

SWEET FLAG (*Acorus*)

LEAF SPOT. **Cylindrosporium acori,** Conn., Kans.; **Ramularia aromatica,** Conn. to Me., Ind., Wis.; **Septocylindrium** sp., N. Y.

RUST. **Uromyces pyriformis** (II, III), Me. to Va., Ill., Miss., Minn.; O, I unknown.

SWEET GALE (*Myrica gale*)

Blight, Twig. **Diplodia** sp., N. J.

Leaf Spot. **Ramularia monilioides,** N. Y.; **Septoria myricata,** N. Y.

Rust. **Cronartium comptoniae,** Me. to N. Y., Wash.; O, I on pine; **Gymnosporangium ellisii** (O, I), Me.

SWEET GUM (*Liquidambar*)

Bacterial Crown Gall. **Agrobacterium tumefaciens,** Md.

Blight, Thread. **Corticium stevensii,** Fla. See *Pellicularia koleroga.*

Canker. **Hymenochaete agglutinans,** Md.; **Nectria** sp.; **Septobasidium** sp., felt canker, Fla.; **Dothiorella** sp., bleeding necrosis, N. J., N. Y.

Leaf Spot. **Cercospora liquidambaris,** Me. to Fla., Tex.; **C. tuberculans,** Miss., La., Mo.; **Exosporium liquidambaris,** Tex.; **Leptothyriella liquidambaris,** Ill., Md., N. C.; **Septoria liquidambaris,** Mass. to Fla., and Tex.

Mistletoe. **Phoradendron flavescens,** Ohio, Tex. to N. C.

Rot, Heart. **Polyporus gilvus,** widespread.

Rot, Root. **Phymatotrichum omnivorum,** Tex.; **Clitocybe tabescens,** Fla.

Rot, Wood. **Daedalea confragosa; Fomes** sp.; **Ganoderma** sp.; **Hydnum** (*Steccherinum*) **ochracearum,** sometimes on living trees; **Polyporus** spp.; **Poria** spp.; **Pleurotus** sp., Miss.; **Schizophyllum commune,** cosmopolitan; **Stereum** spp.

SWEETLEAF (*Symplocos*)

Leaf Gall; Bud Gall. **Exobasidium symploci,** Gulf States, Ind. to N. C.

Leaf Spot. **Septoria symploci,** Fla., Miss., N. C.; **S. stigma,** Ala.; **S. tinctoria,** Ark.

SWEET PEA (*Lathyrus odoratus*)

Anthracnose; Blossom and Shoot Blight. **Glomerella cingulata,** general except on Pacific Coast.

Bacterial Crown Gall. **Agrobacterium tumefaciens,** N. J., Va.

Bacterial Fasciation. **Corynebacterium fascians,** Cal., Col., Conn., Ga., Ind., Mich., Mo., N. Y., N. J., Ohio, Okla., Pa.

Bacterial Leaf Spot. **Pseudomonas pisi,** Ind., Wis.

Bacterial Streak. **Erwinia lathyri,** Del., Ga., Mass., N. J., N. Mex., N. Y., Okla., Pa., Tex., Wash., possibly a complex with virus.

Blight, Gray Mold. **Botrytis cinerea,** probably general.

Blight, Southern. **Sclerotium rolfsii,** Fla.

Damping-Off; Root and Stem Rot. **Pythium** spp., general; **Rhizoctonia solani.**

Dodder. **Cuscuta indecora,** Tex.

Leaf Spot. **Alternaria** sp., secondary, Md., Mass., N. J., N. Y., Pa., Tex.; **Colletotrichum pisi,** Ala., Fla., Ga., S. C.; **Isariopsis griseola,** Conn.; **Myco-**

sphaerella pinodes, also stem spot, Minn., Wis.; **Phyllosticta orobella,** Tex.; **Ramularia** sp., N. Y.

MOLD, White. **Erostrotheca multiformis** (conidial stage *Cladosporium*), Mass., N. J., N. Y., Pa., Tex., in greenhouses.

NEMATODE, Root Knot. **Heterodera marioni,** Mass., N. J., N. Y., Tex.

NEMATODE, Root. **Pratylenchus pratensis,** associated with root blackening, N. J., N. Y.

PHYSIOGENIC Bud Drop. Deficiency of phosphorus and potassium with low light intensity.

POWDERY MILDEW. **Microsphaera alni,** general, especially on greenhouse crops; **Erysiphe polygoni,** often reported but perhaps confused with Microsphaera.

ROT, Root. **Aphanomyces euteiches,** Ind., Mich., Wis.; **Fusarium** spp., occasionally prevalent in greenhouses or garden; **Phymatotrichum omnivorum,** Tex.; **Phytophthora cactorum,** Conn.; **Thielaviopsis basicola,** Conn. to Ohio, Ill., Miss.; also Fla., Col., Pacific Coast.

ROT; Stem Wilt. **Sclerotinia** sp., Md., Pa.

VIRUS, Pea Mosaic. **Marmor leguminosarum.**

VIRUS, Sweet Pea Streak. Suspected virus or complex in Eastern States, perhaps strain of yellow bean mosaic.

VIRUS, Spotted Wilt. **Lethum australiense,** Cal.

WILT, **Verticillium** sp., N. Y.

Treat seed with Arasan or Spergon before planting to aid in control of anthracnose and root rots; keep down aphids with nicotine or other contact insecticides to prevent spread of mosaic; in California control thrips spreading spotted wilt, and dust with sulfur for powdery mildew.

PERENNIAL PEA (*Lathyrus latifolius*)

(An ornamental resembling sweet pea, but without fragrance)

LEAF SPOT. **Cercospora lathyrina,** Ga.; **Ovularia** sp., Cal.

NEMATODE, Root Knot. **Heterodera marioni,** Fla.

MOLD, White. **Erostrotheca multiformis,** Wash.

ROT, Stem. **Ascochyta lathyri,** N. J.

SWEET POTATO (*Ipomoea batatas*)

BACTERIAL Soft Rot. **Erwinia carotovora,** Conn., S. C.

BLIGHT, Leaf. **Phyllosticta batatas,** occasional, N. J. to Fla., Tex., Kans., more prevalent in South; **Choanephora cucurbitarum,** Fla., leaf mold.

BLIGHT, Southern; Cottony Rot. **Sclerotium rolfsii,** common in seedbeds, sometimes gardens, general in South.

LEAF SPOT. **Cercospora** sp., Fla., Okla.; **Colletotrichum** sp., Miss.; **Septoria bataticola,** occasional, N. J. to Ala., Iowa, Tex.

NEMATODE, Brown Ring; Root. **Ditylenchus dipsaci,** N. J.

Nematode, Root Knot. **Heterodera marioni,** general, N. J. to Fla.

Rot, Soil; Pox. **Actinomyces** (*Streptomyces*) **ipomoea,** general, N. J. to Fla., Tex., Ariz., Cal.

Rot, Black. **Endoconidiophora fimbriata,** general on roots, stems; **Diplodia tubericola,** Java black rot, general in South.

Rot, Charcoal. **Macrophomina phaseoli,** N. J. to Fla., Tex., Kans., Cal.

Rot, Gray Mold. **Botrytis cinerea,** on sprouts, cosmopolitan.

Rot, Root. **Diaporthe batatatis,** N. J. to Fla., Tex., Mo., especially in South; **Helicobasidium purpureum,** Kans., Tex.; **Pyrenochaete terrestris,** Cal.; **Phymatotrichum omnivorum,** Ariz., N. Mex., Okla., Tex.; **Phytophthora** sp., N. J., Va.; **Plenodomus destruens,** N. J. to Fla., La., Cal., Kans.; **Pythium** spp., mottle necrosis, leak ring rot.

Rot, Sprout; Stem Canker. **Rhizoctonia solani,** occasional, N. J. to Fla. and Tex.; Ariz., Cal., Ohio, Wash.

Rot, Storage. **Fusarium** spp., general; **Mucor racemosus,** occasional after chilling; **Penicillium** sp., blue mold, cosmopolitan; **Rhizopus** spp., soft rot, general; **Sclerotinia** sp., N. C.; **Trichoderma** spp., Del., N. J.

Rust. **Coleosporium ipomoeae** (II, III), Ala., Miss.

Scurf. **Monilochaetes infuscans,** general.

Virus, Curly Top. **Ruga verrucosans,** Oreg., Tex.

Virus, Feathery Mottle. **Flavimacula ipomeae.**

?Virus, Internal Cork. Suspected virus, Ga., La., Md., Miss., N. C., S. C., Tenn., Va.

?Virus, Mosaic. Suspected virus, occasional on Nancy Hall Variety.

White Rust. **Albugo ipomoeae-panduratae,** general.

Wilt, Stem Rot. **Fusarium oxysporum** f. **batatas,** general, especially in northern range, including Pacific Coast and Western States.

Wilt. **Verticillium albo-atrum,** Cal.

The best way to control diseases is to set disease-free sprouts in field, obtained by treating seed potatoes with organic mercury Semesan Bel, or possibly one of the newer organic materials, and bedding down in sand. Select varieties resistant to Fusarium stem rot, in general the Spanish group.

SWEET VETCH (*Hedysarum*)

Black Mildew. **Parodiella perisporioides,** N. Y.

Leaf Spot. **Septogloeum hedysari,** Wyo.

Nematode, Root Knot. **Heterodera marioni.**

Rust. **Uromyces hedysari-obscuri** (O, I, II, III), Col., Ida., Mont., N. Mex., S. Dak., Utah, Wyo.

SWEET WILLIAM (*Dianthus barbatus*)

?Anthracnose. **Volutella dianthi,** Del., Ind., N. Y.

Blight, Southern. **Sclerotium rolfsii,** Conn., Fla., N. C.

LEAF SPOT. **Phyllosticta** sp. (*?Ascochyta dianthi*), Wash.; **Septoria dianthi,** Ala., Mich., N. Y.

NEMATODE, Leaf and Stem. **Ditylenchus dipsaci,** Oreg.

NEMATODE, Root Knot. **Heterodera marioni.**

ROT, Root. **Pythium ultimum,** ?Cal.

ROT, Stem. **Rhizoctonia solani,** Conn., Ill., Kans., Miss., N. J., N. Y., Pa.

RUST. **Puccinia arenariae** (III), Ala., Conn., Mass., Miss., N. Y., Pa.; **Uromyces caryophyllinus** (II, III), Iowa, Neb.

VIRUS, Curly Top. **Ruga verrucosans,** Cal., Tex.

VIRUS, Yellows. **Chlorogenus callistephi** var. **californicus,** Cal.

WILT. **Fusarium oxysporum** f. **barbati,** Cal., Kans.; **Fusarium** sp., Mass., N. J., S. C. and Va.

Fusarium wilt is one of the more serious diseases with the new growth yellowing, the leaves pointing downward, and plants stunted. There is little to do except the precaution of placing new plants in new or sterilized soil.

SWISS CHARD (*Beta vulgaris* var. *cicla*)

BLIGHT, Southern. **Sclerotium rolfsii,** La., S. C.

DAMPING-OFF, Root Rot. **Rhizoctonia solani,** N. Y.; **Pythium aphanidermatum; P. debaryanum,** Col., Conn., Kans.

DOWNY MILDEW. **Peronospora schachtii,** Cal.

LEAF SPOT. **Cercospora beticola,** general; **Phoma betae,** also root rot; **Ramularia beticola,** Wash.

MOLD, Seed. **Alternaria tenuis,** Cal., Wash.; **Stemphylium botryosum.,** Cal.

NEMATODE, Root Knot. **Heterodera marioni.**

PHYSIOGENIC, Dry Rot; Cracked Stem. Boron deficiency.

ROT, Root. **Phymatotrichum omnivorum,** Tex.

RUST. **Uromyces betae** (II), Cal., Oreg.

VIRUS, Curly top. **Ruga verrucosans.**

VIRUS, Mosaic. **Marmor betae.**

Treat seed before planting with Arasan or Cuprocide.

SYNGONIUM

LEAF SPOT. **Cephalosporium cinnamomeum,** N. Y.

SYNTHYRIS

LEAF SPOT. **Ramularia** sp., Oreg.

RUST. **Puccinia acrophila** (III), Mont. to Col. and Utah; **P. wulfeniae,** Cal., Ida., Oreg., Wash.

TABERNAEMONTANA

LEAF SPOT, Algal; Green Scurf. **Cephaleuros virescens,** Fla.; **Gloeosporium tabernaemontanae,** Fla.

TAENIDIA

Leaf Spot. **Fusicladium angelicae,** Wis.; **Septoria pimpinellae,** Minn.
Rust. **Puccinia angelicae** (O, I, II, III), Ind., Mich., Mo., N. Y., Wis.

TAMARIND (*Tamarindus*)

Nematode, Root Knot. **Heterodera marioni,** Fla.

TAMARISK (*Tamarix*)

Powdery Mildew. **Sphaerotheca humuli,** Ind.
Rot, Root. **Phymatotrichum omnivorum,** Cal., Tex.
Rot, Wood. **Polyporus sulphureus,** Md.

TANSY (*Tanacetum*)

Leaf Spot. **Ramularia tanaceti,** Wis.
Powdery Mildew. **Erysiphe cichoracearum,** Pa.
Nematode, Root Knot. **Heterodera marioni,** Fla.
Rust. **Puccinia absinthii** (O, I, II, III), Wyo.

TELLIMA

Rust. **Puccinia heucherae** (III), Cal., Oreg., Wash., Alaska.
Powdery Mildew. **Sphaerotheca humuli** var. **fuliginea,** Alaska.

TEUCRIUM (Germander)

Downy Mildew. **Peronospora** sp., Okla.
Leaf Spot. **Cercospora teucrii,** N. Y. to Miss., Tex., Wis.; **Phyllosticta decidua,** Tex., Wis.
Powdery Mildew. **Erysiphe cichoracearum,** Ill., Pa., Wis.
Rust. **Puccinia menthae,** Pa.

THALIA

Leaf Spot. **Cercospora thaliae,** La.
Rust. **Puccinia cannae** (II, III), Fla.

TEASEL (*Dipsacus*)

Downy Mildew. **Peronospora dipsaci,** Mo.
Leaf Spot. **Cercospora elongata,** Md., N. Y. to Mo., Wash.
Nematode, Stem and Leaf. **Ditylenchus dipsaci,** Cal., Oreg.
Powdery Mildew. **Phyllactinia corylea,** Wash.

THEA (*Camellia*) SINENSIS (Tea)

Blight, Twig. **Pestalotia guepini,** also leaf spot, S. C.
Leaf Spot; Green Scurf. **Cephaleuros virescens,** Fla., S. C.

THISTLE (*Cirsium*)

Leaf Spot. **Cercospora** spp.; **C. cirsii,** Wash.; **Phyllosticta cirsii,** Iowa; **Septoria cirsii,** Iowa.
Powdery Mildew. **Sphaerotheca humuli,** Md.
Rot, Root. **Rhizoctonia solani,** Ill.
Rust. **Uromyces junci** (O, I), Mo., Nebr., N. Dak.
Smut, Inflorescence. **Thecaphora trailii,** Col., Utah.

THISTLE, BLESSED (*Cnicus benedictus*)

Blight, Southern. **Sclerotium rolfsii,** Ga.

THOROUGH–WAX (*Bupleurum*)

Nematode, Root Knot. **Heterodera marioni,** Cal.

THUJOPSIS (False Arbor-vitae)

Dieback. **Phomopsis occulta,** Cal.

THUNBERGIA

Bacterial Crown Gall. **Agrobacterium tumefaciens,** Conn., Fla.
Nematode, Root Knot. **Heterodera marioni,** Fla.

TIGRIDIA (Tiger-Flower)

Bacterial Scab. **Pseudomonas marginata,** Md.
Nematode, Bulb. **Ditylenchus dipsaci,** in commercial stocks.
Rot, Internal. **Fusarium orthoceras** var. **gladioli;** storage, **Penicillium gladioli.**
Virus, Mosaic. **Marmor iridis,** Oreg., Wash., and in commercial stocks.

THYMUS SERPYLLUM (Mother-of-Thyme)

Rot, Root. **Rhizoctonia solani,** Mass.

TIBOUCHINA (Glory-of-Brazil)

Rot, Root. **Clitocybe tabescens,** Fla.

TOMATO (*Lycopersicon esculentum*)

Anthracnose. **Colletotrichum phomoides,** chiefly ripe rot of fruit, sometimes on leaves, general, especially in Northeast.
Bacterial Canker. **Corynebacterium michiganense,** birds-eye spot; general, but most frequent North and West.
Bacterial Crown Gall. **Agrobacterium tumefaciens,** in experiments.
Bacterial Hairy Root. **Agrobacterium rhizogenes.**
Bacterial Soft Rot. **Erwinia aroidea; E. carotovora,** cosmopolitan.
Bacterial Speck. **Pseudomonas tomato,** occasional East and Central States.

BACTERIAL Spot. **Xanthomonas vesicatoria,** on fruit, leaves, sometimes stem cankers, Northeast.

BACTERIAL Wilt. **Pseudomonas solanacearum,** general, Mass. to Ill., and southward.

BLIGHT, Early; Collar Rot; Fruit Rot. **Alternaria solani,** general.

BLIGHT, Late; Fruit Rot. **Phytophthora infestans,** general in humid regions and seasons, especially East and Southeast.

BLIGHT, Blossom. **Sclerotinia** sp., Cal., Fla., N. Y., Ohio.

BLIGHT, Southern. **Sclerotium rolfsii,** Va. to Fla., Tex., Kans.

BROOMRAPE. **Orobanche ludoviciana,** Wyo.; **O. racemosa,** Cal.

CANKER, Stem. **Helminthosporium** sp., Tex.; **Myrothecium** sp., Tex.

DAMPING-OFF. **Rhizoctonia solani,** also collar rot, stem canker, cosmopolitan; **Pythium** spp.

DODDER. **Cuscuta** spp., Cal., Ida., Md., N. Y., Tex.

DOWNY MILDEW. **Peronospora tabacina,** Ga., N. and S. C.

FRUIT Spot. **Pullularia pullulans,** W. Va., Cal., Okla.

LEAF SPOT. **Ascochyta lycopersici,** Del., Fla., N. J., N. C., Oreg., Va., Wis.; **Septoria lycopersici,** general except Northwest; **Phyllosticta hortorum; Stemphylium** sp., leaf and fruit spot, Cal., Del., Ind.; **S. solani,** Fla., Ga., La., N. J.

MOLD, Leaf. **Botryosporium** sp., Pa., Tex.; **Chaetomium bostrychodes; Cladosporium fulvum,** general in greenhouse.

NEMATODE, Root. **Pratylenchus pratensis,** Md.

NEMATODE, Root Knot. **Heterodera marioni,** general, especially in South.

PHYSIOGENIC Blossom-end Rot. Unbalanced moisture, perhaps calcium deficiency, general. Internal necrosis may be a phase.

Botchy ripening. Malnutrition. Potassium deficiency?

Catface. Fruit abnormalities, growth disturbances.

Oedema; Leaf Hypertrophy. Excessive water absorption and reduced transpiration.

Leafroll, or Leafcurl. Excessive soil moisture.

Sunscald; Fruit Injury. Heat, actinic rays, especially on plants defoliated by disease.

Wilt, Walnut Toxemia. From root excretions of walnut trees, Mich., N. J., Pa., Va.

ROT, Buckeye; Stem Rot. **Phytophthora parasitica,** widespread.

ROT, Charcoal. **Macrophomina phaseoli,** Cal., Tex.

ROT, Gray Mold. **Botrytis cinerea,** occasional.

ROT, Fruit. **Alternaria** sp., black mold; **Aspergillus** spp., green, yellow mold; **Brachysporum tomato,** Kans., Tex.; **Cladosporium herbarum,** green mold, occasional; **Diaporthe phaseolorum,** Miss., Tex.; **Diplodia theobromae,** Ala.; **Glomerella cingulata,** also leaf spot, Fla., La.; **Isaria clonostachoides,** Va., Me., N. J., N. Y.; **Nigrospora oryzae,** Cal.; **Oospora lactis,** sour watery rot, cosmopolitan saprophyte; **Phoma destructiva,** nearly general, but not in North Central States; **Phomopsis** sp.; **Pleospora lycopersici,** Cal.; **Rhizopus stolonifer,** cosmopolitan in transit, field; **Sclerotinia minor,** Tex.; **Trichothecium roseum,** Md., Ohio.

ROT, Nailhead Spot. **Alternaria tomato,** on fruit, stems, Conn. to Fla., N. Dak., Tex.

ROT, Ring. **Myrothecium roridum,** Ohio, Tex., Va., Wis.

ROT, Root. **Aphanomyces cladogamous; Pyrenochaeta terrestris,** secondary, Ill., Iowa, N. J.; **Phymatotrichum omnivorum,** Ariz., Okla., Tex.; **Plectospira myriandra,** Va.; **Thielaviopsis basicola,** Tex.; **Verticillium lycopersici,** Conn., Del., Md., N. J., S. C.

SCAB, Powdery. **Spongospora subterranea,** Pa.

VIRUS, Mosaic. Often tobacco mosaic virus, **Marmor tabaci,** sometimes cucumber, **M. cucumeris,** general. Tobacco etch virus, **Marmor erodens,** causes mosaic in Ky.; yellow mosaic, due to **M. tabaci** var. **aucuba** sometimes found on fruit and foliage.

VIRUS, Big Bud. **?Chlorogenus australiensis,** Cal., Wash.

VIRUS, Bunchy Top. Unidentified, Tex.

VIRUS, Curly Top; Western Yellow Blight. **Ruga verrucosans,** Western States from N. Dak. to Tex., Cal. and Wash.

VIRUS, Fernleaf. Distorting strain of **Marmor tabaci** var. **deformans.**

VIRUS, Tomato Ringspot. **Annulus zonatus,** Col., Ind., Wyo.; ?N. Y.

VIRUS, Shoestring; filiform leaf. **Marmor cucumeris,** occasional in gardens in all sections.

VIRUS, Spotted Wilt. **Lethum australiense,** Pacific States, and Col., Ida., Tex., Utah, occasional in greenhouses in Eastern and Central States, in field, N. J.; **L. australiense** var. **lethale** causes tip-blight, Cal., Md., Oreg., Tex., Utah, W. Va.

VIRUS, Streak; Winter Blight. Complex of potato mottle virus, **Marmor dubium** and tobacco mosaic virus, **Marmor tabaci,** widespread in greenhouses, occasional in Southern States, frequent in East, Central and Pacific States near solanaceous weeds; carried to garden from greenhouse plants.

VIRUS, Single Streak. Necrotic strain of **Marmor tabaci** var. **canadense.**

VIRUS, Witches' Broom. Unidentified, perhaps **Chlorogenus solani,** Tex.

VIRUS, Yellows. **Chlorogenus callistephi,** Ill., Ind., N. Y., Tex.

WART. **Synchytrium endobioticum,** Pa. See under Leaf Galls.

WILT. **Verticillium albo-atrum,** occasional in all regions.

WILT. **Fusarium oxysporum** f. **lycopersici,** general.

Certified tomato seed is produced from crops inspected and certified as free from seed-borne disease by the Agricultural Department of the state where grown and is certainly well worth the few extra pennies it costs. Select varieties resistant to Fusarium wilt, such as Pan American, Marglobe, Pritchard, or Rutgers. Dust with Arasan before planting to prevent damping-off. In purchasing seedlings discard any showing galls of the root-knot nematode on roots or having the slightest symptoms of virus diseases. Do not smoke while working with tomatoes, and do not use tobacco stems as a mulch. Other mulches, however, are helpful in maintaining an even supply of moisture and preventing physiogenic blossom-end rot.

Bordeaux mixture is often injurious to young tomatoes, but either that or a fixed copper or Dithane or Parzate should be used in late foliage sprays to prevent late blight. Zerlate controls early blight and anthracnose and is safe on young plants. Most schedules now alternate—starting (1) with Zerlate, at rate of 2 pounds to 100 gallons of water, about 6 weeks after plants are set in gardens or 30 days after first cluster is in full bloom; (2) repeating 10 days later; (3) copper spray, bordeaux 8–4–100 or fixed copper such as Compound A, 10 days after 2. Since the disastrous summer of 1946 a late-blight warning service is in effect, telling when copper sprays must be started. If the disease is serious, additional sprays may be required late in the season.

Dusts are not quite so effective as sprays but are easier in the home garden. Commercial preparations are available combining 6 to 7% copper with insecticides.

See U. S. Department of Agriculture Farmers' Bulletin No. 1934 for an excellent discussion of tomato diseases, with fine illustrations.

TORENIA

NEMATODE, Root Knot. **Heterodera marioni,** Md.

TRADESCANTIA (Wandering Jew, Spiderwort)

BLIGHT. **Botrytis cinerea,** Alaska.
LEAF SPOT. **Colletotrichum** sp., Tex., N. J.; **Septoria tradescantiae,** Wis. to Tex., S. Dak.
NEMATODE, Root Knot. **Heterodera marioni,** Oreg., Tex.
RUST. **Uromyces commelinae,** Tex.

TRAUTVETERIA

DOWNY MILDEW. **Peronospora ficariae,** Tenn.
LEAF SPOT. **Septoria trautveteriae,** W. Va.
RUST. **Puccinia pulsatillae,** Ida., Oreg., Wash.
SMUT, Leaf and Stem. **Urocystis anemones,** Utah.

TREE–POPPY (*Dendromecon rigida*)

SMUT, Leaf. **Entyloma eschscholtziae,** Cal.

TREE–TOMATO (*Cyphomandra betacea*)

BACTERIAL Canker. **Corynebacterium michiganense,** Cal.
POWDERY MILDEW. **Oidium** sp., Md.

TRILLIUM (Wake-Robin)

LEAF SPOT. **Colletotrichum peckii** (*C. liliacearum?*), N. Y. to N. C., Ill., Minn.; **Gloeosporium trillii,** Cal., Oreg., Wash.; **Heterosporium trillii,** Wash.; **Phyllosticta trillii,** Wash., N. Y., La., Wis.; **Septoria trillii,** New England to S. C., Okla., Wis.; **S. recurvatum,** Ind.

ROT, Stem. **Sclerotium delphinii,** N. H., Pa.

RUST. **Uromyces halstedii** (O, I), Ill., N. Y.; II, III on cutgrass.

SMUT, Leaf. **Urocystis trillii,** Ida., Oreg.

TRITONIA (Montbretia)

BLIGHT, Leaf. **Alternaria** sp., perhaps secondary, N. H.; **Heterosporium** sp. **(H. iridis?),** Oreg., Wash.

BLIGHT, Southern. **Sclerotium rolfsii,** Cal.

ROT, Corm; Yellows. **Fusarium orthoceras** var. **gladioli,** Cal., and commercial stocks.

ROT, Corm. **Stromatinia gladioli** in commercial stocks.

VIRUS, Mosaic. **Marmor iridis?** Cal., Oreg.

TROLLIUS (Globe-Flower)

LEAF SPOT. **Ascochyta,** sp., N. Y.; **Cylindrosporium montenegrinum,** Wyo.; **Phyllosticta trollii,** Wyo.

SMUT, Leaf and Stem. **Urocystis anemones,** Md., N. Y.

TRUMPET–CREEPER, TRUMPET–VINE (*Campsis radicans*)

LEAF BLIGHT. **Cercospora sordida,** Conn. to Ala., Kans. to Tex.

LEAF SPOT. **Phyllosticta tecomae,** Miss.; **Septoria tecomae,** Tex., W. Va.; **Cercospora duplicata,** La.; **C. langloisii.**

MISTLETOE. **Phoradendron flavescens,** Tex.

POWDERY MILDEW. **Erysiphe cichoracearum; Microsphaera alni,** widespread.

Many other fungi are reported on stems and dead branches, but not as causing specific diseases.

TUBEROSE (*Polianthes tuberosa*)

BACTERIAL Soft Rot. **Erwinia carotovora,** N. C.

LEAF SPOT. **Cercospora** sp., Tex.; **Helminthosporium** sp., Tex.

NEMATODE, Root Knot. **Heterodera marioni,** frequently severe.

ROT, Root. **Phythium debaryanum,** Tex.; **Rhizoctonia solani,** N. C.

TULIP (*Tulipa*)

ANTHRACNOSE. **Gloeosporium thümenii** f. **tulipae,** Cal.

BACTERIAL Soft Rot. **Erwinia carotovora,** Wash.

BLIGHT, Botrytis; Tulip Fire. **Botrytis tulipae,** general except far South.

BLIGHT, Southern. **Sclerotium rolfsii,** Cal., Conn., Ga., N. Y., Oreg.

NEMATODE, Bulb. **Ditylenchus dipsaci,** N. Y.

ROT, Basal. **Fusarium** sp., Okla., Wash.

ROT, Gray Bulb. **Rhizoctonia tuliparum,** Northeast.

ROT, Mold. **Penicillium** sp., blue mold; **Aspergillus** spp. black mold, cosmopolitan; **Rhizopus stolonifer,** mushy rot, cosmopolitan.

ROT, Root, Stem. **Rhizoctonia solani,** Mass., N. Y. Bulb rot, Wash.

ROT, Stem; Flower Spot. **Phytophthora cactorum,** Cal., Iowa, N. J., Pa., S. C., Wash.

ROT, White Bulb. **Sclerotinia** sp., Me., Ohio, Wash.

VIRUS, Tulip Breaking; Lily latent-mosaic. **Marmor mite,** mottling flowers and leaves, general.

VIRUS, Tulip Color-Adding. **Marmor tulipae,** dark striping of flowers, no obvious effect on foliage.

Botrytis blight seems to be co-extensive with tulips. In a wet spring leaves are blasted, and buds blighted or open flowers are covered with white spots, followed by the familiar gray mold. Sanitary measures are all important. Spraying in early spring with bordeaux mixture is effective but sometimes injurious. Fermate has been effective in some trials but gives a splotchy effect to foliage and discolors flowers. Tersan is less conspicuous and said to be fairly effective. Zerlate is promising.

Gradual running out of tulips is attributed in large measure to virus disease. Breaking of flowers, once considered a desirable ornamental character, is now recognized as disease and harmful in the long run. Unless aphids are controlled this mottling virus will spread from variegated to solid-color plantings in the garden.

TULIP–TREE (*Liriodendron tulipifera*)

BLIGHT, Seedling. **Rhizoctonia solani,** Ohio, Va.

CANKER. **Dothiorella** sp., Pa.; also **D. minor,** on branches, Md., W. Va.; **Myxosporium** spp., N. Y.; **Nectria** sp., W. Va., N. C.; **N. magnoliae,** Conn. to Ohio southward.

LEAF SPOT. **Cylindrosporium cercosporioides,** Md., W. Va.; **Gloeosporium liriodendri,** Conn. to N. J. and Tex.; **Mycosphaerella liriodendri,** Ga., Mich.; **M. tulipiferae,** Middle Atlantic and Gulf States; **Phyllosticta liriodendrica,** widespread, conidial stage of *Mycosphaerella;* **Ramularia liriodendri,** Ala., Del.

LEAF SPOT, Tar, Black. **Ectostroma liriodendri,** widespread; **Rhytisma liriodendri,** Cal., Tex.

POWDERY MILDEW. **Phyllactinia corylea,** N. Y. to Ala., Mo.; **Erysiphe polygoni,** widespread.

ROT, Heart. **Collybia velutipes,** W. Va.; **Fomes applanatus,** occasional.

ROT, Root. **Phymatotrichum omnivorum,** Tex.

Rot, Seedling Collar. **Cylindrocladium scoparium,** N. J.
Rot, Sapwood. **Schizophyllum commune,** cosmopolitan.
Rot, Wood. **Daedalea extensa; D. unicolor,** sometimes standing trees; **Daldinia vernicosa,** cosmopolitan; **Polyporus** spp., also many stain and timber rots.
Sooty Mold. **Capnodium elongatum,** cosmopolitan.

The most conspicuous fungus on ornamental tulip trees is the black sooty mold growing in the copious honeydew secreted by tuliptree aphids and tuliptree scale. In hot, dry weather leaves sometimes turn yellow and drop prematurely. Leaf spots are seldom serious enough to call for treatment.

TUNG–OIL–TREE (*Aleurites fordii*)

Bacterial Leaf Spot. **Pseudomonas aleuritidis,** Ga., La., Ala.
Blight, Southern. **Sclerotium rolfsii,** Tex.
Blight, Thread. **Pellicularia koleroga** (*Corticium stevensii*), Fla., Miss., La., Tex.
Blight, Web. **Pellicularia filamentosa** (*Corticium microsclerotia*), Ga., Miss.
Canker, Black Rot. **Physalospora rhodina** (imperfect stage *Diplodia*), La., Miss.
Canker, Felt Fungus. **Septobasidium pseudopedicellatum,** La.
Leaf Spot, **Gloeosporium aleuriticum,** Miss.
Nematode, Root Knot. **Heterodera marioni.**
Rot, Nut. **Botryosphaeria ribis,** widespread in tung belt.
Rot, Root. **Clitocybe tabescens,** on isolated trees through tung belt.

Thread blight and nut rot are considered the most serious diseases at present. Annual spraying between June 1 and 15 with 6–6–100 bordeaux mixture keeps blight under control although not eradicated. Good culture to keep trees vigorous is the best recommendation for nut rot, although tests indicate a bordeaux-oil spray will help. A bacterial pathogen for alcoholic slime flux, occasional in late summer, has not yet been proven.

TUPELO, GUM–TREE (*Nyssa*)

Blight, Thread. **Corticium stevensii,** Fla. See **Pellicularia koleroga.**
Canker, **Nectria** sp., Conn.; **Strumella coryneoidea,** Northern Appalachians; **Septobasidium** sp., felt fungus, Fla.
Leaf Spot. **Cercospora nyssae,** Tex.; **Mycosphaerella nyssaecola,** Mass. to Ga., Mich.; **Pirostoma nyssae,** Ill.; **Phyllosticta nyssae,** Southeastern States to Tex.
Mistletoe. **Phoradendron flavescens,** Md., Ind., Tex.
Rot, Heart. **Fomes applanatus; F. connatus,** Conn.
Rot, Root. **Phymatotrichum omnivorum,** Tex.
Rot, Wood. **Daedalea confragosa; D. unicolor; Lentinus** spp., cosmopolitan; **Polyporus** spp., **Poria** spp.; **Stereum** spp.; **Trametes rigida,** Gulf States.
Rust. **Aplopsora nyssae** (II, III), Me. to Ala., Tex.

TURNIP (*Brassica rapa*)

ANTHRACNOSE. **Colletotrichum higginsianum,** N. Y. to Fla., Tex.
BACTERIAL Crown Gall. **Agrobacterium tumefaciens,** Kans.
BACTERIAL Black Rot. **Xanthomonas campestris,** Me. to Fla., Minn., Tex.
BACTERIAL Soft Rot. **Erwinia carotovora,** general, Ga.
BACTERIAL Spot. **Pseudomonas maculicola,** Conn., Ga., Tex., Mass.; **Xanthomonas vesicatoria** var. **raphani,** Ind.
BLACK LEG. **Phoma lingam,** Conn., Mass.
BLIGHT, Southern. **Sclerotium rolfsii,** Fla., Tex.
CLUB ROOT. **Plasmodiophora brassicae,** Me. to S. C., Cal., Col., Minn., Tex., Wash.
DAMPING-OFF. **Pythium ultimum,** Wis.
DOWNY MILDEW. **Peronospora parasitica,** Mass. to Fla., Ill., Tex.
LEAF SPOT; White Spot. **Cercosporella albomaculans,** Mass. to Fla., Tex., Ind.
LEAF SPOT. **Alternaria brassicae,** general; **A. oleracea,** Conn., Fla., Mass., Md., Tex.; **Cercospora** sp., Ala., Fla., Ga., Miss.; **Phyllosticta** sp., Tex., W. Va.; **Ramularia** sp., Ala., Fla., Wash.; **Septomyxa affine,** Ala.
MOLD, Seed. **Alternaria tenuis,** cosmopolitan; **Stemphylium botryosum,** occasional.
NEMATODE, Root Knot. **Heterodera marioni,** N. C. to Fla., Okla., Tex.
PHYSIOGENIC Brown Heart. Boron deficiency, Conn., Mass., Me.
POWDERY MILDEW. **Erysiphe polygoni,** Northeastern States to Fla., Tex., Ill.
ROT, Root. **Phymatotrichum omnivorum,** Tex.
ROT, Watery Soft. **Sclerotinia sclerotiorum,** Conn., Md., Miss., Tex., Wash.
SCAB. **Actinomyces** (*Streptomyces*) **scabies,** Conn., Mich., N. J., Wash.
WHITE RUST; White Blister. **Albugo candida,** general.
VIRUS, Curly Top. **Ruga verrucosans,** Cal.
VIRUS, Mosaic. **Marmor brassicae,** Ala., Cal., Conn., Fla.
WILT; Yellows. **Fusarium oxysporum** f. **conglutinans,** Ind., Miss.

In general turnip diseases and their control are the same as for other crucifers. Rutabagas are rather resistant to clubroot.

TURPENTINE–MYRTLE (*Syncarpia*)

NEMATODE, Root Knot. **Heterodera marioni,** Fla.

TURTLE–HEAD (*Chelone*)

LEAF SPOT. **Septoria mariae-wilsonii,** Me. to Pa., Ohio, Wis.
POWDERY MILDEW. **Erysiphe** spp., and **E. cichoracearum,** Del., Ind., Mass., Mich., Miss., N. C., N. Y., Ohio, Pa., Wis.; **E. polygoni,** Mass., Mich., N. Y.
RUST. **Puccinia andropogonis** var. **penstemonis** (O, I), Conn., Mass., N. J., N. Y., Pa., Tenn.; II, III on Andropogon.

UMBRELLA–PINE (*Sciadopitys verticillata*)

Blight, Twig. **Diplodia pinea,** N. J.
Leaf Spot. **Phyllosticta** sp., R. I.
Rot, Root; Damping-Off. **Rhizoctonia solani,** Conn.

UNICORN–PLANT (*Proboscidea*)

Bacterial Leaf Spot. **Pseudomonas martyneae,** Kans.
Blight, Southern. **Sclerotium rolfsii,** Tex.
Leaf Spot. **Cercospora beticola,** Kans., Iowa, Tex., Wis.
Rot, Root. **Phymatotrichum omnivorum,** Tex.
Rot, Stem. **Sclerotinia sclerotiorum,** Mass.
Virus, Mosaic. Part **Marmor cucumeris,** perhaps also **M. tabaci,** Iowa, Wis.

UVULARIA (Bellwort, Merrybells)

Leaf Spot. **Sphaeropsis cruenta,** Conn., Ill., Ind., Iowa, Mo., N. Y., Va., Wis.
Rust. **Puccinia sessilis** (O, I), Del., Iowa, Minn., Mo., Miss., N. Y., Wis.; **Uromyces acuminatus** var. **magnatus,** Miss.

VALERIAN, GARDEN HELIOTROPE (*Valeriana*)

Leaf Spot. **Ramularia centranthi,** Cal.; **Septoria valerianae,** Wis.
Powdery Mildew. **Erysiphe cichoracearum,** Col., Utah.
Rot, Root. **Rhizoctonia solani,** N. Y.
Rot, Stem. **Sclerotium delphinii,** Conn., N. J.
Rust. **Puccinia commutata** (O, I, III), N. Y., Oreg.; **P. extensicola** var. **valerianae** (O, I), Col., N. Mex., Utah; II, III on Carex; **P. valerianae** (II, III), Alaska.

RED VALERIAN, JUPITERS–BEARD (*Centranthus ruber*)

Leaf Spot. **Ramularia centranthi,** Cal.

VALERIANELLA (Corn-Salad)

Leaf Gall. **Synchytrium aureum,** Miss.
Leaf Spot. **Septoria valerianellae,** Miss.

VANCOUVERIA

Leaf Spot. **Ramularia vancouveriae,** Cal., Oreg.

VANILLA

Black Mildew. **Lembosia rolfsii,** Fla.
Leaf Spot; Pod Spot. **Botryosphaeria vanillae,** Fla.

VANILLA-LEAF (*Achlys*)

LEAF SPOT. **Ascochyta achlyicola; Stagonospora achlydis,** Oreg.

VELVET BEAN (*Stizolobium*)

BACTERIAL Spot. **Pseudomonas syringae,** Ind.; **P. stizolobii,** N. C.
BLIGHT, Southern. **Sclerotium rolfsii,** Ala., Fla., Ga.
LEAF SPOT. **Cercospora stizolobii,** Ala., Fla., Ga., N. and S. C.; **Mycosphaerella cruenta,** Ga.; **Phyllosticta macunae,** Ala.
NEMATODE, Root Knot. **Heterodera marioni,** Cal.
ROT, Pod Spot. **Fusarium** sp., Tex.
ROT, Root. **Phymatotrichum omnivorum,** Ariz., Tex.; **Phytophthora parasitica,** Fla.

VERATRUM (False-Hellebore)

LEAF SPOT. **Ascochyta veratrina,** Wash.; **Cylindrosporium veratrinum,** N. Y., Va., Utah; **Cercosporella terminalis,** N. Y.; **Phyllosticta melanoplaca,** N. Y.
LEAF SPOT, Tar. **Phyllachora melanoplaca,** N. Y.
RUST. **Puccinia atropuncta** (II, III), Mo., N. C., Okla., Tenn., Va., W. Va.; O, I on composites; **P. veratri,** Cal., Miss., N. Mex., Oreg., Wash.

VERBENA, GARDEN (*V. hortensis*)

BLIGHT, Flower. **Botrytis cinerea,** Mass.
NEMATODE, Root Knot. **Heterodera marioni,** Md.
POWDERY MILDEW. **Erysiphe cichoracearum,** general.
ROT, Charcoal, Stem. **Macrophomina phaseoli,** Okla.
ROT, Root. **Phymatotrichum omnivorum,** Tex.; **Rhizoctonia solani,** N. Y.; **Thielaviopsis basicola,** Pa.

VERBENA (Native Species)

DODDER. **Cuscuta arvensis.** Okla.
DOWNY MILDEW. **Plasmopara halstedii,** N. Mex.
LEAF SPOT. **Ascochyta verbenae,** Wis.; **Cercospora verbenicola,** Ala., La., Tex. and other spp., Ill., Kans., Miss.; **Phyllosticta texensis,** Tex.; **Septoria verbenae,** Vt. to Miss., Tex. and S. Dak.
POWDERY MILDEW. **Erysiphe cichoracearum,** general.
RUST. **Puccinia aristidae** (O, I), Ariz.; II, III on grasses; **P. vilfae** (O, I), Ind. to Okla. and S. Dak., Kans., Mo.

VERBESINA (Crownbeard)

DOWNY MILDEW. **Plasmopara halstedii,** N. Mex., Tex.
LEAF SPOT. **Cercospora fulvella,** Tex.; **Colletotrichum** sp., Ariz.; **Phyllosticta verbesinae,** Tex.

NEMATODE Root Knot. **Heterodera marioni,** Ala.

POWDERY MILDEW. **Erysiphe cichoracearum,** S. C., Va.

ROT, Root. **Phymatotrichum omnivorum,** Tex.; **Helicobasidium purpureum,** Tex.

RUST. **Coleosporium viguierae** (II, III), Ariz., Fla., N. C., Tex.; O, I, unknown; **Puccinia abrupta** (II, III), Tex., Cal.; **P. cognata** (O, I, II, III), Ark., La., N. C., Tenn., Tex.; **P. verbesiniae** (O, I, II, III), Md. to Ala., La.

VERONICA (Speedwell)

DOWNY MILDEW. **Peronospora grisea,** Cal., Ga., Ill., Ind., Kans., Mo., N. Y., Tex., Wis.

LEAF GALL. **Sorosphaera veronicae,** Col., Miss.; **Synchytrium globosum,** La.

LEAF SPOT. **Cercospora tortipes,** Wis.; **Gloeosporium veronicae,** N. Y.; **Ramularia veronicae,** Tex., Okla., Wis.; **Septoria veronicae,** Cal., Fla., Mich., Ohio, Wis.

NEMATODE, Root Knot. **Heterodera marioni,** Fla.

ROT, Root and Stem. **Fusarium** sp., N. J.; **Rhizoctonia solani,** Ill., Md.; **Phymatotrichum omnivorum,** Tex.

ROT, Stem. **Sclerotium rolfsii,** Conn., N. J., Ohio.

POWDERY MILDEW. **Sphaerotheca humuli,** Conn., Oreg., Wis.

SMUT, Leaf. **Entyloma veronicae,** Col., Conn., Ill., Iowa, Kans., Miss., Mo., N. Y., Wis.

VIBURNUM

ANTHRACNOSE, Spot. **Sphaceloma viburni,** Cal., Wash.

BACTERIAL Crown Gall. **Agrobacterium tumefaciens,** Wash.

BACTERIAL Leaf Spot. **Pseudomonas viburni,** Ill., Iowa, ?N. J.

BLIGHT, Leaf. **Micropeltis viburni,** N. Y.

BLIGHT, Shoot. **Botrytis cinerea,** Wash.

BLIGHT, Thread. **Corticium stevensii,** Fla., N. C. See *Pellicularia koleroga.*

CANKER, Stem Girdle. **Hymenochaete agglutinans,** Pa.

DOWNY MILDEW. **Plasmopara viburni,** general.

LEAF SPOT. **Cercospora tinea,** La.; **C. varia,** Me. to Gulf States, Col., Wis.; **Hendersonia foliorum,** Fla., Tex.; **Helminthosporium beaumontii,** Ala., Tex.; **Phyllosticta lantanoides,** N. Y.; **P. punctata,** Iowa, Wis.; **Ramularia viburni,** Tenn., Wis.

NEMATODE, Root Knot. **Heterodera marioni,** sometimes serious.

POWDERY MILDEW. **Microsphaera alni,** general.

ROT, Root. **Clitocybe tabescens,** Fla.; **Phymatotrichum omnivorum,** Tex.

RUST. **Coleosporium viburni** (II, III), Ill., Iowa, Mich., Wis.; O, I, unknown; **Puccinia linkii** (III), Ida., Mich., Mont., N. H., Wash.

Wilt. **Verticillium albo-atrum,** Ill., Ind.

Viburnum carlesii is extremely sensitive to sulfur and may be injured even by spray drift blown over plants.

VINCA (Periwinkle, Ground-Myrtle)

Blight, Gray Mold. **Botrytis cinerea,** Conn., Wash.

Canker; Dieback. **Phomopsis lirella,** Conn., Md., N. J., Ohio, Pa., Va. This is conidial stage of *Diaporthe vincae.*

Dodder. **Cuscuta indecora,** Tex.

Leaf Spot. **Alternaria** sp., Pa., Tex.; **Colletotrichum** sp., Fla.; **Macrophoma vincae,** also dieback, Ill., N. Y.; **Phyllosticta** sp., Ga., N. J.; **P. minor,** Md., N. J., N. Y., Va.; **P. vincae-majoris,** Cal.

Mold, Leaf. **Cladosporium herbarum,** Md., N. Y., Pa.

Nematode, Root Knot. **Heterodera marioni,** Kans., Ohio.

Rot, Root and Stem. **Rhizoctonia solani,** Ill., Md., N. J., Pa.

Virus. Aster Yellows. **Chlorogenus callistephi.**

VIOLET (*Viola odorata,* Florists' or Sweet Violet, and native species)

Anthracnose. **Colletotrichum violae-tricoloris,** Conn., Mass., Miss., N. J., N. Y., Ohio, Pa.; **C. violae-rotundifoliae,** Ill., Ind., Mich., Okla., N. Y., Tex., Vt., Wis.

Blight, Southern. **Sclerotium rolfsii,** Ala., Ark., Md., Va. to Fla. and Tex.; **S. delphinii,** Cal., Conn., N. Y., Vt.

Downy Mildew. **Bremiella megasperma,** Fla., N. J., Ill., Iowa, Minn.

Leaf Gall. **Synchytrium aureum,** N. Y., Wis.

Leaf Spot. **Alternaria** sp., Md., Mass., Mich., Minn., N. J., N. Y., Tex.; **A. violae,** Conn. to Ga., Tex., and Wis.; **Ascochyta violicola,** Alaska; **A. violae,** Ind., Iowa, Pa., Wis.; **Centrospora acerina,** Cal., Alaska; **Cercospora granuliformis,** Me. to Ala., Okla. and S. Dak.; **C. violae,** Mass. to Fla., Tex. and N. Dak.; **C. murina,** Ind., Kans.; **Cryptostictis violae,** Ill.; **Cylindrosporium violae,** Mont.; **Gloeosporium violae,** Miss.; **Heterosporium** sp., Alaska; **Marssonina violae,** Mass. to S. C., Iowa and Minn.; **Phyllosticta violae,** Mass. to Fla., Kans., and Minn., Cal.; **P. nigrescens,** Cal.; **Ramularia lactea,** Col., Miss., Mont., Alaska; **R. agrestis,** Nebr., Oreg.; **R. ioniphila,** Cal., Wis., Alaska; **Septoria violae,** North and N. Central States to Fla., La., Kans.

Nematode, Root Knot. **Heterodera marioni,** Fla. to Cal., occasionally in North, Mass., N. J., Ohio, R. I.

Nematode, Root. **Pratylenchus pratensis.**

Powdery Mildew. **Sphaerotheca humuli,** also var. **fuliginea,** Cal., Col., N. Dak., Oreg., Wis., Wyo.

Rot, Root. **Fusarium oxysporum** var. **aurantiacum,** Fla., Miss., Ohio; **Helicobasidium purpureum,** Tex.; **Phymatotrichum omnivorum,** Tex.; **Rhizoctonia**

solani, Ill., N. Y., Fla., Minn., Miss.; **Thielaviopsis basicola,** Conn. to Miss. and Ohio, also Kans., Mass.

ROT, Wet, Gray Mold. **Botrytis cinerea,** Md., Ohio, Alaska.

RUST. **Puccinia violae** (O, I, II, III), general; **P. effusa** (III), Cal.; **P. ellisiana** (O, I), Northeastern and North Central States to Ala., N. Mex., and Wyo.; II, III on Andropogon; **P. fergussoni** (III), Col., Mont., Utah, Alaska; **Uromyces andropogonis,** Miss., N. C., N. J., Pa., Tenn., W. Va.

SCAB; Spot Anthracnose. **Sphaceloma violae,** Me. to Fla. and Miss., Ill.

SMUT, Leaf and Stem. **Urocystis violae,** Cal., Minn., Tex., Utah, Alaska.

VIRUS, Curly Top. **Ruga verrucosans,** Tex.

Scab or spot anthracnose is perhaps the most important disease of violets in many gardens. Disfiguring scabby lesions are formed on stems and leaves.

VIPERS–BUGLOSS (*Echium vulgare*)

LEAF SPOT. **Cercospora echii.**

ROT, Root. **Rosellinia** sp., Cal.

VIRGINIA CREEPER (*Parthenocissus quinquefolia*)

ANTHRACNOSE, Spot. **Elsinoë parthenocissi.**

BLIGHT, Thread. **Pellicularia koleroga,** Fla.

CANKER, Stem. **Coniothyrium fuckelii,** W. Va.

DOWNY MILDEW. **Plasmopara viticola.**

LEAF SPOT. **Cercospora ampelopsidis,** widespread; **C. psedericola,** Ill., Va.; **Guignardia bidwellii** f. **parthenocissi,** general; **Phleospora ampelopsidis,** Ill., Iowa, Nebr., Wis.

POWDERY MILDEW. **Uncinula necator,** general.

ROT, Root. **Phymatotrichum omnivorum,** Tex.

VITEX (Chaste-Tree)

LEAF SPOT. **Cercospora viticis,** La., Tex.

ROT, Root. **Phymatotrichum omnivorum,** Tex.

WALLFLOWER (*Cheiranthus cheiri*)

BLIGHT, Gray Mold. **Botrytis cinerea,** Wash.

LEAF SPOT. **Heterosporium** sp., Okla.

ROT, Crown. **Rhizoctonia solani,** N. J.

WHITE BLISTER. **Albugo candida,** Minn.

WESTERN WALLFLOWER (*Erysimum asperum*)

CLUB ROOT. **Plasmodiophora brassicae,** N. J.

DOWNY MILDEW. **Peronospora parasitica,** Col., Ida., Iowa.

LEAF SPOT. **Cercospora erysimi,** Wis.

POWDERY MILDEW. **Erysiphe polygoni,** Cal.

Rot, Root. **Rhizoctonia solani,** Tex., Utah.

Rust. **Puccinia aristidae** (O, I), Ariz., Col., N. Dak., Nebr., Utah.

White Rust; White Blister. **Albugo candida,** Ida., Oreg., Tex.

WALNUT (*Juglans*)

(Includes Butternut, Black Walnut, English Walnut, Japanese Walnut)

Anthracnose; Leaf Spot. **Gnomonia leptostyla,** general.

Bacterial Blight. **Xanthomonas juglandis,** N. Y. to Ga., Tex. and Pacific Coast, especially on English (Persian) walnut.

Bacterial Crown Gall. **Agrobacterium tumefaciens,** occasional.

Blight, Seedling. **Sclerotium rolfsii.**

Blight, Leaf. **Cylindrosporium juglandis,** Ala., Tenn. to Tex. and Cal.

Blotch, Leaf. **Marssonina juglandis,** N. Y., Miss., Wash.

Canker. **Nectria** spp. widespread; **Cytospora** sp., Ariz.

Canker; Dieback. **Melanconis juglandis** widespread, especially in East; **Diplodia juglandis,** widespread; **Dothiorella gregaria,** Cal.

Canker, Felt Fungus. **Septobasidium curtisii,** N. C.

Leaf Spot; Downy Spot; White Mold. **Microstroma juglandis,** widespread.

Leaf Spot. **Cercospora juglandis,** Kans., Mass.; **Phleospora multimaculans; Marssonina californica,** Cal.

Mistletoe. **Phoradendron flavescens,** Ind.

Nematode, Root Knot. **Heterodera marioni,** general.

Physiogenic Black End, of Nuts. Probably drought injury, Cal., Oreg.

Freckle Spot. Cause unknown, Oreg., Wash.

Girdle. Incompatibility scions on black walnut roots, Oreg., Wash.

Leaf Scorch, Sunscald, N. J., Oreg.

Rosette. Probably zinc deficiency, Del., Mo., S. C., Cal., Miss.

Yellows, Little Leaf. Mineral deficiency, Cal.; cause unknown, Del., Md., N. J.

Powdery Mildew. **Phyllactinia corylea,** Ind., Ohio; **Microsphaera alni,** widespread.

Rot, Collar. **Phytophthora cactorum,** Cal.; **P. cinnamomi,** Md. to Ala., La.

Rot, Heart. **Fomes igniarius,** and **F. everhartii,** widespread; **Polyporus sulphureus,** widespread.

Rot, Root. **Armillaria mellea,** cosmopolitan; **Phymatotrichum omnivorum,** Tex.

Rot, Wood. **Fomes conchatus; Polyporus** spp.; **Schizophyllum commune,** cosmopolitan; **Daedalea confragosa; D. quercina,** widespread.

Virus, Brooming Disease. Undetermined, N. Y.

Wilt. **Exosporina fawcetti,** on Persian walnut, Cal.

Bacterial blight is the most serious disease of walnuts on the Pacific Coast and is usually controlled with about four copper sprays or dusts. Puratized

Agricultural Spray is recently reported as effective against Marssonina leaf spot of black walnuts.

A toxin, juglone, has been considered injurious to many shrubs growing in the vicinity of black walnut roots, but this observation is somewhat disputed.

WATER–CRESS (*Nasturtium officinale*)

Leaf Spot. **Cercospora nasturtii,** Cal., Conn., Fla., Ind., N. H., Tex., Wis.

Rust. **Puccinia aristidae,** Ariz., Col.

White Rust; White Blister. **Albugo candida,** Minn.

WATER–ELM (*Planera aquatica*)

Rot, Wood. **Daedalea ambigua,** S. C.; **Ganoderma lucidum.**

WATER–HOARHOUND (*Lycopus*)

Leaf Gall. **Synchytrium cellulare,** Wis.

Leaf Spot. **Ascochyta lophanthi,** Mass., Wis.; **Cercospora lycopi; Phyllosticta decidua,** Iowa, Okla., Wis.; **Septoria lycopi,** Wis.

Rust. **Puccinia angustata** (O, I), Me. to Md., Kans., N. Dak.; II, III on **Eriophorum** and **Scirpus.**

WATER–LILY (*Nymphaea odorata*)

Leaf Spot. **Alternaria** sp., Tex.; **Cercospora exotica,** Ill.; **C. nymphaeacea,** Ill., Me., Mich., Mo., Miss., N. J., Tex., Va., Wis.; **Helicoceras nymphaearum,** Md., N. J., N. Y.; **Mycosphaerella pontederiae,** Va., Mich.; **Ovularia nymphaearum,** Wash., N. Y.; **Phyllosticta fatiscens,** Vt.; **P. nymphaeacea,** Tex.

Rot, Leaf and Stem. **Pythium** spp., Mass., N. Y., Wis.

Smut, White. **Entyloma nymphaeae,** Mass. to Va., Okla., Tex.

WATER–LILY, COW–LILY, POND–LILY (*Nuphar*)

Leaf Spot. **Mycosphaerella pontederiae,** Me., Mich., N. Y., Va., Wis.; **Phyllosticta fatiscens,** Iowa, N. J., N. Y.; **P. nymphaeacea,** Tex.; **P. nymphaeicola,** Ill.

Smut, White. **Entyloma nymphaeae,** Conn., Ill., Mass., Wis.

WATERMELON (*Citrullus vulgaris* and var. *citroides*)

Anthracnose. **Colletotrichum lagenarium,** general except Pacific Coast.

Bacterial Soft Rot. **Erwinia aroideae,** W. Va.

Bacterial Spot. **Pseudomonas lachrymans,** Mich.

Blight, Gummy Stem. **Mycosphaerella citrullina,** also stem-end rot, leaf spot, Mass. to Fla., Ariz., Mo.

BLIGHT, Southern. **Sclerotium rolfsii, also fruit rot, N. C. to Fla., Tex.**

DAMPING-OFF. **Rhizoctonia solani,** soil rot, leaf blight; **Pythium** spp. also blossom-end rot, foot rot.

DOWNY MILDEW. **Pseudoperonospora cubensis,** occasional Mass. to Fla., Tex., Wis.

FRUIT SPOT; Flyspeck. **Cribropeltis citrullina,** Ill.

LEAF SPOT. **Alternaria cucumerina,** general except Pacific Coast; **Cercospora citrullina,** N. J. to Fla., Tex.; **Phyllosticta citrullina,** Del., Ga., S. C., Ohio; **Septoria citrulli,** N. J., N. Y.; **S. cucurbitacearum,** Wis.

NEMATODE, Root Knot. **Heterodera marioni,** N. C. to Fla., Ariz., Cal., Okla., Tex.

PHYSIOGENIC Blossom-end Rot. Hot dry weather after moist, cool days. Internal browning. Drought.

POWDERY MILDEW. **Erysiphe cichoracearum,** Ariz., Cal., Fla., Ga., N. C., Tex., Va.

ROT, Fruit. **Fusarium scirpi; Helminthosporium** sp., Tex.; **Diplodia** spp., Md. to Ala., Ariz., Kans.; **Rhizopus** spp., mushy soft rot.

ROT, Charcoal. **Macrophomina phaseoli,** Tex.

ROT, Stem and fruit. **Phytophthora cactorum; P. capsici; P. citrophthora; Sclerotinia sclerotiorum.**

ROT, Root. **Phymatotrichum omnivorum,** Ariz., Tex.; **Thielaviopsis basicola,** Oreg., Utah.

VIRUS, Curly Top. **Ruga verrucosans,** Cal.

VIRUS, Mosaic. Undetermined.

WILT. **Fusarium oxysporum** var. **niveum,** general; **Verticillium albo-atrum,** Cal., N. H., Oreg.

Fusarium wilt is probably the major disease and resistant varieties are available, e.g., Dixie Queen, Wilt Resistant Kleckley No. 6 and Black Kleckley, Miles, Hawkesbury, Stone Mountain Resistant No. 5, Klondike Resistant No. 7.

For anthracnose and leaf spots seed should be treated before planting and spraying or dusting started when vines start to run, using bordeaux mixture or fixed coppers or Zerlate.

WATER–PRIMROSE (*Jussiaea*)

LEAF SPOT. **Alternaria** sp., Okla.; **Cercospora jussiaeae,** Ala., Okla., Tex.; **Colletotrichum jussiaeae,** Ala., Tex.; **Septoria jussiaeae,** Ala., Fla., La., Tex.

RUST. **Aecidium betheli,** Cal.; **Puccinia jussiaeae** (O, I, III), Miss.; **Uredo guaynabensis** (II), Fla.

WATSONIA

ROT, Root. **Armillaria mellea,** Cal.

VIRUS, Mosaic. **Marmor iridis,** Cal.

WAX–MYRTLE (*Myrica cerifera*)

Black Mildew. **Irene calostroma,** Gulf States; **Irenina manca,** Miss.
Blight, Seedling. **Rhizoctonia solani,** N. J.
Leaf Spot. **Phyllosticta myricae,** N. J. to Fla., Tex.; **Septoria myricae,** N. J.
Rot, Root. **Clitocybe tabescens,** Fla.; **Phymatotrichum omnivorum,** Tex.
Rust. **Gymnosporangium ellisii** (O, I), Mass. to Md.

WEIGELA

Bacterial Crown Gall. **Agrobacterium tumefaciens,** Md., Miss.
Leaf Spot. **Cercospora weigelae,** Md., Miss.; **Mycosphaerella weigelae,** N. Y.; **Ramularia diervillae,** Tenn.
Nematode, Root Knot. **Heterodera marioni,** Cal., Md., Miss., Tex.
Rot, Root. **Phymatotrichum omnivorum,** Tex.

WHIPPLEA

Downy Mildew. **Peronospora whippleae,** Cal.

WHORTLEBERRY (*Vaccinium membranaceum*)

Leaf Gall. **Exobasidium parvifolii,** Oreg., Wash.; **E. uliginosi,** rose bloom, Ida., Oreg., Wash.; **E. vaccinii,** red leaf spot, shoot hypertrophy, Ida.
Leaf Spot, Tar. **Rhytisma vaccinii,** Mont., Wyo.
Powdery Mildew. **Microsphaera alni** var. **vaccinii,** Oreg., Wyo.
Rust. **Pucciniastrum** sp. (II), Oreg., Wash.; **P. goeppertianum** (III), witches' broom, Mont. to N. Mex., Cal.; **P. myrtilli** (II, III), Mont., Wyo., Pacific Northwest.

WILLOW (*Salix*)
(Includes Weeping and Pussy Willows)

Bacterial Crown Gall. **Agrobacterium tumefaciens,** Conn., N. J., Tex.
Blight, Willow. Complex of scab and black canker.
Canker, Black. **Physalospora miyabeana,** New England and Eastern N. Y.
Canker, Twig and Branch. **Botryosphaeria ribis,** Va. to Ga., Mo., Md.; **Cryptodiaporthe salicina,** Md., N. Y.; **Discella carbonacea,** Conn.; **Diplodina** sp., Mass.; **Macrophoma,** Ark., Miss., N. and S. C., Tex.
Canker, Dieback. **Valsa sordida** (*Cytospora chrysosperma*), Md., N. J., N. Y., N. Mex., Ohio, Tenn., Wis.; **V. salicina,** Md.
Leaf Spot. **Ascochyta salicis,** Cal.; **Cercospora salicina,** Md.; **Marssonina kriegeriana,** Wis.; **Myrioconium comitatum,** Wis.; **Phyllosticta apicalis,** Kans.; **Ramularia rosea,** Wis.; **Septogloeum salicinum,** Wis.
Leaf Spot, Tar. **Rhytisma salicinum,** Mich.
Powdery Mildew. **Uncinula salicis,** widespread.

Rot, Heart. **Daedalea confragosa,** Pa., Minn., Va.; **Fomes applanatus,** Conn.; **Polyporus farlowii,** Southwest; **Trametes suaveolens,** Conn., Me.

Rot, Root. **Phymatotrichum omnivorum,** Tex.

Rot, Wood. **Ganoderma lucidum,** Md.

Rust. **Melampsora abieti-capraearum** (II, III), Me. to W. Va.; Mo., Wash.; O, I on fir; **M. bigelowii** (II, III), Conn., Nebr., Wash., Wis., Me. to Ind., Minn., O, I on larch.

Scab, Gray; Spot Anthracnose. **Sphaceloma murrayae,** Cal., N. Y., Oreg., R. I., Va., Wash.

Scab; Blight. **Fusicladium saliciperdum** (perfect stage *Venturia chlorospora*), New England, especially, also N. Y., N. J., Pa., N. and S. C., W. Va.

Willow scab, followed by black canker, forms a very destructive blight, killing many trees in New England. Sanitary measures and at least three applications of bordeaux mixture are recommended.

WINTERBERRY (*Ilex verticillata*)

Leaf Spot. **Phyllosticta haynaldi,** W. Va.; **Physalospora ilicis,** N. Y.

Leaf Spot, Tar. **Rhytisma concavum,** Ala., Ohio; **R. prini,** widespread.

Powdery Mildew. **Microsphaera alni,** Wis.

WINTERGREEN, TEABERRY (*Gaultheria*)

Leaf Gall; Red Leaf. **Synchytrium vaccinii,** N. J.

Leaf Spot. **Cercospora gaultheriae,** N. J., Wis.; **Discosia maculicola,** N. J.; **Mycosphaerella gaultheriae,** Me. to Md.; **Phyllosticta gaultheriae,** Northeast; **Venturia gaultheriae,** Mass., N. J., Wis.; **Schizothyrium gaultheriae,** Me. to Va.

Powdery Mildew. **Microsphaera alni,** Md.

WISTERIA (*Wistaria*)

Bacterial Crown Gall. **Agrobacterium tumefaciens,** Conn., Md., Tex.

Canker, Stem. **Nectria cinnabarina,** Conn.

Leaf Spot. **Phyllosticta wistariae,** Mass., Mo., N. J., Tex.; **Septoria wistariae,** Tex.; **Phomatospora wistariae,** Ill.

Nematode, Root Knot. **Heterodera marioni.**

Powdery Mildew. **Erysiphe ?cichoracearum,** Tex.

Rot, Heart. **Pleurotus** sp., W. Va.

Rot, Root. **Phymatotrichum omnivorum,** Tex.

Virus, Mosaic. Unidentified, Miss., N. Y.

WITCH–HAZEL (*Hamamelis*)

Leaf Spot. **Gonatobotryum maculicola,** N. H. to W. Va.; **Monochaetia desmazierii,** Va. to Wis., Ga., Tenn.; **Mycosphaerella** sp., W. Va.; **Phyllosticta**

hamamelidis, Conn. to Miss.; **Ramularia hamamelidis,** N. Y. to W. Va., Okla., Wis.

Powdery Mildew; **Podosphaera biuncinata,** New England to Pa., Ill., and southward; **Phylactinia corylea,** Mich., Wis.

Rot, Wood. **Polyporus** spp.; **Fomes scutellatus,** widespread; **Daldinia concentrica,** cosmopolitan.

WOLFBERRY (*Symphoricarpos occidentalis*)

Leaf Spot. **Cercospora symphoricarpi,** Mont., N. Dak., Wash.

Powdery Mildew. **Microsphaera diffusa,** widespread.

Rust. **Puccinia crandallii** (O, I), Col., Mont., N. Dak., Wyo.; II, III on Festuca, Poa.

WOOD–BETONY (*Pedicularis,* Lousewort)

Leaf Gall. **Synchytrium aureum,** Wis.

Leaf Spot. **Ramularia obducens,** Cal.; **Septoria cylindrospora,** Wis.

Powdery Mildew. **Sphaerotheca humuli,** Cal., Col., Ind., Md., Mich., Wyo., Wis.; and var. **fuliginea,** Minn., Wis., Wyo.

Rust. **Cronartium coleosporioides** (II, III), Cal., Ida., Mont., N. Mex., Wash.; **Puccinia clintonii** (III), Col., Ida., Me., Mich., N. Mex., N. Y., Oreg., Wash., Wis., Wyo.; **P. rufescens** (I, III), Col., Cal., Nev.

WOOD–RUST (*Luzula*)

Rust. **Puccinia obscura** (II, III), Me. to Kans., Wis., Ida., Oreg., Wash.

Smut, Inflorescence. **Cintractia luzulae,** Ind.

WYETHIA

Leaf Spot. **Didymaria conferta,** Oreg., Utah, Wyo.; **Marssonina wyethiae,** Wash., Col.; **Septoria wyethiae,** Cal., Utah.

Nematode, Leaf Gall. **Tylenchus balsamophilus,** Utah.

Rust. **Puccinia balsamorrhizae** (O, I, II, III), Ariz., Cal., Col., Utah.

XANTHOSOMA

Rot, Root. **Armillaria mellea,** Cal.

Rot, Powdery Gray. **Fusarium solani,** Fla.

XEROPHYLLUM (Beargrass, Turkey-Beard)

Rust. **Puccinia atropuncta,** Miss.

YARROW (*Achillea*)

Bacterial Crown Gall. **Agrobacterium tumefaciens.**

Dodder. **Cuscuta** sp., N. H.

Powdery Mildew. **Erysiphe cichoracearum,** Mo., Mont., Pa., S. Dak., Vt., Wis., Alaska.

Nematode, Root Knot. **Heterodera marioni,** Oreg.

Rot, Root and Stem. **Rhizoctonia solani,** Northeastern and North Central States.

Rust. **Puccinia millefolii** (III), Cal., Col., Ida., Mont., N. Mex., Oreg., Utah, Wash., Wyo.

YELLOW–ROOT (*Xanthorhiza*)

Leaf Spot. **Phyllosticta xanthorhizae,** W. Va.

YELLOW–WOOD (*Cladastris*)

Rot, Wood. **Polyporus spraguei,** Md.

YERBA BUENA (*Micromeria chamissonis*)

Rust. **Puccinia menthae** (O, I, II, III), Cal., Ida., Oreg., Wash.

YERBA SANTA (*Eriodictyon*)

Blotch, Sooty. **Coniothecium eriodictyonis,** Cal.

YEW (*Taxus*)

Blight, Needle. **Herpotrichia nigra,** Ida.; **Sphaerulina taxi,** Cal., Idaho, Oreg., Wash.

Blight, Seedling. **Phytophthora cinnamomi,** Md., Va.

Blight, Twig. **Phyllostictina hysterella,** Mont., Wash. (conidial stage of *Physalospora gregaria*); **Pestalotia** sp., Pa.; **P. funerea,** Mass.; **Sphaeropsis** sp., N. J.

Rot, Heart. **Fomes hartigii,** Oreg.; **F. roseus, Polyporus schweinitzii.**

Rot, Root. **Armillaria mellea,** Ida.

YUCCA (Adams-Needle, Joshua-Tree, Spanish Bayonet, Spanish Dagger)

Blight, Flower. **Cercospora floricola,** Tex.

Blight, Leaf. **Kellermannia anomala,** secondary, Fla., Kans., Nebr.

Leaf Spot. **Cercospora concentrica,** general; **Coniothyrium concentricum,** general; **Cylindrosporium angustifolium,** Kans., Miss., Okla., Tex.; **Diplodia circinans,** Tex.; **Epicoccum asterinum,** Tex.; **Gloeosporium yuccogenum,** Mo., Tex.; **Nettiospora yuccifolia,** Ga., Wash.; **Pestalozziella yuccae,** secondary, Tex.; **Stagonospora gigantea,** Cal.

Mold, Leaf. **Torula maculans,** Ariz., Cal., S. C., Tex.; **Alternaria tenuis,** Ga., N. C., W. Va.

Nematode Root Knot. **Heterodera marioni.**

Rot, Stem. **Sclerotium rolfsii,** Md.

Rust. **Aecidium yuccae** (O, I), Nebr.; II, III, unknown.

Many other fungi are found on dead leaves and stems.

ZAUSCHNERIA (Fire-Chalice, California-Fuchsia)

Rust. **Puccinia oenotherae** (O, I, II, III), Cal., Utah.

ZEPHYRANTHES ATAMASCO (Atamasco-Lily, Rain-Lily)

Leaf Spot. **Colletotrichum liliacearum,** N. C.; **Stagonospora curtisii,** Cal.
Rot, Dry; Scale, Speck. **Sclerotium** sp., Oreg.
Rust. **Puccinia cooperiae** (O, I, II, III), Fla., Ala., N. C.

ZIGADENUS

Rust. **Puccinia atropuncta,** Iowa, Mo., N. Dak., Wis.; **P. grumosa** (O, I, II, III), Col., Mont., Wyo.; **Uromyces zygadeni,** Col., Iowa, Mont., Wyo.
Smut, Leaf. **Urocystis flowersii,** Utah.

ZINNIA

Bacterial Wilt. **Pseudomonas solanacearum,** Fla.
Blight. **Alternaria zinniae,** Col., Conn., N. J., N. Y., Pa., S. C.
Blight, Head; Stem Canker. **Botrytis cinerea,** Cal., Conn., N. J., Oreg., Pa.
Blight, Southern. **Sclerotium rolfsii,** Fla., N. J.
Damping-Off; Root Rot. **Rhizoctonia solani,** Cal., N. J., Tex.
Leaf Spot. **Cercospora zinniae,** S. C. to Fla., Ala., Col., Ind., Pa.
Nematode, Root Knot. **Heterodera marioni,** N. J., Pa., Tex.
Nematode, Stem, Leaf. **Aphelenchoides** sp.; **A. ritzema-bosi,** Del., Mass.
Powdery Mildew. **Erysiphe cichoracearum,** general.
Rot, Blossom. **Choanephora** sp., Fla.
Rot, Charcoal. **Macrophomina phaseoli,** Tex.
Rot, Stem; Wilt. **Fusarium** sp., Col., Iowa, Mo., N. Y.; **Phytophthora cryptogea,** N. J.; **Sclerotinia sclerotiorum,** Cal., Col., Mass., Mo., Mont., Oreg., Pa., Wash.
Virus, Curly Top. **Ruga verrucosans,** Cal., Ida., Oreg., Wash.
Virus, Mosaic. Several strains of **Marmor cucumeris,** cucumber mosaic, and unidentified viruses.
Virus, Spotted Wilt. **Lethum australiense,** Cal., Tex.
Virus, Aster Yellows. **Chlorogenus callistephi,** Mich., Pa., and also var. **californicus,** Cal.

Powdery mildew in late summer is the most common disease in home gardens.

LIST OF AGRICULTURAL EXPERIMENT STATIONS IN THE UNITED STATES

Alabama: *Auburn*
Alaska: *Palmer*
Arizona: *Tucson*
Arkansas: *Fayetteville*
California: *Berkeley* 4
Colorado: *Fort Collins*
Connecticut: *New Haven* 4 (State Station)
  Storrs (Storrs Station)
Delaware: *Newark*
Florida: *Gainesville*
Georgia: *Experiment* (State Station)
  Tifton (Coastal Plain Station)
Hawaii: *Honolulu*
Idaho: *Moscow*
Illinois: *Urbana*
Indiana: *Lafayette*
Iowa: *Ames*
Kansas: *Manhattan*
Kentucky: *Lexington* 29
Louisiana: *University Station, Baton Rouge* 3
Maine: *Orono*
Maryland: *College Park*
Massachusetts: *Amherst*
Michigan: *East Lansing*
Minnesota: *University Farm,* St. Paul 1
Mississippi: *State College*
Missouri: *Columbia*
Montana: *Bozeman*
Nebraska: *Lincoln* 1
Nevada: *Reno*
New Hampshire: *Durham*
New Jersey: *New Brunswick*
New Mexico: *State College*
New York: *Geneva* (State Station)
  Ithaca (Cornell Station)

North Carolina: *State College Station, Raleigh*
North Dakota: *Fargo*
Ohio: *Wooster*
Oklahoma: *Stillwater*
Oregon: *Corvallis*
Pennsylvania: *State College*
Puerto Rico: *Rio Piedras*
Rhode Island: *Kingston*
South Carolina: *Clemson*
South Dakota: *Brookings*
Tennessee: *Knoxville*
Texas: *College Station*
Utah: *Logan*
Vermont: *Burlington*
Virginia: *Blacksburg* (*College Station*)
Norfolk 1 (Truck Station)
Washington: *Pullman* (*College Station*)
Puyallup (Western Washington Station)
West Virginia: *Morgantown*
Wisconsin: *Madison* 6
Wyoming: *Laramie*

GLOSSARY

Acervulus, pl. *Acervuli.* A "little heap," an erumpent, cushion-like mass of hyphae bearing conidiophores and conidia, sometimes with setae; characteristic of the Melanconiales (Fig. 10).

Acicular. Needle-like.

Aeciospore. Rust spore formed in an aecium.

Aecium, pl. *Aecia.* A cluster-cup, or cup-like fruiting sorus in the rusts (Figs. 89, 90, 92).

Aerobic. Living or active only in the presence of oxygen.

Amoeboid. Not having a cell wall and changing in form like an amoeba.

Allantoid. Sausage-shaped.

Annulus. A ring; ringlike partial veil around stipe in the mushrooms.

Antheridium, pl. *Antheridia.* Male sex organ in the fungi.

Alternate host. One or other of the two unlike hosts of a heteroecious rust.

Anthracnose. A disease with limited necrotic lesions, caused by a fungus producing nonsexual spores in acervuli (Figs. 12, 13).

Antibiotic. Damaging to life; especially a substance produced by one microorganism to destroy others.

Apothecium, pl. *Apothecia.* The cup- or saucer-like ascus-bearing fruiting body; in the Discomycete section of the Ascomycetes (Figs. 8, 41, 86).

Appressorium. A swelling on a fungus germ tube for attachment to host in early stage of infection; found especially in anthracnose fungi and rusts.

Ascocarp, or *Ascoma.* Any structure producing asci, as an apothecium, perithecium.

Ascomycetes. One of the three main groups of the fungi, bearing sexual spores in asci.

Ascospore. Produced in ascus by free cell formation.

Ascus, pl. *Asci.* Saclike, usually clavate cell containing ascospores, typically 8 (Fig. 8).

Aseptate. Without cross-walls.

Asexual. Vegetative, having no sex organs or sex spores; the imperfect stage of a fungus.

Autoecious. Completing life cycle on one host; term used in rusts.

Bacteria. Microscopic 1-celled organisms increasing by fission.

Bactericide. Substance causing death of bacteria.

Basidiomycetes. Class 3 in the Fungi, characterized by septate mycelium, sometimes with clamp-connections, and sexual spores on basidia (Fig. 9).

Basidiospore. Spore produced on a basidium.

Basidium, pl. *Basidia.* Club-shaped structure, which, after fusion of two nuclei, produces four basidiospores (Fig. 9).

Binucleate. Having two nuclei.

Blight. A disease with sudden, severe leaf damage and often with general killing of flowers and stems.

Blotch. A blot or spot, usually superficial.

Breaking, of a virus. Loss of flower color in a variegated pattern, especially in tulips.

Canker. A lesion on a stem; a plant disease with sharply limited necrosis of the cortical tissue (Figs. 43, 44, 45).

Carrier. Infected plant showing no marked symptoms but source of infection for other plants.

Catenulate. In chains, or in an end-to-end series.

Cerebroid. With brainlike convolutions or folds.

Chemotherapy. Treatment of internal disease by chemical agents that have a toxic effect on the microorganism without injuring the plant.

Chlamydospore. Thick-walled, asexual resting spore formed by the rounding up of any mycelial cell (Fig. 80); also used for smut spores.

Chlorosis. Yellowing of normally green tissue due to partial failure of chlorophyll to develop; often due to unavailability of iron (Figs. 69, 70).

Cilium, pl. *Cilia.* Hairlike swimming organ on bacteria or zoospores.

Cirrhus, pl *Cirrhi.* A tendril or horn of forced out spores.

Clamp-connections. Outgrowths of hyphae which form bridges around septa, thus connecting two cells; in Basidiomycetes (Fig. 9).

Clavate. Club-shaped.

Cleistothecium, pl. *Cleistothecia.* A perithecium without a special opening; in powdery mildews (Fig. 74).

Coalesce. Growing together into one body or spot.

Concentric. One circle within another with a common center.

Coenocytic. Multinucleate.

Columella. Sterile central axis in a mature fruiting body (Fig. 7).

Conidiophore. Simple or branched hypha on which conidia are produced.

Conidium, pl. *Conidia.* Any asexual spore except sporangiospore or chlamydospore.

Conk. Term used in forestry for sporophores of Polyporaceae on trees.

Control. Prevention of, or reduction of loss from, plant disease.

Coremium, pl. *Coremia,* Synnema, a cluster of erect hyphae bearing conidia (Fig. 10).

Coriaceous. Like leather in texture.

Culturing. Artificial propagation of organisms on nutrient media or living plants.

Cystidium, pl. *Cystidia.* Sterile, often swollen cell projecting from hymenium in Basidiomycetes.

Damping-off. Seed decay in soil, or seedling blight.

Decumbent. Resting on substratum with ends turned up.

Decurrent. Running down the stipe or stem.

Diagnosis. Identification of nature and cause of a disease.

Dieback. Progressive death of branches or shoots beginning at tips.

Defoliate. To strip or become stripped of leaves.

Dichotomous. Branching, frequently successive, into two more or less equal arms.

Dimidiate. Having one half smaller than the other; of a perithecium, having outer wall covering only top half.

Discomycetes. The cup fungi, a subclass of Ascomycetes; with apothecia.

Disease. A condition in which use or structure of any part of the living organism is not normal.

Disinfection. Freeing a diseased plant, organ or tissue from infection.

Disinfestation. Killing or inactivating disease organisms before they can cause infection; on surface of seed or plant part, or in soil.

Dissemination. Transport of inoculum from a diseased to healthy plant.

Disjunctor. Cell or projection connecting spores of a chain.

Duster. Apparatus for applying fungicides in dry form.

Echinulate. Having small, pointed spines; used of spores.

Endoconidium, pl. *Endoconidia.* Conidium formed within a hypha.

Enphytotic. A plant disease causing constant damage from year to year.

Epiphytotic. Sudden and destructive development of a plant disease over an extensive area, an epidemic.

Eradicant Fungicide. One which destroys a fungus at its source.

Eradication. Control of disease by eliminating the pathogen after it is already established.

Erumpent. Breaking through surface of substratum.

Excentric. Off center.

Exclusion. Control of disease by preventing its introduction into disease-free areas.

Exudate. Liquid discharge from diseased tissues.

Fasciation. Joining side by side; a plant disease with flattened and sometimes curved shoots.

Fascicle. A small bundle or cluster.

Flag. A branch with dead leaves on an otherwise green tree.

Filiform. Threadlike.

Fimbriate. Fringed, or toothed.

Flagellum, pl. *Flagella.* Whiplike organ on a motile cell; cilium.

Fruiting Body. Fungus structure containing or bearing spores: mushroom, pycnidium, perithecium, apothecium, etc.

Fumigant. A volatile disinfectant, destroying organisms by vapor.

Fungicide. Chemical or physical agent that kills or inhibits fungi.

Fungi Imperfecti. Fungi which have not been connected with the perfect or sexual stage; most are imperfect states of Ascomycetes.

Fungistatic. An agent preventing development of fungi without killing them.

Fungus, pl. *Fungi.* An organism with no chlorophyll, reproducing by sexual or asexual spores, usually with mycelium with well-marked nuclei.

Fusiform. Spindle-like, narrowing toward the ends.

Fusoid. Somewhat fusoid.

Gall. Outgrowth or swelling, often more or less spherical, of unorganized plant cells as result of attack by bacteria, fungi, or other organisms.

Gametangium. Gamete mother cell.

Gamete. A sex cell, especially one formed in a gametangium.

Germ Tube. Hypha produced by a germinated fungus spore.

Gill. Lamella or hymenium-covered plate on underside of cap of a mushroom.

Girdle. A canker which surrounds stem, completely cutting off water supply and thus causing death; girdling roots also cause death.

Glabrous. Smooth.

Gleba. Sporulating tissue in an angiocarpous fruit body.

Globose. Almost spherical.

Gram-negative, Gram-positive. Not being stained, and being stained, by the Gram stain used in classifying bacteria.

Haustorium, pl. *Haustoria.* Special hyphal branch extended into living cell for purpose of absorbing food (Fig. 73).

Heteroecious. Undergoing different parasitic stages on two unlike hosts, as in the rusts.

Heterothallic. Of a fungus, sexes separate in different mycelia.

Holocarpic. Having all the thallus used for a fruiting body.

Homothallic. Both sexes present in same mycelium.

Host. Any plant attacked by a parasite.

Hyaline. Colorless, or nearly transparent.

Hymenium. Spore-bearing layer of a fungus fruiting body.

Hyperplastic. Term applied to a disease producing an abnormally large number of cells.

Hypha, pl. *Hyphae.* Single thread of a fungus mycelium.

Hypoplastic. Term applied to a disease with subnormal cell production.

Hyphopodium, pl. *Hyphopodia*. More or less lobed appendage to a hypha.

Hysterothecium. Oblong or linear perithecium, sometimes considered an apothecium, opening by a cleft.

Immune. Exempt from disease; having qualities which do not permit infection.

Immunization. Process of increasing the resistance of a living organism.

Imperfect State. State of life cycle in which asexual spores, or none, are produced.

Imperfect Fungus. One lacking any sexual reproductive state.

Incubation Period. Time between inoculation and development of symptoms which can be seen.

Inoculation. Placing of inoculum in infection court.

Infection. Process of beginning or producing disease.

Infection Court. Place where an infection may take place, as leaf, fruit, petal, etc.

Indehiscent. Of fruit bodies, not opening, or with no special method.

Innate. Bedded in, immersed.

Inoperculate. Not opening by a lid.

Inoculum. Pathogen or its part, as spores, fragments of mycelium, etc., which can infect plants.

Injury. Result of transient operation of an adverse factor, as an insect bite, or action of a chemical.

Intercellular. Between cells.

Intracellular. Within cells.

Intumescence. Knoblike or pustulelike outgrowth of elongated cells on leaves, stems, etc., caused by environmental disturbances.

Lesion. Localized spot of diseased tissue.

Lamella. Gill.

Locule. A cavity, especially one in a stroma.

Macroconidia. Large conidia.

Macroscopic. Large enough to be seen with the naked eye.

Medulla. Loose layer of hyphae inside a thallus; body of a sclerotium.

Microconidia. Very small spores, now considered spermatia of a fungus also having larger conidia.

Micron. 1/1000 millimeter, unit used for measuring spores.

Microscopic. Too small to be seen except with the aid of a microscope; true of most of the fungus structures shown in line drawings in this book.

Mildew. Plant disease in which the pathogen is a growth on the surface.

Monoecious. Male and female reproductive organs in same individual; in rusts, all stages of life cycle on single species of plant.

Molds. Fungi with conspicuous mycelium or spore masses, often saprophytes.
Multinucleate. Several nuclei in same cell.
Mummy. Dried, shriveled fruit, result of disease.
Muriform. Having cross and longitudinal septa.
Mycelium, pl. *Mycelia.* Mass of fungus hyphae.
Mushroom. An agaric fruit body (Fig. 9).
Mycelia Sterilia. Fungi Imperfecti where spores, except for chlamydospores, are not present.
Mycorrhiza, pl. *Mycorrhizae.* Symbiotic, nonpathogenic association of fungi and roots.

Necrosis. Death of plant cells, usually resulting in tissue turning dark.
Necrotic. As an adjective, killing.
Nematocide. Chemical or physical agent killing nematodes.
Nematodes. Nemas, roundworms, eelworms, cause of some plant diseases.

Obligate Parasite. A parasite that can develop only in living tissues, with no saprophytic stage.
Obovate. Inversely ovate, narrowest at base.
Obtuse. Rounded or blunted, greater than a right angle.
Oogonium, pl. *Oogonia.* Female sex organ in the Oomycetes (Fig. 6).
Oomycetes. Subclass of the Phycomycetes, gametangia of unequal size.
Oospore. Resting spore formed in a fertilized oogonium.
Operculate. With a cover or lid, as in some asci.
Ostiole. Porelike mouth or opening in papilla or neck of a perithecium or pycnidium.

Papilla, pl. *Papillae.* Small, nipplelike projection.
Paraphysis, pl. *Paraphyses.* A sterile hyphal element in the hymenium, especially in the Ascomycetes, usually clavate or filiform.
Paraphysoids. Threads of hyphal tissue between asci, like delicate paraphyses but without free ends.
Pedicel. Small stalk.
Perfect State. Stage of life-cycle in which spores are formed after nuclear fission.
Peridium. Wall or limiting membrane of a sporangium or other fruit body, or of a rust sorus.
Perithecium. Subglobose or flasklike ascocarp of the Pyrenomycetes (Fig. 8).
Parasite. An organism that lives on or in a second organism, usually causing disease in the latter.
Pathogen. Any organism or factor causing disease.
Pathogenic. Capable of causing disease.
Physiogenic Disease. Caused by unfavorable environmental factors.
Physiologic Races. Pathogens of same variety and species structurally the same

but differing in physiological behavior, especially in ability to parasitize a given host.

Phytopathology. Plant pathology, science of plant disease.

Pileus. Hymenium-supporting part of fruit body of a higher fungus; the cap of a mushroom.

Primary Infection. First infection by a pathogen after going through a resting or dormant period.

Promycelium. Basidium of rusts and smuts.

Pulvinate. Cushionlike in form.

Pycnidium, pl. *Pycnidia.* Flasklike fruiting body containing conidia.

Pycnium. Spermagonium in the rusts, the O stage, resembling a pycnidium (Fig. 89).

Resistance. Ability of a host plant to suppress or retard activity of a pathogen.

Resting Spore. A spore, often thick-walled, that can remain alive in a dormant condition for some time, later germinating and capable of initiating infection.

Resupinate. Flat on the substratum with hymenium on outer side.

Rhizoid. Rootlike structure (Fig. 7).

Rhizomorph. A cordlike strand of fungus hyphae.

Ring Spot. Disease symptoms characterized by yellowish or necrotic rings with green tissue inside the ring, as in virus diseases.

Roguing. Removal of undesired individual plants.

Rosette. Disease symptom with stems shortened to produce a bunchy growth habit.

Russet. Brownish roughened areas on skins of fruit, from abnormal production of cork caused by disease, insect, or spray injury.

Rust. A fungus, one of the Uredinales, causing a disease also known as rust.

Saprophyte. An organism which feeds on lifeless organic matter.

Scab. Crustlike disease lesion; or a disease in which scabs are prominent symptoms (Figs. 97, 98, 100).

Sclerotium, pl. *Sclerotia.* Resting mass of fungus tissue, often more or less spherical, normally having no spores in or on it (Figs. 85, 86, 87).

Scorch. Burning of tissue, from infection or weather conditions.

Scutellum. Plate or shieldlike cover, as in Microthyriales.

Septate. Having cross-walls, septa.

Sessile. Having no stem.

Seta, pl. *Setae.* A stiff hair, or bristle, generally dark-colored.

Shothole. A disease symptom in which small round fragments drop out or leaves, making them look as if riddled by shot.

Sign. Any indication of disease other than reaction of the host plant—spores, mycelium, exudate, or fruiting bodies of the pathogen.

Slurry. Thick suspension of chemical; used for seed treatment.

Smut. A fungus of the Ustilaginales, characterized by sooty spore masses; the name also used for the disease caused by the smut.

Sorus, pl. *Sori.* Fungus spore mass, especially of rusts and smuts; occasionally, a group of fruiting bodies.

Sooty Mold. Dark fungus growing in insect honeydew.

Species. One sort of plant or animal; abbreviated as *sp.* singular, and *spp.* plural. A genus name followed by *sp.* means that the particular species is undetermined. *Spp.* following genus name means that several species are grouped together without being named individually.

Spermagonium. Walled structure in which spermatia are produced, a pycnium.

Spermatium, pl. *Spermatia,* a sex cell (+ or −), a pycniospore.

Sporangiole. Small sporangium without a columella and with a small number of spores.

Sporangiophore. Hypha bearing a sporangium.

Sporangium. Organ producing nonsexual spores in a more or less spherical wall (Fig. 6).

Spore. A single- to many-celled reproductive body, in the fungi and lower plants, which can develop a new plant.

Sporidium, pl. *Sporidia.* Basidiospore of rusts and smuts.

Sporophore. Spore-producing or supporting structure—a fruit body; used especially in the Basidiomycetes (Fig. 84).

Sporodochium, pl. *Sporodochia.* Cluster of conidiophores interwoven on a stroma or mass of hyphae (Fig. 10).

Sporulate. To produce spores.

Sterigma, pl. *Sterigmata.* Projection for supporting a spore.

Sprayer. Apparatus for applying chemicals in liquid form.

Strain. An organism or group of organisms differing in origin or minor aspects from other organisms of same species or variety.

Stipe. A stalk. *Stipitate.* Stalked.

Stroma, pl. *Stromata.* Mass of fungus hyphae often including host tissue containing or bearing spores.

Substrate. The substance or object on which a saprophytic organism lives and from which it gets nourishment.

Subiculum, Subicle. Netlike woolly or crustlike growth of mycelium under fruit bodies.

Suscept. A living organism attacked by, or susceptible to, a given disease or pathogen; in many cases a more precise term than host but less familiar.

Susceptible. Unresistant, permitting the attack of a pathogen.

Swarmspore. Zoospore.

Synnema, pl. *Synnemata.* Groups of hyphae sometimes joined together, generally upright and producing spores; coremium.

Systemic. Term applied to disease in which single infection leads to general spread of the pathogen throughout the plant body.

Teliospore. Winter or resting form of rust spore, from which basidium is produced (Figs. 88, 89, 93).

Telium. Sorus producing teliospores.

Thallus. Vegetative body of a thallophyte.

Thallophyte. One of the simpler plants, belonging to the algae, bacteria, fungi, slime molds or lichens.

Tolerant. Capable of sustaining disease without serious injury or crop loss.

Toxin. Poison formed by an organism.

Tylosis, pl. *Tyloses.* Cell outgrowth into cavity of xylem vessel, plugging it.

Urediospore. Summer spore of rusts; 1-celled, verrucose (Fig. 88).

Uredium. Sorus producing urediospores.

Valsoid. Having groups of perithecia with beaks pointing inward, or even parallel with surface, as in Valsa.

Vector. An agent, insect, man, etc., transmitting disease.

Vein-banding. Symptom of virus disease in which regions along veins are darker green than the tissue between veins.

Verrucose. With small rounded processes or warts.

Virulent. Highly pathogenic; with strong capacity for causing disease.

Viruliferous. Virus-carrying; term applied particularly to virus-laden insects.

Virus. An obligately parasitic pathogen capable of multiplying in certain hosts, ultramicroscopic, recognizable by the effects produced in infected hosts.

Wilt. Loss of freshness or drooping of plants due to inadequate water supply or excessive transpiration; a vascular disease interfering with utilization of water.

Witches' Broom. Disease symptom with abnormal brushlike development of many weak shoots.

Yellows. Term applied to disease in which yellowing or chlorosis is a principal symptom.

Zoospore. A swimming spore, swarmspore, capable of independent movement (Fig. 6).

Zygomycetes. Subclass of the Phycomycetes, characterized by gametes of equal size.

Zygospore. Resting spore formed from the union of similar gametes (Fig. 7).

SELECTED BIBLIOGRAPHY

In the preparation of the *Plant Disease Handbook* I have reviewed references which have been accumulating in my files for the past thirty years and have tried to keep abreast of current literature. To cite all the individual articles which have been used would fill another book and be more confusing than helpful. The bibliography presented here is a selected small sampling of the field surveyed. Almost all of the books listed are the exceedingly well-thumbed volumes in my personal library, and I acknowledge a heavy debt to their authors.

The periodicals that come regularly to my desk include *The Plant Disease Reporter, Phytopathology, Review of Applied Mycology, Biological Abstracts, Science, Agricultural Chemicals, Florists Exchange, American Fruit Grower, Arborist's News, Trees, Journal of the New York Botanical Garden, Plants and Gardens* (Brooklyn Botanic Garden Record), *The National Gardener* (Bulletin of the National Council of State Garden Clubs), various garden magazines—*American Home, Better Homes and Gardens, Flower Grower, The Home Garden, Home Gardening in the South, Horticulture, House and Garden, Sun-Up*—and the yearbooks and magazines of four single plant societies—American Camellia Society, American Delphinium Society, American Rose Society, and the New England Gladiolus Society. In addition, I receive vegetable leaflets from Cornell University, fruit-spray schedules from Rutgers University, publicity releases from the Connecticut Experiment Station, miscellaneous bulletins from other experiment stations and the U.S. Department of Agriculture, and publications from most of the state garden clubs.

The bibliography has been divided into four sections. The first, sources for the classification of plant pathogens, is solely for plant pathologists and mycologists. The second, references on garden chemicals and their application, suggests sources of information of particular interest to dealers and professional gardeners. Any gardener, professional or otherwise, would benefit by a subscription to *American Fruit Grower,* if only for the charts on compatibility of spray materials and on weather factors. *Entoma* is a "must" for dealers.

The third section, general references on plant diseases, lists a number of books and bulletins that should interest amateur gardeners as well as professional workers. *The Advance of the Fungi,* by Large, is delightfully written and shows how plant diseases influence world history. The U.S. Department of Agriculture Farmers' Bulletins on trees are excellent. I am indebted to

Diseases and Pests of Ornamental Plants by Dodge and Rickett for many descriptions of diseases of flowering plants and some control measures. *Hunger Signs in Crops* and *Commercial Flower Forcing* provide symptoms of plants suffering from nutritional defects. Boyce's *Forest Pathology* goes into detail on signs and symptoms of tree diseases, many of which are important in home plantings as well as in the forest. Chester's textbook on plant diseases can be read with profit by laymen as well as students.

The last section gives the merest hint of the vast amount of literature available to home gardeners on troubles of their special plants. Farmers' Bulletins on general culture or diseases of many different plants are available for a few cents from the Superintendent of Documents, Washington 25, D.C. Almost any Public Library will have a set of these bulletins from which to make a selection. The single plant societies, in their yearbooks and bulletins, likewise provide a wealth of information for the hobbyist and an exchange of views on the latest garden chemicals. Free for the asking are the bulletins, circulars, and spray schedules from your own state experiment station. Send for a list of publications available and check those that deal with your particular problems.

REFERENCES ON THE CLASSIFICATION OF PLANT PATHOGENS

Ainsworth, G. C., and G. R. Bisby. A dictionary of the fungi. 2nd ed. Imperial Mycological Institute, Kew, Surrey, England. 1945.

Arthur, J. C. Manual of the rusts in United States and Canada. Purdue Research Foundation, Lafayette, Ind. 1934.

Bailey, L. H., and Ethel Zoe Bailey, compilers. Hortus second. The Macmillan Company, New York. 1941.

Bisby, G. R. An introduction to the taxonomy and nomenclature of fungi. Imperial Mycological Institute, Kew, Surrey, England. 1945.

Burkholder, Walter H. *In* Bergey's manual of determinative bacteriology. 6th ed. pp. 82–172, 381–409, 463–478, 638–640. Williams and Wilkins Company, Baltimore. 1948.

Christensen, Clyde M. Keys to the common fleshy fungi. Burgess Publishing Company, Minneapolis. 1946.

Clements, Frederic E., and Cornelius L. Shear. The genera of fungi. The H. V. Wilson Company, New York. 1931.

Couch, J. N. The genus Septobasidium. University of North Carolina Press, Chapel Hill. 1938.

Fitzpatrick, Harry Morton. The lower fungi—Phycomycetes. McGraw-Hill Book Company, Inc. 1930.

Goodey, T. Plant parasitic nematodes and the diseases they cause. E. P. Dutton and Company, New York. 1933.

Holmes, Francis O. Virales. *In* Bergey's manual of determinative bacteriology. 6th ed. pp. 1128–1224. Williams and Wilkins Company, Baltimore. 1948.

Jenkins, Anna E. A specific term for diseases caused by Elsinoë and Sphaceloma. Plant Disease Reporter **31**:71. 1947.

Kelsey, Harlan P., and William A. Dayton, editors. Standardized plant names. 2nd ed. J. Horace McFarland Company, Harrisburg. 1942.

Martin, G. W. Key to the families of fungi. *In* A dictionary of the fungi. 2nd ed. pp. 394–410. Imperial Mycological Institute, Kew, Surrey, England. 1945.

——— Outline of the fungi. Univ. of Iowa Studies in Nat. Hist. **18** (1) :1–64. Univ. of Iowa, Iowa City. 1941.

Miller, L. W., and J. S. Boyle. The Hydnaceae of Iowa. Univ. of Iowa Studies in Nat. Hist. **18** (2) :1–92. 1943.

Rogers, Donald P. The genus Pellicularia (Thelephoraceae). Farlowia **1** (1) : 95–118. 1943.

Salmon, Ernest S. A monograph of the Erysiphaceae. Mem. Torrey Bot. Club **9**:1–292. 1900.

Seymour, Arthur Bliss. Host index of the fungi of North America. Harvard University Press, Cambridge, Mass. 1929.

Snyder, W. C., and H. N. Hansen. The species concept in Fusarium. Amer. Jour. Bot. **27**:64–67. 1940; and **32**:657–665. 1945.

Weiss, Freeman. Check list revision, diseases of economic plants of the United States. Plant Disease Reporter **24**:140–148. 1940 and in subsequent issues to **33**:104–126. 1949.

——— Ovulinia, a new generic segregate from Sclerotinia. Phytopath. **30**:236–244. 1940.

Whetzel, H. H. A synopsis of the genera and species of the Sclerotiniaceae, a family of stromatic inoperculate Discomycetes. Mycologia **37**:648–714. 1945.

Wiltshire, S. P., editor. Common names of the viruses used in the Review of Applied Mycology. Rev. Appl. Myc. **24**:515–556. 1945 (special part issued July, 1946).

Wolf, Frederick A., and Frederick T. Wolf. The Fungi. Vols. I, II. John Wiley and Sons, Inc., New York. 1947.

REFERENCES ON CHEMICALS AND THEIR APPLICATION

American Phytopathological Society Sub-Committee. 1947 fungicide tests: a summation of nation-wide results with newer fungicides. Plant Disease Reporter Sup. **176**:96–142. 1948.

——— Nation-wide results with fungicides in 1948. Fourth annual report. Plant Disease Reporter Sup. **181**:18–87. 1949.

Anonymous. Compatibility chart for insecticides and fungicides. American Fruit Grower **69** (2) :36, 37. 1949.

——— Weather factors in spraying and dusting pome fruits. American Fruit Grower **69** (2) :24–25. 1949.

——— Weather factors in spraying and dusting stone fruits. American Fruit Grower **69** (3) :21. 1949.

Anonymous. New federal act is introduced. AIF News **4** (3) :1–4. 1945.

——— New federal insecticide act's features important to agriculture and industry. AIF News **5** (10) :5. 1947.

Carter, J. C. Organic fungicides. Proc. Twenty-third National Shade Tree Conference: 122–130. 1947.

Christie, Jesse R. Soil fumigation for control of nematodes and other soil-inhabiting organisms. Plant Disease Reporter Sup. **170:**170–189. 1947.

Cohen, Sylvan I. Development of fungicidal aerosols as foliage protectants. Phytopath. **38:**6. 1948.

Davis, Spencer H. Organic fungicides in the control of certain shade and ornamental tree diseases. Phytopath. **38:**575. 1948.

Dimond, A. E., G. H. Plumb, E. M. Stoddard, and J. G. Horsfall. An evaluation of chemotherapy and vector control by insecticides for combating Dutch elm disease. Conn. Agr. Exp. Sta. Bul. **531:**1–70. 1949.

Frear, Donald E. H. Chemistry of insecticides, fungicides and herbicides. 2nd ed. D. Van Nostrand Company, Inc., New York. 1948.

Goldsworthy, Marion C. Development and progress in new fungicides. Agric. Chem. **4** (3) :33–35. 1949.

Horsfall, James G. Fungicides and their action. Chronica Botanica Company, Waltham, Mass. 1945.

Howard, Frank L. Outlook for fungicides. American Fruit Grower **69** (2) :26, 38. 1949.

Langford, G. S., editor. Entoma, a directory of insect and plant pest control. 7th ed. Eastern Branch of the American Association of Economic Entomologists, College Park, Md. 1947. (The 8th edition available early in 1950.)

Liming, O. N. et al. Dutch elm disease control conference report—1949. Trees **9** (4) :6, 7, 15, 18–21. 1949.

Mason, A. Freeman. Spraying, dusting and fumigating of plants. The Macmillan Company, New York. 1932.

McCallan, S. E. A. What every dealer should know about fungicides. Agric. Chem. **3** (7) :23–25, 77–79. 1948.

McClintock, J. A., and Wayne B. Fisher. Spray chemicals and application equipment. The Greenlee Company, Inc., Chicago. 1945.

Miller, Paul R., J. I. Wood, and M. J. O'Brien. Plant disease forecasting makes possible more effective methods of fungicidal control. Agric. Chem. **3** (11) : 28–31, 63–66. 1948.

Rowell, John B. Development of fungicides for turf diseases in 1948. R. I. Agr. Exp. Sta. Pl. Path.-Ent. Report 1948 (3). 1948.

——— and F. L. Howard. Development of fungicidal concentrates and their application with motorized air-blast equipment to row crops. R. I. Agr. Exp. Sta. Pl. Path.-Ent. Report 1948 (1). 1948.

Westcott, Cynthia. The gardener's bug book. American Garden Guild, Inc.

and Doubleday & Company, Inc. 1946. (Chapter III, on spraying, dusting, fumigation, is designed to be used with this Plant Disease Handbook.)

Young, H. C. Recent developments in fungicides and their evaluation, nature, compatibility and use. Proc. Twenty-fourth National Shade Tree Conference: 47–58. 1948.

Zentmeyer, George A. Recent trends in the field of fungicides. Trees **9** (3) :21–22, 26, 30. 1949.

GENERAL REFERENCES ON PLANT DISEASES

American Phytopathological Society. Committee on Standardization of Fungicidal Tests. Definitions of fungicide terms. Phytopath. **33:**624–626. 1943.

——— Report of the Committee on Technical Words. Phytopath. **30:**361–368. 1940.

Boyce, John Shaw. Forest pathology. 2nd ed. McGraw-Hill Book Company, Inc., New York. 1948.

Brierley, Philip. Viruses described primarily on ornamental or miscellaneous plants. Plant Disease Reporter Sup. **150:**410–482. 1944.

Chester, K. Starr. Nature and prevention of plant diseases. 2nd ed. The Blakiston Company, Philadelphia. 1947.

——— Nature and prevention of the cereal rusts as exemplified in the leaf rust of wheat. Chronica Botanica Company, Waltham, Mass. 1946.

——— Virus diseases of the stone fruits. Plant Disease Reporter **24:**74–78. 1940.

Chupp, Charles. Manual of vegetable-garden diseases. The Macmillan Company, New York. 1925.

Cook, Melville T. Viruses and virus diseases of plants. Burgess Publishing Company, Minneapolis. 1947.

Cox, C. E., and W. E. Jeffers. Root-knot. Univ. of Maryland Ext. Bul. **113:**1–23. 1946.

Dickson, James G. Diseases of field crops. McGraw-Hill Book Company, Inc., New York. 1947.

Dodge, Bernard O., and Harold W. Rickett. Diseases and pests of ornamental plants. Rev. ed. The Ronald Press Company, New York. 1948.

Dunlap, A. A., J. F. Rosborough, and E. E. Miller. Plant diseases in Texas and their control. Texas Agr. Ext. Bul. **b132:**1–73. 1944.

Elliott, Charlotte. Manual of bacterial plant pathogens. The Williams and Wilkins Company, Baltimore. 1930.

Felt, Ephraim Porter, and R. Howard Rankin. Insects and diseases of ornamental trees and shrubs. The Macmillan Company, New York. 1932.

Fenska, Richard R. Tree experts manual. A. T. De La Mare Company, Inc., New York. 1943.

Forsberg, Junius L. Diseases of ornamental plants. Colorado Agricultural and Mechanical College, Fort Collins. 1946.

Fowler, Marvin E., and G. F. Gravatt. Reducing damage to trees from construction work. U. S. Dept. Agr. Farmers' Bul. **1967**:1–26. 1945.

Garrett, S. D. Root disease fungi. Chronica Botanica Company, Waltham, Mass. 1944.

Hambidge, Gove, editor. Hunger signs in crops, a symposium. American Society of Agronomy and National Fertilizer Association. Printer, Judd and Detweiler, Inc., Washington, D. C. 1941.

Heald, Frederick Deforest. Manual of plant diseases. McGraw-Hill Book Company, Inc., New York. 1926.

Large, E. C. The advance of the fungi. Henry Holt and Company, New York. 1940.

Laurie, Alex, and D. C. Kiplinger. Commercial flower forcing. 4th ed. The Blakiston Company, Philadelphia. 1944.

Marshall, Rush P., and Alma M. Waterman. Common diseases of important shade trees. U. S. Dept. Agr. Farmers' Bul. **1987**:1–53. 1948.

——— Care of damage shade trees. U. S. Dept. Agr. Farmers' Bul. **1896**:1–34. 1942.

Moore, W. C. Diseases of bulbs. Ministry of Agriculture and Fisheries (Great Britain) Bul. **117**:1–176. 1939.

Parks, T. H., and T. H. King. Control of garden insects and diseases. Ohio State Univ. Agr. Ext. Bul. **76**:1–64. 1947.

Pirone, P. P. Maintenance of shade and ornamental trees. 2nd ed. Oxford University Press, New York. 1948.

——— Diseases of ornamental plants. N. J. Agr. Exp. Sta. Circ. **385**:1–80. 1939.

Post, Kenneth. Florist crop production and marketing. Orange Judd Publishing Company, New York. 1949.

Smith, Ralph E. Diseases of flowers and other ornamentals. Cal. Agr. Ext. Circ. **118**:1–108. 1940.

——— Diseases of truck crops. Cal. Agr. Ext. Circ. **119**:1–112. 1940.

——— Diseases of fruits and nuts. Cal. Agr. Ext. Circ. **120**:1–166. 1941.

U. S. Department of Agriculture. Trees. The Yearbook of Agriculture. Washington. 1949.

Weiss, Freeman. Viruses described primarily on leguminous vegetable and forage crops. Plant Disease Reporter Sup. **154**:32–80. 1945.

——— Viruses, virus diseases and similar maladies on potatoes, *Solanum tuberosum*. Plant Disease Reporter Sup. **155**:82–140. 1945.

Westcott, Cynthia. The plant doctor. Rev. ed. J. B. Lippincott Company, Philadelphia. 1940.

Whitcomb, W. D. Spraying of home fruit orchard by the arborist. Arborist's News **10**:9–14. 1945.

Wood, Jessie I., and Paul R. Miller, compilers. Losses from plant diseases: effects on crop industries and on farm life. Plant Disease Reporter Sup. **186**:254–282. 1949.

REFERENCES TO DISEASES OF SPECIAL PLANTS

AZALEA

Gill, D. L. Azalea petal blight control brought up to date. Home Gardening for the South **8**:19–21. 1948.

Hume, H. Harold. Azaleas, kinds and culture. The Macmillan Company, New York. 1948.

Weiss, Freeman. A flower-spot disease of cultivated azaleas. U. S. Dept. Agr. Circ. **556**:1–26. 1941.

Westcott, Cynthia. Azalea petal blight can be controlled. Home Gardening for the South **5**:134–139. 1945.

CAMELLIA

Gill, D. L. Camellia flower blight in the South. Plant Disease Reporter **32**:317–318. 1948.

Hansen, H. N., and H. Earl Thomas. Flower blight of camellias. Phytopath. **30**:166–170. 1940.

——— Camellia flower blight. American Camellia Yearbook **1946**:43–45. 1946.

West, Erdman. Camellia diseases, 1946–1947. American Camellia Yearbook **1947**:116–121. 1947.

CARNATION

Brierley, Philip, and F. F. Smith. Carnation and gladiolus virus diseases pose serious problems. Florists Review **99** (2567) :31–33. 1947.

Guba, E. F. Carnation wilt diseases and their control. Mass. Agr. Exp. Sta. Bul. **427**:1–64. 1945.

McCully, Kenneth F. Commercial carnation growing. Sim Carnation Co., Inc. Saugus, Mass. 1949.

CHRYSANTHEMUM

Brierley, Philip, and Floyd F. Smith. Chrysanthemum stunt. Phytopath. **39**:501. 1949.

DeWorth, A. F. Commercial production of chrysanthemums in the South. Florists Exchange **110** (18) :20–21, 67–69; and **110** (19) :17, 54–57. 1948.

CITRUS FRUITS

Fawcett, Howard S. Citrus diseases and their control. 2nd ed. McGraw-Hill Book Company, Inc., New York. 1936.

Klotz, L. J., and H. S. Fawcett. Color handbook of citrus diseases. University of California Press, Berkeley. 1941.

DELPHINIUM

Baker, Kenneth F. Diseases of delphinium in California. American Delphinium Society Yearbook **1947:**15–30. 1947.

ELM

Dimond, A. E., and G. H. Plumb. Combating the Dutch elm disease. Conn. Agr. Exp. Sta. Special Bulletin. 1949.

Swingle, R. U., R. R. Whitten, and H. C. Young. The identification and control of elm phloem necrosis and Dutch elm disease. Ohio Agr. Exp. Sta. Special Circ. **80:**1–11. 1949.

GLADIOLUS

Magie, Robert O. The Curvularia and other important leaf and flower diseases of gladiolus in Florida. Gladiolus Magazine **12** (1) :13–16. 1948.

McClellan, W. D., K. F. Baker, and C. J. Gould. The Botrytis disease of gladiolus in the United States. Gladiolus Magazine **12** (3) :22–24, 42. 1948.

Nelson, Ray. Diseases of gladiolus. Mich. Agr. Exp. Sta. Special Bul. **350:**1–63. 1948.

GRAPE

Braun, Alvin J. A three-spray schedule for control of black rot of grapes. Phytopath. **37:**3, 4. 1947.

Demaree, J. B. Control of grape diseases and insects in eastern United States. Farmers' Bul. **1893:**1–28. 1942.

Suit, R. F. Field results on the control of certain grape diseases in New York. N. Y. (Geneva) Agr. Exp. Sta. Bul. **712:**1–26. 1945.

GRASS

Kirby, R. S., and H. W. Thurston, Jr. Prevention of turf diseases. Penn. State College Agr. Ext. mimeographed circular. March, 1949.

United States Department of Agriculture. Grass. The Yearbook of Agriculture, Washington, 1948.

MIMOSA

Hepting, G. H. A vascular wilt of the mimosa tree (*Albizzia julibrissin*) . U. S. Dept. Agr. Circ. 535. 1939.

Pirone, P. P. Mimosa wilt found in New Jersey. Jour. N. Y. Bot. Gard. **50:**226–229. 1949.

Toole, E. Richard, and George H. Hepting. Selection and propagation of Albizzia for resistance to Fusarium wilt. Phytopath. **39:**63–70. 1949.

NARCISSUS

Gould, Charles J. Narcissus diseases in Washington. Wash. Agr. Exp. Sta. Popular Bul. **194.** 1949.

OAK

Dietz, S. M., and Roy A. Young. Oak wilt—a serious disease in Iowa. Iowa State College Bul. P91. 1948.

Young, Roy A. Studies on oak wilt, caused by *Chalara quercina*. Phytopath. **39:**425–441. 1949.

PECAN

Phillips, Arthur M., and John R. Cole. Insects and diseases of the pecan in Florida. Fla. Agr. Exp. Sta. Bul. **411:**1–62. 1945.

POTATO

Lombard, P. M., B. E. Brown, and T. P. Dykstra. Potato production in the northeastern and north central states. U. S. Dept. Agr. Farmers' Bul. **1958.** Rev. 1948.

RASPBERRY

Jeffers, Walter F., and Mark W. Woods. Raspberry diseases in Maryland. Univ. of Md. Ext. Bul. **93:**1–25. 1942.

Suit, R. F. Control of spur blight of red raspberries. New York (Geneva) Agr. Exp. Sta. Bul. **710:**1–14. 1945.

ROSE

Allen, R. C. Roses for every garden. M. Barrows and Company, Inc., New York, 1948.

Massey, L. M. Keeping roses healthy. In each issue of American Rose Magazine.

Zimmerman, P. W. 2,4–D injury on roses. American Rose Annual **1949:**71–72. 1949.

STRAWBERRY

Demaree, J. B. Diseases of strawberries. U. S. Dept. Agr. Farmers' Bul. **1891.** Rev. 1949.

TOMATO

Doolittle, S. P. Tomato diseases. U. S. Dept. Agr. Farmers' Bul. **1934.** Rev. 1948.

As stated above, the few references selected for citation can only hint at the vast amount of literature on diseases of flowers and vegetables, fruits, nuts, and shade trees available to gardeners as well as technical workers. Speaking as a rose hobbyist I heartily recommend the stimulation that comes with membership in one of the single-plant societies. The list increases year by year. Some have a permanent address, some change address with changing officers, but your nearest botanical library or garden center should be able to supply information on how to join any of the following: African Violet Society of America, American Amaryllis Society, Begonia Society, Camellia Society, Carnation Society, Dahlia Society, Delphinium Society, Forestry Association, Iris Society, Orchid Society, Pelargonium Society, Penstemon Society, Peony Society, Primrose Society, Rhododendron Society, Rock Garden Society, Rose Society, Chrysanthemum Society of America, Epiphyllum Society of America, Gourd Society of America, Herb Society of America, Holly Society of America, National Chrysanthemum Society, and the National Tulip Society.

INDEX

This is a selective index. It includes common and Latin names of the host plants in Chapter 5, common names of the diseases described in Chapter 4 and Latin names of their pathogens. Entries under plant names are chiefly for the purpose of providing cross references to disease names and are not to be construed as providing a complete check list of the diseases of each plant. For that, the host section itself must suffice.

Orders and families given in Chapter 3 are indexed, and genera described in Chapter 4. Chemicals listed in Chapter 2 are indexed, but not their use in control of specific diseases. Names of scientists and authors mentioned in the text are included but not those in the Bibliography.

Boldface type indicates illustrations.